SRa MATH
Explorations and Applications

Make thinking a basic skill on the road of life.

Solve the persistent problems of teaching elementary mathematics by teaching children how to *think* mathematically.

REPORT CARD

Subjects	1	2	3	4
Math	✓	✓	✓	✓
Knows and uses basic facts		✓	✓	✓
Demonstrates understanding of the math concepts using manipulatives and abstract thinking		✓	✓	✓
Solves word problems		✓	✓	
Uses problem-solving strategies to solve real-world problems				
Language Arts				

Visit our website
www.SRA-4KIDS.com

Introducing

SRA MATH
Explorations and Applications

Take the right path to teaching mathematics.

This comprehensive, research-based program challenges students to think every day, on every page, at every juncture. It's the answer that teachers need to make math instruction effective and math learning enjoyable.

Level K   Level 1   Level 2   Level 3

MATEMÁTICAS
Exploraciones y aplicaciones
Complete program available in Spanish

Level 4

Level 5

Level 6

Also Available

- ◆ **Professional Development Handbook**
- ◆ **Program Guide**
- ◆ **Test Preparation Practice Workbook**
- ◆ **Lesson Plans**
- ◆ *Minds on Math*
- ◆ *Math CrossSections*
- ◆ *Science, Math & YOU*
- ◆ *Cooperate 1, 2, and 3*
- ◆ *Junior Thinklab™*
- ◆ *Thinklab™*
- ◆ *Scoring High in Math*

Take along the essentials for the journey.

Core Materials

- Student Editions (K–2) in consumable format that introduce, integrate, and practice concepts and skills
- Student Editions (3–6) in hardbound format filled with lessons that integrate concept development, practice, and problem solving
- Thinking Story Books (Levels 1–3) for teachers to read to the class
- Teacher's Guides that provide the road map along with practice, reteaching, and enrichment support
- Basic Manipulative Kits needed for Cube Games and Mental Math Activities

Lesson Support Materials

- Practice Activities in Workbook and Blackline Master formats
- Enrichment Activities in Workbook and Blackline Master formats
- Reteaching Activities in Workbook and Blackline Master formats
- Assessment Masters
- Home Connections Masters
- Literature Library (K–3)

Manipulative Support Materials

- Game Mat Packages (K–6) for skill practice and problem solving
- Primary Manipulative Kit (K–2) to introduce basic concepts
- Primary Overhead Manipulative Kit (K–2)
- Intermediate Manipulative Kit (3–6) for variety in concept presentation
- Intermediate Overhead Manipulative Kit (3–6)
- Teacher Manipulative Kit for classroom demonstrations

Technology Support Materials

- *Math Explorations and Applications* Software (1–6) provides extra skill practice for every lesson.
- *The Cruncher* (4–6) offers a student-friendly spreadsheet application for appropriate lessons.
- *My Silly CD of Counting* CD-ROM (K) helps build the concept of counting.
- TI-108™ Calculator Package (K–3)
- Math Explorer™ Calculator Package (4–6)
- Primary Overhead Calculator (K–3)
- Intermediate Overhead Calculator (4–6)

Professional Development

- Professional Development Handbook

It's mathematics, taken off the beaten path.

Math Explorations and Applications helps students learn the real basics: traditional arithmetic skills, computation, and problem solving.

◆ **Concept Integration.** The program's organization, scope, and sequence allow integration and thorough study of math concepts.

◆ **In-Depth Study.** Lessons devote the number of pages needed to teach a concept, not artificially dividing every topic into the same lesson length. Sometimes it takes more than two pages to effectively cover the important points in a lesson.

◆ **Concepts in Context.** Skills and concepts are taught and retaught in different contexts—never in isolation.

◆ **Variety of Presentations.** Explore, Practice, Problem Solving, and Projects address a variety of learning styles so that students stay interested and motivated as they learn to think.

◆ **Cumulative Review of Content.** Once a skill has been introduced, it is integrated, practiced, and reviewed in mixed practice and in context throughout the grade level. Lesson by lesson, students accumulate the skills they need to master more complicated math concepts, as they continually review previously introduced skills.

◆ **Life-Long Learning.** As they see mathematics used to solve realistic problems, students begin to view strong math skills as useful, lifelong tools they can use both inside and outside the classroom.

◆ **Focus on Computation *and* Problem Solving.** *Math Explorations and Applications* develops and provides practice of traditional skills in problem-solving settings such as games. This makes efficient use of teacher and student time and effort.

Developing concepts in context paves the road to understanding.

Math Explorations and Applications introduces and integrates concepts so that students make connections and build on what they already know.

◆ **Early Introduction of Concepts.**
An early age-appropriate introduction to concepts such as algebra, geometry, multiplication, and division builds understanding and connections from the very beginning. Because most students actually begin to use the principles of more advanced math concepts like algebra long before the eighth grade, *Math Explorations and Applications* helps students feel comfortable with these concepts from the very start.

◆ **Core Concept Development at Every Level.** Operations, thinking skills, problem solving, mental math, estimation, data organization, geometry, probability, and statistics are emphasized at all grade levels.

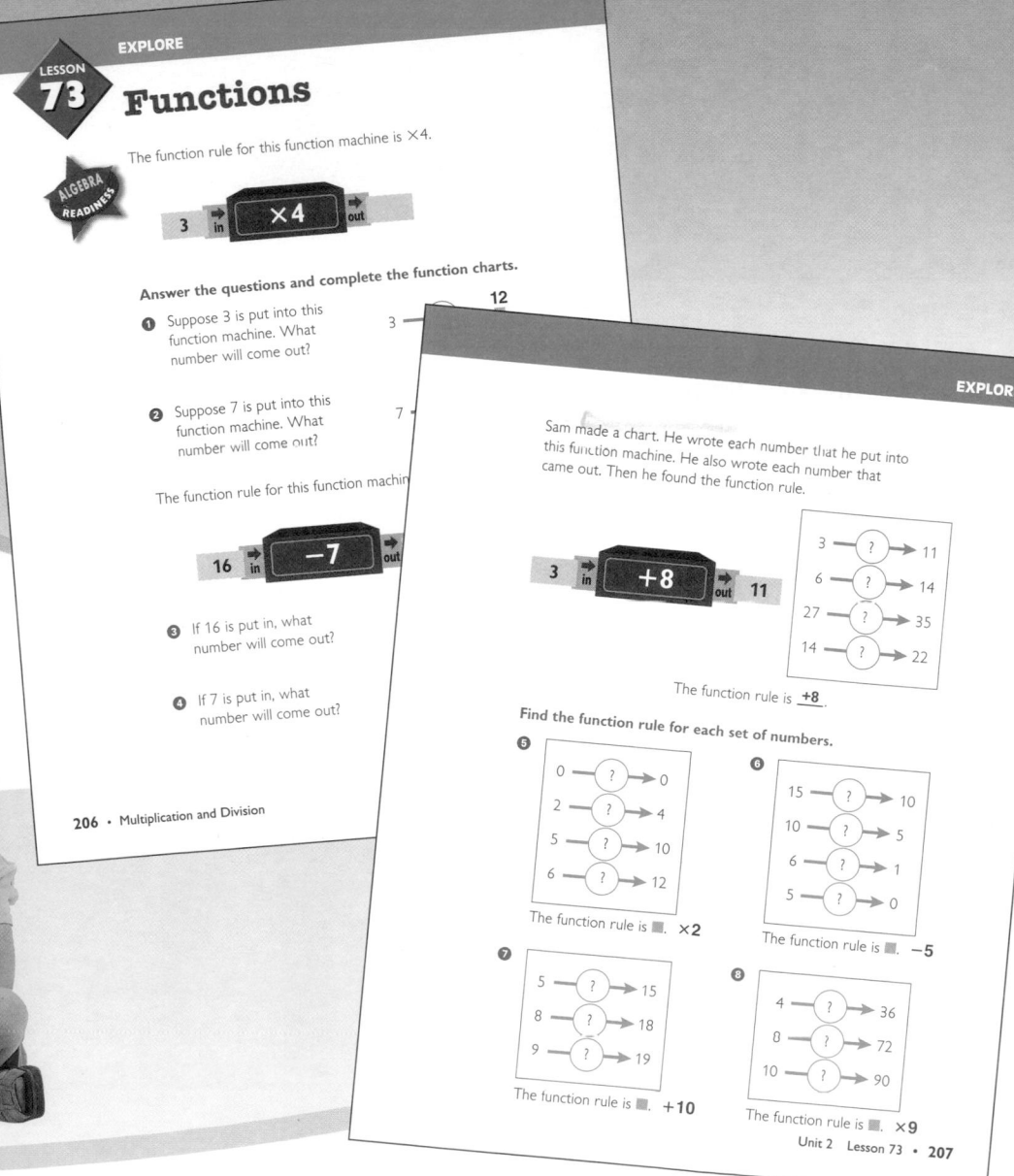

Level 3

◆ **Concepts in Context.** Concepts are developed in different contexts to help students recognize their natural connections. For example, the concept of fractions is developed in relation to time, money, and measurement.

◆ **Intelligent Use of Manipulatives.** Intelligent use of hands-on activities and manipulatives establishes concepts in the concrete, showing students a variety of ways to solve a problem. Students are encouraged to use these tools where appropriate, then to move beyond these tools as quickly as possible toward the goal of abstract thinking.

◆ **Realistic Problem-Solving Models.** Exciting **Act It Out** lessons model problem-solving strategies by having students physically work through new concepts.

◆ **Emphasizing Natural Concept Relationships** By drawing on the natural relationships that exist among concepts, students learn to make connections between concepts so that they can understand them more effectively.

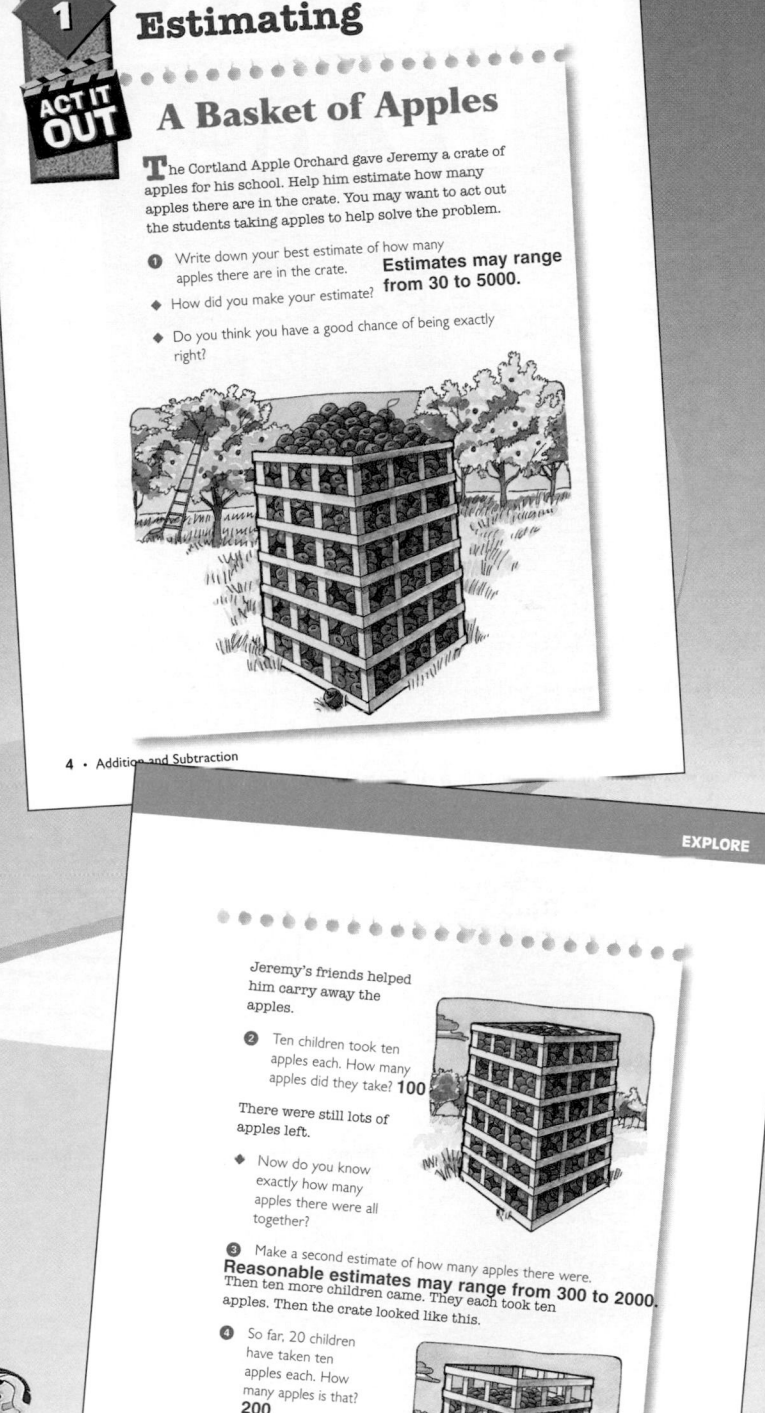

Step by step, students learn the basics by heart and mind.

Computational skills are essential for efficient mathematical thinking. But skill practice can be enjoyable and is one more opportunity to challenge students to think mathematically.

◆ **Practice** pages often have hidden patterns that help students understand number relationships and encourage mathematical thinking on every problem on every page.

PRACTICE

Remember, to find the area of a rectangle, multiply the length by the width.

What is the area of the rectangle?

Area = 3 × 5 square centimeters

5 cm

3 cm   3 cm

5 cm

Let's turn the rectangle on its side.

Area = 5 × 3 square centimeters

3 cm

5 cm   5 cm

3 cm

◆ Did the area of the rectangle change? **no**
◆ Does 3 × 5 = 5 × 3? **yes**
◆ What is 3 × 5? **15**
◆ What is 5 × 3? **15**

Rule: The order in which two numbers are multiplied makes no difference to the answer.

Multiply. Compare the problems in each pair.

6 2 × 5 = n **10**
5 × 2 = n

7 1 × 8 = n **8**
8 × 1 = n

8 10 × 4 = n **40**
4 × 10 = n

9 5 × 5 = 2
5 × 5 =

10 9 × 0 = n **0**
0 × 9 = n

11 3 × 4 = n **12**
4 × 3 = n

12 3 × 9 = n **27**
9 × 3 = n

13 5 × 8 =
8 × 5 =

14 6 × 9 = n **54**
9 × 6 = n

15 7 × 9 = n **63**
9 × 7 = n

16 6 × 4 = n **24**
4 × 6 = n

17 4 × 8
8 × 4

18 2 × 4 = n **8**
4 × 2 = n

19 3 × 5 = n **15**
5 × 3 = n

20 9 × 1 = n **9**
1 × 9 = n

21 4 ×
2 ×

Unit 2 Lesso

Level 4

◆ **Mixed Practice** pages throughout each grade level review concepts from all lessons and encourage students to think about what they're doing and how they do it.

MIXED PRACTICE

ALGEBRA READINESS

Multiply. Solve for n.

7 6 × 5 = n **30**
8 8 × 6 = n **48**
9 4 × 7 = n **28**

10 3 × 2 = n **6**
11 7 × 3 = n **21**
12 6 × 6 = n **36**

13 4 × 10 = n **40**
14 3 × 7 = n **21**
15 2 × 5 = n **10**

16 7 × 5 = n **35**
17 2 × 6 = n **12**
18 4 × 4 = n **16**

PROBLEM SOLVING

Solve.

Carolyn has seven nickels. She wants to buy a fan that costs 95¢.

19 How much money does Carolyn have in cents? **35¢**

20 How much more does she need to buy the fan? **60¢**

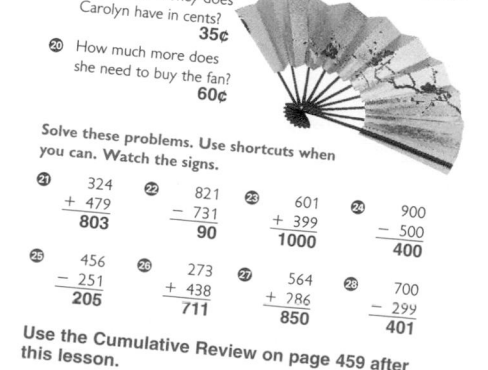

Solve these problems. Use shortcuts when you can. Watch the signs.

21
324
+ 479
803

22
821
− 731
90

23
601
+ 399
1000

24
900
− 500
400

25
456
− 251
205

26
273
+ 438
711

27
564
+ 286
850

28
700
− 299
401

Use the Cumulative Review on page 459 after this lesson.

Unit 2 Lesson 48 • 145

Level 3

Multiplication Table Game

Math Focus:
- Practicing basic facts–multiplying two factors of 5 or less
- Using a multiplication table

Object of the Game: To have more counters at the end of the game

Players: Two

MATERIALS

Two cubes   36 counters or pennies

SET UP

▶ Every circle on the mat must be covered with a counter.
▶ Players roll the 0–5 number cube. The person who rolls the higher number goes first.

HOW TO PLAY

❶ Players take turns rolling both cubes and making multiplication sentences out of the numbers. For example, if a 4 and a 2 are rolled, the player could say either "4 times 2 equals 8" or "2 times 4 equals 8."

❷ After giving the multiplication sentence, players check their answers by looking under the appropriate counter. If correct, the player keeps the counter; if incorrect, the player replaces the counter.

❸ Once the counter on a circle has been won, the circle remains empty. A player who cannot make a multiplication sentence that applies to a covered circle cannot win a counter that turn.

❹ The player with more counters at the end of the game wins.

✗	0	1	2	3	4	5
0	0	0	0	0	0	0
1	0	1	2	3	4	5
2	0	2	4	6	8	10
3	0	3	6	9	12	15
4	0	4	8			
5	0	5	10			

PRACTICE

LESSON 47 Estimating Products

CO OPERATIVE LEARNING

GAME

Mul-Tack-Toe Game

Players:	Two
Materials:	Two Mul-Tack-Toe cards (like those below), two 0–5 cubes (red), eight counters or coins for each player
Object:	To cover three boxes in a line
Math Focus:	Multiplication facts

RULES

1. Each player chooses one of the two Mul-Tack-Toe cards.

2. Players take turns rolling the two 0–5 cubes.

3. Both players calculate the product of the two numbers rolled. If the product is on a player's card, he or she puts a counter on that box.

4. The first player to cover three boxes in a line (horizontally, diagonally, or vertically) wins the round.

15	16	6
25	4	5
10	0	2

Card 1

12	1	10
0	4	20
8	9	15

Card 2

142 • Multiplication and Division

Level 3

◆ **Games** are not just for fun. Throughout the program, games provide extensive, serious practice with traditional arithmetic. They also offer opportunities to identify and solve interesting problems. Students don't even realize how much math they're practicing!

MENTAL MATH

Interactive **Mental Math** activities in every lesson in the Teacher's Guide help students develop the ability to manipulate numbers in their minds, easily and with common sense.

Problem Solving—Applications

Children learn to solve problems by solving problems.

Problem-solving strategies are integrated throughout *SRA Math Explorations and Applications*, never taught in isolation. Instead of memorizing rote strategies, students learn to:

- recognize a problem,
- select an appropriate strategy,
- solve the problem, and
- reflect on their reasoning.

◆ **Thinking Stories** model mathematical thinking and problem-solving strategies. They demonstrate that real-life "problems" can appear in unexpected places.

INTEGRATED **PROBLEM SOLVING**

◆ **LESSON 150** Counting to One Million

In the last lesson your teacher read the first part of this story to you. Now read this part yourself.

THINKING STORY

Mr. Muddle's Time Machine

Part 2

The next day Mr. Muddle bought two hands for his clock. They were both the same length and looked exactly alike. He put the hands on carefully. "There," he said, "this clock looks better than most. There's something uneven about most clocks."

426 • Geometry

INTEGRATED **PROBLEM SOLVING**

One afternoon Mark and Manolita stopped by to see how Mr. Muddle's time machine was working. "The clock works just fine," said Mr. Muddle. "Listen to it tick. But sometimes I can't tell what time it is. Look at it now."

One hand was pointing at 11. The other hand was pointing at 4 "It could be almost any time," said Mr. Muddle. "I can't tell."

"It's not that bad," said Mark. "There are only two different times it could be."

"And I think I know which is the right time," said Manolita.

Work in groups. Discuss your answers and how you figured them out. Then compare your answers with those of other groups.

❶ Why is it hard to tell what time it is with Mr. Muddle's clock? **Because the hands are the same length.**

❷ Look at the clock in the picture. What are the two times that it could be? **11:20 or 3:55**

❸ Which of these is the right time? Look for a clue in the story. **3:55; the story takes place in the afternoon**

Unit 4 Lesson 150 • 427

Level 3

- **Word Problems** throughout the student books are carefully crafted to involve multiple operations, cumulative content, and sometimes, insufficient information so that students always have to think.

MIXED PRACTICE

COOPERATIVE LEARNING

GAME

Roll a 15 Game

Players:	Two
Materials:	Two 0–5 cubes (red), two 5–10 cubes (blue)
Object:	To get the sum closer to 15
Math Focus:	Addition, subtraction, and mathematical reasoning

RULES

1. Roll the cubes one at a time.
2. Add the numbers as you roll. The sum of all the cubes you roll should be as close to 15 as possible.
3. You may stop after two, three, or four rolls.
4. The player with the sum closer to 15 wins the round.

If you rolled:	The sum would be:
7 and 1 and 4 and 7	19
8 and 5	13
4 and 4 and 8	16
9 and 3 and 3	15
5 and 10	15

ANOTHER WAY TO PLAY THIS GAME

Start at 20 and subtract the numbers rolled. Try to get as close to 5 as possible.

MATH JOURNAL **In your Math Journal describe your strategy for playing this game.**

Use the Cumulative Review on page 534 after this lesson.

Unit 1 Lesson 4 • 15

Level 4

- **Games** provide lots of opportunities for students to identify problems and develop strategies for their solution.

Problem-Solving Strategies and Methods integrated throughout the program

- Act it out
- Check reasonableness
- Choose a strategy
- Choose the appropriate operation
- Choose the method
- Conduct an experiment
- Eliminate possibilities
- Identify extra information
- Identify needed information
- Interpret data
- Interpret the quotient and remainder
- Make an organized list
- Solve a simpler/similar problem
- Solve multistep problems
- Use a formula
- Use estimation
- Use guess and check/test
- Use logical reasoning
- Use manipulatives
- Use/draw a picture or diagram
- Use/find a pattern
- Use/make a model
- Use/make a table
- Work backwards
- Write a number sentence
- Write an equation

- **Projects** at the end of each unit allow students to solve complex problems, many of which require outside research and data analysis.

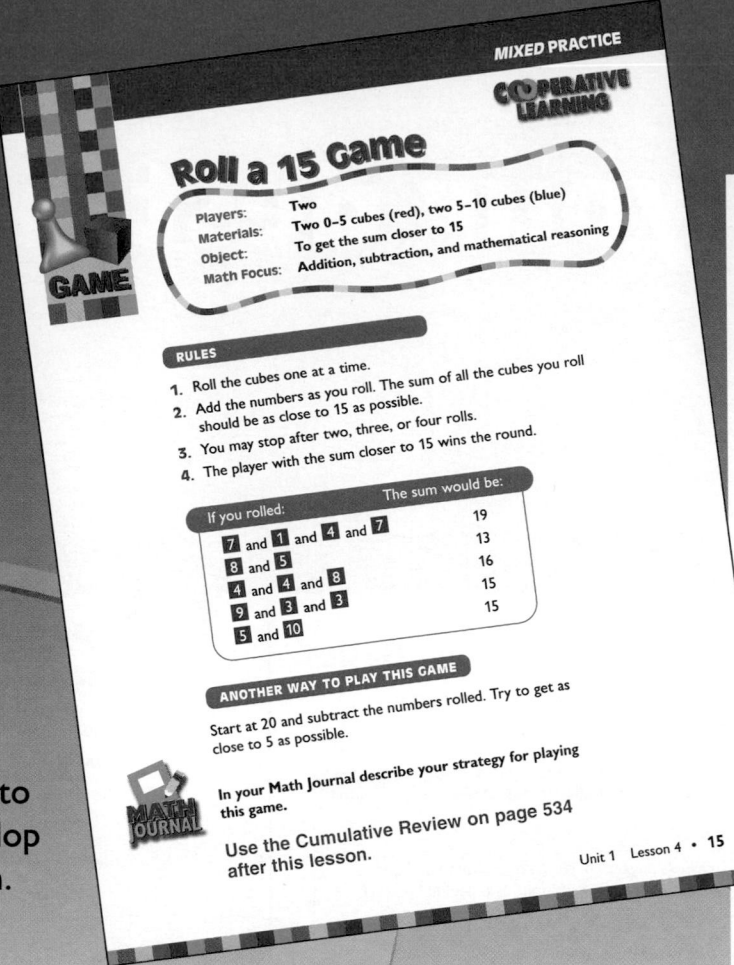

UNIT 2 WRAP-UP PROJECT

COOPERATIVE LEARNING

Number Tricks

Put your hands in front of you. Stretch out your fingers. Think of your fingers as being numbers from 1 through 10, as shown. Now, bend down finger number 3. You have two fingers up on the left and seven fingers up on the right. What is 9 × 3? Do you see any connection?

27; The number of fingers to the left of the finger you put down is the tens digit, and the number of fingers to the right of the finger you put down is the ones digit.

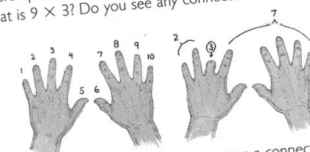

Bend down finger number 4. Do you see a connection between your fingers and 4 × 9? What happens when you bend down finger number 8? **see above**

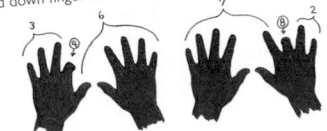

Does this work for 10 × 9? How about for 0 × 9? **yes; no**

224 • Multiplication and Division

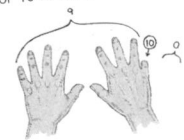

Why does this work? If you multiply 7 by 10, you get seven tens. So put up seven fingers. Now, if you subtract 7, you have one fewer ten (so put down finger number 7). But you need three more ones (because 10 − 7 = 3), so put up three fingers.

MATH JOURNAL **In your Math Journal write about how this trick can help you remember the multiples of 9.**

Try this number trick on your friends. Start with a two-digit number that has two different digits. Reverse the digits. Subtract the lesser number from the greater number.

Then, reverse the digits of this last number and add. The sum will be 99.

For example, if you start with 48, the reversed number is 84. 84 − 48 = 36

Reverse the digits, and add: 36 + 63 = 99.

If you started with a three-digit number, what would the final number be? **1089**

Unit 2 Wrap-Up • 225

Level 3

To reach your destination,

Math Explorations and Applications gives teachers the support they need to challenge students to think mathematically, not to just complete exercises.

◆ **Lesson Planner** offers a quick overview of the lesson objectives, materials, and resources.

◆ **Context of the Lesson** explains how this lesson fits into sequence with others.

◆ A clear, three-step lesson plan lays out how to **Warm-Up, Teach,** and **Wrap-Up** each lesson.

◆ **Problem of the Day** presents an interesting problem for students to ponder in every lesson.

◆ **Mental Math** provides basic fact and abstract-thinking practice in every lesson.

◆ **Why teach it at this time?** or **Why teach it in this way?** provides an explanation of the authors' philosophy as it relates to this specific lesson.

LESSON 106

Student Edition pages 298–299

Practicing Basic Operations

LESSON PLANNER

Objectives

✓ to assess mastery of students' ability to add and subtract decimals (with up to two decimal places)

▶ to provide practice in adding and subtracting decimals

Context of the Lesson This is the 15th of 15 lessons on decimals. This lesson also contains the 22nd of 24 Mastery Checkpoints.

Materials
graph paper (optional)
play money (optional)

Program Resources
Thinking Story Book, pages 88–89
Practice Master 106
Enrichment Master 106
Assessment Master
For extra practice:
CD-ROM* Lesson 106

❶ Warm-Up ⏱ 5 MINUTES

Problem of the Day Present this problem: Fay called her friend Samir and asked him to meet her at the library. Fay lives 3.4 kilometers away from the library, while Samir lives 1.62 kilometers away. Who must travel farthest to the library? (Fay: 3.4 > 1.62) How much farther? (1.78 km: 3.40 – 1.62 = 1.78)

MENTAL MATH Review addition and subtraction of decimals. On the chalkboard write: 4.2 – 1.14 = _____. Show that the problem can be done by changing 4.2 to the equivalent 4.20 and then subtracting. Then have students respond quickly by writing their answers on paper as you read the following problems aloud.

a. 3.57 – 2.4 = (1.17)
b. 15.63 – 4.7 = (10.93)
c. 5.3 – 2.02 = (3.28)
d. 9.1 + 6.04 = (15.14)
e. 8.35 + 3.2 = (11.55)
f. 7.06 – 1.3 = (5.76)

298 Fractions and Decimals

MIXED PRACTICE

LESSON 106

Practicing Basic Operations

Solve these problems. Watch the signs.

❶   5.3
   – 2.1
   3.2

❷   5.47
   – 3.6
   1.87

❸   2.4
   – 1.87
   0.53

❹   4.71
   + 5.62
   10.33

❺   5.62
   + 4.71
   10.33

❻   5.62
   – 4.71
   0.91

❼   3.8
   + 1.2
   5.0

❽   4.07
   – 3.7
   0.37

❾   12.13
   – 8.6
   3.53

❿ 5.81 – 3.28 = ■ **2.53**   ⓫ 9.03 + 9.3 = ■ **18.33**

⓬ 2.66 – 1.7 = ■ **0.96**   ⓭ 7.56 + 9.33 = ■ **16.89**

⓮ 4.2 – 1.75 = ■ **2.45**   ⓯ 3.44 – 2.07 = ■ **1.37**

⓰ 5.4 + 8.17 = ■ **13.57**   ⓱ 12.1 + 4.79 = ■ **16.89**

Number correct ■

298 • Fractions and Decimals

RETEACHING

Students who fall short of the mastery objective should be checked to determine the nature of the difficulty. If the trouble lies with multidigit addition and subtraction of whole numbers, reteach the appropriate algorithms using concrete materials. If the difficulty is adding and subtracting decimals, have students solve problems both with and without concrete objects such as play money*. Use graph paper if students have difficulty lining up the decimal points and columns.

PRACTICE p. 106

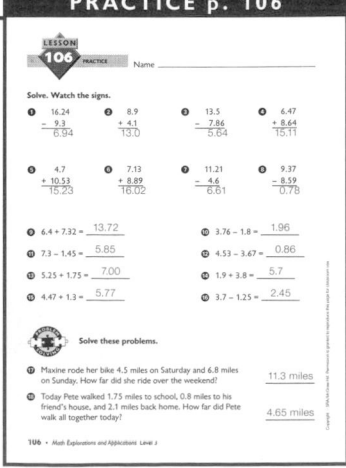

*available separately

---

you need a clear road map.

Solve.

18 Each time Amy adds a book to her bookshelf, she records how much room is left on the shelf. All her books are the same thickness. Copy and complete Amy's table.

Space on Amy's Bookshelf

Number of Books	5	6	7	8	9	10	11	12	13
Space Used	1.03	0.99	0.95	0.91	0.87	0.83	0.79	0.75	0.71

Make up five problems using the map below and solve them. Write your problems in your Math Journal and explain how to solve them.

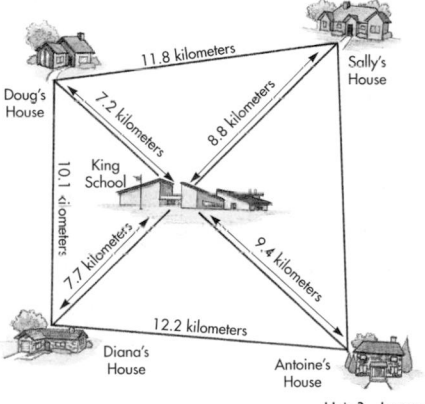

11.8 kilometers — Doug's House — Sally's House
7.2 kilometers — 8.8 kilometers
King School
10.1 kilometers
7.7 kilometers — 9.4 kilometers
12.2 kilometers
Diana's House — Antoine's House

Unit 3 Lesson 106 • 299

❷ Teach

Using the Student Pages Tell students that the problems on page 298 are a test. Allow students enough time to finish. When all students have finished, have them proofread their papers as a group. Remember to focus attention on the number of correct rather than the number of incorrect answers. Then have students complete page 299.

 Using the Thinking Story Have students complete three problems from among those following "Mosquito Lake" on pages 88–89 of the Thinking Story Book.

❸ Wrap-Up

In Closing Ask students what they must remember to do when adding or subtracting numbers with decimals. Students should say they must write more zeros as necessary so that each number in the problem has the same number of decimal places.

Mastery Checkpoint 22

Students should demonstrate mastery of the addition and subtraction of decimals (with up to two decimal places) by correctly answering 12 of the 17 problems on page 298. The results of this assessment may be recorded on the Mastery Checkpoint Chart. You may also wish to assign the Assessment Master on page 41 to determine mastery.

ENRICHMENT p. 106

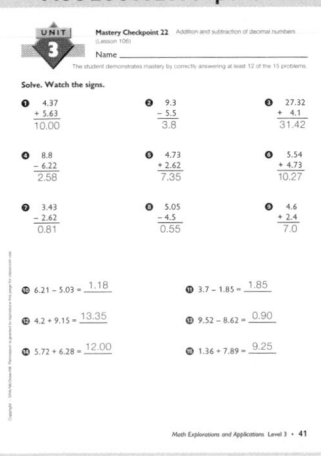

LESSON 106 ENRICHMENT   Name _____

The chart below shows the average yearly rainfall in ten U.S. cities. Use the chart to help you write and solve the number sentence that answers each question below.

City	Average Yearly Rain (in inches)	City	Average Yearly Rain (in inches)
Chicago, Illinois	33.34	New York, New York	42.82
El Paso, Texas	7.82	Pittsburgh, Pennsylvania	36.30
Los Angeles, California	12.08	Phoenix, Arizona	7.11
Minneapolis, Minnesota	26.36	Richmond, Virginia	44.07
New Orleans, Louisiana	59.74	Washington, D.C.	39.00

❶ What is the difference in rainfall between New Orleans and Phoenix?   52.63 inches

❷ Is the combined rainfall of Chicago and El Paso greater than the rainfall in New York?   no; 33.34 + 7.82 < 42.82

❸ What is the difference?   33.4 + 7.82 = 41.16; 42.82 − 41.16 = 1.66

❹ The combined rainfall of Phoenix and Minneapolis is nearest to the amount of rainfall in what single city?   7.11 + 26.36 = 33.47; Chicago

106 • Math Explorations and Applications Level 3

ASSESSMENT p. 41

UNIT 3   **Mastery Checkpoint 22**   Addition and subtraction of decimal numbers (Lesson 106)   Name _____

The student demonstrates mastery by correctly answering at least 12 of the 17 problems.

Solve. Watch the signs.

❶ 4.37 + 5.63 = 10.00   ❷ 9.3 − 5.5 = 3.8   ❸ 27.32 + 4.1 = 31.42

❹ 8.8 − 6.22 = 2.58   ❺ 4.73 + 2.62 = 7.35   ❻ 5.54 + 4.73 = 10.27

❼ 3.43 − 2.62 = 0.81   ❽ 5.05 − 4.5 = 0.55   ❾ 4.6 + 2.4 = 7.0

❿ 6.21 − 5.03 = 1.18   ⓫ 3.7 − 1.85 = 1.85

⓬ 4.2 + 9.15 = 13.35   ⓭ 9.52 − 8.62 = 0.90

⓮ 5.72 + 6.28 = 12.00   ⓯ 1.36 + 7.89 = 9.25

Math Explorations and Applications Level 3 • 41

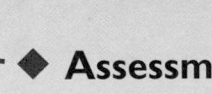

Assessment Criteria

Did the student . . .

✓ make up at least five word problems with solutions based on page 299?

✓ demonstrate mastery of the addition and subtraction of decimals?

Homework To reinforce the lesson concept, have students play the "Harder Rummage Sale" game with a household member.

Unit 3 Lesson 106 **299**

Level 3

◆ **Program Resources** are referenced at point of use.

◆ **Mastery Checkpoint** provides opportunities for teachers to check for student understanding of core skills and concepts.

◆ **Practice, Enrichment,** and **Reteaching** blackline masters and strategies are included for every lesson.

◆ **Assessment Criteria** tie informal assessment to the Lesson Objectives.

◆ **Homework** ideas are always included in Levels 3–6 for added practice and reinforcement.

Assessment

Assessment tools help students stay on track.

Math Explorations and Applications aligns teaching and assessment to support learning. With a variety of options, teachers can select appropriate methods to monitor student progress.

Self-Assessment. *Are You Shiny or Rusty?* activities offer nonthreatening timed tests so that students can see how quickly and accurately they can recall the basic arithmetic facts.

Performance Assessment. Strategies in the Teacher's Guide and the Assessment Book provide opportunities for students to show what they know.

Portfolio Assessment. Suggestions throughout the Teacher's Guide give students an opportunity to demonstrate their mathematical growth.

Informal Assessment

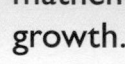 **Assessment Criteria.** In every lesson teachers are reminded what to look for as they informally assess student responses.

◆ **Varied Opportunities.** Every Game, Thinking Story, and Act It Out provides an opportunity for teachers to informally assess students' mathematical thinking.

◆ **Mental Math Exercises.** Daily interactive Mental Math activities offer opportunities for informal assessment and self-assessment.

Formal Assessment

◆ **Unit Assessment.** Mid-Unit Reviews, Unit Reviews, and Unit Tests provide ready-made formal assessment of students' comprehension.

◆ **Mastery Checkpoints.** These checkpoints and corresponding evaluations in the Assessment Books indicate times that teachers can check for mastery of specific skills and concepts.

◆ **Mastery Checkpoint Charts.** Mastery Checkpoints give teachers an easy way to keep track of students' mastery of specific skills.

◆ **Standardized-Format Tests.** Multiple-choice computation tests provide practice taking standardized tests at the same time they provide one more opportunity to assess students' math skills.

SRA® MATH

Explorations and Applications

It will change the way students think about math . . . for a lifetime.

Math Explorations and Applications is a program with proven results for more than 25 years.

◆ The program was developed one grade level at a time, building on valuable field test results to ensure consistency and continuity throughout all grade levels.

◆ Successfully field-tested in urban, suburban, and rural schools, *Math Explorations and Applications* ensures effectiveness in any teaching situation.

◆ Teaching strategies throughout the program are based on substantial bodies of research indicating how children learn best.

◆ Written and updated by a team of distinguished and committed authors, *Math Explorations and Applications* reflects time-tested strategies with proven results.

◆ We have listened carefully to teachers who use the program. This edition of *Math Explorations and Applications* reflects the many valuable suggestions and comments we have received from talented teachers over the years. We look forward to receiving your comments.

Exceeds ~~Meets~~ NCTM Standards!

Authorship

Dr. Stephen S. Willoughby
Mathematics Educator

Stephen S. Willoughby has taught mathematics at all levels, from first grade through graduate courses in schools in Massachusetts, Connecticut, Wisconsin, New York, and Arizona, including the University of Wisconsin and New York University. He is now Professor of Mathematics at the University of Arizona. He received bachelor's and master's degrees from Harvard University and a doctorate from Columbia University

Dr. Willoughby was President of the National Council of Teachers of Mathematics from 1982 to 1984 and Chairman of the Council of Scientific Society Presidents in 1988. He was a member of the national Board of Advisors for SQUARE ONE TV, chairman of the United States Commission on Mathematics Instruction, and a member of the Education Testing Services Mathematics Advisory Committee for the successor to the National Teacher's Examination, and is now a member of the Education Advisory Panel of New American Schools Development Corporation (NASDC).

Dr. Willoughby has published more than 200 articles and books on mathematics and mathematics education and was senior author of the innovative K–8 mathematics series *Real Math™* published by Open Court.

Dr. Carl Bereiter
Cognitive Psychologist

Carl Bereiter is a professor in the Centre for Applied Cognitive Science, Ontario Institute for Studies in Education, University of Toronto. He holds a Ph.D. in educational psychology from the University of Wisconsin. He has done research and developed educational materials in such diverse areas as preschool education, thinking skills, writing, elementary school mathematics, and science understanding. He is also active in the development of advanced computer-based technology for schools. His scholarly contributions have been recognized by award of a Guggenheim Fellowship, appointments to the Center for Advanced Study in the Behavioral Sciences, election to the National Academy of Education, and an honorary Doctor of Laws from Queens University. His books include *Arithmetic and Mathematics* (1968), *Thinking Games* (1975 with Valerie Anderson), *The Psychology of Written Composition* (1987, with Marlene Scardamalia), and *Surpassing Ourselves: An Inquiry into the Nature and Implications of Expertise* (1993, also with Marlene Scardamalia) and the forthcoming *Education and Mind in the Knowledge Age.*

Dr. Peter Hilton
Mathematician

Peter Hilton is Distinguished Professor of Mathematics Emeritus at the State University of New York (Binghamton) and Distinguished Professor at the University of Central Florida. He holds M.A. and Doctorate of Philosophy degrees from Oxford University and a Ph.D. from Cambridge University. He has an honorary doctorate of humanities from Northern Michigan University, an honorary doctorate of science from the Memorial University of Newfoundland, and an honorary doctorate of science from the Autonomous University of Barcelona. In addition to his activity in research and teaching as a mathematician, he has a continuing interest in mathematics education and has served on many national and international committees and as chairman of the United States Commission on Mathematics Instruction. Dr. Hilton is the author of several important books, his most recent being *Mathematical Reflections*, jointly with Derek Holton and Jean Pedersen, and many research articles on algebraic topology, homological algebra, group theory, and category theory.

Dr. Joseph H. Rubinstein
Biologist and Educator

Joseph H. Rubinstein is Professor of Education and Chairperson of the Department of Education at Coker College, Hartsville, South Carolina. He received B.A., M.S., and Ph.D. degrees in biology from New York University, completing his studies in 1969. His interest in elementary education was kindled by his participation in the late 1960s in an experimental science curriculum development project, the Conceptually Oriented Program in Elementary Science (COPES). During that time he worked in the New York City public schools helping elementary school teachers implement science programs in their classrooms. Dr. Rubinstein served as the Director of Open Court Publishing Company's Mathematics and Science Curriculum Development Center during the development of *Real Math™*, the precursor to *SRA Math Explorations and Applications*. In 1984 he joined the faculty of Coker College, where his principal duties include training prospective teachers to teach mathematics and science.

T16

Reviewers

Dr. Prentice Baptiste
Manhattan, KS

Debney Biggs
Shreveport, LA

Pat Dahl
Vancouver, WA

Karen Hardin
Houston, TX

Susan Humphries
BelAir, MD

Tucky Marchica
Inverness, IL

Dr. Marilyn Neil
Birmingham, AL

Bill Smith
Haddonfield, NJ

Bob Winkler
Overland Park, KS

Game Mat Testers

Grace Brethren Elementary School
Columbus, OH

Huber Ridge Elementary School
Westerville School District
Westerville, OH

St. Paul's Elementary School
Columbus Diocese
Westerville, OH

Tremont Elementary School
Upper Arlington School District
Upper Arlington, OH

TEACHER'S GUIDE
Level 6

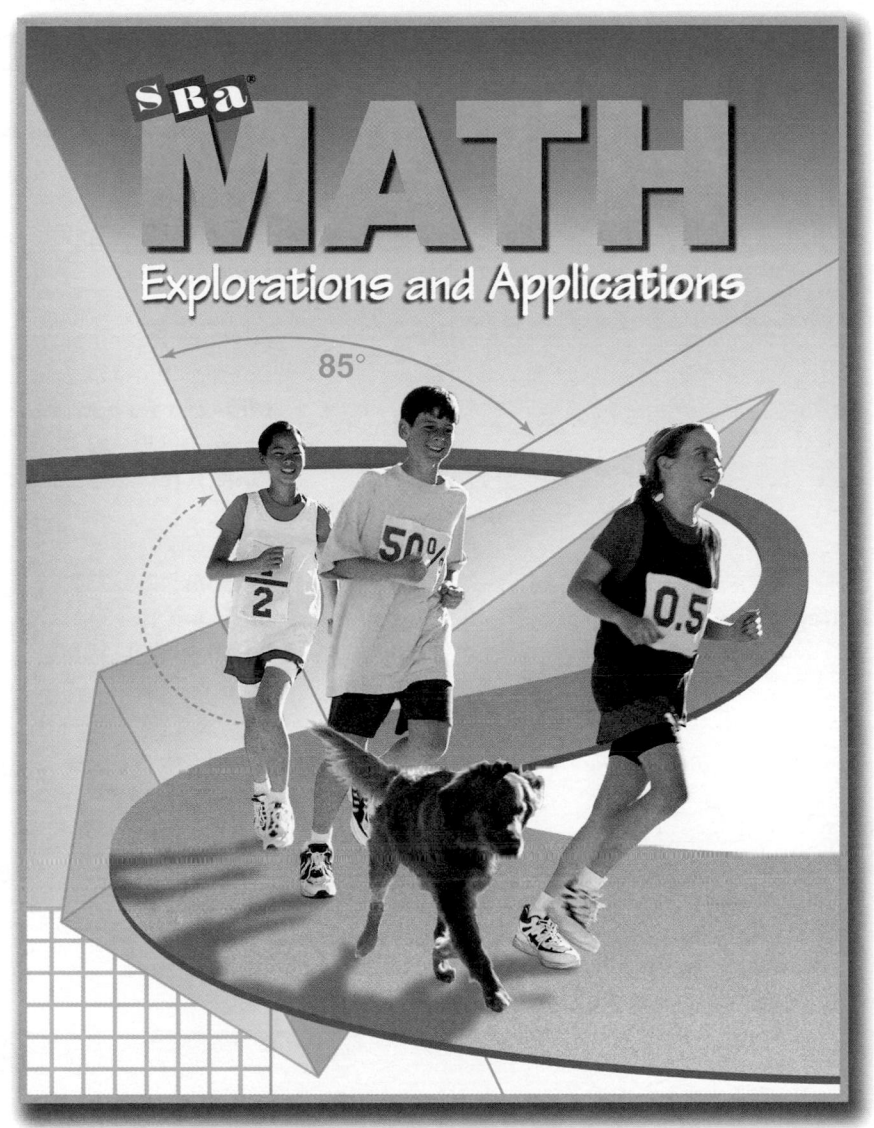

Stephen S. Willoughby
Carl Bereiter
Peter Hilton
Joseph H. Rubinstein

**SRA
McGraw-Hill**

Columbus, Ohio

*A Division of The **McGraw·Hill** Companies*

TABLE OF CONTENTS

Program Overview T2–T3
Program Organization T4–T5
Student Edition Features
    Explore T6–T7
    Practice T8–T9
    Problem Solving T10–T11
Teacher's Guide Features Lesson Cycle T12–T13
Assessment T14
Program Philosophy T15
Authors and Contributors T16
Program Organization T19
Components Chart T20
Managing Resources and Assessment T21
Manipulatives Chart T23
Games and Thinking Stories T24
Expanded Counting T25
Finger Sets T26
Student Edition Table of Contents T27
Pacing the First Half of the Book T32

STUDENT EDITION PAGES
Unit 1
    Whole Numbers and Integers 2A–99
    Lessons 1–13 4–47
    Mid-Unit Review 48–49
    Lessons 14–26 50–95
    Unit 1 Test 96–97
Unit 2
    Decimals and Exponents 100A–173
    Lessons 27–37 102–135
    Mid-Unit Review 136–137
    Lessons 38–47 138–169
    Unit 2 Test 170–171

Unit 3
    Percents and Number Theory 174A–235
    Lessons 48–54 176–199
    Mid-Unit Review 200–201
    Lessons 55–64 202–231
    Unit 3 Test 232–233
    Pacing the Second Half of the Book 236A–236B
Unit 4
    Fractions and Mixed Numbers 236C–339
    Lessons 65–81 238–291
    Mid-Unit Review 292–293
    Lessons 82–94 294–335
    Unit 4 Test 336–337
Unit 5
    Algebra Readiness 340A–435
    Lessons 95–111 342–393
    Mid-Unit Review 394–397
    Lessons 112–123 398–431
    Unit 3 Test 432–433
Unit 6
    Geometry 436A–551
    Lessons 124–137 438–483
    Mid-Unit Review 484–487
    Lessons 138–156 488–547
    Unit 6 Test 548–549

Cumulative Review 552–587
Tables of Measurement and Formulas 588–591
Glossary 592–599
Game Directory 600–602
Game Mats 603–629
Index 630–640
Scope and Sequence 641–644

SRA/McGraw-Hill

*A Division of The **McGraw·Hill** Companies*

1999 imprint

Copyright © 1998 by SRA/McGraw-Hill. All rights reserved.
Except as permitted under the United States Copyright Act,
no part of this publication may be reproduced or distributed
in any form or by any means, or stored in a database or
retrieval system, without prior written permission from the
publisher.

Printed in the United States of America.

Send all inquiries to:
SRA/McGraw-Hill
250 Old Wilson Bridge Road, Suite 310
Worthington, OH 43085

ISBN 0-02-687866-6

2 3 4 5 6 7 8 9 WEB 02 01 00 99 98

Acknowledgments

Photo Credits
p. T1, (l) ©Jeff Smith/Fotosmith; (r) ©Timothy Fuller; **T3,** ©Aaron Haupt; **T4,** ©Jeff
Smith/Fotosmith; **T5,** ©Aaron Haupt; **T6,** ©Jeff Smith/Fotosmith; **T7,** ©Jeff
Smith/Fotosmith; **T8,** (l) ©Jeff Smith/Fotosmith; (r) ©Timothy Fuller; **T9,** ©Jeff
Smith/Fotosmith; **T10,** ©Jeff Smith/Fotosmith; **T11,** ©Jeff Smith/Fotosmith; **T13,** ©Jeff
Smith/Fotosmith; **T14,** ©Timothy Fuller; **T15,** ©Jeff Smith/Fotosmith; **T32, T33, T236B,**
©1997/PhotoDisc.

Cover Credits
Front cover photo, Fotosmith; **Design and Illustration,** Morgan-Cain & Associates;
Back cover photo, ©Timothy Fuller and Jeff Smith/Fotosmith.

TEACHING THE PROGRAM

Math Explorations and Applications is based upon the idea of making mathematics real for students. It builds upon what children already know when they enter school and upon what they learn from their experiences outside school. It helps children see that mathematics is useful and important in their own lives, and it makes learning mathematics enjoyable.

Math Explorations and Applications is based upon everyday teaching and learning. In the Teacher's Guide are all the activities that go together to make up the total learning experience. These activities have been tried, criticized, revised, and tried again by hundreds of teachers.

Math Explorations and Applications is based upon sound theory, research, and extensive field testing. It is a program that works.

In every grade the program emphasizes thinking skills, problem-solving strategies, real applications, mental arithmetic, estimation, approximation, measurement, organizing data, geometry, probability, statistics, and algebra. In addition, computational skills are introduced at appropriate levels and are reviewed and maintained in that level and in subsequent levels.

PROGRAM ORGANIZATION

There are three ways that *Math Explorations and Applications* has been carefully organized to introduce and reinforce concepts.

Early Introduction of Concepts

Math Explorations and Applications makes a point of exposing students to core problems and concepts from the beginning. For example, in traditional teaching, students first learn the plus sign and later are introduced to the minus sign. When signs are introduced one at a time, students learn to pay no attention to the sign because it is always the same. Students are trained in this way not to figure out the problem but to follow the pattern.

Similar confusion arises in the traditional teaching of subtraction of multidigit numbers. First, children learn to subtract with numbers that require no regrouping (65 – 32, for example). When they are later introduced to regrouping (62 – 35, for example), they are often confused because they have learned an easy and automatic way to subtract, which turns out to work only sometimes.

In *Math Explorations and Applications*, plus and minus signs are introduced at the same time in Level 1. In Level 2, multidigit subtraction problems that require regrouping, as well as those that do not, are introduced early on. Core mathematical concepts are emphasized in an age-appropriate manner at every level. The early introduction of concepts causes much less trouble and confusion later on because students don't have to unlearn patterns that they have begun to rely on. Furthermore, when students reach middle school and high school, they will already have a firm foundation in core mathematical concepts such as probability, statistics, geometry, and algebra.

Revisiting Concepts

While it is convenient to package teaching into neat, isolated units that deal with a single topic, the learning that goes on in children's minds cannot be so neatly packaged. Children learn, forget, and relearn. They catch a glimmer of an idea, lose it, catch it again, and finally get hold of it firmly enough that it becomes a solid part of understanding. In *Math Explorations and Applications*, concepts like inequalities, missing addends, and base 10 are developed and reviewed continuously over the whole year so that they become part of the child's working knowledge.

Throughout the year concepts and skills are introduced and reappear again and again in subsequent lessons and in Mixed Practice so that students never lose them. For example, basic addition, subtraction, multiplication, and division are a major focus of at least one third of the lessons in Level 3 and are practiced in virtually every Practice and Mixed Practice exercise.

Presenting Concepts in Different Contexts

In Level 4 of *Math Explorations and Applications*, multiplication is introduced and reinforced in more than 50 lessons throughout the entire year in all the following contexts:

one-digit number multiplication	conversion graphs
two-digit number multiplication	multidigit numbers
three-digit number multiplication	money
algebra readiness	multiplication facts
area	multiples of 10
commutative property (order of factors)	powers of 10
decimals	problem solving
division	repeated addition
	skip counting
	square numbers
	whole numbers

The thoughtful organization at every level of *Math Explorations and Applications* ensures that students are introduced to mathematics concepts and skills in context at appropriate age levels. They encounter these concepts and use these skills again and again throughout the year and in subsequent years in different, age-appropriate contexts.

> " There are reasons for almost everything we do in mathematics. Children should be encouraged to discover, or at least see, those reasons. Understanding the reasons will help them remember how to do the mathematics; but more important, it will help them understand that the mathematics is related to their reality and that mathematics can be used to help them understand the real world. "
>
> —Stephen S. Willoughby
> *Mathematics Education for a Changing World*

COMPONENTS CHART

A variety of resources that present math concepts in a way all students can learn!

Components	Levels						
	K	1	2	3	4	5	6
Student Edition	✓	✓	✓	✓	✓	✓	✓
Teacher's Guide	✓	✓	✓	✓	✓	✓	✓
Thinking Story Book		✓	✓	✓			
Game Mat Package	✓	✓	✓	✓	✓	✓	✓
Reteaching Masters		✓	✓	✓	✓	✓	✓
Reteaching Workbook		✓	✓	✓	✓	✓	✓
Reteaching Workbook TE		✓	✓	✓	✓	✓	✓
Practice Masters	✓	✓	✓	✓	✓	✓	✓
Practice Workbook	✓	✓	✓	✓	✓	✓	✓
Practice Workbook TE	✓	✓	✓	✓	✓	✓	✓
Enrichment Masters	✓	✓	✓	✓	✓	✓	✓
Enrichment Workbook	✓	✓	✓	✓	✓	✓	✓
Enrichment Workbook TE	✓	✓	✓	✓	✓	✓	✓
Assessment Masters	✓	✓	✓	✓	✓	✓	✓
Home Connections Masters	✓	✓	✓	✓	✓	✓	✓
Literature Library	✓	✓	✓	✓			
Primary Manipulative Kit	✓	✓	✓				
Primary Overhead Manipulative Kit	✓	✓	✓				
Intermediate Manipulative Kit				✓	✓	✓	✓
Intermediate Overhead Manipulative Kit				✓	✓	✓	✓
Teacher Manipulative Kit	✓	✓	✓	✓	✓	✓	✓
Basic Manipulative Kit	✓	✓	✓	✓	✓	✓	✓
Primary Overhead Calculator	✓	✓	✓	✓			
Intermediate Overhead Calculator					✓	✓	✓
TI-108™ Calculator Package	✓	✓	✓	✓			
Math Explorer™ Calculator Package					✓	✓	✓
Math Explorations and Applications CD-ROM Program		✓	✓	✓	✓	✓	✓
The Cruncher CD-ROM Program and Guide					✓	✓	✓
My Silly CD of Counting CD-ROM	✓						
Professional Development Handbook	✓	✓	✓	✓	✓	✓	✓

In *Math Explorations and Applications* there are a variety of resources for students and teachers to use to introduce and demonstrate concepts and to practice math skills. These carefully integrated materials each play an important and well-thought-out role in the program as a whole.

TEACHER'S GUIDE

This comprehensive manual gives specific advice for every lesson and lesson component, as well as teaching tips, explanations, and background information.

STUDENT EDITION

The Student Edition provides practice with written problems. It is also used to present games and activities. It is not, however, the main source of concept presentation or skill practice. Student Edition pages supplement the teacher's concept presentation and the practice provided by Mental Math exercises, activities, games, and Thinking Stories.

BASIC MANIPULATIVES

Basic Manipulatives—Number Cubes, Number Wheels, and Number Strips—are used throughout *Math Explorations and Applications* in Games and in Mental Math activities that appear in the Teacher's Guide. The Basic Manipulatives allow all students to participate in every Mental Math activity in a nonthreatening way. Mental Math activities provide essential, regular practice in basic math facts. Furthermore, they allow the teacher to informally assess each student's mathematical skill.

The Number Cubes used at Levels 1 and 2 allow students to make any integer from 0 through 100. The students use the cubes to form numbers in games and to show answers during Mental Math exercises. In Levels 3–6, students use Number Wheels for display. Each wheel can be dialed to show any digit from 0 to 9. The wheels allow students to make any integer from 0 through 99,999.

Most Mental Math activities are done in the following three steps. The pace should be lively enough to keep things moving yet not so fast that students have insufficient time to think.

1. "Find." The teacher presents the problem either orally or on the chalkboard. The students find the answer and arrange their Number Cubes or Number Wheel in a position to display it.

2. "Hide." The students hide the answer against their chests. The teacher waits for most of the students to have an answer. Teachers do not need to wait for every student to find and hide an answer, but long enough so that students who are making progress toward a solution have time to finish. Add a "peek-to-be-sure" step to keep all students involved while waiting for the next command.

3. "Show." The students hold up their Number Cubes or Number Wheel so that the teacher can see the response. The teacher quickly checks the responses, shows or tells the correct answer, and quickly moves to the next problem. Only the teacher and the students who got a wrong answer need know about it. Teachers can give these students extra teaching later on.

PRIMARY AND INTERMEDIATE MANIPULATIVE KITS

In the real world, students experience number in many different representations. If in mathematics instruction they are given only one way of representing number—whether with rods, blocks, coins, sticks, or tally marks—they are liable to become dependent upon that one method. In *Math Explorations and Applications* all these ways—and more—of representing number are used.

Whenever appropriate, manipulatives are used to show the connection between the real world and the mathematics. The use of manipulatives is discontinued after a sufficient connection has been made so that the abstract nature of mathematics is not obscured.

LESSON SUPPORT MATERIALS

A variety of extra activities is available to support lesson concepts and skills. Activities in the Practice Workbook provide extra practice in computational skills. Enrichment activities offer extensions, and Reteaching activities help those who have not yet grasped the lesson concept or skill. These activities are keyed to each lesson. Assessment masters provide the Mastery Checkpoints, Mid-Unit Reviews, and Unit Tests.

TECHNOLOGY SUPPORT MATERIALS

◆ Calculators are suggested for use in appropriate lessons.

◆ SRA **Cruncher** suggestions are also provided at point of use when a spreadsheet application would be appropriate or would facilitate solving a problem.

◆ The *Math Explorations and Applications* Software provides extra practice for specific skills in a motivating format.

PACING

Math Explorations and Applications is intended to be taught at a lively pace but not to be rushed through at the expense of achievement. Lessons are generally written to fill a 45-minute time period. Teachers should move quickly from activity to activity. Introductions and lesson closures should be short because these tend to be ineffective and often lose students' attention.

The efficient lesson plans in *Math Explorations and Applications* help teachers gives their students the chance to practice skills, to solve thinking problems, and to do enrichment activities. Here are some tips for using the resources efficiently.

Be prepared. Having necessary materials ready is, of course, important. To help, sections in the Lesson Plans entitled "Looking Ahead" and "Materials" will be useful. This is a good reason to read the lesson in advance.

Watch the clock. The clock can tell a teacher when he or she has concentrated on an activity too long, even before students show signs of restlessness. Teachers should keep an eye on the clock to make sure they don't spend too much time talking or shifting from one activity to another.

Extend lessons to more than one day. Teachers may occasionally find it necessary to spend an extra day on some lessons. This is expected. It is recommended that more than one day be spent on many lessons. The time gained by extending a lesson should go to more teaching and drill on related skills, to related games, or to a review of prerequisite skills.

> " *Whole-class response activities encourage practice, allow students to correct their own errors, and allow the teacher to identify difficulties that individual students are having or that are common to the entire class.* "
>
> —Stephen S. Willoughby
> *Mathematics Education for a Changing World*

If you have more than forty-five minutes a day for math. Below are some ideas for extending parts of the lessons.

◆ Lengthen game periods by five minutes each (more when new games are introduced).

◆ Repeat whole-group activities when you feel that the students will remain interested.

◆ Lengthen Mental Math exercises by up to five minutes.

◆ Lengthen demonstrations and seminars by two or three minutes at most.

◆ Use the Enrichment masters.

If you have less than forty-five minutes a day for math. Many teachers will be tempted to forgo Games or Thinking Stories in a time crunch, but these elements of *Math Explorations and Applications* are vital for developing mathematical intelligence, without which computational skills have little value. Try these suggestions if there is little time.

◆ Present the Thinking Stories during reading or some other time outside the regular math period.

◆ Conduct games outside the regular math period. Set up game-playing sessions every Friday, for example. Be aware, however, that not all games can be transferred to special sessions, because sometimes a game provides practice that will help students complete a particular lesson.

◆ Complete Mental Math exercises during five-minute periods at the beginning or end of the day or right before or after lunch. These sessions are not always essential to a particular lesson, but they do provide regular drill with Mental Math and basic math facts.

ASSESSMENT

Math Explorations and Applications is unusually rich in opportunities to keep track of—and do something about—individual student progress.

In the Teacher's Guide

Each lesson in the Teacher's Guide provides at least two different assessment suggestions. One is Assessment Criteria, which provides questions teachers can ask themselves as they observe students completing the lesson activities. Additional suggestions include the following:

◆ Informal assessment (interviews, observation, and oral assessment)

◆ Formal assessment (Tests, Reviews, Mastery Checkpoints, and Mastery Checkpoint Masters)

◆ Self-Assessment

◆ Portfolio and Performance Assessment

In the Student Edition

A formal Mid-Unit Review as well as a Unit Review and a Unit Test are provided in the Student Edition in Levels 1–6. Self-Assessments and timed tests are included throughout the Student Editions for students to evaluate their own performances.

In the Assessment Book

In the Assessment Book, there is a master for each Mastery Checkpoint, and an additional Mid-Unit Review and two Unit Tests, one in standardized (multiple-choice) format. Each unit also provides Performance Assessment activities and Portfolio Assessment suggestions. The Assessment Book includes additional information on the various alternative assessment options that are provided in the program, as well as suggestions for using rubrics to grade these assessments.

Informal Daily Assessment

Use Mental Math, Games, Thinking Stories, and Student Edition pages for day-to-day observation and assessment of how well each student is learning the skills and grasping concepts. Because of their special nature, these activities are an effective and convenient means of monitoring. Games, for example, allow the teacher to watch students practice particular skills under conditions more natural to students than most classroom activities. Mental Math activities allow the teacher to get feedback from each student, to give immediate feedback to each student, and to keep all the students actively involved.

To follow through on daily monitoring, consider the Reteaching strategy or master in each lesson to provide immediate help to students who are having difficulty.

Mastery Checkpoints and Charts

To help teachers formally yet conveniently monitor the progress of each student, there are more than 20 skills identified at each grade level that are important for future progress. These skills are listed on the Mastery Checkpoint Chart in the Assessment Book for each grade level. Each skill is described in detail in the Mastery Checkpoint section of the Teacher's Guide lesson in which teachers can formally assess that skill. These Mastery Checkpoints are an opportunity for teachers to monitor how well students have mastered basic skills and to provide extra help to those who are having trouble. Mastery Checkpoints are placed in the lesson in which most, but not all, of the students are expected to have achieved adequate proficiency in the skill. Teachers should not hold up the class waiting for every student to demonstrate success.

Using the Mastery Checkpoint Chart

◆ Fill in the names of all the students in the class.

◆ When a Mastery Checkpoint is encountered in the Teacher's Guide, follow the suggestions for observing and assessing each student's success.

◆ ✓ Place a check mark in the appropriate column of the Mastery Checkpoint Chart beside the name of each student who demonstrates success on the objective in question.

◆ **P** Pencil in a *P* in the appropriate column for each student who grasps the concept but still needs further practice to sharpen his or her skill. Assign extra practice to students whose names you marked with a *P*.

◆ **T** Pencil in a *T* for each student who has not yet grasped the idea and needs further teaching. Give extra teaching or Reteaching to students whose names you marked with a *T*.

◆ Change Ts to Ps and Ps to check marks when students demonstrate success on the objective. Do not hold up the entire class, however, waiting for all students to demonstrate success. More teaching and practice on a particular skill is always given in a later lesson, usually the following one. At that time teachers can focus on those students who need extra help.

> " *Observation of game-playing activity resembles observation of real-life-out-of-school activities as closely as anything we are likely to see in school. Such observation will often give greater insight into a child's thought patterns than anything else the teacher can do.* "
>
> —Stephen S. Willoughby
> *Mathematics Education for a Changing World*

MANIPULATIVE KITS

Component	Game Mat Package (K-6)	Basic (K)	Basic (1-2)	Basic (3-6)	Primary (K-2)	Primary Overhead (K-2)	Intermediate (3-6)	Intermediate Overhead (3-6)	Teacher (K-6)
Angle Ruler							✓		
Attribute Blocks					✓	✓			
Base-10 Blocks				✓	✓	✓	✓		
Beakers									✓
Bills	✓*					✓		✓	
Classifying Counters					✓				
Clock Faces (demonstration or individual)					✓	✓	✓	✓	✓
Coins	✓*					✓		✓	
Counters (opaque or two-sided)	✓				✓	✓	✓	✓	
Cubes (interlocking)					✓		✓		
Decimal Set							✓		
Dual-Dial Scale									✓
Fraction Cubes							✓		
Fraction Tiles					✓	✓		✓	
Funnels							✓		
Geoboard					✓	✓			
Geometric Solids					✓				
Geometric Volume Set							✓		
Math Balance									✓
Metric Grids								✓	
Mirrors					✓		✓		
Number Cubes—0-5 and 5-10 Units	✓	✓	✓	✓					
Number Cubes—0-5 and 5-10 Tens			✓						
Number Line (walk-on)					✓				
Number Strips		✓	✓						
Number Tiles						✓		✓	
Number Wheels				✓					
Pattern Blocks					✓	✓			
Place Markers	✓								
Place Value Pad							✓		
Precision Balance									✓
Protractors							✓		
Shape Set					✓			✓	
Spinners and Dice (blank)						✓	✓	✓	
Stopwatch									✓
Tape Measure					✓		✓		
Thermometer (classroom, demonstration, or individual)					✓	✓	✓	✓	✓
Venn Diagram/Graphing Mat									✓

*not in the Kindergarten package

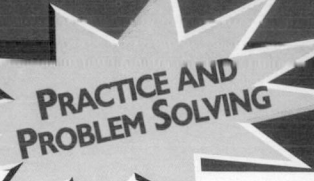

GAMES AND THINKING STORIES

GAMES

Games do not provide just fun or enrichment in *Math Explorations and Applications;* they are a vital, almost daily part of the program. Games give students a chance to develop their mathematical skills and understandings in situations in which those skills and understandings count. Games provide practice. They give students a means of becoming proficient in the mathematical skills to which they've been introduced. Some games give students a chance to work out important mathematical ideas and problem-solving strategies. Games also give the teacher an opportunity for informal assessment. By observing game-playing sessions, teachers can quickly assess how well individual students have learned the skill being practiced.

Each game involves the use of specific skills, but there is usually also a certain amount of luck involved, so the more able student does not always win. When a lesson plan prescribes a game, it does so because the principal skills involved in that game need attention at that time. Some lesson plans suggest that students play games of their choice. The Game Directory lists principal skills involved in each game to help the teacher select those games that will give each student an appropriate form of practice. Game Mats and Cube Games are the two types of games used in *Math Explorations and Applications*.

GAME MATS

Many of the games in *Math Explorations and Applications* are board games found in the Game Mat package for each grade level. There are five Game Mats in Kindergarten, 13 in Levels 1–3, and 14 in Levels 4–6. In each Game Mat package there are 15 copies of each Game Mat, as well as enough counters, place markers, Number Cubes, and money so that the entire class can play a game at the same time. Also included is A Guide for Using the Game Mats and an overhead transparency of each game for introducing the games to the class. Many of the Game Mats are offered in both a standard and a harder version. A copy of each game can also be found in the back of this Teacher's Guide.

CUBE GAMES

Many games don't require Game Mats. They use Number Cubes or sometimes require no materials at all. These games, presented in the Student Edition in Levels 3–6 and in the Teacher's Guide in Levels K–2, reinforce basic math skills and involve mathematical reasoning.

INTRODUCING GAMES

Here are some tips for making sure that games are played correctly.

◆ Familiarize yourself with each game by playing it before showing the students how to play it.

◆ Show, don't just tell, how a game is played. Games should be demonstrated in front of the class when they are first introduced. Overhead Game Mats are provided for this purpose. Verbalize the rules as you demonstrate.

◆ Make sure each student can see when a game is demonstrated.

◆ Supervise to see that students get off to the right start after you've introduced a game.

◆ Let students who know the game rules help those who haven't played it.

ORGANIZING SUCCESSFUL GAME SESSIONS

◆ Mixing ability levels from time to time, however, keeps some students from having an oppressive sense of their slowness.

◆ Change groupings from day to day. Students can learn different things by playing with different partners.

◆ Assign a referee to each group. The referee sees that the rules are followed, reminds players when it is their turn, settles disputes, keeps track of scores, and in some games acts as banker. Associate a sense of honor and responsibility around the role of the referee so that students will be willing to serve as referee.

◆ Encourage students to play games during free time—in school and at home—as well as during the scheduled game periods.

◆ Allow students to make up and name their own variations of the games. Whenever students regularly misinterpret a rule, there's a good chance they have discovered a new and, to them, more interesting version of the game. Be alert, however, to avoid versions that reduce the skill-practice value of the game.

◆ Encourage parents, teacher aides, or older students to participate in game-playing sessions with students.

◆ Stress enjoyment rather than competition. Emphasize sportsmanship, fair play, and giving each player a turn.

◆ Teach students to control their excitement and to speak in a low voice.

◆ Make Game Mats accessible. Store Game Mats so that students can find and return them by themselves.

THINKING STORIES

Thinking Stories are an essential part of *Math Explorations and Applications*. The stories and related thinking problems tap into the child's world of fantasy and humor. They are aimed at developing quantitative intelligence—creativity and common sense in the use of mathematics. The stories allow students to discover the power of their own mathematical common sense and of their innate capacity for reasoning. The stories and problems are filled with surprises, so students cannot apply arithmetic routinely. Instead they must apply mathematical common sense to choose which operation to use, to recognize which data are relevant to the questions asked, to determine whether an answer is absurd, and to decide when calculation isn't necessary.

THINKING STORY CHARACTERS

The various characters in the stories appear in all grade levels. The children in the stories age with each grade level so that they are about the same age as the students reading the stories. All the characters have peculiar thinking patterns that students come to know. Mr. Muddle, for example, is always forgetting things. Ferdie jumps to conclusions, and Mr. Breezy provides too much information. Students are challenged to listen carefully and to try to outthink the characters.

READING THE THINKING STORIES

The Thinking Stories are designed to be read to students. They appear in the Teacher's Guide and in separate Thinking Story books in Levels 1–3. At Levels 4–6 the Thinking Stories appear in three to five or more parts in the student book so that students have an option to read them individually or in groups, depending upon their reading abilities. As the stories unfold, students are asked questions that prompt them to think ahead of the characters—to spot what is wrong with what a character has done or said, to anticipate what is going to happen as a result, or to think of other possibilities that the character hasn't considered.

Following each story is a selection of short problems. Like the story questions, these problems generally require more thinking than computation and have a mixture of difficulty levels.

PACING

Most teachers spend about 15 minutes reading a Thinking Story and discussing the corresponding questions. In many lessons teachers may spend about five minutes on three or four of the questions that follow the story.

The Introduction to the Storybook for Levels 1–3 contains a briefing on the characters and useful hints on presenting stories and problems.

Table of Contents

Whole Numbers and Integers

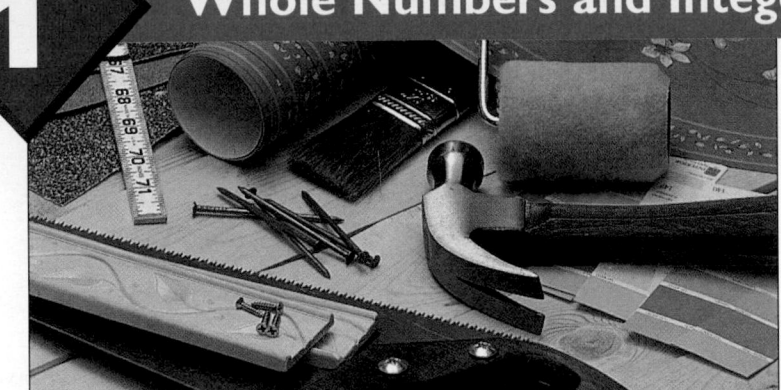

HOW TO PACE THE PROGRAM T32

UNIT 1 PLANNER   Unit Overview, Lesson Plans, Unit Connections, Assessment Overview, Program Resources 2a
     • School to Work Connection: Decorators Use Math 2

LESSON 1   Measuring and Visualizing CHECKPOINT 4
   PRACTICE/PROBLEM SOLVING

LESSON 2   Place Value CHECKPOINT 8
   MIXED PRACTICE/PRACTICE
     • Game: Roll and Regroup a Number Game

LESSON 3   Estimating with Fractions CHECKPOINT 12
   PRACTICE/PROBLEM SOLVING

LESSON 4   Adding and Subtracting 14
   MIXED PRACTICE
     • Game: Roll- Sub-Add Game

LESSON 5   Multiplying and Dividing 16
   MIXED PRACTICE
     • Game: Multifact Game

LESSON 6   Applying Basic Facts 18
   MIXED PRACTICE
     • Game: Cubo

LESSON 7   Mental Arithmetic 20
   MIXED PRACTICE/PROBLEM SOLVING/INTEGRATED PROBLEM SOLVING
     • Thinking Story: Mr. Muddle's Extra-Large Problems, Part 1

LESSON 8   Multidigit Addition 24
   PRACTICE

LESSON 9   Multidigit Subtraction CHECKPOINT 28
   PRACTICE/MIXED PRACTICE/ PROBLEM SOLVING

LESSON 10   Addition and Subtraction Applications 32
   PROBLEM SOLVING/MIXED PRACTICE
     • Game: Don't Go Over 1000 Game

LESSON 11   Powers and Multiples of 10 36
   PRACTICE/INTEGRATED PROBLEM SOLVING
     • Thinking Story: Mr. Muddle's Extra-Large Problems, Part 2

LESSON 12   Multidigit Multiplication CHECKPOINT 40
   PRACTICE/MIXED PRACTICE

LESSON 13   Applying Multiplication 44
   PROBLEM SOLVING/MIXED PRACTICE
     • Game: Roll a Problem Game

Mid-Unit Review ASSESSMENT 48

LESSON 14   Division CHECKPOINT 50
   MIXED PRACTICE/PROBLEM SOLVING

LESSON 15   Dividing by a One-Digit Divisor CHECKPOINT 54
   PRACTICE

LESSON 16   Dividing by a Multidigit Divisor 58
   PRACTICE/MIXED PRACTICE/PROBLEM SOLVING
     • Game: Roll a Problem Game (Division)

LESSON 17   Division Applications 64
   PRACTICE/PROBLEM SOLVING/MIXED PRACTICE
     • Game: Roll and Divide Game

LESSON 18   Arithmetic Applications CHECKPOINT 68
   PROBLEM SOLVING/INTEGRATED PROBLEM SOLVING
     • Thinking Story: Mr. Muddle's Extra-Large Problems, Part 3

LESSON 19   Using Your Calculator 72
   MIXED PRACTICE
     • Game: Key Keys Game

LESSON 20   Calculator or Mental Arithmetic? CHECKPOINT 74
   MIXED PRACTICE/PROBLEM SOLVING
     • Game: Approximation Game

LESSON 21   Rounding 78
   PRACTICE/PROBLEM SOLVING

LESSON 22   Using Negative Numbers 82
   PRACTICE/MIXED PRACTICE

LESSON 23   Computing with Negative Numbers 84
   MIXED PRACTICE/PROBLEM SOLVING/INTEGRATED PROBLEM SOLVING
     • Thinking Story: Mr. Muddle's Extra-Large Problems, Part 4

LESSON 24   Multiplying Positive and Negative Numbers 88
   EXPLORE/PRACTICE

LESSON 25   Unit 1 Review ASSESSMENT 90

LESSON 26   Unit 1 Practice 92
   MIXED PRACTICE/PROBLEM SOLVING
     • Game: Numbo Jumbo

UNIT 1 TEST 96

Unit 1 Wrap-Up Project: Clever Counting 98

Table of Contents

Decimals and Exponents

UNIT 2 PLANNER — Unit Overview, Lesson Plans, Unit Connections, Assessment Overview, Program Resources 100a
• School to Work Connection: Gas Station Attendants Use Math 100

LESSON 27 — Adding and Subtracting Decimals CHECKPOINT 102
PRACTICE/*MIXED* PRACTICE/PROBLEM SOLVING
• Game: Harder Roll a Decimal Game

LESSON 28 — Applying Decimals............................ 106
PROBLEM SOLVING/*MIXED* PRACTICE/*INTEGRATED* PROBLEM SOLVING
• Thinking Story: Efficiency Experts, Part 1

LESSON 29 — Decimals and Powers of 10................... 110
PRACTICE

LESSON 30 — Multiplying Decimals and Whole Numbers....... 114
PRACTICE

LESSON 31 — Multiplying Decimals CHECKPOINT.............. 116
PRACTICE/PROBLEM SOLVING

LESSON 32 — Precision with Customary Measurements 120
EXPLORE/PRACTICE

LESSON 33 — Reporting Metric Measurements 122
EXPLORE/PROBLEM SOLVING

LESSON 34 — Solving Problems Using Decimals 124
PROBLEM SOLVING/*MIXED* PRACTICE
• Game: Make 25 Game

LESSON 35 — Understanding Division by Decimals............ 128
PRACTICE

LESSON 36 — Dividing by Decimals CHECKPOINT.............. 130
PRACTICE/PROBLEM SOLVING/*MIXED* PRACTICE

LESSON 37 — Arithmetic with Decimals..................... 134
MIXED PRACTICE/PROBLEM SOLVING

Mid-Unit Review ASSESSMENT 136

LESSON 38 — Keeping Sharp 138
MIXED PRACTICE/PROBLEM SOLVING/*INTEGRATED* PROBLEM SOLVING
• Thinking Story: Efficiency Experts, Part 2

LESSON 39 — Exponents 142
EXPLORE/PRACTICE/PROBLEM SOLVING
• Algebra Readiness

LESSON 40 — Counting Possibilities 146
EXPLORE/PROBLEM SOLVING

LESSON 41 — Writing Powers of 10 148
EXPLORE/PRACTICE/*INTEGRATED* PROBLEM SOLVING
• Thinking Story: Efficiency Experts, Part 3

LESSON 42 — Multiplying and Dividing Using Exponents 152
EXPLORE/*MIXED* PRACTICE

LESSON 43 — Approximation with Exponents CHECKPOINT 154
PRACTICE/PROBLEM SOLVING/*MIXED* PRACTICE

LESSON 44 — Interpreting Multidigit Numbers................ 158
PROBLEM SOLVING/PRACTICE

LESSON 45 — Scientific Notation............................ 162
EXPLORE/PRACTICE

LESSON 46 — Unit 2 Review ASSESSMENT...................... 164

LESSON 47 — Unit 2 Practice............................... 166
MIXED PRACTICE/PROBLEM SOLVING

UNIT 2 TEST ASSESSMENT.................................... 170

Unit 2 Wrap-Up Project: Planning a Trip..................... 172

Calculator

Table of Contents

UNIT 3 PLANNER	Unit Overview, Lesson Plans, Unit Connections, Assessment Overview, Program Resources	174a
	• School to Work Connection: Bankers Use Math	174
LESSON 48	Percents	176
	PRACTICE/*MIXED* PRACTICE	
	• Game: Tips Game	
LESSON 49	Computing Percent Discounts	180
	PRACTICE/*MIXED* PRACTICE	
LESSON 50	Percents on a Calculator	182
	PRACTICE/PROBLEM SOLVING/*MIXED* PRACTICE	
	• Game: $50 Price Game	
LESSON 51	Sales Tax and Discounts CHECKPOINT	186
	PROBLEM SOLVING/*MIXED* PRACTICE/*INTEGRATED* PROBLEM SOLVING	
	• Thinking Story: Competition, Part 1	
LESSON 52	Calculating Interest	190
	EXPLORE/PRACTICE	
LESSON 53	Compound Interest	192
	EXPLORE/PRACTICE/PROBLEM SOLVING	
LESSON 54	Reversing Percent Problems	196
	EXPLORE/PROBLEM SOLVING	

	Mid-Unit Review ASSESSMENT	200
LESSON 55	Applying Percents CHECKPOINT	202
	PROBLEM SOLVING	
LESSON 56	Keeping Sharp	204
	MIXED PRACTICE/*INTEGRATED* PROBLEM SOLVING	
	• Algebra Readiness	
	• Thinking Story: Competition, Part 2	
LESSON 57	Multiples of 9	208
	EXPLORE	
	• Act It Out: Tricky Nines	
LESSON 58	Finding Divisibility Rules	210
	EXPLORE/PRACTICE	
LESSON 59	Using Divisibility Rules	214
	PROBLEM SOLVING/*MIXED* PRACTICE	
LESSON 60	Factors	218
	PRACTICE/*INTEGRATED* PROBLEM SOLVING	
	• Thinking Story: Competition, Part 3	
LESSON 61	Prime and Composite Numbers	222
	EXPLORE/*INTEGRATED* PROBLEM SOLVING	
	• Thinking Story: Competition, Part 4	
LESSON 62	Checking Products	226
	EXPLORE/PRACTICE	
LESSON 63	Unit 3 Review ASSESSMENT	228
LESSON 64	Unit 3 Practice	230
	MIXED PRACTICE	
UNIT 3 TEST ASSESSMENT		232
Unit 3 Wrap-Up Project: A Birthday Present		234

PACING THE REST OF THE YEAR..............................236a

UNIT 4 PLANNER — Unit Overview, Lesson Plans, Unit Connections, Assessment Overview, Program Resources 236c
  • School to Work Connection: Firefighters Use Math......236

LESSON 65 — **Fractions of Whole Numbers**................238
PRACTICE/PROBLEM SOLVING/*MIXED* PRACTICE
  • Algebra Readiness
  • Game: Fractions of 60 Game

LESSON 66 — **Multiplying Fractions**.........................242
PRACTICE

LESSON 67 — **Decimal Equivalents of Fractions**..............244
EXPLORE/*MIXED* PRACTICE/*INTEGRATED* PROBLEM SOLVING
  • Game: Up to 1 Game
  • Thinking Story: Energy Savers, Part 1

LESSON 68 — **Equivalent Fractions** 248
PRACTICE

LESSON 69 — **Reducing Fractions**...........................250
EXPLORE/*MIXED* PRACTICE
  • Game: Greatest Common Factor Game

LESSON 70 — **Multiplying and Reducing Fractions**.............254
EXPLORE/*MIXED* PRACTICE/*INTEGRATED* PROBLEM SOLVING
  • Thinking Story: Energy Savers, Part 2

LESSON 71 — **Comparing Fractions**.........................258
EXPLORE/PRACTICE

LESSON 72 — **Adding and Subtracting Fractions**...............262
PRACTICE

LESSON 73 — **Adding and Subtracting Special Fractions** CHECKPOINT............264
MIXED PRACTICE
  • Game: Circo 11 Game

LESSON 74 — **Least Common Multiples of Three or More Numbers** 266
EXPLORE/*MIXED* PRACTICE/*INTEGRATED* PROBLEM SOLVING
  • Thinking Story: Energy Savers, Part 3

LESSON 75 — **Probability** 270
PROBLEM SOLVING
  • Game: Roll a 15 Game

LESSON 76 — **Analyzing Probability** 274
MIXED PRACTICE/PROBLEM SOLVING
  • Game: Anything but 10 Game

LESSON 77 — **Practice with Fractions and Decimals**...........278
MIXED PRACTICE/PROBLEM SOLVING

LESSON 78 — **Improper Fractions and Mixed Numbers** 280
PRACTICE/*MIXED* PRACTICE

LESSON 79 — **Practice with Decimal Equivalents** 282
MIXED PRACTICE/PRACTICE/*INTEGRATED* PROBLEM SOLVING
  • Game: Up to 2 Game
  • Thinking Story: Energy Savers, Part 4

LESSON 80 — **Adding and Subtracting Mixed Numbers** CHECKPOINT 286
PRACTICE/*MIXED* PRACTICE
  • Game: Make 1 Game

LESSON 81 — **Using Mixed Numbers**.........................290
PROBLEM SOLVING

Mid-Unit Review ASSESSMENT 292

LESSON 82 — **Keeping Sharp**................................294
PROBLEM SOLVING/*MIXED* PRACTICE
  • Game: Up to 2 Game

LESSON 83 — **Division by Fractions**..........................298
EXPLORE/*MIXED* PRACTICE
  • Act It Out: A Material Problem with Fractions

LESSON 84 — **Functions** 302
MIXED PRACTICE
  • Algebra Readiness

LESSON 85 — **Dividing Fractions** CHECKPOINT 304
EXPLORE/PRACTICE/PROBLEM SOLVING

LESSON 86 — **Using Maps and Charts**........................308
PROBLEM SOLVING

LESSON 87 — **Ratios** 310
PRACTICE/PROBLEM SOLVING

LESSON 88 — **Averages and Rates** CHECKPOINT 314
PRACTICE/PROBLEM SOLVING

LESSON 89 — **Mean, Median, and Mode** 318
PRACTICE/*MIXED* PRACTICE/PROBLEM SOLVING

LESSON 90 — **Choosing an Appropriate Average**.............322
PROBLEM SOLVING

LESSON 91 — **Solving Proportions** 324
EXPLORE/PROBLEM SOLVING

LESSON 92 — **Similar Figures** 328
PRACTICE/PROBLEM SOLVING

LESSON 93 — **Unit 4 Review** ASSESSMENT.....................330

LESSON 94 — **Unit 4 Practice**...............................332
MIXED PRACTICE/PROBLEM SOLVING
  • Game: Inverso Game

UNIT 4 TEST ASSESSMENT 336

Unit 4 Wrap-Up Project: Fair Advertising....................338

■ Calculator

UNIT
5
Algebra Readiness

UNIT 5
PLANNER
Unit Overview, Lesson Plans, Unit Connections,
Assessment Overview, Program Resources 340a
  • School to Work Connection:
    Government Workers Use Math 340

LESSON 95   Creating a Graph 342
             PROBLEM SOLVING

LESSON 96   Interpreting a Graph 346
             PROBLEM SOLVING

LESSON 97   Misleading Graphs. 348
             PROBLEM SOLVING

LESSON 98   Organizing Data CHECKPOINT 350
             EXPLORE/PRACTICE
               • Act It Out: Is Business Booming?

LESSON 99   Ordered Pairs and Function Rules CHECKPOINT . . . 354
             PRACTICE
               • Algebra Readiness

LESSON 100   Translation, Rotation, Reflection, and Symmetry . . 356
             PRACTICE/PROBLEM SOLVING

LESSON 101   Graphing Functions. 362
             PRACTICE
               • Algebra Readiness

LESSON 102   Graphing Data. 364
             PROBLEM SOLVING

LESSON 103   Making and Interpreting Line Graphs. 368
             PRACTICE

LESSON 104   Graphing Functions: Negative Values. 370
             EXPLORE/PROBLEM SOLVING
               • Algebra Readiness

LESSON 105   Practice with Graphing. 374
             MIXED PRACTICE/INTEGRATED PROBLEM SOLVING
               • Game: Get the Point Game
               • Thinking Story: Diet for a Small Terrier, Part 1

LESSON 106   Graphing Composite Functions. 378
             PRACTICE
               • Algebra Readiness

LESSON 107   Inverse Functions 380
             PRACTICE
               • Algebra Readiness

LESSON 108   Keeping Sharp 382
             MIXED PRACTICE/PROBLEM SOLVING/INTEGRATED PROBLEM SOLVING
               • Thinking Story: Diet for a Small Terrier, Part 2

LESSON 109   Determining Rules from Ordered Pairs. 386
             PROBLEM SOLVING/MIXED PRACTICE
               • Algebra Readiness
               • Game: Find the Function Rule Game

LESSON 110   Interpreting Data 388
             PROBLEM SOLVING/MIXED PRACTICE

LESSON 111   Using Formulas 390
             PROBLEM SOLVING
               • Algebra Readiness

Mid-Unit Review ASSESSMENT 394

LESSON 112   Standard Notation for Functions 398
             PRACTICE
               • Algebra Readiness

LESSON 113   Finding Terms of Sequences CHECKPOINT 400
             PROBLEM SOLVING/MIXED PRACTICE
               • Algebra Readiness

LESSON 114   Graphing Linear Functions. 402
             EXPLORE/PROBLEM SOLVING
               • Algebra Readiness

LESSON 115   Order of Operations 406
             PRACTICE/INTEGRATED PROBLEM SOLVING
               • Thinking Story: Diet for a Small Terrier, Part 3

LESSON 116   Graphing Nonlinear Functions. 410
             EXPLORE
               • Algebra Readiness

LESSON 117   More Nonlinear Functions. 412
             MIXED PRACTICE
               • Algebra Readiness

LESSON 118   Graphing a Perimeter Function 414
             PROBLEM SOLVING

LESSON 119   Determining the Function Rule. 416
             EXPLORE/PROBLEM SOLVING/MIXED PRACTICE
               • Algebra Readiness

LESSON 120   Finding Circumference 420
             EXPLORE/MIXED PRACTICE

LESSON 121   Average Monthly Temperature. 424
             PROBLEM SOLVING

LESSON 122   Unit 5 Review ASSESSMENT 426

LESSON 123   Unit 5 Practice. 428
             PRACTICE/MIXED PRACTICE

UNIT 5 TEST ASSESSMENT 432

Unit 5 Wrap-Up Project: Library Research 434

Table of Contents

Geometry

UNIT 6 PLANNER — Unit Overview, Lesson Plans, Unit Connections, Assessment Overview, Program Resources 436a
• School to Work Connection: Architects Use Math 436

LESSON 124 — Area of a Rectangle 438
PRACTICE
• Algebra Readiness

LESSON 125 — Surface Area 440
PRACTICE/PROBLEM SOLVING/INTEGRATED PROBLEM SOLVING
• Thinking Story: On the Move, Part 1

LESSON 126 — Volume of a Rectangular Prism 444
PRACTICE/PROBLEM SOLVING
• Algebra Readiness

LESSON 127 — Area and Volume 448
MIXED PRACTICE
• Algebra Readiness

LESSON 128 — Area of a Right Triangle 452
PRACTICE/MIXED PRACTICE
• Algebra Readiness

LESSON 129 — Parallelograms 456
PRACTICE/MIXED PRACTICE
• Algebra Readiness

LESSON 130 — Area of a Triangle 460
PRACTICE/MIXED PRACTICE
• Algebra Readiness

LESSON 131 — Area of a Trapezoid 464
EXPLORE/PRACTICE
• Algebra Readiness

LESSON 132 — Areas of Figures on a Grid 466
EXPLORE/PRACTICE

LESSON 133 — Triangles and Quadrilaterals 468
PRACTICE/PROBLEM SOLVING

LESSON 134 — Classifying Figures 472
PROBLEM SOLVING/MIXED PRACTICE/INTEGRATED PROBLEM SOLVING
• Game: Three Questions Game
• Thinking Story: On the Move, Part 2

LESSON 135 — Determining Lengths from Given Areas 476
PROBLEM SOLVING
• Algebra Readiness

LESSON 136 — Square Roots 478
EXPLORE/PRACTICE/PROBLEM SOLVING

LESSON 137 — Estimating Measures 482
PROBLEM SOLVING

Mid-Unit Review ASSESSMENT 484

LESSON 138 — Multiplying and Dividing by Powers of 10 488
MIXED PRACTICE

LESSON 139 — The Metric System 490
PRACTICE/MIXED PRACTICE/PROBLEM SOLVING

LESSON 140 — The Customary System 494
PRACTICE

LESSON 141 — Estimating Volume 496
PROBLEM SOLVING

LESSON 142 — Keeping Sharp 498
MIXED PRACTICE/PROBLEM SOLVING/INTEGRATED PROBLEM SOLVING
• Thinking Story: On the Move, Part 3

LESSON 143 — Angles and Rotation 502
EXPLORE/PRACTICE/MIXED PRACTICE

LESSON 144 — Measuring Angles 506
PRACTICE/MIXED PRACTICE

LESSON 145 — Corresponding Angles and Vertical Angles 510
EXPLORE/MIXED PRACTICE

LESSON 146 — Straight and Supplementary Angles CHECKPOINT . . 514
EXPLORE/MIXED PRACTICE

LESSON 147 — Angles of Polygons 518
PRACTICE/EXPLORE/PROBLEM SOLVING

LESSON 148 — Points, Lines, and Planes 522
EXPLORE

LESSON 149 — Congruent and Similar Figures 526
PRACTICE

LESSON 150 — Compass Constructions 528
EXPLORE

LESSON 151 — Circle Graphs 534
EXPLORE/PRACTICE

LESSON 152 — Right Triangles: Squares of Sides 538
EXPLORE

LESSON 153 — Unit 6 Review ASSESSMENT 540

LESSON 154 — Unit 6 Practice 542
MIXED PRACTICE

LESSON 155 — More Practice 544
MIXED PRACTICE

LESSON 156 — Practice 546
MIXED PRACTICE

UNIT 6 TEST ASSESSMENT 548

Unit 6 Wrap-Up Project: Melting Ice Cubes 550

Resources

Cumulative Review 552-587

Tables of Measurement and Formulas 588-591

Glossary 592-599

Game Directory 600-602

Game Mats 603-629

Index 630-639

Scope and Sequence 641-644

▤ Calculator

Dear Student,

You'll find a lot of things in this *Math Explorations and Applications* book. You'll find stories with Mr. Muddle, Ferdie, Portia, Manolita, Marcus, and their friends, whom you may remember from earlier years.

You'll find games that will give you a chance to practice and put to use many of the skills you will be learning.

You'll find stories and examples that will show you how mathematics can help you solve problems and cut down on your work.

You'll be reading and talking about many of the pages with your class. That's because mathematics is something people often learn together and do together.

Of course, this book isn't all fun and games. Learning should be enjoyable, but it also takes time and effort. Most of all, it takes thinking.

We hope you enjoy this book. We hope you learn a lot. And we hope you think a lot.

The Authors of *Math Explorations and Applications*

PACING

HOW TO PACE THE PROGRAM

The lessons in this book are designed to be taught at a lively pace. Students should move quickly from activity to activity. In this way, they will remain alert and interested in what they are learning.

The lively pace is also important because there is much for students to learn at this grade level. Yet, 45 minutes a day is about all that most teachers can devote to mathematics. Therefore, it's important to get as much from those minutes as possible. Here are some tips to help you make the most of your time:

Tips for Making the Most of Your Time

- **Prepare items you'll need for a lesson ahead of time.** See the Lesson Planner sections titled Materials and Program Resources for a complete listing of the items you'll need. The Looking Ahead feature under the Wrap-Up alerts you to any advance preparation needed for an upcoming lesson.
- **Read the lesson plan in advance.** This will save you time and make the lesson run more smoothly.
- **Keep introductions and explanations brief.** You will lose your students' attention if you try to say too much.

HOW TO EXTEND YOUR LESSONS

You might need to spend an extra day teaching some lessons. Lessons that might take an extra day are noted in the individual Lesson Planner and in the Unit Overview Planning Chart—but only you can be the judge. When you decide to let a lesson run two days, try dividing it as follows:

Day 1

- Do all suggested activities, but not the Student Edition pages.
- Use extra time to review the skills students will need for the lesson.
- Modify the Reteaching Strategy/Master and Practice Master suggestions for use with the entire class.
- Don't greatly lengthen the demonstration period (K–3).

Day 2

- Review the Mental Math exercises from the preceding day.
- Provide additional teaching and practice on related skills.
- Devote time to a related Cube Game or Game Mat.
- Allow plenty of time for students to do the Student Edition activities.

WHEN YOU HAVE MORE THAN 45 MINUTES FOR MATH

Tips for Making the Best Use of Extra Time

- Lengthen game periods by five minutes each (more when new games are introduced).
- Repeat whole-group activities when you feel that students will remain interested.
- Lengthen Mental Math exercises by up to five minutes each.
- Lengthen demonstrations and activities by two or three minutes at most.
- Use the Reteaching, Practice, and Enrichment Masters. You might also want to use the various Cross-Curricular Connections strategies provided throughout the Teacher's Guide.

WHEN YOU HAVE FEWER THAN 45 MINUTES FOR MATH

Tips for Making the Best Use of Less Time

- Don't eliminate the games or the Thinking Stories. These help develop mathematical intelligence.
- Do the Thinking Story activities outside the regular mathematics period. There might be time the first thing in the morning, right after lunch, or when you have a read-aloud period.
- Conduct games outside the regular mathematics period—every Friday, perhaps— especially if you have another adult or older student to assist you. If a game provides practice that will help students do the Student Edition exercise, play the game during the lesson.
- Conduct Mental Math on basic facts outside the regular mathematics period.
- Reduce a few lesson components by a minute or two.
- Introduce the Problem of the Day at the start of school each morning instead of at the start of the regular mathematics period.

UNIT 1

Whole Numbers and Integers

REVIEWING ARITHMETIC

OVERVIEW

This unit begins with a review of whole number and decimal place value and the meaning of fractions and mixed numbers. The students review basic facts in addition, subtraction, multiplication, and division. Students practice skills in multidigit addition and multiplication and apply those skills to practical problems. They also review division by one-digit and multidigit divisors. Finally, students review negative numbers and the realistic situations in which these numbers appear.

Integrated Topics in This Unit Include:

♦ reviewing place value for whole numbers and decimals

♦ comparing decimals

♦ writing and estimating fractions and mixed numbers

♦ mastering addition, subtraction, multiplication, and division facts

♦ reviewing and applying multidigit addition and subtraction

♦ reviewing multidigit multiplication and applying multiplication

♦ reviewing multidigit division and interpreting remainders

♦ reviewing negative numbers and their uses

♦ computing with negative numbers

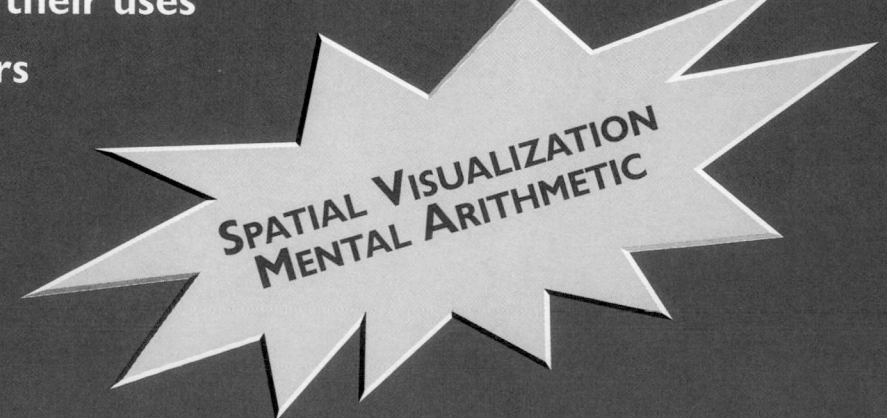

SPATIAL VISUALIZATION
MENTAL ARITHMETIC

"The vision articulated in the 5–8 standards is of a broad, concept-driven curriculum, one that reflects the full breadth of relevant mathematics and its interrelationships with technology. This vision is built on five overall curricular goals for students: learning to value mathematics, becoming confident in their ability, becoming a mathematical problem solver, learning to communicate mathematically, and learning to reason mathematically."

—NCTM Curriculum and Evaluation Standards for School Mathematics

 ## GAMES

Motivating Mixed Practice

Games provide **basic math skills** practice in cooperative groups. Playing the games also develops **mathematical reasoning.**

Roll and Regroup a Number	Lesson 2	page 9
Roll-Sub-Add	Lesson 4	page 14
Busy Bee Game Mat	Lesson 4	page 15
Multifact	Lesson 5	page 16
Marathon 1 Game Mat	Lesson 5	page 17
Marathon 2 Game Mat	Lesson 5	page 17
Cubo	Lesson 6	page 18
Cube-O-Mat Game Mat	Lesson 7	page 22
Harder Cube-O-Mat Game Mat	Lesson 7	page 22
Transaction Game Mat	Lesson 9	page 30
Don't Go Over 1000	Lesson 10	page 34
Roll a Problem	Lesson 13	page 46
Roll a Problem (Division)	Lesson 16	page 62
Roll and Divide	Lesson 17	page 66
Key Keys	Lesson 19	page 73
Approximation	Lesson 20	page 75
Roller Coaster 1 Game Mat	Lesson 20	page 76
Roller Coaster 2 Game Mat	Lesson 20	page 76
Numbo Jumbo	Lesson 26	page 95

 ## THINKING STORY

Integrated Problem Solving

Thinking Stories provide opportunities for students to work in **cooperative groups** and develop **logical reasoning** while they integrate **reading skills** with mathematics.

Mr. Muddle's Extra-Large Problems

Part 1	Lesson 7	pages 22–23
Part 2	Lesson 11	pages 38–39
Part 3	Lesson 18	pages 70–71
Part 4	Lesson 23	pages 86–87

Story Summary "Mr. Muddle's Extra-Large Problems" examines the supply and demand issues involved in building a successful small business, using Mr. Muddle's T-shirt shop as a model. As students progress through the story, they will learn how market testing tells storekeepers what products to keep in stock (in Mr. Muddle's case, how many T-shirts of each size). Students will use multiplication and addition skills to evaluate Mr. Muddle's mistakes and near-mistakes.

PROJECT

Making Connections

The Unit Project makes real-world connections. Students work in **cooperative groups** to solve problems and to communicate their findings. The project presented in the Unit Wrap-Up asks students to compare and contrast our numeration system (Hindu-Arabic numerals) with numeration systems used in other cultures and times. Students should conduct research and do some calculations in those systems as well. Students may work on this project during their free time throughout the unit.

LESSON	PACING	PRIMARY OBJECTIVE	FEATURE	RESOURCES	NCTM STANDARD
1 Measuring and Visualizing 4–7	2 days	✓ to evaluate students' ability to estimate and measure length		Reteaching Strategy Practice Master 1 Enrichment Master 1 Assessment Master	12, 13
2 Place Value 8–11	1 day	✓ to assess students' understanding and use of numbers	Game	Reteaching Master Practice Master 2 Enrichment Master 2 Assessment Masters	3, 5, 6, 8
3 Estimating with Fractions 12–13	1 day	✓ to assess students' familiarity with fractional notation and the use of fractions		Reteaching Strategy Practice Master 3 Enrichment Master 3 Assessment Masters	4, 5, 7
4 Adding and Subtracting 14–15	1 day	to review addition and subtraction facts	Game	Reteaching Strategy Practice Master 4 Enrichment Master 4	7
5 Multiplying and Dividing 16–17	1 day	to review and practice multiplication and division facts	Game	Reteaching Strategy Practice Master 5 Enrichment Master 5	7
6 Applying Basic Facts 18–19	1 day	to practice whole-number arithmetic with the four basic operations	Game	Reteaching Strategy Practice Master 6 Enrichment Master 6	6, 7
7 Mental Arithmetic 20–23	1 day	to practice mental arithmetic	Thinking Story Game	Reteaching Strategy Practice Master 7 Enrichment Master 7	1, 2, 3, 4, 7, 12
8 Multidigit Addition 24–27	1 day	to practice adding multidigit numbers		Reteaching Strategy Practice Master 8 Enrichment Master 8	1, 2, 3, 4, 7
9 Multidigit Subtraction 28–31	1 day	✓ to evaluate students' ability to do multidigit addition and subtraction	Game	Reteaching Strategy Practice Master 9 Enrichment Master 9 Assessment Master	7
10 Addition and Subtraction Application 32–35	1 days	to practice multidigit addition and subtraction and reading a map	Game	Reteaching Strategy Practice Master 10 Enrichment Master 10	1, 2, 3, 4, 7, 12
11 Powers and Multiples of 10 36–39	1 day	to review how to multiply powers and multiples of 10 mentally	Thinking Story	Reteaching Master Practice Master 11 Enrichment Master 11	1, 2, 3, 4, 7
12 Multidigit Multiplication 40–43	1 day	✓ to assess students' ability to do multidigit multiplication		Reteaching Master Practice Master 12 Enrichment Master 12 Assessment Master	7
13 Applying Multiplication 44–47	1 day	to practice multidigit multiplication and approximation	Game	Reteaching Strategy Practice Master 13 Enrichment Master 13	1, 4, 7
Mid-Unit Review 48–49				Assessment Masters	

	LESSON	PACING	PRIMARY OBJECTIVES	FEATURE	RESOURCES	NCTM STANDARD
14	Division 50–53	1 day	✓ to assess mastery of division facts and ability to present answers in appropriate forms	♦	Reteaching Strategy Practice Master 14 Enrichment Master 14 Assessment Master	1, 4, 7
15	Dividing by a One-Digit Divisor 54–57	1 day	✓ to assess students' ability to divide a multidigit dividend by a single-digit divisor	♦	Reteaching Master Practice Master 15 Enrichment Master 15 Assessment Master	3, 7
16	Dividing by a Multidigit Divisor 58–63	2 days	to introduce and practice using shortcuts to divide	Game	Reteaching Master Practice Master 16 Enrichment Master 16	6, 7
17	Division Applications ... 64–67	1 day	to provide practice in mental arithmetic and word problems	Game	Reteaching Strategy Practice Master 17 Enrichment Master 17	1, 2, 3, 4, 7
18	Arithmetic Applications 68–71	1 day	✓ to evaluate students' ability to decide which operation is appropriate to solve a given word problem	♦ Thinking Story	Reteaching Strategy Practice Master 18 Enrichment Master 18 Assessment Masters	1, 2, 3, 4, 7
19	Using Your Calculator 72–73	1 day	to familiarize students with the capabilities of a calculator	Game	Reteaching Strategy Practice Master 19 Enrichment Master 19	7
20	Calculator or Mental Arithmetic 74–77	1 day	✓ to assess students' ability to approximate answers to arithmetic problems	♦ Game	Reteaching Strategy Practice Master 20 Enrichment Master 20 Assessment Master	3, 7
21	Rounding 78–81	1 day	to practice using rounding and approximation		Reteaching Master Practice Master 21 Enrichment Master 21	1, 2, 3, 4, 7
22	Using Negative Numbers 82–83	1 day	to review negative numbers		Reteaching Master Practice Master 22 Enrichment Master 22	4, 5, 6
23	Computing with Negative Numbers ... 84–87	1 day	to practice using negative numbers mentally and with a calculator	Thinking Story	Reteaching Strategy Practice Master 23 Enrichment Master 23	1, 2, 3, 4, 5, 6, 7
24	Multiplying Positive and Negative Numbers 88–89	1 day	to provide an intuitive introduction to the multiplication of integers		Reteaching Strategy Practice Master 24 Enrichment Master 24	6, 7
25	Unit 1 Review 90–91		to review whole numbers and integers		Practice Master 25 Enrichment Master 25	
26	Unit 1 Practice.......... 92–95		to practice with whole numbers and integers	Game	Practice Master 26 Enrichment Master 26	
	Unit 1 Test 96–97		to review whole numbers and integers	♦	Assessment Masters	
	Unit 1 Wrap-Up 98–99			Project		

UNIT CONNECTIONS

INTERVENTION STRATEGIES

In this Teacher's Guide there will be specific strategies suggested for students with individual needs—ESL, Gifted and Talented, Special Needs, Learning Styles, and At Risk. These strategies will be given at the point of use. Here are the icons to look for and the types of strategies that will accompany them:

English as a Second Language
These strategies, designed for students who do not fluently speak the English language, will suggest meaningful ways to present the lesson concepts and vocabulary.

Gifted and Talented
Strategies to enrich and extend the lesson will offer further challenges to students who have easily mastered the concepts already presented.

Special Needs
Students who are physically challenged or who have learning disabilities may require alternative ways to complete activities, record answers, use manipulatives, and so on. The strategies labeled with this icon will offer appropriate methods of teaching lesson concepts to these students.

Learning Styles
Each student has his or her individual approach to learning. The strategies labeled with this icon suggest ways to present lesson concepts so that various learning modalities—such as tactile/kinesthetic, visual, and auditory—can be addressed.

At Risk
These strategies highlight the relevancy of the skills presented, making the connection between school and real life. They are directed toward students who appear to be at risk of dropping out of school before graduation.

TECHNOLOGY CONNECTIONS

The following materials, designed to reinforce and extend lesson concepts, will be referred to throughout this Teacher's Guide. It might be helpful to order the software, videos, and laser discs or to check them out of the school media center or local community library. If the school does not provide Internet access, consider visiting a local library, college, or business specializing in Internet services. Some students may be able to access the Internet at home.

 *Look for this* **Technology Connection** *icon.*

- Eisenhower National Clearinghouse: http://www.enc.org; Telnet: enc.org (login using the word "guest"); or dial (800) 362-4448 (Internet)
- *Turbo Math Facts,* from Mordic Software, Mac, for K-6
- *Word Problem Square Off: Level A,* from Gamco, Mac, for grades 3-8 (software)
- *Mighty Math Calculating Crew,* from Edmark, Mac, IBM, for grades 3-5 (software)
- *Numbers Munchers,* from MECC, Mac, IBM, for grades 2-6 (software)
- *Core Concepts in Math: Problem Solving Series,* by BFA/Systems Impact, laser disc for grades 5-9 (laser disc)
- *Modumath: Arithmetic, Dividing Whole Numbers, Part 1,* from VTAE, VHS, IBM, for grades 6-12 (video, software, or laser disc)
- *Math Mystery Theatre, Mission Division: World's Secret Formula,* from EdCon/Imperial International, VHS, for grades 2-8 (video)
- *Math Mystery Theatre: Mathman and Chikadee vs. the Questioner,* from EdCon/Imperial International, VHS, for grades 2-8 (video)
- *Mastering Math,* by Queue, Mac, IBM, for grades 5-12
- *Mental Math Games,* from Waterford, IBM, for K-8
- *Modumath: Arithmetic, Rounding Numbers* from VTEA, VHS, IBM, for grades 6-12 (video, software, or laser disc)
- *Modumath: Arithmetic, Signed Numbers,* from VTAE, VHS, IBM, for grades 6-12 (video, software, or laser disc)
- *Troggle Trouble,* from MECC, Mac, IBM, for grades 1-6 (software)

CROSS-CURRICULAR CONNECTIONS

This Teacher's Guide offers specific suggestions on ways to connect the math concepts presented in this unit with other subjects that students are studying. Students can connect math concepts with topics they already know about, and they can find examples of math in other subjects and in real-world situations. These strategies are given at the point of use.

Look for these icons:

 Geography

 Social Studies

 Science

 Art

 Language Arts

 Health

 Music

 Math

 Physical Education

 Careers

LITERATURE CONNECTIONS

These books will be presented throughout the Teacher's Guide at the point where they could be used to introduce, reinforce, or extend specific lesson concepts. You may want to locate these books in your school or your local community library.

 *Look for this* **Literature Connection** *icon.*

- ♦ *Skyscraper* by Tim Ostler, Gloucester Press, 1988
- ♦ *You Can't Count a Billion Dollars and Other Little Known Facts About Money* by Barbara Sealing, Ivy Books, 1991
- ♦ *Anno's Mysterious Multiplying Jar* by Masaichiro and Mitsumasa Anno, Philomel Books, 1983
- ♦ *The Sneaky Square + 113 Other Math Activities for Kids* by Richard Sharp and Seymour Metzner, Tab Books, 1990
- ♦ *Arithmetic* by Carl Sandburg, Harcourt Brace Jovanovich, 1993
- ♦ *Rand McNally Children's Atlas of the United States* by Rand McNally, Rand McNally, 1992
- ♦ "Top Dog" in *Math Mini-Mysteries* by Sandra Markle, Atheneum, 1993
- ♦ *How to Count Sheep Without Falling Asleep* by Ralph Leighton and Carl Feyman, Prentice-Hall, 1976
- ♦ *Sarah Plain and Tall* by Patricia MacLachlan, Harper & Row, 1987
- ♦ *Counting on Frank* by Rod Clement, Stevens Children's Books, 1991
- ♦ *Pumpkins* by Mary Lynn Ray, Harcourt Brace Jovanovich, 1992
- ♦ *Cookies* by William Jaspersohn, Macmillan, 1993
- ♦ *Dear Mr. Henshaw* by Beverly Cleary, Dell, 1983
- ♦ *What Do You Mean by Average?* by Elizabeth James, Lothrop, Lee & Shepard Co., 1978
- ♦ *All the Money in the World* by Bill Brittain, HarperCollins, 1979
- ♦ *Math Fun with Money Puzzlers* by Rose Wyler, J. Messner, 1992
- ♦ *Toothpaste Millionaire* by Jean Merrill, Houghton Mifflin, 1972
- ♦ "Approximation" in *Math Smart Junior: Math You'll Understand* by Marcia Lerner, Random House, 1995
- ♦ *Dominoes: Basic Rules and Variations* by Reiner F. Muller, Sterling Publishing Co., 1995
- ♦ "Negative Numbers" in *Math Smart Junior: Math You'll Understand* by Marcia Lerner, Random House, 1995

ASSESSMENT OPPORTUNITIES AT-A-GLANCE

LESSON	PORTFOLIO	PERFORMANCE	FORMAL	SELF	INFORMAL	CUMULATIVE REVIEW	MULTIPLE-CHOICE	MASTERY CHECKPOINTS	ANALYZING ANSWERS
1			✓					✓	
2			✓		✓			✓	
3			✓		✓			✓	
4	✓			✓		✓			
5				✓					
6					✓				
7				✓					
8	✓					✓			✓
9			✓					✓	✓
10	✓								
11					✓				
12			✓			✓		✓	
13					✓				
Mid-Unit Review	✓	✓	✓						
14			✓					✓	✓
15			✓	✓		✓		✓	
16		✓							
17	✓								
18			✓					✓	
19				✓		✓			
20			✓					✓	
21		✓							
22					✓				
23		✓				✓			
24					✓				
25	✓	✓	✓						
26						✓			
Unit Test			✓				✓		

ASSESSMENT OPTIONS

PORTFOLIO ASSESSMENT

Throughout this Teacher's Guide are suggested activities in which students draw pictures, make graphs, write about mathematics, and so on. Keep students' work to assess growth of understanding as the year progresses.

Lessons 4, 8, 10, Mid-Unit Review, 17, and 25

PERFORMANCE ASSESSMENT

Performance assessment items focus on evaluating how students think and work as they solve problems. Opportunities for performance assessment can be found throughout the unit. Rubrics and guides for grading can be found in the front of the Assessment Blackline Masters.

Mid-Unit Review and Lessons 16, 21, 23, and 25

FORMAL ASSESSMENT

A Mid-Unit Review, Unit Review, and Unit Test help assess students' understanding of concepts, skills, and problem solving. The *Math Explorations and Applications* CD-ROM Test Generator can create additional unit tests at three ability levels. Also, Mastery Checkpoints are provided periodically throughout the unit.

Lessons 1, 2, 3, 9, 12, Mid-Unit Review, 14, 15, 18, 20, 25, and Unit Test

SELF ASSESSMENT

Throughout the program students are given the opportunity to check their own math skills.

Lessons 4, 5, 7, and 15

INFORMAL ASSESSMENT

A variety of assessment suggestions are provided, including interviews, oral questions or presentation, debates, and so on. Also, each lesson includes Assessment Criteria, a list of questions about each student's progress, understanding, and participation.

Lessons 2, 3, 6, 11, 13, 19, 22, and 24

CUMULATIVE REVIEW

Cumulative Reviews, covering material presented thus far in the year, are provided in the unit for use as either assessment or practice.

Lessons 4, 8, 12, 15, 19, 23, and 26

MULTIPLE-CHOICE TESTS (STANDARDIZED FORMAT)

Each unit provides a unit test in standardized format, presenting students with an opportunity to practice taking a test in this format.

MASTERY CHECKPOINT

Mastery Checkpoints are provided throughout the unit to assess student proficiency in specific skills. Checkpoints reference appropriate Assessment Blackline Masters and other assessment options. Results of these evaluations can be recorded on the Mastery Checkpoint Chart.

Lessons 1, 2, 3, 9, 12, 14, 15, 18, and 20

ANALYZING ANSWERS

Analyzing answers items suggest possible sources of student error and offer teaching strategies for addressing difficulties.

Lessons 8, 9, and 14

Look for these icons:

> **"Although assessment is done for a variety of reasons, its main goal is to advance students' learning and inform teachers as they make instructional decisions."**
>
> **—NCTM Assessment Standards**

 # MASTERY CHECKPOINTS

WHAT TO EXPECT FROM STUDENTS AS THEY COMPLETE THIS UNIT

❶ MEASURING—LESSON 1

At about this time most students should be able to use appropriate metric units to estimate and measure length with accuracy. They should also have an understanding of the decimal structure of the metric system.

❷ UNDERSTANDING AND USING NUMBERS—LESSON 2

By this time most students should have a solid understanding of the use and significance of numbers in counting, measuring, comparing, and ordering.

❸ UNDERSTANDING FRACTIONS AND MIXED NUMBERS—LESSON 3

At about this time most students should be able to demonstrate mastery of fractions and mixed numbers. Mastery may be assessed by observing students during the Mental Math exercises and during written work.

❹ ADDITION AND SUBTRACTION— LESSON 9

By this time most students should demonstrate mastery of addition and subtraction (multidigit problems and basic facts) by correctly answering at least 20 of the first 25 problems on page 30 in a reasonable amount of time.

❺ MULTIPLICATION—LESSON 12

At this time most students should demonstrate mastery of multiplying multidigit numbers by getting correct answers and using correct procedures in at least 80% of the problems.

❻ INTERPRETING ANSWERS TO DIVISION PROBLEMS—LESSON 14

At about this time most students should be proficient in deciding what form of answer is appropriate in situations that call for division (for example, rounding quotients up, down, or not at all; leaving the remainder as a whole number; or expressing the quotient in decimal or fraction form).

❼ DIVISION (WITH SINGLE-DIGIT DIVISORS)— LESSON 15

At this time most students should demonstrate mastery using the division algorithm to divide by a one-digit divisor by correctly answering at least 80% of the computation problems.

❽ ARITHMETIC APPLICATIONS—LESSON 18

By this time most students should be able to choose the correct operation to use to solve a word problem or to decide that no calculations are needed. Students can demonstrate this ability by using the appropriate operation in at least 80% of the word problems.

❾ APPROXIMATION—LESSON 20

By this time most students should be able to approximate answers to arithmetic problems. As a regular part of your classroom activities, you can ask students to approximate the answer when you are about to do a computation problem together. This practice can encourage the useful habit of estimating to get an idea of the expected size of the answer before calculating.

PROGRAM RESOURCES

THESE ADDITIONAL COMPONENTS OF *MATH EXPLORATIONS AND APPLICATIONS* CAN BE PURCHASED SEPARATELY FROM SRA/McGRAW-HILL.

LESSON	BASIC MANIPULATIVE KIT	GAME MAT PACKAGE	TEACHER MANIPULATIVE KIT	INTERMEDIATE MANIPULATIVE KIT	INTERMEDIATE OVERHEAD MANIPULATIVE KIT	THE CRUNCHER SOFTWARE	MATH EXPLORATIONS AND APPLICATIONS CD-ROM
1				interlocking cubes			Lesson 1
2	Number Cubes, Number Wheels	play money		base-10 materials	base-10 materials bills, coins		Lesson 2
3				counters	counters		Lesson 3
4	Number Cubes	Busy Bee Game					Lesson 4
5	Number Cubes	Marathon 1 and Marathon 2 Games					Lesson 5
6	Number Cubes						Lesson 6
7		Cube-O-Mat and Harder Cube-O-Mat Games					Lesson 7
8	Number Wheels			base-10 materials	base-10 materials		Lesson 8
9		Transaction Game		base-10 materials	base-10 materials		Lesson 9
10	Number Cubes					spreadsheet	Lesson 10
11				base-10 materials place value chart	base-10 materials		Lesson 11
12							Lesson 12
13	Number Cubes						Lesson 13
14		play money			bills, coins		Lesson 14
15				base-10 materials	base-10 materials		Lesson 15
16	Number Cubes	play money			bills, coins		Lesson 16
17	Number Cubes					project	Lesson 17
18						spreadsheet	Lesson 18
19							Lesson 19
20		Roller Coaster and Harder Roller Coaster Games					Lesson 20
21							Lesson 21
22						spreadsheet	Lesson 22
23							Lesson 23
24							Lesson 24
25							Lesson 25
26							Lesson 26

UNIT 1

Student Edition pages 2–3

Whole Numbers and Integers

INTRODUCING THE UNIT

Using the Student Pages Begin your discussion of the opening unit photo by asking students, "How do decorators use numbers?" Then read aloud the paragraph on the student page that highlights decorating as a career. This helps make the connection between school and work and encourages students to explore how math is used in the real world.

ACTIVITY Inform students that if a client chooses paper or fabric with a pattern, it is the decorator's job to ensure that there will be enough extra paper or fabric to allow for a continuous pattern. Ask students to figure out how many square feet of carpet would be needed to cover your classroom.

FYI Tell students that it is possible to trace the origins of decorating as far back as 10,000 years, to the cave paintings that illuminated the walls at such sites as the Lascaux caves in France. Some cave art may be even older. Although these paintings may have a religious significance as well, they clearly have a decorative element. Wall paintings were a feature of ancient societies from China to Egypt to Europe and South America. Egyptian wall paintings with their vibrant colors and hieroglyphics, or picture writing, are among the most famous. The more recently discovered murals of the Mayans are equally bright and graphic. Also well known are the beautiful painted walls of the city of Pompeii in the ancient Roman empire, which unlike the earlier examples, were made purely for the decoration of homes. Stress that the urge to improve and decorate dwellings extends even to the animal kingdom, where such creatures as the bower bird search fastidiously for objects—usually blue in color—to decorate nests with walls carefully plastered in mud.

Pleasure in furnishings and decor has led to many innovations in style and function that have remained in use for thousands of years. Suggest to students that they visit a museum to see ancient Egyptian or Chinese artifacts. Many home furnishings from living rooms of 2000 years ago will seem familiar to them today.

UNIT 1

Whole Numbers and Integers

REVIEWING ARITHMETIC

- **measurement**
- **place value**
- **basic operations**
- **negative numbers**
- **multiplying integers**

Decorators use math . . .

A decorator spends only part of the time looking for things that clients want in their homes. A lot of time is spent in people's homes measuring floors for carpeting, rooms for furniture, furniture for fabric, and walls for wallpaper. Wallpaper and fabric come in rolls of a certain width, and decorators must decide how much to buy.

2

Thinklab™ 2

SRA's *Thinklab™ 2* provides a series of creative and logical problem-solving opportunities for individual students. The problems are designed to appeal to different cognitive abilities.

▶ Use Problems 1–10 with this unit to reinforce object manipulation (ways and means of dealing with specific data).

▶ Use Problems 11–20 with this unit to reinforce creative insight (extrapolation from, and beyond, given data).

Make the point for students that success in the decorating business today is as dependent on careful mathematical estimates as is success in running a restaurant or painting houses. Knowing exactly what materials will be needed and in what quantity is the key to making a profit. Of course, other talents are required as well. Understanding the client's taste, keeping in mind how much money the client wishes to spend, and knowing about style and quality when choosing furnishings are also crucial. But a primary tool of a good decorator is the calculator. Figuring out the areas of complicated spaces such as stairwells and kitchens means knowing geometry. Areas from walls to countertops to floors to ceilings all come into play. The materials used to cover each of these places must be purchased in as correct a quantity as possible or money is wasted—usually the decorator's money. Point out that a decorator may save even more money by calculating the materials needed for more than one job at once. All this takes careful planning and good math.

Home Connections You may want to send Home Connections Blackline Masters pages 36–37 home the first week of school to introduce families to *Math Explorations and Applications*. Then use the Masters on pages 38–39 the following week to introduce this unit.

Unit Project This would be a good time to assign the "Clever Counting" project on pages 98 and 99. Students can begin working on the project in cooperative groups in their free time as you work through the unit. The Unit Project is a good opportunity for students to compare our base-10 system with other systems.

 *Cooperate 3*

Cooperate 3, published by SRA, provides a series of creative and logical problem-solving opportunities for cooperative groups. The problems are designed to provide practice in problem solving, communication, reasoning, and making connections. *Cooperate 3* presents the following cognitive strategies—perceiving spatial relations, ordering and sequencing, logical deduction, establishing and testing hypotheses, sequential exploration, identifying starting points, attending to detail, organizing information, and screening irrelevant information.

Each Problem Card emphasizes a principal strategy as well as reinforcing other strategies.

▶ Use Problem Cards 1–2 with this unit to emphasize logical deduction.

▶ Use Problem Cards 3–4 with this unit to emphasize organizing information.

▶ Use Problem Card 5 with this unit to emphasize ordering and sequencing.

✔ ASSESSMENT

This is the first Mastery Checkpoint at this grade level. Throughout each unit of each grade level, at benchmarks specified on the Mastery Checkpoint Chart, you are able to assess students' progress.

MASTERY CHECKPOINT CHARTS

The Mastery Checkpoint Chart contains a listing of the mastery objectives that are considered important for future progress in mathematics. These benchmarks appear on a chart in the Assessment Blackline Master Book on pages vii-viii. You can determine each student's mastery of specific objectives by his or her performance of the mastery objective in the lesson and/or by using the specific

Tips on Using the Mastery Checkpoint Chart

◆ Fill in the names of all students in your class.

◆ For each checkpoint on the Mastery Checkpoint Chart, the Teacher's Guide gives opportunities to assess either by observation or by using the Student Edition page(s). Students can also be given the Assessment Blackline Master for that specific Checkpoint.

◆ Place a check mark (✔) in the appropriate column of the Mastery Checkpoint Chart beside the name of each student who demonstrates success on the objective in question.

◆ Pencil in a *P* in the appropriate column for each student who, in your judgment, grasps the necessary idea for accomplishing the objective but needs further practice to sharpen his or her skill. Assign extra practice to identified students.

◆ Pencil in a *T* for each student who has not grasped the necessary idea and therefore needs further teaching. Give extra teaching to identified students.

◆ Replace *T*s or *P*s with check marks when students demonstrate mastery of a skill.

Mastery Checkpoint test provided in the Assessment Blackline Master Book. Those students who are having difficulty with a skill should receive extra help before continuing on in the unit. But an entire class should not be held up until all students learn the skill. Each lesson provides you with either a Reteaching Strategy or a Reteaching Master that will help you present the lesson concept in a slightly different way.

ASSESSMENT OPPORTUNITIES IN THE PROGRAM

The *Math Explorations and Applications* program offers many opportunities to assess students' skills. Activities that students engage in on a daily basis, such as Mental Math exercises, games, response exercises, Thinking Story discussions, and Student Edition exercises allow you to steadily monitor individual progress.

In the Teacher's Guide

Each lesson in the Teacher's Guide provides at least two different assessment suggestions. One is Assessment Criteria, which gives you questions to ask yourself while you observe students playing a game, completing an activity, participating in a Thinking Story discussion, or working in cooperative groups. The additional suggestions include the following types of assessment:

- informal assessment (interviews, observation, and oral)
- formal assessment (tests, reviews, and checkpoints)
- self assessment
- alternative assessment (portfolio and performance)

In the Student Editions

A formal Mid-Unit Review as well as a Unit Review and a Unit Test are provided in the Student Edition in levels 1–6. The exception is Kindergarten, which has a Mid-Book Review and a Book Test. There are also self-assessments throughout the Student Editions in which students are asked to evaluate their own performance.

In the Assessment Blackline Masters

In the Assessment Blackline Master book there is a page for each Mastery Checkpoint, an additional Mid-Unit Review, and two Unit Tests, one in standardized format. Each unit also provides Performance Assessment activities and Portfolio Assessment suggestions. There is also additional information on the various alternative assessment options that are provided in this program and suggestions for grading these assessments using rubrics.

DAILY MONITORING

The following activities will help you assess your students' progress on a daily basis:

- **Cube Games and Game Mats**
  These allow you to watch students practice specific skills under conditions natural to them.

- **Mental Math Exercises**
  These exercises, which involve Number Wheels and Number Cubes, allow you to see everyone's responses, give immediate feedback, and involve the entire class.

- **Student Edition Exercises**
  These help you determine which skills your students can use on paper and which they need to practice.

- **Thinking Story Sessions**
  These help you determine whether or not your students are able to apply their knowledge of math concepts to everyday common sense problems.

Student Edition pages 4–7

Measuring and Visualizing

LESSON PLANNER

Objectives

✓ to evaluate students' ability to estimate and measure length in metric units

▶ to review the use of numbers in estimation and measurement

▶ to provide practice in measuring

▶ to provide opportunities to help students develop spatial perception and to understand the relationship between a two-dimensional perspective and a three-dimensional object

Context of the Lesson This is the first of three lessons reviewing measurement; place value; and the use of numbers, including whole numbers, decimals, and fractions. This lesson also contains the first Mastery Checkpoint, which assesses students' ability to estimate and measure length in metric units.

 MANIPULATIVES

metersticks
(1 for every
4–5 students)

stacking or
interlocking
cubes*

two-cm square
graph paper

Program Resources

Practice Master 1

Enrichment Master 1

Assessment Master

For extra practice:
  CD-ROM* Lesson 1

Note: This lesson may take more than one day.

➊ Warm-Up

 Problem of the Day Present the following problem to the class: Which of the following measurements—4 meters, 40 centimeters, or 40 meters—might be the height of a typical classroom? (4 m) Have students suggest other objects, heights, or lengths that match each measurement. (Answers will vary.)

Problem-Solving Strategies Ask students who have solved the Problem of the Day to share how they solved it and any strategies they used.

MENTAL MATH Introduce the following exercise that provides practice in estimating measures with standard units for length, weight, and volume. Use a technique similar to the following:

(continued on page 5)

Measuring and Visualizing

Kim and Paul wanted to tile the floor of their clubhouse. They decided to measure the floor to see how many tiles they would need.

But one end of their meterstick had been broken. It looked like this:

They used the stick anyway. Paul measured the length of the clubhouse. He was able to fit the stick along the length of the room about five times with a little room left over. But he still didn't know how long the room was. Can you help him?

◆ The stick is broken at the 99-centimeter mark. About how long is the broken meterstick? **about 99 cm**

◆ If the stick were not broken, how many centimeters would there be in five lengths of the stick? (There are 100 centimeters in a meter.) **500**

◆ How many centimeters are there in five lengths of the broken meterstick? Try to figure this out in your head. **495**

Paul said the clubhouse floor is five sticks long plus about 5 centimeters.

◆ How many centimeters is that? **500**

4 • Whole Numbers and Integers

Why teach it this way?

All Student Edition questions preceded by a ◆ are discussion questions, to be read and discussed with the whole class. As a rule, numbered questions and problems can be done by students on their own or in groups, but some might also best be discussed with the class.

COOPERATIVE LEARNING Help students working in cooperative groups to find ways to contribute in a collaborative fashion in doing the activities on pages 4–5 and 6–7. Suggest that each member of the group take on a different task or portion of a task so that all members can participate. Brainstorm with the class to discuss the different aspects of the task so that it can be divided up fairly.

*available separately

Kim used the broken meterstick to measure the width of the clubhouse.

She started at one wall and marked off 99 centimeters.

Then she moved the stick and marked off another 99 centimeters.

Then she moved the stick again and marked off another 99 centimeters.

◆ How many centimeters has she marked off so far? **297**

Then Kim tried to mark off another 99 centimeters. But there was not enough room.

◆ How could you measure the last section?

Kim measured the last section. It was 60 centimeters long.

◆ How many centimeters wide is the clubhouse? **357**

Suppose the meterstick was broken at the 98-centimeter mark.

◆ How many centimeters long would five lengths of the stick be? **490**

Answers will vary. She could use the stick to measure the last section.

Now try these in your head.

Suppose the meterstick is broken at this centimeter mark:	How long would this many lengths be in centimeters?	
❶ 97	4	**388**
❷ 95	6	**570**
❸ 92	3	**276**

Work in groups. Measure the length and width of your classroom with a regular meterstick. Compare your results with those of other groups.

Save your results in your Math Journal. You'll need them for Lesson 13.

Literature Connection Have students read *Skyscraper* by Tim Ostler to see an example of measurement used in everyday life.

Technology Connection You may wish to refer students or parents to the Internet access for the Eisenhower National Clearinghouse. ENC's address is: http://www.enc.org, or if you have Telnet: enc.org (log in using the word "guest"). Your ENC user name is your last name and the last four digits of your phone number. Or dial (800) 362–4448 from your terminal. This Internet resource provides access to activity guides, reference materials, and web sites for teachers and students.

Mental Math (continued)

1. Present an object to the class.

2. Have students provide estimates of its length, weight, or volume.

3. Have a student measure to check the estimates.

4. Present other objects and have students provide estimates expressed in the same units as the first. Then have a student measure to check the estimates before you move on to the next object.

② Teach

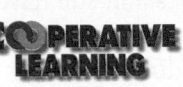

Using the Student Pages Do pages 4 and 5 with the class. Stop at the discussion questions so students can think about, answer, and discuss them. This story is continued in Lesson 13. If students have difficulty with the third discussion question on page 4, help them see that they do not have to multiply 99 × 5 but can subtract 5 from 500.

COOPERATIVE LEARNING Read page 5, discuss the questions, and have students do the three problems. Then have them do the measuring activity in groups. Answers to the second discussion question on page 5 will vary, so accept any reasonable answers, such as using a shorter measuring stick or turning the **meterstick** over and measuring from the wall to the mark.

> . . . *thinking is the ultimate basic skill in mathematics.*
>
> —Stephen S. Willoughby,
> *Teaching Mathematics: What Is Basic?*

◆ LESSON 1 Measuring and Visualizing

Teach

Using the Student Pages Read the top of page 6 with students. Have a volunteer stack the **cubes*** the way Alan did in the story. Ask students to look at the stack from two different viewpoints to get the perspective shown on the page. Next, discuss the "map" and be sure everyone sees that it correctly describes the stack. Have another student add the four extra cubes as shown in the second map. Again, ask students to decide what the two perspectives will look like and then check by actually looking. Note that the perspective for the altered stack will be the same as that for the original; adding more cubes as shown does not change the perspective.

There are several possible maps and answers to the problems on page 7. You may want to have **graph paper** available. Have students work in small groups to build stacks of cubes that give the indicated views. Then have them see if they can add or remove any cubes and still have the same views. Encourage students to spend time as needed experimenting, discussing, and deciding. You may need to mention that *maximum* means the greatest possible number and *minimum* means the least possible number.

LEARNING STYLES

Meeting Individual Needs
Some students may have difficulty visualizing how a two-dimensional illustration can be seen as a representation of a three-dimensional object. Provide nets or actual objects they can manipulate to develop a better understanding of the relationships between solid objects and their flat representations.

◆ LESSON 1 Measuring

Alan was stacking cubes. He made one stack three cubes high. Then he put four more cubes around the bottom cube. When he looked at the pile of cubes from the south, it looked like this.

When he looked at the stack of cubes from the west, it looked just the same.

Using graph paper, Alan kept track of how many cubes were in each stack looking down from above. He called this a map.

Alan decided to put four more cubes in the design. On his "map" his record looked like this.

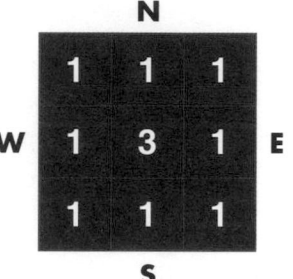

◆ How did that change the view from the south?
It stayed the same.

◆ How did the view from the west look?
It was the same as before the four new cubes were put in the design.

Explain your answers to these two questions in your Math Journal.
There were already cubes visible in each of the three positions in the bottom layer. Cubes behind other cubes don't affect the new.

RETEACHING

Students who have difficulty with this lesson should be observed carefully during the next few lessons to see whether the difficulty stems from the nature of the exercises or from a general lack of number sense.

In the meantime give specific help where needed—for example, in how to measure—and note which students are likely to need extensive extra work.

PRACTICE p. 1

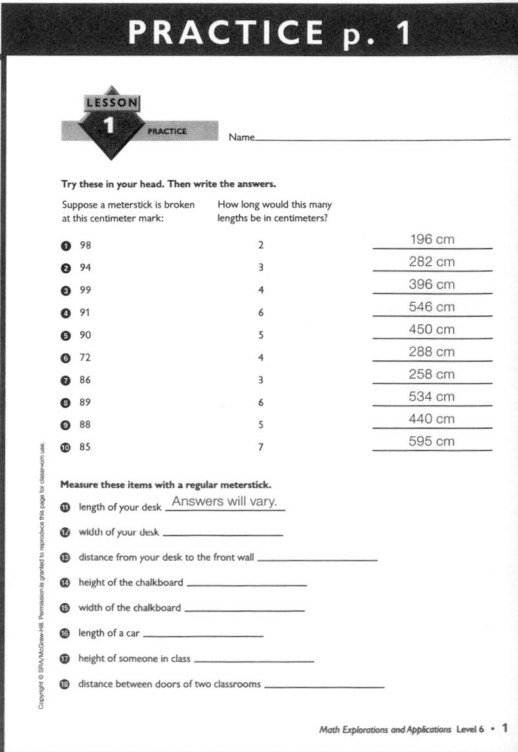

*available separately

A different stack of cubes looked like this from the south:

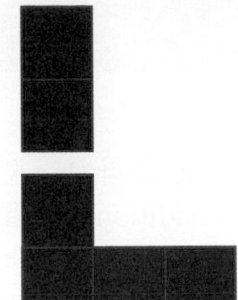

And like this from the west:

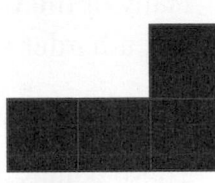

◆ Draw a "map" of this stack. Are there any other possible maps that could make those two views? **no**

For another stack the view from the south was this:

And the view from the west was this:

◆ How many cubes are in this stack? Are you sure? **There are at least four cubes and at most 10 cubes.**
◆ What is the maximum number of cubes that might be in the stack? **10**
◆ What is the minimum number possible? **4**

Draw a map for the maximum number and a map for the minimum number of cubes that could be in this stack.

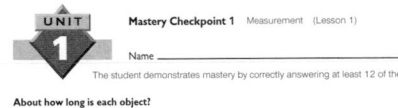

 The length of all of the blood vessels in the human body laid end to end would be about 60,000 miles for a child and about 100,000 miles for an adult. (The distance around the equator is less than 25,000 miles.)

Unit 1   Lesson 1 • **7**

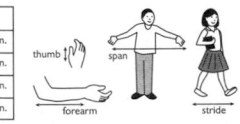

❸ Wrap-Up ⏱ 5 MINUTES

In Closing Summarize the lesson by asking students to suggest other ways that Kim and Paul could have measured the floor.

Mastery Checkpoint 1
At this time most students should be able to use appropriate metric units to estimate and measure length with accuracy. They should also have an understanding of the decimal structure of the metric system. These abilities may be assessed by observing students as they work or by using Assessment Blackline Masters page 1. The results of this assessment may be recorded on the Mastery Checkpoint Chart.

Assessment Criteria

Did the student . . .

✓ contribute to the discussion?

✓ communicate strategies used?

✓ accurately visualize the three-dimensional objects on pages 6–7?

✓ exhibit understanding of measuring, estimating, and converting metric units of length?

Homework Have students measure a room at home and draw a labeled diagram of it.

LOOKING AHEAD Have students save the results of their measurements for use in Lesson 13. Although results for students' measurements will vary, variations should not exceed 1 centimeter times the number of meterstick lengths needed to measure the dimensions.

 # GAMES

THE ROLE OF GAMES

Games are an important component of the *Math Explorations and Applications* program. They offer students an opportunity to practice the mathematical skills to which they've been introduced and to develop logical reasoning as they use mathematical strategies. They make learning fun. Games also offer you another way to assess how well your students have learned each skill. There are two types of games presented in this program—Game Mats and Cube Games.

Game Mats

There are five Game Mats in Kindergarten, thirteen in levels 1–3, and fourteen in levels 4–6. In the Game Mat package, you receive 15 copies of each Game Mat, counters, place markers,

Number Cubes, and money (not in Kindergarten). In addition, you have *A Guide for Using the Game Mats* and a color transparency for each Game Mat. Each game involves the use of several math skills including mathematical reasoning and probability. Many of the Game Mats are offered in a standard and a harder version.

Cube Games

These games, presented in the Student Edition in levels 3–6 and in the Teacher's Guide for K–2, reinforce basic math skills and involve mathematical reasoning.

TIPS FOR TEACHING GAMES

After reading the rules for each game, which are provided in the lesson where the Cube Game is introduced or on each Game Mat, take the following steps:

- **Play the game yourself.** This will help you identify any difficulties your students might have.
- **Demonstrate how the game is played.** Making sure that everyone can see, say the rules aloud as you play another student or as two or more students play together. For the Game Mats, you may want to use the color overhead transparencies to demonstrate how each game is played.
- **Restate how the game is played.** Ask students to restate the object of the game and rules of the game in their own words to be sure everyone understands how to play.
- **Supervise students' play.** Be sure they get off to the right start.

Tips for Organizing Successful Game Sessions

◆ **Stress enjoyment rather than competition.** Emphasize sportsmanship, fair play, and taking turns.

◆ **In general, place students of the same ability together.** This way all students have a more equal chance of winning.

◆ **Change groupings from day to day.** Students can learn different things by playing with different partners.

◆ **Be sure students are challenged by a game.** Most Game Mats have a standard and a harder version. Some Cube Games suggest variations to the game.

◆ **Assign one referee for the day or one for each group.** Students sometimes get so absorbed in their own efforts that they do not follow the rules. A referee can monitor players' moves, keep track of scores, and in some games act as banker.

◆ **Make Game Mats accessible.** Store mats so that students can find and return them without your help. (You might want to laminate the mats.)

MENTAL MATH EXERCISES

Mental Math exercises offer an easy and practical technique for drilling students' math skills and assessing their performance. With these exercises students usually use either the Number Wheel (Levels 3–6) or Number Cubes (Levels K–6) to display their answers to your oral questions.

NUMBER WHEELS

Number Wheels have five wheels, each of which can be dialed to show any digit from 0 through 9. This allows students to make any integer from 0 through 99,999. To show the number 2047, for example, a student rotates the thousands wheel to show a 2, turns the hundreds wheel to show a 0, and so on. Different colors are used to identify each of the five wheels. On the back of the Number Wheels, the digits 0 through 9 are repeated with the addition of a decimal point.

Tips for Using Number Wheels and Cubes

◆ **Add a "peek-to-be-sure" step.** This should occur between the "Hide" and "Show" steps of the procedure. It asks students who have already found answers to check them. This keeps them involved as they wait for the "Show" command.

◆ **Use good judgment to decide when to give the "Show" command.** Give students who are progressing toward a solution time enough to finish, but avoid prolonged waiting because this calls attention to slower students.

◆ **Encourage your students.** Mental Math exercises allow an active exchange between you and your students. Use this opportunity to give your students plenty of positive reinforcement.

NUMBER CUBES

Number Cubes allow students to make any integer from 0 through 100. In levels 3–6, students use the 0–5 (red) and 5–10 (blue) Number Cubes. To show the number 73, for example, a student should find the 7 face on the 5–10 cube and place that next to the 3 face on the 0–5 cube.

In levels 1 and 2, each student should be given four cubes—two units cubes, 0–5 (red) and 5–10 (blue), and two tens cubes, 0–5 (yellow) and 5–10 (green). To show the number 43, for example, a student should find the 4 face on the 0–5 tens cube and place that next to the 3 face on the 0–5 units cube.

HOW TO USE WHEELS AND CUBES

1. Present the class with a problem (orally or on the chalkboard) and say "Find."
2. Students determine the answer and dial it on their Number Wheels or position it on their Number Cubes.
3. Say "Hide."
4. Students hide their answers by holding their Wheels or Cubes against their chests.
5. Say "Show," when you see that most students have an answer.
6. Students hold up their Wheels or Cubes so you can see their responses.
7. Check students' responses.
8. Show and/or say the correct answer.
9. Move on to the next problem.

Sometimes the problems in a Mental Math exercise will be complex enough to require paper and pencil. In these cases, have students show their answers to you as you walk around the room.

Place Value

Place Value

LESSON PLANNER

Objectives

▶ to provide practice with place value as it relates to whole numbers and decimals

▶ to provide practice with numerical sequence

▶ to provide practice in comparing decimals

✓ to assess students' understanding and use of numbers

Context of the Lesson This is the second of three lessons reviewing the use of numbers and place value. This lesson also contains a Mastery Checkpoint for understanding and use of numbers. Inequalities and use of the three common relation signs will come up in varying contexts throughout the year.

MANIPULATIVES

base-10
  materials*
  (optional)
calculators*
  (optional)
play money*
  (optional)

Program Resources

Number Cubes (0–5 and 5–10)
Number Wheels
Reteaching Master
Practice Master 2
Enrichment Master 2
Assessment Master

For extra practice:
  CD-ROM* Lesson 2

① Warm-Up ⏱

Problem of the Day Write the number 5204.36 on the chalkboard. Ask students to explain how they could increase this number by 500, by changing only one of the digits. (Change the 2 in the hundreds place to a 7.)

Problem-Solving Strategies Ask students who have solved the Problem of the Day to share how they solved it and any strategies they used.

Provide problems such as "What number comes after 956?" (957) and "What is the number before 1235?" (1234) Begin with questions that are easy for the class, then gradually introduce more difficult ones such as numbers with decimals. Have students use their Number Wheels to respond.

When the 1990 Census was taken, the total population of the United States was estimated to be 248,709,873. This lesson will show you how to read that number, and other numbers, by using place value.

Millions			Thousands					
hundreds	tens	ones	hundreds	tens	ones	hundreds	tens	ones
2	4	8	7	0	9	8	7	3

This number is two hundred forty-eight million, seven hundred nine thousand, eight hundred seventy-three.

The 2 stands for 2 hundred millions.	200,000,000
The 4 stands for 4 ten millions.	40,000,000
The 8 stands for 8 millions.	8,000,000
The 7 stands for 7 hundred thousands.	700,000
The 0 stands for 0 ten thousands.	0
The 9 stands for 9 thousands.	9,000
The 8 stands for 8 hundreds.	800
The 7 stands for 7 tens.	70
The 3 stands for 3 ones.	3

The value of each place is ten times that of the place to the right: *tens* are ten times *ones*, *hundred thousands* are ten times *ten thousands*, and so on.

Write the numbers in standard form.

❶ 9000 + 500 + 40 + 3 **9543**   ❷ 6000 + 700 + 80 + 9 **6789**

❸ 70,000 + 200 + 3 **70,203**   ❹ 3 + 500 + 20,000 **20,503**

❺ 20 + 9000 + 50,000 **59,020**   ❻ 2 + 300 + 200,000 **200,302**

❼ 4000 + 70 + 30,000 + 1 **34,071**   ❽ 6 + 50 + 8000 **8056**

Copy and complete the number sequences.

❾ 3995, 3996, ▪, ▪, ▪, ▪, ▪, 4002   ❿ 5678, 5679, ▪, ▪, ▪, ▪, ▪, 5685
3997, 3998, 3999, 4000, 4001   **5680, 5681, 5682, 5683, 5684**

⓫ 9996, 9997, ▪, ▪, ▪, ▪, ▪, 10,003   ⓬ 6098, 6099, ▪, ▪, ▪, ▪, ▪, 6105
9998; 9999; 10,000; 10,001; 10,002   **6100, 6101, 6102, 6103, 6104**

8 • Whole Numbers and Integers

Why teach it this way?

Tell students that for decimals less than 1, we will follow the convention of writing the 0 in the ones place, except when we write money amounts or for some multiplications. There are three reasons for following this convention:

1. It is the Standard International (SI) convention.

2. It makes it clearer that there is a decimal point in the number. For example, it is less likely for .7 to be read as 7 if the 0 is included.

3. Most calculators display numbers between 0 and 1 with a 0 in the ones place.

We will omit the 0 in cases in which the ones-place 0 might confuse rather than clarify, as in some problems involving the multiplication of decimals.

A student should not be marked wrong for giving a correct answer in which the zero is omitted.

Roll and Regroup A Number Game

COOPERATIVE LEARNING

Players:	Two or more
Materials:	One 0–5 cube, one 5–10 cube
Object:	To make the greatest number
Math Focus:	Addition facts, place value, regrouping, and mathematical reasoning

RULES

1. Draw boxes on your paper like this:

   hundreds   tens   ones

2. The first player rolls both cubes. Every player writes the sum of the cubes in the hundreds box, the tens box, or the ones box.

3. The cubes are rolled twice more, and each time every player writes the sum of the numbers in one of the remaining boxes.

4. After the three rolls, the players find the value of their numbers, regrouping where necessary.

5. The player who makes the greatest number is the winner of the round.

SAMPLE GAME

Numbers rolled:			David wrote:			Maria wrote:			Corrine wrote:		
5 **3**	First roll			8				8	8		
8 **3**	Second roll		11	8			11	8	8		11
10 **4**	Third roll		11	8	14	14	11	8	8	14	11

David regrouped 11 hundreds, 8 tens, and 14 to get 1194.
Maria regrouped 14 hundreds, 11 tens, and 8 to get 1518.
Corrine regrouped 8 hundreds, 14 tens, and 11 to get 951.
Maria won this round.

MATH JOURNAL

Can you describe the strategies you used to play this game? Write each idea in your Math Journal.

Unit 1   Lesson 2 • **9**

② Teach

GAME **Using the Student Pages** You may wish to demonstrate the "Roll and Regroup a Number" game on page 9, which provides practice with place value, first so that students who finish early can play.

Go over the table on page 8 and do the first one or two problems with the class. Have students do the remaining problems on their own. In discussing the example, explain that in order to make multidigit numbers easier to read, we often break them up by inserting commas after every three digits, starting from the right. Provide a few examples. You may wish to point out to students that 1000 million is called a *billion*, 1000 billion is called a *trillion*, and the names *quadrillion, quintillion, sextillion, septillion, octillion, nonillion,* and *decillion* follow.

The "Roll and Regroup a Number" game can be played by the whole class or by as few as two players. When you introduce the game, take a place at the chalkboard and act as the leader. This game provides practice with place value and with mathematical reasoning as students decide where to place each number. For a variation on this game and the "Roll a Problem" games that come later, use slips of paper numbered 0 through 10 instead of cubes. This method lends itself well to whole-group participation. The lead player draws slips two at a time from a container and calls out both numbers. The other players write the sum of numbers in the boxes drawn on their sheets of paper immediately after the numbers are called out and before the next draw. Decide beforehand whether to put the slips aside or to return them to the container after they are drawn. Each method produces a different strategy for winning.

SOCIAL STUDIES CONNECTION

Social Studies Connection Have students browse through an almanac or other source to find numerical data that have changed over time and can be compared, such as data related to population. They also can compare magazine and newspaper circulation, box-office figures for movies, sales of CDs and videos, and production data for various items. To compare decimal numbers, students can research scores in Olympic gymnastic and swimming events. Encourage students to look for trends in the data.

LITERATURE CONNECTION

Literature Connection For an interesting collection of little-known facts related to money and finance, refer to *You Can't Count a Billion Dollars* by Barbara Sealing.

◆ LESSON 2 Place Value

Teach

Using the Student Pages Go over the examples on page 10 and the exercises on pages 10–11. Remind students that the small ends of the > and < signs always point to the lesser number and that if the two numbers are the same value, we use the equal sign (=). Solve one or two of the inequality problems (41–55) on page 11 with the class. Then have students work independently on these pages.

◆ LESSON 2 Place Value

To determine the winners of many Olympic races, participants' times are measured using decimals. For example, in the 1996 Summer Olympics, Gary Neiwand won the cycling sprint in 10.129 seconds. This is how you use place value to read decimal numbers like this one.

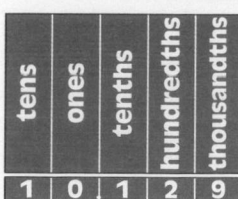

This number is ten and one hundred twenty-nine thousandths. Another way to say it is ten point one two nine.

The 1 stands for 1 ten.	10.
The 0 stands for 0 ones.	0.
The 1 stands for 1 **tenth.**	0.1
The 2 stands for 2 **hundredths.**	0.02
The 9 stands for 9 **thousandths.**	0.009

We can tell the place value of any **digit** in a number by the **decimal point.** The decimal point is always between the ones and the tenths place.

On both sides of the decimal point, each place has a value ten times that of the place to the right.

5	5	5	5	5

The purple 5 stands for 5 thousandths.	0.005
The orange 5 stands for 5 hundredths.	0.05
The blue 5 stands for 5 tenths.	0.5
The red 5 stands for 5 ones.	5.
The green 5 stands for 5 tens.	50.

What does the 7 stand for in each of these numbers? Show it in two ways. The first one has been done for you.

13 363.721 **7 tenths, 0.7**

14 635.567 **7 thousandths, 0.007**

15 457.318 **7 ones, 7**

16 567.105 **7 ones, 7**

17 749.956 **7 hundreds, 700**

18 892.713 **7 tenths, 0.7**

19 971.324 **7 tens, 70**

20 214.271 **7 hundredths, 0.07**

21 639.257 **7 thousandths, 0.007**

10 • Whole Numbers and Integers

Meeting Individual Needs
For kinesthetic learners, work with a **calculator***, adding machine, or counter. Students, given a number, can find the next number by adding 1 or find the preceding number by subtracting 1. If available, use a device such as a bicycle odometer on which they can see what happens when the 10 or the 100 is changed.

In addition, you may wish to use **base-10 materials*** or **play money***. Have students manipulate the materials to group them into tens, hundreds, and so on to form numbers.

10 Whole Numbers and Integers

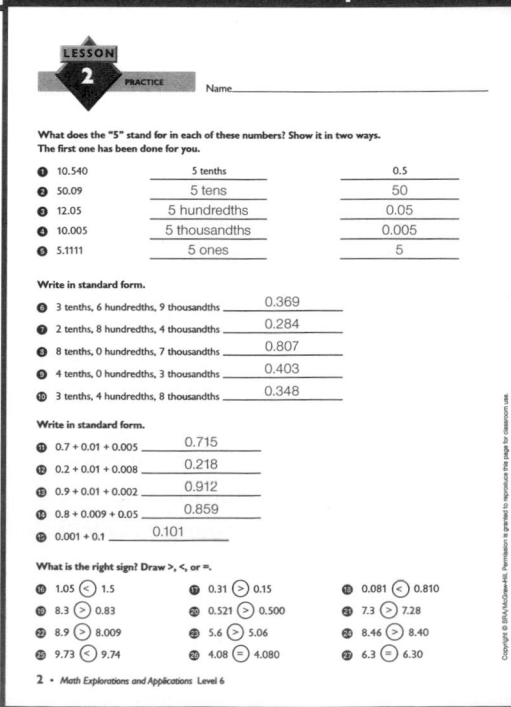

Write in standard form.

22 2 tenths, 4 hundredths, 6 thousandths
0.246

23 3 tenths, 3 hundredths, 5 thousandths
0.335

24 3 tenths, 5 hundredths, 0 thousandths
0.350

25 4 tenths, 0 hundredths, 9 thousandths
0.409

26 0 tenths, 6 hundredths, 4 thousandths
0.064

27 2 tenths, 7 hundredths, 0 thousandths
0.270

28 5 tenths, 0 hundredths, 3 thousandths
0.503

29 0 tenths, 0 hundredths, 4 thousandths
0.004

30 7 ones, 4 tenths, 2 hundredths
7.42

31 6 ones, 8 hundredths, 7 thousandths
6.087

Write in standard form.

32 0.7 + 0.05 + 0.002
0.752

33 0.03 + 0.005 + 0.1
0.135

34 0.009 + 0.02 + 0.5
0.529

35 0.6 + 0.03 + 0.001
0.631

36 0.007 + 0.9 + 0.06
0.967

37 0.3 + 0.007
0.307

38 0.02 + 0.004
0.024

39 0.08 + 0.7 + 0.002
0.782

40 2 + 0.6 + 0.04
2.64

Sometimes we put 0s in places to the right of the decimal point to help make the arithmetic easier. This is helpful when we are comparing decimals.

Which is greater, 0.94 or 0.904?

We can put a 0 after 0.94, making it 0.940, so that both decimals have the same number of places after the decimal point. (0.940 has the same value as 0.94, assuming we know that 0.94 is precise to the thousandths place.)

Now it is easier to see that 0.940 is greater than 0.904.

Copy each pair of numbers but replace ● with <, >, or =.

41 0.9 ● 0.009 **>**

42 0.5 ● 0.50 **=**

43 0.32 ● 0.23 **>**

44 0.63 ● 0.613 **>**

45 0.498 ● 0.4 **>**

46 9.35 ● 9.53 **<**

47 0.479 ● 0.5 **<**

48 8.0 ● 0.8 **>**

49 8.78 ● 8.8 **<**

50 0.71 ● 0.7 **>**

51 0.06 ● 0.59 **<**

52 3.28 ● 2.34 **>**

53 0.42 ● 0.419 **>**

54 0.5 ● 0.62 **<**

55 0.2 ● 0.195 **>**

Unit 1   Lesson 2 • **11**

③ Wrap-Up

In Closing Summarize the lesson by asking students to share the strategies they used to compare whole numbers and decimals.

Informal Assessment Observe students as they play the game and work on the exercises on pages 8, 10, and 11. Students who do not appear to have an adequate understanding of place value should be checked individually and given additional help. For others, playing the "Roll and Regroup a Number" game will provide useful practice.

Mastery Checkpoint 2

At the beginning of sixth grade most students should have a solid understanding of the use and significance of numbers in counting, measuring, comparing, and ordering. They can demonstrate mastery of place value by getting at least 80% of the problems correct on pages 8, 10, and 11 or on Assessment Blackline Masters pages 2–3 in a reasonable amount of time. The results of this assessment may be recorded on the Mastery Checkpoint Chart.

Assessment Criteria

Did the student . . .

✓ correctly answer at least 80% of the problems on pages 8, 10, and 11?

✓ explain how to compare whole numbers and decimal numbers?

Homework Have students play the "Roll and Regroup a Number" game with a family member for further practice with place value. A copy of this game can also be found on page 6 of the Home Connections Blackline Masters.

ENRICHMENT p. 2

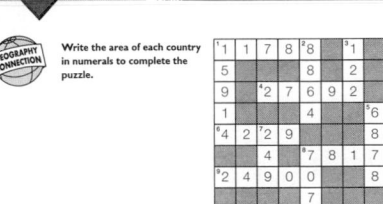

LESSON 2 ENRICHMENT   Name _____

Write the area of each country in numerals to complete the puzzle.

Across
1. The area of Belgium is eleven thousand, seven hundred eighty-eight square miles.
4. The area of Sierra Leone is twenty-seven thousand, six hundred ninety-two square miles.
6. The area of Jamaica is four thousand, two hundred twenty-nine square miles.
8. The area of Slovenia is seven thousand, eight hundred seventeen square miles.
9. The area of Latvia is twenty-four thousand, nine hundred square miles.
10. The area of Gambia is four thousand, three hundred sixty-one square miles.

Down
1. The area of Switzerland is fifteen thousand, nine hundred fourteen square miles.
2. The area of Belize is eight thousand, eight hundred sixty-four square miles.
3. The area of Malta is one hundred twenty-two square miles.
5. The area of Kuwait is six thousand, eight hundred seventy-eight square miles.
7. The area of Tonga is two hundred forty-nine square miles.
8. The area of Fiji is seven thousand, seventy-six square miles.

Write the countries in order of size, from largest to smallest.

Sierra Leone, Latvia, Switzerland, Belgium, Belize, Slovenia, Fiji, Kuwait, Gambia, Jamaica, Tonga, Malta

2 • Math Explorations and Applications Level 6

ASSESSMENT p. 2

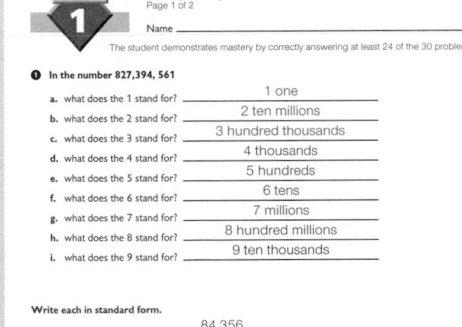

UNIT 1   Mastery Checkpoint 2   Understanding and using numbers (Lesson 2)
Page 1 of 2
Name _____

The student demonstrates mastery by correctly answering at least 24 of the 30 problems.

1 In the number 827,394,561
a. what does the 1 stand for? 1 one
b. what does the 2 stand for? 2 ten millions
c. what does the 3 stand for? 3 hundred thousands
d. what does the 4 stand for? 4 thousands
e. what does the 5 stand for? 5 hundreds
f. what does the 6 stand for? 6 tens
g. what does the 7 stand for? 7 millions
h. what does the 8 stand for? 8 hundred millions
i. what does the 9 stand for? 9 ten thousands

Write each in standard form.

2 80,000 + 4,000 + 300 + 50 + 6   84,356

3 3000 + 500 + 70 + 6   3576

4 5000 + 30   5030

5 4 + 300 + 50,000   50,304

6 sixty thousand seven hundred thirty-eight   60,738

Draw <, >, or = to make each statement true.

7 51 (>) 15

8 325 (>) 235

9 2056 (=) 2056

10 3065 (<) 3650

11 90 (<) 900

12 276 (>) 267

13 562 (<) 652

14 39 (>) 38

15 3124 (=) 3124

16 223 (>) 222

2 • Math Explorations and Applications Level 6

Estimating with Fractions

LESSON PLANNER

Objectives

✓ to assess students' familiarity with fractional notation and the use of fractions

▶ to provide practice in estimating fractional quantities

▶ to provide practice in determining whether a given use of fractions makes sense

Context of the Lesson This lesson is the third of three designed to refamiliarize students with the use of numbers. It contains a Mastery Checkpoint on fractions and mixed numbers. The focus of the lesson is on using fractions in context, understanding fractional notation, understanding that a fraction is a number, and mentally manipulating fractions.

 MANIPULATIVES

counters

Program Resources

Practice Master 3

Enrichment Master 3

Assessment Masters

For extra practice:
CD-ROM* Lesson 3

 **Warm-Up** ⏱ 5 MINUTES

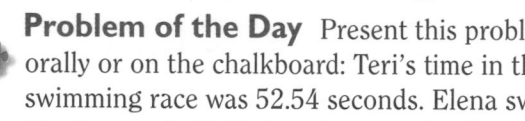 **Problem of the Day** Present this problem orally or on the chalkboard: Teri's time in the swimming race was 52.54 seconds. Elena swam the race in 52.45 seconds. Belinda's time was 51.99 seconds. Who came in first? Who finished last? (Belinda; Teri)

Problem-Solving Strategies Ask students who have solved the Problem of the Day to share how they solved it and any strategies they used.

MENTAL MATH Give problems in which you draw line segments or geometric figures on the chalkboard, shade a portion of each, say and write the fraction you shaded, and have students tell whether your answer is reasonable. Use common fractions, such as $\frac{1}{2}$, $\frac{3}{4}$, and $\frac{2}{5}$. When giving unreasonable answers, make them obviously so.

 **Teach**

Using the Student Pages Avoiding uncommon fractions like $\frac{13}{79}$ and $\frac{3}{11}$, write a few fractions such as $\frac{1}{2}$, $\frac{3}{4}$, and $\frac{2}{5}$ on the chalkboard.

Estimating with Fractions

Not all amounts can be expressed as a whole number. In this lesson you will use **fractions** and **mixed numbers** to make estimates.

1 About how full is the fuel tank?

    a. $\frac{1}{2}$ **b.** $\frac{1}{4}$ **c.** $\frac{3}{4}$

2 About what fraction of the fence has Carla painted?

    a. $\frac{3}{10}$ **b.** $\frac{5}{10}$ **c.** $\frac{7}{10}$

3 About what fraction of the fence does Carla still have to paint?

    a. $\frac{3}{10}$ **b.** $\frac{5}{10}$ **c.** $\frac{7}{10}$

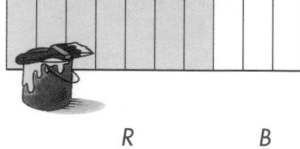

The point A is the number 0, and the point B is the number 1.

4 What fraction tells us where point Q is?

    a. $\frac{1}{2}$ **b.** $\frac{1}{4}$ **c.** $\frac{1}{10}$

5 What fraction tells us where point R is?

    a. $\frac{3}{8}$ **b.** $\frac{3}{6}$ **c.** $\frac{3}{4}$

Number line: J, T, V, Z marked at 0 1 2 3 4 5 6 7

6 What number tells us where point T is?

    a. $2\frac{1}{2}$ **b.** $3\frac{1}{2}$ **c.** $2\frac{9}{10}$

7 What number tells us where point Z is?

    a. $4\frac{4}{5}$ **b.** $5\frac{1}{4}$ **c.** $5\frac{3}{4}$

8 What number tells us where point J is?

    a. $\frac{1}{10}$ **b.** $\frac{1}{2}$ **c.** $\frac{9}{10}$

9 What number tells us where point V is?

    a. $3\frac{3}{4}$ **b.** $4\frac{1}{4}$ **c.** $3\frac{1}{2}$

12 • Whole Numbers and Integers

RETEACHING

Some students may have difficulty with written fractional notation. To help these students, emphasize that the "downstairs," or bottom, number (denominator) tells into how many equal parts something has been divided. Present fractions with only the denominator written, for example: $\frac{}{4}$ of a square. Ask how many equal parts should be produced (4). Have students divide a square into fourths. Then write various numbers—one at a time—in the numerator. Explain again what the numerator means. Then have students shade the appropriate parts of figures, or use other concrete materials to review the meaning of the entire fraction.

PRACTICE p. 3

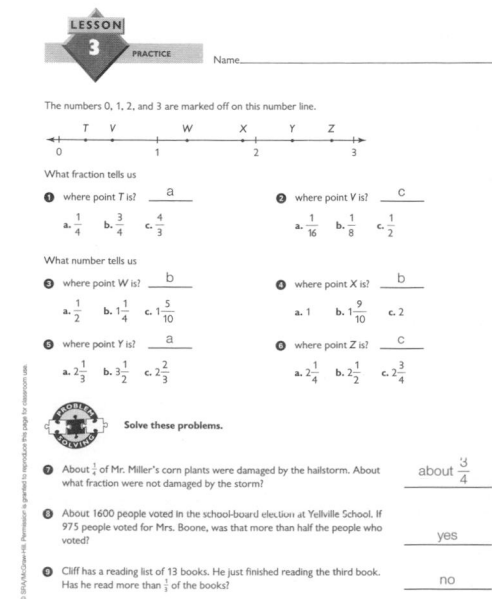

Solve these problems.

10 A concert will last two hours. Can the entire concert be recorded on an audiotape that plays $\frac{3}{4}$ of an hour on each side? **no**

11 Ms. Dimitrov was driving from Sayville to Oceanside. She drove about $\frac{1}{3}$ of the way in one hour and used 10 liters of gasoline.

a. At that speed about how long will the trip take? **about 3 hours**

b. About how much gasoline will she use on the entire trip? **about 30 L**

12 About $\frac{3}{10}$ of Earth's surface is land. About what fraction is water? **about $\frac{7}{10}$**

13 Arturo sleeps about eight hours each day.

a. About what fraction of the day is that? $\frac{1}{3}$

b. About what fraction of a week does Arturo sleep? $\frac{1}{3}$

c. About what fraction of a year does Arturo sleep? $\frac{1}{3}$

d. About what fraction of a year is Arturo awake? $\frac{2}{3}$

14 There are 29 people in Chitra's class. Eighteen voted to have their class party on Tuesday, and the rest voted for Wednesday. Did the majority vote for Tuesday? **yes**

15 A portable tape player that usually sells for $40 is on sale for $27.95. Is that more than $\frac{1}{4}$ off the regular price? **yes**

16 What is the sale price of the headphones? **$20**

17 Sarah invited 15 people to a party, and 12 people came to it. Did over $\frac{2}{3}$ of the people she invited attend the party? **yes**

SALE
Regularly $30
NOW
1/3 off

Unit 1 Lesson 3 • 13

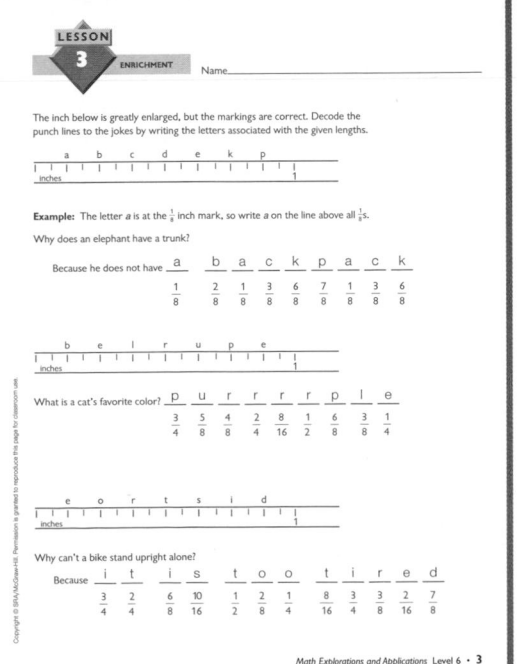
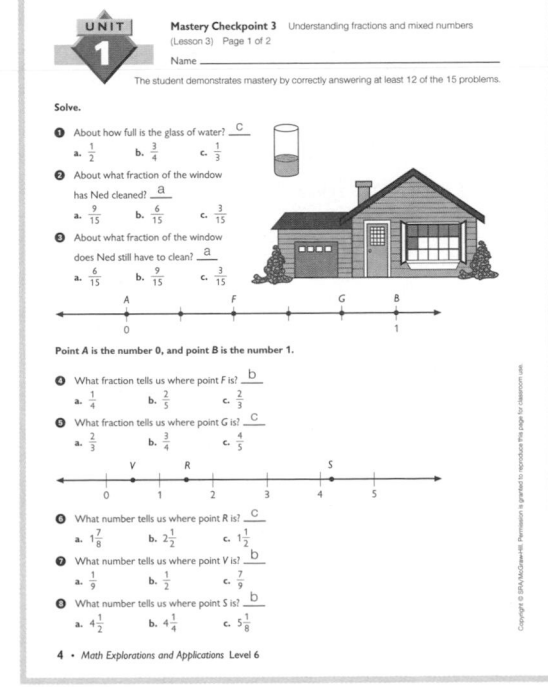
Ask students to name each, in unison. Make sure that students understand that the lower number in a fraction tells how many equal parts into which the whole has been divided. As needed, use **counters*** or other objects and pencil and paper to show how this concept applies to numbers. After making sure that most of the students are comfortable working with fractions, have the class work independently on the problems on page 12.

Have the students do page 13 on their own. Encourage them to draw pictures or visualize the situations to help them understand the problems. Then discuss the questions and answers with the whole class.

❸ Wrap-Up

In Closing Summarize the lesson by asking students this question: Jerry gave his friends Tameka, Juan, and Sue pieces of his apple. If he divided it equally, what fraction of the apple does he have left? $\left(\frac{1}{4}\right)$

Informal Assessment Ask students as they work on the problems on page 12 what the bottom and top numbers refer to in order to be sure they understand the fractions.

Mastery Checkpoint 3

At about this time most students should be able to demonstrate mastery of fractions and mixed numbers. Mastery may be assessed by observing students during the Mental Math exercises and during work on and discussion of pages 12 and 13 or Assessment Blackline Masters pages 4–5. The results of this assessment may be recorded on the Mastery Checkpoint Chart.

Assessment Criteria

Did the student . . .

✓ make a reasonable estimate of the fractions of figures or lengths that were shaded?

✓ correctly answer at least 75% of the exercises and problems?

✓ use sensible strategies to solve the problems?

Homework Ask students to share an example of how they use fractions at home.

LESSON 4

Student Edition pages 14–15

Adding and Subtracting

LESSON PLANNER

Objective

▶ to review and provide practice with addition and subtraction facts through 10 + 10

Context of the Lesson This is the first of 15 lessons that review operations with whole numbers, including basic facts and the standard algorithms for addition, subtraction, multiplication, and division with one-digit divisors.

 MANIPULATIVES

Program Resources

"Busy Bee" Game Mat

Number Cubes (0–5 and 5–10)

Practice Master 4

Enrichment Master 4

For additional math integration:
  Math Throughout the Day*

For extra practice:
  CD-ROM* Lesson 4
  Cumulative Review, page 552

❶ Warm-Up ⏱

 **Problem of the Day** Present this problem orally or on the chalkboard: Kevin spends $\frac{1}{6}$ of every day watching TV. Helen spends five hours each day in front of the TV. Inez watches television for 0.25 of a day. Of the three, who watches the most TV? (Inez)

Problem-Solving Strategies Ask students who have solved the Problem of the Day to share how they solved it and any strategies they used.

 Give practice in the basic arithmetic facts for the numbers 0–20, adjusting the speed to the ability of the class. Emphasize quick recall of these basic arithmetic facts.

❷ Teach

Using the Student Pages Have students play the "Roll-Sub-Add" Game. Demonstrate the "Roll-Sub-Add" game by playing it with a student or by having two students play. When one player gets a certain score, encourage others to show ways to match or improve upon that score. This game provides practice with mental

14 Whole Numbers and Integers

MIXED PRACTICE

LESSON 4 GAME

Adding and Subtracting

C∞PERATIVE LEARNING

Roll-Sub-Add Game

Players:	Two or more
Materials:	Two 0–5 cubes, two 5–10 cubes
Object:	To come as close as possible to the goal score for each round
Math Focus:	Addition facts and mathematical reasoning

RULES

1. The first player rolls all the cubes and makes a score as close to 0 as possible. To do this, he or she may add, subtract, or both. The player uses the number on each cube once and only once. Two or three cubes may be put together to make a multidigit number.

2. Other players take turns following the same procedure.

3. The player whose score is closest to 0 is the winner of the round.

4. For the second round the goal is changed to 1, but the rules remain the same. The goal is increased by 1 for each new round.

5. The game ends when the goal of 10 (or some other agreed-upon number) has been reached or when time has run out.

SAMPLE GAME

Goal	Tamika rolled:	Tamika made:	Rick rolled:	Rick made:
0	5 1 2 7	5 + 1 + 2 − 7 = 1	8 8 1 0	8 + 1 − 8 + 0 = 1
1	8 5 3 2	8 + 2 − 5 − 3 = 2	8 2 6 3	8 + 2 − 6 − 3 = 1
2	8 8 2 0	82 − 80 = 2	7 5 5 0	5 + 5 − 7 + 0 = 3

14 • Whole Numbers and Integers

Music Connection Briefly explain the idea of time signatures in music, or ask a volunteer to do so. Have groups of students look at sheet music and figure out the number of beats per song. Make sure that each group contains at least one student who can read music. Or, you could do this activity with the class as a whole.

RETEACHING

Pinpoint the particular facts with which a student is struggling. Try to relate each to a fact the student has mastered. For example, if the student knows that 7 + 7 = 14, but doesn't readily know the answer to 7 + 8, ask him or her to give the relationship between the two facts and between the two answers (7 + 8 is 1 more than 7 + 7). These students can practice with a partner using flash cards, appropriate mathematics games, or additional speed tests. The partner should be encouraged to provide positive feedback and helpful suggestions for remembering answers.

*available separately

Solve for *n*. Watch the signs.

① $7 + 8 = n$ **15** ② $n = 2 + 7$ **9** ③ $7 + 7 = n$ **14** ④ $n = 6 + 5$ **11**

⑤ $13 - 4 = n$ **9** ⑥ $n = 17 - 7$ **10** ⑦ $n = 8 + 9$ **17** ⑧ $12 - 8 = n$ **4**

⑨ $8 + 5 = n$ **13** ⑩ $n = 16 - 9$ **7** ⑪ $n = 15 - 6$ **9** ⑫ $4 + 7 = n$ **11**

⑬ $10 + 10 = n$ **20** ⑭ $n = 7 + 5$ **12** ⑮ $15 - 5 = n$ **10** ⑯ $n = 7 + 6$ **13**

⑰ $15 - 9 = n$ **6** ⑱ $n = 6 + 6$ **12** ⑲ $n = 9 + 7$ **16** ⑳ $n = 10 - 3$ **7**

㉑ $2 + 8 = n$ **10** ㉒ $n = 15 - 8$ **7** ㉓ $n = 14 - 8$ **6** ㉔ $n = 12 - 9$ **3**

㉕ $13 - 7 = n$ **6** ㉖ $n = 14 - 7$ **7** ㉗ $12 - 4 = n$ **8** ㉘ $6 + 4 = n$ **10**

㉙ $18 - 9 = n$ **9** ㉚ $n = 13 - 8$ **5** ㉛ $9 + 6 = n$ **15** ㉜ $11 - 7 = n$ **4**

㉝ $10 + 6 = n$ **16** ㉞ $n = 9 + 9$ **18** ㉟ $11 - 8 = n$ **3** ㊱ $n = 10 + 9$ **19**

㊲ $8 + 8 = n$ **16** ㊳ $n = 4 + 4$ **8** ㊴ $n = 5 + 9$ **14** ㊵ $11 - 2 = n$ **9**

Add or subtract. Watch the signs.

㊶ $\begin{array}{r} 5 \\ +\ 5 \\ \hline \mathbf{10} \end{array}$ ㊷ $\begin{array}{r} 4 \\ +\ 9 \\ \hline \mathbf{13} \end{array}$ ㊸ $\begin{array}{r} 18 \\ -\ 8 \\ \hline \mathbf{10} \end{array}$ ㊹ $\begin{array}{r} 17 \\ -\ 9 \\ \hline \mathbf{8} \end{array}$ ㊺ $\begin{array}{r} 2 \\ +\ 9 \\ \hline \mathbf{11} \end{array}$

㊻ $\begin{array}{r} 16 \\ -\ 8 \\ \hline \mathbf{8} \end{array}$ ㊼ $\begin{array}{r} 9 \\ +\ 3 \\ \hline \mathbf{12} \end{array}$ ㊽ $\begin{array}{r} 17 \\ -\ 8 \\ \hline \mathbf{9} \end{array}$

㊾ $\begin{array}{r} 16 \\ -\ 6 \\ \hline \mathbf{10} \end{array}$ ㊿ $\begin{array}{r} 16 \\ -\ 7 \\ \hline \mathbf{9} \end{array}$ ⑤① $\begin{array}{r} 15 \\ -\ 7 \\ \hline \mathbf{8} \end{array}$

⑤② $\begin{array}{r} 8 \\ +\ 4 \\ \hline \mathbf{12} \end{array}$ ⑤③ $\begin{array}{r} 14 \\ -\ 5 \\ \hline \mathbf{9} \end{array}$ ⑤④ $\begin{array}{r} 16 \\ -\ 10 \\ \hline \mathbf{6} \end{array}$

⑤⑤ $\begin{array}{r} 14 \\ 9 \\ \hline \mathbf{5} \end{array}$ ⑤⑥ $\begin{array}{r} 13 \\ 9 \\ \hline \mathbf{4} \end{array}$ ⑤⑦ $\begin{array}{r} 12 \\ 5 \\ \hline \mathbf{7} \end{array}$

⑤⑧ $\begin{array}{r} 6 \\ +\ 8 \\ \hline \mathbf{14} \end{array}$ ⑤⑨ $\begin{array}{r} 3 \\ +\ 8 \\ \hline \mathbf{11} \end{array}$ ⑥⓪ $\begin{array}{r} 11 \\ -\ 6 \\ \hline \mathbf{5} \end{array}$

SELF ASSESSMENT

Are You Shiny or Rusty?

On this page did you get

Very shiny — 54 or more right

Shiny — 48–53 right

A bit rusty — 42–47 right

Rusty — Fewer than 42 right

Keep in shape by practicing your number facts for addition and subtraction.

Use the Cumulative Review on page 552 after this lesson.

Unit 1 Lesson 4 • **15**

---

arithmetic. A copy of this game can also be found on page 7 of the Home Connections Blackline Masters.

Then have students complete page 15 as a timed exercise, as described on page 49 of this Teacher's Guide. Explain that people need to be able to give arithmetic facts quickly and accurately so that they can focus more of their attention on how to solve more difficult problems.

 **Introducing the "Busy Bee" Game Mat**

You may wish to demonstrate the "Busy Bee" game by playing it with a student as the rest of the class watches. Play long enough for students to understand the rules and to see how the blocking procedure works. This game provides practice with mental arithmetic and mathematical reasoning. Complete instructions for playing are on the Game Mat. A copy of this game can also be found on page 603 of this Teacher's Guide.

❸ Wrap-Up ⏱ 5 MINUTES

In Closing Summarize the lesson by asking a few students to describe their winning strategies for the "Roll-Sub-Add" game. Invite others to explain any ideas they use to help them remember basic addition or subtraction facts.

Encourage students to keep a record of their time and score on the exercises on page 15 so they can begin competing against their own past performances. Similar self-assessments will be provided in upcoming lessons.

Portfolio Assessment Ask students to write down the addition and subtraction facts that are hardest for them to remember. Then challenge them to think of and record a way they can speedily recall each fact. Have students keep these records in their Math Portfolios.

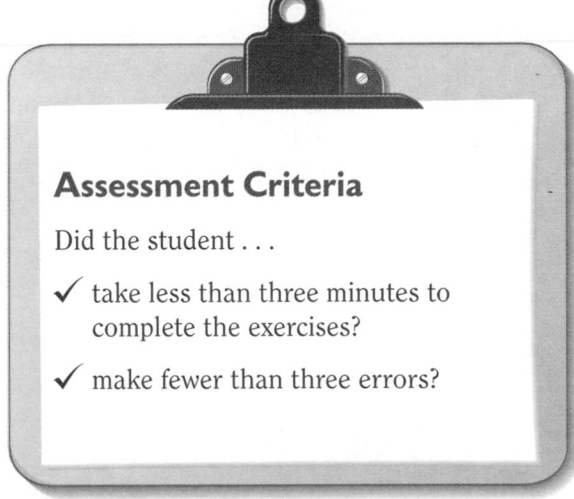

Assessment Criteria

Did the student . . .

✓ take less than three minutes to complete the exercises?

✓ make fewer than three errors?

Homework Ask students to write down three ways in which they use arithmetic facts in games or sports they play.

Unit 1 Lesson 4 **15**

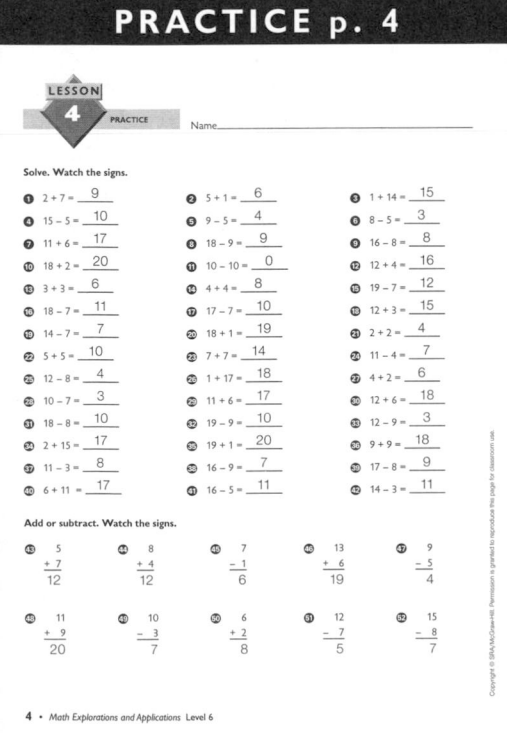
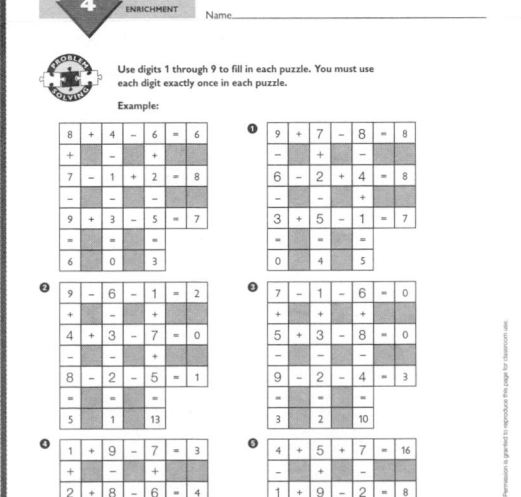

Multiplying and Dividing

LESSON PLANNER

Objective

▶ to review and provide practice with multiplication facts through 10 × 10 and their related division facts

Context of the Lesson
This is the second of 15 lessons that review operations with whole numbers.

 MANIPULATIVES

flash cards (optional)

Program Resources

"Marathon 1" Game Mat

Number Cubes (0–5 and 5–10)

Practice Master 5

Enrichment Master 5

For additional math integration:
  Math Throughout the Day*

For extra practice:
  CD-ROM* Lesson 5

❶ Warm-Up

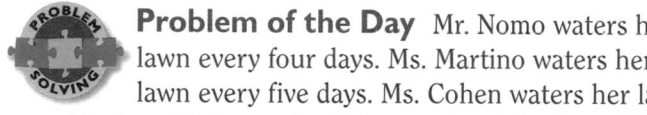

Problem of the Day Mr. Nomo waters his lawn every four days. Ms. Martino waters her lawn every five days. Ms. Cohen waters her lawn every six days. Today, each of them watered the lawn. When is the next time all three will water their lawns on the same day? (in 60 days, because 60 is the least common multiple of 4, 5, and 6)

Problem-Solving Strategies Ask students who have solved the Problem of the Day to share how they solved it and any strategies they used.

 Have students practice speedy recall of basic multiplication and division facts through 10 × 10. Present problems like these:

a. 7 × 6 = (42)   b. 56 ÷ 8 = (7)   c. 9 × 4 = (36)

d. 48 ÷ 6 = (8)   e. 72 ÷ 8 = (9)   f. 3 × 7 = (21)

g. 5 × 6 = (30)   h. 24 ÷ 3 = (8)   i. 8 × 5 = (40)

❷ Teach

 Using the Student Pages Demonstrate the "Multifact" game by playing several rounds with the class. Emphasize that a player need not use

---

Multiplying and Dividing

 COOPERATIVE LEARNING

Multifact Game

Players:	Two or more
Materials:	Two 0–5 cubes, two 5–10 cubes
Object:	To make a score that is closest to 25
Math Focus:	Multiplication facts, multidigit addition and subtraction, and mental arithmetic

RULES

1. Take turns rolling all four cubes. Make two multiplication problems from any of the numbers rolled. Each number may be used once in each problem. For example, if you roll 7, 2, 3 and 5, you could make 7 × 2 and 3 × 2, but you could not make 3 × 3.

2. Find the products of both problems, and add or subtract them to get your score for the round.

3. The player whose score is closest to 25 wins the round.

SAMPLE GAME

Juan rolled:

2 3 7 8

Juan made:
3 × 7 and 3 × 2
He added the products.
His score was 27.

Emily won this round.

Sam rolled:

4 8 6 2

Sam made:
4 × 6 and 6 × 8
He subtracted the products.
His score was 24.

Emily rolled:

5 0 9 5

Emily made:
5 × 5 and 9 × 0
She added the products.
Her score was 25.

 **Music Connection** Encourage students who have an interest in music to make up a song, such as a rap song, to help them remember basic facts.

RETEACHING

Identify students who have trouble with multiplication and division facts and, if possible, which facts are causing the most difficulty. Have these students work with a partner using **flash cards**. As you did with addition and subtraction, have them try to relate the problematic facts to known facts (9 x 7, for example, must be 7 less than 10 x 7, and therefore 63). The partner should provide encouragement and pointers for remembering answers.

*available separately

Solve for n. Watch the signs.

1. $56 \div 7 = n$ **8**
2. $n = 5 \times 5$ **25**
3. $n = 7 \times 7$ **49**
4. $6 \times 8 = n$ **48**
5. $n = 9 \times 4$ **36**
6. $8 \times 9 = n$ **72**
7. $8 \times 4 = n$ **32**
8. $n = 80 \div 8$ **10**
9. $n = 54 \div 6$ **9**
10. $45 \div 5 = n$ **9**
11. $n = 72 \div 9$ **8**
12. $50 \div 5 = n$ **10**
13. $60 \div 6 = n$ **10**
14. $n = 64 \div 8$ **8**
15. $9 \times 7 = n$ **63**
16. $3 \times 8 = n$ **24**
17. $n = 9 \times 3$ **27**
18. $n = 48 \div 6$ **8**
19. $45 \div 9 = n$ **5**
20. $n = 72 \div 8$ **9**
21. $32 \div 4 = n$ **8**
22. $36 \div 9 = n$ **4**
23. $n = 2 \times 9$ **18**
24. $n = 9 \times 6$ **54**
25. $35 \div 5 = n$ **7**
26. $n = 60 \div 10$ **6**
27. $24 \div 8 = n$ **3**
28. $30 \div 6 = n$ **5**
29. $n = 63 \div 7$ **9**
30. $n = 5 \times 9$ **45**

Multiply or divide. Watch the signs.

31. $2 \times 7 = $ **14**
32. $7)\overline{70} = $ **10**
33. $9)\overline{63} = $ **7**
34. $7 \times 5 = $ **35**
35. $6 \times 6 = $ **36**
36. $8)\overline{56} = $ **7**
37. $7)\overline{49} = $ **7**
38. $8)\overline{40} = $ **5**
39. $7 \times 8 = $ **56**
40. $4)\overline{36} = $ **9**
41. $8 \times 5 = $ **40**
42. $10 \times 10 = $ **100**
43. $9)\overline{54} = $ **6**
44. $8 \times 2 = $ **16**
45. $7)\overline{42} = $ **6**
46. $9)\overline{81} = $ **9**
47. $10 \times 6 = $ **60**
48. $8 \times 8 = $ **64**

SELF ASSESSMENT

Are You Shiny or Rusty?

On this page did you get

Very shiny	44 or more right
Shiny	39–43 right
A bit rusty	34–38 right
Rusty	Fewer than 34 right

Keep in shape by practicing your number facts.

Unit 1 Lesson 5 • **17**

---

every number rolled. As an example, point out that Juan did not use the 8 and Sam did not use the 2. Ask students to explain why these players may have made each of these choices. Then have students play the game in pairs or small groups. This game provides practice in multiplication facts.

Next, have students do page 17 as a timed exercise. Those students who have difficulty completing these problems with speed and accuracy should be given extra help.

GAME Introducing the "Marathon 1" Game Mat
Demonstrate the "Marathon 1" game by playing it with a student. This game provides practice with mathematical reasoning and solving missing-fact multiplication problems. "Marathon 2" is a variation of the same game, using different numbers. A copy of these games can be found on pages 620–621 of this Teacher's Guide.

❸ Wrap-Up 5 MINUTES

In Closing Summarize the lesson by asking a few students to describe their winning strategies for the "Multifact" game. Invite others to explain any tricks they have used to help them remember any basic multiplication or division facts that once eluded them.

SELF ASSESSMENT As you did in the previous lesson, encourage students to keep a record of their time and score on the exercises on page 17. In future self-assessments they can compete against their best past performances.

Assessment Criteria

Did the student . . .

✓ make fewer than three errors?

✓ take less than three minutes to complete the exercises?

Homework Encourage students who would benefit from additional fact practice to work with an adult at home. The adult can time the student's performance on a self-made test or present flash cards of the facts that are stumbling blocks.

Literature Connection *Anno's Mysterious Multiplying Jar* by Masaidiro and Mitsumaso Anno provides multiplication practice through a description of a jar's contents.

PRACTICE p. 5

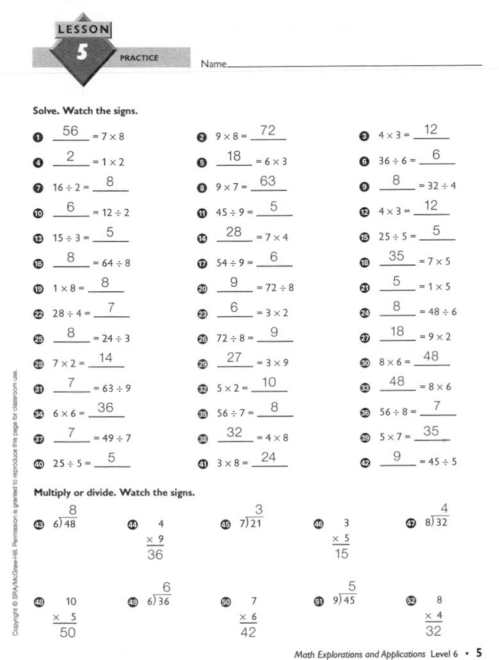

LESSON 5 PRACTICE Name_____

Solve. Watch the signs.

1. $56 = 7 \times 8$
2. $9 \times 8 = \underline{72}$
3. $4 \times 3 = \underline{12}$
4. $\underline{2} = 1 \times 2$
5. $\underline{18} = 6 \times 3$
6. $36 \div 6 = \underline{6}$
7. $16 \div 2 = \underline{8}$
8. $9 \times 7 = \underline{63}$
9. $\underline{8} = 32 \div 4$
10. $\underline{6} = 12 \div 2$
11. $45 \div 9 = \underline{5}$
12. $4 \times 3 = \underline{12}$
13. $15 \div 3 = \underline{5}$
14. $\underline{28} = 7 \times 4$
15. $25 \div 5 = \underline{5}$
16. $\underline{8} = 64 \div 8$
17. $54 \div 9 = \underline{6}$
18. $\underline{35} = 7 \times 5$
19. $1 \times 8 = \underline{8}$
20. $\underline{9} = 72 \div 8$
21. $\underline{5} = 1 \times 5$
22. $28 \div 4 = \underline{7}$
23. $\underline{6} = 3 \times 2$
24. $\underline{8} = 48 \div 6$
25. $\underline{8} = 24 \div 3$
26. $72 \div 8 = \underline{9}$
27. $\underline{18} = 9 \times 2$
28. $\underline{7} = 63 \div 9$
29. $5 \times 2 = \underline{10}$
30. $\underline{48} = 8 \times 6$
31. $6 \times 6 = \underline{36}$
32. $56 \div 7 = \underline{8}$
33. $56 \div 8 = \underline{7}$
34. $\underline{7} = 49 \div 7$
35. $\underline{32} = 4 \times 8$
36. $5 \times 7 = \underline{35}$
37. $\underline{7} = 49 \div 7$
38. $3 \times 8 = \underline{24}$
39. $\underline{9} = 45 \div 5$

Multiply or divide. Watch the signs.

$6)\overline{48}$ = **8** $7)\overline{21}$ = **3** $8)\overline{32}$ = **4**

$\times 9 = 36$ $\times 5 = 15$

$\times 5 = 50$ $6)\overline{36}$ = **6** $7 \times 6 = 42$ $9)\overline{45}$ = **5** $\times 4 = 32$

Math Explorations and Applications Level 6 • 5

ENRICHMENT p. 5

LESSON 5 ENRICHMENT Name_____

COOPERATIVE LEARNING

Players: Two
Materials: 30 centimeter cubes or 30 square pieces of cardboard, colored pencils
Object: To color four squares in a row

Rules

1. The first player takes some cubes. That player arranges the cubes to make a rectangle and says a multiplication fact and a division fact that is shown by the arrangement. If a correct fact is given, the player gets to color any square below.
2. The second player tries to make a different rectangle and states a different pair of facts. (Different numbers must be used.) If a fact is correctly stated, he or she colors in a square.
3. The first player tries to make another rectangle. If a player cannot make a rectangle, but the opponent can, he or she gets to color in a square.
4. When no different rectangles can be made, put the cubes back. The second player draws the cubes and play continues.
5. Continue until a player colors four squares in a row—horizontally, vertically, or diagonally.

1×12 and $12 \div 1$ or 12×1 and $12 \div 12$

2×6 and $12 \div 2$ or 6×2 and $12 \div 6$

3×4 and $12 \div 3$ or 4×3 and $12 \div 4$

Game 1   Game 2

Math Explorations and Applications Level 6 • 5

Applying Basic Facts

LESSON PLANNER

Objectives

▶ to diagnose and correct deficiencies in students' knowledge of the basic addition, subtraction, multiplication, and division facts

▶ to provide practice in whole-number arithmetic with the four basic operations

Context of the Lesson This is the third of 15 lessons reviewing operations with whole numbers.

MANIPULATIVES	Program Resources
none	Number Cubes (0–5 and 5–10)
	Practice Master 6
	Enrichment Master 6
	For extra practice:
	CD-ROM* Lesson 6

❶ Warm-Up

Problem of the Day Present this problem orally: Geraldo had 20 cents. His sister gave him double this amount. He then spent 35 cents. Walking home, he found a penny on the ground. How much money did he have then? (26 cents)

Problem-Solving Strategies Ask students who have solved the Problem of the Day to share how they solved it and any strategies they used.

Tell students to use the numbers 1, 2, 4, 6, and 7 in any combination to write as many basic facts as they can. Explain that they can use each number more than once in a fact. (Answers will vary; sample answers: 4 + 2 = 6; 6 × 7 = 42; 11 – 4 = 7; 24 ÷ 6 = 4)

❷ Teach

Using the Student Pages Demonstrate the "Cubo" game on page 18 by playing it a few times with the entire class. Roll four cubes and write the numbers on the chalkboard. Have students first describe different ways to score 21 or a number close to 21. Record their responses on the chalkboard. Use parentheses when

---

Applying Basic Facts

Cubo

C🟠OPERATIVE LEARNING

Players:	Two or more
Materials:	Two 0–5 cubes, two 5–10 cubes
Object:	To score as close to 21 as possible
Math Focus:	Mental arithmetic with all four operations

RULES

1. Roll all four cubes on each turn.

2. Use any combination of the four operations (addition, subtraction, multiplication, and division) on the numbers rolled to make a number as close to 21 as possible. Use the number on each cube once and only once. (If two cubes have the same number, you must use both.)

If you rolled:	You could make these scores:	By doing these operations, for example:
3	19	6 – 3 = 3; 3 × 6 = 18; 18 + 1 = 19
6	23	3 × 6 = 18; 18 + 6 = 24; 24 – 1 = 23
6	21	6 – 1 = 5; 5 × 3 = 15; 15 + 6 = 21
1	21	6 – 3 = 3; 6 + 1 = 7; 3 × 7 = 21

3. The player who scores 21 or closest to it is the winner of the round.

OTHER WAYS TO PLAY THIS GAME

1. Make the goal a number other than 21.

2. Use more or fewer than four cubes.

3. Choose a set of numbers (0 to 10, 10 to 20, and so on), and try to make all the scores in the set. (It may not be possible to make every score.)

Literature Connection *The Sneaky Square and 113 Other Math Activities for Kids* by Richard Sharp and Seymour Metzner provides math puzzles and enrichment activities.

RETEACHING

Provide additional practice for those students who are still experiencing difficulty recalling the basic facts. These students can work with a peer tutor in ways described in the previous lessons.

Solve for *n*. Watch the signs.

❶ $7 \times 8 = n$ **56**
❷ $n = 17 - 8$ **9**
❸ $14 - 6 = n$ **8**
❹ $7 + 8 = n$ **15**
❺ $n = 36 \div 9$ **4**
❻ $7 + 7 = n$ **14**
❼ $49 \div 7 = n$ **7**
❽ $n = 15 - 9$ **6**
❾ $4 \times 6 = n$ **24**
❿ $16 - 7 = n$ **9**
⓫ $n = 5 + 4$ **9**
⓬ $n = 12 - 5$ **7**
⓭ $4 + 9 = n$ **13**
⓮ $4 \times 8 = n$ **32**
⓯ $10 - 4 = n$ **6**
⓰ $7 \times 9 = n$ **63**
⓱ $0 + 7 = n$ **7**
⓲ $n = 3 + 8$ **11**
⓳ $7 \times 6 = n$ **42**
⓴ $n = 0 \times 8$ **0**
㉑ $18 - 9 = n$ **9**
㉒ $5 + 9 = n$ **14**
㉓ $7 - 0 = n$ **7**
㉔ $n = 8 \times 8$ **64**
㉕ $10 + 8 = n$ **18**
㉖ $n = 0 \div 8$ **0**
㉗ $15 - 9 = n$ **6**
㉘ $9 + 8 = n$ **17**
㉙ $8 \times 3 = n$ **24**
㉚ $15 \div 3 = n$ **5**
㉛ $n = 48 \div 8$ **6**
㉜ $n = 9 + 7$ **16**
㉝ $4 + 8 = n$ **12**
㉞ $n = 81 \div 9$ **9**
㉟ $n = 35 \div 7$ **5**
㊱ $n = 12 - 6$ **6**
㊲ $n = 6 \times 6$ **36**
㊳ $12 - 9 = n$ **3**
㊴ $n = 30 \div 6$ **5**

㊵ $n = 19 - 10$ **9**
㊶ $45 \div 9 = n$ **5**
㊷ $n = 8 \times 9$ **72**
㊸ $n = 12 - 8$ **4**
㊹ $n = 54 \div 6$ **9**
㊺ $n = 6 + 7$ **13**
㊻ $8 \times 5 = n$ **40**
㊼ $9 - 3 = n$ **6**
㊽ $5 \times 5 = n$ **25**
㊾ $n = 5 + 5$ **10**
㊿ $8 + 8 = n$ **16**

SELF ASSESSMENT

Are You Shiny or Rusty?

Very shiny	45 or more right
Shiny	40–44 right
A bit rusty	35–39 right
Rusty	Less than 35 right

Keep in shape by practicing your number facts for addition, subtraction, multiplication, and division.

Unit 1 Lesson 6 • **19**

---

applicable, but point out that the game can easily be played without them. Make sure students understand the "Cubo" rules and how each of the sample scores was obtained. This game provides practice in basic facts. Then have students complete page 19 on their own as a timed exercise.

❸ Wrap-Up  5 MINUTES

In Closing Give students the following arithmetic facts orally and have them write down the answers as quickly as possible. Then have them add up all their answers to arrive at a total. (59)

a. 6×3 (18)
b. $9 + 12$ (21)
c. $28 \div 7$ (4)
d. $33 - 17$ (16)

ALTERNATIVE ASSESSMENT

Informal Assessment Observe students as they play "Cubo" to see how easy or difficult it is for students to choose sensible combinations of facts to create their scores. Check for speed and accuracy as they recall the facts at their disposal.

Assessment Criteria

Did the student . . .

✓ regularly obtain scores close to 21 in "Cubo"?

✓ correctly answer 80% of the exercises on page 19?

✓ complete all the exercises in under three minutes?

Homework Have students play "Cubo" with a family member to practice basic facts and mathematical reasoning. A copy of this game can also be found on page 9 of the Home Connections Blackline Masters.

SPECIAL NEEDS

Meeting Individual Needs

If a student still has not mastered the great majority of the basic facts, the difficulty may be serious enough to require the help of a learning disabilities specialist or other specialized personnel.

THINKING STORIES

WHAT ARE THINKING STORIES?

Thinking Stories are short stories about common sense mathematical problems, many of which people face every day. Thinking Stories are designed to be read aloud to an entire class. Some Thinking Stories apply lesson concepts, and some introduce or pre-teach an upcoming lesson concept, but the majority of stories simply require students to use their mathematical knowledge and logical reasoning, because real life presents us with a variety of problems at the same time.

The same characters are used in all grade levels. The children in the stories are always the same age as the students at that grade level. Students become familiar with each character and how each one reacts to specific situations.

Levels K–3

In Kindergarten, the Thinking Stories are found in the Teacher's Guide in each lesson. In levels 1–3, the Thinking Stories are presented in both the Teacher's Guide and in a separate book. Interspersed in each story are questions that will prompt your students to think ahead of the story characters. The questions might ask students to identify what is wrong with what a character has done or said, to anticipate what is going to happen as a result, or to think of other possibilities that the character hasn't considered. There are also many additional problems in the separate Thinking Story book (levels 1–3) that can be used at any time.

Levels 4–6

In levels 4–6, the Thinking Stories are presented in the Student Editions. After listening to the story as a class, students can reread the story, either by themselves or in small groups, and discuss the questions at the end.

WHAT ARE THE EXTRA STORY PROBLEMS IN LEVELS 1–3?

In the separate Thinking Story book, there are additional story problems that follow each story. They require students to use the same thinking skills that the story characters used. These problems can be used at any time.

Tips for Using the Thinking Story Books (Levels 1–3)

◆ **Read the stories aloud.** Give students time to think about each question, but not so much time that they forget the point of the story.

◆ **Discuss the problems.** Ask your students how they arrived at their answers. Encourage debate. There are often many ways to solve a problem.

◆ **Encourage students to think carefully.** Speed should not be emphasized.

◆ **When possible, let students use Number Cubes.** This will encourage *all* students to respond.

◆ **Recognize sensible answers.** Even if a student gives an incorrect answer, he or she probably thought carefully about it and should be praised.

◆ **Encourage students to act out or use manipulatives to solve difficult problems.** This technique may help students organize their thinking.

WHAT MAKES THINKING STORIES AND STORY PROBLEMS UNIQUE?

The characters in the stories and problems have peculiarities that your students will come to know. Mr. Muddle, for example, easily forgets things. Ferdie jumps to conclusions without thinking. Mr. Breezy gives more information than is needed and, therefore, makes easy problems seem difficult. Ms. Eng, on the other hand, provides insufficient information to solve the questions and problems she poses. Your students will learn to recognize these peculiarities and avoid them in their own thinking. The stories and problems are filled with so many surprises that your students will be challenged as well as entertained.

WHEN SHOULD I USE THE STORIES AND PROBLEMS?

In Kindergarten, the problems are provided with each individual lesson in the Teacher's Guide. In levels 1–3, the Teacher's Guide will instruct you which of the 20 story selections to use and when to use them. In general, you will be directed to read one story about every five or six lessons. On days when no stories are read, the Teacher's Guide will suggest you read problems—usually three or four—to your students. If it has been a day or two since you read a particular story, you might want to read it again before presenting new story problems. Stories and problems become more difficult as the year progresses.

WHICH THINKING SKILLS ARE STRESSED IN THE STORIES AND PROBLEMS?

Math Skills
- Choosing which operation to use
- Recognizing relevant information
- Recognizing absurd or unreasonable answers
- Deciding when calculation isn't necessary
- Recognizing incorrect answers

Language Arts Skills
- Characterization
- Predicting what will happen in a story
- Making inferences
- Summarizing what has happened in a story
- Listening for details
- Drawing conclusions
- Evaluating information
- Recognizing cause-and-effect relationships
- Forming generalizations

LESSON 7

Student Edition pages 20–23

Mental Arithmetic

LESSON PLANNER

Objectives

▶ to provide practice in mental arithmetic

▶ to provide practice in working with multidigit numbers in estimating areas on a map

▶ to help students develop the broad ability to use mathematical common sense

Context of the Lesson This is the fourth of 15 lessons reviewing operations with whole numbers. Many of these lessons provide review and practice with estimating and approximating. Subsequent lessons formally review approximation techniques. This lesson also contains part 1 of the first Thinking Story, "Mr. Muddle's Extra-Large Problems."

MANIPULATIVES

Program Resources

"Cube-O-Mat" and "Harder Cube-O-Mat" Game Mats

Practice Master 7

Enrichment Master 7

For career connections: Careers and Math*

For additional math integration: Math Throughout the Day*

For extra practice: CD-ROM* Lesson 7

① Warm-Up

 Problem of the Day Present the following problem to students: I'm thinking of three numbers, each 10 apart, whose sum is 450. What are the numbers? (140, 150, 160)

Problem-Solving Strategies Ask students who have solved the Problem of the Day to share how they solved it and any strategies they used.

MENTAL MATH Present the following mixed computation problems. Have students do the operations in the sequence presented and show the correct final answers.

a. $5 + 6 + 7 + 8 = (26)$ b. $35 \div 5 \times 5 = (35)$

c. $3 \times 3 \times 3 + 10 = (37)$ d. $49 - 49 \times 5 + 2 = (2)$

e. $45 - 5 \times 10 \times 0 = (0)$ f. $8 \times 8 - 10 + 10 \div 8 = (8)$

20 Whole Numbers and Integers

MIXED **PRACTICE**

LESSON 7

Mental Arithmetic

You've learned about place value and have practiced your number facts. In this lesson you'll put it all together to solve problems mentally.

Solve for the variable. Do the problems in your head. Then write the answers.

1. $4 \times 4 = n$ **16**   2. $40 \times 4 = n$ **160**   3. $3 + 9 = x$ **12**

4. $30 + 90 = n$ **120**   5. $30 + 95 = y$ **125**   6. $6 \div 3 = x$ **2**

7. $60 \div 3 = n$ **20**   8. $600 \div 3 = r$ **200**   9. $10 \times 10 = m$ **100**

10. $10 \times 100 = n$ **1000**   11. $8 + 7 = x$ **15**   12. $8 \times 7 = n$ **56**

13. $80 \times 7 = y$ **560**   14. $100 - 20 = r$ **80**   15. $100 - 25 = n$ **75**

16. $37 + 10 = n$ **47**   17. $37 + 100 = m$ **137**   18. $3700 + 1000 = t$ **4700**

19. $3700 + 100 = n$ **3800**   20. $3700 + 10 = z$ **3710**   21. $16 - 9 = n$ **7**

22. $16 - 10 = y$ **6**   23. $16 - 11 = x$ **5**   24. $16 - 12 = r$ **4**

25. $160 - 120 = t$ **40**   26. $160 - 115 = n$ **45**   27. $16 \times 10 = m$ **160**

28. $16 \times 5 = s$ **80**   29. $16 \times 2 = n$ **32**   30. $16 \times 1 = y$ **16**

 **Solve these problems.**

31. Anna wants to purchase a bicycle that costs $139.95. If she can save $2.50 per week, how many weeks will it take to save enough money? **56**

32. A theater has 5000 seats. There are two performances a day, and about $\frac{1}{2}$ of the seats are used at each performance. About how much money would the theater collect each day if tickets cost

a. $2 each? **about $10,000**

b. $3 each? **about $15,000**

c. $2.50 each? **about $12,500**

20 • Whole Numbers and Integers

 **Why teach it this way?**

"Mr. Muddle's Extra-Large Problems, Part 1," is the first part of a four-part Thinking Story selection in Unit 1. Each unit contains a three- or four-part story or three or four different stories, as well as problems relating to the stories, which encourage students to apply mathematical common sense to real or fanciful situations. Students may remember many of the Thinking Story characters from earlier grades. These stories are a central focus of the program.

Technology Connection Refer students to the software *Turbo Math Facts* from Nordic Software (Mac, for grades K–6) for further practice with basic computation (addition, subtraction, multiplication, and division).

*available separately

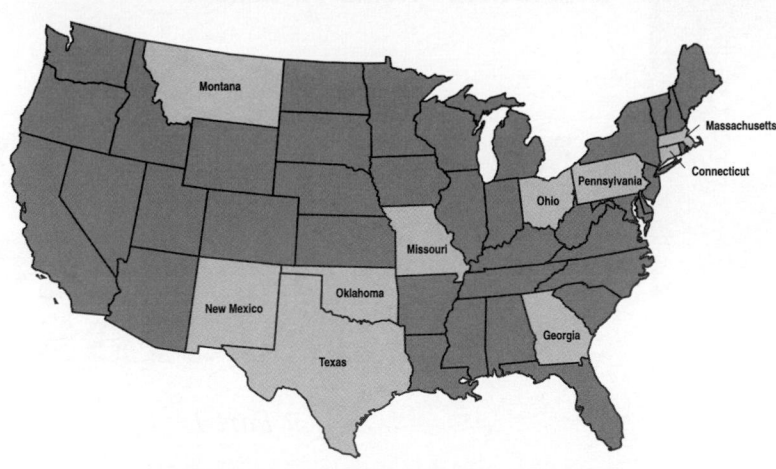

State	Area (square kilometers)
Montana	376,991
Massachusetts	20,300
Missouri	178,446
Ohio	106,067

GEOGRAPHY CONNECTION

Arizona is the state directly west of New Mexico. It looks to be about $\frac{3}{4}$ or $\frac{4}{5}$ the size of Montana. Since the area of Montana is 376,991 km², you could estimate the area of Arizona to be about 300,000 km².

Use the map and the chart to estimate the area in square kilometers of the following states. In each problem four areas are given in square kilometers, but only one is correct. Choose the correct area.

33 New Mexico   **a.** 150,289   **(b.)** 314,334   **c.** 105,321   **d.** 567,402

34 Georgia   **(a.)** 150,010   **b.** 472,809   **c.** 210,450   **d.** 102,946

35 Pennsylvania   **a.** 46,315   **b.** 256,947   **(c.)** 116,083   **d.** 437,231

36 Oklahoma   **a.** 392,025   **b.** 53,702   **c.** 108,257   **(d.)** 177,877

37 Texas   **a.** 45,327   **(b.)** 678,358   **c.** 392,621   **d.** 192,849

38 Connecticut   **(a.)** 12,550   **b.** 194,327   **c.** 56,240   **d.** 376,294

Unit 1   Lesson 7   •   **21**

❷ Teach

Using the Student Pages You may wish to demonstrate the "Cube-O-Mat" and "Harder Cube-O-Mat" Game Mats before beginning work on pages 20–23 so students who finish early can play.

Encourage students to do problems 1–30 on page 20 mentally. If necessary, show how solving one problem, for example $4 \times 4 = n$, can help solve the next one, $40 \times 4 = n$. Challenge students to try to solve the word problems without pencil or paper. Then go over the first problem on page 21 with the class. Ask students to look at the map and compare the size of New Mexico with that of each of the four states whose areas are given in the chart. Dialogue with students: "Is New Mexico larger than Massachusetts?" (yes) "Is it larger than Ohio?" (yes) "Is it larger than Missouri?" (yes) "Is it larger than Montana?" (no) "So New Mexico is larger than Missouri but smaller than Montana. Which of the choices for the area given in problem 33 is greater than Missouri's area of 178,446 and less than Montana's area of 376,991?" (314,334) "Then the answer for the area of New Mexico must be 314,334 square kilometers." If students understand this method of estimating area, let them finish the page working independently or in small groups. If they have difficulty with this method, finish the page as a whole-class activity.

Using the Thinking Story "Mr. Muddle's Extra-Large Problems, Part 1," on pages 22–23 focuses on some of the inventory problems connected with operating a small retail business and on the importance of organizing information in a way that makes it easy to use. One way to handle Thinking Stories is to have students work in groups to read the story and discuss the questions. Make sure each group includes a good reader. Groups should discuss and try to agree on answers. You may also have students work individually or you can do the story and problems with the class. If students work individually or in groups, the whole class should come together to discuss the questions.

Answers to Thinking Story Questions:

Although most students will come up with answers like the ones below, accept any reasonable responses.

1. By selling all of the extra-large and large sizes and few of the smaller ones, Mr. Muddle gradually is left with more and more of the smaller sizes.

2. Sizes people wanted: 83 extra-large, 89 large, 42 medium, 20 small. Number of shirts of each size sold: 36 extra-large, 36 large, 31 medium, 15 small.

3. It is difficult to answer questions from Mr. Muddle's record. For example, it is hard to determine quickly which sizes there are more of, because the different sizes are hard to count and are mixed together. One possible improvement would be for students to organize the information in a table.

Unit 1 Lesson 7   **21**

Teach

4. Mr. Muddle sells more extra-large and large T-shirts than small or medium ones on every day except Saturday and Monday. On Monday he sells no larger sizes at all because he has run out of them. It should be noted that the number of extra-large and large T-shirts sold that week, which was 36 of each, was the same number as in the new box he opened.

5. About 60 extra-large and 60 large. One possible solution is for students to notice that when there are enough T-shirts, about three-fourths of the people who go into the store buy a shirt. If about 80 people each want extra-large and large shirts in one week, Mr. Muddle can be expected to sell about 60 (three-fourths of 80) of each size. Or, because on weekdays Mr. Muddle typically sells eight or nine T-shirts of each larger size, this is a reasonable estimate for Monday. On Saturdays twice the number of people go into the store as on a weekday, so Mr. Muddle sells twice as many shirts, or 16 to 18 of each size. Students can add these estimates to the actual sales for the other days to get a total of about 60 extra-large and 60 large shirts.

MATH JOURNAL Have students discuss Marcus's idea of asking what customers want and keeping a record of their responses. Also discuss Mr. Muddle's practice of circling his "star customers." Have students write in their Math Journals the advice they would give Mr. Muddle.

GAME **Introducing the "Cube-O-Mat" and "Harder Cube-O-Mat" Game Mats** These Game Mats use the rules of "Cubo" and provide practice with the basic arithmetic facts as well as practice in looking ahead. If the Game Mats are not available, use copies of pages 606 and 607 of this *Teacher's Guide,* in which students capture squares by marking them with different-colored pencils instead of placing counters on the Game Mat. Complete directions are on the Game Mat. When everyone understands the rules, students should play in pairs or in small groups.

THINKING STORY

Mr. Muddle's Extra-Large Problems

Part 1

"How is your T-shirt business doing?" Manolita asked. "Not too well," said Mr. Muddle. "People like my T-shirts, but often they don't buy any. They say they can't find any that fit."

Willy looked through the piles of T-shirts neatly stacked on the counter.

"No wonder," Willy said. "You have a few medium T-shirts, and all the rest are small. You need some large and extra-large sizes. That's what most people buy."

"Something must be wrong," said Mr. Muddle. "The company is supposed to send me the same number of every size."

Mr. Muddle opened a box that had just come. Sure enough, it held 36 small, 36 medium, 36 large, and 36 extra-large T-shirts.

"Maybe you should order more of some sizes than others," Marcus said. "I have an idea. For the next week ask all the customers who come in what sizes they want. Write down what they tell you."

Mr. Muddle did just that. Here is the record he showed Marcus the next week:

LITERATURE CONNECTION

Literature Connection Have students read "Arithmetic," a poem by Carl Sandburg about aspects of arithmetic.

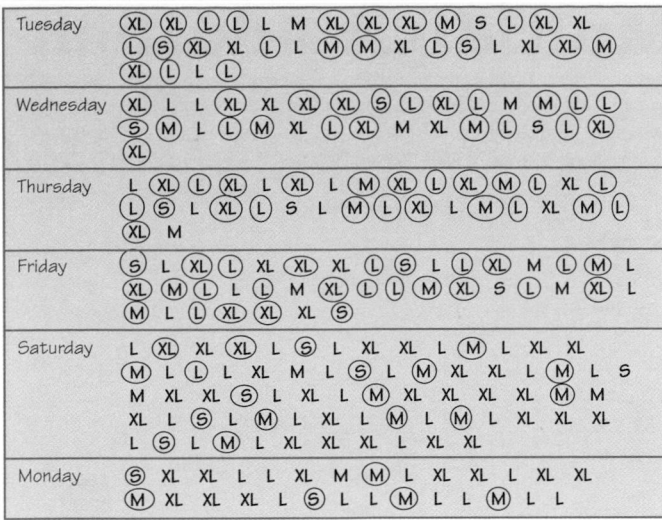

Tuesday	XL XL L L M XL XL XL M S L XL XL L S XL XL L L M M XL L S L XL XL M XL L L L
Wednesday	XL L XL XL XL S L XL L M M L S M L L XL XL M XL M L S L XL XL
Thursday	L XL L XL L XL L M XL L XL M L XL L L S L XL L S L M L XL L M L XL M L XL M
Friday	S L XL L XL XL L S L XL M L M L XL M L L L M L XL L M L S L M XL L M L XL XL XL S
Saturday	L XL XL XL L S L XL XL L M L XL XL M L L L XL M L S L M XL XL L M L S M XL XL S L XL L M XL XL XL M M XL L S L M L XL L M L XL XL XL L S L M L XL L XL L XL L XL
Monday	S XL XL L L XL M M L XL XL L XL XL M XL XL XL L S L L M L L M L L

"What are the circles for?" Manolita asked.

"They mark my star customers," Mr. Muddle answered. "Each one of them bought a T-shirt."

. . . to be continued

Work in groups. Discuss how you figured out your answers. Compare them with other groups.
Answers are in margin.

❶ If each new box holds the same number of each size, how could Mr. Muddle end up with only small and medium T-shirts?

❷ Figure out from Mr. Muddle's record how many people wanted each size of T-shirt. How many T-shirts of each size did he sell that week?

❸ What do you think of Mr. Muddle's way of keeping a record? Show a better way to do it.

❹ Look at the record of T-shirts sold on Saturday and Monday. How are those days different from the other days? How could you explain this difference?

❺ How many large and extra-large T-shirts could Mr. Muddle have sold that week if he had had enough for everyone who wanted one?

Unit 1   Lesson 7   • **23**

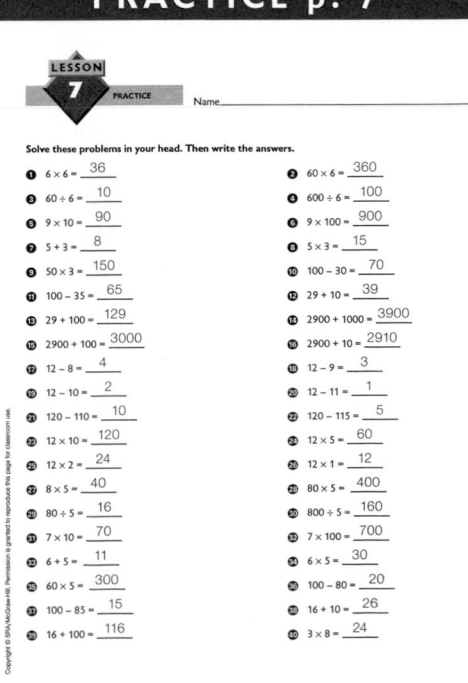

❸ Wrap-Up   5 MINUTES

In Closing Summarize the lesson by asking students to share the strategies they used to solve the problems on page 20 mentally and to choose the correct area of each state.

Encourage students to keep a record of the number of correct answers they get for the first 30 exercises on page 20. Point out that they will be able to compare these results with their results on similar self-assessments in upcoming lessons.

Assessment Criteria

Did the student . . .

✓ correctly answer at least 75% of the computation problems?

✓ explain how she or he solved the problems about state areas?

✓ contribute to the Thinking Story discussion?

Homework Make copies of the "Cube-O-Mat" Game Mat and have students play the game with a family member to practice with basic operations. A copy of this Game Mat can be found on pages 606–607 of this Teacher's Guide.

ESL Meeting Individual Needs

Students with limited proficiency in English may have difficulty with the language in the Thinking Stories. You may want to read the Thinking Stories aloud to them, stopping as necessary to explain or to act out words you think students may not understand. Use gestures and vocal inflection to help convey the humor and confusion in each situation, or invite small groups of students to act out different sections of the story.

Unit 1 Lesson 7 **23**

Multidigit Addition

LESSON PLANNER

Objectives

▶ to review the standard algorithm for multidigit addition, including column addition

▶ to provide practice in adding multidigit numbers

▶ to provide practice in using addition to solve word problems

Context of the Lesson This is the fifth of 15 lessons reviewing operations with whole numbers. Multidigit addition was taught in the second-grade program and has been reviewed in each subsequent grade. The standard algorithm for multidigit subtraction is reviewed in the next lesson.

 MANIPULATIVES

base-10 materials* (optional)

Program Resources

Number Wheels

Practice Master 8

Enrichment Master 8

For extra practice:
  CD-ROM* Lesson 8
  Cumulative Review, page 553

1 Warm-Up ⏱ 5 MINUTES

 **Problem of the Day** Present this problem to the class: Sen-Pei wants to use her calculator to subtract 247 from 408. However, the 7 and 0 keys on her calculator are stuck. How can she still do the subtraction using the calculator? (Answers will vary. Sample answers: subtract 246 from 418, then subtract 11; add 5 or any number with a 5 in the ones place to both, 413 – 252.)

Problem-Solving Strategies Ask students who have solved the Problem of the Day to share how they solved it and any strategies they used.

 Have students solve the following problems, using Number Wheels to show their answers:

a. 420 + 200 = (620)   b. 560 + 300 = (860)

c. 70 + 35 = (105)   d. 16 + 32 = (48)

Multidigit Addition

For a popular concert, 83,576 tickets were sold on the first day. On the second day 19,806 tickets were sold. How many tickets were sold? To find out, find the **sum** of 83,576 and 19,806.

83,576 + 19,806 = ?

Remember:

83,576 + 19,806	Line up corresponding digits.
1 83,576 + 19,806 2	Add the digits in the ones place. 6 + 6 = 12 Write 2. "Carry" 1.
1 83,576 + 19,806 82	Add the next column. 1 + 7 + 0 = 8 Write 8.
1 1 83,576 + 19,806 382	Add the next column. 5 + 8 = 13 Write 3. Carry 1.
11 1 83,576 + 19,806 3,382	Add the next column. 1 + 3 + 9 = 13 Write 3. Carry 1.
11 1 83,576 + 19,806 103,382	Add the next column. 1 + 8 + 1 = 10 Write 10. There were 103,382 tickets sold.

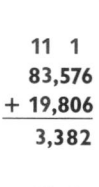

24 • Whole Numbers and Integers

Why teach it this way?

Mixing in addition problems that can be solved without using the standard algorithm helps students to recognize that they need not use paper and pencil or a calculator every time they work with numbers.

 **Technology Connection** You may wish to use the software *Word Problem Square Off: Level A* from Gamco (Mac, for grades 3–8) for further practice with one- and two-step problems, addition/subtraction of up to four digits, and multiplying/dividing through 9 x 9.

*available separately

Add. Use shortcuts when you can.

1 86 + 86 = **172**	**2** 75 + 98 = **173**	**3** 46 + 53 = **99**	**4** 207 + 359 = **566**	**5** 617 + 849 = **1466**
6 86 + 731 = **817**	**7** 500 + 700 = **1200**	**8** 406 + 79 = **485**	**9** 342 + 658 = **1000**	**10** 305 + 609 = **914**
11 2346 + 7654 = **10,000**	**12** 346 + 235 = **581**	**13** 5000 + 2476 = **7476**	**14** 4962 + 1 = **4963**	**15** 8219 + 1 = **8220**
16 5999 + 1 = **6000**	**17** 99,999 + 1 = **100,000**	**18** 99,999 + 2 = **100,001**	**19** 60 + 20 = **80**	**20** 80 + 70 = **150**
21 800 + 700 = **1500**	**22** 8000 + 7000 = **15,000**	**23** 493 + 7 = **500**	**24** 493 + 507 = **1000**	**25** 1493 + 3507 = **5000**

Solve these problems.

26 Lin's family went on vacation for 21 days near Cape Canaveral, Florida. When they got back, Lin gave Fred five NASA postcards for his postcard collection. How many postcards does Fred have now? **not enough information given**

27 Lin's family began their vacation on June 25. What was the last day of their vacation? **July 15**

28 Lin had 98 seashells in her collection. During her vacation she found 14 shells on the beach. How many shells does she have now? **112**

Unit 1 Lesson 8 • **25**

② Teach

Using the Student Pages Review the standard algorithm for column addition by going over page 24 with the class. Emphasize that the process is the same in each column. Point out that it is not necessary to write the carried numbers when doing addition problems.

Have students do page 25 on their own. The direction line on this page, "Use shortcuts when you can," appears on almost every page of multidigit arithmetic exercises. Each of these pages contains some items that can be done more easily without using the standard algorithm. For example, problem 2 on this page can be solved using mental math, because the sum of 75 + 98 must be 2 less than the sum of 75 + 100 (2 less than 175). Also, in problems such as 500 + 700 or 800 + 700, students can find the answer by using basic arithmetic facts.

A good understanding of the commutative principle will reduce by almost half the number of addition facts that must be learned, and is therefore, well worth knowing and stating explicitly (but not necessarily with the formal name).

—Stephen S. Willoughby, *Mathematics Education for a Changing World*

Meeting Individual Needs

If students have the addition facts memorized but have trouble with the algorithm, focus on the steps.

You may wish to use **base-10 materials*** with kinesthetic learners to help explain why the algorithm works. One strategy you can use with auditory learners is to have them say what they are doing as they work through a problem. For instance, using the example on page 24, students can say together, "Start on the right with the ones column: 6 + 6 = 12. Write the 2 in the answer space and the 1 at the top of the next column (tens) and add: 1 + 7 + 0 = 8." They can continue in this manner.

*available separately

◆ LESSON 8 Multidigit Addition

Teach

Using the Student Pages Review the methods shown for adding columns of numbers. Then have students work independently on the problems. When they finish they can play "Cubo" on page 18 to practice basic facts. A copy of "Cubo" can also be found on page 9 of the Home Connections Blackline Masters.

Meeting Individual Needs

For students who can add two multidigit numbers but have difficulty adding a column of numbers, you might find the following technique helpful (when adding numbers with three or more digits, the numbers must be written with extra space between the digits). First, students add the ones digits of the first two numbers and write the sum slightly off to the side. If there is a 10 in the answer, they should write a 1 at the top of the tens column and add the ones part of the answer to the ones digit of the next number, and so on. For example, in the problem:

```
   27
   26
 + 39
```

students add 7 and 6 and write 3 near the ones column and 1 at the top of the tens column. They may cross out the 7 and the 6.

```
  1
  2̸7̸
  2̸6̸3
 + 39
```

They would then add 3 + 9 to get 12, writing the 2 in the ones column of the answer space and another 1 at the top of the tens column. The final answer should look something like this:

```
  1
  1
  2̸7̸
  2̸6̸3
 + 39
 ─────
   92
```

◆ LESSON 8 Multidigit Addition

356 + 829 + 54 = ?

There are many ways to add more than two numbers.

One way is to add the numbers in pairs.

```
   356      Add one pair.
 + 829
 ─────
  1185
```

```
  1185      Then add the other number to that sum.
 +  54
 ─────
  1239
```

It's not necessary to add the numbers in order. For example, to add 999 + 667 + 1, first add 999 + 1 to get 1000. Then it's easy to add 667 + 1000 to get 1667.

Another way is to add the numbers in a column.

```
   1          11          11
  356        356         356
  829        829         829
 + 54       + 54        + 54
 ────       ────        ─────
   9    →    39    →    1239
```

The second method is usually faster.

Add. How many can you do without using paper and pencil?

㉙ 42 + 57 + 64 = ■ **163**
㉚ 250 + 250 + 250 + 250 = ■ **1000**
㉛ 843 + 71 + 64 = ■ **978**
㉜ 9473 + 8597 + 6492 + 2179 = ■ **26,741**
㉝ 4000 + 5000 + 7000 = ■ **16,000**
㉞ 150 + 250 + 150 + 250 = ■ **800**
㉟ 123 + 456 + 789 = ■ **1368**
㊱ 29 + 39 + 50 = ■ **118**
㊲ 25 + 25 + 25 + 25 = ■ **100**
㊳ 999 + 999 + 999 = ■ **2997**
㊴ 9999 + 9999 + 9999 = ■ **29,997**
㊵ 1001 + 1002 + 999 + 998 = ■ **4000**
㊶ 480 + 310 + 612 = ■ **1402**
㊷ 528 + 63 + 816 = ■ **1407**
㊸ 375 + 400 + 125 = ■ **900**
㊹ 705 + 208 + 413 = ■ **1326**

26 • Whole Numbers and Integers

Literature Connection Rand McNally's *Children's Atlas of the United States* is a good source for population arithmetic problems. You may wish to have students add the populations of different states to determine the number of people in a certain section of the country.

RETEACHING

Have students who are proficient with the addition algorithm but never use shortcuts work with peer tutors who can present problems and ask, "How can you solve this without using paper and pencil?" These tutors should present both problems that can easily be done using a shortcut and problems that cannot.

Add. How many can you do without using paper and pencil?

㊺	㊻	㊼	㊽	㊾
750	979	300	55	402
750	365	300	55	508
750	489	350	+ 55	311
+ 750	685	+ 5	**165**	+ 203
3000	+ 944	**955**		**1424**
	3462			

㊿	51	52	53	54
777	625	473	722	391
888	450	695	278	523
+ 999	175	+ 829	410	+ 754
2664	+ 250	**1997**	+ 306	**1668**
	1500		**1716**	

Solve these problems.

55 Chan, Rachel, and Jody collect postcards. Jody has 80. So does Rachel. Chan has 42. How many do they have all together? **202**

56 Lauren, Kim, and Brandon also collect postcards. Lauren has 15 more than Kim, who has 23 more than Brandon. Brandon has 56. How many do they have all together? **229**

57 The Blue Flags played three home games last week. On Monday about 3000 people were at the game. On Wednesday about 5000 people watched them play. About 11,000 people were at Saturday's game. About how many tickets were sold for the games last week? **about 19,000**

58 For their next home game the Blue Flags have sold about 4500 regularly priced tickets, about 1200 student tickets, and about 1500 senior citizen tickets. About how many tickets have been sold? **about 7200**

Use the Cumulative Review on page 553 after this lesson.

Unit 1   Lesson 8 • **27**

PRACTICE p. 8

ENRICHMENT p. 8

---

❸ Wrap-Up

In Closing Summarize the lesson by asking students to explain how to use the algorithm for adding columns of numbers. Additionally, ask students to describe how to identify problems that they can solve mentally, without using the algorithm.

ANALYZING ANSWERS Sometimes students see things in word problems that are not intended and so arrive at unexpected but reasonable and defensible answers. It is important for students to know, for example, when a problem can be solved by arithmetic and when it cannot and when an approximation is more appropriate than a precise calculation. For these reasons, many of the word problems in this program are open-ended, intentionally do not provide enough information, or can be solved by approximation. It is essential not to criticize students for giving an unexpected answer that they have thought through and that makes sense in light of their interpretation of the text. Be supportive of students who think through problems.

ALTERNATIVE ASSESSMENT **Portfolio Assessment** Have students write an explanation of how they can sometimes use their knowledge of basic facts and mental math to find the sum of two or more numbers. Make sure they put this explanation in their Math Portfolios.

Assessment Criteria

Did the student . . .

✓ communicate strategies used to solve the addition and word problems?

✓ correctly answer over 80% of the computation problems?

Homework Invite students to formulate two word problems that classmates can solve by adding multidigit numbers.

Multidigit Subtraction

LESSON PLANNER

Objectives

✓ to evaluate students' ability to do multidigit addition and subtraction, including speedy recall of addition and subtraction facts

▶ to review the standard algorithm for multidigit subtraction

▶ to provide practice in subtracting multidigit numbers

Context of the Lesson This is the sixth of 15 lessons reviewing operations with whole numbers and contains Mastery Checkpoint 4, for assessing students' ability to do multidigit addition and subtraction.

 MANIPULATIVES

atlas (optional)

base-10 materials* (optional)

Program Resources

"Transaction" Game Mat

Practice Master 9

Enrichment Master 9

Assessment Master

For additional math integration:
Math Throughout the Day*

For extra practice:
CD-ROM* Lesson 9

 # ① Warm-Up ⏱

Problem of the Day Present this problem orally: Two numbers have a sum of 12,000 and a difference of 1000. What are the numbers? (6500 and 5500)

Problem-Solving Strategies Ask students who have solved the Problem of the Day to share how they solved it and any strategies they used.

 Provide the following multidigit addition and subtraction problems for students to do mentally.

a. 75 + 20 = (95)	**b.** 75 + 75 = (150)
c. 76 + 25 = (101)	**d.** 176 + 25 = (201)
e. 85 − 10 = (75)	**f.** 85 − 20 = (65)
g. 85 − 25 = (60)	**h.** 185 − 25 = (160)
i. 185 − 26 = (159)	**j.** 274 + 25 = (299)

Multidigit Subtraction

For a new magazine the publisher printed 50,026 copies. Of those, 39,478 were sold. How many were not sold? To find out, subtract 39,478 from 50,026.

$$50{,}026 - 39{,}478 = ?$$

Remember:

$$\begin{array}{r} 50{,}026 \\ -\,39{,}478 \\ \hline \end{array}$$

Line up the corresponding digits. Subtract the digits in the ones place. It is not possible, because 6 is less than 8. Look for the next nonzero digit in the **minuend.** It's the 2. Remember, the minuend is the number from which another number is subtracted.

$$\begin{array}{r} \overset{1\ 16}{50{,}0\cancel{2}\cancel{6}} \\ -\,39{,}478 \\ \hline \end{array}$$

Regroup the 2 tens and 6 to make 1 ten and 16.

$$\begin{array}{r} \overset{1\ 16}{50{,}0\cancel{2}\cancel{6}} \\ -\,39{,}478 \\ \hline 8 \end{array}$$

Now subtract the ones.
$16 - 8 = 8$
Write 8.

$$\begin{array}{r} \overset{1\ 16}{50{,}0\cancel{2}\cancel{6}} \\ -\,39{,}478 \\ \hline 8 \end{array}$$

Subtract the tens.
It is not possible, because 1 is less than 7. Look for the next nonzero digit in the minuend. It's the 5.

$$\begin{array}{r} \overset{4\ 9\ 9\ 11}{\cancel{50{,}0}\overset{16}{\cancel{26}}} \\ -\,39{,}478 \\ \hline 8 \end{array}$$

Regroup the 500 hundreds and 1 ten to make 499 hundreds and 11 tens.

$$\begin{array}{r} \overset{4\ 9\ 9\ 11}{\cancel{50{,}0}\overset{16}{\cancel{26}}} \\ -\,39{,}478 \\ \hline 10{,}548 \end{array}$$

Now finish the subtraction.
There were 10,548 unsold copies.

Why teach it this way?

Mixing in problems that can be solved mentally allows students to recognize that they do not need to use paper and pencil or a calculator every time they work with numbers. In this lesson students have the opportunity to use mental math strategies to do many of the subtraction problems.

*available separately

Subtract. Use shortcuts when you can.

❶	❷	❸	❹	❺
94 − 37 **57**	68 − 43 **25**	127 − 85 **42**	249 − 37 **212**	645 − 79 **566**

❻	❼	❽	❾	❿
63 − 62 **1**	100 − 1 **99**	800 −300 **500**	432 −431 **1**	703 −504 **199**

⓫	⓬	⓭	⓮	⓯
1000 −999 **1**	1600 −700 **900**	1800 −500 **1300**	1800 −501 **1299**	1800 −510 **1290**

⓰	⓱	⓲	⓳	⓴
407 −349 **58**	506 −247 **259**	3007 −1248 **1759**	1000 − 1 **999**	4091 −1095 **2996**

㉑	㉒	㉓	㉔	㉕
1000 − 2 **998**	100 − 3 **97**	18,000 −7,000 **11,000**	500 −400 **100**	2400 −900 **1500**

㉖	㉗	㉘	㉙	㉚
63 − 37 **26**	630 −370 **260**	6300 −3700 **2600**	63,000 −37,000 **26,000**	63,005 −37,005 **26,000**

Solve these problems.

❸❶ The world's highest mountain is Mount Everest, 8848 meters above sea level. The highest mountain in North America is Mount McKinley, 6194 meters above sea level.

   a. How much higher than Mount McKinley is Mount Everest?
   2654 m
   b. How far apart are the two mountains?
   not enough information given

❸❷ The lowest point on Earth is the Dead Sea, 397 meters below sea level. The lowest point in North America is Death Valley, 86 meters below sea level. How much lower is the Dead Sea than Death Valley? **311 meters**

❷ Teach

Using the Student Pages You may wish to demonstrate the "Transaction" Game Mat before students begin the problems on pages 28–31 so they can play when they are finished.

Review the standard algorithm for subtraction by reviewing page 28 with the class. Again, as when reviewing addition, emphasize that the process is the same in each column, no matter how many columns there are. Explain that it is not necessary to cross out and rewrite a number to which 10 is being added—putting a small 1 near the number is sufficient.

Have students work independently on page 29. Point out that they may be able to do many problems without pencil and paper. Note that for problem 31b, there is no way to obtain the answer from the information given in the problem. Interested students can find out an approximate answer by researching in an **atlas** or other reference source.

Geography Connection Invite interested students to make up their own problems about comparing heights and finding the distances between peaks within a country of their choosing from another part of the world.

Literature Connection Have students read "Top Dog" in *Math Mini-Mysteries* by Sandra Markle. Ask them to use the chart to compare the number of registered dogs of different breeds.

◆ LESSON 9 Multidigit Subtraction

Teach

Using the Student Pages Have students do these computations and word problems on their own. Use the first 25 problems (problems 33–57) on page 30 as an assessment. Encourage students to use mental math wherever they can do so. Check students' work carefully to see whether they have achieved the level of mastery specified in the Mastery Checkpoint section.

PROBLEM SOLVING When discussing students' answers to the problems on page 31, ask a volunteer to explain how to solve problem 64 using estimation.

GAME **Using the "Transaction" Game Mat** Have students play the "Transaction" game in groups of two or three. This Game Mat provides practice in multidigit addition and subtraction. Complete instructions for playing can be found on the Game Mat. A copy of the "Transaction" Game Mat can also be found on page 628 of this Teacher's Guide.

◆ LESSON 9 Multidigit Subtraction

Solve these problems. Use shortcuts when you can.

㉝ 386 + 249 = **635**	㉞ 548 − 267 = **281**	㉟ 4705 + 3846 = **8551**	㊱ 4705 − 3846 = **859**	㊲ 2783 + 4596 = **7379**
㊳ 10,000 + 3,507 = **13,507**	㊴ 10,000 − 3,507 = **6,493**	㊵ 4567 − 3456 = **1111**	㊶ 4567 + 3456 = **8023**	㊷ 750 − 250 = **500**
㊸ 750 + 250 = **1000**	㊹ 1000 − 250 = **750**	㊺ 1000 − 1 = **999**	㊻ 6450 + 3275 = **9725**	㊼ 3450 + 6275 = **9725**
㊽ 10,000 − 2,500 = **7,500**	㊾ 638 − 495 = **143**	㊿ 208 − 129 = **79**	(51) 3003 − 4 = **2999**	(52) 897 + 6 = **903**
(53) 375 + 625 + 100 = **1100**	(54) 4050 + 3720 + 1000 + 8975 = **17,745**	(55) 50 + 50 + 25 + 25 = **150**	(56) 6297 + 3426 + 9351 + 7644 = **26,718**	(57) 453 + 2974 + 5190 + 68 = **8685**

PROBLEM SOLVING

Solve these problems.

(58) Angelo lives 15 kilometers from the city of Sioux Falls. Janine lives 10 kilometers from Sioux Falls.

a. Who lives farther from Sioux Falls? **Angelo**

b. How much farther? **5 km**

c. How far apart do Angelo and Janine live? **not enough information given (but between 5 and 25 km)**

(59) Anya lives 6 miles from her friend Douglas and 4 miles from her friend Tarrah.

a. What is the farthest distance apart Douglas and Tarrah could live? **10 mi**

b. What is the closest Douglas and Tarrah could live? **2 mi**

(60) Mr. Warren has seven cats, five dogs, and about 100 chickens on his farm. How many eggs do the chickens lay each day?
not enough information given

30 • Whole Numbers and Integers

RETEACHING

MANIPULATIVES If students have subtraction facts memorized but have difficulty with the subtraction algorithm, focus on the steps of the algorithm. Have students repeat the steps in unison for a specific problem. For instance, for the example on page 28, they would say, "Start at the right. Subtract 8 from 6. I can't. Regroup the two 10s and 6 to make one 10 and 16. Subtract 8 from 16. . . ." Although they may use different words, the idea here is to get students to say what they are doing because it can help them to remember. Simultaneously using **base-10 materials*** to show why the algorithm works can also help.

PRACTICE p. 9

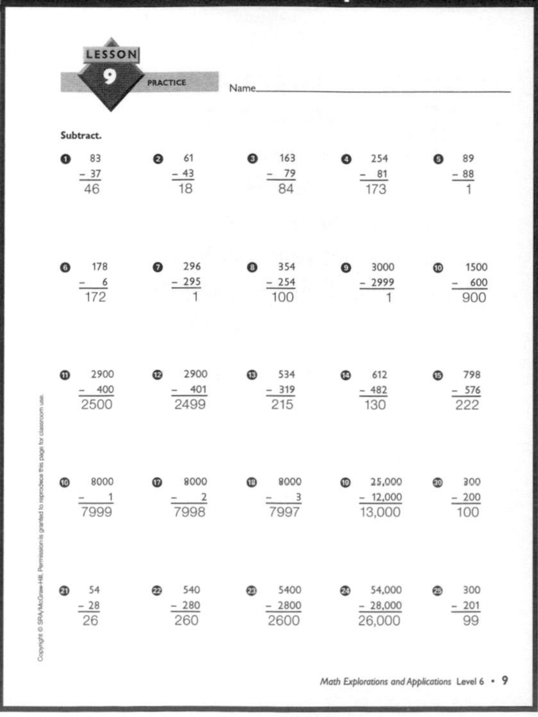

LESSON 9 PRACTICE Name________

Subtract.

❶ 83 − 37 = 46	❷ 61 − 43 = 18	❸ 163 − 79 = 84	❹ 254 − 81 = 173	❺ 89 − 88 = 1
❻ 178 − 6 = 172	❼ 296 − 295 = 1	❽ 354 − 254 = 100	❾ 3000 − 2999 = 1	❿ 1500 − 600 = 900
⓫ 2900 − 400 = 2500	⓬ 2900 − 401 = 2499	⓭ 534 − 319 = 215	⓮ 612 − 482 = 130	⓯ 798 − 576 = 222
⓰ 8000 − 1 = 7999	⓱ 8000 − 2 = 7998	⓲ 8000 − 3 = 7997	⓳ 25,000 − 12,000 = 13,000	⓴ 300 − 200 = 100
㉑ 54 − 28 = 26	㉒ 540 − 280 = 260	㉓ 5400 − 2800 = 2600	㉔ 54,000 − 28,000 = 26,000	㉕ 300 − 201 = 99

Math Explorations and Applications Level 6 • 9

*available separately

Solve these problems.

Ms. Arbuncle wants to buy a car. She has checked the prices of three used cars. The Hubmobile sells for $7843, the Folkwagon sells for $8209, and the Ritzwheel sells for $9078. But Ms. Arbuncle also wants to purchase insurance, which will cost $2053 for the Hubmobile, $1704 for the Folkwagon, and $1577 for the Ritzwheel.

61. How much will she have to pay to buy the Hubmobile with the insurance she wants? **$9896**

62. How much will she have to pay for the Folkwagon with the insurance she wants? **$9913**

63. How much will she have to pay for the Ritzwheel with the insurance she wants? **$10,655**

64. Ms. Arbuncle has $10,000 to spend on a car and insurance. Are there any of the cars she cannot afford to buy with the insurance she wants? If so, which can she not afford to buy? **Yes, she cannot afford to buy the Ritzwheel.**

65. For those cars she can afford, how much money will Ms. Arbuncle have left after she pays for the car and insurance? **If she buys the Hubmobile, she will have $104 left. If she buys the Folkwagon, she will have $87 left.**

Unit 1   Lesson 9 • **31**

❸ Wrap-Up

5 MINUTES

In Closing Summarize the lesson by asking students to explain how to use the algorithm for subtracting columns of multidigit numbers. Then ask students to share the mental math strategies they have used to do the subtractions.

ANALYZING ANSWERS Use the following procedures to help students who fall short of the mastery objective. Ask those who misread or ignored the operation signs to correct their errors and pay closer attention to the signs in the future. For those who made procedural errors or who have difficulty when regrouping is required, check to see whether the difficulty is with the facts or with the algorithm. If it is with the algorithm, focus on the steps; if it is with the facts, give extra practice of the type suggested in earlier lessons.

Mastery Checkpoint 4

By this time most students should demonstrate mastery of addition and subtraction (multidigit problems and basic facts) by getting at least 20 of the first 25 problems correct on page 30 in a reasonable amount of time. You can also assign Assessment Blackline Masters page 6. The results of this assessment may be recorded on the Mastery Checkpoint Chart.

Assessment Criteria

Did the student . . .

✓ correctly answer at least 80% of the computation and word problems?

✓ communicate strategies employed for using an algorithm and for using mental math?

✓ demonstrate ability in multidigit addition and subtraction?

Homework Invite students to use data about mountains other than those mentioned in the lesson to formulate multidigit addition and subtraction problems for classmates to solve.

Addition and Subtraction Applications

LESSON PLANNER

Objectives

▶ to provide practice in approximating and then finding the sum of two multidigit numbers

▶ to provide practice in solving realistic problems involving multidigit addition and subtraction

▶ to provide practice in reading a map and planning routes

Context of the Lesson This is the seventh of 15 lessons reviewing operations with whole numbers. The next lesson begins a review of multidigit multiplication.

 MANIPULATIVES
calculators*
road map
(optional)

Program Resources
Number Cubes (0–5 and 5–10)
Practice Master 10
Enrichment Master 10
The Cruncher*
For extra practice:
CD-ROM* Lesson 10

1 Warm-Up

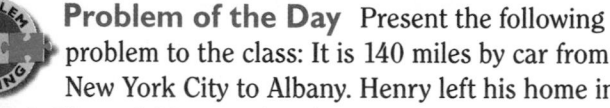

⏱ 5 MINUTES

Problem of the Day Present the following problem to the class: It is 140 miles by car from New York City to Albany. Henry left his home in New York City at 3:30 P.M. When he was halfway to Albany, Henry realized that he had left his suitcase at home and needed to return to get it. He drove back on the same route, picked up the suitcase, and then started out again for Albany. Assuming that he encounters no more detours along the way, how many miles will Henry's round-trip from New York City to Albany be? (420 miles)

Problem-Solving Strategies Ask students who have solved the Problem of the Day to share how they solved it and any strategies they used.

 Have students use mental math to solve the following problems.

(continued on page 33)

Addition and Subtraction Applications

Road atlases provide the highway distances between places on a map. Travelers can use this information to plan their trips.

This map shows driving distances in miles between selected cities in the United States.

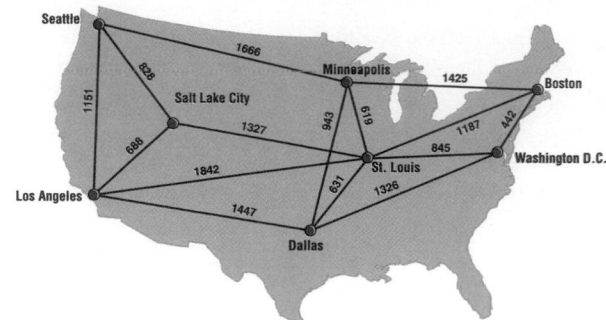

GEOGRAPHY CONNECTION

Use the map to answer these questions.

1 How many miles is it from Los Angeles to Salt Lake City? **688**

2 How many miles is it from Los Angeles to St. Louis if you go through Salt Lake City? **2015**

3 How many miles is it from Los Angeles to St. Louis if you go through Dallas? **2078**

4 If you were going from Dallas to Washington, D.C., how much farther would it be to go through St. Louis? **150 mi**

5 If you were going from Dallas to Minneapolis, how much farther would it be to go through St. Louis? **307 mi**

6 Suppose you were going from Dallas to Boston and you wanted to visit St. Louis and Washington, D.C.

    a. Would it be shorter to visit St. Louis first or Washington, D.C., first?

    b. How many miles shorter? **1440**   **St. Louis**

Why teach it this way?

Reading maps and estimating distances on maps is a useful and common real-life application of multidigit computation.

*available separately

7 How many miles is a round trip from Seattle to Los Angeles and back to Seattle? **2302**

8 Which round trip is shorter:

    a. Minneapolis–Dallas–St. Louis–Minneapolis?

    b. Minneapolis–St. Louis–Dallas–Minneapolis?
neither (They are the same distance.)

9 Put the following trips in order from shortest to longest:

    a. Dallas–Minneapolis–Boston   **c, b, a**

    b. Dallas–St. Louis–Boston

    c. Dallas–Washington, D.C.–Boston

10 Put the following trips in order from shortest to longest:

    a. Los Angeles–Seattle–Minneapolis   **b, c, a**

    b. Los Angeles–Salt Lake City–St. Louis–Minneapolis

    c. Los Angeles–Dallas–St. Louis–Minneapolis

11 How many miles long is the shortest path from Los Angeles to Washington, D.C., as shown on the map? **2687**

12 How many miles long is the shortest path from Seattle to Dallas shown on the map? Do you think this is the shortest possible path between Seattle and Dallas? **2598; no**

13 Suppose you were going from Seattle to St. Louis.

    a. Would it be shorter to go through Minneapolis or Salt Lake City? **Salt Lake City**

    b. How much shorter? **130 miles**

Challenge: Plan a trip that is less than 3000 miles and includes as many of the cities on the map as possible. The trip can start in any city and end in any city (not necessarily the one in which you start). Compare your answer with others in the class. **One 5-city route that totals 2849 miles is Boston–Washington, D.C.–St. Louis–Minneapolis–Dallas.**

Superchallenge: (Use a calculator to help you with this problem, but think and plan before you calculate.) Plan a trip that lets you visit all eight cities on the map. The total distance should be as short as you can make it. You need not return to the original city. **The students should use a trial and error approach. One reasonable trip is Seattle–Salt Lake City–Los Angeles–Dallas–Minneapolis–St. Louis–Washington, D.C.–Boston–a total of 5812 miles.**

Technology Connection You may wish to refer students to the software *Mighty Math Calculating Crew* from Edmark (Mac, IBM, for grades 3–5) for further practice with one- to three-digit addition, subtraction, multiplication, and division, estimating, 3-D geometry (solids and nets) and problem solving.

Mental Math (continued)

a.	25 + 10 = (35)	**b.**	75 + 20 = (95)
c.	200 − 30 = (170)	**d.**	170 + 300 = (470)
e.	470 − 5 = (465)	**f.**	465 + 34 = (499)
g.	95 + 105 = (200)	**h.**	499 + 499 = (998)

❷ Teach

Using the Student Pages You may wish to demonstrate the "Don't Go over 1000" game on page 35 to provide practice with addition. Students may begin playing as they finish their work on pages 32–34.

Briefly discuss some local distances in miles to help students get a feel for how long a unit of length a mile is. Talk about places students know that are about 1 mile, 2 miles, and 5 miles from the school.

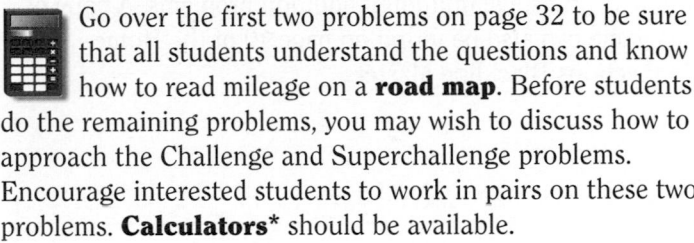 Go over the first two problems on page 32 to be sure that all students understand the questions and know how to read mileage on a **road map**. Before students do the remaining problems, you may wish to discuss how to approach the Challenge and Superchallenge problems. Encourage interested students to work in pairs on these two problems. **Calculators*** should be available.

Students can use a blank **Cruncher*** spreadsheet to record the distance between each pair of cities.

◆ LESSON 10 Addition and Subtraction Applications

Teach

Using the Student Pages You may wish to do problem 14 on page 34 with the class so that you can help students to read the mileage table correctly. Have students do the rest of the problems on page 34 on their own. The problems involving speed anticipate the review of division in Lesson 14. Students may solve them using trial and error, or whatever means they find appropriate.

Using the "Don't Go Over 1000" Game Demonstrate the "Don't Go Over 1000" game by playing it with one or two students. Then have students play the game in groups of two or three. This game challenges students to use mathematical reasoning to create numbers and solve multidigit addition problems. A copy of this game can also be found on page 10 of the Home Connections Blackline Masters.

> *Observation of game-playing activity resembles observation of real-life-out-of-school activities as closely as anything we are likely to see in school. Such observation will often give greater insight into a child's thought patterns than anything else the teacher can do.*
>
> –Stephen S. Willoughby,
> *Mathematics Education for a Changing World*

◆ LESSON 10 Addition and Subtraction Applications

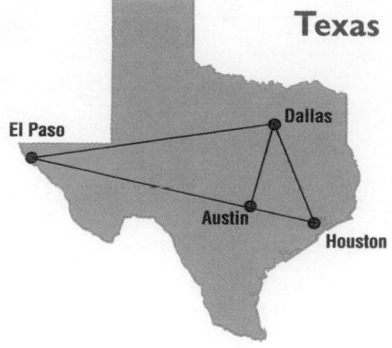

Texas Distances	
From/To	**Miles**
Austin–Dallas	195
Dallas–Houston	246
Houston–Austin	186
Houston–El Paso	769

Texas

Solve these problems using the table and the map above.

14 How far would you travel if you drove from Austin to Dallas to Houston and then back to Austin? **627 mi**

15 You take the trip described in problem 14. If you drive at an average speed of 50 miles per hour, about how many hours would you spend driving? **about $12\frac{1}{2}$**

16 If during your trip from Austin you had a meeting in Dallas that lasted for three hours and a dinner in Houston that lasted for two hours, about how long would the entire trip take?
about $17\frac{1}{2}$ hours

17 If you left Austin at 5:00 A.M., about what time would you get back to Austin? **about 10:30 P.M.**

18 How long is the drive from El Paso to Houston and back? **1538 mi**

19 If you drove 50 miles per hour from El Paso to Houston and back, about how many hours would you spend driving? Assuming you drive ten hours each day, how many days would that be?
about 31; about 3

20 You are planning to drive from Dallas to Houston. You expect your average speed will be 50 miles an hour and that you will make a 30-minute stop for lunch. What is the latest you could leave to be in Houston by 2:00 P.M.? **about 8:30 A.M.**

34 · Whole Numbers and Integers

Literature Connection You may wish to have students read *How to Count Sheep Without Falling Asleep* by Ralph Leighton and Carl Feyman. The book is a fictional account of how our number system evolved.

To help students who have difficulty with the map-reading problems on pages 32 and 33, draw a simpler map with easier numbers (20 or less). Have students traverse the paths with their fingers and then answer the questions. When they see how to get the answers, have them try to work out the original problems with the greater numbers.

Don't Go Over 1000 Game

COOPERATIVE LEARNING

GAME

Players:	Two or more
Materials:	Two 0–5 cubes, two 5–10 cubes
Object:	To get the sum closest to but not over 1000
Math Focus:	Place value, multidigit addition, and mathematical reasoning

RULES

1. Roll all four cubes. If you roll a 10, roll that cube again.

2. Combine three of the numbers rolled to make a three-digit number.

3. Roll all four cubes again. Make a second three-digit number and add it to your first number.

4. You may stop after your second roll, or you may make another three-digit number and add it to your previous sum. You may roll and add as many times as you want.

5. The player whose sum is closest to but not over 1000 is the winner.

SAMPLE GAME

Anita rolled: Anita wrote:

`5` `3` `4` `6`   643

`3` `6` `7` `2`   + 327
                    ———
                    970

Anita stopped.

Miguel rolled: Miguel wrote:

`0` `5` `9` `1`   519

`3` `7` `7` `1`   + 137
                    656

`8` `2` `3` `9`   +329
                    ———
                    985

Miguel stopped after his third roll.

Miguel was the winner.

Can you describe how you played this game? Write your strategies in your Math Journal.

---

❸ Wrap-Up

In Closing Summarize the lesson by asking students to explain how to read a driving distance map to a person who is seeing one for the first time.

Portfolio Assessment Have students write an explanation of the strategies they could use to find three trips from the mileage chart that totaled 1000 miles. Then ask them to write an explanation of their strategy for winning the "Don't Go Over 1000" game. This explanation should focus on their reasons for the way they combined the digits to form their second three-digit number and their decision about when to stop rolling.

Assessment Criteria

Did the student . . .

✓ understand how to read and use the mileage map?

✓ understand how to interpret the mileage chart?

✓ demonstrate ability to estimate sums and differences of multidigit numbers?

Homework Invite students to work with a family member to solve road map problems similar to those in the lesson.

GIFTED & TALENTED **Meeting Individual Needs**
Provide a road map of a region in the United States or elsewhere. Give the mileage between two places on that map. Challenge students to use that marked length to estimate other distances on the map. For example, if you label the distance between New York City and Albany as 140 miles, ask students to use this information to approximate other distances within New York State, such as between Albany and Buffalo or Syracuse and Binghamton.

PRACTICE p. 10

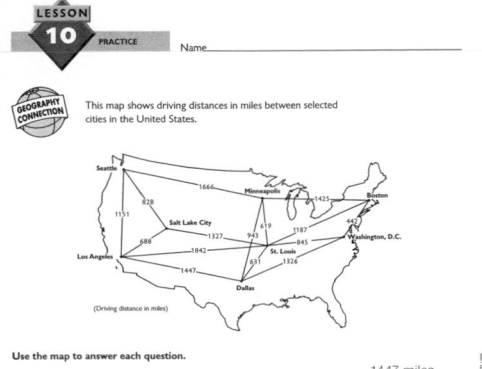

LESSON 10 PRACTICE   Name_____

GEOGRAPHY CONNECTION This map shows driving distances in miles between selected cities in the United States.

(Driving distance in miles)

Use the map to answer each question.

1. How many miles is it from Los Angeles to Dallas? — 1447 miles

2. Is Seattle or Dallas closer to Los Angeles? — Seattle

3. If you were going from Los Angeles to Minneapolis, would it be shorter to go through Dallas or through St. Louis? — Dallas

4. Suppose you live in Boston and are going to St. Louis and Minneapolis on your vacation. How much longer would the trip be if you go to Washington, D.C., too? — 100 miles

5. Which round trip is shorter?
   a. Seattle–Minneapolis–St. Louis–Salt Lake City–Seattle
   b. Los Angeles–Dallas–St. Louis–Salt Lake City–Los Angeles — b

10 • Math Explorations and Applications Level 6

ENRICHMENT p. 10

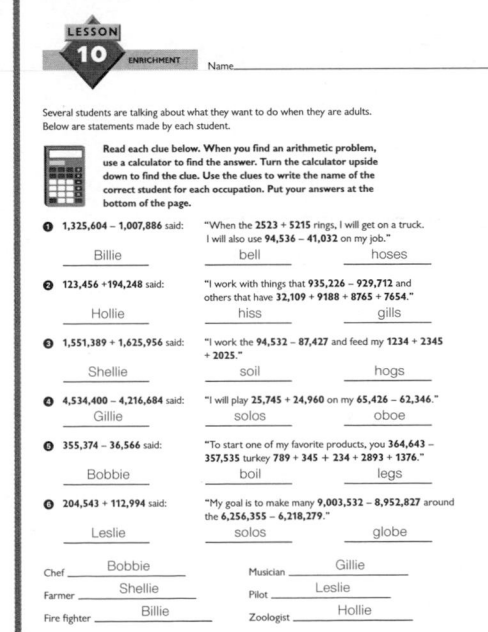

LESSON 10 ENRICHMENT   Name_____

Several students are talking about what they want to do when they are adults. Below are statements made by each student.

Read each clue below. When you find an arithmetic problem, use a calculator to find the answer. Turn the calculator upside down to find the clue. Use the clues to write the name of the correct student for each occupation. Put your answers at the bottom of the page.

1. 1,325,604 – 1,007,886 said: "When the 2523 + 5215 rings, I will get on a truck. I will also use 94,536 – 41,032 on my job."
   Billie   bell   hoses

2. 123,456 + 194,248 said: "I work with things that 935,226 – 929,712 and others that have 32,109 + 9188 + 8765 + 7654."
   Hollie   hiss   gills

3. 1,551,389 + 1,625,956 said: "I work the 94,532 – 87,427 and feed my 1234 + 2345 + 2025."
   Shellie   soil   hogs

4. 4,534,400 – 4,216,684 said: "I will play 25,745 + 24,960 on my 65,426 – 62,346."
   Gillie   solos   oboe

5. 355,374 – 36,566 said: "To start one of my favorite products, you 364,643 – 357,535 turkey 789 + 345 + 234 + 2893 + 1376."
   Bobbie   boil   legs

6. 204,543 + 112,994 said: "My goal is to make many 9,003,532 – 8,952,827 around the 6,256,355 – 6,218,279."
   Leslie   solos   globe

Chef	Bobbie	Musician	Gillie
Farmer	Shellie	Pilot	Leslie
Fire fighter	Billie	Zoologist	Hollie

10 • Math Explorations and Applications Level 6

Powers and Multiples of 10

LESSON PLANNER

Objectives

▶ to review how to multiply powers and multiples of 10 mentally and to provide practice with that skill

▶ to help students develop the broad ability to use mathematical common sense

Context of the Lesson This is the eighth of 15 lessons reviewing operations with whole numbers. This review of multiplying by powers of 10 and multiplying multiples of 10 will help prepare students for the upcoming review of multidigit multiplication. This lesson contains the second part of "Mr. Muddle's Extra-Large Problems," a four-part Thinking Story.

✋ **MANIPULATIVES**

base-10 materials* (optional)

place-value charts* (optional)

Program Resources

Reteaching Master

Practice Master 11

Enrichment Master 11

For career connections:
   Careers and Math

For extra practice:
   CD-ROM* Lesson 11

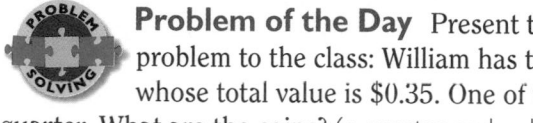

① Warm-Up ⏱ 5 MINUTES

Problem of the Day Present the following problem to the class: William has two coins whose total value is $0.35. One of them is not a quarter. What are the coins? (a quarter and a dime [one is not a quarter; the other is.])

Problem-Solving Strategies Ask students who have solved the Problem of the Day to share how they solved it and any strategies they used.

  Present the following problems, and ask students to show thumbs up if the answer is greater than 200 or thumbs down if it is not.

a. 125 + 75 (thumbs down)   b. 125 + 49 (thumbs down)

c. 126 + 76 (thumbs up)   d. 150 + 51 (thumbs up)

e. 129 + 70 (thumbs down)   f. 500 – 200 (thumbs up)

g. 500 – 250 (thumbs up)   h. 299 – 98 (thumbs up)

i. 300 – 125 (thumbs down)   j. 275 – 76 (thumbs down)

Powers and Multiples of 10

Because our number system is based on 10, there are many shortcuts for working with powers of 10. In this lesson you'll learn a quick way to multiply by a power or a multiple of 10.

$26 \times 1000 = ?$

Remember:

26×1000	Count the 0s in the power of 10. A power is the product of the multiplication of a number by itself. $1000 = 10 \times 10 \times 10$. It is the third power of 10. There are three 0s.
26	Write the number being multiplied: 26.
26,000	Write three 0s to the right of 26.

Multiply.

❶ 3×10 **30**	❷ 3×100 **300**	❸ 45×100 **4500**	❹ 45×1000 **45,000**
❺ 1000×78 **78,000**	❻ 10×78 **780**	❼ 100×5 **500**	❽ $10,000 \times 5$ **50,000**
❾ 989×10 **9890**	❿ 100×989 **98,900**	⓫ 6789×10 **67,890**	⓬ 100×6789 **678,900**
⓭ 63×100 **6300**	⓮ 63×1000 **63,000**	⓯ $10,000 \times 51$ **510,000**	⓰ 51×1000 **51,000**

$7 \times 800 = ?$

Remember:

7×800	Count the 0s in the multiple of 10. There are two 0s.
7×800	Multiply the nonzero digits. $7 \times 8 = 56$
56	Write 56.
5600	Write two 0s to the right of 56.

Multiply.

⓱ 9×60 **540**	⓲ 9×600 **5400**	⓳ 7×700 **4900**	⓴ 7×7000 **49,000**
㉑ 300×4 **1200**	㉒ 3000×4 **12,000**	㉓ 40×6 **240**	㉔ 4000×6 **24,000**
㉕ 5×700 **3500**	㉖ 70×5 **350**	㉗ 9×90 **810**	㉘ 9000×9 **81,000**
㉙ 20×8 **160**	㉚ 80×2 **160**	㉛ 8×200 **1600**	㉜ 8000×2 **16,000**

36 • Whole Numbers and Integers

Why teach it this way?

This review of multiplying by powers of 10 and by multiples of 10 helps prepare students for the upcoming review of multidigit multiplication. Mental multiplication skills can also help students know if their written answers make sense.

90 × 700 = ?

Remember:

90 × 700	Count the 0s in both factors. There are three 0s.
90 × 700	Multiply the nonzero digits. 9 × 7 = 63
63	Write 63.
63,000	Write three 0s to the right of 63.

Be careful when the product of the nonzero digits has a 0.

80 × 50	There are two 0s.
40	8 × 5
4000	Write two 0s to the right of 40.

Multiply.

33 40 × 20 **800**		**34** 400 × 20 **8000**		**35** 30 × 400 **12,000**		**36** 30 × 4000 **120,000**	
37 90 × 30 **2700**		**38** 90 × 3000 **270,000**		**39** 10 × 100 **1000**		**40** 8 × 1000 **8000**	
41 90 × 70 **6300**		**42** 100 × 63 **6300**		**43** 27 × 10 **270**		**44** 70 × 700 **49,000**	
45 60 × 700 **42,000**		**46** 20 × 50 **1000**		**47** 200 × 50 **10,000**		**48** 60 × 600 **36,000**	
49 60 × 60 **3600**		**50** 80 × 90 **7200**		**51** 800 × 900 **720,000**		**52** 4 × 500 **2000**	
53 40 × 50 **2000**		**54** 90 × 60 **5400**		**55** 900 × 6 **5400**		**56** 100 × 100 **10,000**	
57 10 × 70 **700**		**58** 100 × 11 **1100**		**59** 12 × 100 **1200**		**60** 60 × 4 **240**	
61 40 × 60 **2400**		**62** 600 × 40 **24,000**		**63** 40 × 600 **24,000**		**64** 500 × 80 **40,000**	
65 50 × 30 **1500**		**66** 8 × 7000 **56,000**		**67** 50 × 1000 **50,000**		**68** 60 × 800 **48,000**	

Solve these problems.

69 There are about 50 books on each of the 20 shelves in the classroom. About how many books are on the shelves? **about 1000**

70 Will 1000 books in the school library fit onto 40 shelves that can hold up to 30 books each? **yes**

Unit 1   Lesson 11 • **37**

② Teach

Using the Student Pages Go over these pages with the class. When students begin the numbered problems, have them write out only the final answers, not the problems, on their papers. Ask students to discuss the advantages of learning mental multiplication skills such as multiplying by powers of 10 and by multiples of 10.

SPECIAL NEEDS **Meeting Individual Needs**

If students have difficulty mentally multiplying powers of 10, emphasize these steps: Begin by writing the product of the first digits of the factors. Then, to the right of the product, write one 0 for each 0 in the factors. Once students can follow the procedure, have them practice. Keep in mind that review of multiplying multiples of 10 is given periodically throughout the year.

Technology Connection Refer students to the software *Number Munchers* from MECC (Mac, IBM, for grades 2–6) for further practice with multiples, factors, prime numbers, equalities, and inequalities.

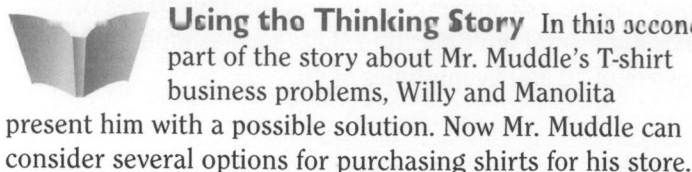

◆ LESSON 11 Powers and Multiples of 10

Teach

Using the Thinking Story In this second part of the story about Mr. Muddle's T-shirt business problems, Willy and Manolita present him with a possible solution. Now Mr. Muddle can consider several options for purchasing shirts for his store.

Answers to Thinking Story Questions:

1. Buying two boxes at the listed price of $1120 saves $32 off the cost of buying two boxes separately (2 x $576 = $1152). But two boxes still cost much more than one box.

2. He should order as many boxes as possible at a time, getting only one size in each box. That way he gets the lowest rate per box and avoids paying the extra $30 per box of mixed sizes.

3. He should order one box containing a single size and one box containing a mixture of the three other sizes. That way he will have to pay the extra $30 for only one box. If he plans carefully, he should be able to get along by ordering two boxes some weeks and one box other weeks.

4. He will save $30. He has to pay the basic $1120 for two boxes. If both are mixed, he has to pay an extra $60. If only one is mixed, he pays an extra $30.

Have students read the story, discuss the information in the table on page 38, and then answer the questions. After discussing students' answers, ask them to predict what will happen in the next installment of the story. Have them write their predictions and explain their reasoning in their Math Journals.

Meeting Individual Needs

AT RISK / **MANIPULATIVES**

Although some students may not yet have a solid understanding of base-10 place value, they should learn the rules for multiplying powers of 10. At this time, emphasize these rules, but begin a program of extra help to develop understanding of place value. Use **base-10 materials*** and **place-value charts***. You may wish to consult the Teacher's Guides for Levels 3 and 4 for additional approaches.

◆ LESSON 11 Powers and Multiples of 10

THINKING STORY

Mr. Muddle's Extra-Large Problems

Part 2

You may want to refer to the earlier part of this Thinking Story on pages 22–23.

"I think we've solved your problem, Mr. Muddle," said Willy. "To have enough of every size, you should get about 60 extra-large, 60 large, 30 medium, and 15 small T-shirts each week."

"Oh, dear," said Mr. Muddle. "That's too many. There are 144 T-shirts in a box. To get what you say I need, I'd have to buy two boxes a week. I can't afford to do that every week. See how much they cost!"

Mr. Muddle showed his friends the price list.

Quality T-Shirts Price List (All prices subject to change.)		
Number of Boxes	Price	You Save
1	$576.00	
2	$1,120.00	$32.00
3	$1,670.00	$58.00
4	$2,200.00	$104.00

Each additional box, add $520.00. Above prices are for boxes with one shirt size. Add $30.00 per box for boxes with mixed size.

38 • Whole Numbers and Integers

Literature Connection You may wish to have students read *Sarah Plain and Tall* by Patricia MacLachlan. Have students multiply to determine the number of miles the children walked to and from school in 180 days.

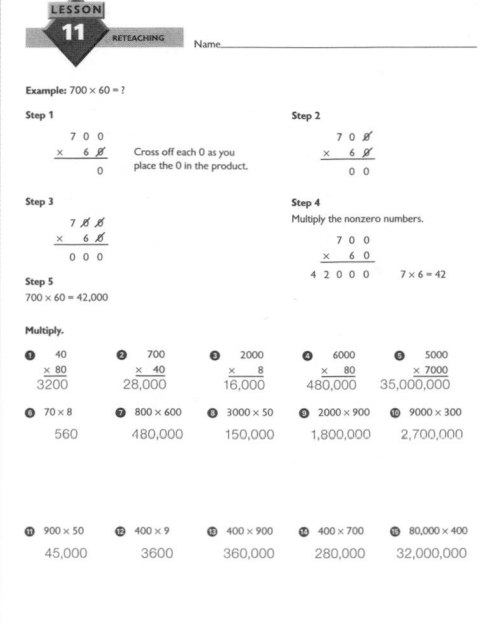

"It won't cost you more money to buy two boxes instead of one," said Manolita. "This price list says it will cost you $32 less."

. . . to be continued

Work in groups. Discuss your answers and how you figured them out. Then compare your answers with those of other groups. **Answers are in margin.**

❶ Is Manolita right in saying two boxes cost less than one box?

❷ If Mr. Muddle had enough money and enough storage space, what would be the cheapest way for him to buy T-shirts?

❸ If Mr. Muddle can never afford to buy more than two boxes at a time, what would be a good way for him to order T-shirts? Will he need to order two boxes every week to have enough of every size?

❹ How much money will Mr. Muddle save if he orders one box of a single size and one box of mixed sizes, instead of two boxes of mixed sizes?

PRACTICE p. 11

LESSON
11 PRACTICE   Name_____

Multiply.

❶ 10 × 1000 = 10,000		❷ 3 × 100 = 300
❸ 71 × 100 = 7100		❹ 71 × 1000 = 71,000
❺ 1000 × 59 = 59,000		❻ 10 × 59 = 590
❼ 100 × 3 = 300		❽ 10,000 × 3 = 30,000
❾ 521 × 10 = 5210		❿ 100 × 521 = 52,100

⓫ 60 × 3 = 180		⓬ 600 × 3 = 1800
⓭ 5 × 500 = 2500		⓮ 5 × 5000 = 25,000
⓯ 200 × 8 = 1600		⓰ 2000 × 8 = 16,000
⓱ 80 × 2 = 160		⓲ 8000 × 2 = 16,000
⓳ 3 × 400 = 1200		⓴ 40 × 3 = 120

㉑ 50 × 700 = 35,000		㉒ 50 × 70 = 3500
㉓ 20 × 800 = 16,000		㉔ 20 × 8000 = 160,000
㉕ 70 × 40 = 2800		㉖ 70 × 4000 = 280,000
㉗ 20 × 200 = 4000		㉘ 5 × 3000 = 15,000
㉙ 30 × 50 = 1500		㉚ 100 × 79 = 7900

㉛ 13 × 100 = 1300		㉜ 100 × 14 = 1400
㉝ 10 × 90 = 900		㉞ 1000 × 10 = 10,000
㉟ 200 × 200 = 40,000		㊱ 400 × 5 = 2000
㊲ 40 × 50 = 2000		㊳ 2 × 600 = 1200
㊴ 20 × 60 = 1200		㊵ 3 × 400 = 1200

Math Explorations and Applications Level 6 • 11

ENRICHMENT p. 11

LESSON
11 ENRICHMENT   Name_____

Here is another puzzle. First you must find the numbers that you will use to fill in the puzzle at the bottom of the page. Write the answer to each computation in the blank. Then decide where each answer will go in the puzzle and fill in the answers.

40 × 60 = 2400	70 × 900 = 63,000	2 × 3 × 100 = 600
7 × 300 = 2100	99 × 10 = 990	7926 + 6280 = 14,206
60 × 70 = 4200	30 × 600 = 18,000	82,106 − 61,074 = 21,032
910 × 6 = 5460	800 × 30 = 24,000	62,000 − 30,480 = 31,520
80 × 500 = 40,000		

Possible solution given.

2	4	0	0		1	4	2	0	6
1			4						0
0			0		2	1	0	0	
3	1	5	2	0	4		8		
2		4		0	2	4	0	0	0
		6	3	0	0	0		0	
9	9	0			0		0		

Math Explorations and Applications Level 6 • 11

---

❸ Wrap-Up

In Closing Summarize the lesson by asking students to explain the procedure for multiplying by a power of 10 using mental math. Have them explain how to quickly multiply by a multiple of 10.

 **Informal Assessment** Have students choose one problem each from page 36 and page 37. Ask them to use mental math to explain how they found each answer.

Assessment Criteria

Did the student . . .

✓ correctly answer at least 75% of the computation problems?

✓ effectively communicate his or her problem-solving strategies?

✓ contribute to the Thinking Story discussion?

Homework Invite interested students to speak with a store owner to find out more about how he or she decides what numbers and sizes of T-shirts or other items to purchase. Students can share their findings with the class.

GIFTED & TALENTED **Meeting Individual Needs**
Some students may figure out other procedures for mentally multiplying multiples of 10. For example, to multiply 30 × 400, some might think: 3 × 400 is 1200, so 30 × 400 is 12,000. Encourage students to use whatever method works best for them.

LESSON 12
Multidigit Multiplication

LESSON 12
Multidigit Multiplication

LESSON PLANNER

Objectives

▶ to review the standard algorithm for multiplication with a one-digit multiplier

▶ to review the standard algorithm for multidigit multiplication

▶ to provide practice in multiplying multidigit numbers

✓ to assess students' ability to do multidigit multiplication, including speedy recall of the multiplication facts

Context of the Lesson
This is the ninth of 15 lessons reviewing operations with whole numbers. A checkpoint for assessing mastery of multiplication is provided here. However, work with multiplication occurs regularly throughout the year in varying contexts, including decimals, fractions, and exponents.

 **MANIPULATIVES**

Program Resources

Reteaching Master

Practice Master 12

Enrichment Master 12

Assessment Master

For extra practice:
CD-ROM* Lesson 12
Cumulative Review, page 554

❶ Warm-Up 🕐 5 MINUTES

Problem of the Day Present this problem on the chalkboard: All of the following are nirts: 24, 56, 96, 8, 160
None of these are nirts: 28, 7, 164, 36, 180
Which of these is a nirt: 16, 44, 240, 110? (16 and 240)
What is a nirt? (nirts are multiples of 8)

Problem-Solving Strategies Ask students who have solved the Problem of the Day to share how they solved it and any strategies they used.

At every game of the seven-game home stand, the stadium was filled to capacity. Tickets were sold for all 47,826 seats. How many tickets were sold for the home stand? You can multiply to find out.

$7 \times 47,826 = ?$

Remember:

$$
\begin{array}{r}
47,826 \\
\times 7 \\
\hline
2
\end{array}
$$
$7 \times 6 = 42$
Write 2.
Remember the 4.

$$
\begin{array}{r}
47,826 \\
\times 7 \\
\hline
82
\end{array}
$$
$7 \times 2 = 14$
Add 4 and get 18.
Write 8. Remember the 1.

$$
\begin{array}{r}
47,826 \\
\times 7 \\
\hline
782
\end{array}
$$
$7 \times 8 = 56$
Add 1 and get 57.
Write 7. Remember the 5.

$$
\begin{array}{r}
47,826 \\
\times 7 \\
\hline
4782
\end{array}
$$
$7 \times 7 = 49$
Add 5 and get 54.
Write 4. Remember the 5.

$$
\begin{array}{r}
47,826 \\
\times 7 \\
\hline
334,782
\end{array}
$$
$7 \times 4 = 28$
Add 5 and get 33.
Write 33.

There were 334,782 tickets sold.

Check to be sure that your answer makes sense.
The answer should be more than $7 \times 40,000$, which is 280,000.
The answer should be less than $7 \times 50,000$, which is 350,000.
The number 334,782 is between 280,000 and 350,000.

 **Literature Connection**
For more practice with determining the different ways to use multiplication to find answers, invite students to read *Counting on Frank* by Rod Clement.

*available separately

Multiply. Check to be sure that your answers make sense.

❶ 73
× 5
365

❷ 56
× 8
448

❸ 83
× 7
581

❹ 59
× 9
531

❺ 47
× 4
188

❻ 41
× 6
246

❼ 609
× 6
3654

❽ 753
× 4
3012

❾ 821
× 8
6568

❿ 537
× 7
3759

⓫ 987
× 1
987

⓬ 430
× 3
1290

⓭ 700
× 5
3500

⓮ 5
× 700
3500

⓯ 400
× 9
3600

⓰ 60
× 8
480

⓱ 8
× 60
480

⓲ 500
× 9
4500

⓳ 40
× 80
3200

⓴ 90
× 60
5400

㉑ 600
× 80
48,000

㉒ 70
× 9000
630,000

㉓ 800
× 800
640,000

㉔ 70
× 70
4900

㉕ 500
× 20
10,000

㉖ 630
× 7
4410

㉗ 63
× 7
441

㉘ 6300
× 70
441,000

㉙ 6300
× 700
4,410,000

㉚ 700
× 63
44,100

Solve these problems.

㉛ Sharifa has $35. She wants to treat five friends to a baseball game. Each ticket costs $4.95. Does she have enough money? **yes**

㉜ A school has 80 students and 14 adults going on a field trip. Can the students be put into 14 groups with no more than six students in each group? **yes**

㉝ A theater group is selling tickets to a play for $7 apiece. The theater can seat 200 people. If the show is a sell-out, how much money will the group collect?
$1400

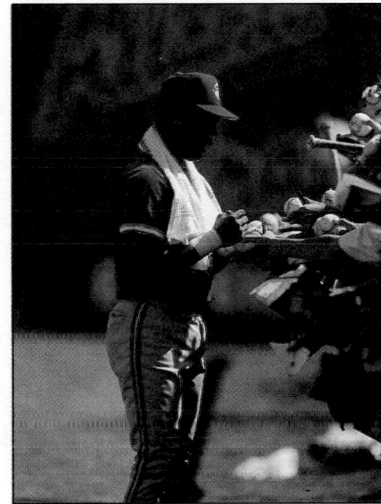

Technology Connection Use the laser disc *Core Concepts in Math: Problem Solving Series,* by BFA/Systems Impact (for grades 5–9) to provide further practice with column multiplication, long division, and problem-solving strategies.

MENTAL MATH Present these problems one at a time on the chalkboard:

a. $2 \times 10 = (20)$

b. $2 \times 20 = (40)$

c. $2 \times 60 = (120)$

d. $2 \times 59 = (118)$

e. $3 \times 20 = (60)$

f. $3 \times 40 = (120)$

g. $3 \times 50 = (150)$

h. $3 \times 49 = (147)$

i. $5 \times 7 = (35)$

j. $50 \times 70 = (3500)$

k. $50 \times 7 = (350)$

l. $70 \times 5 = (350)$

m. $60 \times 6 = (360)$

n. $60 \times 60 = (3600)$

o. $60 \times 600 = (36,000)$

❷ Teach

Using the Student Pages Go over the examples on pages 40 and 42 with the class as a review. Emphasize the importance of checking answers to be sure they make sense. Note that the method described at the bottom of page 40 is only one of many ways to check for reasonableness. Then have students do the problems on pages 41 and 43 on their own.

SPECIAL NEEDS **Meeting Individual Needs**
For students having difficulty, work through examples, pausing occasionally to ask, "What do we do next?" For example, for the problem on page 40, the first steps might go like this:

1. **What do we do first?** (Multiply each top digit by the ones digit of the multiplier.)

2. **What is 7 × 6?** (42)

3. **What do we do with 42?** (Write the 2 in the ones place and save the 4 for the tens place.)

Note: **Some students get confused when they write the 4 above the tens place in the multiplicand. Suggest that these students write it elsewhere on the page and cross it off when it is used.**

4. **What's next?** (Multiply 7 × 2, getting 14, and add 4, getting 18.)

5. **What do we do with the 18?** (Write the 8 in the tens column and save the 1 for the next column.)

Continue in this manner for this and other problems, as needed.

◆ LESSON 12 Multidigit Multiplication

Teach

Using the Student Pages Review the multidigit algorithm with the class. The examples on pages 40 and 42 show how it is always possible to multiply multidigit numbers, but there are many situations for which there is a much more efficient procedure for finding the answer, for example, when the multiplier has a 0 in it.

In the first and second grades, seven tens was defined as 70, 70 tens as 700, and so on. Because multiplication is commutative in that the order of the factors does not change the results, 10 × 7 must be 7 × 10, and so on. Because 80 is 8 × 10, we can get the answer to 80 × 584 (problem 42) by multiplying 8 × 584 and writing a 0 after the product (which moves each digit one place to the left).

Discuss these facts before the class starts working on the problems on page 43. Point out that when partial products with only 0s are multiplied, the 0s need not be written. The next partial product should be started directly below the next nonzero digit in the multiplier. It may be helpful for students to write one of the 0s to help keep track of where to write subsequent partial products. (See problems 1 and 2 below.)

```
1.      742
      × 606
       4452
      4452
```

```
2.      742
      × 606
       4452
      44520
```

Remind students to check that their answers make sense.

◆ LESSON 12 Multidigit Multiplication

To multiply by a multiplier with more than one digit, follow the procedure as in the example on page 40. Put the ones digit of each **partial product** below the digit of the multiplier you are using.

537 × 47,826 = ?

```
    47,826
  ×    537
   334782
```
Multiply by the ones digit.
Write this partial product (334,782) so that its ones digit (2) is in the ones column.

```
    47,826
  ×    537
   334 782
  1 434 78
```
Multiply by the tens digit.
Write this partial product (143,478 tens) so that its ones digit (8) is in the tens column.

```
     47,826
  ×     537
    334 782
   1 434 78
  23 913 0
```
Multiply by the hundreds digit.
Write this partial product (239,130 hundreds) so that its ones digit (0) is in the hundreds column.

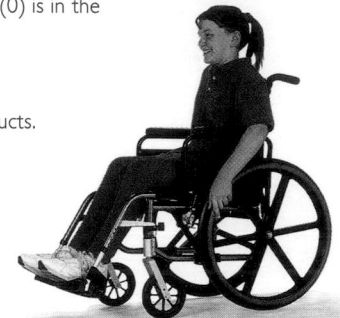

```
       47,826
  ×       537
      334 782
     1 434 78
    23 913 0
    25,682,562
```
Add the partial products.

Check to be sure that your answer makes sense.
  The answer should be more than 500 × 40,000, which is 20,000,000.
  The answer should be less than 600 × 50,000, which is 30,000,000.
  25,682,562 is between 20,000,000 and 30,000,000.
So the answer makes sense.

Multiply. Check your answers to be sure they make sense.

㉞ 58	㉟ 73	㊱ 95	㊲ 647	㊳ 312
× 46	× 39	× 22	× 508	× 960
2668	**2847**	**2090**	**328,676**	**299,520**

42 • Whole Numbers and Integers

Multiply. Check your answers to be sure they make sense.

(39) 26 × 71 = **1846**
(40) 584 × 8 = **4672**
(41) 584 × 10 = **5840**
(42) 584 × 80 = **46,720**
(43) 584 × 88 = **51,392**
(44) 584 × 800 = **467,200**
(45) 742 × 100 = **74,200**
(46) 742 × 6 = **4452**
(47) 742 × 600 = **445,200**
(48) 742 × 606 = **449,652**
(49) 742 × 60 = **44,520**
(50) 832 × 502 = **417,664**
(51) 368 × 79 = **29,072**
(52) 368 × 790 = **290,720**
(53) 3680 × 790 = **2,907,200**

Watch the signs.

(54) 5103 − 746 = **4357**
(55) 5103 + 746 = **5849**
(56) 5103 × 746 = **3,806,838**
(57) 1000 − 648 = **352**
(58) 1648 − 1000 = **648**
(59) 1000 + 648 = **1648**
(60) 1000 × 648 = **648,000**
(61) 2000 − 648 = **1352**
(62) 2000 × 648 = **1,296,000**
(63) 648 + 200 = **848**
(64) 512 + 47 = **559**
(65) 512 − 47 = **465**
(66) 512 × 7 = **3584**
(67) 512 × 4 = **2048**
(68) 512 × 47 = **24,064**

PROBLEM SOLVING

Solve these problems.

(69) Last week, José swam 20 laps of the pool on Monday, Tuesday, Wednesday, and Thursday. He swam 30 laps on both Friday and Saturday.

a. How many laps did he swim all together? **140**

b. If each lap is 50 meters, how far did José swim last week? **7000 m**

(70) José is swimming in a smaller pool in which laps are 40 meters. He plans to swim twice as many laps on Monday, Tuesday, Wednesday, and Thursday as he did last week, and the same number of laps as last week on Friday and Saturday.

a. How many laps will he swim this week if he follows his plan? **220**

b. How many meters will he swim this week? **8800**

Use the Cumulative Review on page 554 after this lesson.

Unit 1 Lesson 12 • 43

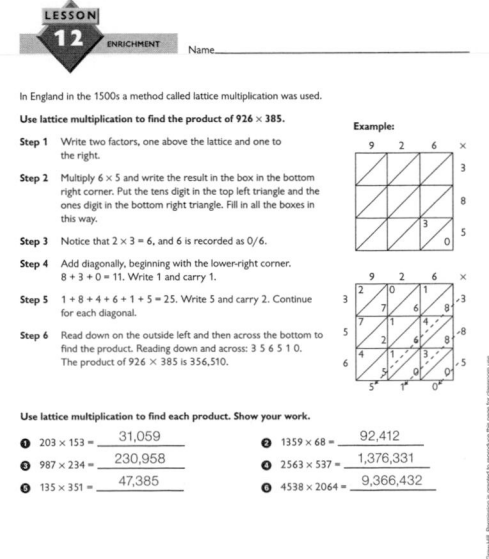

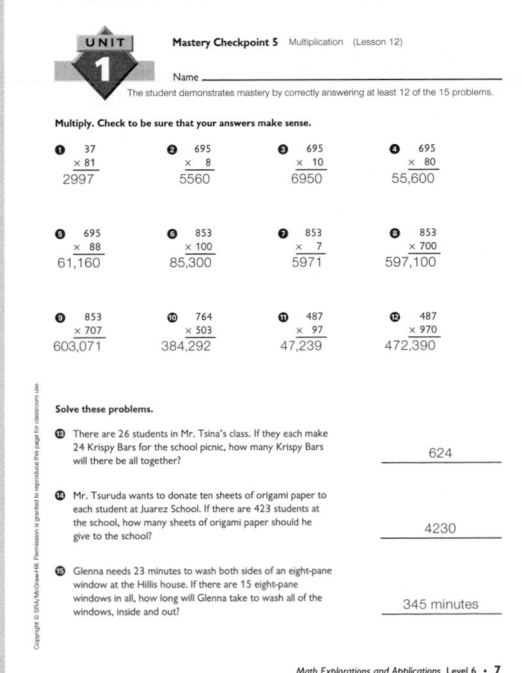

③ Wrap-Up

5 MINUTES

In Closing To summarize the lesson, ask students to explain what a partial product is and describe the steps in the procedure for multiplying multidigit numbers.

Mastery Checkpoint 5

At this time most students should demonstrate mastery of multiplying multidigit numbers by getting correct answers and using correct procedures for at least 80% of the problems on Assessment Blackline Masters page 7 or the first set of problems on page 43. The results of this assessment may be recorded on the Mastery Checkpoint Chart.

Assessment Criteria

Did the student . . .

✓ use knowledge of place value and basic facts to do the problems with one-digit and multidigit multipliers?

✓ use a more efficient multiplying process when a multidigit multiplier contained a 0?

Homework Assign Practice Master 12 to provide practice with multidigit multiplication.

ENRICHMENT p. 12

LESSON 12 ENRICHMENT Name__________

In England in the 1500s a method called lattice multiplication was used.

Use lattice multiplication to find the product of 926 × 385.

Step 1 Write two factors, one above the lattice and one to the right.

Step 2 Multiply 6 × 5 and write the result in the box in the bottom right corner. Put the tens digit in the top left triangle and the ones digit in the bottom right triangle. Fill in all the boxes in this way.

Step 3 Notice that 2 × 3 = 6, and 6 is recorded as 0/6.

Step 4 Add diagonally, beginning with the lower-right corner. 8 + 3 + 0 = 11. Write 1 and carry 1.

Step 5 1 + 8 + 4 + 6 + 1 + 5 = 25. Write 5 and carry 2. Continue for each diagonal.

Step 6 Read down on the outside left and then across the bottom to find the product. Reading down and across: 3 5 6 5 1 0. The product of 926 × 385 is 356,510.

Example:

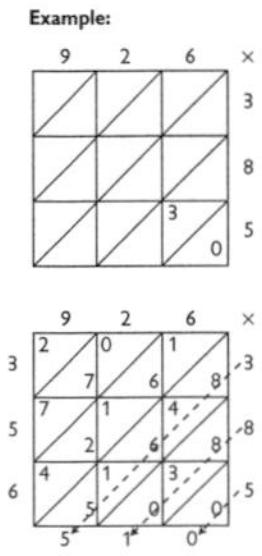

Use lattice multiplication to find each product. Show your work.

1. 203 × 153 = 31,059
2. 1359 × 68 = 92,412
3. 987 × 234 = 230,958
4. 2563 × 537 = 1,376,331
5. 135 × 351 = 47,385
6. 4538 × 2064 = 9,366,432

12 • *Math Explorations and Applications* Level 6

ASSESSMENT p. 7

UNIT 1 **Mastery Checkpoint 5** Multiplication (Lesson 12)

Name__________

The student demonstrates mastery by correctly answering at least 12 of the 15 problems.

Multiply. Check to be sure that your answers make sense.

1. 37 × 81 = 2997
2. 695 × 8 = 5560
3. 695 × 10 = 6950
4. 695 × 80 = 55,600
5. 695 × 88 = 61,160
6. 853 × 100 = 85,300
7. 853 × 7 = 5971
8. 853 × 700 = 597,100
9. 853 × 707 = 603,071
10. 764 × 503 = 384,292
11. 487 × 97 = 47,239
12. 487 × 970 = 472,390

Solve these problems.

13. There are 26 students in Mr. Tsina's class. If they each make 24 Krispy Bars for the school picnic, how many Krispy Bars will there be all together? 624

14. Mr. Tsuruda wants to donate ten sheets of origami paper to each student at Juarez School. If there are 423 students at the school, how many sheets of origami paper should he give to the school? 4230

15. Glenna needs 23 minutes to wash both sides of an eight-pane window at the Hillis house. If there are 15 eight-pane windows in all, how long will Glenna take to wash all of the windows, inside and out? 345 minutes

Math Explorations and Applications Level 6 • 7

LESSON 13
Applying Multiplication

Student Edition pages 44–47

LESSON PLANNER

Objectives

▶ to provide an opportunity to solve a practical problem by using multidigit multiplication

▶ to provide practice in solving word problems that involve multiplication

▶ to provide practice with multidigit multiplication and approximation

Context of the Lesson This is the tenth of 15 lessons reviewing operations with whole numbers. In this lesson, review of an intuitive idea of area is presented. Review of division begins in the next lesson.

 MANIPULATIVES

playing cards (optional)

Program Resources

Number Cubes (0–5)

Practice Master 13

Enrichment Master 13

For extra practice:
CD-ROM* Lesson 13

---

❶ Warm-Up
5 MINUTES

 **Problem of the Day** Present the following problem orally: A rectangular room in a seven-room house has an area of 140 square feet and a perimeter of 48 feet. What are the dimensions of the room? (14 feet by 10 feet)

Problem-Solving Strategies Ask students who have solved the Problem of the Day to share how they solved it and any strategies they used.

 **MENTAL MATH** Write these problems one at a time on the chalkboard:

a. 7 × 7 = (49)	**b.** 70 × 70 = (4900)
c. 700 × 7 = (4900)	**d.** 7 × 70 = (490)
e. 5 × 4 = (20)	**f.** 50 × 30 = (1500)
g. 50 × 29 = (1450)	**h.** 49 × 5 = (245)
i. 20 × 20 = (400)	**j.** 20 × 19 = (380)
k. 21 × 20 = (420)	**l.** 21 × 21 = (441)
m. 9 × 10 = (90)	**n.** 90 × 10 = (900)
o. 900 × 100 = (90,000)	**p.** 98 × 10 = (980)

LESSON 13
Applying Multiplication

You can make a diagram on grid paper to help you solve problems involving area. In this lesson you'll see how to use a diagram to plan an arrangement of tiles on a floor.

Remember that Paul and Kim measured the floor of their clubhouse so they could tile it. The floor is 500 centimeters long and 357 centimeters wide. The tiles they want to buy are square. Each tile is 25 centimeters on a side. Paul and Kim made this diagram to plan how to arrange the tiles.

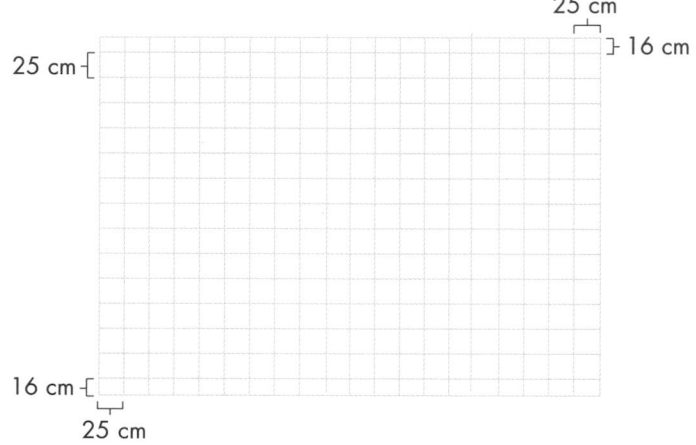

◆ How many whole tiles will they put down? **260**

◆ How many tiles will they need to cut? **40**

◆ How many tiles will they need to purchase? **300**

COOPERATIVE LEARNING Guide students who work on the Challenge activity in a group to figure out a way for all members of the group to participate meaningfully in the process. Invite groups struggling with this idea to observe other groups at work.

The tiles that Kim and Paul want to buy come in boxes of 24. Each box costs $8.00.

◆ How many boxes will they need to buy? **13**

◆ How many extra whole tiles will they have? **12**

◆ How much will the tiles cost (not including tax)? **$104**

◆ **Challenge:** If you were tiling your classroom floor, how many tiles would you need if each tile were 25 centimeters by 25 centimeters? (If you have already measured your classroom, use those results.) **Answers will vary depending on the size of the classroom floor.**

Solve these problems.

❶ Roger wants to make five kites. For each kite he needs two unbroken bamboo strips—one that is 60 centimeters long and one 80 centimeters long. Bamboo strips are 100 centimeters long and cost 75¢ each.

　　a. How many bamboo strips does Roger need to buy? **10**

　　b. How much will it cost him (not counting the tax)? **$7.50**

❷ Ms. Yamato is planning to buy carpeting for her living room. The carpeting she likes is 5 meters wide and costs $59.95 a meter. Her living room is 7 meters long and five meters wide.

　　a. How much carpeting should she buy? **7 m**

　　b. How much will it cost? **$419.65**

❸ There are 26 students in Rebecca's class who are going to a soccer game. The tickets are $6.75. Rebecca said that it will cost $17.55 for everyone to go. Was she right? Explain how you can tell. **No, she was**

t right. These **tickets would cost over $120.**

❹ Andre is putting baseball cards into an album. He bought 11 packs of 12 cards each to put in the album. Each page has spaces for nine cards, and Andre has 15 empty pages.

　　a. How many cards does Andre have to put in the album? **132**

　　b. Will all of the cards fit in the album? **yes**

　　c. How many empty spaces or how many leftover cards will Andre have after he puts the cards in the album?
3 empty spaces

Unit 1　Lesson 13　•　**45**

❷ Teach

Using the Student Pages Before beginning work on these pages, you may wish to demonstrate the multiplication variation of the "Roll a Problem" game on page 46, which provides practice with multiplication. Students who finish pages 44 and 45 early can play the game immediately.

This story is a continuation of the clubhouse story in Lesson 1 (pages 4 and 5). Review the story and the discussion questions with the class. Point out that instead of using two rows of tiles 16 cm wide, Paul and Kim could have used one row 25 cm wide and one row 7 cm wide.

You might wish to have students work in small groups to do the Challenge question. Remind them that they measured the length and width of the classroom in Lesson 1. (You may wish to calculate the answer yourself so that you can tell whether students' answers are reasonable.) Discuss the results; then have students work on problems 1–4 on their own.

ESL **Meeting Individual Needs**
　　Some students may have difficulty reading and understanding the word problems. Consider pairing these students with more proficient readers who can help by asking useful guiding questions or even acting out the situation in a problem.

◆ **LESSON 13** Applying Multiplication

Teach

GAME **Using the Student Pages** Demonstrate the "Roll a Problem" game by playing a few rounds with the entire class. Some students may remember the game from earlier grades. *Note:* Although they can be played by small groups, these games are often more fun when played with the entire class. Choose a student to act as leader. A copy of this game can also be found on page 11 of the Home Connections Blackline Masters.

We suggest that you first have students play the game with a two-digit multiplicand and multiplier, as described on page 46. After one or two games, modify it by using a three-digit multiplicand and a two-digit multiplier. Then change to an addition version and later to a subtraction version. In subtraction the strategy is especially difficult and interesting if the difference is to be the least possible but not negative.

MANIPULATIVES If a deck of **playing cards** is available, you can use it to generate the numbers after removing the face cards and by reading the 10 as 0. This approach has the advantage of bringing all ten digits into play and substantially increasing the number of different answers.

Then go over one or two problems on page 47 with the class. Have students do the rest of the page independently. Some students may remember the format from earlier grades. Emphasize that they need not calculate precise answers, but can choose the correct answer in each case by eliminating the two obviously wrong choices. For example, in the first problem, the answer must be less than 900 (30 x 30) and greater than 400 (20 x 20). Whenever you are working with problems like these, allow some time after students finish to discuss methods they used to find the answers.

◆ **LESSON 13** Applying Multiplication

COOPERATIVE LEARNING

Roll a Problem Game

Players:	Two or more
Materials:	One 0–5 cube
Object:	To get the greatest product
Math Focus:	Multidigit multiplication, place value, and mathematical reasoning

RULES

1. Use blanks to outline a multiplication problem on your paper, like this:

$$\underline{\qquad}\ \ \underline{\qquad}$$
$$\times \underline{\qquad}\ \ \underline{\qquad}$$
$$\overline{}$$

2. The first player rolls the cube four times.

3. Each time the cube is rolled, write that number in one of the blanks in your outline.

4. When all the blanks have been filled, find the product of the two numbers.

5. The player with the greatest product wins the round.

OTHER WAYS TO PLAY THIS GAME

1. Try to get the least product.

2. Multiply a one-digit number and a three-digit number.

3. Multiply two three-digit numbers.

4. Use a 5–10 cube. If you roll a 10, roll that cube again.

5. Instead of a cube, use ten slips of paper numbered 0 through 9. The first player draws the slips one at a time from a container.

MATH JOURNAL

If you played the game again, would you use the same strategy? In your Math Journal, write about the strategies you used.

46 • Whole Numbers and Integers

Literature Connection

Students can create multiplication problems that represent the expenses and profits of a large pumpkin production as they read *Pumpkins* by Mary Lynn Ray.

RETEACHING

Pair students who have trouble approximating answers with tutors who present problems like those on page 47. Tutors should use guiding questions to help students find a reasonable range for an answer. For example, they might say, "To get an idea of how large 17 x 39 is, think of two numbers close to these but greater that are easy to multiply." After helping the student to see that 20 x 40 (800) is a good choice, the tutor can say, "Think of two numbers that are easy to multiply and will give an answer that is less than 17 x 39." Finally, the tutor should ask, "What can you say about the product of 17 x 39?"

In each problem two of the answers are incorrect and one is correct. Choose the correct answer. Discuss your methods for finding the answers. What methods worked best?

5 23 × 29 a. 967 b. 367 **c.** 667

6 17 × 77 **a.** 1309 b. 6309 c. 1609

7 49 × 92 a. 3508 **b.** 4508 c. 5508

8 63 × 36 a. 2868 **b.** 2268 c. 3868

9 89 × 32 a. 1848 b. 2348 **c.** 2848

10 6973 − 3937 a. 1336 b. 336 **c.** 3036

11 6973 + 3937 a. 8910 **b.** 10,910 c. 3910

12 947 × 21 **a.** 19,887 b. 17,887 c. 1887

13 327 × 32 a. 40,464 **b.** 10,464 c. 1464

14 821 × 89 **a.** 73,069 b. 83,069 c. 16,069

15 456 × 52 a. 20,002 b. 2372 **c.** 23,712

16 593 × 42 a. 204,906 b. 34,906 **c.** 24,906

17 3377 + 167 **a.** 3544 b. 5044 c. 5344

18 1871 − 1387 a. 1484 **b.** 484 c. 84

19 1812 − 1776 a. 136 b. 1036 **c.** 36

20 367 + 274 **a.** 641 b. 341 c. 441

21 413 × 211 a. 67,143 b. 77,143 **c.** 87,143

22 387 × 195 a. 85,465 **b.** 75,465 c. 87,465

23 2492 − 363 **a.** 2129 b. 2329 c. 1929

24 1540 + 12,249 a. 27,649 b. 2789 **c.** 13,789

Unit 1 Lesson 13 • **47**

❸ Wrap-Up

In Closing Summarize the lesson by asking students to explain in a short paragraph the importance of proficiency in approximating an answer to a multidigit multiplication problem.

Informal Assessment Ask students to choose a few of the problems on page 47 and to explain orally how they arrived at their answers. In addition, ask them to describe the strategy they would use to get the greatest product and one they would use to get the least product in the "Roll a Problem" game.

Assessment Criteria

Did the student . . .

✓ explain how to solve the problems on page 45?

✓ explain how to choose the correct answers on page 47?

✓ communicate a reasonable strategy for winning the "Roll a Problem" game?

Homework Challenge students to first predict, then compute, the number of 25-cm tiles they would need to tile a room at home.

Mid-Unit Review

The Mid-Unit Review pinpoints troublesome skill areas for students, allowing plenty of time for additional practice and reteaching before the unit ends. If students did not do well on the Mid-Unit Review and have completed additional practice, you may want to use the Mid-Unit Review provided on Assessment Blackline Masters pages 8–9.

Using the Student Pages Have students complete problems 1–55 on pages 48 and 49 on their own. You might treat this review as a formal assessment of students' skills and have students complete this review as a timed test. See suggestions on page 49.

Mid-Unit Review

Write the numbers in standard form.

❶ $5000 + 600 + 80 + 5$ **5685**

❷ $8000 + 200 + 30 + 9$ **8239**

❸ $4000 + 50 + 1$ **4051**

❹ $30,000 + 600 + 20$ **30,620**

❺ $5 + 800 + 400,000$ **400,805**

❻ $0.6 + 0.04 + 0.005$ **0.645**

❼ $0.03 + 0.006 + 0.1$ **0.136**

❽ $0.008 + 0.3$ **0.308**

❾ 3 tenths, 5 hundredths, 3 thousandths **0.353**

❿ 0 tenths, 7 hundredths, 2 thousandths **0.072**

Copy each pair of numbers but replace ● with > , <, or =.

⓫ 3.9 ● 4.1 **<**

⓬ 0.6 ● 0.06 **>**

⓭ 0.778 ● 0.8 **<**

Point A is the number 0, and the point B is the number 1.

⓮ What fraction tells us where point R is?

a. $\frac{1}{2}$ (b.) $\frac{3}{4}$ c. $\frac{7}{8}$

⓯ What fraction tells us where point S is?

a. $\frac{1}{6}$ b. $\frac{2}{30}$ (c.) $\frac{1}{3}$

Solve for the variable. Watch the signs.

⓰ $6 + 8 = n$ **14**

⓱ $13 - 7 = n$ **6**

⓲ $n = 8 + 5$ **13**

⓳ $24 \div 6 = m$ **4**

⓴ $9 \times 7 = n$ **63**

㉑ $n = 54 \div 6$ **9**

㉒ $n = 70 \times 5$ **350**

㉓ $2400 + 10 = y$ **2410**

㉔ $z = 5 \times 500$ **2500**

㉕ $n = 4 \times 50$ **200**

㉖ $10 \times 100 = n$ **1000**

㉗ $s = 90 - 50$ **40**

48 • Whole Numbers and Integers

Add or subtract. Use shortcuts when you can.

28 $\begin{array}{r} 100 \\ -\ 27 \\ \hline \mathbf{73} \end{array}$	**29** $\begin{array}{r} 2100 \\ +\ 70 \\ \hline \mathbf{2170} \end{array}$	**30** $\begin{array}{r} 2000 \\ -\ 6 \\ \hline \mathbf{1994} \end{array}$	**31** $\begin{array}{r} 5000 \\ +3034 \\ \hline \mathbf{8034} \end{array}$	**32** $\begin{array}{r} 4001 \\ 2000 \\ 2020 \\ +3980 \\ \hline \mathbf{12,001} \end{array}$
33 $\begin{array}{r} 6999 \\ +\ 1 \\ \hline \mathbf{7000} \end{array}$	**34** $\begin{array}{r} 3006 \\ +2238 \\ \hline \mathbf{5244} \end{array}$	**35** $\begin{array}{r} 65,000 \\ -30,334 \\ \hline \mathbf{34,666} \end{array}$	**36** $\begin{array}{r} 400 \\ 200 \\ +209 \\ \hline \mathbf{809} \end{array}$	**37** $\begin{array}{r} 5000 \\ 2359 \\ +3034 \\ \hline \mathbf{10,393} \end{array}$

Multiply.

38 $\begin{array}{r} 800 \\ \times\ 60 \\ \hline \mathbf{48,000} \end{array}$	**39** $\begin{array}{r} 100 \\ \times\ 100 \\ \hline \mathbf{10,000} \end{array}$	**40** $\begin{array}{r} 700 \\ \times\ 80 \\ \hline \mathbf{56,000} \end{array}$	**41** $\begin{array}{r} 1000 \\ \times\ 24 \\ \hline \mathbf{24,000} \end{array}$	**42** $\begin{array}{r} 539 \\ \times\ 7 \\ \hline \mathbf{3773} \end{array}$
43 $\begin{array}{r} 67 \\ \times\ 9 \\ \hline \mathbf{603} \end{array}$	**44** $\begin{array}{r} 832 \\ \times\ 15 \\ \hline \mathbf{12,480} \end{array}$	**45** $\begin{array}{r} 302 \\ \times\ 46 \\ \hline \mathbf{13,892} \end{array}$	**46** $\begin{array}{r} 730 \\ \times\ 50 \\ \hline \mathbf{36,500} \end{array}$	**47** $\begin{array}{r} 306 \\ \times\ 80 \\ \hline \mathbf{24,480} \end{array}$

Choose the correct answer.

48 17×248 **a.** 4206   **(b.)** 4216   **c.** 42,106

49 $8305 - 2919$ **(a.)** 5386   **b.** 11,224   **c.** 6386

50 $3206 + 3811$ **a.** 6917   **b.** 7117   **(c.)** 7017

51 314×62 **(a.)** 19,468   **b.** 17,928   **c.** 16,828

52 $928 - 359$ **a.** 531   **b.** 1287   **(c.)** 569

53 $853 + 2496$ **a.** 1099   **(b.)** 3349   **c.** 3029

Solve these problems.

54 Art hiked for about 6 hours. About what fraction of the day is that?   **about $\frac{1}{4}$**

55 Of the 32 students in Corrine's class, 14 are wearing sneakers today. Are the majority of her classmates wearing sneakers?   **no**

Unit 1 Mid-Unit Review • **49**

ASSESSMENT p. 8

UNIT 1   Mid-Unit Review   (Use after Lesson 13.)   Page 1 of 2

Name

The student demonstrates mastery by correctly answering at least 24 of the 30 problems.

Solve. Watch the signs.

1 $\begin{array}{r} 369 \\ +732 \\ \hline 1101 \end{array}$	**2** $\begin{array}{r} 865 \\ \times\ 36 \\ \hline 31,140 \end{array}$	**3** $\begin{array}{r} 10,712 \\ -\ 965 \\ \hline 9747 \end{array}$	**4** $\begin{array}{r} 10,712 \\ +\ 965 \\ \hline 11,677 \end{array}$
5 $\begin{array}{r} 8650 \\ \times\ 360 \\ \hline 3,114,000 \end{array}$	**6** $\begin{array}{r} 13,532 \\ -\ 9,415 \\ \hline 4117 \end{array}$	**7** $\begin{array}{r} 274 \\ \times\ 55 \\ \hline 15,070 \end{array}$	**8** $\begin{array}{r} 14,673 \\ +10,269 \\ \hline 24,942 \end{array}$
9 $\begin{array}{r} 4028 \\ -2037 \\ \hline 1991 \end{array}$	**10** $\begin{array}{r} 3618 \\ \times\ 22 \\ \hline 79,596 \end{array}$	**11** $\begin{array}{r} 3609 \\ -1720 \\ \hline 1889 \end{array}$	**12** $\begin{array}{r} 4028 \\ +2037 \\ \hline 6065 \end{array}$

Solve these problems.

13 If 226 people each donated $10 to the soup kitchen, how much money would the soup kitchen get? $2260

14 The "Travels Under the Sea" dance show will have three performances. Tickets will be $2 for children and $4 for adults.

   a. If 100 children and 80 adults come to each performance, how much ticket money will be collected at each performance? $200 + $320 = $520

   b. How much money will that be for all three performances? $1560

15 A discontinued model of ski boot is on sale for $\frac{3}{4}$ off the regular price. The regular price of the boots is $100. How much do the boots cost now? $25

8 • *Math Explorations and Applications Level 6*

Timed Test Throughout the Teacher's Guide there are suggestions for sets of exercises to be completed as a "timed test." This usually occurs on pages of basic facts where the focus is on speedy recall. It gives each student a chance to improve as the year goes on. Invite students to keep their scores or the pages showing their work in their Math Journals or keep the pages in their Math Portfolios so that they can track their improvement.

Here are some suggestions for giving timed tests:

▶ Before students begin, they should number their papers in the same way as the problems in the book.

▶ Have all students start at the same time.

▶ Write 0 on the chalkboard as you tell them to start; after one minute erase the 0 and write 1; after two minutes write 2; and so on. Have students write that number at the tops of their papers when they finish the test so they know how long they took to complete the test.

▶ Grade the papers yourself or have students correct their own papers as you call out the answers. Encourage the students to brainstorm ways to improve their times on future tests.

Home Connections You may want to send Home Connections Blackline Masters pages 40–41 home, which provide additional activities families can complete together. These activities apply the skills being presented in this unit.

Portfolio Assessment The Portfolio Assessment task provided on Assessment Blackline Masters page 86 can be used at this time to evaluate students' ability to solve complex problems involving arithmetic.

Performance Assessment The Performance Assessment Task 1 provided on Assessment Blackline Masters pages 62–63 can be used at this time to evaluate students' proficiency with place value, addition, subtraction, and multiplication. You may want to administer this assessment with individual students or in small groups.

Unit Project This would be a good time to assign the "Clever Counting" project on pages 98 and 99. Students can begin working on the project in cooperative groups in their free time as you work through the unit. The Unit Project is a good opportunity for students to compare our base-10 system with other systems.

Division

LESSON PLANNER

Objectives

▶ to provide practice with simple division with remainders

▶ to review, through realistic situations, the meaning of division and remainders

▶ to show with examples when it is appropriate to round up or down in a division problem

✓ to assess mastery of division facts and ability to present answers in appropriate forms

Context of the Lesson This lesson, the 11th of 15 lessons reviewing operations with whole numbers, contains a checkpoint for mastery of basic division facts. Standard division algorithms are reviewed in the next three lessons.

 MANIPULATIVES

flash cards, division (optional)

play money* (optional)

Program Resources

Practice Master 14

Enrichment Master 14

Assessment Master

For extra practice: CD-ROM* Lesson 14

1 Warm-Up

Problem of the Day Present this problem orally or on the chalkboard: Jessica claims that she can multiply 9 × 49 easily without using pencil and paper. Describe a method she could use to do it. (One way: multiply 9 × 50; subtract 9 from the product.)

Problem-Solving Strategies Ask students who have solved the Problem of the Day to share how they solved it and any strategies they used.

 Give practice with problems focusing on inverse operations. Mix in missing-term problems. Here's a suggested sequence:

a. 3 × 9 = (27), 27 ÷ 3 = (9), n × 9 = 27 (n = 3)

b. 5 × 4 = (20), 20 ÷ 4 = (5), n × 5 = 20 (n = 4)

(continued on page 51)

Division

Mrs. Katz has 24 oranges to put in packages to sell in her store. She wants to put the same number of oranges in each package, but no more than six will fit in a package.

◆ How many ways can Mrs. Katz package the oranges so that there are none left to sell individually? **4**

Divide.

8 ① 7)56	**7** ② 6)42	**9** ③ 8)72	**4** ④ 9)36	**5 R2** ⑤ 3)17
8 R2 ⑥ 8)66	**6** ⑦ 4)24	**7 R1** ⑧ 7)50	**5 R4** ⑨ 6)34	**8 R3** ⑩ 5)43
7 ⑪ 9)63	**6 R2** ⑫ 3)20	**5** ⑬ 7)35	**6** ⑭ 8)48	**7** ⑮ 3)21
9 ⑯ 9)81	**8 R2** ⑰ 7)58	**7 R5** ⑱ 6)47	**8 R5** ⑲ 6)53	**9 R2** ⑳ 4)38
9 R3 ㉑ 8)75	**8** ㉒ 8)64	**5 R2** ㉓ 4)22	**5** ㉔ 5)25	**7 R3** ㉕ 4)31
7 ㉖ 7)49	**7 R1** ㉗ 9)64	**5 R3** ㉘ 7)38	**9 R5** ㉙ 9)86	**4** ㉚ 8)32

Besides the United States and Canada, other countries whose basic unit of money is called the dollar include Australia, Liberia, New Zealand, and Singapore.

50 · Whole Numbers and Integers

 **Technology Connection** Use the video, laser disc, or software *Modumath: Arithmetic, Dividing Whole Numbers, Part 1* from VTAE (VHS, IBM, for grades 6–12) for further practice with 90 basic division facts, word problems, and using multiplication to check division.

*available separately

Often in real life the answer to division problems must be interpreted. In this lesson you'll explore situations that call for different ways to interpret answers in division problems.

Frank made 30 cupcakes. He put them in boxes to sell at a bake sale. Only four fit in a box.

◆ How many boxes will he fill? **7**

◆ How many cupcakes will be left over? **2**

◆ What can he do with them? **Answers may include Frank will eat the cupcakes, sell them separately, give them away, and so on.**

There are 30 members of the Rocky Hill Ski Club. They are planning to go skiing at High Hills Ski Center next weekend. With all the skis and gear, only four persons can go in one car.

◆ How many cars will they need to take? **8**

◆ Why can't they take $7\frac{1}{2}$ cars? **They can't take half a car.**

Bonita has a board that is 30 centimeters long. She wants to divide it into four equal pieces to make a square frame. She wants the frame to be as large as possible.

◆ How long should she make each of the small pieces? **7.5 cm**

◆ Will part of the board be left? **no**

Unit 1   Lesson 14 • **51**

Mental Math (continued)

c. $600 \times 200 = (120{,}000)$, $120{,}000 \div 600 = (200)$,
$n \times 200 = 120{,}000$ ($n = 600$)

d. $60 + 40 = (100)$, $100 - 60 = (40)$, $n + 40 = 100$ ($n = 60$)

e. $40 - 20 = (20)$, $20 + 20 = (40)$, $n - 20 = 20$ ($n = 40$)

f. $25 \times 4 = (100)$, $100 \div 4 = (25)$, $n \times 4 = 100$ ($n = 25$)

❷ Teach

Using the Student Pages If necessary, briefly review writing remainders before students do problems 1–30 on page 50 on their own. Guide students to check their answers by using the inverse operation, multiplication. When students have completed the discussion problem about Mrs. Katz's oranges, go over it with the whole class. If a student suggests that Mrs. Katz can make 24 packages of one orange each, remind them that the problem says that she does not want to sell any oranges individually.

Go over pages 51–52 carefully with all students. Be sure they see why each answer is in a different form even though the division problem, $30 \div 4$, is the same.

Literature Connection You may wish to use *Cookies* by William Jaspersohn to create division problems related to the production of Famous Amos cookies.

◆ LESSON 14   Division

Teach

Using the Student Pages After going over page 52, ask students to work independently on the problems on page 53. Again, the arithmetic is the same in each problem and students must recognize which form of the answer is appropriate. Students may need assistance with division by a two-digit divisor, which is formally reviewed in Lesson 16.

ESL **Meeting Individual Needs**
Students who have difficulty with English may not understand all of the words in the word problems. Have them work with another student to paraphrase each problem. Encourage students to use a strategy such as drawing a diagram, acting it out, and so on to communicate and solve the problem.

◆ LESSON 14   Division

Ms. Chen gave Donald, Carlos, Rose, and Dorothy 30 bananas that weren't eaten at the school picnic. She told them to share the bananas equally.

◆ How many whole bananas did each one get? **7**

◆ In order to share equally and use all the bananas, what must they have done with the last two bananas?
They must have cut the bananas in half.

◆ How many bananas did each one get? **$7\frac{1}{2}$**

Pat has a rock collection. She has boxes that are 4 centimeters high to hold individual rocks. There are 30 centimeters between the shelves on which she stacks the boxes.

◆ How many boxes can she stack on a shelf? **7**

◆ How much space will be left over? **2 cm**

◆ Can she use the leftover space to stack more rocks? **If the rocks are no more than 2 cm high; she cannot use the boxes she has.**

For each of these problems, we did the same division problem:

$$4\overline{)30}$$

But we looked at the answers differently in each case. We obtained as possible answers:

$$7\text{ R2, }8,\ 7.5,\ 7\frac{1}{2},\ 7$$

Whenever you divide to find the answer to a problem, you must decide which is the right answer. Sometimes you'll round up or down to the nearest whole number; sometimes you'll show the remainder; sometimes you'll use a fraction or a decimal answer. There may even be other possibilities for the answer to the problem or the way to present it. It all depends on the situation.

52 • Whole Numbers and Integers

RETEACHING

Encourage students who are still having difficulty recalling the division facts to work in pairs to help each other. They may use **flash cards,** for example, or simply make up problems and do them orally. If a sizable number of students in the class are still less than proficient, drills with the whole class would be appropriate.

PRACTICE p. 14

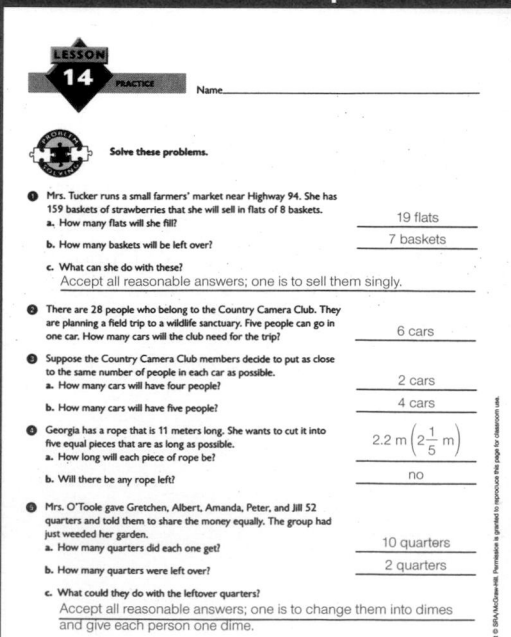

LESSON 14 PRACTICE   Name_____

Solve these problems.

❶ Mrs. Tucker runs a small farmers' market near Highway 94. She has 159 baskets of strawberries that she will sell in flats of 8 baskets.
  a. How many flats will she fill?   19 flats
  b. How many baskets will be left over?   7 baskets
  c. What can she do with these?
  Accept all reasonable answers; one is to sell them singly.

❷ There are 28 people who belong to the Country Camera Club. They are planning a field trip to a wildlife sanctuary. Five people can go in one car. How many cars will the club need for the trip?   6 cars

❸ Suppose the Country Camera Club members decide to put as close to the same number of people in each car as possible.
  a. How many cars will have four people?   2 cars
  b. How many cars will have five people?   4 cars

❹ Georgia has a rope that is 11 meters long. She wants to cut it into five equal pieces that are as long as possible.
  a. How long will each piece of rope be? $2.2\text{ m}\left(2\frac{1}{5}\text{ m}\right)$
  b. Will there be any rope left?   no

❺ Mrs. O'Toole gave Gretchen, Albert, Amanda, Peter, and Jill 52 quarters and told them to share the money equally. The group had just weeded her garden.
  a. How many quarters did each one get?   10 quarters
  b. How many quarters were left over?   2 quarters
  c. What could they do with the leftover quarters?
  Accept all reasonable answers; one is to change them into dimes and give each person one dime.

14 • Math Explorations and Applications Level 6

Solve the following problems. Write a short sentence as an answer to each problem, giving your answer and your reason for choosing that answer. **Reasons will vary. Accept all reasonable explanations.**

31 All 1032 students from the Worthington School must be taken by bus on a field trip. No more than 40 students are allowed on one bus. How many busses will be needed? **26**

32 Mr. Alonzo has 1032 pieces of construction paper that he wants to divide equally among the 40 people in his class. How many pieces should each person get? **$25\frac{4}{5}$**

33 Mr. Alonzo has 1032 marbles that he wants to divide equally among the 40 people in his class. How many marbles should each person get? **25 with 32 left over**

34 The total cost of a party was $1032. Each of the 40 people at the party had to pay an equal share of the cost. How much should each person pay? **$25.80**

35 Angie the tailor has 1032 inches of material with which to make vests. Each vest requires 40 inches of material. How many vests can she make? **25**

36 The school board has told Ms. Miller, the principal, that she must have exactly the same number of students in each of the 40 classes in her school. There are 1032 students in the school. How many students should be in each class? **impossible**

Unit 1   Lesson 14 • **53**

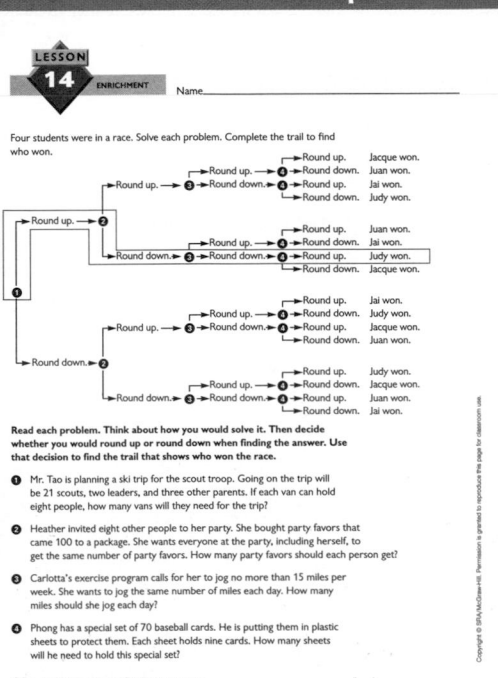
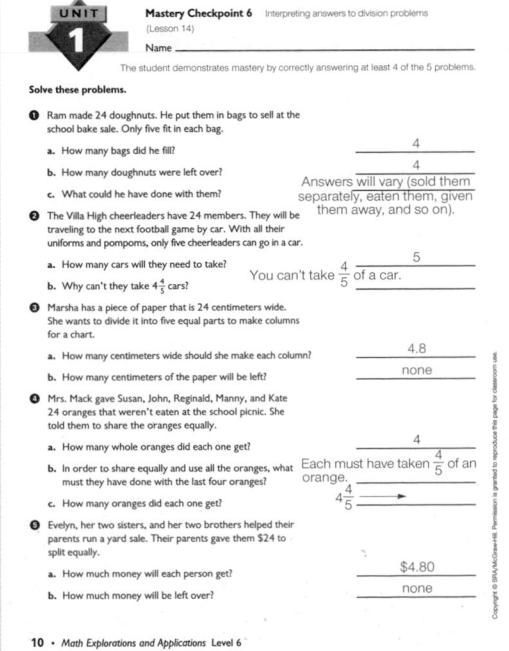
❸ Wrap-Up

In Closing Summarize the lesson by asking students to explain and provide examples of how a situation can dictate the way to present the answer to a division problem.

 For students who can find quotients but have difficulty finding remainders, do some problems such as $50 \div 7$ with **play money*** or other objects. Tell a story or have the students make up a story and keep track of the division process this way:

$$\begin{array}{r} 7 \\ 7\overline{)50} \\ -49 \\ \hline 1 \end{array}$$

 **Mastery Checkpoint 6**

At this time most students should be proficient in deciding which form of answer is appropriate in situations that call for division (for example, rounding quotients up, down, or not at all; leaving the remainder as a whole number; or expressing the quotient in decimal or fraction form). This understanding may be assessed by observing students as they work on pages 51–53 or on Assessment Blackline Masters page 10.

Assessment Criteria

Did the student . . .

✓ explain how to choose the appropriate form for expressing a quotient?

✓ correctly answer at least 90% of the division problems on page 50?

✓ demonstrate mastery of basic division facts?

Homework Assign Practice Master 14 for further practice with division.

Student Edition pages 54–57

Dividing by a One-Digit Divisor

Dividing by a One-Digit Divisor

LESSON PLANNER

Objectives

▶ to review and provide practice with the long and short forms of the algorithm for dividing a multidigit dividend by a one-digit divisor

▶ to compare the short-division algorithm with the standard division algorithm

✓ to assess students' ability to divide a multidigit dividend by a single-digit divisor

Context of the Lesson This lesson, the 12th of 15 lessons reviewing operations with whole numbers, contains a checkpoint for assessing mastery of division by one-digit divisors. This topic was introduced in Level 4 and reviewed in Level 5. Division by two-digit numbers was introduced in the fifth grade and will be reviewed in the next lesson.

 **MANIPULATIVES**

base-10 materials*
  (optional)
play money*
  (optional)
flash cards
  (optional)

Program Resources

Reteaching Master

Practice Master 15

Enrichment Master 15

Assessment Master

For extra practice:
  CD-ROM* Lesson 15
  Cumulative Review, page 555

At a charity dinner, $18,432 was raised. The money is to be divided among seven charities. How much will each charity receive? Find out by dividing.

$18,432 \div 7 = ?$

$$7\overline{)18,432}$$

Since 1 is less than 7, start by dividing 18 by 7. That is, use 18 as a partial dividend. The **dividend** is the number to be divided.

$$\begin{array}{r} 2 \\ 7\overline{)18,432} \\ \underline{14} \\ 4 \end{array}$$

There are two, but not three, 7s in 18.
Write 2 above the 8.
Multiply 2 × 7 and write 14 below the 18.
Subtract 14 from 18, leaving 4.

$$\begin{array}{r} 2\,6 \\ 7\overline{)18,432} \\ \underline{14} \\ 4\,4 \\ \underline{4\,2} \\ 2 \end{array}$$

"Bring down" the next digit (4) and divide 44 by 7, getting 6.
Write 6 above the 4 you brought down.
Multiply 6 × 7 and write 42 below the 44.
Subtract 42 from 44, leaving 2.

$$\begin{array}{r} 2\,63 \\ 7\overline{)18,432} \\ \underline{14} \\ 4\,4 \\ \underline{4\,2} \\ 23 \\ \underline{21} \\ 2 \end{array}$$

Bring down the 3.
There are three, but not four, 7s in 23.
3 × 7 = 21
23 − 21 = 2

$$\begin{array}{r} 2\,633 \\ 7\overline{)18,432} \\ \underline{14} \\ 4\,4 \\ \underline{4\,2} \\ 23 \\ \underline{21} \\ 22 \\ \underline{21} \\ 1 \end{array}$$

Bring down the 2.
There are three, but not four, 7s in 22.
3 × 7 = 21
22 − 21 = 1
The answer is 2633, but there is a remainder of 1.
Each charity will get $2633, with $1 left over.

54 • Whole Numbers and Integers

① Warp-Up ⏱ 5 MINUTES

 Problem of the Day Present this problem orally: What is the greatest whole number that rounds to 6000 when rounded to the nearest 100, and to 5950 when rounded to the nearest 10? (5954)

Problem-Solving Strategies Ask students who have solved the Problem of the Day to share how they solved it and any strategies they used.

MENTAL MATH Ask students to show thumbs up if there is a remainder or thumbs down if there is not for the following problems:

a. 25 ÷ 8 = (thumbs up)   **b.** 14 ÷ 7 = (thumbs down)

c. 35 ÷ 5 = (thumbs down)   **d.** 81 ÷ 9 = (thumbs down)

(continued on page 55)

 **teach it this way?**

The long form for one-digit divisors is reviewed in this lesson because it is used as a model for two-digit divisor problems and also because it makes it easier to identify specific difficulties students may be having.

COOPERATIVE LEARNING Students can play the "Roll a Problem (Division)" game (page 63) or the "Roll and Divide" game (page 67) in small groups for further practice with the division algorithm.

*available separately

⑭ b. Answers will vary. Students may suggest that Mrs. Ortiz should make a profit or that she should charge extra to cover the cost of caring for and feeding the puppies.

Check to be sure that your answer is correct.

Multiply the quotient by the divisor and add the remainder.

```
                    2633  ———— quotient (answer to a division problem)
  2 633R1        ×    7   ———— divisor (number we're dividing by)
 7)18,432           18,431
                 +      1  ———— remainder (number left over)
                    18,432
```

The result should be the same as the dividend. It is, so the answer is correct.

Divide. If the answer is not a whole number, leave the remainder as shown in the example.

7	**919**	**4509**	**1457**
❶ 8)56	❷ 9)8271	❸ 7)31,563	❹ 5)7285
208	**1020**	**58**	**688 R3**
❺ 4)832	❻ 6)6120	❼ 7)406	❽ 9)6195
187	**781**	**6 R3**	**236 R6**
❾ 5)935	❿ 3)2343	⓫ 6)39	⓬ 8)1894

Solve these problems.

⑬ Mrs. Ortiz bought seven puppies for $875. She wants to know how much this is per puppy. How much did she pay for each puppy? **$125**

⑭ Mrs. Ortiz wants to sell six of the puppies and keep one.
 a. How much must she charge for each puppy so that she gets back her $875 but sells only six of them? (Assume that she will charge the same for each puppy.) **at least $145.84**
 b. If you were Mrs. Ortiz, what price would you charge for each puppy? **See above.**

⑮ Mrs. Ortiz decides to keep two puppies instead of one.
 a. If she still wants to get back $875, how much must she charge for each puppy? **$175**
 b. Mrs. Ortiz is able to sell one of the five remaining puppies for $200. How much must she charge for the others to get a total of at least $875? **$168.75**

Mental Math (continued)

 e. 100 ÷ 25 = (thumbs down) f. 66 ÷ 3 = (thumbs down)
 g. 25 ÷ 2 = (thumbs up) h. 325 ÷ 5 = (thumbs down)
 i. 110 ÷ 10 = (thumbs down) j. 19 ÷ 9 = (thumbs up)

❷ Teach

Using the Student Pages Review the algorithm and the checking procedure with all students before they do the computation problems on their own. Then discuss the word problems after students have finished page 55.

For problem 14b, some students may suggest that finding good homes for the puppies is more important than making a profit.

Literature Connection You may wish to have students read *Dear Mr. Henshaw* by Beverly Cleary. Challenge them to determine how many recipes of 2, 3, or 4 pounds of moose meat would be needed to use 1000 pounds.

Meeting Individual Needs For students who do not understand the algorithm, consider using **base-10 materials***, or **play money***, to demonstrate it. Or, you may wish to have them simply carry out the steps of the algorithm as they say them aloud. Use a problem such as **543,296 ÷ 7.** (77,613.7)

*available separately

◆ LESSON 15 Dividing by a One-Digit Divisor

Teach

Using the Student Pages Review the short form of the algorithm with the class. Emphasize the importance of checking to see whether the answer makes sense. At this point most students should see that the short form of division is essentially the same as the long form, except that there is less writing in the short form. Students may use whichever form they prefer.

You may wish to do the first discussion problem with the class. The procedures are essentially the same, but the work, when finished, will look like this on paper:

Standard Form	Short Form
456	4 5 6
7)3192	7)3 1³9⁴2
28	
39	
35	
42	
42	

Note that the intermediate results, 39 and 42, are written out in the standard form but are indicated only by writing the tens digit above and to the left of the ones digit in the short form. The products, 28, 35, and 42, are not written out in the short form, even though they are computed.

Have students do problems 16–30 on page 57 on their own. Remind them to check their answers.

Meeting Individual Needs
Social learners having trouble with multiplication or division facts may benefit from practice with partners using visual aids, such as **flash cards,** or playing games. Check students regularly until they are proficient at answering pairs of questions such as "How many 6s in 49?" (8) and "What's left?" (1)

◆ LESSON 15 Dividing by a One-Digit Divisor

You've learned the procedure for long division. Now you'll review the procedures for short division.

$543,296 \div 7 = ?$

7)543,296 — 7 is greater than 5.
54 is the next partial dividend.

7
7)54⁵3,296 — $7 \times 7 = 49$
$54 - 49 = 5$
Write the 5 in front of the 3.
53 is the new partial dividend.

7 7
7)54⁵3ᵢ296 — $7 \times 7 = 49$
$53 - 49 = 4$
Write the 4 in front of the 2.
42 is the new partial dividend.

7 7 6
7)54⁵3ᵢ296 — $6 \times 7 = 42$
$42 - 42 = 0$
There's no need to write 0 in front of the 9.
9 is the new partial dividend.

7 7 61
7)54⁵3ᵢ29²6 — $1 \times 7 = 7$
$9 - 7 = 2$
26 is the new partial dividend.

7 7 61 3
7)54⁵3ᵢ29²6 — $3 \times 7 = 21$
$26 - 21 = 5$
The answer is 77,613 with 5 left over.
Depending on the situation, you might use 77,613 or 77,614.

Check your answer to be sure that it makes sense.

77,613 is a little less than 80,000.

$7 \times 80,000$ is 560,000.

543,296 is a little less than 560,000.

So the answer makes sense.

56 • Whole Numbers and Integers

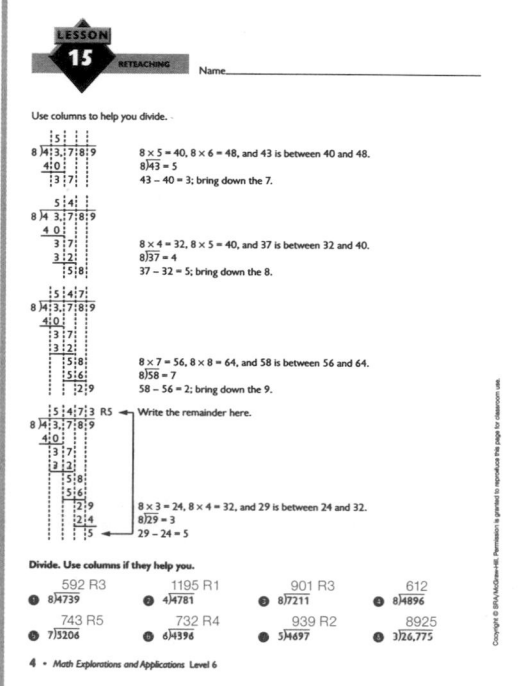
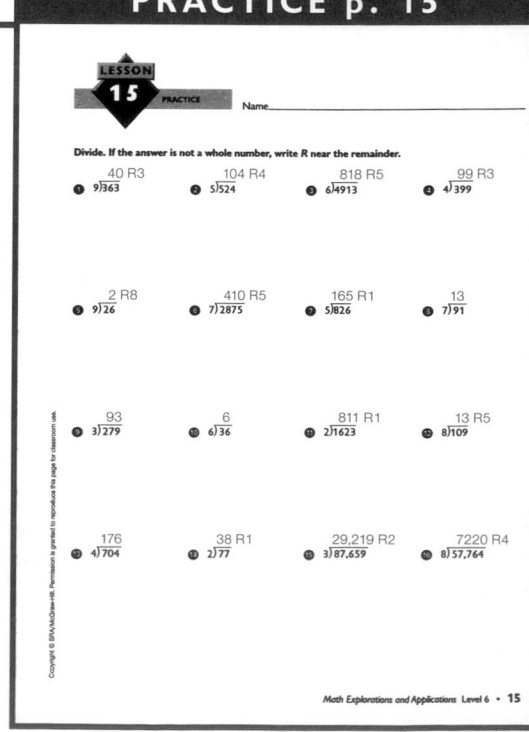

Compare the procedures for division (page 54) and short division (page 56).

◆ Make sure you get the same answer when you do a problem either way.

Solve these division problems. There are no remainders. Check your answers to be sure that they make sense.

⑯ 49,380 ÷ 5
9876

⑰ 76,136 ÷ 8
9517

⑱ 47,016 ÷ 2
23,508

⑲ 64,251 ÷ 3
21,417

⑳ 9872 ÷ 4
2468

㉑ 33,282 ÷ 9
3698

㉒ 51,884 ÷ 7
7412

㉓ 82,734 ÷ 6
13,789

㉔ 45,186 ÷ 6
7531

㉕ 25,581 ÷ 3
8527

㉖ 4356 ÷ 6
726

㉗ 19,912 ÷ 8
2489

Solve these problems.

㉘ Mr. and Mrs. Singh drove 3555 kilometers in the last five days. If they drove about the same amount each day, about how many kilometers did they drive each day? **about 711**

㉙ Mr. and Mrs. Perez have a 1125 kilometer trip to make in two days. They want to drive about twice as far the first day as the second. How far should they drive the first day? **750 km**

㉚ Three friends are making a 2070 kilometer trip over three days. They want to drive the same distance each day and share the driving equally. How far should each person drive on the first day? **230 km**

Use the Cumulative Review on page 555 after this lesson.

Unit 1   Lesson 15 • **57**

In Closing Summarize the lesson by asking students to explain the similarities and differences between the long and short forms of the division algorithm.

Encourage students to keep a record of their results on the computation problems on pages 55 and 57.

Mastery Checkpoint 7

At this time most students should demonstrate mastery using the division algorithm to divide by a one-digit divisor by getting at least 80% of the computation problems correct on page 57 or on Assessment Blackline Masters page 11 in a reasonable amount of time.

Assessment Criteria

Did the student . . .

✓ correctly answer at least ten of the first 12 problems on page 55?

✓ demonstrate mastery of both the long and short forms of the division algorithm?

Homework Assign the following problem: Manuel wants to give away his sports card collection by giving the same number of each kind of card to three friends. How should he evenly divide his collection if he has 330 baseball cards, 720 basketball cards, and 1035 football cards? (110 baseball cards, 240 basketball cards, and 345 football cards for each friend)

ENRICHMENT p. 15

LESSON 15 ENRICHMENT   Name_____

Two daughters and two mothers went fishing. Each person caught the same number of fish. There were nine fish caught all together. How can this be?

Use short division to complete each problem. If there is a 0 in the answer, lightly shade that section. The shaded sections will show how many people went fishing. Write your solution to the riddle below the puzzle

The 1128 cans were packed in boxes of eight each. How many boxes were there? **141**	A grocer sold 5216 loaves of bread in four months. What was the average number sold each month? **1304**	The grocer counted 416 cans of green beans, 253 cans of wax beans, and 132 cans of yellow beans. How many cans was that? **801**	In six days 1230 customers came in the store. What was the average number of customers per day? **205**
One day 620 people bought groceries. Only 195 paid cash. How many did not pay cash? **425**	There are 25 crackers in a box. How many crackers are in three boxes? **75**	A gross is 144 of an item. How many items are in 3 gross? **432**	How many items are in 5 gross? **720**
Eggs are sold by the dozen or half dozen. How many eggs are in 3½ dozen? **42**	How many eggs are in 10½ dozen? **126**	The grocer paid $252.50 for five cases of exotic fruit. How much did each case cost? **$50.50**	How many oranges are in nine bags if each bag holds a dozen oranges? **108**
Cans of vegetables come 24 to a case. How many cans are in 31 cases? **744**	In a three-month period, the store sold 1896 magazines. What was the average number of magazines sold per month? **632**	Packaged pasta comes 18 boxes to a case. The grocer received 396 boxes of pasta. How many cases were received? **22**	A ton is 2000 pounds. How many pounds are in 4½ tons? **9000**
The butcher had 42 packages of ground beef. Each weighed 1.5 pounds. How many pounds of ground beef were there in all? **63**	A ream of paper has 500 sheets. How many sheets of paper are in six reams of paper? **3000**	There are 20 packages of baseball cards in a box and 15 cards in each package. How many cards are in three boxes? **900**	The grocer ordered 945 newspapers. They come nine to a bundle. How many bundles of newspapers were ordered? **105**

A grandmother, mother, and daughter went fishing (3 people).

Math Explorations and Applications Level 6 • **15**

ASSESSMENT p. 11

UNIT 1   Mastery Checkpoint 7   Division (with one-digit divisors)   (Lesson 15)

Name_____

The student demonstrates mastery by correctly answering at least 16 of the 20 problems.

Solve these division problems. There are no remainders. Check your answers to be sure that they make sense.

❶ 8967 / 5)44,835
❷ 32,604 / 2)65,208
❸ 2489 / 9)22,401
❹ 1961 / 8)15,688

❺ 3552 / 4)14,208
❻ 7321 / 7)51,247
❼ 834 / 6)5004
❽ 1331 / 5)6655

❾ 5829 / 8)46,632
❿ 5324 / 7)37,268
⓫ 9316 / 3)27,948
⓬ 463 / 7)3241

⓭ 1963 / 4)7852
⓮ 8527 / 6)51,162
⓯ 6249 / 7)43,743
⓰ 5167 / 3)15,501

⓱ 4478 / 5)22,390
⓲ 2792 / 8)22,336
⓳ 3659 / 9)32,931
⓴ 4286 / 7)30,002

Math Explorations and Applications Level 6 • **11**

Unit 1 Lesson 15   **57**

Student Edition pages 58–63

Dividing by a Multidigit Divisor

LESSON PLANNER

Objectives

▶ to review the standard algorithm for dividing by two-digit numbers

▶ to introduce and provide practice in using shortcuts to divide

▶ to provide practice with division

Context of the Lesson This is the 13th of 15 lessons reviewing operations with whole numbers. Practice in using division to solve word problems is provided in the next lesson.

 MANIPULATIVES

calculators*

play money*
 (optional)

Program Resources

Number Cubes (0–5)

Reteaching Master

Practice Master 16

Enrichment Master 16

For extra practice:
 CD-ROM* Lesson 16

Note: This lesson may take more than one day.

---

① Warm-Up ⏱

Problem of the Day Present the following problem to the class: Advance tickets for a play cost $10.50. At the door the tickets cost $1.50 more. A total of 320 tickets were sold in advance. If all ticket sales totaled $5160, how many tickets were sold at the door? (150)

Problem-Solving Strategies Ask students who have solved the Problem of the Day to share how they solved it and any strategies they used.

MENTAL MATH Ask students to show thumbs up if there is a remainder and thumbs down if there is no remainder for the following problems.

a. 81 ÷ 9 (thumbs down)

b. 5 ÷ 5 (thumbs down)

(continued on page 59)

58 Whole Numbers and Integers

PRACTICE

LESSON 16

Dividing by a Multidigit Divisor

In this lesson you'll review a method for dividing by a multidigit divisor in which you first make an **approximation** of the answer.

139,196 ÷ 73 = ?

73)139,196	It is sensible to first approximate an answer.
70)139,196	Round 73 to 70.
7)13,919.6	139,196 divided by 70 is the same as 13,919.6 divided by 7.
$\dfrac{1\,9}{7)13,919.6}$	The approximate answer is *about 1900.*

Now do the division.

73)139,196	Since 73 × 1 is greater than 13, a 0 could be written above 3, but this isn't necessary. Use 139 as the partial dividend.
$\begin{array}{r} 1 \\ 73)\overline{139,196} \end{array}$	Estimate the quotient by mentally dropping the last digit of both divisor and partial dividend. Since 7 × 1 = 7 and 7 × 2 = 14, use 1 as your *trial quotient.*
$\begin{array}{r} 1 \\ 73)\overline{139,196} \\ \underline{73} \\ 66 \end{array}$	1 × 73 = 73 139 − 73 = 66
$\begin{array}{r} 1 \\ 73)\overline{139,196} \\ \underline{73} \\ 661 \end{array}$	Bring down the 1 and use 661 as the new partial dividend.

58 • Whole Numbers and Integers

Why teach it this way?

It is often useful in everyday life to perform mental calculations. Learning time-saving mental math strategies for multiplication or division is beneficial because it empowers students to apply their math skills and number sense outside of the classroom.

58 Whole Numbers and Integers

```
        1 9
73)139,196
       73
       66 1
       65 7
          4
```

Since 7 × 9 = 63, try 9 as the next trial quotient.
9 × 73 = 657
If 657 were greater than 661, you'd cross out 9
and try 8.
661 − 657 = 4

```
      1 90
73)139,196
      73
      66 1
      65 7
         49
```

Bring down the 9. Since 73 is greater than 49,
the next digit of the quotient is 0.
(It is essential to write this 0 to show that
there are no tens in the quotient. If you
omit the 0, the 9 in the hundreds place
might seem to be in the tens place.)

```
               6
      1 907
73)139,196
      73
      66 1
      65 7
         496
         511
         438
          58
```

Bring down the 6.
Because 7 × 7 = 49, try 7 as the trial quotient.
Since 511 is greater than 496, 7 is too large.
Try 6.

Depending on the situation, 1907 or 1906 may be the best answer
to this problem. Clearly, 1907 is closer, because the remainder, 58,
is more than half of the divisor.

Check: Is 1907 close to 1900, the approximation we made first?
Yes, so the answer makes sense.

**The following problems have no remainders. Find the quotient in
each problem.**

❶ 2924 ÷ 86 **34**   ❷ 33,696 ÷ 432 **78**   ❸ 15,964 ÷ 52 **307**

❹ 28,569 ÷ 321 **89**   ❺ 60,207 ÷ 61 **987**   ❻ 29,240 ÷ 860 **34**

◆ Look around. Is there an easy way to do problem 6?

Unit 1   Lesson 16 • **59**

Mental Math (continued)

c. 492 ÷ 7 (thumbs up)

d. 560 ÷ 8 (thumbs down)

e. 1400 ÷ 2 (thumbs down)

f. 333 ÷ 9 (thumbs down)

g. 2500 ÷ 5 (thumbs down)

h. 2000 ÷ 4 (thumbs down)

i. 17 ÷ 7 (thumbs up)

j. 236 ÷ 3 (thumbs up)

❷ Teach

Using the Student Pages Do pages 58
and 59 with the class, discussing each step.
Emphasize that sometimes the trial quotient is
not the correct one, as is the case in the sixth step. Explain
that because crossing off or erasing digits may make an
answer harder to read, final quotients can be rewritten
above the work and circled. After discussing the check step,
explain that the division can be carried on. Write a decimal
point after the 6 in the dividend and after the 6 in the
quotient and continue. Do this step on the chalkboard,
explaining to students that the division process stays the
same, regardless of on which side of the decimal point it
takes place. However, emphasize the importance of putting
in the decimal points to identify place value.

◆ LESSON 16   Dividing by a Multidigit Divisor

Teach

Using the Student Pages To provide practice with division, demonstrate the "Roll a Problem" game first, so that students may begin playing when they finish their work on pages 60–62. Play several rounds with the class.

Point out to students that they can solve many of the problems on page 60 using mental math. Some of these problems may not appear to be solvable without pencil and paper. Discuss the examples that show how to easily multiply by a power of 10, or by 25, 50, 75, or other numbers that are factors of 100 or 1000. Provide additional examples as needed. You may wish to ask students to explain how they would use mental math to divide by 250, 500, and 750.

◆ LESSON 16   Dividing by a Multidigit Divisor

You know you can multiply by 10 easily. Multiplying by 100, 1000, and so on is equally easy ($7 \times 100 = 700$, $7 \times 1000 = 7000$, and so on).

You can also multiply by numbers like 25 easily. Think of 25 as $\frac{100}{4}$. Then, $25 \times 36 = \frac{100}{4} \times 36 = 100 \times \frac{1}{4} \times 36 = 100 \times 9 = 900$. So, to multiply 36 by 25, take $\frac{1}{4}$ of 36 (9) and write two 0s after it: 900.

Multiply 25×36 the usual way.

◆   Is the answer 900?

To multiply 50×36, you can use the fact that 50 is $\frac{100}{2}$.

◆   Try doing that multiplication the short way. What is your answer?

To multiply 75×36, remember that $75 = \frac{3}{4}$ of 100. Since $\frac{1}{4}$ of 36 is 9, $\frac{3}{4}$ of 36 is $3 \times 9 = 27$. Finally, $27 \times 100 = 2700$.

In a similar way you can see that $36 \times 5 = 36 \times \frac{1}{2} \times 10 = 18 \times 10 = 180$. Or, $36 \times 250 = 36 \times \frac{1}{4} \times 1000 = 9 \times 1000 = 9000$.

Similar procedures can be used to divide easily. For example, what is $700 \div 25$? Since $25 = \frac{100}{4}$, $700 \div 25 = 700 \div 100 \times 4 = 7 \times 4 = 28$.

Do the following multiplication and division problems, using shortcuts whenever possible.

7 $18 \div 2$ **9**	**8** 18×5 **90**	**9** $38 \div 2$ **19**	**10** 38×5 **190**
11 $17 \div 2$ **8.5**	**12** 17×5 **85**	**13** 335×2 **670**	**14** $335 \div 5$ **67**
15 $24 \div 4$ **6**	**16** 24×25 **600**	**17** 24×50 **1200**	**18** 24×75 **1800**
19 $92 \div 4$ **23**	**20** 92×25 **2300**	**21** 92×50 **4600**	**22** 92×75 **6900**
23 $96 \div 4$ **24**	**24** 96×25 **2400**	**25** 96×50 **4800**	**26** 96×75 **7200**
27 96×250 **24,000**	**28** 96×750 **72,000**	**29** 92×250 **23,000**	**30** 6×4 **24**
31 $600 \div 25$ **24**	**32** 9×4 **36**	**33** $900 \div 25$ **36**	**34** 11×4 **44**
35 $1100 \div 25$ **44**	**36** 64×25 **1600**	**37** 64×75 **4800**	**38** 65×25 **1625**

Literature Connection Have students read *What Do You Mean by Average?* by Elizabeth James. They can use this story as a guide for determining averages for different attributes of students in the class, such as average amount of pocket change or average amount of time spent doodling during a school day.

Solve the following multiplication and division problems, using shortcuts whenever possible. Find the value of *n* in each case.

㊴ $10 \times 76 = n$ **760**
㊵ $100 \times 76 = n$ **7600**
㊶ $25 \times 76 = n$ **1900**
㊷ $50 \times 76 = n$ **3800**
㊸ $75 \times 76 = n$ **5700**
㊹ $1000 \times 428 = n$ **428,000**
㊺ $250 \times 428 = n$ **107,000**
㊻ $750 \times 428 = n$ **321,000**
㊼ $500 \times 428 = n$ **214,000**
㊽ $107{,}000 \div 250 = n$ **428**
㊾ $321{,}000 \div 428 = n$ **750**
㊿ $214{,}000 \div 500 = n$ **428**
(51) $32{,}528 \div 19 = n$ **1712**
(52) $20{,}093 \div 71 = n$ **283**
(53) $167{,}162 \div 83 = n$ **2014**
(54) $44 \times 25 = n$ **1100**
(55) $44 \times 50 = n$ **2200**
(56) $44 \times 75 = n$ **3300**
(57) $196 \div 4 = n$ **49**
(58) $196 \times 25 = n$ **4900**
(59) $196 \times 50 = n$ **9800**
(60) $196 \times 75 = n$ **14,700**
(61) $14 \div 4 = n$ **3.5**
(62) $14 \times 25 = n$ **350**
(63) $14 \times 50 = n$ **700**
(64) $14 \times 75 = n$ **1050**
(65) $18 \div 4 = n$ **4.5**
(66) $18 \times 25 = n$ **450**
(67) $50 \times 18 = n$ **900**
(68) $75 \times 18 = n$ **1350**

Solve these problems.

SOCIAL STUDIES CONNECTION

(69) Douglas has been saving all of the quarters he has received in change for the past several months. He has 38 quarters.
a. How many cents worth of quarters does he have? **950¢**
b. What are his quarters worth in dollars and cents? **$9.50**

(70) The 76 sixth graders at William McKinley School are raising money for a computer. If each student raises $50, how much money will they raise? **$3800**

(71) The Census Bureau projects that by 2050, the United States population will be 394,000,000.
a. If that population were distributed evenly among the states, how many people would live in each state? **7,880,000**
b. Do you think the population will be distributed evenly among all the states? Why or why not? **no; Answers will vary but may mention that the population is distributed unevenly at present and that this trend will probably continue.**

Assign the problems on page 61 for independent work, directing students to use mental math whenever it makes sense. Invite students to use **calculators*** to check their answers.

For problem 71, students may also mention the different sizes of various states to explain why the population might not be evenly distributed.

Technology Connection Refer students to the video *Math Mystery Theatre, Mission Division: World's Secret Formula* from EdCon/Imperial International (VHS for grades 2–8) for further practice with division word problems.

*available separately

◆ **LESSON 16 Dividing by a Multidigit Divisor**

Teach

Using the Student Pages Assign the word problems on page 62 for independent work. Before beginning, you may find it useful to discuss what an odometer is and to go over the relationship between mileage driven, gallons of gas used, and average miles per gallon. Invite knowledgeable students to share what they know about the gas mileage that cars typically get.

Have students play the "Roll a Problem (Division)" game on page 63 in pairs, in small groups, or with the class. This game provides practice in multidigit division and mathematical reasoning as students choose where to place each digit. A copy of this game can also be found on page 12 of the Home Connections Blackline Masters.

◆ **LESSON 16 Dividing by a Multidigit Divisor**

Solve these problems.

72 Ms. Lopez drives to work each day, about 250 days a year. The round trip is 36 miles. About how many miles does she drive to and from work in a year? **9000**

73 Ms. Lopez records the reading on her odometer at the beginning of each year. Last year on January 1 the odometer read 43,298. This year on January 1 the odometer read 56,037. How many miles did she drive all together last year? About how much of that was for something other than going to and from work? **12,739; 3739 mi**

74 Ms. Lopez believes her car gets an average of about 25 miles per gallon. Approximately how many gallons of gas did she use last year? **about 510**

75 The last four times Ms. Lopez bought gas, she recorded the mileage shown on her odometer and also how much gas she bought. Here is her record. Use it to calculate her average mileage on a gallon of gas for as many of the times as is possible. Why can you not find the average for the first time she bought gas? Do you need the number of gallons she put in the car for the first time? Explain. **You cannot find the average for the first time she bought gas since you do not know how many miles she drove while using the 11 gallons of gas. You need to know the odometer reading from the last time she bought gas.**

Odometer reading:	62,573	62,873	63,113	63,437
Gallons gas bought:	11	12	10	12
Average mpg		**25**	**24**	**27**

76 Ms. Okamoto is about to make a 450-mile trip. She filled her 16 gallon gas tank, and she wants to refill it when it is half full.

a. Assuming her car continues to get about 25 miles per gallon, after how many miles should she plan on stopping for gas? **200**

b. About how many times will she need to stop for gas on her trip? **2**

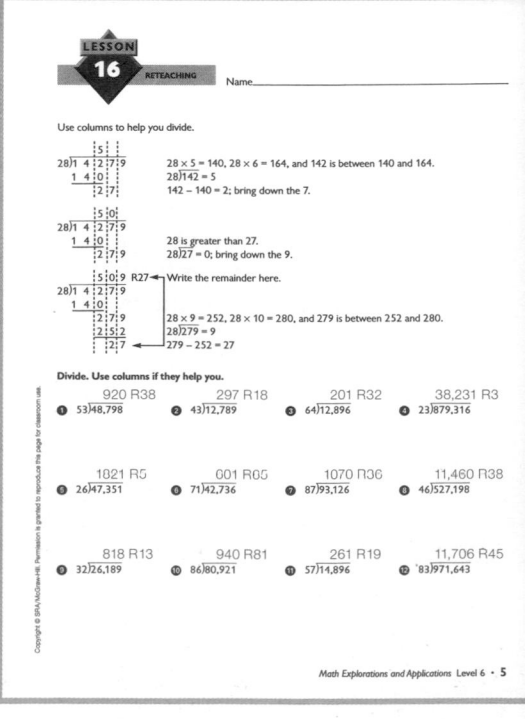

LESSON 16 RETEACHING   Name_____

Use columns to help you divide.

28)142,79   28 × 5 = 140, 28 × 6 = 164, and 142 is between 140 and 164.
             28)142 = 5
             142 − 140 = 2; bring down the 7.

28)142,79   28 is greater than 27.
             28)27 = 0; bring down the 9.

28)142,79 R27 ← Write the remainder here.
             28 × 9 = 252, 28 × 10 = 280, and 279 is between 252 and 280.
             28)279 = 9
             279 − 252 = 27

Divide. Use columns if they help you.

1. 53)48,798 **920 R38**
2. 43)12,789 **297 R18**
3. 64)12,896 **201 R32**
4. 23)879,316 **38,231 R3**
5. 26)47,351 **1821 R5**
6. 71)42,736 **001 R05**
7. 87)93,126 **1070 R36**
8. 46)527,198 **11,460 R38**
9. 32)26,189 **818 R13**
10. 86)80,921 **940 R81**
11. 57)14,896 **261 R19**
12. 83)971,643 **11,706 R45**

Math Explorations and Applications Level 6 • 5

Roll a Problem Game (Division)

COOPERATIVE LEARNING

GAME

Players:	Two or more
Materials:	One 0–5 cube
Object:	To get the greatest quotient
Math Focus:	Multidigit division, place value, and mathematical reasoning

RULES

1. Outline a division problem on your paper, like this:

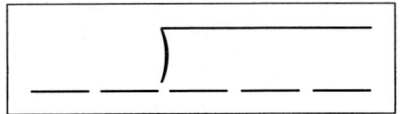

2. The lead player rolls the cube. Write the number in any of the five blanks.

3. The lead player rolls the cube again. Write the number in any of the remaining blanks. Zero may not be written in the first blank, except when it comes on the last roll.

4. Repeat step 3 until all the blanks are filled.

5. Divide the three-digit number by the two-digit number. Carry out the division as far as necessary to see who has the greatest quotient.

6. The player with the greatest quotient wins.

OTHER WAYS TO PLAY THIS GAME

1. The least quotient wins. Zero may not be written in the first blank under the division sign except when it comes on the last roll.

2. Change the number of digits in the divisor or the dividend.

3. Use a 5–10 cube. If a 10 is rolled, roll that cube again.

4. Instead of a cube, use ten numbered cards or slips of paper.

Unit 1   Lesson 16 • **63**

---

③ Wrap-Up 🕐 5 MINUTES

In Closing To summarize the lesson, ask students to explain how they decide what trial quotients to use in a two-digit divisor problem.

ALTERNATIVE ASSESSMENT

Performance Assessment Ask students to create three division problems with no remainders and to then trade with a classmate and solve each other's problems. Then ask them to explain a way to find the product of 96 × 50 using mental math.

Assessment Criteria

Did the student . . .

✓ demonstrate proficiency in dividing by two-digit divisors?

✓ demonstrate understanding of how to multiply by 25, 50, and 75 using mental math?

✓ understand the rules and objective of the "Roll a Problem (Division)" game?

Homework Ask students to explain to a family member the shortcut for multiplying by 25, 50, and 75 well enough that the family member can apply the technique successfully.

SPECIAL NEEDS • MANIPULATIVES •

Meeting Individual Needs You may wish to use **play money***
to explain the algorithm in the following way:

Suppose 25 people want to divide $8764 equally. Using play money, start with eight $1000 bills, seven $100 bills, six $10 bills, and four $1 bills. Can you give each person a $1000 bill? No. Then change the eight $1000 bills for 80 $100 bills; you now have 87 $100 bills. If you give each person three, you will have 12 $100 bills left over. Change them for 120 $10 bills and distribute the 126 $10 bills, five to each person, which leaves $14 undistributed. Each person gets zero $1 bills.

PRACTICE p. 16

LESSON 16 PRACTICE Name_____

Divide. There will be no remainders. Check your answers to be sure that they make sense.

❶ 53)1855 35	❷ 547)14,769 27	❸ 13)728 56	❹ 198)37,026 187
❺ 51)153 3	❻ 326)95,844 294	❼ 82)1722 21	❽ 97)5335 55
❾ 54)3834 71	❿ 294)7644 26	⓫ 32)1248 39	⓬ 21)2142 102
⓭ 589)34,162 58	⓮ 118)8378 71	⓯ 662)3310 5	⓰ 896)8064 9

16 • *Math Explorations and Applications Level 6*

ENRICHMENT p. 16

LESSON 16 ENRICHMENT Name_____

In the division below, letters are used instead of numbers. Find the numbers for the problem. Each letter stands for a different digit.

```
                1
             R K A M
   QEU)S E R E S N E
        S A U R
        N N M S
        M A R R
        S N U N
        S M A N
            0
          E P E
          Q E U
          K M K
```

Puzzle Hints:

• M is 1 because QEU × 1 = QEU and P is 0 because N − N = 0.

• N − M = 0 because there is no letter beneath them.
  So, A must be greater than N, and 1 was borrowed from N to subtract A from N. If (N − 1) − M = 0 and M = 1, then N = 2.

• P − E = M
  We can't subtract from 0 in a division problem, so we must have borrowed.
  0 − E = 1.
  If E is greater than U, then E = 9.
  If E is less than U, then E = 8.

A = 7	P = 0
E = 9	Q = 5
M = 1	R = 8
K = 3	S = 4
N = 2	U = 6

16 • *Math Explorations and Applications Level 6*

*available separately

Division Applications

LESSON PLANNER

Objectives

▶ to provide practice in mental arithmetic

▶ to provide practice in solving word problems with solutions that mostly involve division

Context of the Lesson This is the 14th of 15 lessons reviewing operations with whole numbers.

 MANIPULATIVES

Program Resources

Number Cubes (0–5 and 5–10)

Practice Master 17

Enrichment Master 17

The Cruncher*: *Recipe Converter*

For extra practice:
CD-ROM* Lesson 17

❶ Warm-Up 🕔 5 MINUTES

 **Problem of the Day** Present the following problem: The sum of three consecutive numbers is 138. What are the numbers? (45, 46, and 47; to find the middle number divide 138 by 3)

Problem-Solving Strategies Ask students who have solved the Problem of the Day to share how they solved it and any strategies they used.

 Introduce a new type of mental math activity in which you ask students if there is enough money to make certain purchases. Ask them to respond thumbs up if there is enough or thumbs down if there is not:

I have $40. Do I have enough to buy . . .

a. a sweater for $29.99 and a cassette for $10.99? (thumbs down)

b. a hat for $17.99 and an apple for $0.85? (thumbs up)

c. a hamster for $5.99 and a hamster cage for $34.99? (thumbs down)

d. five packs of trading cards for $2.95 each and an album for $19.95? (thumbs up)

e. six movie tickets for $5.75 each? (thumbs up)

Division Applications

In this lesson you'll use what you know about arithmetic to solve problems mentally.

Solve these problems in your head. Then write the answers.

❶ 30 × 3 **90** ❷ 60 × 3 **180** ❸ 600 × 3 **1800**

❹ 1800 ÷ 3 **600** ❺ 1800 ÷ 30 **60** ❻ 1800 ÷ 300 **6**

❼ 16 + 10 **26** ❽ 160 + 5 **165** ❾ 160 + 15 **175**

❿ 175 − 15 **160** ⓫ 12 ÷ 12 **1** ⓬ 24 ÷ 12 **2**

⓭ 48 ÷ 12 **4** ⓮ 4 × 12 **48** ⓯ 5 × 12 **60**

⓰ 50 × 12 **600** ⓱ 600 ÷ 12 **50** ⓲ 60 ÷ 12 **5**

⓳ 60 ÷ 6 **10** ⓴ 60 ÷ 3 **20** ㉑ 2 × 75 **150**

㉒ 150 ÷ 75 **2** ㉓ 150 ÷ 50 **3** ㉔ 150 ÷ 25 **6**

㉕ 300 ÷ 25 **12** ㉖ 3000 ÷ 25 **120** ㉗ 3025 ÷ 25 **121**

㉘ 4 × 25 **100** ㉙ 4 × 250 **1000** ㉚ 1000 ÷ 4 **250**

For each problem several answers are given, but only one is correct. Choose the correct answer.

㉛ How many minutes are there in one week?

   a. 1,000,000
   b. 39,475
   c. 10,080 ✓
   d. 100,800

㉜ Ms. Abdul's salary is $27,120 per year. How much does she earn each month?

   a. $22,600
   b. $2260 ✓
   c. $312
   d. $3120

⬛ Why teach it this way?

Some of the problems on pages 65 and 66 require students to make approximations. Many students are uncomfortable with estimates and would prefer problems that have exact answers. Emphasize that in everyday life, many of the math problems we need to solve involve making estimates and that for many problem situations we face, estimates make much more sense than exact answers. You may wish to brainstorm with students a list of questions for which estimates make the best answers.

Solve these problems.

33 Mr. DeAngelo sold 1012 pairs of shoes in the 22 days he worked last month. About how many pairs of shoes did he sell each day?
about 46

34 Mr. Peterson found an old recipe for 24 loaves of bread. He wants to use the recipe to make two loaves of bread. The original recipe calls for 36 kilograms of flour and 156 grams of salt.

a. How much flour should he use? **3 kg**

b. How much salt should he use? **13 g**

35 Eva has 320 pictures that she took during the summer. She puts her pictures in an album, 12 on a page. How many pages will she need for these pictures? **27**

36 Sara is planning a backpacking trip. The trip is for six days, and she can hike about 15 kilometers a day. About how many kilometers can she cover during the entire trip? **about 90**

37 Francesca's scout troop is chartering a bus to go to summer camp. The cost of the bus is $196. There are 35 scouts going to camp. How much will each scout pay for her trip? **$5.60**

38 For a cookout at camp, Francesca's troop plans on having two hot dogs and two hot dog buns for each of the 35 scouts. Hot dogs come in packages of ten, and hot dog buns come in packages of eight. How many packages of hot dogs and hot dog buns does the troop need?
7 packages of hot dogs, 9 packages of hot dog buns

39 Mr. Kim earns $12 an hour. He just received a paycheck for $936. How many hours did he work during that pay period? **78**

Unit 1   Lesson 17   •   **65**

❷ Teach

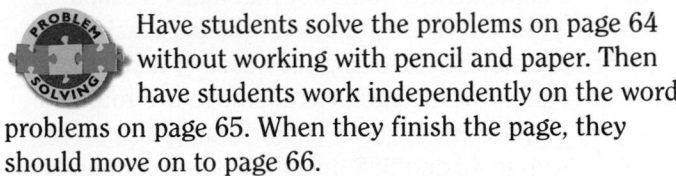

Using the Student Pages To provide practice with division, demonstrate the "Roll and Divide" game on page 67 first, so that students may begin playing as they finish their work on pages 64–66.

Have students solve the problems on page 64 without working with pencil and paper. Then have students work independently on the word problems on page 65. When they finish the page, they should move on to page 66.

Students can use **The Cruncher*:** *Recipe Converter* spreadsheet to help them create and solve problems similar to problem 34 on page 65.

Technology Connection You may wish to refer students to the video *Math Mystery Theatre: Mathman and Chickadee vs. The Questioner* from EdCon/Imperial International (VHS, for grades 2–8) for further practice with division word problems.

◆ LESSON 17 Division Applications

Teach

Using the Student Pages Have students do the estimation problems on page 66 independently. Point out that many reasonable answers are possible. When going over the page, ask students to explain the reasoning they used to make their estimates. You may wish to guide students to use rounded numbers to do problems 40 and 41. For example, in problem 40, round 37 up to 40 and 888 down to 880, a multiple of 40. Another sensible pair of numbers to use is 30 and 900. Ask students what additional information they would need to answer all the questions for problem 41. Encourage students to draw a picture if they are having difficulty visualizing the property in question 45.

As students finish the problems, they should play the "Roll and Divide" game on page 67 in pairs or in small groups. This game provides practice with division facts and mathematical reasoning as students decide what problems to create. You may wish to demonstrate the game by playing three or four rounds with two students as the rest of the class watches. Try to be sure that everyone understands that the answer to the problem that is made must be a whole number, that the score is 0 if this is not possible, and that the winner of one round starts the next. A copy of this game can also be found on page 13 of the Home Connections Blackline Masters.

Students can use a blank **Cruncher*** spreadsheet to help them keep score.

◆ LESSON 17 Division Applications

Solve these problems.

40 Matt read an 888-page book in 37 hours last month. About how many pages per hour is that? **about 24**

41 Matt counted the number of words on three different pages of the book that looked typical to him. There were 483 words on one of the pages, 503 words on a second page, and 511 words on the third page.

  a. About how many words do you think there are in the entire book? **about 444,000**

  b. About how many words per hour did Matt read? **about 12,000**

  c. About how many words per minute is that? **about 200**

42 Ms. Whitman has a large rectangular lawn that is 374 feet long and 285 feet wide. She wants to put fertilizer on the lawn. Each bag of fertilizer is supposed to cover 5000 square feet. How many bags of fertilizer should she buy? If each bag of fertilizer costs $5, how much will she spend on fertilizer? **22; $110**

43 An airplane flew 2425 miles in five hours. What was its average speed in miles per hour? **485 mph**

44 Don and Juwan can plant an average of 80 seedling trees in an hour. They intend to plant 400 trees on each acre of their property.

  a. How long will they need to complete one acre? **5 hours**

  b. How many hours will they need to plant trees on all 160 acres of their property? **800**

  c. How many trees will they plant on the 160 acres? **64,000**

  d. If they plant trees for 12 hours each day, how many days will they need to complete the job? **67**

45 Don and Juwan's property is in the shape of a rectangle composed of squares 1 acre in area. The property is 16 squares long and 10 squares wide. On each acre they are planting 400 trees in the shape of a square, with 20 trees on each side. Viewed from above, the trees will be in the shape of a rectangle. How many rows of trees will there be, and how many trees will be in each row? **200 rows of 320 trees each, or 320 rows of 200 trees each**

66 • Whole Numbers and Integers

Literature Connection Have students read *All the Money in the World* by Bill Brittain. Ask them to explain how Jason should divide and manage his money.

RETEACHING

You may wish to pair students with different reading levels to work on word problems in this lesson. Students with weaker reading skills or ESL students can be paired with stronger readers, with whom they can discuss the meanings of the problems. You may wish to pair game-playing partners as well.

*available separately

GAME

Roll and Divide Game

COOPERATIVE LEARNING

Players:	Two or more
Materials:	Two 0–5 cubes, two 5–10 cubes
Object:	To create a division problem without a remainder but with the greatest divisor
Math Focus:	Mental arithmetic (multiplication and division)

RULES

1. The first player rolls all four cubes and uses one or two of the numbers rolled as the digits of the dividend. (Neither the divisor nor the dividend can be 0, although each may contain a 0.) Another number rolled is used as the divisor. The answer cannot have a decimal or fractional part. There cannot be a remainder. A player's score is 0 if he or she cannot follow this rule to make a problem.

2. The other players follow the same procedure.

3. In each round the player with the greatest divisor wins and starts the next round. If two players have the same divisor, the player with the greater quotient wins.

SAMPLE GAME

Round 1:

Miguel rolled: `0` `4` `7` `9` He made: $49 \div 7 = 7$. His divisor was 7.

Judith rolled: `5` `6` `0` `6` She made $60 \div 6 = 10$. Her divisor was 6.

So Miguel won this round.

Round 2:

Miguel rolled: `4` `4` `8` `8` He made: $48 \div 8 = 6$. His divisor was 8.

Judith rolled: `10` `10` `5` `0` She made: $510 \div 10 = 51$. Her divisor was 10.

Judith won this round.
(She could also have used $100 \div 10 = 10$ or $10 \div 10 = 1$.)

Unit 1 Lesson 17 • **67**

③ Wrap-Up ⏱ 5 MINUTES

In Closing To summarize the lesson, ask students to describe the strategy they used in the game.

Portfolio Assessment Have students write in their Math Journals a word problem involving whole-number computation for which an estimate makes better sense than an exact answer.

Assessment Criteria

Did the student . . .

✓ correctly answer at least 90% of the mental arithmetic problems on page 64?

✓ make reasonable estimates when appropriate or obtain the correct answers for at least nine of the 13 word problems on pages 65–66?

✓ develop a successful strategy for playing the game?

Homework Ask students to formulate two problems similar to problems 31 and 32 on page 64 for classmates to solve in class the next day. Challenge them to be sure that each of the distracting answers is a result of a common error.

PRACTICE p. 17

LESSON **17** PRACTICE Name_____

Solve these problems.

❶ Craig and Charlotte are covering a wall with paper so that the class can make a mural about holidays. The wall is 16 meters long and 3 meters high. The paper is 1 meter wide and comes in rolls that are 10 meters long.
a. What is the total amount of paper they need? — 48 m²
b. How many rolls of paper should they get from the storeroom? — 5 rolls

❷ Nilo is planning to bicycle from Madison to Springfield, a distance of 550 miles. If he can ride about 50 miles a day, about how many days will it take him to make the trip? — about 11 days

❸ Mr. Mehta has a recipe for beef stew, but the recipe is for 60 people. He wants to make it for 15 people. The recipe calls for 20 pounds of beef, 24 pounds of potatoes, 40 large onions, and 15 bunches of carrots.
a. How much beef should he use? — 5 lb
b. How many pounds of potatoes should he use? — 6 lb
c. How large large onions should he use? — 10 onions
d. About how many bunches of carrots should he use? — about 4 bunches

❹ The Nature Club in Northfield is planning a trip to the state park in Southville, 125 kilometers away. The cost to charter a bus is $216.00. Each bus can carry 40 passengers. Everyone going on the trip will share equally in the cost of transportation. How much will it cost each person if
a. 36 people go on the trip? — $6.00
b. 40 people go on the trip? — $5.40
c. 66 people go on the trip? (Be careful!) — $6.55
d. 80 people go on the trip? — $5.40

❺ Marta delivers newspapers six days a week. She has 120 people on her route. How many papers does she deliver in a week? — 720 papers

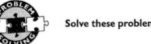

Math Explorations and Applications Level 6 • **17**

ENRICHMENT p. 17

LESSON **17** ENRICHMENT Name_____

Your grandfather tells you that he will take you to the zoo a million seconds from now. How long will you have to wait to go to the zoo?

Without looking any further, guess how long that will be.

You can use your calculator to find how many days are in a million seconds.

1,000,000 sec ÷ 60 sec/min = 16,666.666667 ÷ 60 min/hr = 277.777778
277.777778 ÷ 24 hr/day = 11.574074 days

Your grandfather will take you to the zoo in about $11\frac{1}{2}$ days.

How long do you think each of the following would take? Give your answer in one of the following units: minutes, days, months, years, decades (ten years), or centuries (100 years). Make a guess, and then find the exact answer by using a calculator.

❶ You won a million dollars. You are going to spend $1000 a day. How long will it take to spend all of the money? — 2.7 years

❷ You won a billion dollars. You are going to spend $2000 a day. How long will it take to spend all of the money? — 13.7 centuries

❸ NASA has just created a walkway to the sun. You walk at a rate of 3 miles per hour. It is 93 million miles to the sun. How long will it take to walk to the sun and back? — 70.8 centuries

❹ Take your pulse. How long will it take for your heart to beat one million times? — Answers will vary, but should be between 5 and 12 days.

❺ Pat ran for president of the United States. He said he shook hands with three million people. It took ten seconds for each handshake. How long would it take for three million handshakes? — 347 days

Math Explorations and Applications Level 6 • **17**

Student Edition pages 68–71

LESSON 18 Arithmetic Applications

Arithmetic Applications

LESSON PLANNER

Objectives

✓ to evaluate students' ability to decide which operation, if any, is appropriate to solve a given word problem

▶ to provide practice in whole-number arithmetic with the four basic operations

▶ to help students develop the broad ability to use mathematical common sense

Context of the Lesson This lesson, the last of 15 lessons reviewing operations with whole numbers, provides a Mastery Checkpoint for assessing students' ability to choose the correct operation for solving a word problem. This lesson also contains the third part of "Mr. Muddle's Extra-Large Problems," a four-part Thinking Story.

MANIPULATIVES none

Program Resources

Practice Master 18

Enrichment Master 18

Assessment Masters

The Cruncher*

For career connections:
  Careers and Math*

For extra practice:
  CD-ROM* Lesson 18

① Warm-Up

5 MINUTES

Problem of the Day It is 10:30 A.M. What time will it be 2400 hours from now? What time will it be 2401 hours from now? (10:30 A.M.; 11:30 A.M.)

Problem-Solving Strategies Ask students who have solved the Problem of the Day to share how they solved it and any strategies they used.

MENTAL MATH Ask the class if $200 is enough money to purchase the following items. Students should indicate "yes" with thumbs up and "no" with thumbs down.

a. two plane tickets at $99.90 each (thumbs up)

b. a dress for $69.50 plus a coat for $130.00 (thumbs up)

(continued on page 69)

In this lesson you'll use what you know about addition, subtraction, multiplication, and division to solve these problems.

Solve these problems.

1 Juanita earns $2.50 per hour mowing lawns. How much will she earn for eight hours of work? **$20.00**

2 For most people adult height is about double the height at the age of two. Philip was 87 centimeters tall when he was two years old. About how tall would you expect him to be when he is 21? **about 174 cm**

3 Mr. Redhawk earns $33,600 a year but is paid once a month. How much does he earn each month? **$2800**

4 Mr. Goldstein earns $2541.67 each month. Before he is paid, deductions are made for taxes ($612), insurance ($228), and savings ($42.75). What is his take-home pay each month? **$1658.92**

5 At $30,500 per year, how much does Mr. Goldstein earn in a week? **about $586.54**

6 Which job has a higher annual salary, one that pays $21,000 per year or one that pays $425 each week? **one that pays $425 each week**

7 Which job has a higher annual salary, one that pays $1100 every two weeks or one that pays $2300 each month? **one that pays $1100 every two weeks**

8 Mr. Ramirez earns $31,200 per year. Mrs. Ramirez earns $2600 each month. What is the total of their annual salaries? **$62,400**

Why teach it this way?

The Thinking Story activity and the word problems provide an opportunity for students to appreciate that many real-life situations involve whole-number operations and call for critical thinking and the application of problem-solving skills.

Technology Connection Refer students to the software *Mastering Math* by Queue (Mac, IBM, for grades 5–12) for further practice with identifying which operation to apply to an equation, using survival math (paying bills, measuring for recipes, etc.), solving word problems, rounding, estimating, and much more.

9 Mrs. Kelly has $1678.56 in her checking account. She has the following bills: electricity, $31.74; gas, $43.82; telephone, $26.59; grocery store, $207.57; service station, $57; doctor, $235; rent, $600; and insurance, $145. Does she have enough money in her checking account to pay her bills? **yes**

10 If Mrs. Kelly's checking-account balance is $1678.56 and she writes checks for a total of $1346.72, how much money will she have left in her checking account? **$331.84**

11 Arturo's class is going to the state capital. The cost to charter a bus is $116.64. If the 18 students share the cost equally, how much will each student pay? **$6.48**

12 Sofi had 750 stamps in her collection. She traded 25 stamps with Jerome, swapping one for one. How many stamps does she have now? **750**

13 Sofi has her stamps in an album with 50 pages. If the same number of stamps were on each page, how many would be on a page? **15**

14 Deanna saved in her bank account exactly half of the money she received for her birthday. She deposited $37.50 in her savings account. How much money did she receive? **$75.00**

15 Deanna wants to use the other half of her birthday money to buy a book for $5.95, a CD for $14.97, and a necklace for $18.50. Can she afford all three purchases? **no**

Unit 1 Lesson 18 • **69**

Mental Math (continued)

c. three puppies at $80.00 each (thumbs down)

d. ice skates for $125.00 plus a costume for $55.00 (thumbs up)

② Teach

Using the Student Pages Have students solve these problems on their own. When discussing students' answers, point out that for problem 9 it is not necessary to add the actual amounts of all the bills, because an approximation will suffice. Explain that rounding each amount up to the nearest $10, or even the nearest $50, when estimating the sum will indicate that the amount in the account is more than enough to pay all the bills.

Students can use blank **Cruncher*** spreadsheets to create and solve wage problems similar to those on page 68.

Literature Connection For further practice with whole-number operations, have students do some of the puzzles and games in *Math Fun with Money Puzzlers* by Rose Wyler.

*available separately

◆ **LESSON 18 Arithmetic Applications**

Teach

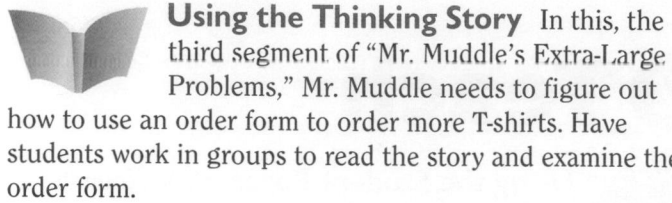

Using the Thinking Story In this, the third segment of "Mr. Muddle's Extra-Large Problems," Mr. Muddle needs to figure out how to use an order form to order more T-shirts. Have students work in groups to read the story and examine the order form.

Answers to Thinking Story Questions:

1. He would get 72 T-shirts of each size, which would be enough of each size to last him for a week, but he would keep on accumulating too many small shirts. Both boxes would contain mixed sizes, so he would have to pay the extra $30 for each box.

2. He should get four boxes, each containing one size: an equal number of each size packed in the most economical way.

3. Her idea is good in that ordering one size per box saves money and means not ordering more of the small T-shirts, which Mr. Muddle does not need. On the other hand, it will probably result in a shortage of medium shirts because Mr. Muddle has only 26 and can expect to sell 30 in a week. The savings of $30, however, may offset the risk of having disappointed customers.

4. Plans should be discussed in terms of cost and maintaining the needed number of each size. One economical plan is: first week—order one box of extra-large and one mixed box containing 132 large and 12 medium; second week—one box of large and one box of medium; third week—one box of extra-large; fourth week—no need to order because there will be enough of each size left over. Good plans should: take account of the shirts Mr. Muddle has already (enough smalls so that he need not order any for the next four weeks); work in units of 12 because the shirts are in bags of 12; and order boxes containing a single size.

5. If four or more boxes are ordered, it would be possible to change the order to include at least one box containing a single size.

Ask students to consider and list in their Math Journals the different mathematical skills they have used to answer the questions about Mr. Muddle's orders and inventory. Then have them write about other aspects of running a small business that might require these skills.

◆ **LESSON 18 Arithmetic Applications**

THINKING STORY

Mr. Muddle's Extra-Large Problems

Part 3

You may want to refer to earlier parts of this Thinking Story on pages 22–23 and 38–39 to refresh your memory.

Mr. Muddle counted the T-shirts in his store. He found that he had 26 medium, 87 small, and none at all of the large and extra-large sizes.

"I'd better order some more T-shirts right away," he said. He took an order form out of his desk.

"How many shirts of each size did you say I need each week?" Mr. Muddle asked.

"You need 60 extra large, 60 large, 30 medium, and 15 small," Marcus answered.

"How can I get that number?" Mr. Muddle muttered. "This order form is so confusing. I used to just write a "1" in the bottom box. Then everything was taken care of for me. I know! I'll write a "2" in the box instead. Then I'll be sure to get enough of every size."

"I have a better idea," said Manolita. "Just order one box of large T-shirts and one box of the extra-large size. That way you'll save money."

"I think you need a long-term plan," said Marcus.

. . . to be continued

RETEACHING

Help students who fall short of mastery by giving them problems similar to those in this lesson but with lesser numbers. Ask these students to talk through their approach to each problem—what information is given, what they need to find out, and what they will do to solve the problem.

PRACTICE p. 18

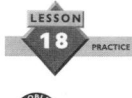

LESSON 18 PRACTICE   Name_____

Solve these problems.

❶ Jonah's class is going to the science museum for a field trip. There are 24 students and two teachers who will go on the trip. Tickets to the museum are $1.75. The bus will cost $78.00. The group plans to stop on the way back at a smorgasbord restaurant, where each meal will cost $3.50.
   a. How much will all the museum tickets cost? — **$45.50**
   b. How much will all the meals cost? — **$91.00**
   c. What will the total cost for the trip be? — **$214.50**
   d. Everyone going is sharing equally in the cost. How much will each person pay? — **$8.25**

❷ Mrs. Renoir's salary is $18,600 a year. She is paid twice a month. From each paycheck, deductions are made for taxes ($99), the credit union ($25), and an investment plan ($18).
   a. What is the amount that she earns on each paycheck (before deductions)? — **$775.00**
   b. What is the amount of Mrs. Renoir's take-home pay each pay period? — **$633.00**

❸ Mr. Bennett wants to fertilize his garden. The garden is 50 meters long and 40 meters wide. The store sells a bag of fertilizer that covers 1000 square meters. The bag costs $5.50.
   a. How many bags would he need? — **2 bags**
   b. How much would the fertilizer cost? — **$11.00**

❹ Barney bought five tickets to a concert. Each ticket cost $8.50. He gave $50 to the ticket seller, who said that $2.50 more was needed. Barney said there was a mistake. The ticket seller thought for a moment and then agreed.
   a. Who made the mistake? — **the ticket seller**
   b. When the mistake was corrected, what amount of money went to whom? — **$7.50 in change went to Barney.**

18 • *Math Explorations and Applications Level 6*

Quality T-Shirts Order Form

Orders are accepted for boxes only. Each box contains 12 bags of 12 T-shirts. Show number of bags of each size per box, or save money by ordering only one size per box.

Single Sizes

Size	Number of Boxes
Small	_____
Medium	_____
Large	_____
X-Large	_____

Total Price	$_____
(see current price list)	

Mixed Sizes

Number of Bags
(Each column must add up to 12.)

	First Box	Second Box	Third Box
Small			
Medium			
Large			
X-Large			

Number of boxes	

Price	$_____

(include extra charge for mixed boxes)

Easy Ordering Method:

Enter the total number of boxes you want. Don't bother to fill out the rest of the form. We will ship equal numbers of each size, packed to save you the most money.

Number of boxes	

Work in groups. Discuss your answers and how you figured them out. Compare your answers with others.

Answers are in margin.

❶ What will happen if Mr. Muddle writes a "2" in the bottom box? What do you think of that way of ordering?

❷ What would happen if Mr. Muddle wrote a "4" in the bottom box?

❸ What is good and what is bad about Manolita's idea?

❹ Work out an ordering plan for Mr. Muddle that will cover the next four weeks. Mr. Muddle can't afford to order more than two boxes at a time. Save him as much money as you can. Be sure that he always has enough T-shirts of every size.

❺ A **super challenge** question: Why doesn't the order form have room for more than three boxes of mixed sizes?

Unit 1   Lesson 18   •   **71**

---

❸ Wrap-Up

In Closing Ask students to explain why it is important to have a plan for a business.

Mastery Checkpoint 8

By this time most students should be able to choose the correct operation to use to solve a word problem or to decide that no calculations are needed. Students can demonstrate this ability by using the appropriate operation in at least 80% of the word problems on pages 68–69 or on Assessment Blackline Masters pages 12–13. Results may be recorded on the Mastery Checkpoint Chart.

Assessment Criteria

Did the student . . .

✓ use the appropriate operation in at least 12 of the word problems on pages 68-69?

✓ correctly answer at least 11 of the problems?

✓ participate in the Thinking Story discussion?

Homework Provide catalog order forms or have students find one at home. Ask them to fill out a mock order for an assortment of items of their choice, to arrive at a total within a specified range (e.g., $100-$150). Have students swap forms and compare their orders.

ENRICHMENT p. 18

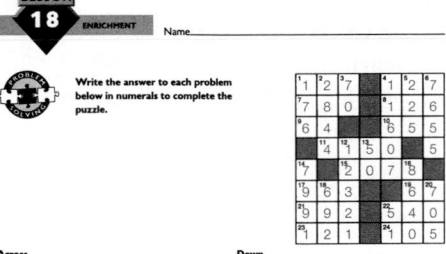

ASSESSMENT p. 12

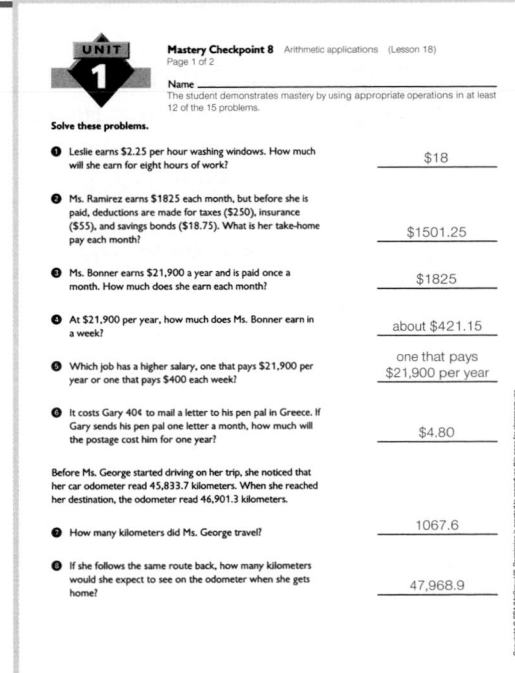

Using Your Calculator

LESSON PLANNER

Objectives

▶ to familiarize students with the keys on a calculator

▶ to provide students with the opportunity to investigate the capabilities of a calculator

Context of the Lesson This is the first of three lessons dealing with calculators and approximating.

 MANIPULATIVES

calculators*

Program Resources

Practice Master 19

Enrichment Master 19

For extra practice:
CD-ROM* Lesson 19
Cumulative Review, page 556

① Warm-Up

 Problem of the Day Present the following problem to the class: The division key on Sam's calculator is broken. He used the method below to divide 2103 by 66.

2103 – 660 – 660 – 660 – 66 = 57 (remainder)
10 + 10 + 10 + 1 = 31
2103 ÷ 66 = 31 R 57

Use Sam's method to divide 1446 by 36.

1446 – 360 – 360 – 360 – 360 = 6 (remainder)
10 + 10 + 10 + 10 = 40
1446 ÷ 36 = 40 R6

Problem-Solving Strategies Ask students who have solved the Problem of the Day to share how they solved it and any strategies they used.

MENTAL MATH Write these problems one at a time on the chalkboard:

a. 32 × 10 = (320) **b.** 32 × 100 = (3200)

c. 32 × 50 = (1600) **d.** 32 × 25 = (800)

e. 10 × 108 = (1080) **f.** 100 × 108 = (10,800)

g. 50 × 108 = (5400) **h.** 25 × 108 = (2700)

Using Your Calculator

 A calculator is a useful tool. To use your calculator effectively, you need to know what its special features are. Answer as many of the following questions as you can. Some of them may not apply to your calculator. **Answers will vary depending on the type of calculators students have. Sample responses are given.**

❶ What is the greatest number your calculator is able to display?
99,999,999

❷ What happens if the answer to a problem you give the calculator has more digits than the calculator display can show (for example, the problem 7,777,777 × 8,888,888)? **The calculator shows an E for error.**

❸ What is the difference between the ⬛ and ⬛ keys? **The ⬛ key clears everything. The ⬛ key clears only the last number entered.**

❹ How can you store a number in the calculator's memory? How can you display a number already in the memory? **Clear the memory by pressing the ⬛ key. Then enter the number and press the ⬛ key. To display the number already in memory, press the ⬛ key.**

❺ What does the ⬛ key do? **It divides 1 by the number entered.**

❻ Can your calculator display fractions? If so, how? **Some calculators can only display fractions as decimals. Other calculators may have keys such as ⬛ that can be used to enter a fraction bar.**

❼ Can your calculator add and subtract fractions? If not, can you use your calculator to check your answers when you add and subtract fractions? How can you do this? **Calculators that can display fractions can also add and subtract fractions. Check answers by finding decimal equivalents of the numbers in the problem and in the answer.**

❽ Does your calculator round to the last decimal place it shows? (Hint: Find 2 ÷ 3. How does this tell you whether the calculator rounds?) **no; the answer is shown as 0.6666666 instead of 0.6666667**

❾ Does your calculator "remember" more digits than it shows? How might you find out this information? **Yes; enter the decimal equivalent of a fraction such as $\frac{1}{7}$, then multiply by 10. Then one more digit appears.**

 **Literature Connection** Have students read about how Rufus uses a number of calculations to determine his costs and profits in *Toothpaste Millionaire* by Jean Merrill.

RETEACHING

If some students have difficulty learning to use a calculator, have others help them learn. Be sure that a student needing help is using the calculator if there is only one calculator per pair.

*available separately

GAME

Key Keys Game

C⚬⚬PERATIVE LEARNING

Players:	One or more
Materials:	One calculator per player
Object:	To reach a given number using only permitted keys
Math Focus:	Mental arithmetic (all four operations), using a calculator, and mathematical reasoning

RULES

1. Choose several keys ("permitted keys") including one number.

2. Try to get the display to show another number you select. See who can get to the selected number with the fewest steps. (You don't have to push ▤ after each operation.)

SAMPLE GAME

Min and Oliver chose these keys: ➕, ➖, ✖, ➗, ▤, 7

They wanted to reach the number 22.

Min reached 22 in ten steps:

7, ➗, 7, ➕, 7, ➕, 7, ➕, 7, ▤

Oliver won the round.

Oliver reached 22 in eight steps:

7, 7, ➕, 7, 7, ➗, 7, ▤

Can you do these? Count your steps.

1. Permitted keys: ➕, ➖, ✖, ➗, ▤, 8

   Try to reach: **a.** 24 **b.** 11 **c.** 19 **d.** 640 **e.** 2 **f.** 56

2. Permitted keys: ➕, ➖, ✖, ➗, ▤, 9

   Try to reach: **a.** 45 **b.** 81 **c.** 82 **d.** 360 **e.** 4 **f.** 98

   Permitted keys: ➕, ➖, ✖, ➗, ▤, 5

   Try to reach: **a.** 25 **b.** 550 **c.** 280 **d.** 165 **e.** 11 **f.** 13

Use the Cumulative Review on page 556 after this lesson.

---

② Teach

 Using the Student Pages To provide practice with a **calculator***, demonstrate how to play the "Key Keys" game first, so that students can begin playing as they finish their work on page 72. Have students work with partners as they try to find answers to the questions on page 72. Then go over findings with the class, asking students to explain their answers and to demonstrate what they have learned about their calculators' features. Advise students to turn their calculators off when they are not in use.

 Demonstrate the "Key Keys" game by going over the sample game on page 73. This game provides practice in mental arithmetic and thinking ahead, as well as practice in using a calculator. Point out that it may not be necessary to push ▤ after each step. If there are few calculators, have students write their answers on paper, and take turns checking solutions with the calculator.

③ Wrap-Up 🕐 5 MINUTES

 In Closing Have students distinguish between times when it would be useful to use a calculator and times when it would be easier to use mental math.

 **ALTERNATIVE ASSESSMENT** **Informal Assessment** Observe students as they explore their calculators. Be sure they are tackling each question thoroughly, and that they understand the different features of a calculator and what it will display.

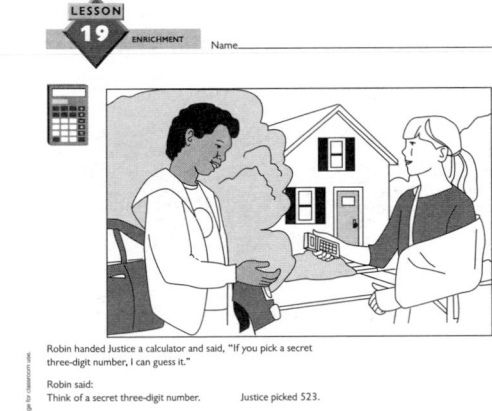
Assessment Criteria

Did the student . . .

✓ find answers to all the questions on page 72?

✓ demonstrate how to reach 80% of the numbers presented in the "Key Keys" game?

Homework Invite students to choose a previously introduced game and play it with a family member.

*available separately

Calculator or Mental Arithmetic?

LESSON PLANNER

Objectives

✓ to assess students' ability to approximate answers to arithmetic problems

▶ to provide practice in mental arithmetic involving situations in which the mind is faster than the calculator

Context of the Lesson This is the second of three lessons reviewing the use of calculators and methods and applications of approximation; the lesson contains Mastery Checkpoint 9 to assess this skill.

 **MANIPULATIVES**
calculators*

Program Resources
"Roller Coaster 1" and
"Roller Coaster 2" Game Mats
Practice Master 20
Enrichment Master 20
Assessment Master
For additional math integration:
Math Throughout the Day*
For extra practice:
CD-ROM* Lesson 20

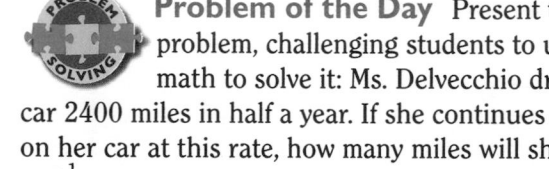

❶ Warm-Up

5 MINUTES

 Problem of the Day Present the following problem, challenging students to use mental math to solve it: Ms. Delvecchio drove her new car 2400 miles in half a year. If she continues to put mileage on her car at this rate, how many miles will she have driven in $3\frac{1}{4}$ years? (15,600 miles)

Problem-Solving Strategies Ask students who have solved the Problem of the Day to share how they solved it and any strategies they used.

MENTAL MATH Ask students to suggest pairs of two-digit factors for each of the following products: (Answers may vary.)

a. 200 (20 × 10)   b. 4000 (50 × 80)
c. 3000 (60 × 50)   d. 2400 (40 × 60)
e. 480 (40 × 12)   f. 750 (25 × 30)

Calculator or Mental Arithmetic?

Are all problems quicker to solve with a calculator? Have a race to find out.

COOPERATIVE LEARNING Do this with a partner. One of you must use a calculator; the other, any other method. The player using a calculator must press all the keys indicated. See how fast each of you can find the answers.

❶ $7 \times 8 = n$
56
❷ $70 \times 8 = n$
560
❸ $700 \times 8 = n$
5600
❹ $7000 \times 8 = n$
56,000
❺ $7 \times 80 = n$
560
❻ $7 \times 800 = n$
5600
❼ $7 \times 8000 = n$
56,000
❽ $70 \times 80 = n$
5600
❾ $700 \times 80 = n$
56,000
❿ $70 \times 800 = n$
56,000
⓫ $700 \times 800 = n$
560,000
⓬ $7000 \times 8000 = n$
56,000,000
⓭ $7 + 8 = n$
15
⓮ $70 + 8 = n$
78
⓯ $7 + 80 = n$
87
⓰ $7000 + 80 = n$
7080
⓱ $8 - 7 = n$
1
⓲ $80 - 7 = n$
73
⓳ $8000 - 70 = n$
7930
⓴ $8000 - 700 = n$
7300
㉑ $90 \times 700 = n$
63,000
㉒ $600 \times 80 = n$
48,000
㉓ $5000 \times 800 = n$
4,000,000
㉔ $50 \times 600 = n$
30,000
㉕ $900 \times 600 = n$
540,000
㉖ $5 \times 90 = n$
450
㉗ $80 \times 80 = n$
6400
㉘ $600 \times 70 = n$
42,000
㉙ $700 \times 7 = n$
4900
㉚ $100 \times 80 = n$
8000
㉛ $600 \times 60 = n$
36,000
㉜ $40 \times 800 = n$
32,000
㉝ $56 \div 7 = n$
8
㉞ $560 \div 70 = n$
8
㉟ $5600 \div 700 = n$
8
㊱ $5600 \div 7 = n$
800
㊲ $5600 \div 70 = n$
80
㊳ $810 \div 9 = n$
90
㊴ $810 \div 90 = n$
9
㊵ $4900 \div 70 = n$
70
㊶ $640 \div 80 = n$
8
㊷ $50 \times 50 = n$
2500
㊸ $500 \times 5 = n$
2500
㊹ $50 + 50 = n$
100
㊺ $50 + 5 = n$
55
㊻ $500 + 5 = n$
505
㊼ $50 - 40 = n$
10
㊽ $50 - 4 = n$
46
㊾ $500 - 4 = n$
496
㊿ $30 \times 900 = n$
27,000
㉛ $300 \times 90 = n$
27,000

◆ Which person finished first? Did most of the pairs have the same winner?
Answers will vary.

How can you decide when it would be faster to use a calculator or to use mental arithmetic? Record your strategies in your Math Journal.

Why teach it at this time?

Approximation is an important concept and skill that will require considerable teaching and practice for many students. The next lesson formalizes an efficient method of approximating and provides more practice. Throughout the remainder of the year, students will be practicing approximation in various contexts. Point out to students that many types of problems can be solved more quickly and with less chance of error mentally than with a calculator.

 **Technology Connection** Refer students to the software *Mental Math Games* from Waterford (IBM, for grades K–8) for further practice with mental math skills, math facts, equations, fractions, decimals, and percentages.

*available separately

Approximation Game

 C∞PERATIVE LEARNING

GAME

Players: Three or more
Materials: One calculator for the lead player
Object: To get the most points by making close approximations
Math Focus: Place value, using a calculator, and mathematical reasoning

RULES

1. Make a game form like this:

Round	Approximation	Point for Correct First Digit	Points for Correct Number of Digits	Score for Round
1				
2				

2. Decide how many rounds will be played. List them on the game form and add a space at the bottom for the total.

3. The lead player writes a problem on the board (for example, 73 3 59) and uses the calculator to find the answer.

4. Each player writes an approximate answer on the game form.

5. The lead player rounds the correct answer to a number with only one nonzero digit and writes it on the board, saying the first digit and the number of digits in the answer.

6. Look at your approximation and score yourself as follows: one point for the correct first digit and two points for the correct number of digits. Record your points on your game form.

If your approximation was:	And the correct answer is:	Then you would score:
4000	3652 → 4000	three points
50,000	44370 → 40,000	two points
900	9231 → 9000	one point

7. The player with the greatest total score at the end of the game is the winner.

Literature Connection Have students read Marcia Lerner's story "Approximation," which is about children trying to guess the number of leaves on a tree. You may wish to challenge students to come up with a method for approximating the number of trees and bushes in a local park.

② Teach

Using the Student Pages Before students begin work on these pages, demonstrate the "Approximation" game and the "Roller Coaster 1" Game Mat. These games provide practice with approximation. Students can play one of these games when they finish pages 74–77.

Before starting the lesson, you may wish to discuss the following ideas if you haven't already done so.

1. A number like 7000 is the same as 7×1000 (7000 means seven thousands).

2. A number like 1000 (1 with some number of 0s after it) can be written $10 \times 10 \times 10$ (as many factors of 10 as there are 0s in the number).

3. When you multiply three or more numbers together, the order in which you multiply does not change the answer ($3 \times 4 \times 5 = 12 \times 5 = 3 \times 20 = 4 \times 15 = 60$).

4. All the above can be put together to answer a question like problem 12 as follows:

   $7000 \times 8000 = 7 \times 10 \times 10 \times 10 \times 8 \times 10 \times 10 \times 10$

   $= 56 \times 10 \times 10 \times 10 \times 10 \times 10 \times 10$

   $= 56,000,000$

   Another way to look at this is that 7000×8000 must be 56 followed by as many 0s (6) as there are in the two factors.

5. In a problem like 50×400, the answer is 20 followed by three 0s, or 20,000 (do not count the 0 from the 20).

6. Division is essentially the reverse of multiplication. So to get an answer to $56,000 \div 700$, divide 56 by 7, getting 8, and subtract the number of 0s in 700 (two) from the number in 56,000 (three). Write that 0 to the right of the 8. The answer is 80.

 Have students follow the directions on page 74 by working in pairs to determine whether a **calculator*** or mental arithmetic provides answers more quickly.

  The "Approximation" game provides practice with estimating and rounding answers to arithmetic problems. Play four or five rounds with the class, then discuss procedures for improving approximations. If no student suggests the following method, describe it or a method similar to it. Round each number to the closest number with only one nonzero digit, calculate the answer, and then adjust the answer if the numbers were increased or decreased substantially by rounding.

*available separately

◆ LESSON 20 Calculator or Mental Arithmetic?

Teach

Using the Student Pages Have students do pages 76 and 77 on their own. You may wish to have students form groups to discuss their answers to the word problems on page 77 before you discuss these problems with the class as a whole.

Introducing the "Roller Coaster 1" and "Roller Coaster 2" Game Mats The "Roller Coaster 1" Game Mat provides practice in approximating answers to multidigit multiplication problems. Demonstrate the game by playing with two or three students as the rest of the class watches. Be sure students realize that exact and rounded answers are included in the circles on the Game Mat, but emphasize that players need not give these answers to win a counter. Students who find the game too easy may enjoy playing the harder version on the back of the Game Mat. The "Roller Coaster 2" Game Mat involves approximating answers to problems using all four basic operations. Complete directions for playing can be found on the Game Mats. A copy of these Game Mats can also be found on pages 624–625 of this Teacher's Guide.

AT RISK **Meeting Individual Needs**
To emphasize the usefulness of developing approximation skills, provide examples of common real-life situations in which students need to quickly estimate an answer to a problem. For example, discuss the many occasions on which students need to figure out quickly whether they have enough money to buy a snack or two or a comic book, or whether they have enough to go to a movie.

◆ LESSON 20 Calculator or Mental Arithmetic?

In this lesson you'll use your approximating skills and number sense to find correct answers and tell when answers don't make sense.

In each case two of the answers are clearly wrong and one is correct. Choose the correct answer. Watch the signs!

52 843 × 629 =	a. 53,427	**b.** 530,247	c. 5,300,427
53 5043 × 75 =	a. 3725	b. 37,825	**c.** 378,225
54 86,658 ÷ 429 =	**a.** 202	b. 2562	c. 22,602
55 73,492 + 876 =	a. 15,468	b. 159,168	**c.** 74,368
56 642 × 593 =	a. 38,706	**b.** 380,706	c. 3,800,706
57 3487 − 94 =	a. 2647	**b.** 3393	c. 3581
58 3487 × 94 =	**a.** 327,778	b. 247,778	c. 467,778
59 3487 + 94 =	a. 3393	b. 128	**c.** 3581
60 3478 ÷ 94 =	**a.** 37	b. 4	c. 420
61 954 × 8 =	a. 762	**b.** 7632	c. 8062
62 57 × 68 =	**a.** 3876	b. 2876	c. 4876
63 475 × 71 =	**a.** 33,725	b. 27,725	c. 41,725
64 29 × 32 =	a. 98	**b.** 928	c. 9298
65 24 × 1765 =	a. 4260	b. 63,260	**c.** 42,360
66 28,764 ÷ 423 =	a. 728	b. 7	**c.** 68

Solve these problems.

67 A school has 20 classes. Each class has 25, 26, 27, or 28 students. Are there more than 600 students in the school? **no**

68 Karim has $150.00. Does he have enough money to buy six concert tickets that cost $24.50 each? **yes**

RETEACHING

For each set of problems on page 74 (e.g., 1–12), let students do the first one or two on their own. Ask whether they see any patterns in the problems and answers. Once students can solve these problems quickly using mental math, ask them to see if they can do them more quickly and accurately using **calculator***. They will probably find that using a calculator takes as long or longer, and if they work too quickly they may find that they are making mistakes keying in numbers.

PRACTICE p. 20

LESSON 20 PRACTICE Name_____

In each problem two of the answers are clearly wrong and one is correct. Choose the correct answer.

1 571 × 880 = _a_   a. 502,480   b. 582,480   c. 365,180
2 2654 × 25 = _b_   a. 97,210   b. 66,350   c. 112,540
3 57,222 ÷ 561 = _c_   a. 52   b. 82   c. 102
4 38,137 + 521 = _a_   a. 38,658   b. 38,018   c. 39,658
5 984 × 711 = _b_   a. 559,324   b. 699,624   c. 611,695
6 8651 − 42 = _a_   a. 8609   b. 8097   c. 8693
7 7321 × 86 = _a_   a. 629,606   b. 569,306   c. 538,316
8 2179 + 50 = _c_   a. 2159   b. 2129   c. 2229
9 4872 ÷ 56 = _a_   a. 87   b. 68   c. 56
10 888 × 5 = _b_   a. 4540   b. 4440   c. 4040
11 32 × 79 = _a_   a. 2528   b. 1758   c. 3228
12 811 × 36 = _b_   a. 23,896   b. 29,196   c. 19,940
13 33 × 96 = _c_   a. 2658   b. 4288   c. 3168
14 46 × 1925 = _b_   a. 101,300   b. 88,550   c. 116,850
15 31,720 ÷ 488 = _b_   a. 35   b. 65   c. 95

In each division problem two of the answers are clearly wrong and one is correct. Choose the correct answer.

16 435 ÷ 87 = _c_   a. 3   b. 8   c. 5
17 216 ÷ 18 = _b_   a. 18   b. 12   c. 8
18 3750 ÷ 250 = _c_   a. 9   b. 18   c. 15
19 824 ÷ 103 = _b_   a. 72   b. 8   c. 12
20 8160 ÷ 68 = _a_   a. 120   b. 90   c. 10

20 • Math Explorations and Applications Level 6

---

*available separately

Solve these problems.

69 Patty can read about 45 pages per hour in the book she's reading. The book has 1231 pages and she is now on page 92. Using a calculator, she decides she will have to spend 253 hours reading before she finishes the book. Do you agree? If not, about how long do you think it will take for her to finish the book? **disagree; 25.3 hours**

70 Chiyo runs 5 miles each morning, every day of the year. She believes she will run about 1800 miles in a year. Do you agree? If not, about how many miles do you think she will run in a year? **agree**

71 Carlos pays 25 cents to ride the bus to school each day and 25 cents to ride it home. He goes to school about 180 days each year. About how much does he spend to ride the bus each year? **$90.00**

72 Joe has $20. He wants to buy some ballpoint pens that cost $1.98 each. About how many of the pens can he buy? **no more than 10**

73 Mary, Mike, and Mavis are all twelve years old. Mary estimates that she has been alive for 4400 days. Mike believes he's been alive for 44,000 days, and Mavis estimates she's been alive for 440 days. Tell whether each estimate is reasonable and why you think so. **Only Mary's estimate is reasonable. Ten years is 3650 days, so twelve years is slightly longer. The other estimates have misplaced decimals.**

74 Jin wants to buy a jacket for $89, a pair of slacks for $73, and two shirts for $21 each. He has $300 to spend. Does he have enough money to buy all of these clothes? If not, about how much more money does he need? If he does have enough, about how much extra money will he have left after buying the clothes? **yes; $96 extra**

75 Jin had been saving about $30 a week towards his new clothes. He thought it would take him four months to save $300. Was he correct? If not, about how many months did it take? **no; It took him about 2½ months (10 weeks).**

Unit 1   Lesson 20 • **77**

---

❸ Wrap-Up

In Closing To summarize the lesson, ask students to explain how they use their approximation skills. Ask them to provide an example to demonstrate how to find an approximate answer.

✓ Mastery Checkpoint 9

By this time, most students should be able to approximate answers to arithmetic problems. You can assess this ability by checking students' work on page 76 and by observing them during appropriate mental math activities or by using Assessment Blackline Masters page 14. The results of this assessment may be recorded on the Mastery Checkpoint Chart. In addition, as a regular part of your classroom activities, you can ask students to approximate the answer when you are about to do a computation problem together. This practice can encourage the useful habit of estimating to get an idea of the expected size of the answer before calculating.

Assessment Criteria

Did the student . . .

✓ correctly answer 12 out of 15 of the multiple-choice problems on page 76?

✓ demonstrate approximation skills when playing the two games presented in the lesson?

✓ show improvement in his or her ability to approximate answers to computation problems?

Homework Have students play the "Approximation" game with a family member for additional practice in approximation. A copy of this game can also be found on page 15 of the Home Connections Blackline Masters.

Unit 1 Lesson 20   **77**

LESSON PLANNER

Objectives

▶ to teach how to round to a given place

▶ to teach students to consider the situation when deciding how much and in what direction to round

▶ to provide students with a sense of how precisely a number needs to be expressed in light of how the number will be used

▶ to provide practice in using rounding and approximation to solve word problems

Context of the Lesson
This is the third of three lessons reviewing the use of calculators and methods of approximation. Students will use rounding and approximation techniques in future lessons and in real life to help them decide whether answers make sense.

 MANIPULATIVES

Program Resources

Reteaching Master

Practice Master 21

Enrichment Master 21

For extra practice:
CD-ROM* Lesson 21

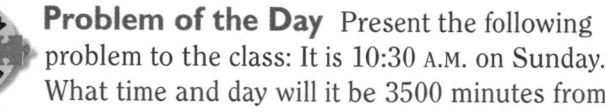 **Warm-Up** 5 MINUTES

 Problem of the Day Present the following problem to the class: It is 10:30 A.M. on Sunday. What time and day will it be 3500 minutes from now? (8:50 P.M. Tuesday)

Problem-Solving Strategies Ask students who have solved the Problem of the Day to share how they solved it and any strategies they used.

MENTAL MATH Introduce a new type of drill. Present students with a problem, and have students show thumbs up if the answer is within the stated bounds and thumbs down if it is over or under the stated bounds. Begin with problems for which the answer must be more than 100 but less than 200 to be within the bounds. Write the problems one at a time on the chalkboard so that students can see the relationship between problems in the same column. This kind of drill is continued periodically throughout the year. Here are three suggested sequences of problems:

(continued on page 79)

Rounding

Which number is easier to work with, 88,978 or 90,000?

Multiples of 10, 100, 1000, and so on are usually easier to work with than most other numbers. So when we are estimating or approximating, we often round numbers to a multiple of 10, 100, and so on.

We may round to the nearest multiple below. We call that **rounding** down. Or we may round to the nearest multiple above. We call that rounding up. Sometimes we round to the nearest multiple. How much we round and in what direction depends on the problem we are trying to solve.

Let's practice rounding to the nearest multiple.

Round 1248 to the nearest 10, 100, and 1000.

To the nearest 10: Since 48 is between 40 and 50, but closer to 50, 1248 rounds to 1250.

To the nearest 100: Since 248 is between 200 and 300, but closer to 200, 1248 rounds to 1200.

To the nearest 1000: Since 1248 is between 1000 and 2000, but closer to 1000, it rounds to 1000.

Round 45 to the nearest 10.

The number 45 is between 40 and 50 and is equally close to both. Most people use the rule to round up. So to round 45 to the nearest ten, we can round 45 up to 50. Sometimes how we round depends more on the situation than on following a rule. We will see an example of this on page 80.

Round 62.2 to the nearest whole number.

The number 62.2 is between 62 and 63 but closer to 62.

78 • Whole Numbers and Integers

Social Studies Connection Provide time for students to bring in newspaper articles or examples of news reports with rounded numbers and discuss them with the class. They may find examples in which figures have been reported more precisely than is warranted; for instance, census figures are not correct to the nearest whole number, although they are often reported that way.

19 two possible answers: 73,000,000 and 74,000,000; If you round to the nearest hundred thousand first, you may not round to the nearest million.

Round each of the following numbers to the nearest million.

1 73,474,362
73,000,000

2 1,973,425
2,000,000

3 14,298,755
14,000,000

4 645,043,171
645,000,000

5 73,500,000
See right.

6 211,000
0
5 74,000,000 or 73,000,000

7 800,000
1,000,000

8 73,500,001
74,000,000

9 95,724,000
96,000,000

Round each of the following numbers to the nearest hundred thousand.

10 73,474,362
73,500,000

11 106,876
100,000

12 53,493
100,000

13 525,672
500,000

14 1,263,000
1,300,000

15 6,539,000
6,500,000

16 472,311
500,000

17 251,998
300,000

18 832,599
800,000

19 How many possible correct answers are there to problem 5 above? What are they? Look at problems 10, 5, and 1, and explain why it might not be a good idea to round a number first to the nearest hundred thousand and then to the nearest million. **See above.**

Round each of the following numbers to the nearest whole number.

20 73.65
74

21 81.04
81

22 0.73
1

23 6.52
7

24 0.31
0

25 56.4
56

26 56.5
57 or 56

27 17.09
17

28 56.6
57

29 0.49
0

30 4.52
5

31 0.65
1

32 417.8
418

33 6.85
7

34 12.49
12

35 10.06
10

Round each of the following numbers to the nearest hundred.

36 843.6
800

37 589.702
600

38 1111
1100

39 9999
10,000

40 500
500

41 47
0

42 53
100

43 672
700

44 888
900

45 447
400

46 2763
2800

47 364.9
400

48 74
100

49 1859
1900

50 739
700

51 802
800

Unit 1   Lesson 21   •   **79**

Technology Connection Refer students to the video, laser disc, or software *Modumath: Arithmetic, Rounding Numbers* from VTAE (VHS, IBM, for grades 6–12) for further practice with rounding numbers to a degree of accuracy.

Mental Math (continued)

a. 35 × 2 (thumbs down)

35 × 3 (thumbs up)

35 × 4 (thumbs up)

35 × 5 (thumbs up)

35 × 6 (thumbs down)

b. 75 × 2 (thumbs up)

75 × 3 (thumbs down)

75 × 4 (thumbs down)

76 × 4 (thumbs down)

77 × 4 (thumbs down)

c. 51 × 2 (thumbs up)

51 × 3 (thumbs up)

51 × 4 (thumbs down)

51 × 5 (thumbs down)

❷ Teach

Using the Student Pages Before you discuss the examples of rounding to the nearest multiple on page 78, to emphasize that a number such as 90,000 is easier to work with than a number such as 88,978, ask the class to multiply mentally 88,978 × 6 and 90,000 × 6. Draw a number line on the chalkboard for some of the examples and have students find the given number on the line. Explain that first they should look for the digit just to the right of the place they are rounding to. So when rounding to the nearest tenth, look at the digit in the hundredths place. If it is greater than 5 or if it is 5 and there are nonzero digits to the right, round up (3.7863 → 3.8). If it is less than 5, round down (3.7463 → 3.7). If it is 5 and there are no more nonzero digits, round up or down depending on the situation.

Have students work individually on the problems on page 79.

Unit 1 Lesson 21 **79**

◆ LESSON 21 Rounding

Teach

Using the Student Pages Discuss with the class the sample problem on page 80 and its solution. Again, emphasize how the problem can be solved by using approximation and by rounding in a direction that gives a useful answer. Then have students work in small groups on the three discussion questions and discuss their answers with the class afterward. Ask students to justify their rounding strategies. Point out that by rounding differently we can arrive at different approximate answers and that the degree to which we round depends on the situation.

Assign the problems on page 81 for students to work on independently or in pairs. In either case, students should justify their answers to one another in groups or pairs.

If students have difficulty applying approximation skills, work with them whenever situations arise during regular classroom activities that call for approximation—for example, when discussing the finances of a field trip or when discussing multidigit numbers during a social studies or science lesson. Emphasize that approximation is a way of reducing work, even though this may conflict with students' tendency to want a precise answer.

◆ LESSON 21 Rounding

How much we round and whether we round up or down depends on the problem we are trying to solve.

Example:

Mr. and Mrs. Taylor and their three children have been at the amusement park most of the day, and Mr. and Mrs. Taylor have about $20 left to spend. Jack asks his parents if the whole family can go on the cable car, which costs $3.35 per person. Mrs. Taylor thinks, "$3.35 is less than $4. Five times $4 is $20. Five times $3.35 will be less than $20. So we have enough money."

If Mrs. Taylor had rounded $3.35 down to $3.00, she would have known that five tickets for the ride would be more than $15, but she would not have been sure that they were less than $20. Notice that rounding to $3.00 is rounding to the nearest dollar but that it is not as useful as rounding up in this situation.

Discuss solutions to the following questions. Try to find solutions that avoid paper and pencil calculations.

◆ Jessica is traveling to Endville, 2089 kilometers away. She wants to spend three days driving. About how far should she plan to drive each day? **about 700 km**

◆ Carlos is going to make 24 stuffed animals for a bazaar. He needs 90 centimeters of fabric for each animal. Will he have enough fabric if he buys 18 meters (1800 centimeters) of fabric? 24 meters (2400 centimeters) of fabric? **no; yes**

◆ Frances saved $23.57. Packages of sports cards are on sale for $2.47 each. Does Frances have enough money to purchase ten packs? seven packs? **no; yes**

80 • Whole Numbers and Integers

Literature Connection Have students read the directions and play "Multiplications" on page 69 of *Dominoes: Basic Rules and Variations* by Reiner F. Maler. Have students estimate their answers before finding the answer tiles.

RETEACHING p. 6

LESSON 21 RETEACHING   Name_____

You can use a number line to help you round a number.

Example 1:
Round 15.38 to the nearest whole number.

15.00 ———————————— 16.00
          15.38

15.38 is closer to 15 than to 16.
15.38 rounded to the nearest whole number is 15.

Example 2:
Round 236 to the nearest hundred.

200 210 220 230 240 250 260 270 280 290 300
                236

236 is closer to 200 than to 300.
236 rounded to the nearest hundred is 200.

Round to the nearest ten.
1. 14 __10__   2. 27 __30__   3. 536 __540__   4. 753 __750__

Round to the nearest whole number.
5. 18.9 __19__   6. 27.3 __27__   7. 489.6 __490__   8. 214.3 __214__

Round to the nearest hundred.
9. 453 __500__   10. 215 __200__   11. 2897 __2900__   12. 3142 __3100__

Round to the nearest thousand.
13. 4897 __5000__   14. 3451 __3000__   15. 27,416 __27,000__   16. 53,926 __54,000__

6 • Math Explorations and Applications Level 6

Explain how to solve each of the following without actually doing the paper and pencil calculations.

52 Mr. Hilton has a $20 bill, three $5 bills, and less than a dollar of change in his pocket. He wants to spend $4.98 on milk, $22.89 on meat, and $4.53 on vegetables. Does he have enough money to do that? **Add Mr. Hilton's cash: $20 + $15 = $35. Round the price of each item up to the nearest dollar. Then add the prices: $5 + $23 + $5 = $33. Since this is less than $35, he has enough money.**

53 Jeremy can run for a long time at a rate of about 7.2 miles per hour. He wants to run 27.4 miles in less than four hours. Will he be able to do that? **Round 7.2 miles per hour down to 7 miles per hour and multiply by 4. Jeremy can run over 28 miles in 4 hours.**

54 Maria can ride her bicycle for long periods of time at an average speed of 12 miles per hour. She wants to ride 50 miles in less than five hours. Will she be able to do it? **Divide 50 miles by 5. This is 10 miles per hour. Since Maria rides faster than that, she can make the trip.**

55 Brittany can ride her bicycle for long periods of time at a rate of about 18 miles per hour. She wants to ride 100 miles in no more than five hours. Will she be able to do it? **Divide 100 by 5. This is 20 miles per hour. Since Brittany doesn't ride that fast, she can't make the trip.**

56 If Mrs. Littman drives her car an average of 53 miles an hour for 8 hours and 17 minutes, will she go farther than 200 miles? Will she go farther than 400 miles? Will she go farther than 600 miles? **Round 53 down to 50 and multiply by 8. She will go a little farther than 400 miles.**

 **③ Wrap-Up**

 **In Closing** To summarize the lesson, ask students to explain in their Math Journals the procedure for rounding numbers. Ask them to describe instances in which they should round up or in which they should round down.

Performance Assessment Have students round the following number to the nearest tenth, to the nearest whole number, and to the nearest ten: 247.238. (247.2; 247; 250)

Assessment Criteria

Did the student . . .

✓ correctly answer at least 42 of the 51 rounding problems on page 79?

✓ demonstrate understanding of the rounding procedure?

✓ express understanding of the usefulness of approximations?

Homework Have students look through newspapers to find examples of both rounded and exact numbers. Ask them to round sensibly each of the exact numbers they find.

PRACTICE p. 21

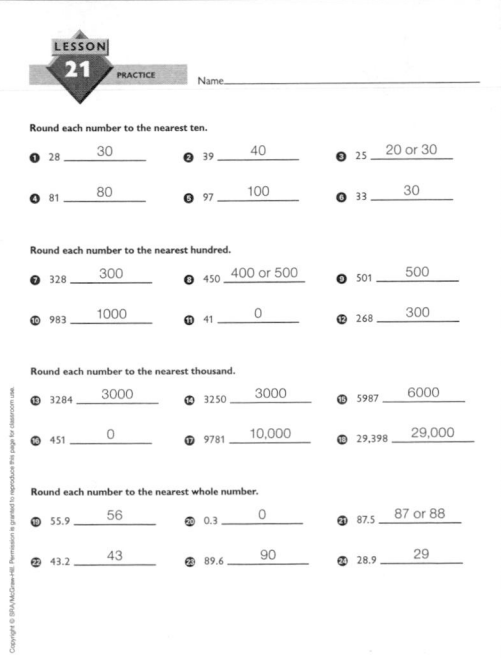

ENRICHMENT p. 21

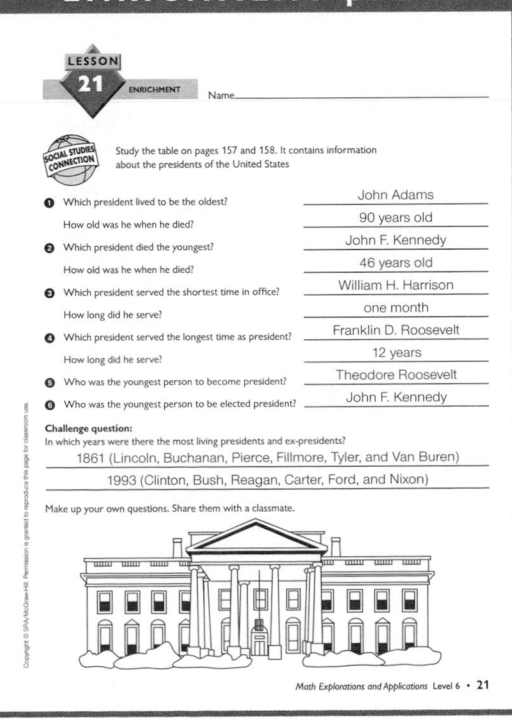

LESSON 22

Using Negative Numbers

LESSON 22

Using Negative Numbers

Objectives

▶ to review negative numbers

▶ to demonstrate the usefulness of negative numbers through realistic examples

Context of the Lesson This is the first of three lessons on negative numbers. The next lesson reviews using negative numbers on the calculator and Lesson 24 introduces multiplication of a negative number by a positive number. Here, as in Level 5, work with negative numbers is restricted to operations that have a physical model. More practice with signed numbers is provided in Unit 5.

 MANIPULATIVES

Program Resources

Reteaching Master

Practice Master 22

Enrichment Master 22

The Cruncher*

For extra practice:
CD-ROM* Lesson 22

① Warm-Up ⏱ 5 MINUTES

 **Problem of the Day** Present this problem orally: Anna is taking an ocean voyage. She peeked out the porthole of her cabin while the ship was still in port and saw that the water line was 5 meters below the porthole. If the tide raises the water level at a rate of 0.75 meters an hour, how soon will the water reach her porthole? (It never will; the boat rises along with the tide.)

Problem-Solving Strategies Ask students who have solved the Problem of the Day to share how they solved it and any strategies they used.

MENTAL MATH Have students answer these questions in unison:

a. $50 - 75 = (-25)$
b. $15 - 25 = (-10)$
c. $17 - 18 = (-1)$
d. $23 - 25 = (-2)$
e. $3 - 18 = (-15)$
f. $7 - 7 = (0)$
g. $6 - 3 = (3)$
h. $28 - 35 = (-7)$

Student Edition pages 80–81

In many real-life situations we need to describe things using numbers that are less than 0. In this lesson you'll review how to identify and name these negative numbers.

◆ Can you think of times when it might be useful to use numbers less than 0? **Answers will vary but might include using temperature, for example.**

Suppose the temperature is 10°C and it goes down 15°C. What will the temperature be?

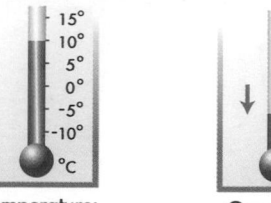  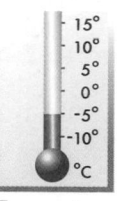

Temperature: 10°C | Goes Down 15°C | Temperature: 5° below 0°

We can then write this problem in this way: $10 - 15 = (-5)$
-5 is read "negative 5."

We often call a temperature of 5° below 0°C a temperature of $-5°C$.

You can show negative numbers on a number line.

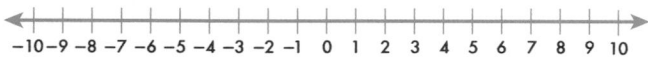

$-10\ -9\ -8\ -7\ -6\ -5\ -4\ -3\ -2\ -1\quad 0\quad 1\quad 2\quad 3\quad 4\quad 5\quad 6\quad 7\quad 8\quad 9\quad 10$

Write the missing items.

		Temperature Before Change	Temperature Change	Temperature After Change
	❶	15°C	up 5°	■ 20°C
(5° below 0°C)	❷	10°C	down 15°	■ −5°C
(10° below 0°C)	❸	−5°C (5° below 0°C)	down 5°	■ −10°C
(8° below 0°C)	❹	−10°C	up 2°	■ −8°C
	❺	−5°C	up 5°	■ 0°C

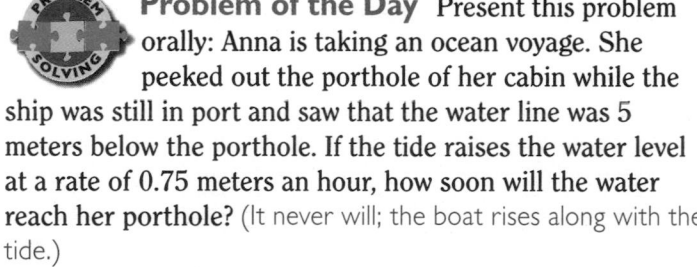 **Geography Connection** Choose a total of five cities in the United States that span a variety of climates and altitudes. Challenge students to predict the average high and low temperatures for each city at this time of year. Have them check their predictions in the temperature chart in the weather section of tomorrow's newspaper.

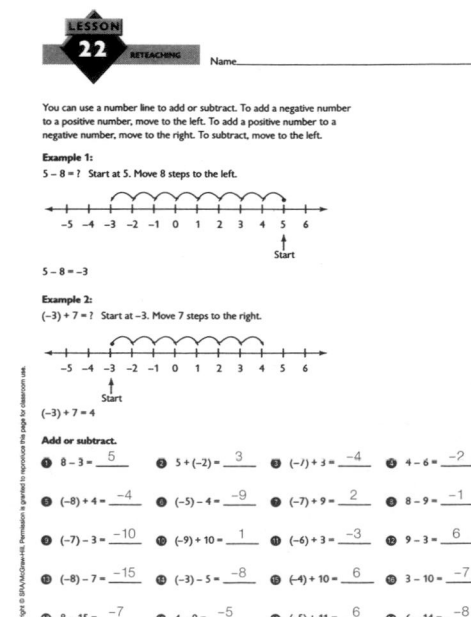

*available separately

Diego's bank allows customers temporarily to have a negative **balance** in their accounts.

Diego's balance was $5. He then wrote a check for $15. What was his new balance?

We can write that problem in this way:

$(5) + (-15) = (-10)$

Diego's new balance was −$10.

Write the missing items.

	If Diego's balance was:	And he did this:	Then his new balance would be:	
6	$15	deposited $5	■ $20	
7	$50	wrote check for $20	■ $30	
8	$5	wrote check for $25	■ −$20	(or $20 overdrawn)
9	−$25	deposited $25	■ $0	

Add or subtract. Watch for negative numbers.

10 10 + 20 **30** **11** 10 − 20 **−10** **12** 20 − 20 **0** **13** 15 − 20 **−5**

14 15 − 25 **−10** **15** 0 − 25 **−25** **16** (−10) + 10 **0** **17** (−10) − 10 **−20**

18 7 − 16 **−9** **19** 16 − 7 **9** **20** 12 − 4 **8** **21** 4 − 12 **−8**

22 8 − 3 **5** **23** 8 − 8 **0** **24** 8 − 10 **−2** **25** 8 − 14 **−6**

26 (−6) + 1 **−5** **27** (−6) + 4 **−2** **28** (−7) + 13 **6** **29** (−7) + 0 **−7**

30 (−2) + 12 **10** **31** 10 − 12 **−2** **32** 15 − 8 **7** **33** 9 − 14 **−5**

Unit 1   Lesson 22 • **83**

---

② Teach

Using the Student Pages Explain to students that there are real-world problems for which negative numbers provide a solution. Work together on problems 1–9, and then assign problems 10–33 for individual work. *Note:* Parentheses are shown around negative numbers because the negative symbol looks like the subtraction sign. Later on, if there is no doubt about the meaning of the sign, the parentheses are omitted. Students can use a blank **Cruncher*** spreadsheet to help with these problems.

③ Wrap-Up

In Closing Summarize the lesson by asking students to explain why negative numbers are useful in expressing temperatures or bank balances. Ask them to tell what the temperature would be if it dropped 6° Celsius from a starting temperature of 3° Celsius. (−3°C)

 **Informal Assessment** Observe students as they work on problems 10–33. Ask them to explain why they need to use negative numbers when the number being subtracted is greater than the number from which it is subtracted.

Assessment Criteria

Did the student . . .

✓ correctly answer at least 70% of the computation problems?

✓ communicate an understanding of the concept of negative numbers?

✓ explain why some addition or subtraction results in an answer that is a negative number?

Homework Have students write and solve three application problems involving negative numbers.

Literature Connection For an explanation of negative numbers in a story about friends who are pulled "below the surface of numbers," have students read the story "Negative Numbers" in *MathSmart Junior* by Marcia Lerner.

*available separately

LESSON 23
Computing with Negative Numbers
Student Edition pages 84–87

23 Computing with Negative Numbers

LESSON PLANNER

Objectives

▶ to teach the use of negative numbers on the calculator

▶ to provide practice in using negative numbers mentally and with a calculator, and in solving word problems

▶ to help students develop the broad ability to use mathematical common sense

Context of the Lesson This is the second of three lessons on negative numbers and contains the fourth part of "Mr. Muddle's Extra-Large Problems," a four-part Thinking Story.

MANIPULATIVES
calculators*

Program Resources
Practice Master 23
Enrichment Master 23
For career connections:
    Careers and Math*
For extra practice:
    CD-ROM* Lesson 23
    Cumulative Review, page 557

Add or subtract. Do not use a calculator. Watch for negative numbers.

1	100 − 50	**2**	50 − 100	**3**	100 − 200	**4**	150 − 200
	50		**−50**		**−100**		**−50**
5	(−100) + 150	**6**	(−100) − 150	**7**	(−150) − 100	**8**	(−150) + 100
	50		**−250**		**−250**		**−50**
9	0 − 250	**10**	0 + 250	**11**	75 − 100	**12**	175 − 200
	−250		**250**		**−25**		**−25**
13	125 − 50	**14**	125 − 150	**15**	(−50) + 75	**16**	(−50) + 25
	75		**−25**		**25**		**−25**

Look on your calculator for a key that looks like this **+/−** or this **+/−**. You can use the **+/−** key on a calculator to compute with negative numbers.

Look at these examples.

Problem:	Push:		
50 − 20	 5 0 − 2 0 = ⟶	30.
20 − 50	2 0 − 5 0 = ⟶	−30.
(−40) + 30	4 0 +/− + 3 0 = ⟶	−10.
(−5) − 20	5 +/− − 2 0 = ⟶	−25.

17 Now use your calculator to do problems 1–16. See if you get the same answers you got before.

Use your calculator to explore subtracting a negative number.

FANTASTIC FACT Mountains over 3280 feet above sea level cover over one fourth of Earth's land surface.

1 Warm-Up ⏱ 5 MINUTES

Problem of the Day Present the following problem to students: Leo bought a bag of pretzels. He ate six of them and then shared the rest equally with two friends. One friend ate five pretzels and then had 13 left. How many pretzels were in the bag Leo bought? (60)

Problem-Solving Strategies Ask students who have solved the Problem of the Day to share how they solved it and any strategies they used.

MENTAL MATH Provide practice with multiplication facts by asking students to show thumbs up if the answer is greater than 60 but less than 70, and thumbs down if not.

a. 4 × 5 (thumbs down)   **b.** 4 × 10 (thumbs down)

c. 4 × 15 (thumbs down)   **d.** 4 × 16 (thumbs up)

(continued on page 85)

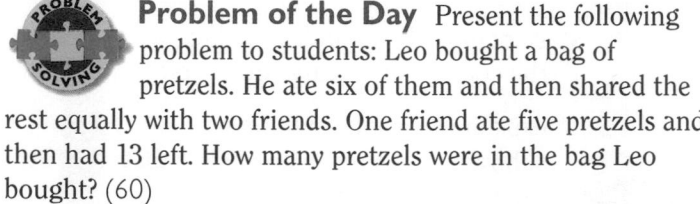

Literature Connection Have students do some of the investigations and activities in *Calculators* by Marion Smoothey.

*available separately

GEOGRAPHY CONNECTION

The chart below shows the highest and lowest points in each continent. The distances are measured from sea level. For example, a height of 29,028 feet means that the point is 29,028 feet above sea level. A distance of −1302 feet means that the point is 1302 feet below sea level.

Continent	Name and Place of Highest Point	Feet from Sea Level	Name and Place of Lowest Point	Feet from Sea Level
Asia	Mt. Everest (Nepal-Tibet)	29,028	Dead Sea (Israel-Jordan)	−1302
Africa	Mt. Kilimanjaro (Tanzania)	19,340	Lake Assal (Ethiopia)	−512
North America	Mt. McKinley (Alaska)	20,320	Death Valley (California)	−282
South America	Mt. Aconcagua (Argentina)	22,834	Valdes Peninsula (Argentina)	−131
Antarctica	Vinson Massif	16,864	not known	not known
Europe	Mt. El' brus (Russia)	18,510	Caspian Sea (Russia)	−92
Australia	Mt. Kosciusko (New South Wales)	7310	Lake Eyre (South Australia)	−52

Use the chart to solve these problems.

18 How high above sea level is Mount McKinley? **20,320 ft**

19 What is the difference in feet between the highest and lowest points on Earth? **30,330 ft**

20 What is the difference between the highest and the lowest points in North America? **20,602 ft**

21 How much higher is the highest point in Africa than the highest point in Europe? **830 ft**

22 How much lower is the lowest point in South America than the lowest point in Australia? **79 ft**

Unit 1   Lesson 23 • **85**

Mental Math (continued)

e.	4 × 20 (thumbs down)	**f.**	4 × 21 (thumbs down)
g.	15 × 1 (thumbs down)	**h.**	15 × 2 (thumbs down)
i.	15 × 3 (thumbs down)	**j.**	15 × 4 (thumbs down)
k.	15 × 5 (thumbs down)	**l.**	5 × 1 (thumbs down)
m.	5 × 2 (thumbs down)	**n.**	5 × 4 (thumbs down)
o.	5 × 15 (thumbs down)	**p.**	5 × 16 (thumbs down)
q.	20 × 2 (thumbs down)	**r.**	20 × 3 (thumbs down)
s.	20 × 4 (thumbs down)	**t.**	20 × 5 (thumbs down)
u.	2 × 30 (thumbs down)	**v.**	2 × 33 (thumbs up)
w.	2 × 40 (thumbs down)	**x.**	2 × 41 (thumbs down)
y.	2 × 25 (thumbs down)	**z.**	2 × 31 (thumbs up)

❷ Teach

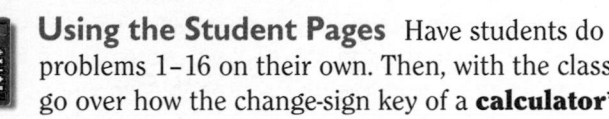

Using the Student Pages Have students do problems 1–16 on their own. Then, with the class, go over how the change-sign key of a **calculator*** works. Depending on how many calculators are available, have students work on problem 17 individually, in pairs, or in small groups. Then have students work on page 85, using calculators if necessary. Students who finish early can formulate additional problems, based on data from the chart, for others to solve.

REAL-WORLD CONNECTION

Real-World Connection Invite students to think about advertisements they see on TV or in newspapers and magazines. Ask them to tell which ones they think are questionable or deceptive and to explain why they think so.

TECHNOLOGY CONNECTION

Technology Connection Refer students to the video, laser disc, or software *Modumath: Arithmetic, Signed Numbers* from VTAE (VHS, IBM, for grades 6–12) for further practice with grouping positive and negative numbers on a number line, comparing signed numbers, and identifying absolute value of a given number.

GIFTED & TALENTED Meeting Individual Needs
   Ask your more advanced students to use a calculator to explore what happens when a negative number is subtracted from another number. Challenge them to explain why it happens. (The answer will be the same as if you added the opposite of the number. One example is subtracting −7° F from 57° F. Because you are trying to find the distance between −7 and 57, the answer is 64. A number line that includes negative numbers will help students visualize how this works.)

*available separately

◆ LESSON 23 Computing with Negative Numbers

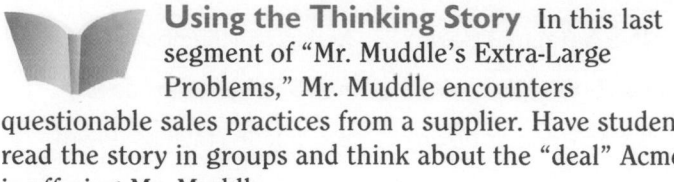

Using the Thinking Story In this last segment of "Mr. Muddle's Extra-Large Problems," Mr. Muddle encounters questionable sales practices from a supplier. Have students read the story in groups and think about the "deal" Acme is offering Mr. Muddle.

Answers to Thinking Story Questions:

1. "Extra-medium" doesn't make sense. It is unclear whether it would be smaller or larger than medium.

2. Roughly $3.95 per shirt. Normally, Mr. Muddle sells 165 shirts a week and receives one delivery a week, and he would have to pay Acme $2.95 for quality cloth and 70¢ for lettering for each shirt. He would pay $25 for the weekly delivery, which comes to about 15¢ a shirt. He sells about 700 T-shirts a month, so the service charge of $100 would add another 14¢ to the cost of each shirt. This adds up to $3.94. Although the sign is expensive, presumably it will last a long time and so not add an appreciable amount to the cost of each shirt.

3. Acme's cost per shirt is slightly lower than that of Quality, but in view of Acme's tricky sales practices, he could not be confident of getting a better deal. There might be other unmentioned costs to his "free" T-shirts, or perhaps they would not be delivered at all. Mr. Muddle seems to be aware of this when he says he wouldn't be proud to sell Acme T-shirts. There is no clear right answer to this question, but students should be asked to consider the value of dealing with a reputable company.

 Ask students to think back on all the decisions Mr. Muddle has made and to write a description of the kind of business person they think he is. Ask them to explain how they might do things if they were in his place.

◆ LESSON 23 Computing with Negative Numbers

Mr. Muddle's Extra-Large Problems

Part 4

You may want to refer to previous parts of this Thinking Story on pages 22-23, 38-39, and 70-71.

One day a woman walked into Mr. Muddle's T-shirt store. She said, "Mr. Muddle, I'm vice president of the Acme T-Shirt Company. I have an offer you won't be able to refuse. We will give you all the T-shirts you want, absolutely free! All you have to do is put a sign in your window that says 'We Proudly Sell Acme T-Shirts.'"

"Great," said Mr. Muddle. "Maybe at last I'll start to make money on my store."

"You'll be rich in no time," said the woman. "Would you like to place your first order right now?"

"You bet," said Mr. Muddle. "Since they're free, I'll take 1000 of each size."

"That's the spirit," said the woman. "Six thousand T-shirts!"

"You have six different sizes?" Mr. Muddle asked.

"Of course. Large, extra-large, small, extra-small, medium, and extra-medium. I guess you'll want the shirts made of our extra-special cloth. They will cost you only $2.95 a shirt. Believe me, it's worth it."

"All right," said Mr. Muddle. "Nothing but the best for my customers."

86 · Whole Numbers and Integers

C○PERATIVE LEARNING Invite students to work as "advertising teams" to design an advertisement and an order form for the Acme T-shirt company or another (imaginary) company that uses deceptive strategies to fool customers. Doing so may help students recognize deceptive business practices when they encounter them. Have groups share their efforts with the class.

Aside from continuing any extra help begun in earlier lessons, reteaching is not essential at this time. You may want to assign Enrichment Master 23.

Use the Cumulative Review on page 557 after this lesson.

"Do you want any lettering on the T-shirts?"

"Oh, yes," Mr. Muddle said. "All my T-shirts say 'T-Shirt' across the front."

"That's 10¢ a letter . . . for seven letters . . . 70¢ a shirt."

"Seven letters? I count six," said Mr. Muddle.

"You forgot the hyphen in 'T-Shirt.' But what's another dime when the shirts are free? Then there's the delivery charge—$25 per delivery, large or small."

Mr. Muddle started to look worried. "That's strange. The other company delivers free."

"Ah, but we have same-day delivery. We deliver them the same day you get them."

"Oh, that's all right then," replied Mr. Muddle.

"Then there's the service charge—only $100 a month. That's all. Except for the sign, of course. You put it in the window: 'We Proudly Sell Acme T-Shirts.' It's $450."

"No," said Mr. Muddle. "I can't do it. I know I'd save lots of money if I sold Acme T-shirts. But I don't think I would feel proud anymore."

. . . the end

Work in groups. Discuss your answers and how you figured them out. Then compare your answers with those of other groups. **Answers are in margin.**

❶ What is silly about the sizes Acme T-shirts come in?

❷ About how much would each "free" Acme T-shirt cost Mr. Muddle? You may have to work hard on this problem. Salespeople like the vice president from the Acme T-Shirt Company don't make it easy to figure out what things really cost.

❸ Would Mr. Muddle be better off getting his T-shirts from the Acme T-Shirt Company or staying with the other company? Explain your answer.

Unit 1 Lesson 23 • **87**

❸ Wrap-Up

5 MINUTES

In Closing To summarize the lesson, ask students to explain how to compute with negative numbers using a calculator.

Performance Assessment Provide a few addition and subtraction problems for students to solve with a calculator. Observe as they use the calculator.

Assessment Criteria

Did the student . . .

✓ demonstrate an ability to use a calculator to add and subtract with negative numbers?

✓ participate in the Thinking Story discussion?

✓ understand why Mr. Muddle made his decision in the Thinking Story?

Homework Assign Practice Master 23 for further practice in working with negative numbers.

> *We can remember—always—that at the heart of problem solving is the most basic and human skill of all—thinking.*
>
> –Stephen S. Willoughby,
> *Teaching Mathematics: What Is Basic?*

PRACTICE p. 23

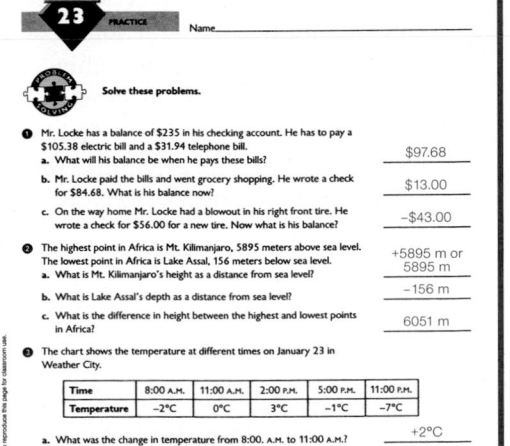

LESSON 23 PRACTICE   Name_____

Solve these problems.

❶ Mr. Locke has a balance of $235 in his checking account. He has to pay a $105.38 electric bill and a $31.94 telephone bill.
  a. What will his balance be when he pays these bills? — $97.68
  b. Mr. Locke paid the bills and went grocery shopping. He wrote a check for $84.68. What is his balance now? — $13.00
  c. On the way home Mr. Locke had a blowout on his right front tire. He wrote a check for $56.00 for a new tire. Now what is his balance? — –$43.00

❷ The highest point in Africa is Mt. Kilimanjaro, 5895 meters above sea level. The lowest point in Africa is Lake Assal, 156 meters below sea level.
  a. What is Mt. Kilimanjaro's height as a distance from sea level? — +5895 m or 5895 m
  b. What is Lake Assal's depth as a distance from sea level? — –156 m
  c. What is the difference in height between the highest and lowest points in Africa? — 6051 m

❸ The chart shows the temperature at different times on January 23 in Weather City.

Time	8:00 A.M.	11:00 A.M.	2:00 P.M.	5:00 P.M.	11:00 P.M.
Temperature	–2°C	0°C	3°C	–1°C	–7°C

  a. What was the change in temperature from 8:00 A.M. to 11:00 A.M.? — +2°C
  b. What was the change in temperature from 11:00 A.M. to 2:00 P.M.? — +3°C
  c. What was the change in temperature from 2:00 P.M. to 5:00 P.M.? — –4°C
  d. What was the change in temperature from 5:00 P.M. to 11:00 P.M.? — –6°C
  e. What was the change in temperature from 11:00 A.M. to 11:00 P.M.? — –7°C
  f. What was the change in temperature from 2:00 P.M. to 11:00 P.M.? — –10°C
  g. What were the highest and lowest temperatures on January 23? — can't tell

Math Explorations and Applications Level 6 • 23

ENRICHMENT p. 23

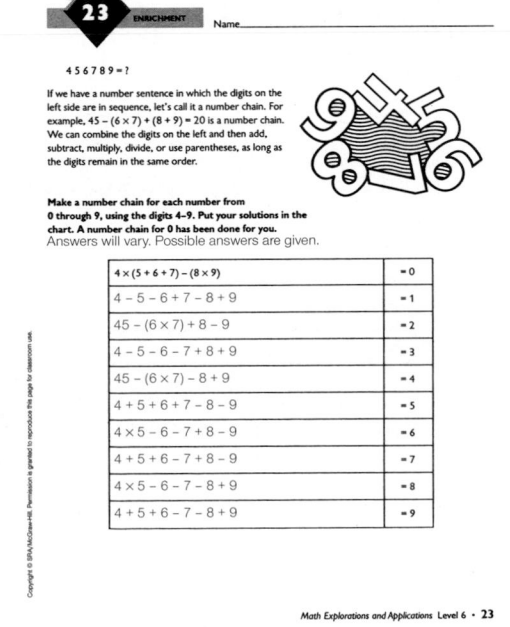

LESSON 23 ENRICHMENT   Name_____

4 5 6 7 8 9 = ?

If we have a number sentence in which the digits on the left side are in sequence, let's call it a number chain. For example, 45 – (6 × 7) + (8 + 9) = 20 is a number chain. We can combine the digits on the left and then add, subtract, multiply, divide, or use parentheses, as long as the digits remain in the same order.

Make a number chain for each number from 0 through 9, using the digits 4–9. Put your solutions in the chart. A number chain for 0 has been done for you. Answers will vary. Possible answers are given.

4 × (5 + 6 + 7) – (8 × 9)	= 0
4 – 5 – 6 + 7 – 8 + 9	= 1
45 – (6 × 7) + 8 – 9	= 2
4 – 5 – 6 – 7 + 8 + 9	= 3
45 – (6 × 7) – 8 + 9	= 4
4 + 5 + 6 + 7 – 8 – 9	= 5
4 × 5 – 6 – 7 + 8 – 9	= 6
4 + 5 + 6 – 7 + 8 – 9	= 7
4 × 5 – 6 – 7 – 8 + 9	= 8
4 + 5 + 6 – 7 – 8 + 9	= 9

Math Explorations and Applications Level 6 • 23

*available separately

Multiplying Positive and Negative Numbers

LESSON PLANNER

Objective

▶ to provide an intuitive introduction to the multiplication of integers

Context of the Lesson This is the third of three lessons on negative numbers. It covers the multiplication of integers, which is an important concept in later mathematics, especially algebra.

MANIPULATIVES
calculators*

Program Resources
Practice Master 24
Enrichment Master 24
For extra practice:
CD-ROM* Lesson 24

① Warm-Up ⏱ 5 MINUTES

Problem of the Day Present this problem: Amy says that she can do the calculation 50 × 4.264 × 2 × 0.025 × 4 in her head and in less than six seconds. Explain how she can do this. (One possible answer: multiply 50 x 2 x 0.025 to get 2.5, then multiply 2.5 x 4 to get 10, and finally multiply 10 x 4.264 to get 42.64.)

Problem-Solving Strategies Ask students who have solved the Problem of the Day to share how they solved it and any strategies they used.

MENTAL MATH Ask students to find each of the following products:

a. 57 x 1000 = (57,000)   b. 2.8 x 100 = (280)

c. 0.35 x 1000 = (350)   d. 33.8 x 1000 = (33,800)

ESL Meeting Individual Needs
You may find it useful to be sure that students understand the mathematical meaning of "negative" so that no one considers these numbers lacking in positive qualities. Emphasize that in mathematical language, negative numbers designate quantities less than 0, while positive numbers designate quantities greater than 0.

Multiplying Positive and Negative Numbers

If you save $5 every week for 50 weeks, how much money will you have saved? Did you add 5 over and over until you got your answer, or did you use a quicker way to find the answer?

If you borrow $4 from a friend every week for seven weeks, how much will you owe your friend after the seven weeks?

Borrowing $4 is like saving negative $4 (−$4), and being in debt $28 is like having saved −$28. Because of this sort of thinking, we say that $7 \times -4 = -28$. Or, in general, a positive number times a negative number is a negative number.

You know that with positive numbers the order in which you multiply two numbers doesn't influence the product. For example, 7×8 is the same as 8×7. We would like that same rule to apply to all numbers, so we say that $-4 \times 7 = 7 \times -4 = -28$.

Find the value of *n* in each of the following problems.

① $7 \times -3 = n$
−21

② $4 \times -6 = n$
−24

③ $n = 9 \times -5$
−45

④ $n = 20 \times -5$
−100

⑤ $48 \times -5 = n$
−240

⑥ $n = 50 \times -48$
−2400

⑦ $n = 25 \times -40$
−1000

⑧ $n = 25 \times -80$
−2000

⑨ $n = 80 \times -25$
−2000

⑩ $-3 \times 7 = n$
−21

⑪ $-6 \times 8 = n$
−48

⑫ $-80 \times 6 = n$
−480

Why teach it this way?

Multiplication involving integers is initially difficult for many students, so this introduction to the process is an informal one. Mastery is not expected at this time.

 **Language Arts Connection** Have students write a paragraph explaining why the product of two negative integers is positive.

RETEACHING

Because this lesson provides an informal, intuitive introduction to multiplying integers, no reteaching is recommended at this time. Further practice with integers is provided in the unit on functions and graphing. You may want to assign Enrichment Master 24.

Find the value of *n* in each of the following problems.

⑬ $n = -5 \times 48$
−240

⑭ $n = -25 \times 80$
−2000

⑮ $75 \times 80 = n$
6000

⑯ $75 \times -80 = n$
−6000

⑰ $-80 \times 75 = n$
−6000

⑱ $250 \times -20 = n$
−5000

⑲ $-250 \times 20 = n$
−5000

⑳ $n = -750 \times 20$
−15,000

㉑ $12 \times 6 = n$
72

㉒ $12 \times -6 = n$
−72

㉓ $n = -6 \times 12$
−72

㉔ $20 \times -50 = n$
−1000

㉕ $50 \times 20 = n$
1000

㉖ $n = -10 \times 10$
−100

㉗ $-100 \times 10 = n$
−1000

㉘ $45 \times 40 = n$
1800

㉙ $n = -40 \times 45$
−1800

㉚ $60 \times 70 = n$
4200

㉛ $60 \times -70 = n$
−4200

㉜ $n = 25 \times -8$
−200

㉝ $-60 \times 12 = n$
−720

㉞ $16 \times 4 = n$
64

㉟ $n = 11 \times -8$
−88

㊱ $n = -7 \times 5$
−35

㊲ Consider the following four multiplication problems:

$3 \times 4 = ?$ $3 \times -4 = ?$ $-3 \times 4 = ?$ $-3 \times -4 = ?$

What should the answer to the last problem be? Should it be the same as the answer to either the second or third problem? Why or why not? Discuss this with your friends. What do you think is a reasonable answer to the question "What is -3 times -4?" Would you choose the rule that the product of two negative numbers is positive, or that the product of two negative numbers is negative? **12; no; The product of two negative numbers is a positive number.**
Because people find it most convenient to use the rule that a negative number multiplied by a negative number equals a positive number, most calculators have been programmed to follow this rule.

㊳ Write a problem that could be solved by multiplying a negative number by a positive number. **Answers will vary.**

The lowest temperature ever recorded on Earth was −89°C (−129°F) at Vostok, Antarctica on July 21, 1983.

Unit 1 Lesson 24 • **89**

PRACTICE p. 24

Solve. Watch the signs.

❶ −486 + 157 = _−329_
❷ 5309 × (−26) = _−138,034_
❸ −2000 − 156 = _−2156_
❹ 728 × (−300) = _−218,400_
❺ 5100 ÷ (−897) = _4203_
❻ 5000 × 819 = _4,095,000_
❼ −589 + (−647) = _−1236_
❽ 829 − (−417) = _1246_
❾ 112 × 43 = _4816_
❿ (−3200) × 180 = _−576,000_
⓫ 31 × (−151) = _−4681_
⓬ 762 × 493 = _375,666_
⓭ 100 × 3000 = _300,000_
⓮ 768 × (−50) = _−38,400_
⓯ 191 × (−63) = _−12,033_
⓰ (−18) − 43 = _−61_
⓱ 127 × (−127) = _−16,129_
⓲ 64 × (−64) = _−4096_
⓳ 351 × (−35) = _−12,285_
⓴ 56 − 13 = _43_

⓫ −13 × 75 = _−975_
⓬ 102 × −7 = _−714_
⓭ 3000 − 249 = _2751_
⓮ 166 − 82 = _84_
⓯ 800 × (−1473) = _−1,178,400_
⓰ −24 × 96 = _−2304_
⓱ 114 − 876 = _−762_
⓲ 35 + (−59) = _−24_
⓳ 1700 − 944 = _756_
⓴ −1010 × 500 = _−505,000_
㉒ 812 − 439 = _373_
㉓ 35 + (−409) = _−374_
㉔ −300 × 1000 = _−300,000_
㉕ 434 − 23 = _411_
㉖ 210 × 4 = _840_
㉗ (−43) − 18 = _−61_
㉘ 30 × (−18) = _−540_
㉙ −511 × 1300 = _−664,300_
㉚ −1000 + 995 = _−5_
㉛ 13 − 56 = _−43_

ENRICHMENT p. 24

Complete each multiplication problem. Use the code to find the letter for that answer. Write the letter next to the answer. Read the letters from left to right to find the answer to the riddle.

−64	×	−63	F	−56	Y	−48	W	−45	D	−42	B
−40	Q	−36	I	−32	P	−30	J	−24	E	−21	'
−18	N	−16	S	16	H	18	M	21	Z	24	U
30	space	32	R	36	A	40	O	42	T	45	C
48	V	56	G	63	K	64	L				

−9 × −4 = _36 A_   −2 × 9 = _−18 N_   5 × 6 = _30 space_

−6 × 4 = _24 E_   8 × 8 = _64 L_   8 × −3 = _−24 E_

−4 × 8 = _−32 P_   −4 × −4 = _16 H_   −6 × −6 = _36 A_

−3 × 6 = _−18 N_   −7 × −6 = _42 T_   −7 × 3 = _−21 '_

4 × −4 = _−16 S_   −6 × −5 = _30 space_   2 × −8 = _−16 S_

−8 × −2 = _16 H_   6 × 6 = _36 A_   −9 × 5 = _−45 D_

−8 × −5 = _40 O_   −6 × 8 = _−48 W_

What is as big as an elephant and does not weigh anything? _an elephant's shadow_

---

② Teach

Using the Student Pages Before doing the problems on pages 88 and 89, ask students to try to provide real-life examples of multiplying a negative number by a positive one. Students may suggest situations involving deep-sea diving, digging in the ground, football (negative yardage gained) or golf (strokes below par) statistics, or temperatures.

Have students read the top of page 88 and do the problems on pages 88 and 89. Problem 37 requires some discussion. Guide students to conclude, by examining the pattern, that –3 x –4 must be the opposite of –3 x 4, so it should be 12. Be sure they understand that this is true because it is logical and not because the calculator says so.

③ Wrap-Up

In Closing To summarize the lesson, ask students to describe the patterns they have noticed when integers are multiplied.

Informal Assessment Circulate and observe students as they work on the problems. To help assess their understanding, you may wish to ask students to give real-life problems for some of the computations.

Assessment Criteria

Did the student . . .

✓ come up with good examples of multiplication of integers?

✓ correctly answer at least 75% of the problems?

✓ give a good argument for his or her answer to problem 37?

Homework Have students write a paragraph in their Math Journals explaining the usefulness of negative numbers.

LESSON 25 — Unit 1 Review

Student Edition pages 90–91

Using the Student Pages Use this Unit Review as a preliminary unit test to indicate areas in which an individual student is having difficulty or in which the entire class may need help. If students do well on the Unit Review, you may wish to skip directly to the next unit. If not, you may want to spend a day or so helping students overcome their individual difficulties before they take the Unit Test.

Next to each instruction line is a list of the lessons in the unit covered in that set of problems. Students can refer to the specific lesson for additional instruction if they need help. You can also use this information to make additional assignments based on the previous lesson concepts.

 **Problems 1–16** Students who miss more than three of these problems about basic facts and whole numbers should be assessed individually to determine the nature of their difficulty. Reteach these students using an appropriate strategy from the lesson that teaches the corresponding difficult concepts. For example, you may wish to have students play an appropriate version of the "Roll a Problem" game (pages 46 and 63) or the "Don't Go Over 1000" game (page 35).

ASSESSMENT

LESSON 25 Unit 1 Review

Lessons 8, 9, 12, 15, and 16 — Solve these problems. Watch the signs.

1. 783 + 246 = **1029**
2. 4038 − 896 = **3142**
3. 5309 × 73 = **387,557**
4. 6)7404 = **1234**
5. 8)7704 = **963**
6. 4038 + 896 = **4934**
7. 5309 − 4000 = **1309**
8. 35)15,960 = **456**
9. 783 × 246 = **192,618**
10. 4038 × 89 = **359,382**
11. 9)3843 = **427**
12. 7)2247 = **321**
13. 5309 + 4873 = **10,182**
14. 783 − 246 = **537**
15. 8)8352 = **1044**
16. 80)83,520 = **1044**

Lessons 13 and 20 — In each problem two of the answers are clearly wrong and one is correct. Choose the correct answer.

17. 728 × 542 — a. 39,456 **(b.) 394,576** c. 3,913,456
18. 7523 × 806 — **(a.) 6,063,538** b. 663,538 c. 60,063,538
19. 7523 + 803 — **(a.) 8326** b. 15,326 c. 5326
20. 3014 − 876 — a. 5862 **(b.) 2138** c. 3962
21. 47,705 ÷ 145 — a. 9306 b. 4076 **(c.) 329**
22. 2409 ÷ 73 — a. 2113 b. 213 **(c.) 33**
23. 682 × 47 — a. 36,524 **(b.) 32,054** c. 22,864
24. 451 + 926 — **(a.) 1377** b. 5277 c. 13,477
25. 8194 − 3475 — **(a.) 4719** b. 5321 c. 7429
26. 90,272 ÷ 28 — a. 32 b. 324 **(c.) 3224**

90 • Whole Numbers and Integers

RETEACHING

Students who have difficulty with this Unit Review should have further opportunity to review and to practice the skills before they proceed on with the next unit. For each set of problems there are specific suggestions for reteaching. These suggestions can be found in the margins.

90 Whole Numbers and Integers

Lessons 22 and 24

Solve. Watch for negative numbers.

㉗ 5 + 20 **25**   ㉘ 5 − 20 **−15**   ㉙ (−5) + 20 **15**

㉚ (−5) − 20 **−25**   ㉛ 13 − 8 **5**   ㉜ 8 − 13 **−5**

㉝ (−13) − 8 **−21**   ㉞ (−8) − 13 **−21**   ㉟ 5 × −4 **−20**

㊱ −3 × 6 **−18**   ㊲ −2 × 1 **−2**   ㊳ 7 × −8 **−56**

Solve these problems.

㊴ How many students are in 14 classes of 25 students each? **350**

㊵ As many as 50 children can be transported on one ABC school bus. How many buses are needed to transport 342 children? **7**

Lessons 9, 13, 17, 18, and 22

㊶ You can get 3 kilograms of dog food for $4.77 or 7 kilograms of the same dog food for $10.46. In which container does the dog food cost less per kilogram? **7-kilogram container**

㊷ If the temperature is 15°C now, what will it be if it

a. goes down 5°C? **10°C**

b. goes down 15°C? **0°C**

c. goes up 8°C? **23°C**

d. goes down 30°C? **−15°C (15° below 0°C)**

㊸ One kilogram of hamburger costs $4.19.

a. How much will 7 kilograms cost? **$29.33**

b. How much will 4 kilograms cost? **$16.76**

c. How much will 10 kilograms cost? **$41.90**

㊹ Leo has $12.00. With it he has to pay $1.20 for lunch five times next week and buy a notebook that costs $1.49. Does he have enough money so that he can buy a $5.00 ticket for the high school football game today? **no**

㊺ Suki is crushing aluminum cans to send to the recycling center. She has about 600 cans to crush and can crush two cans every minute. About how long will it take Suki to crush all the cans? **300 minutes (5 hours)**

Unit 1 Review • 91

Problems 17–26 Students who miss any of these approximation problems or who do them by calculating the exact answer should be checked individually. If the trouble is with rounding, follow the suggestions in the Reteaching for Lesson 20, or assign Reteaching page 6. You might have students play the "Approximation" game (page 75) as well.

Problems 27–38 Students who miss more than two of these problems should act out each of the missed problems using a number line or thermometer. Keep in mind that those students who are consistently off by one may be counting the starting number as a step.

Problems 39–45 Students who have trouble with these word problems should be encouraged to act them out or to draw pictures to illustrate the concepts of the problem. Working out the problems in this way will make the situation clearer.

Portfolio Assessment If you have not already assigned the Portfolio Assessment task provided on Assessment Blackline Masters page 86, it can be used at this time to evaluate students' ability to solve a complex problem involving arithmetic.

Performance Assessment The Performance Assessment Task 2 provided on Assessment Blackline Masters page 64 can be used at this time to evaluate students' proficiency with division and integers. You may want to administer this assessment with individual students or in small groups.

Unit Project If you have not already assigned the "Clever Counting" project on pages 98 and 99, you may wish to do so at this time. This project is a good opportunity for students to compare our base-10 system with other systems.

PRACTICE p. 25

LESSON 25 PRACTICE Name_____

Add.

❶ 5327 + 8496 = 13,823

❷ 3872 + 149 = 4021

❸ 287 + 8493 = 8780

❹ 5271 + 8046 = 13,317

Subtract.

❺ 7891 − 5206 = 2685

❻ 4738 − 1296 = 3442

❼ 5203 − 498 = 4705

❽ 2714 − 489 = 2225

Add or subtract. Watch the signs.

❾ 5279 − 3841 = 1438

❿ 2309 + 147 = 2456

⓫ 8591 + 4268 = 12,859

⓬ 5234 − 1496 = 3738

Multiply. Check your answers to be sure they make sense.

⓭ 52 × 76 = 3952

⓮ 429 × 25 = 10,725

⓯ 781 × 603 = 470,943

⓰ 3000 × 80 = 240,000

Divide. There will be no remainder.

⓱ 426, 7⟌2982

⓲ 502, 4⟌2008

⓳ 259, 6⟌1554

⓴ 4528, 3⟌13,584

Add or subtract. Watch the signs.

㉑ (−8) + 15 **7**   ㉒ (−8) − 15 **−23**   ㉓ 8 − 15 **−7**   ㉔ (−15) − 8 **−23**

In each problem two of the answers are clearly wrong and one is correct. Choose the correct answer.

㉕ 7502 × 26 **c**   a. 1952   b. 19,552   c. 195,052

㉖ 41,246 ÷ 82 **a**   a. 503   b. 53   c. 50

Math Explorations and Applications Level 6 • 25

ENRICHMENT p. 25

LESSON 25 ENRICHMENT Name_____

Five girls participated and won events at Peru Middle School's track and field meet. Of these girls, two competed in both the shot put and discus events (field events), and three competed in the 50-meter dash, the 100-meter dash, and the hurdles (track events). No girl participated in both track and field events. Each girl won exactly one competition. From the clues below, find each girl's full name and the event she won.

- The 100-meter dash winner lost to Li in another event.
- Li and Julie (who isn't Wong) were not in any of the same events.
- In one event Nicole beat Garcia and the 50-meter dash winner.
- Steele did not participate in field events.
- Wong, who did not win the discus throw, was not in any event with Angie or Kayla.
- Garcia (who is not Angie) did not win the 100-meter dash.

Below is a table that might help you solve the puzzle. Put an X to indicate a definite "no" and an O to indicate a definite "yes."

Example: According to the first clue, Li was in the track events but did not win the 100-meter dash. So Xs have been entered to show that shot put, discus, and 100-m dash are "no."

	Brindle	Garcia	Li	Steele	Wong	shot put	discus	50-m dash	100-m dash	hurdles
Angie	X	X	O	X	X	X	X	O	X	X
Julie	O	X	X	X	X	X	O	X	X	X
Kayla	X	O	X	X	X	X	X	X	X	O
Nicole	X	X	X	O	X	X	X	X	O	X
Sierra	X	X	X	X	O	O	X	X	X	X
shot put	X	X	X	X	O					
discus	O	X	X	X	X					
50-m dash	X	X	O	X	X					
100-m dash	X	X	X	O	X					
hurdles	X	O	X	X	X					

Angie Li, 50-m dash;
Julie Brindle, discus;
Kayla Garcia, hurdles;
Nicole Steele, 100-m dash;
Sierra Wong, shot put

Math Explorations and Applications Level 6 • 25

LESSON
26

LESSON
26

Student Edition pages 92–95

Unit 1 Practice

Using the Student Pages The purpose of these pages is to provide additional practice for those students who demonstrated a need for it on the Unit Review. You may wish to assign only the specific exercises in this Unit Practice for which students need further reinforcement. Each instruction line gives the lessons in the unit it covers so that you or students can refer to the specific lesson for additional review and instruction.

 Students who do not require additional practice on specific concepts may enjoy playing the "Numbo Jumbo" game on page 95. This game provides practice with logical reasoning. You may also wish to have them play any other games you have played so far, such as the various "Roll a Problem" games. These students may also help by practicing flashcard drills and playing appropriate games with students who need remedial practice or by actually teaching certain procedures to other students.

 You may want to use the Cumulative Review on page 558 after this lesson.

Unit 1 Practice

Add.

Lesson 8

① 3847
+ 6952
10,799

② 8340
+ 7396
15,736

③ 4783
+ 2875
7658

④ 3872
+ 846
4718

⑤ 7903
+ 3408
11,311

⑥ 9994
+ 9876
19,870

⑦ 403
+ 7828
8231

⑧ 5743
+ 6921
12,664

Lesson 9

Subtract.

⑨ 5302
− 461
4841

⑩ 5871
− 3942
1929

⑪ 5003
− 2769
2234

⑫ 4872
− 2171
2701

⑬ 10,000
− 3,462
6538

⑭ 6047
− 382
5665

⑮ 43,571
− 488
43,083

⑯ 2576
− 1849
727

Lessons 8 and 9

Watch the signs.

⑰ 4321
+ 3456
7777

⑱ 4321
− 3456
865

⑲ 9878
+ 5676
15,554

⑳ 9878
− 5676
4202

㉑ 4823
+ 759
5582

㉒ 6104
− 586
5518

㉓ 403
− 397
6

㉔ 403
+ 397
800

Lessons 11 and 12

Multiply. Check your answers to be sure that they make sense.

㉕ 200
× 4
800

㉖ 534
× 9
4806

㉗ 6395
× 7
44,765

㉘ 308
× 21
6468

㉙ 78
× 54
4212

㉚ 69
× 73
5037

㉛ 59
× 96
5664

㉜ 879
× 302
265,458

㉝ 607
× 865
525,055

㉞ 703
× 71
49,913

㉟ 300
× 800
240,000

㊱ 2000
× 90
180,000

92 • Whole Numbers and Integers

Lesson 15 Divide. Answers will be whole numbers. There will be no remainder.

37 8)4032 = **504** **38** 6)534 = **89** **39** 5)3915 = **783** **40** 7)59,479 = **8497**

41 9)40,752 = **4528** **42** 3)534 = **178** **43** 4)11,352 = **2838** **44** 2)13,578 = **6789**

Lesson 16 Divide. Round decimal quotients to the nearest whole number.

45 50)473,200 = **9464** **46** 25)473,210 = **18,928.4→18,928** **47** 25)905 = **36.2→36**

48 25)700 = **28** **49** 25)6120 = **244.8→245** **50** 75)5750 = **76.6→77**

Lessons 22 and 24 Watch the signs.

51 5 + 10 = **15** **52** 5 − 10 = **−5** **53** (−5) + 10 = **5** **54** (−5) − 10 = **−15**

55 10 − 20 = **−10** **56** 10 + 20 = **30** **57** (−10) − 20 = **−30** **58** (−10) + 20 = **10**

59 7 − 8 = **−1** **60** 8 − 7 = **1** **61** (−7) − 8 = **−15** **62** (−8) − 7 = **−15**

63 6 × −9 = **−54** **64** −25 × 4 = **−100** **65** −30 × 70 = **−2100** **66** 16 × −5 = **−80**

Lessons 13 and 20 In each problem two of the answers are clearly wrong and one is correct. Choose the correct answer.

67 438 × 694 =   **a.** 3372   **b.** 33,972   **(c.)** 303,972

68 6805 × 79 =   **a.** 5595   **b.** 53,595   **(c.)** 537,595

69 4567 × 824 =   **a.** 373,208   **(b.)** 3,763,208   **c.** 37,863,208

70 6 × 7863 =   **a.** 478   **b.** 4718   **(c.)** 47,178

71 597 × 68 =   **a.** 4596   **(b.)** 40,596   **c.** 401,596

72 742,014 ÷ 78 =   **(a.)** 9513   **b.** 95,113   **c.** 950,413

73 291,312 ÷ 408 =   **a.** 74   **(b.)** 714   **c.** 7314

74 264,128 ÷ 64 =   **a.** 427   **(b.)** 4127   **c.** 41,027

75 46,890 ÷ 45 =   **a.** 142   **(b.)** 1042   **c.** 10,342

76 3145 ÷ 37 =   **a.** 5   **b.** 8   **(c.)** 85

Unit 1 Practice • **93**

Technology Connection Refer students to the software *Troggle Trouble* from MECC (Mac, IBM, for grades 1–6) for further practice with basic math facts, operations, calculator skills, story problems, and puzzles.

◆ **LESSON 26 Unit 1 Practice**

◆ **LESSON 26 Unit 1 Practice**

Lessons 9, 13, 17, 18, and 22

Solve these problems.

77 If 50 cubes (all the same weight) weigh 194 grams, how much does each cube weigh? **3.88 g**

78 If 194 people each gave $50 to the local college, how much would the college get? **$9700**

79 Mr. Muñoz's hens laid 194 eggs, but 50 of the eggs were broken in an accident. There are 12 eggs in a dozen. How many dozens of unbroken eggs did Mr. Muñoz have that he could sell? **12**

80 Mary can read about 50 pages in an hour. One day she read a book that was 194 pages long, and then she spent an hour reading another book.

a. About how many pages did she read that day? **about 244**

b. About how many hours did she read that day? **about 5**

81 If you have to cook a 6-kilogram turkey about five hours at 170°C, how long and at what temperature would you cook two 6-kilogram turkeys? **about 5 hours at 170°C**

82 If the temperature is 10°C, what will the temperature be

a. when it goes down 10°C? **0°C**

b. when it goes up 10°C? **20°C**

c. when it goes down 20°C? **−10°C (10° below 0°C)**

d. when it goes down 5°C? **5°C**

e. when it goes down 25°C? **−15°C (15° below 0°C)**

83 Tickets to the class play cost $1.98. About $240 has been collected so far. About how many people have bought tickets? **about 120**

84 Jesse is preparing to mail flyers about the next club meeting. He can fold, staple, and put address labels on three flyers every minute. How long will it take him to finish 75 flyers? **25 minutes**

85 Ms. Lee earns about $3200 each month. About how much does she earn each year? **about $38,400**

94 • Whole Numbers and Integers

RETEACHING

Students who have difficulty with this Unit Practice should have further opportunity to review and to practice the skills before they proceed on with the next unit. Beside each set of problems is a reference to the lesson or lessons from which the problems were taken. You may want to review the individual lessons with students who are having difficulty with them.

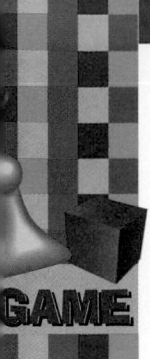

Numbo Jumbo

C⊙⊙PERATIVE LEARNING

Players:	Two
Materials:	None
Object:	To determine the other player's number
Math Focus:	Mathematical reasoning

GAME

RULES

1. The first player chooses and writes down secretly any two-digit number in which no digit is repeated. Numbers that start with 0 (such as 07) are acceptable.

2. The second player says a two-digit number.

3. The first player responds with the letter *T* for each digit the second player guesses correctly and has in the correct position, *P* for each digit the second player guesses correctly but has in the wrong spot, and *F* for each digit he or she guesses incorrectly.

4. Repeat steps 2 and 3 until the first player responds with *TT*.

   Here are some suggestions:

   A. The first player should announce *T*s first, then *P*s, and then *F*s to avoid giving information about the order of the digits.

   B. Both players should record every guess and every response.

SAMPLE GAME

Glenda wrote 94 on her paper and hid it from Michael.

Michael guessed: 57 46 68   Glenda responded: FF PF FF

Michael stopped to think. He said to himself "5, 7, 6, and 8 cannot occur. Four is in the ones place, so all I have to find is the other number."

Michael guessed: 01 93 94   Glenda responded: FF TF TT

ANOTHER WAY TO PLAY THIS GAME

Use three-digit numbers instead of two-digit numbers.

Use the Cumulative Review on page 558 after this lesson.

Unit 1 Practice • **95**

GAME **Introducing the "Numbo Jumbo" Game**
Students who have finished any necessary practice may play the "Numbo Jumbo" game in pairs. The purpose of this game is to encourage the use of logic, planning, and organization to discover needed information. With 3-digit numbers the use of indirect reasoning becomes important, and good players will learn the desirability of getting *FFF* as a response, since this gives considerable (negative) information.

PRACTICE p. 26

LESSON 26 PRACTICE   Name_____

Solve these problems.

1. If a farmer harvests about 550 apples per tree, how many peck-sized bags will she need to hold the apples from each tree? A peck-sized bag holds 25 to 30 apples.
   19 to 22 bags

2. A service club at school is selling bumper stickers at $2.50 each. The club has collected about $170 so far. About how many bumper stickers have been sold?
   68 bumper stickers

3. Ben must keep a minimum balance of $2500.00 in his checking account to avoid paying a service fee. He wants to write a check for $342.00. His account has $2781.04 in it. What is the minimum Ben must deposit to avoid paying a service fee?
   $60.96

4. The road between Apple and Orange is about 534 kilometers. Richard left Apple three hours ago and has been driving at 95 kilometers an hour. If he continues at the same speed, about how many more hours will he be on the road to Orange?
   about 3 hours

5. A van can transport eight people. How many vans will be needed to transport 105 people to the game?
   14 vans

6. Mr. Browne changes the oil in his car every 2500 miles. The last oil change was at 8450 miles. He has driven 1247 miles since the last oil change. How many more miles can Mr. Browne drive before it is time for another oil change?
   1253 miles

26 • Math Explorations and Applications Level 6

ENRICHMENT p. 26

LESSON 26 ENRICHMENT   Name_____

Travis, Ryan, Roberto, Michelle, Heather, and Brenda were talking about the jobs listed in the help-wanted section. Use the clues below to decide who chose each job.

Help Wanted Travel Agent Intern Learn to use computers to schedule travel. Must have excellent math and map skills.	Help Wanted Sales Trainee Carpet Central Company needs enthusiastic people to train in sales.	Help Wanted Apprentice Installer Carpet Central Company will train new tile-and-carpet installers.
Help Wanted Accounting Intern Learn to use computer-based accounting. Must have excellent computational skills.	**Help Wanted Surveying Apprentice** Must like to work out-of-doors. Need measurement and math skills.	**Help Wanted Inventory Trainee** Will help check orders and stock shelves. Must have good organizational skills.

Each person chose a different job.
The jobs chosen by boys were: inventory trainee, accounting intern, and one of the Carpet Central Company jobs.
Heather's job title included the word *Trainee*.
Ryan's mother is a carpenter and he wanted to start as an apprentice.
Michelle did not want to work outdoors.
Roberto chose the job that would help him prepare for college, where he hopes to become a certified public accountant (CPA).

Travis, inventory trainee; Ryan, apprentice installer; Roberto, accounting intern; Michelle, travel agent intern; Heather, sales trainee; Brenda, surveying apprentice

	Accounting Intern	Surveying Apprentice	Inventory Trainee	Travel Agent Intern	Sales Trainee	Apprentice Installer
					Carpet Central Company	
Travis	X	X	O	X	X	X
Ryan	X	X	X	X	X	O
Roberto	O	X	X	X	X	X
Michelle	X	X	X	O	X	X
Heather	X	X	X	X	O	X
Brenda	X	O	X	X	X	X

26 • Math Explorations and Applications Level 6

Unit Test

Using the Student Pages The Unit Test on Student Edition pages 96 and 97 provides an opportunity to formally evaluate your students' proficiency with concepts developed in this unit. It is similar in content and format to the Unit Review. Students who did well on the Unit Review may not need to take this test. Students who did not do well on the Unit Review should be provided with additional practice opportunities, such as the Unit Practice pages, before taking the Unit Test. As an alternative, you may wish to have these students take the Unit Test on Assessment Blackline Masters pages 15–17 or the Unit Test in standardized format, provided on Assessment Blackline Masters pages 94–100.

Unit Test

Watch the signs.

❶ 356 × 78 **27,768** ❷ 356 − 78 **278** ❸ 356 + 78 **434** ❹ 1274 × 91 **115,934**

❺ 1274 + 91 **1365** ❻ 1274 − 91 **1183** ❼ 1274 ÷ 91 **14** ❽ 7990 ÷ 85 **94**

❾ 4007 − 2409 **1598** ❿ 5386 + 825 **6211** ⓫ 679 × 48 **32,592** ⓬ 11,984 ÷ 14 **856**

⓭ 5992 ÷ 7 **856** ⓮ 30,168 ÷ 9 **3352** ⓯ 52,824 ÷ 6 **8804** ⓰ 18,075 ÷ 5 **3615**

In each problem two of the answers are clearly wrong and one is correct. Choose the correct answer.

⓱ 4673 × 75,154   **a.** 351,194,642 **b.** 35,194,624 **c.** 3,904,624

⓲ 672 × 4960   **a.** 33,120   **b.** 333,120   **c.** 3,333,120

⓳ 716,103 ÷ 753   **a.** 951   **b.** 9451   **c.** 94,451

⓴ 5,718,016 ÷ 1024   **a.** 584   **b.** 5584   **c.** 55,484

㉑ 4673 + 75,154   **a.** 129,827   **b.** 12,827   **c.** 79,827

㉒ 75,154 − 4673   **a.** 28,481   **b.** 70,481   **c.** 2481

Add or subtract. Watch for negative numbers.

㉓ (−5) + 5 **0** ㉔ (−5) − 5 **−10** ㉕ (−5) − 10 **−15**

㉖ 13 − 7 **6** ㉗ 7 − 13 **−6** ㉘ (−7) − 13 **−20**

㉙ (−8) + 7 **−1** ㉚ (−8) − 7 **−15** ㉛ 8 − 7 **1**

㉜ −7 × 2 **−14** ㉝ 8 × 9 **72** ㉞ 25 × −3 **−75**

PROBLEM SOLVING

Solve these problems.

㉟ Gloria's checking-account balance was $63. Then she wrote a check for $73. What was her new balance? **−$10 or $10 overdrawn**

㊱ Happy Cow Dairy sells milk in 2-liter cartons for $1.32 or in 10-liter cartons for $6.50. In which container does the milk cost less per liter? **10-L container**

37 At the Quick-Service store a liter of milk costs 73¢ and a loaf of bread costs 90¢. How much will John pay for 2 liters of milk and three loaves of bread? **$4.16**

38 Celia's class is making Thanksgiving nut cups for the hospital. The students can make 30 nut cups in ten minutes. How long will it take them to make 600 nut cups? **200 minutes or 3 hours and 20 minutes**

39 Mr. Chen wants the class to finish the nut cup project in five days. Will they finish on time if they work on the nut cups 30 minutes each day? **no**

40 At the beginning of the day the odometer on the school bus showed 49,723 kilometers. At the end of the day the odometer showed 49,916 kilometers.

   a. How many kilometers did the bus travel that day? **193**

   b. How much farther must the bus travel before the odometer shows 50,000 kilometers? **84 km**

41 A Hubmobile car can transport six people. How many Hubmobile cars will be needed to transport 27 people? **5**

42 A stationery store sells a box of 24 pencils for $1.98. Do you think the store will sell you one pencil for 6¢? **no**

43 Tomás was born on April 29, 1985. In what year will he

   a. graduate from high school? **can't tell**

   b. be 30 years old? **2015**

   c. be 75 years old? **2060**

44 Mr. Havel wants to fertilize his lawn. Each bag of fertilizer is supposed to cover 75 square feet. Mr. Havel's front lawn is 144 square feet and the back lawn is 200 square feet. How many bags of fertilizer will Mr. Havel need to buy (assuming he doesn't already have some)? **5 bags**

45 Vanessa stopped for lunch at a fast-food restaurant. She wanted a hamburger for $1.89, a salad for $1.29, and a lemonade for $0.89. She had $5 with her. Could she buy the lunch she wanted? **yes**

Unit 1 Test • **97**

ASSESSMENT p. 15

UNIT 1 | Unit 1 Test (Use after Lesson 26.) | Page 1 of 3

Name _____

The student demonstrates mastery by correctly answering at least 36 of the 45 problems.

Solve. Watch the signs.

1 7)6498 → 928 R2

2 41)85,602 → 2087 R35

3 7934 + 8972 = 16,906

4 6407 × 42 = 269,094

5 536 × 66 = 35,376

6 16)4176 → 261

7 846 + 787 = 1633

8 8473 − 509 = 7964

9 5)1605 → 321

10 10,001 − 7,450 = 2551

11 8)51,412 → 6426 R4

12 3047 − 2052 = 995

13 15)21,645 → 1443

14 88)5142 → 58 R38

15 2302 × 32 = 73,664

16 4862 + 999 = 5861

17 4516 × 27 = 121,932

18 6009 − 1998 = 4011

Math Explorations and Applications Level 6 • **15**

PRESENTING THE PROJECT

Project Objectives

▶ to show that disparate and distant societies developed counting procedures that seem quite dissimilar but have a great deal in common

▶ to contrast the base-10 place value system with other systems

MANIPULATIVES

books such as *Ethnomathematics*, or various history of mathematics books or encyclopedias that provide information about numeration systems

Students should work independently or in groups with relatively little teacher supervision on this project. To begin the project, they should complete the activities on page 98.

Portfolio Assessment After students complete page 98, they should keep the papers they have written in their Math Portfolios after you have seen and commented on them.

When to Assess the Project Assessment should occur throughout all stages of a project.

▶ **Before a project,** find out what students already know and what their needs, interests, and experiences are.

▶ **During a project,** assess to check progress, provide assistance, or modify activities, if necessary.

▶ **After a project,** assess to find out what students learned, evaluate the quality of the learning, and gauge the effectiveness of the project approach.

What to Assess In projects students have the opportunity to demonstrate a variety of competencies. Teachers can choose to evaluate students on any or all of the following:

▶ **Basic skills** include reading, writing, arithmetic and other mathematics, speaking, and listening.

▶ **Thinking skills** include thinking creatively, making decisions, solving problems, thinking visually, knowing how to learn, and reasoning.

▶ **Interpersonal skills** include individual responsibility, self-esteem, ability to work in a group, self-management, and integrity.

COOPERATIVE LEARNING

CLEVER COUNTING

People in all cultures and all times have needed to count. Different cultures develop different ways of expressing numbers.

The Romans developed a numeration system that we still see in use today. Originally, the Roman numerals for 1 through 10 were I, II, III, IIII, V, VI, VII, VIII, VIIII, and X.

SOCIAL STUDIES CONNECTION

◆ Do you see a possible connection between these symbols and finger counting? Explain. **Each "1" stands for a finger, "V" stands for a hand, and "X" stands for two hands.** Later the symbols IV and IX were used instead of IIII and VIIII. What does it mean when the "I" is written before the "V" and the "X"? Why do you suppose this change was made? **It means one less than "V" or "X". This change was probably made to make numbers** Try doing the following problems using only Roman numerals (don't **easier to** convert to your usual system or use a calculator). **write and read.**

Use the Roman numerals, including L = 50, C = 100, D = 500, and M = 1000.

MMMMDLXXVI + MCCCCLXXII
MMMMMMXXXXVIII

MMMCCLXXVIII − MDCCCLXVIIII
MCCCCVIIII

CLXXXVIII × XVIII
MMMCCCLXXXIIII
Show all your work for these problems in Roman numerals.

How to Assess Record and use information in ways that you determine will be helpful to you and your students. Below are some ideas for routine forms of assessment that can provide regular feedback.

▶ **Observations** can take the form of watching, listening, discussing, questioning, challenging, or answering students' questions.

▶ **Checklists** can help you focus on specific aspects of your students' learning and behavior.

▶ **Interviews** of individuals, pairs, or small groups can provide valuable insights into students' thoughts about a project and the project approach, as well as how students view themselves and others.

▶ **Group assessment** can focus on how well all members of the group fulfill their roles, enabling the group to function successfully.

Many other number systems have been used.

CULTURE	NUMBER SYSTEM BASED ON	REGION
Babylonians	60	Middle East
Mayans	20	South America
Yuki	8	North America
Nahuatl	addition	Central America
Hindu-Arabic	10	Asia
Computers	2	everywhere

Conduct library research to investigate these or other numeration systems, and do some calculations in those systems as well.

MATH JOURNAL

In your Math Journal discuss how difficult arithmetic is in our system, which uses place value as well as base 10, as compared with a system that does not use place value.

Unit 1 Wrap-Up • **99**

▶ **Student self-assessment** provides an opportunity to understand your students' perception of their own strengths, problems, and work habits, as well as their perception of the value of the project.

▶ **Portfolio assessment** can be accomplished by collecting samples of students' work on this project and throughout the unit.

What Is a Math Project? Math projects in *Math Explorations and Applications* are real-world problem-solving activities in which students use many different mathematics skills. These mathematics projects are not word problems that focus on one skill area; rather, students must draw from all that they already know about mathematics to complete them. They offer students freedom to problem-solve on their own or ask teachers and classmates to help them with the necessary mathematics skills.

Why Use Projects in Mathematics? Projects give students a reason to learn mathematics. They provide for students a direct route to mathematics literacy and are a powerful way for students to apply math concepts in real-world applications. As with the problems and projects people face in their daily lives, the problem-solver has to make decisions as to which skills to use to complete the project. These projects are suggestions only; you and your students may wish to generate and implement your own ideas so different math skills are explored and used.

Creating a Project Environment Projects invite students to explore and experiment. When students begin a project, you may want to arrange the classroom furniture to be more conducive to group work. Students will be better able to focus on the project if resources are readily available in the classroom, so you may wish to gather materials ahead of time.

The Teacher's Role During a project the teacher's role is to serve as a "guide on the side" rather than a "sage on the stage" by helping students find information, asking questions that encourage students to think about the problem and use their problem-solving skills, and encouraging students to generate more questions to explore in the project. For these projects, you are not expected to know all the answers or to be able to solve all the problems but rather to model good problem-solving and investigative behaviors.

Grouping Projects can be completed by individual students, but students often learn more by working together. Ideally, cooperative group projects should mix students of different ability levels so that all students learn from each other. Successful group work does not just happen. Groups need to establish expectations of the roles and responsibilities of every member of the group. Encourage group members to take specific roles that ensure that everyone makes an overall contribution to the project.

UNIT 2

Decimals and Exponents

UNDERSTANDING POWERS OF 10

OVERVIEW

This unit begins with a review of adding and subtracting decimals, followed by a review of multiplying and dividing decimals by powers of 10 and of common metric units of length, weight, and volume. Students then review multiplying decimals by whole numbers and by decimals. Students learn the meaning of precision in measurement and use a calculator to compute perimeters and areas. The unit develops an algorithm for dividing by a decimal. Students apply their skills with decimal operations to real-life applications. Finally, students are introduced to exponential and scientific notation.

Integrated Topics in This Unit Include:

◆ adding and subtracting decimals

◆ multiplying and dividing decimals by powers of **10**

◆ reviewing common metric units of length, weight, and volume and converting between units

◆ multiplying whole numbers by decimals and decimals by decimals

◆ reporting measures with an appropriate level of precision

◆ dividing by a decimal

◆ applying operations with decimals

◆ writing numbers using exponential notation

◆ counting outcomes of independent events

◆ calculating with multidigit numbers using exponents

◆ using scientific notation to write multidigit numbers

**PRECISION
SCIENTIFIC NOTATION**

> "*Instruction that facilitates students' understanding of the underlying structure of arithmetic should employ informal explorations and emphasize the reasons why various kinds of numbers occur, commonalities among various arithmetic processes, and relationships between number systems.*"
>
> —*NCTM Curriculum and Evaluation Standards for School Mathematics*

GAMES

Motivating Mixed Practice

Games provide **basic math skills** practice in cooperative groups. Playing the games also develops **mathematical reasoning.**

Harder Roll a Decimal	Lesson 27	page 104
Harder Transaction Game Mat	Lesson 27	page 104
Make 25	Lesson 34	page 126

THINKING STORY

Integrated Problem Solving

Thinking Stories provide opportunities for students to work in **cooperative groups** and develop **logical reasoning** while they integrate **reading skills** with mathematics.

The Efficiency Experts

Part 1	Lesson 28	pages 108–109
Part 2	Lesson 38	pages 140–141
Part 3	Lesson 41	pages 150–151

Story Summary "The Efficiency Experts" examines methods people can use to operate more efficiently in their homes and at their jobs. A team of "experts" is consulted by clients who want to expend less time and energy performing certain daily tasks. Students will learn to evaluate each time- and energy-saving measure the team suggests, using probability skills in Part 1 and mapping and measuring skills in Parts 2 and 3.

PROJECT

Making Connections

The Unit Project makes real-world connections. Students work in **cooperative groups** to solve problems and to communicate their findings.

The project presented in the Unit Wrap-Up asks students to plan a trip for their class, including researching how much transportation, meals, and lodging would cost. Then the students should develop plans to raise the needed money.

Students may work on this project during their free time throughout the unit.

UNIT 2 DECIMALS AND EXPONENTS LESSON PLANS

	LESSON	PACING	PRIMARY OBJECTIVES	FEATURE	RESOURCES	NCTM STANDARD
27	Adding and Subtracting Decimals 102–105	1 day	✓ to evaluate students' ability to add and subtract decimals	Game	Reteaching Master Practice Master 27 Enrichment Master 27 Assessment Master	6, 7
28	Applying Decimals 106–109	1 day	to practice solving word problems by adding and subtracting decimals	Thinking Story	Reteaching Strategy Practice Master 28 Enrichment Master 28	1, 2, 3, 4, 7
29	Decimals and Powers of 10 110–113	1 day	to practice multiplying and dividing decimals by powers of 10 and converting various units in the metric system		Reteaching Master Practice Master 29 Enrichment Master 29	7, 13
30	Multiplying Decimals and Whole Numbers 114–115	1 day	to practice multiplying decimals and whole numbers		Reteaching Strategy Practice Master 30 Enrichment Master 30	6, 7
31	Multiplying Decimals 116–119	1 day	✓ to evaluate students' ability to multiply with decimals		Reteaching Master Practice Master 31 Enrichment Master 31 Assessment Master	3, 4, 6, 7
32	Precision with Customary Measurements 120–121	1 day	to introduce the concept of precision of a reported measurement		Reteaching Strategy Practice Master 32 Enrichment Master 32	13
33	Reporting Metric Measurements 122–123	1 day	to teach the meaning of *precision* as it relates to metric measurements		Reteaching Strategy Practice Master 33 Enrichment Master 33	12, 13
34	Solving Problems Using Decimals 124–127	1 day	to provide applications of multiplying decimals	Game	Reteaching Strategy Practice Master 34 Enrichment Master 34	1, 2, 3, 4, 7
35	Understanding Division by Decimals 128–129	1 day	to introduce division by a decimal and practice in approximating quotients		Reteaching Strategy Practice Master 35 Enrichment Master 35	6, 7
36	Dividing by Decimals 130–133	1 day	✓ to evaluate students' ability to divide with decimal divisors		Reteaching Master Practice Master 36 Enrichment Master 36 Assessment Master	1, 2, 3, 4, 7
37	Arithmetic with Decimals 134–135	1 day	to provide real-life applications of decimal operations		Reteaching Strategy Practice Master 37 Enrichment Master 37	1, 2, 3, 4, 7
	Mid-Unit Review 136–137	1 day			Assessment Masters	
38	Keeping Sharp 138–141	1 day	to practice facts and computation	Thinking Story	Reteaching Strategy Practice Master 38 Enrichment Master 38	1, 2, 3, 4, 7, 12
39	Exponents 142–145	1 day	to introduce exponential notation		Reteaching Master Practice Master 39 Enrichment Master 39	1, 5
40	Counting Possibilities 146–147	1 day	to introduce the principle of counting outcomes		Reteaching Strategy Practice Master 40 Enrichment Master 40	11

	LESSON	PACING	PRIMARY OBJECTIVES	FEATURE	RESOURCES	NCTM STANDARD
41	**Writing Powers of 10**................ **148–151**	1 day	to help students work with multidigit numbers expressed in exponential form	**Thinking Story**	Reteaching Strategy Practice Master 41 Enrichment Master 41	1, 2, 3, 4, 7
42	**Multiplying and Dividing Using Exponents**...... **152–153**	1 day	to introduce multiplication and division with numbers in exponential form		Reteaching Strategy Practice Master 42 Enrichment Master 42	5, 7
43	**Approximating with Exponents**............. **154–157**	1 day	to teach how to use exponents in approximating; ✓ to evaluate students' ability to multiply and divide numbers in exponential form		Reteaching Strategy Practice Master 43 Enrichment Master 43 Assessment Master	1, 2, 3, 4, 5, 7
44	**Interpreting Multidigit Numbers**............... **158–161**	1 day	to provide practice in using exponents to solve problems involving multidigit numbers		Reteaching Strategy Practice Master 44 Enrichment Master 44	2, 4, 7
45	**Scientific Notation** ... **162–163**	1 day	to practice using scientific notation to write multidigit numbers		Reteaching Master Practice Master 45 Enrichment Master 45	5
46	**Unit 2 Review** **164–165**		to review decimals and exponents		Practice Master 46 Enrichment Master 46	
47	**Unit 2 Practice** **166–169**		to practice with decimals and exponents		Practice Master 47 Enrichment Master 47	
	Unit 2 Test **170–171**		to review decimals and exponents		Assessment Masters	
	Unit 2 Wrap-Up **172–173**			**Project**		

UNIT CONNECTIONS

INTERVENTION STRATEGIES

In this Teacher's Guide there will be specific strategies suggested for students with individual needs–ESL, Gifted and Talented, Special Needs, Learning Styles, and At Risk. These strategies will be given at the point of use. Here are the icons to look for and the types of strategies that will accompany them:

English as a Second Language
These strategies, designed for students who do not fluently speak the English language, will suggest meaningful ways to present the lesson concepts and vocabulary.

Gifted and Talented
Strategies to enrich and extend the lesson will offer further challenges to students who have easily mastered the concepts already presented.

Special Needs
Students who are physically challenged or who have learning disabilities may require alternative ways to complete activities, record answers, use manipulatives, and so on. The strategies labeled with this icon will offer appropriate methods of teaching lesson concepts to these students.

Learning Styles
Each student has his or her individual approach to learning. The strategies labeled with this icon suggest ways to present lesson concepts so that various learning modalities–such as tactile/kinesthetic, visual, and auditory–can be addressed.

At Risk
These strategies highlight the relevancy of the skills presented, making the connection between school and real life. They are directed toward students who appear to be at risk of dropping out of school before graduation.

TECHNOLOGY CONNECTIONS

The following materials, designed to reinforce and extend lesson concepts, will be referred to throughout this Teacher's Guide. It might be helpful to order the software, videos, and laser discs or to check them out of the school media center or local community library.

Look for this **Technology Connection** *icon.*

◆ *Modumath: Arithmetic, Adding and Subtracting Decimal Fractions,* from VTAE, VHS, IBM, for grades 6–12 (video, software, or laser disc)

◆ *Math Mystery Theatre: The Ten Percenters,* from EdCon/Imperial International, VHS, for grades 2–8 (video)

◆ *Math Mystery Theatre, Decimal Disagreement: The War of the Rose,* from EdCon/Imperial International, VHS, for grades 2–8 (video)

◆ *Math Mystery Theatre: Decimal Disaster, or The Case of the Maltese Fraction,* from EdCon/Imperial International, VHS, for grades 2–8 (video)

◆ *Classroom Grade Level Math Programs,* from Jostens Home Learning; Mac, IBM, for grades K-8 (software)

◆ *Core Concepts in Math: Mastering Equations, Roots and Exponents,* from BFA/Systems Impact, Mac, IBM, for grades 5–9 (software or laser disc)

◆ *The Wonderful Problems of Fizz & Martina–Volume 3: Fizz & Martina Do Hollywood,* from Tom Snyder Productions, VHS, for grades 3–6 (video)

CROSS-CURRICULAR CONNECTIONS

This Teacher's Guide offers specific suggestions on ways to connect the math concept presented in this unit with other subjects students are studying. Students can connect math concepts with topics they already know, and they can find examples of math in other subjects and in real-world situations. These strategies will be given at the point of use.

Look for these icons:

 Geography
 Health

 Social Studies
 Music

 Science
 Math

 Art
 Physical Education

 Language Arts
 Careers

LITERATURE CONNECTIONS

These books will be presented throughout the Teacher's Guide at the point where they could be used to introduce, reinforce, or extend specific lesson concepts. You may want to locate these books in your school or your local community library.

 *Look for this* **Literature Connection** *icon.*

♦ *Smart Spending* by Lois Schmitt, Scribner, 1989

♦ "Lunch Money" in *Lunch Money and Other Poems about School* by Carol Diggery Shields, Dutton Children's Books, 1995

♦ *Jason and the Money Tree* by Sonia Levitin, Harcourt Brace Jovanovich, 1974

♦ *Matilda* by Roald Dahl, Viking Kestrel, 1988

♦ *The Kids' Complete Guide to Money* by Kathy S. Kyte, Knopf (Distributed by Random House), 1984

♦ *How Much and How Many?* by Jeanne Bendick, F. Watts, 1989

♦ *Gold and Silver, Silver and Gold* by Alvin Schwartz, Farrar, Straus & Giroux, 1988

♦ *Supergrandpa* by David M. Schwartz, Lothrop, Lee & Shepard, 1991

♦ *Buy Now, Pay Later* by Thompson Yardley, Millbrook Press, 1991

♦ *Amazing Biofacts* by Susan Goodman, P. Bedrick Books, 1993

♦ *Take Me to Your Liter: Math and Science Jokes* by Charles Keller, Pippin Press, 1991

♦ *The Rajah's Rice* by David Barry, Scientific American Books for Young Readers, 1994

♦ *The Westing Game* by Ellen Raskin, Dutton, 1978

♦ *Magnification* by Beth B. Norden, Lodestar Books, 1993

♦ *How Much is a Million?* by David M. Schwartz, Mulberry Books, 1994

♦ *Math and Society* by Robert Gardner and Edward A. Shore, Franklin Watts, 1975

ASSESSMENT OPPORTUNITIES AT-A-GLANCE

LESSON	PORTFOLIO	PERFORMANCE	FORMAL	SELF	INFORMAL	CUMULATIVE REVIEW	MULTIPLE-CHOICE	MASTERY CHECKPOINTS	ANALYZING ANSWERS
27			✓					✓	
28					✓				
29		✓							✓
30					✓	✓			✓
31			✓					✓	
32	✓								
33					✓				
34		✓							
35					✓				
36			✓			✓		✓	
37					✓				
Mid-Unit Review	✓	✓	✓						
38				✓					
39	✓								
40	✓								
41	✓					✓			
42		✓							
43			✓					✓	
44					✓				
45					✓				
46	✓	✓	✓						
47						✓			
Unit Test			✓				✓		

✓ ASSESSMENT OPTIONS

PORTFOLIO ASSESSMENT

Throughout this Teacher's Guide are suggested activities in which students draw pictures, make graphs, write about mathematics, and so on. Keep students' work to assess growth of understanding as the year progresses.

Lessons 32, Mid-Unit Review, 39, 40, 41, and 46

PERFORMANCE ASSESSMENT

Performance assessment items focus on evaluating how students think and work as they solve problems. Opportunities for performance assessment can be found throughout the unit. Rubrics and guides for grading can be found in the front of the Assessment Blackline Masters.

Lessons 29, 34, Mid-Unit Review, 42, and 46

FORMAL ASSESSMENT

A Mid-Unit Review, Unit Review, and Unit Test help assess students' understanding of concepts, skills, and problem solving. The *Math Explorations and Applications* CD-ROM Test Generator can create additional unit tests at three ability levels. Also, Mastery Checkpoints are provided periodically throughout the unit.

Lessons 27, 31, 36, Mid-Unit Review, 43, 46, and Unit Test

SELF ASSESSMENT

Throughout the program students are given the opportunity to check their own math skills.

Lesson 38

INFORMAL ASSESSMENT

A variety of assessment suggestions are provided, including interviews, oral questions or presentation, debates, and so on. Also, each lesson includes Assessment Criteria, a list of questions about each student's progress, understanding, and participation.

Lessons 28, 30, 33, 35, 37, 44, and 45

CUMULATIVE REVIEW

Cumulative Reviews, covering material presented thus far in the year, are provided in the unit for use as either assessment or practice

Lessons 30, 36, 41, and 47

MULTIPLE-CHOICE TEST (STANDARDIZED FORMAT)

Each unit provides a unit test in standardized format, presenting students with an opportunity to practice taking a test in this format.

MASTERY CHECKPOINT

Mastery Checkpoints are provided throughout the unit to assess student proficiency in specific skills. Checkpoints reference appropriate Assessment Blackline Masters and other assessment options. Results of these evaluations can be recorded on the Mastery Checkpoint Chart.

Lessons 27, 31, 36, and 43

ANALYZING ANSWERS

Analyzing answers items suggest possible sources of student error and offer teaching strategies for addressing difficulties.

Lessons 29 and 30

Look for these icons:

> **"***Large pieces of work, like performance tasks, projects, and portfolios, provide opportunities for students to demonstrate growth in mathematical power.***"**
>
> —*NCTM Assessment Standards*

 **MASTERY CHECKPOINTS**

WHAT TO EXPECT FROM STUDENTS AS THEY COMPLETE THIS UNIT

⑩ ADDITION AND SUBTRACTION OF DECIMALS—LESSON 27

By this time most students should demonstrate mastery of addition and subtraction of decimals by correctly answering at least 26 of the first 30 problems on page 103. You may also use Assessment Blackline Master page 18 to assess student's ability. Students who fall short of this objective should be given extra help. Results of this assessment may be recorded on the Mastery Checkpoint Chart.

⑪ MULTIPLICATION WITH DECIMALS—LESSON 31

By this time most students should demonstrate mastery of multiplication of decimals by correctly answering at least 26 of the 33 problems on page 118 or meeting the objective on Assessment Blackline Master page 19. Students who fall short of this objective should be given extra help. Results of this assessment may be recorded on the Mastery Checkpoint Chart.

⑫ DIVISION WITH DECIMAL DIVISORS—LESSON 36

By this time most students should demonstrate mastery of division of decimals by correctly answering at least 17 of the 21 problems on page 131 or meeting the objective on Assessment Blackline Master page 20. Students who fall short of this objective can be given extra help. Results of this assessment may be recorded on the Mastery Checkpoint Chart.

⑬ MULTIPLYING AND DIVIDING WITH EXPONENTS—LESSON 43

By this time most students should understand how to multiply and divide numbers in exponential form. You can assess this understanding by observing students during work on and discussion of problems 18–47 on page 156 or by assigning Assessment Blackline Master page 23. Students who consistently have difficulty multiplying and dividing with exponents should be given extra help. Results of this assessment may be recorded on the Mastery Checkpoint Chart.

UNIT 2

PROGRAM RESOURCES

THESE ADDITIONAL COMPONENTS OF *MATH EXPLORATIONS AND APPLICATIONS* CAN BE PURCHASED SEPARATELY FROM SRA/McGRAW-HILL.

LESSON	BASIC MANIPULATIVE KIT	GAME MAT PACKAGE	TEACHER MANIPULATIVE KIT	INTERMEDIATE MANIPULATIVE KIT	INTERMEDIATE OVERHEAD MANIPULATIVE KIT	THE CRUNCHER SOFTWARE	MATH EXPLORATIONS AND APPLICATIONS CD-ROM
27	Number Cubes	Harder Transaction Game					Lesson 27
28	Number Cubes, Number Wheels						Lesson 28
29			weights	tape measure liter container base-10 materials	base-10 materials	spreadsheet	Lesson 29
30				base-10 materials decimal mods			Lesson 30
31						spreadsheet	Lesson 31
32				tape measure rulers			Lesson 32
33							Lesson 33
34	Number Cubes					spreadsheet	Lesson 34
35							Lesson 35
36							Lesson 36
37			scale weights	ruler tape measure		spreadsheet	Lesson 37
38	Number Cubes			interlocking cubes			Lesson 38
39							Lesson 39
40				counters	counters		Lesson 40
41							Lesson 41
42							Lesson 42
43							Lesson 43
44	Number Cubes		stopwatch			spreadsheet	Lesson 44
45							Lesson 45
46							Lesson 46
47							Lesson 47

UNIT 2
Decimals and Exponents

INTRODUCING THE UNIT

Using the Student Pages Begin your discussion of the opening unit photo by asking students, "How are decimals used at the gas station?" Then read aloud the paragraph on the student page that highlights working in a gas station. This helps make the connection between school and work and encourages students to explore how math is used in the real world.

ACTIVITY Ask students to find the prices per gallon for different gasolines at one gas station in your community. Have students compare their data with their fellow classmates.

FYI Tell students that the job of pumping gas is as old as the automobile. While the first cars were invented around the turn of the century, in the United States it was not until the advent of the Model T Ford in 1913 that gas stations really multiplied. Before that time gas was more frequently used for motorcycles, which up until World War I remained a popular form of family transportation, particularly with the attachment of a sidecar. Two-wheeled transport would remain popular in America and a fixture at the gas pump. However, it was the car that really made profits for the oil industry. Because of its vast size and consistently rising economy, the United States and the car were a good fit. People needed a way to conquer great distances. Just getting from one city to another in the West used to mean days or weeks of uncomfortable travel in horse-drawn carriages or traveling only where and when the trains did. Large oil companies made sure they had gas stations wherever cars could go, and each company competed for loyal customers. Between the turn of the century and today, little has changed at the pump, except the price of gas. Point out that in 1920 a gallon of regular gas cost a nickel.

UNIT 2
Decimals and Exponents

UNDERSTANDING POWERS OF 10

- operations with decimals
- precision in measurement
- exponential notation
- counting outcomes

SCHOOL TO WORK CONNECTION

Gas station attendants use math . . .

The gas station attendant pumps gas that is measured to the nearest tenth of a gallon. The pump computes how many dollars and cents the customer owes for the gas. The customer chooses the type of gasoline according to price (given to thousandths of a dollar) or according to the octane rating (given as a percent).

100

Thinklab™ 2

SRA's *Thinklab™ 2* provides a series of creative and logical problem-solving opportunities for individual students. The problems are designed to appeal to different cognitive abilities.

▶ Use Problems 21–25 with this unit to integrate object manipulation, creative insight, logical analysis, quantitative thinking, and brainstorming and to incorporate social interaction.

▶ Use Problems 26–35 with this unit to reinforce logical analysis (absorbing multiple data, testing hypotheses, and planning a set of operations).

▶ Use Problems 36–45 with this unit to reinforce quantitative thinking (interpreting and synthesizing data).

Urge students to consider what they notice when they pull into a gas station. Invariably they will see signs with numbers on them, and those numbers nearly always feature decimals. Explain that fuel companies gauge their prices on their own expenses. They must purchase oil, refine it or pay to have it refined, and ship it—usually across great distances. The largest ships in the world are oil tankers, which get bigger every few years. Once the gas gets to this country, it must be further transported to thousands of gas stations. Taxes are added to the final price that a customer pays at the pump, though in the United States people pay a fraction of the taxes that are added in most other countries. Point out that the task facing a gas station attendant is to convert all those decimals—the number of gallons and the price per gallon, both usually ending in a fraction or decimal—to the correct amount to charge the customer. They must then make change. While this is usually done with the aid of automation, the attendant must be able to estimate the proper amount in case there is an error.

Home Connections You may want to send home Home Connections Blackline Masters pages 42–43 to introduce this unit.

Unit Project This would be a good time to assign the "Planning a Trip" project on pages 172 and 173. Students can begin working on the project in cooperative groups in their free time as you work through the unit. This project is a good opportunity for students to apply the concepts of estimation and planning strategies to real-world problem solving.

 *Cooperate 3*

Cooperate 3, published by SRA, provides a series of creative and logical problem-solving opportunities for cooperative groups. The problems are designed to provide practice in problem solving, communication, reasoning, and making connections. *Cooperate 3* presents the following cognitive strategies—perceiving spatial relations, ordering and sequencing, logical deduction, establishing and testing hypotheses, sequential exploration, identifying starting points, attending to detail, organizing information, and screening irrelevant information. Each Problem Card emphasizes a principal strategy as well as reinforcing other strategies.

▶ Use Problem Card 6 with this unit to emphasize ordering and sequencing.

▶ Use Problem Cards 7–8 with this unit to emphasize establishing and testing hypotheses.

▶ Use Problem Cards 9–10 with this unit to emphasize perceiving spatial relations.

LESSON 27

Student Edition pages 102–105

Adding and Subtracting Decimals

LESSON PLANNER

Objectives

▶ to review addition and subtraction of decimals

✓ to evaluate students' ability to add and subtract decimals

Context of the Lesson This is the first of 11 lessons on operations with decimals. Much of the work is review. This lesson contains a checkpoint for assessing mastery of addition and subtraction of decimals.

✋ **MANIPULATIVES**

almanacs and other reference sources (optional)

Program Resources

"Harder Transaction" Game Mat

Number Cubes

Reteaching Master

Practice Master 27

Enrichment Master 27

Assessment Master

For additional math integration:
  Math Throughout the Day*

For extra practice:
  CD-ROM* Lesson 27

---

❶ Warm-Up ⏱ 5 MINUTES

Problem of the Day Present the following problem to the class: A hardball pitcher threw the ball at a speed of 91.5 mph and a softball pitcher threw at a speed of 0.016 miles per second. Who threw the ball faster and by how much? (the hardball pitcher, by about 33.9 mph or 0.009 mi/sec)

Problem-Solving Strategies Ask students who have solved the Problem of the Day to share how they solved it and any strategies they used.

Have students show thumbs up if the answer is possibly right or thumbs down if it is obviously wrong for the following:

a. 600 + 320 = 920 (thumbs up)

b. 200 × 420 = 800 (thumbs down)

(continued on page 103)

Adding and Subtracting Decimals

You know how to add decimals—the same way you add whole numbers. Line up the decimal points to make sure you add thousandths to thousandths, hundredths to hundredths, and so on.

Examples:

0.38 + 0.25 = ?

$$\begin{array}{r} 1 \\ 0.38 \\ + 0.25 \\ \hline 0.63 \end{array}$$ Line up the decimal points.
Add.

0.937 + 0.3 = ?

$$\begin{array}{r} 0.937 \\ + 0.3 \\ \hline \end{array}$$ Occasionally, you may have to add decimals that don't have the same number of digits after the decimal point.

$$\begin{array}{r} 0.937 \\ + 0.300 \\ \hline 1.237 \end{array}$$ To help line up the digits, you may put 0s to the right of 0.3 so that both decimals have the same number of digits after the decimal point. You may do this because 0.3 and 0.300 have the same value. However, you may be indicating greater precision than is appropriate.

Subtraction with decimals is also the same as subtraction with whole numbers after you line up the decimal points.

Examples:

0.38 − 0.25 = ?

$$\begin{array}{r} 0.38 \\ - 0.25 \\ \hline 0.13 \end{array}$$ Line up the decimal points.
Subtract.

Literature Connection

Students can learn to become informed consumers by reading *Smart Spending* by Lois Schmitt.

0.937 − 0.3 = ?

$$\begin{array}{r} 0.937 \\ -\ 0.300 \\ \hline 0.637 \end{array}$$

You may write 0s to help you in lining up decimal points, just as in addition.

Add or subtract. Watch the signs.

1 0.4 + 0.1 **0.5**   **2** 0.4 − 0.1 **0.3**   **3** 0.33 + 0.25 **0.58**

4 0.33 − 0.25 **0.08**   **5** 0.375 − 0.167 **0.208**   **6** 0.375 + 0.167 **0.542**

7 0.417 + 0.333 **0.750**   **8** 0.417 − 0.333 **0.084**   **9** 0.5 + 0.33 **0.83**

10 0.5 − 0.33 **0.17**   **11** 0.8 − 0.3 **0.5**   **12** 0.8 + 0.3 **1.1**

13 0.67 + 0.2 **0.87**   **14** 0.67 − 0.2 **0.47**   **15** 0.4 + 0.28 **0.68**

16 0.4 − 0.28 **0.12**   **17** 6.8 + 3.2 **10.0**   **18** 6.8 − 3.2 **3.6**

19 5.9 − 4.7 **1.2**   **20** 5.9 + 4.7 **10.6**   **21** 2.4 + 1.2 **3.6**

22 2.4 − 1.2 **1.2**   **23** 5.4 − 5.4 **0**   **24** 5.4 + 5.4 **10.8**

25 2.4 + 0.18 **2.58**   **26** 2.4 − 0.18 **2.22**   **27** 1 + 0.5 **1.5**

28 1 − 0.5 **0.5**   **29** 6.1 + 3.1 **9.2**   **30** 6.1 − 3.1 **3.0**

Solve these problems.

31 George has a piece of rope 5.5 meters long. He cut off a piece 2.4 meters long. How long is the remaining piece? **3.1 m**

32 Mr. Engle bought three packages of ground beef at the store. They weighed 0.97 kilograms, 1.09 kilograms, and 2.00 kilograms. How much ground beef did he buy all together? **4.06 kg**

Unit 2   Lesson 27   •   **103**

Technology Connection Refer students to the video, laser disc, or software *Modumath: Arithmetic, Adding & Subtracting Decimal Fractions* (VHS, IBM, for grades 6–12) for further practice determining which is the greater or lesser of two decimal fractions, adding and subtracting decimal fractions, and word problems involving decimal fractions.

Mental Math (continued)

c. 10 × 300 = 310 (thumbs down)

d. 40 × 30 = 1200 (thumbs up)

e. 700 − 55 = 645 (thumbs up)

f. 90 × 90 = 180 (thumbs down)

g. 330 − 29 = 301 (thumbs up)

h. 63 − 62 = 61 (thumbs down)

i. 55 + 155 = 210 (thumbs up)

j. 22 + 222 = 244 (thumbs up)

❷ Teach

Using the Student Pages To provide practice adding and subtracting decimals, demonstrate the "Harder Roll a Decimal" game on page 105 and the "Harder Transaction" Game Mat first, so that students may play as they finish their work on pages 102–104.

Go over pages 102 and 103 with students, and be sure that they understand these two important concepts:

▶ Adding and subtracting decimals is exactly the same as adding and subtracting whole numbers, once the decimal points have been aligned.

▶ The ones digit is the first digit to the left of the decimal point. We can assume that there is a decimal point to the right of any whole number.

If students understand these concepts, they can see why it is possible to write 0s to the right of any number with a decimal point without changing the value of the number: 2.45, 2.450, and 2.4500 have the same value. Have students do problems 1–32 on page 103 on their own.

Note that although some of the computation problems in this lesson involve numbers that do not have the same number of decimal places, such problems arise infrequently in real situations. Numbers other than whole numbers usually arise from measurements, which are always approximations. The number of places reported generally tells how precise the measurement is believed to be, so writing additional 0s may change the apparent precision of the number.

GIFTED & TALENTED **Meeting Individual Needs** Challenge students to formulate problems like the one in the Problem of the Day for classmates to solve. Refer students to **almanacs** and other reference sources for their data.

◆ LESSON 27 Adding and Subtracting Decimals

Teach

Using the Student Pages Assign the problems on page 104 for independent work. Have students check answers with a partner.

 When they finish, have students play the "Harder Roll a Decimal" game in pairs. Principal skills involved in this game are subtracting decimals and using place value to choose where to place digits.

Introducing the "Harder Transaction" Game Mat Demonstrate the "Harder Transaction" game for the class by playing it with one or two students. This game provides practice in adding and subtracting amounts of money expressed in dollars and cents. The rules are the same as for the "Transaction" game introduced in Lesson 9. Complete instructions can be found on the Game Mat or on the copy on page 629 of this Teacher's Guide.

SPECIAL NEEDS Meeting Individual Needs

For students who can add and subtract multidigit numbers and understand decimals but have trouble adding and subtracting decimals, try this procedure. Give a problem like 3.785 + 24.6. Have students write 3.785 on their papers. Then ask where 24.6 should be written. (under 3.785 with points aligned) Write the decimal point there. Then ask which digit in 24.6 stands for ones. (4) Where should we write the 4? (under the 3) Where should we write the 6? (under the 7) Now the problem should look like this:

$$3.785$$
$$+ \ 24.6$$

If they prefer, students may write 0s under the 8 and 5. Do several more problems in a similar way. As you, a parent, an adult aide, or an able student supervise a student having difficulty, the four steps of the procedure should be emphasized.

1. Write the numbers with the decimal points directly above and below one another.

2. Add or subtract as with whole numbers.

3. Place the decimal point in the answer directly below the points in the addends.

4. Ask, "Does the answer make sense?" A student who, for example, adds 3.5 and 0.27 and gets 6.2 should see that the answer ought to be less than 4 and that 6.2 is therefore wrong.

◆ LESSON 27 Adding and Subtracting Decimals

Solve these problems.

33 Sam works at Robert's Fast Food restaurant. A customer ordered two BIG BOB sandwiches for $1.98 each, a milkshake for $1.29, potato chips for $0.59, and a dessert for $1.09. He handed Sam a ten-dollar bill. Sam's cash register showed that the customer should receive $93.07 in change. Is anything wrong? What mistake do you think Sam may have made? How much change should the customer receive? **yes; Sam may have entered $100.00 instead of $10.00; $3.07**

34 Abigail went to the grocery store to buy three containers of milk for $1.08 apiece, a head of lettuce for $1.27, a loaf of bread for $1.89, and some cheese for $2.53. She has a $50 bill, a $20 bill, a $10 bill, and a $5 bill in her pocket. Which should she give the clerk in order to receive the least amount of change? How much change should she receive? **$10 bill; $1.07**

35 Miguel has put the following ten items in his grocery basket so far: milk ($1.87), orange juice ($0.97), cottage cheese ($2.57), bread ($1.98), meat ($7.50), lettuce ($0.89), carrots ($1.84), crackers ($2.53), popcorn ($2.89), and bagels ($0.78). He has $28. Can he also afford to buy ice cream that costs $3.99? If he can't afford the ice cream, how much more money would he need to buy it? If he can afford the ice cream and buys it, how much change should he receive if he gives the clerk $28? **yes; 19¢ or $0.19**

36 David had a balance in his checkbook of $342.05. He wrote a check for $73.16. What is his new balance? **$268.89**

37 Phyllis went to a discount art store to buy pictures to decorate her house. She wanted to buy five pictures for $4.99 each, three other pictures for $6.99 each, and a large picture for $24.98. She had $60 with her. Could she pay for all the pictures? If so, how much money would she have left after paying for them? If not, how much more money would she need in order to pay for the pictures? **no; $10.90**

Major Reductions Sale

104 • Decimals and Exponents

RETEACHING p. 8

LESSON 27 RETEACHING   Name_____

Use the column markings to help you add or subtract.

Example:
0.976 + 1.3402 = ?

| 0 | . | 9 | 7 | 6 | |
| 1 | . | 3 | 4 | 0 | 2 |

Align the decimal points.
Align the ones digits, tenths digits, and so on.

| 0 | . | 9 | 7 | 6 | 0 |
| 1 | . | 3 | 4 | 0 | 2 |

Write 0s if it helps you, then add.

0	.	9	7	6	0
1	.	3	4	0	2
2	.	3	1	6	2

The decimal point in the answer will line up with the decimal point in the problem.

Add or subtract.

1 4.73 − 2.047 =   2.683
2 0.97 + 0.0047 =   0.9747
3 8.406 + 15.2 =   23.606
4 483.9 + 29.47 =   513.37

5 0.97 + 3.406 =   4.376
6 4.3 − 0.529 =   3.771
7 23.879 − 15.48 =   8.399
8 286.947 − 189.75 =   97.197

9 7.432 + 15.2 =   22.632
10 11.6 + 5.942 =   17.542
11 43.98 + 27.402 =   71.382
12 387.92 + 486.587 =   874.507

13 8.47 + 29.47 =   37.94
14 12.7 − 8.934 =   3.766
15 83.906 − 47.88 =   36.026
16 7.84 + 0.36 =   8.20

8 • Math Explorations and Applications Level 6

PRACTICE p. 27

LESSON 27 PRACTICE   Name_____

Add or subtract. Watch the signs.

1 0.9 − 0.5 = 0.4
2 0.9 + 0.5 = 1.4
3 0.66 + 0.3 = 0.96
4 0.66 − 0.3 = 0.36
5 0.9 + 0.36 = 1.26

6 0.9 − 0.36 = 0.54
7 7.2 + 1.9 = 9.1
8 7.2 − 1.9 = 5.3
9 8.6 − 4.5 = 4.1
10 8.6 + 4.5 = 13.1

11 0.2 + 0.6 = 0.8
12 0.7 − 0.6 = 0.1
13 3.7 − 1.8 = 1.9
14 9.62 + 2.47 = 12.09
15 8.12 + 4.99 = 13.11

16 2.6 − 1.43 = 1.17
17 9.2 − 6.87 = 2.33
18 3.65 + 0.5 = 4.15
19 5.91 − 2.698 = 3.212
20 2.110 + 8.621 = 10.731

Add or subtract. Watch the signs.

21 0.2 + 0.8 = 1.0
22 0.4 − 0.3 = 0.1
23 0.86 + 0.79 = 1.65
24 0.86 − 0.79 = 0.07
25 0.244 − 0.161 = 0.083
26 0.244 + 0.161 = 0.405
27 0.791 + 0.015 = 0.806
28 0.791 − 0.015 = 0.776
29 0.6 + 0.21 = 0.81
30 0.6 − 0.21 = 0.39
31 9.6 − 9.6 = 0
32 3.8 − 1.2 = 2.6
33 9.6 + 9.6 = 19.2
34 3.9 + 0.16 = 4.06
35 3.9 − 0.16 = 3.74
36 3 + 0.2 = 3.2
37 3 − 0.2 = 2.8
38 4.9 + 2.6 = 7.5
39 4.9 − 2.6 = 2.3

Math Explorations and Applications Level 6 • 27

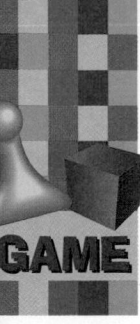

Harder Roll a Decimal Game

COOPERATIVE LEARNING

GAME

Players:	Two
Materials:	One 0–5 cube, one 5–10 cube
Object:	To get the greater total score
Math Focus:	Place value, comparing decimal numbers, subtracting decimal numbers, and mathematical reasoning

 **RULES**

1. Before play begins, agree on the number of rounds.

2. Roll the 0–5 cube. If a 0 is rolled, roll that cube again. Write a decimal point followed by as many blanks as the number rolled. If you roll a 3, you would write this: __ __ __.

3. Roll the 5–10 cube as many times as there are blanks in your decimal. If you roll a 10, roll that cube again.

4. Each time you roll the 5–10 cube, write that number in one of your blanks.

5. After both players have made decimals, subtract the lesser decimal from the greater decimal. Award the difference to the person who made the greater decimal.

6. After an agreed-upon number of rounds, add up your score. The player with the greater total is the winner.

 SAMPLE GAME

Round	Andrea's Roll	Dan's Roll	Andrea's Score	Dan's Score
1	.76	.966		.206
2	.957	.676	.281	
3	.97775	.9665	.01125	
4	.8	.9576		.1576
5	.99	.866	.124	
6	.86855	.8875		.01895
Total			.41625	.38255

Andrea was the winner.

Unit 2   Lesson 27 • **105**

ENRICHMENT p. 27

ASSESSMENT p. 18

---

③ Wrap-Up ⏱ 5 MINUTES

In Closing Ask students to give the place value of the second digit to the left of the decimal point and of the second digit to the right of the decimal point. (tens; hundredths)

Mastery Checkpoint 10

By this time, most students should demonstrate mastery of addition and subtraction of decimals by getting correct answers to at least 26 of the first 30 problems on page 103. You may also use Assessment Blackline Masters page 18 to assess students' ability. Results of this assessment may be recorded on the Mastery Checkpoint Chart.

Assessment Criteria

Did the student . . .

✓ correctly answer at least 26 of the first 30 problems on page 103?

✓ demonstrate an understanding of how the procedures for adding and subtracting decimals are the same as those for adding and subtracting whole numbers?

✓ understand the rules of the games and play several rounds with a partner?

Homework Invite students to play the "Harder Roll a Decimal" game with a family member for further practice working with decimals. A copy of this game can also be found on page 17 of the Home Connections Blackline Masters.

Applying Decimals

LESSON PLANNER

Objectives

▶ to provide practice in solving word problems by adding and subtracting decimals

▶ to help students develop the broad ability to use mathematical common sense

Context of the Lesson This lesson, the second of 11 lessons on operations with decimals, contains the first part of "The Efficiency Experts," a three-part Thinking Story. The next lesson reviews multiplication and division of decimals by powers of 10.

 MANIPULATIVES

Program Resources

Practice Master 28

Enrichment Master 28

For career connections:
  Careers and Math*

For extra practice:
  CD-ROM* Lesson 28

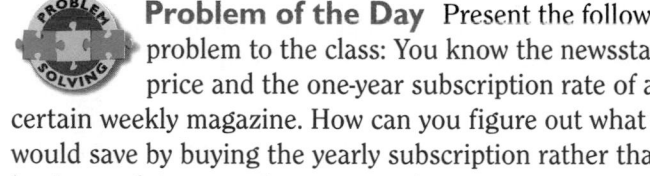

① Warm-Up

5 MINUTES

Problem of the Day Present the following problem to the class: You know the newsstand price and the one-year subscription rate of a certain weekly magazine. How can you figure out what you would save by buying the yearly subscription rather than buying each issue at the newsstand? (Multiply the newsstand price by 52; subtract the subscription price from that product.)

Problem-Solving Strategies Ask students who have solved the Problem of the Day to share how they solved it and any strategies they used.

 **MENTAL MATH** Provide practice in approximation by presenting the following equations to the class. Ask students to quickly indicate thumbs down if the answer is obviously wrong or thumbs up if it is possibly correct.

a. 0.8 – 0.4 = 0.4 (thumbs up)

b. 0.78 – 0.45 = 0.33 (thumbs up)

c. 8.4 + 0.59 = 0.899 (thumbs down)

d. 0.3 + 0.09 = 0.39 (thumbs up)

(continued on page 107)

106 Decimals and Exponents

Applying Decimals

Solve these problems.

① Dewayne had a $10 bill and spent some money at the grocery store. Now he has $3.47. How much money did he spend at the grocery store? **$6.53**

② Abe is 1.60 meters tall. Last year he was 1.52 meters tall. How much has he grown since last year? **0.08 m (or 8 cm)**

③ Winona has a board that is 2.50 meters long. If she cuts off 1.75 meters of the board, how much will be left? **0.75 m (or 75 cm)**

④ Rosalind has a 2-kilogram bag of flour. She wants to bake a cake that uses 0.25 kilogram of flour, some bread that uses 1.5 kilograms of flour, and a batch of cookies that uses 0.35 kilogram of flour. Does she have enough flour? **no**

⑤ Mr. Gonzales checked his odometer before he started driving this morning. It read 2545.3 miles. At noon it was 2563.7, and when he arrived home at 5 P.M., it was 2622.8. Did he drive more in the morning or the afternoon? **afternoon**

⑥ The balance in Sonia's checking account was $30.63. She then deposited $403.36. What was the new balance? **$433.99**

⑦ Darrell and Nathan timed each other in the 50-meter dash. Darrell took 10.7 seconds, and Nathan took 9.8 seconds. How much less time did Nathan take? **0.9 seconds**

⑧ Mrs. Cooper went to the grocery store this morning. She wanted only five items: a loaf of bread for $0.75, a box of cereal for $2.79, a can of soup for $0.32, a pound of apples for $0.97, and a pineapple for $1.99. The clerk asked Mrs. Cooper for $10.24. Could that have been right? How can you tell?

no; rounding each price up to the nearest dollar gives a total of $8

106 • Decimals and Exponents

 **COOPERATIVE LEARNING** You may wish to have students work with partners on the problems on pages 106–107, discussing what each problem asks, what information is given, and what strategy and/or operation to use to find the solution.

---

106 Decimals and Exponents

*available separately

Solve.

⑨ Philip wrote down the deposits and the amounts of the checks he had written all month, but he didn't bother doing the arithmetic. He started with a balance of $12.73. What was his balance at the end of the month? Was there ever a time when his balance was negative? **$11.98; no**

Amount of Check	Amount of Deposit	Balance
		12.73
10.00		**2.73**
	148.57	**151.30**
43.86		**107.44**
102.78		**4.66**
	100.00	**104.66**
54.61		**50.05**
83.07	200.00	**166.98**
150.00		**16.98**
5.00		**11.98**

⑩ Two months later Philip's records looked like this. Find his balance at the end of that month. **$28.91**

Amount of Check	Amount of Deposit	Balance
		12.53
	148.57	**161.10**
35.42		**125.68**
90.00		**35.68**
25.00		**10.68**
	100.00	**110.68**
8.57		**102.11**
63.25	200.00	**238.86**
150.00		**88.86**
60.00		**28.86**

Unit 2   Lesson 28   •   **107**

Technology Connection Invite students to view the video *Math Mystery Theatre: The Ten Percenters* from EdCon/Imperial International (VHS, for grades 2–8) for further practice in solving word problems involving decimals and percents.

Mental Math (continued)

e.   0.4 + 0.23 = 0.27 (thumbs down)

f.   0.91 – 0.60 = 0.31 (thumbs up)

g.   0.2 + 2.74 = 29.4 (thumbs down)

h.   0.55 – 0.50 = 0.05 (thumbs up)

i.   0.5 + 3.9 = 0.44 (thumbs down)

② Teach

Using the Student Pages Have students work independently on page 106. When everyone has finished, discuss the problems. Point out that problem 8 can be solved quickly by rounding amounts up to the nearest dollar. As needed, help students read the check register on page 107. Make sure they understand that writing checks withdraws, or subtracts, money from the account and deposits are additions to the account. Discuss other factors that, in real life, need to be taken into account when balancing a checkbook, such as per-check charges or other transaction charges, minimum balances, and so on.

> *Special stories that involve serious problem solving may be of help if written properly and treated effectively in the class . . . Such stories should mix questions that are simple and straightforward with others that may require considerable thought or that may not even have one simple, correct answer. They should not, of course, rely heavily on the most recently taught skills since that reduces the need to think. Children should discuss these questions with the entire class.*
>
> –Stephen S. Willoughby,
> *Mathematics Education for a Changing World*

◆ **LESSON 28** Applying Decimals

Teach

Using the Thinking Story In the first of three segments of "The Efficiency Experts," Ferdie, Portia, Manolita, and Marcus begin their business as efficiency experts by offering advice to two customers. Have students work in groups to read the story and discuss the suggestions these "efficiency experts" make for solving their clients' problems.

Answers to Thinking Story Questions:

1. One alternative is for Mr. Eng to let his glasses hang by a chain around his neck when he is not using them. This would be much less expensive than Manolita's suggestion and would eliminate the need to hunt for the glasses. However, Mr. Eng might find the chain annoying or unattractive.

2. No. Mr. Breezy would have to carry around many more keys, and he might have even more trouble keeping track of the ones he had already tried.

3. He would have more chances of getting the right key, but he would also have more chances of getting the wrong key. The probability of getting the right key stays the same. As it is, he has one chance in 12 of finding the right key on the first try. If he made four copies of each key, he would have four chances in 48 of getting the right key, which is equivalent to one in 12.

4. Yes. Mr. Breezy would have only half as many keys to search through each time.

5. Suggestions may include labeling the keys in some way or getting new keys made in different colors of metal. But remembering which label or color goes with which key could be difficult. An effective but more expensive solution would be to change locks so that a number of them use the same key.

Ask students to write a description in their Math Journals of the training and skills they think efficiency experts should have. Ask them to explain why they themselves would or would not enjoy work as an efficiency expert.

◆ **LESSON 28** Applying Decimals

THINKING STORY

Efficiency Experts

Part 1

Ferdie, Portia, Manolita, and Marcus went into business as efficiency experts. That means they thought up quicker, easier, or cheaper ways to do things.

Their first customer was Mr. Eng. He said, "I have to wear glasses when I read, but not other times. As a result, my glasses are never where I need them. Suppose I am down in my workshop and I need to read the label on a can. But my glasses are in the living room, where I put them down after reading a book. If I sit down in the living room to read, then my glasses are sure to be upstairs in the bedroom. I'm always running around. Can you help me?"

The children thought about Mr. Eng's problem. Finally Manolita came up with an idea. "Why don't you buy four or five pairs of glasses? Leave them in different parts of the house. Then you won't have to walk so far to find a pair."

Mr. Eng tried the idea and said it worked fine.

The next customer was Mr. Breezy. He had a problem with keys. "I have six keys to different doors in my house and six keys to different doors in my dog-training school," he said. He showed them the key ring with the 12 keys on it. "All the keys look pretty much alike. I waste a lot of time trying different keys every time I want to lock or unlock a door."

108 • Decimals and Exponents

Literature Connection Have students read "Lunch Money" by Carol Diggery Shields. Then ask each of them to create two of their own problems based on searching for lunch money at home.

"That's easy," said Ferdie. "Your problem is really the same as Mr. Eng's. You can solve it the same way. Just get four or five keys made for every lock. Put them on your key ring. Then each time you try a key, you will have four or five chances of getting the right one instead of only one chance."

"I have a different idea," said Portia. "Get two key rings—a silver ring for your house keys and a gold ring for your dog-school keys. Then you won't have to hunt through so many keys to find the right one."

"I don't see how that will help," said Ferdie. "He'll still have all the same keys as before."

. . . to be continued

Work in groups. Discuss your answers and how you figured them out. Then compare your answers with those of other groups. **Answers are in margin.**

① What is another way of solving Mr. Eng's problem? In what ways is your idea better than or worse than Manolita's idea?

② Would Ferdie's idea help Mr. Breezy? Why or why not?

③ Was Ferdie right when he said that Mr. Breezy would have more chances of getting the key on the first try? Give a reason for your answer.

④ Would Portia's idea help Mr. Breezy? Why or why not?

⑤ What is another way of solving Mr. Breezy's problem? In what ways is your idea better than or worse than Portia's idea?

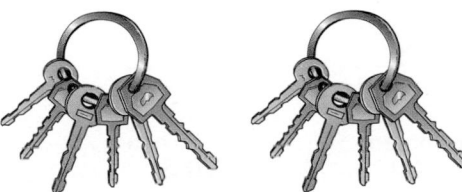

Unit 2   Lesson 28 • **109**

---

❸ Wrap-Up

In Closing To summarize the lesson, ask students to suggest ways that an efficiency expert might be able to help them.

Informal Assessment Circulate through the class as students do the problems on page 106. Ask them to explain the strategy they are using to solve the problem on which they are working.

Assessment Criteria

Did the student . . .

✓ correctly answer at least six of the eight problems on page 106?

✓ participate in the discussion of the answers to the Thinking Story questions?

✓ support his or her answers to the Thinking Story questions with logical reasoning?

Homework Ask students to think about the problems facing the first two clients in the Thinking Story. Then have them list five inefficient daily activities around their homes and act as efficiency experts by talking with family members about those activities. Invite students to share the results of their discussions.

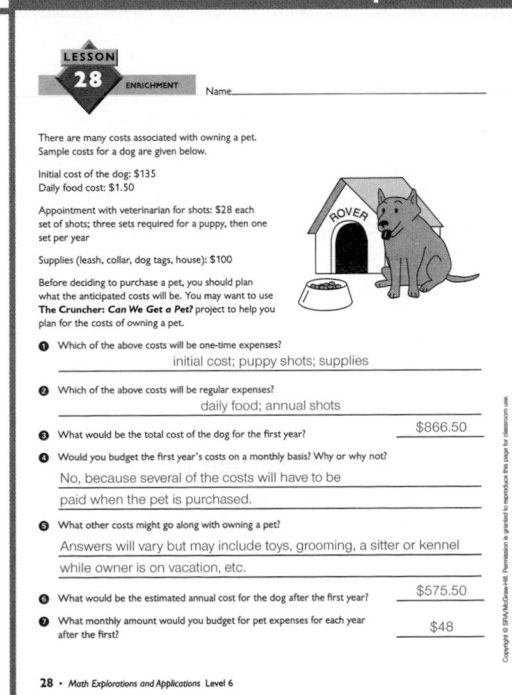

PRACTICE p. 28

LESSON 28 PRACTICE Name_____

Solve these problems.

① Aaron weighs 134.2 kilograms. Last year he weighed 125.4 kilograms. How many kilograms has he gained?
8.8 kilograms

② Libby had $5.00 and paid for a school basketball ticket. How much was the basketball ticket?
can't tell, but less than or just $5.00

③ Tanisha had 2.5 meters of fabric. She used 0.75 meter to make a bike bag.
  a. How much fabric was left? **1.75 meters**
  b. Did she have enough fabric left to make another bike bag just like the first one? **yes**

④ Mr. Villa's odometer read 3860.3 miles when he started driving this morning. At noon it read 4077.5 miles, and this evening it was 4164.6 miles.
  a. How far did Mr. Villa drive today? **304.3 miles**
  b. Did he drive more in the morning or afternoon? **morning**

⑤ The balance in Marissa's checking account is now $313.83. Yesterday afternoon she wrote a check for $93.43 and deposited $119.37 in her account. What was her balance yesterday morning?
$287.89

⑥ Ling bought three books at $3.25 each, a magazine for $1.25, and a newspaper for $0.75 at the bookstore. The clerk asked Ling for $18.50, but Ling said that was too much.
  a. Who was right? **Ling**
  b. How might the error have been made?
It's most likely that the clerk put the decimal point in the wrong place in ringing up the newspaper; however, accept all reasonable answers.

28 • *Math Explorations and Applications Level 6*

ENRICHMENT p. 28

LESSON 28 ENRICHMENT Name_____

There are many costs associated with owning a pet. Sample costs for a dog are given below.

Initial cost of the dog: $135
Daily food cost: $1.50

Appointment with veterinarian for shots: $28 each set of shots; three sets required for a puppy, then one set per year

Supplies (leash, collar, dog tags, house): $100

Before deciding to purchase a pet, you should plan what the anticipated costs will be. You may want to use **The Cruncher: Can We Get a Pet?** project to help you plan for the costs of owning a pet.

① Which of the above costs will be one-time expenses?
initial cost; puppy shots; supplies

② Which of the above costs will be regular expenses?
daily food; annual shots

③ What would be the total cost of the dog for the first year? **$866.50**

④ Would you budget the first year's costs on a monthly basis? Why or why not?
No, because several of the costs will have to be paid when the pet is purchased.

⑤ What other costs might go along with owning a pet?
Answers will vary but may include toys, grooming, a sitter or kennel while owner is on vacation, etc.

⑥ What would be the estimated annual cost for the dog after the first year? **$575.50**

⑦ What monthly amount would you budget for pet expenses for each year after the first? **$48**

28 • *Math Explorations and Applications Level 6*

Unit 2 Lesson 28 **109**

Decimals and Powers of 10

LESSON PLANNER

Objectives

▶ to review and provide practice in multiplying and dividing decimals by powers of 10

▶ to review some common metric units of length, weight, and volume, and the decimal nature of the metric system

▶ to provide practice in converting between various units of measure in the metric system

Context of the Lesson
This is the third of 11 lessons on operations with decimals.

✋ MANIPULATIVES

base-10 materials* (optional)

meterstick or tape measure* (optional)

1-gram weight* (optional)

1-liter container* (optional)

Program Resources

Reteaching Master

Practice Master 29

Enrichment Master 29

The Cruncher*

For extra practice:
CD-ROM* Lesson 29

① Warm-Up 5 MINUTES

 **Problem of the Day** Present this problem orally or on the chalkboard: Jerome is about to cut shelves from a 12-meter board. If he makes four cuts, how many shelves will he make? If all the shelves are the same length, how long will each one be? (5 shelves, each 2.4 m or 240 cm long)

Problem-Solving Strategies Ask students who have solved the Problem of the Day to share how they solved it and any strategies they used.

 Present an object to the class. Ask students to estimate its length, weight, or volume in a few different standard units of measure. Then have students measure to check the estimates. You will need to have a **meterstick** or **tape measure***, a **1-gram weight***, and a **1-liter container*** available for reference. Repeat the process with several other objects, using the same units each time and having students measure to check the estimates before the next object is presented.

Decimals and Powers of 10

You know that the value of a digit's place in a number is ten times as much as the place to its right. So you can multiply by a power of 10 just by moving the decimal point to the right.

To multiply by 10, move the decimal point one place to the right. You may need to write in a 0.

Examples:

10 × 9 ⟶ 9.0. ⟶ 90

12.3 × 10 ⟶ 1 2.3. ⟶ 123

10 × 13.57 ⟶ 1 3.5.7 ⟶ 135.7

To multiply by 100, move the decimal point two places to the right. You may need extra 0s in writing your answer.

Examples:

100 × 6 ⟶ 6.0 0. ⟶ 600

23.4 × 100 ⟶ 2 3.4 0. ⟶ 2340

100 × 15.97 ⟶ 1 5.9 7. ⟶ 1597

To multiply by any power of 10, count the number of 0s in the power of 10. Then move the decimal point that many places to the right. You may need to write in extra 0s.

Multiply.

① 10 × 1.9 **19**	**②** 1000 × 1.9 **1900**	**③** 100 × 0.36 **36**
④ 0.36 × 1000 **360**	**⑤** 1.96 × 10 **19.6**	**⑥** 1000 × 1.96 **1960**
⑦ 100 × 0.973 **97.3**	**⑧** 0.973 × 10,000 **9730**	**⑨** 100 × 5.6 **560**
⑩ 5.6 × 10,000 **56,000**	**⑪** 0.07 × 10 **0.7**	**⑫** 100 × 0.07 **7**
⑬ 10 × 0.89 **8.9**	**⑭** 0.89 × 1000 **890**	**⑮** 10 × 23.7 **237**
⑯ 1000 × 23.7 **23,700**	**⑰** 1.05 × 10 **10.5**	**⑱** 100 × 1.05 **105**
⑲ 10 × 1.932 **19.32**	**⑳** 1.932 × 1000 **1932**	**㉑** 19.32 × 10 **193.2**

 **Social Studies Connection** Have groups of students research skyscrapers around the world. They could share their research with the class in a presentation or with a poster. Make sure they include information on the height, in meters, of skyscrapers and any other relevant measurements that they may find. Have them decorate their posters or visual presentation aids with original art or magazine clippings.

*available separately

You know that the value of a digit's place in a number is one-tenth the value of the place to its left. So you can divide by a power of 10 just by moving the decimal point to the left.

To divide by 10, move the decimal point one place to the left. You may need to write in a 0.

Examples:

$9 \div 10 \longrightarrow 0.9. \longrightarrow 0.9$

$77 \div 10 \longrightarrow 7.7. \longrightarrow 7.7$

$12.48 \div 10 \longrightarrow 1.2.48 \longrightarrow 1.248$

To divide by 100, move the decimal point two places to the left. You may need to write in extra 0s.

Examples:

$68 \div 100 \longrightarrow 0.68. \longrightarrow 0.68$

$5 \div 100 \longrightarrow 0.05. \longrightarrow 0.05$

$229.3 \div 100 \longrightarrow 2.29.3 \longrightarrow 2.293$

To divide by any power of 10, count the 0s in the power of 10. Then move the decimal point that many places to the left. You may need to write in extra 0s.

Divide.

22 $33 \div 10$
3.3

23 $33 \div 100$
0.33

24 $7.5 \div 10$
0.75

25 $7.5 \div 100$
0.075

26 $19.6 \div 10$
1.96

27 $19.6 \div 1000$
0.0196

28 $219.7 \div 10$
21.97

29 $219.7 \div 1000$
0.2197

30 $0.3 \div 10$
0.03

31 $0.3 \div 100$
0.003

32 $1.05 \div 10$
0.105

33 $1.05 \div 100$
0.0105

34 $20.3 \div 100$
0.203

35 $20.3 \div 10,000$
0.00203

36 $0.02 \div 10$
0.002

37 $0.02 \div 100$
0.0002

38 $5000 \div 10$
500

39 $5000 \div 1000$
5

40 $270 \div 1000$
0.270

41 $270 \div 10$
27

42 $27 \div 10$
2.7

Unit 2 Lesson 29 • **111**

② Teach

Using the Student Pages Briefly review the procedures for multiplying and dividing decimals by powers of 10. Have students work on these pages independently.

Use concrete materials, such as **centimeter cubes*** and **decimeter rods***, to help students understand the concept that there must be many small units to make one large unit.

Literature Connection
In *Jason and the Money Tree* by Sonia Levitin, Jason's money tree grows ten-dollar bills. Invite students to create multiplication problems with decimals to determine the value of a portion of Jason's crop.

*available separately

◆ LESSON 29 Decimals and Powers of 10

Teach

Using the Student Pages Go over this page and the discussion questions with the class. The work with metric units here and on the following page applies the material reviewed on pages 110–111. Emphasize the decimal nature of the metric system and the ease of conversion among units of measure.

Have students work independently or in small groups on the two problems on page 112. Go over the examples on page 113, and then have students do the problems on their own.

Students can use a blank **Cruncher*** spreadsheet to create tables for the metric units of weight and volume.

Answers to first discussion question:

Other metric units of weight that students name should include all those that correspond to the units of length given in the table: *milligram, centigram, decigram, dekagram, hectogram, and kilogram*. Their symbols are, respectively, *mg, cg, dg, dag, hg,* and *kg*. Students who mention other units of weight and volume, such as *megagram* and *nanoliter*, should be praised for their knowledge. Point out that those units mentioned on this page are the most common, and not even all of these are in common use.

◆ LESSON 29 Decimals and Powers of 10

The basic unit of length in the metric system is the *meter*. Its symbol is *m*. The following table shows some metric units of length:

Unit	Symbol	Relationship to the Meter	Number of Meters
millimeter	mm	one-thousandth of a meter	0.001
centimeter	cm	one-hundredth of a meter	0.01
decimeter	dm	one-tenth of a meter	0.1
meter	m	one meter	1
dekameter	dam	ten meters	10
hectometer	hm	one hundred meters	100
kilometer	km	one thousand meters	1000

The *gram* is a metric unit of weight. Its symbol is *g*. Other metric units of weight correspond to the metric units of length. For example, a milligram is one thousandth of a gram.

◆ What are some other metric units of weight and their symbols? **See margin.**

◆ How are they related to the gram? **They are related to the gram in the same way the various units of length are related to the meter.**

43 Use a computer or other means to draw and complete a table for metric units of weight. **See the table of metric measures on pages 588–589.**

The *liter* is a metric unit of capacity. Its symbol is *L*. Other metric units of capacity correspond to the metric units of length and weight.

◆ What are some metric units of capacity and their symbols? **Metric units of volume include the *milliliter (mL), centiliter (cL), deciliter (dL), dekaliter (daL), hectoliter (hL)* and *kiloliter (kL)*.**

◆ How are they related to the liter? **They are related to the liter in the same way as the various units of length are related to the meter.**

44 Use a computer or other means to draw a table, and complete the table for metric units of capacity. **See the table of metric measures on pages 588–589.**

FANTASTIC FACT The meter is defined as the distance travelled by light in a vacuum in $\frac{1}{299{,}792{,}458}$ of a second.

112 · Decimals and Exponents

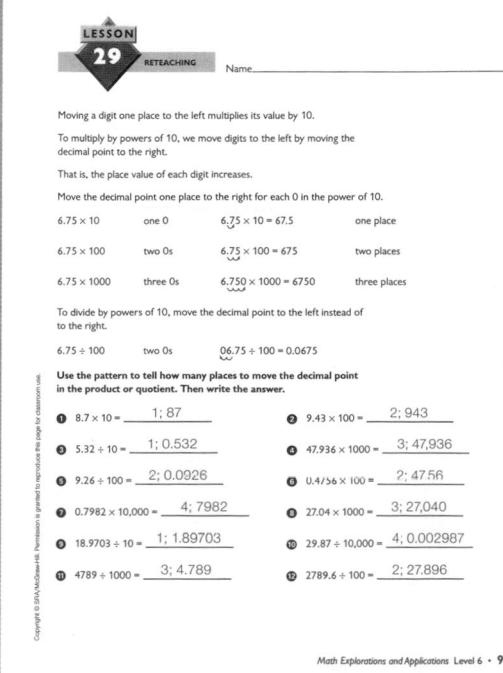

*available separately

The meter is divided or multiplied by powers of 10 to produce the other metric units of length. For this reason it is easy to change from one unit of length to another in the metric system.

To convert from larger to smaller units, multiply by moving the decimal point right. To convert from smaller to larger units, divide by moving the decimal point to the left.

It is just as easy to change from one unit of weight or volume to another.

Example: 14 m = ■ cm

Remember:
0.01 m = 1 cm
1 m = 100. cm   Multiply by 100.
14 m = 1400. cm   Multiply by 100.

Example: 70 g = ■ kg

Remember:
1000 g = 1 kg
1 g = 0.001 kg   Divide by 1000.
70 g = 0.070 kg   Divide by 1000.

Example: 3.02 L = ■ mL

Remember:
0.001 L = 1 mL
1 L = 1000 mL   Multiply by 1000.
3.02 L = 3020 mL   Multiply by 1000.

Complete these conversions.

45 3 m = ■ cm
300

46 312 cm = ■ m
3.12

47 2 kg = ■ mg
2,000,000

48 300 g = ■ kg
0.3

49 31.2 cm = ■ m
0.312

50 500 mL = ■ L
0.5

51 1.5 L = ■ mL
1500

52 200 mg = ■ g
0.2

53 50 mL = ■ L
0.05

54 4000 mm = ■ m
4

55 200 g = ■ kg
0.2

56 10 m = ■ dm
100

57 11 g = ■ mg
11,000

58 0.5 L = ■ mL
500

59 52.35 mg = ■ g
0.05235

Solve this problem.

60 Natasha has a pet hamster named Goldie. Natasha weighed and measured Goldie and found that the hamster weighs 120 grams and is 13 centimeters long.

a. What is Goldie's weight in kilograms? **0.12**

b. What is Goldie's length in meters? **0.13**

Unit 2   Lesson 29 • **113**

PRACTICE p. 29

ENRICHMENT p. 29

---

③ Wrap-Up 5 MINUTES

In Closing Summarize the lesson by asking students to explain and then demonstrate on the chalkboard the procedure for multiplying and dividing by powers of 10 and for converting from one metric unit of measurement to another.

To help students who move the decimal point in the wrong direction when multiplying or dividing by a power of 10, guide them first to decide whether the answer will be greater than or less than the number being multiplied or divided. Then remind them that the number of 0s in the multiplier or divisor shows how many places to move the decimal point in the answer.

Performance Assessment Have students write a description of how to convert between units in the metric system. Have them include an explanation of why you can move the decimal point to the right to convert from a larger unit of measurement to a smaller one.

Assessment Criteria

Did the student . . .

✓ contribute to the solution of the discussion questions?

✓ correctly answer at least 75% of the computation problems on pages 110, 111, and 113?

Homework Have students write a short paragraph detailing the benefits and disadvantages of the metric system compared to the customary measuring system commonly used in the United States.

Multiplying Decimals and Whole Numbers

Student Edition pages 114–115

LESSON PLANNER

Objectives

▶ to review and provide practice in multiplying decimals and whole numbers

▶ to provide practice in approximating the product of two decimals

Context of the Lesson This is the fourth of 11 lessons on operations with decimals.

 MANIPULATIVES

base-10 materials* (optional)

Program Resources

Practice Master 30

Enrichment Master 30

For extra practice:
CD-ROM* Lesson 30
Cumulative Review, page 559

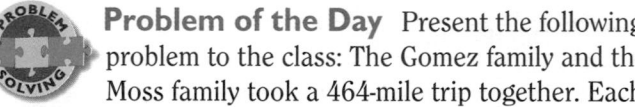

❶ Warm-Up ⏱ 5 MINUTES

Problem of the Day Present the following problem to the class: The Gomez family and the Moss family took a 464-mile trip together. Each family took its own car. The Gomez car used 16 gallons of gas and the Moss car used 14 gallons. The Gomez family used Super Duper gas at $1.45 per gallon, while the Moss family used Super Duper Deluxe gas at $1.75 per gallon. Which family got the better gas mileage? Which spent more on gas? (Moss; Moss)

Problem-Solving Strategies Ask students who have solved the Problem of the Day to share how they solved it and any strategies they used.

 Continue the estimating measurements activity begun in the previous lesson. You may wish to ask students who give their measurements in one unit to convert them to another in the same measurement system.

❷ Teach

Using the Student Pages Go over these pages with the class. When you discuss multiplying a decimal by a whole number on page 114, you may wish to use physical models

114 Decimals and Exponents

Multiplying Decimals and Whole Numbers

Jamal wants to buy seven jars of poster paint that cost $0.54 each. What will the total cost be?

$$7 \times 0.54 = ?$$

To find the answer, we could simply add 0.54 seven times:

$$7 \times 0.54 = 0.54 + 0.54 + 0.54 + 0.54 + 0.54 + 0.54 + 0.54$$
$$= 3.78$$

We can think of this another way. Write $0.54 as 54¢. Since 7×54 is 378, the total cost is 378¢. In dollars and cents, that is $3.78. So $7 \times \$0.54$ is $3.78.

$$
\begin{array}{r}
54 \\
\times\ 7 \\
\hline
378
\end{array}
\qquad
\begin{array}{r}
0.54 \\
\times\ 7 \\
\hline
3.78
\end{array}
$$

Remember: **When you multiply a decimal by a whole number, multiply as though the decimal were a whole number, too. Then write the decimal point in the product as many places from the right as it is in the decimal factor.**

Example: 83×2.741

$$
\begin{array}{r}
2.741 \quad \longleftarrow \text{ This decimal point is three places from the right.} \\
\times \qquad 83 \\
\hline
8\,223 \\
+\ 219\,28 \\
\hline
227.503 \quad \longleftarrow \text{ So put this decimal point three places from the right.}
\end{array}
$$

Multiply.

❶ 2.4 × 7 **16.8**	❷ 0.6 × 5 **3.0**	❸ 0.65 × 5 **3.25**	❹ 3.65 × 5 **18.25**
❺ 0.1 × 8 **0.8**	❻ 2.1 × 8 **16.8**	❼ 0.4 × 6 **2.4**	❽ 0.04 × 6 **0.24**
❾ 3.2 × 3 **9.6**	❿ 43.2 × 3 **129.6**	⓫ 20 × 0.8 **16.0**	⓬ 22 × 0.8 **17.6**

114 • Decimals and Exponents

 **Literature Connection**

Matilda by Roald Dahl takes place in England. You may wish to have students convert money amounts in the story from pounds to dollars using current exchange rates for more practice with decimals.

RETEACHING

 Some students may have difficulty because they do not have a feel for magnitude when it is expressed in decimal notation. Have these students work with concrete materials, such as **base-10 blocks*** or metric units of length.

Other students may benefit from working with you to count from the right to place the point in a product. You can provide further practice by having students play the "Roll a Problem" Game (Multiplication), modified to work with decimals.

---

114 Decimals and Exponents

*available separately

Rosa was about to buy a package of dog treats at the supermarket.

"That can't be right," said Rosa.

◆ Why not? **If the price and weight are rounded up, the cost is $12.**

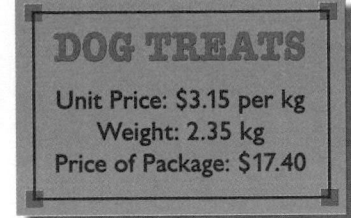

DOG TREATS

Unit Price: $3.15 per kg
Weight: 2.35 kg
Price of Package: $17.40

Linda, Pablo, and Jim were shopping for a carpet. "I like that one," Linda told the saleswoman.

When the saleswoman asked the family how much carpet they needed, they said that the room was 4.62 meters long and 3.56 meters wide.

The saleswoman took out her calculator, pressed a few keys, and said, "That's 164.472 square meters."

"That can't be," said Jim.

◆ Why not? **Students should realize that 164.472 cannot be the product of 4.62 × 3.56, because the product must be less than 5 × 4, or 20.**

In each case one answer is correct. Decide which one is correct without using a calculator.

⑬ 4.3 × 6.4 =   a. 2.752   **(b.)** 27.52   c. 275. 2

⑭ 2.5 × 15.3 =   **(a.)** 38.25   b. 382.5   c. 3825

⑮ 3.3 × 3.3 =   a. 1.089   **(b.)** 10.89   c. 108.9

⑯ 10.14 × 10.51 =   a. 1.065714   b. 10.65714   **(c.)** 106.5714

⑰ 1.04 × 25.6 =   a. 266.24   **(b.)** 26.624   c. 2.6624

⑱ 9.4 × 11.8 =   **(a.)** 110.92   b. 11.092   c. 1.1092

⑲ 17.5 × 2.1 =   a. 3675   b. 367.5   **(c.)** 36.75

⑳ 2.9 × 2.9 =   a. 0.841   **(b.)** 8.41   c. 84.1

㉑ 26.7 × 10.2 =   **(a.)** 272.34   b. 27.234   c. 2.7234

㉒ 62.3 × 1.08 =   a. 6728.4   b. 672.84   **(c.)** 67.284

㉓ 5.72 × 34 =   a. 19.448   **(b.)** 194.48   c. 1944.8

㉔ 18.6 × 4.9 =   **(a.)** 91.14   b. 911.4   c. 9114

㉕ 0.4 × 1.3 =   a. 0.052   **(b.)** 0.52   c. 5.2

Use the Cumulative Review on page 559 after this lesson.

Unit 2 Lesson 30 • 115

---

other than money. For example, find the combined length of four sticks that are each 0.35 meters long. You can convert to centimeters here just as the example on page 114 converts to cents. Go over the situations and discussion questions on page 115. Make sure students understand that the package price is the product of the price per kilogram and the weight in kilograms. Point out that even if students do not know how to find an exact answer to 2.35 × 3.15, they can tell that $74.03 is wrong, because the product must be less than 3 × 4, or 12. Have students do problems 13–25 on their own.

❸ Wrap-Up

In Closing Ask students how many spaces to the right of the decimal point will be in the answer for the following:

a. 47 × 0.68 (2)

b. 62.37 × 4 (2)

c. 7.332 × 42 (3)

d. 16 × 7 (0)

e. 17.8 × 232 (1)

f. 1876 × 0.19777 (5)

 Encourage students who make errors in the placement of the decimal point to check their answers to see that they make sense. For example, a student who gets an answer of 13.68 to the problem 45.6 × 3 can be asked for the answer to 45 × 3. Seeing that the answer to that is 135 and recognizing that the answer to 45.6 × 3 should be a little greater than 135 can help these students see that 13.68 cannot be correct.

 **Informal Assessment** Observe students as they work on the problems on page 114. Ask them to explain how they know where to place the decimal point in the product. Have students explain the process they used on page 115.

Assessment Criteria

Did the student . . .

✓ correctly answer at least 75% of the computation problems on page 114?

✓ contribute to the discussion on page 115?

✓ choose at least 70% of the correct answers in the exercise set on page 115?

Homework Have students practice estimating decimal products by using data from ten different supermarket products. For example, students can estimate how much 6 pounds of corn at $0.29 per pound would cost ($1.80). Make sure they check their estimates.

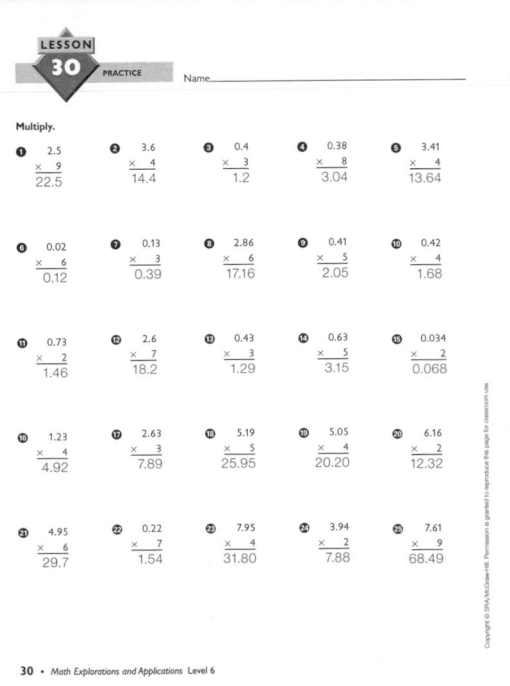

PRACTICE p. 30

LESSON 30 PRACTICE   Name_____

Multiply.

❶ 2.5 × 9 = 22.5
❷ 3.6 × 4 = 14.4
❸ 0.4 × 3 = 1.2
❹ 0.38 × 8 = 3.04
❺ 3.41 × 4 = 13.64

❻ 0.02 × 6 = 0.12
❼ 0.13 × 3 = 0.39
❽ 2.86 × 6 = 17.16
❾ 0.41 × 5 = 2.05
❿ 0.42 × 4 = 1.68

⓫ 0.73 × 2 = 1.46
⓬ 2.6 × 7 = 18.2
⓭ 0.43 × 3 = 1.29
⓮ 0.63 × 5 = 3.15
⓯ 0.034 × 2 = 0.068

⓰ 1.23 × 4 = 4.92
⓱ 2.63 × 3 = 7.89
⓲ 5.19 × 5 = 25.95
⓳ 5.05 × 4 = 20.20
⓴ 6.16 × 2 = 12.32

㉑ 4.95 × 6 = 29.7
㉒ 0.22 × 7 = 1.54
㉓ 7.95 × 4 = 31.80
㉔ 3.94 × 2 = 7.88
㉕ 7.61 × 9 = 68.49

30 • Math Explorations and Applications Level 6

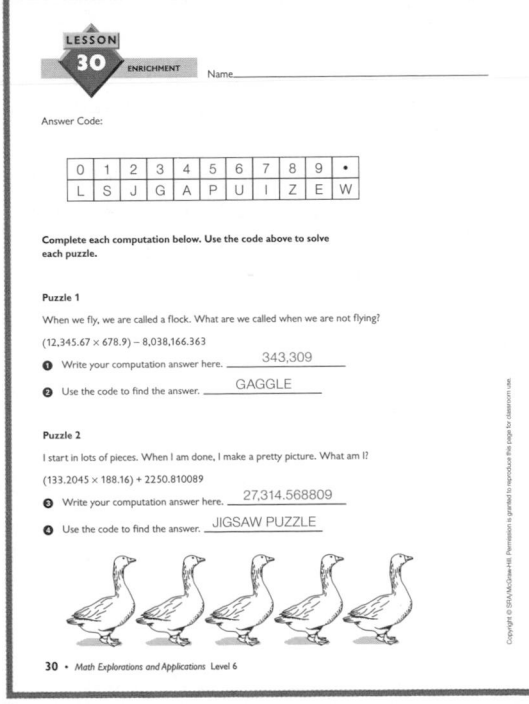

ENRICHMENT p. 30

LESSON 30 ENRICHMENT   Name_____

Answer Code:

0	1	2	3	4	5	6	7	8	9	•
L	S	J	G	A	P	U	I	Z	E	W

Complete each computation below. Use the code above to solve each puzzle.

Puzzle 1

When we fly, we are called a flock. What are we called when we are not flying?

(12,345.67 × 678.9) − 8,038,166.363

❶ Write your computation answer here.   343,309

❷ Use the code to find the answer.   GAGGLE

Puzzle 2

I start in lots of pieces. When I am done, I make a pretty picture. What am I?

(133.2045 × 188.16) + 2250.810089

❸ Write your computation answer here.   27,314.568809

❹ Use the code to find the answer.   JIGSAW PUZZLE

30 • Math Explorations and Applications Level 6

Unit 2 Lesson 30 **115**

Student Edition pages 116–119

Multiplying Decimals

LESSON PLANNER

Objectives

✓ to evaluate students' ability to multiply with decimals

▶ to help students develop, through an area model, an algorithm for multiplying two decimals

Context of the Lesson This is the fifth of 11 lessons on operations with decimals. It provides Mastery Checkpoint 11 for assessing mastery of multiplication with decimals.

 MANIPULATIVES

newspaper (optional)

Program Resources

Reteaching Master

Practice Master 31

Enrichment Master 31

Assessment Master

The Cruncher*

For extra practice:
   CD-ROM* Lesson 31

① Warm-Up

Problem of the Day Present the following problem to the class: What is the product of the two numbers that have a sum of 10 and a difference of 5? (18.75; the numbers are 2.5 and 7.5.)

Problem-Solving Strategies Ask students who have solved the Problem of the Day to share how they solved it and any strategies they used.

 **MENTAL MATH** Help students understand the following method for solving problems mentally. (Note that there are many reasonable ways of finding these answers.)

a.   64
      +44
      ———
      108   is the answer

     Think   64 + 40 = 104
                 104 + 4 = 108

b.   83
      +55
      ———
      138   is the answer

     Think   83 + 50 = 133
                 133 + 5 = 138

c.   71
      +42
      ———
      113   is the answer

     Think   71 + 40 = 111
                 111 + 2 = 113

(continued on page 117)

Multiplying Decimals

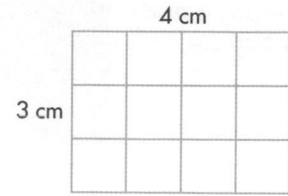

4 cm

3 cm

To find the area of a rectangle, multiply the length and the width. Your answer will be in square units. The area of the rectangle above is 3 centimeters × 4 centimeters, or 12 square centimeters.

Often we have to multiply two decimals when we are finding areas. Suppose we want to find the area of a rectangle that is 0.3 meter long and 0.25 meter wide. The area is 0.3 × 0.25 square meter.

Let's draw that rectangle in a square that is 1 meter on a side (1 square meter). The rectangle is yellow. See the illustration on the next page.

One side of the square is marked off in hundredths. The other side is in tenths. We want to find the area of the yellow rectangle. It is three tenths of a meter long and 25 hundredths of a meter wide.

◆   How many tenths in one whole? **10**

◆   How many hundredths in one whole? **100**

◆   How many small rectangles are there in the entire square? **1000**

◆   What part of the large square is each small rectangle? **one-thousandth**

◆   How many of the small rectangles are in the yellow rectangle? **75**

◆   How did you find that? **Explanations will vary. One possible solution is that there are 3 rows of 25 rectangles each, and 3 × 25 = 75.** The area of the yellow rectangle is $\frac{75}{1000}$ of a square meter, or 0.075 square meter. So we say that 0.3 × 0.25 is 0.075.

116 • Decimals and Exponents

 **CULTURAL DIVERSITY** Introduce students to the currency exchange rates table in the financial section of the **newspaper**. Demonstrate how to interpret the table to figure out how many francs, pounds, marks, etc. $10, $100, or some other amount of American money will buy.

*available separately

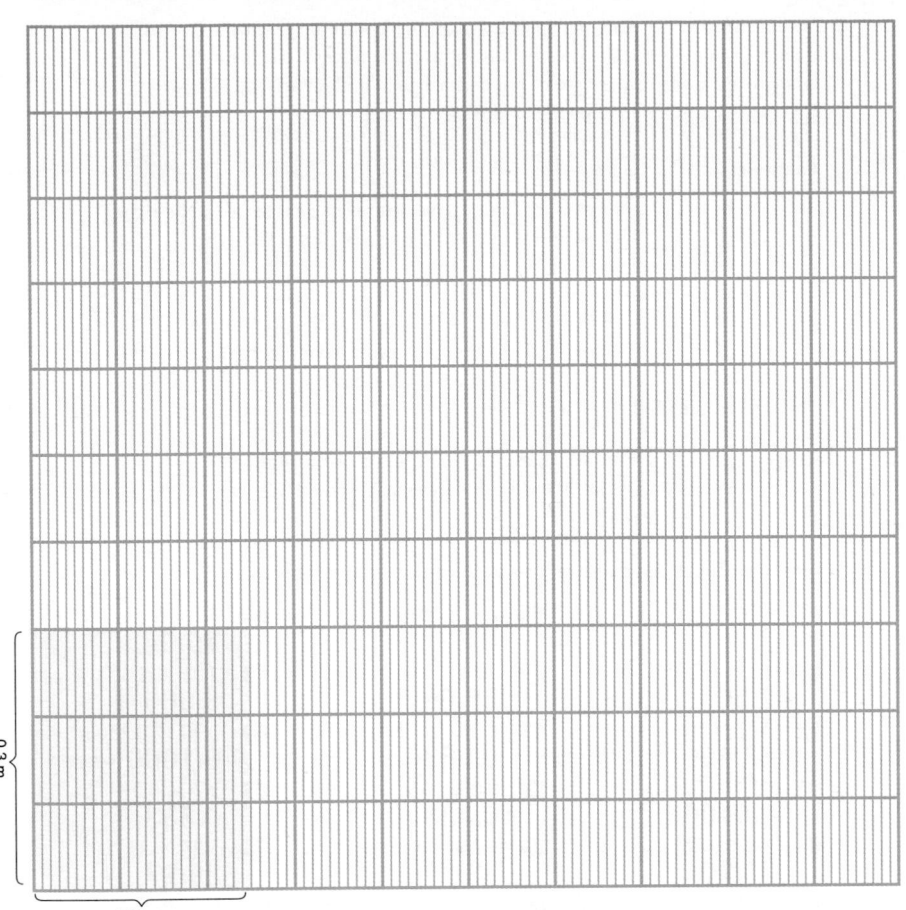

0.3 m

0.25 m

Notice that we found the number of small rectangles by multiplying two whole numbers (3 and 25). The size of each small rectangle is determined by the size of the units of the two factors: (tenths × hundredths = thousandths).

We can use this idea whenever we multiply two decimals. The number in the answer, if we ignore the decimal point, is the product of the numbers in the factors.

To place the decimal point, we look at the number of decimal places in each factor.

Unit 2   Lesson 31 • **117**

d.   49
   +25
   ‾‾‾
   74   is the answer

Think 49 + 20 = 69
       69 + 5 = 74

❷ Teach

Using the Student Pages Discuss the material on page 116 with students. You may wish to do several examples for which you draw the appropriate rectangles on the chalkboard. You may wish to draw a square divided into tenths, another square showing hundredths, and finally a drawing similar to the one on page 117 showing thousandths. You can use explanations for the sixth discussion question similar to the following: Because the side is divided into tenths and the top into hundredths, the entire square is divided into 10 × 100, or 1000, small rectangles. Each small rectangle is one thousandth of the square meter. Of the 1000 small rectangles, 25 × 3, or 75, are in the yellow rectangle that is 0.25 meters wide and 0.3 meters high.

Go over the concepts on page 117 with the class.

Why **teach it this way?**

Computation problems are provided to reinforce the mechanics of multiplying decimals. Students should realize, however, that the existence of a numerical answer calculated to several decimal places does not necessarily imply that the answer is that precise. If lengths are measured to the nearest hundredth of a meter, for instance, the area of a room 3.12 m × 7.16 m is about 22.34 m², but not necessarily 22.3392 m² merely because 3.12 × 7.16 = 22.3392.

Literature Connection Have students read *The Kids' Complete Guide to Money* by Kathy S. Kyte. Reading this book can help students manage money and make intelligent kid-sized financial decisions.

◆ LESSON 31 Multiplying Decimals

Teach

Using the Student Pages

Do several examples such as the one at the top of page 118, focusing on the steps. Point out that multiplication of decimals is done exactly the same way as multiplication with whole numbers, but with the extra step of placing the decimal point in the product. Emphasize that in order to place the decimal point, students must count the digits to the right of the point in each factor and add those numbers together. That total is the number of digits that should be to the right of the decimal point in the product.

 Have students do problems 1–33 on page 118 on their own, as well as the word problems on page 119. Ask students to approximate the answers to the word problems before solving them to make sure their actual answers make sense.

Students can use a blank **Cruncher*** spreadsheet to explore patterns found when multiplying decimals.

◆ LESSON 31 Multiplying Decimals

To multiply two decimals, multiply as though there were no decimal points. Then place the point in the answer as many places from the right as there are digits to the right of the decimal point in the two factors together. This is easier to understand with an example.

Example: $10.1 \times 3.48 = ?$

$$
\begin{array}{r}
3.4\,8 \\
\times\ \ 1\,0.1 \\
\hline
3\,4\,8 \\
\times\,3\,4\,8\,0 \\
\hline
3\,5.1\,4\,8 \\
\end{array}
$$

3.48 ◄──── This decimal point is two places from the right.

× 10.1 ◄──── This point is one place from the right.

35.148 ◄──── 2 + 1 = 3 So place the point three places from the right in the answer.

The answer is 35.148.

Check to see that the answer makes sense. It should be more than 10×3 and less than 11×4. Is 35.148 between 30 and 44? Yes, so the answer makes sense.

Multiply. Check your answers to be sure they make sense.

1 4×0.8 **3.2**	**2** 0.4×0.8 **0.32**	**3** 75×0.2 **15.0**
4 7.5×0.2 **1.50**	**5** 101×0.66 **66.66**	**6** 1.01×6.6 **6.666**
7 3.02×21 **63.42**	**8** 0.302×0.21 **0.06342**	**9** 0.40×0.25 **0.1000**
10 0.04×0.25 **0.0100**	**11** 0.037×9 **0.333**	**12** 3.7×0.09 **0.333**
13 42×0.55 **23.10**	**14** 4.2×5.5 **23.10**	**15** 3.57×11 **39.27**
16 35.7×1.1 **39.27**	**17** 606×2.2 **1333.2**	**18** 6.06×0.22 **1.3332**
19 1.540×21 **32.340**	**20** 1.540×0.21 **0.32340**	**21** 35×7.2 **252**
22 3.5×72 **252**	**23** 8.4×6.9 **57.96**	**24** 0.84×0.69 **0.5796**
25 5.1×0.09 **0.459**	**26** 51×0.9 **45.9**	**27** 73.8×2.3 **169.74**
28 7.38×23 **169.74**	**29** 47×9.45 **444.15**	**30** 4.7×9.45 **44.415**
31 4.7×94.5 **444.15**	**32** 75×10.3 **772.5**	**33** 75×1.03 **77.25**

118 • Decimals and Exponents

---

*available separately

Solve these problems.

34 Antonio bought 12 cans of juice for $2.53 each. How much did he have to pay for them? **$30.36**

35 Jefferson's weekly paycheck is $243.57. How much does he receive in one year? **about $12,665.64**

36 One pencil costs $0.57. How much will 20 pencils cost? **$11.40**

37 Patrick lives 0.7 miles from school. If he rides his bicycle to school and back every day from Monday through Friday, how many miles does he ride in a week? **7**

38 Each of the Gumper quintuplets weighs exactly 51.3 kilograms. How much do they weigh all together? **256.5 kg**

39 Each of the Gumper quintuplets can jump across a puddle that is 3.74 meters wide. How wide a puddle can they jump all together? **3.74 m**

40 Each of the Gumper quintuplets has $43.57 in her pocket. How much money do they have all together? **$217.85**

41 How much will it cost for the Gumper quintuplets to go to a movie if tickets cost $4.75 each? **$23.75**

42 The quintuplets have some coupons for the movie theater that say, "Buy one ticket, get another ticket free." Using the coupons, how much will it cost them to go to a movie? **$14.25**

❸ Wrap-Up  5 MINUTES

In Closing To summarize the lesson, ask students to explain the procedure for multiplying two decimal numbers.

Mastery Checkpoint 11

By this time, most students should demonstrate mastery of multiplication with decimals by getting correct answers to at least 26 of the 33 problems on page 118 or meeting the objective on Assessment Blackline Masters page 19. The results of this assessment may be recorded on the Mastery Checkpoint Chart. Students who fall short of this objective should be given extra help, using the Reteaching Master on page 10 or other methods.

Assessment Criteria

Did the student . . .

✓ correctly answer at least 80% of the problems on page 118?

✓ demonstrate understanding of the multiplication algorithm for decimals?

Homework Have students use store flyers or newspaper ads to formulate several multiplication word problems involving money. Students can distribute these in class the next day for classmates to solve.

SPECIAL NEEDS Meeting Individual Needs

Emphasize that students should follow the practice of treating each problem involving multiplication of decimals at first as if there were no decimal points and then deciding how to locate the decimal point in the product, using the rules for determining where to place the point.

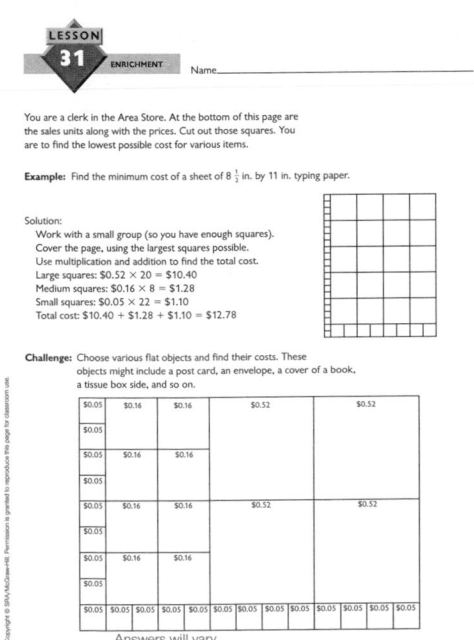
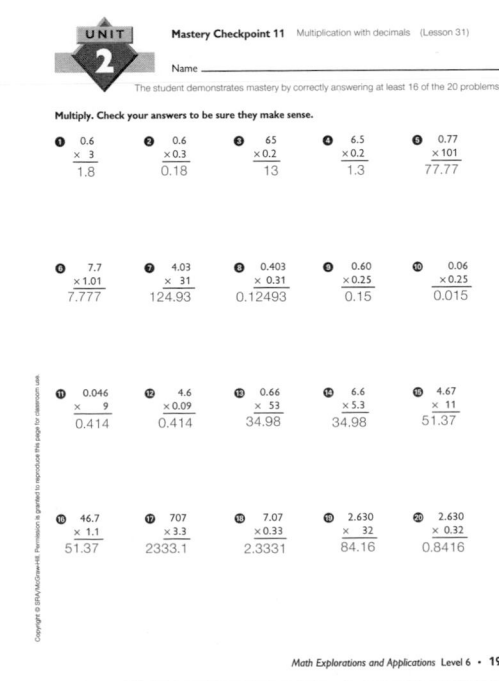

Precision with Customary Measurements

LESSON PLANNER

Objectives

▶ to call students' attention to the need for some means of indicating the precision of a reported measurement

▶ to introduce the usual convention for indicating the precision of a reported measurement

Context of the Lesson Measurements carried out to different decimal places indicate different levels of precision. This is the first lesson to introduce the concept formally, and this concept will be used in future lessons.

 MANIPULATIVES

measuring instruments with customary units of length*

Program Resources

Practice Master 32

Enrichment Master 32

For extra practice:
CD-ROM* Lesson 32

❶ Warm-Up ⏱ 5 MINUTES

 Problem of the Day Present the following problem to the class: Mr. Fleury's property is in the shape of a square 100 feet long on each side. He wants to fence in the property. The fence needs to have a post every 10 feet. How many fence posts will Mr. Fleury need? (40)

Problem-Solving Strategies Ask students who have solved the Problem of the Day to share how they solved it and any strategies they used.

MENTAL MATH Have students complete the following:

a. 12 ft = _____ yd (4)   **b.** 48 in. = _____ ft (4)

c. 3 yd = _____ in. (108)   **d.** 18 in. = _____ ft (1.5)

e. 8 ft = _____ yd ($2\frac{2}{3}$)   **f.** 4.5 yd = _____ ft (13.5)

Precision with Customary Measurements

  **COOPERATIVE LEARNING** **Work in groups to measure the length of your classroom. Share your results with the class. Did each get the same result?**

When you report a measurement, such as 3 feet 2 inches, people assume you believe the true measurement is closer to 3 feet 2 inches than to either 3 feet 1 inch or 3 feet 3 inches.

◆ What is the measurement exactly halfway between 3 feet 1 inch and 3 feet 2 inches? **3 ft 1$\frac{1}{2}$ in**

◆ What is the measurement exactly halfway between 3 feet 2 inches and 3 feet 3 inches? **3 ft 2$\frac{1}{2}$ in**

So if you say a length is 3 feet 2 inches, you mean that the length is between 3 feet 1$\frac{1}{2}$ inches and 3 feet 2$\frac{1}{2}$ inches.

3 ft   3 ft 1 in   3 ft 2 in   3 ft 3 in

In general you should be careful not to report a measurement that would give the impression it is more precise than it really is. So, to say the length of your school room is 27 feet, 3 and $\frac{5}{16}$ inches gives the impression you believe your measurement is correct to the nearest sixteenth of an inch.

◆ Were all of the class's measurements within $\frac{1}{16}$ inch of each other?

This is unlikely, given the usual methods of measuring and all the things that might go wrong as you are trying to measure the length of the room.

 **Solve these problems.**

❶ Suppose you hear that a new mall has opened 10 miles from your school.
  a. Do you think the mall is exactly 10 miles from your school? **probably not**
  b. What is the closest the mall could be to school? **probably about 9.5 miles**
  c. What is the farthest the mall could be from school? **probably about 10.5 m**

❷ Suppose a county map reports a street is 52,799 feet long.
  a. What is the shortest length the street could have? **probably about 52,798$\frac{1}{2}$**
  b. What is the longest length the street could have? **probably about 52,799$\frac{1}{2}$**

▇▇▇ teach it this way?

By actually making and reporting measurements, students are better able to appreciate the importance of reporting measurements precisely.

 **COOPERATIVE LEARNING** Encourage groups to assign roles during the measuring. While some students are laying down the measuring tool, another can read the measurement and another can record it. Another student can present the group's findings to the class. Set up the activity so that groups do not get in each other's way. You may wish to have groups measure different regions in the school to avoid confusion.

RETEACHING

Some students might benefit by working in small groups on the problems on page 121. Encourage students to talk over the answers and come to consensus on each. The key idea in this lesson and the next is that precision must be considered when reporting and interpreting measurements. It is not necessary for students to master the details at this time.

*available separately

Between what two measures would you assume the true measure is if somebody reported each of the following measurements?

3 3 feet 4 inches **3 feet $3\frac{1}{2}$ inches** **4** 5 yards, 2 feet, 7 inches **5 yards, 2 feet,** and 3 feet $4\frac{1}{2}$ inches **$6\frac{1}{2}$ inches and 5 yards, 2 feet, $7\frac{1}{2}$ inches**

5 27 miles **$26\frac{1}{2}$ miles and** **6** 27.3 miles **27.25 miles and 27.35 miles** **$27\frac{1}{2}$ miles**

7 27.0 miles **8** 7 inches **$6\frac{1}{2}$ inches and $7\frac{1}{2}$ inches** **26.95 miles and 27.05 miles**

9 18 yards **10** 54 feet **$53\frac{1}{2}$ feet and $54\frac{1}{2}$ feet** **$17\frac{1}{2}$ yards and $18\frac{1}{2}$ yards**

11 648 inches **$647\frac{1}{2}$ inches and** **12** 8 feet **$7\frac{1}{2}$ feet and $8\frac{1}{2}$ feet** **$648\frac{1}{2}$ inches**

13 8 feet, 3 inches **14** 6 miles **$5\frac{1}{2}$ miles and $6\frac{1}{2}$ miles** **8 feet $2\frac{1}{2}$ inches, 8 feet $3\frac{1}{2}$ inches**

15 $4\frac{1}{2}$ feet **$4\frac{1}{4}$ feet and $4\frac{3}{4}$ feet** **16** 12 yards **$11\frac{1}{2}$ yards and $12\frac{1}{2}$ yards**

17 37 feet **$36\frac{1}{2}$ feet and $37\frac{1}{2}$ feet** **18** 57 pounds **$56\frac{1}{2}$ pounds and $57\frac{1}{2}$ pounds**

19 1216 gallons **20** 13 years **$12\frac{1}{2}$ years and $13\frac{1}{2}$ years** **$1215\frac{1}{2}$ gallons and $1216\frac{1}{2}$ gallons**

21 Discuss the relationship between the three measurements in problems 9–11. **They are the same measurement. 648 inches is more precise than 54 feet, which is more precise than 18 yards**

How would you report the measurements given below with the possible indicated error?

22 10 feet, possible error of $\frac{1}{2}$ foot **10 feet** **23** 10 feet, possible error of $\frac{1}{2}$ inch **120 inches**

24 1 mile, possible error of $\frac{1}{20}$ mile **1.0 mile** **25** 1 mile, possible error of $\frac{1}{2}$ yard **1760 yards**

26 1 mile, possible error of $\frac{1}{2}$ foot **5280 feet** **27** 1 mile, possible error of $\frac{1}{2}$ inch **63,360 inches**

28 8 inches, possible error of $\frac{1}{2}$ inch **8 inches** **29** 12 miles, possible error of 0.05 mile **12.0 miles**

30 9 yards, possible error of $\frac{1}{2}$ yard **9 yards** **31** 9 yards, possible error of $\frac{1}{2}$ foot **9 yards, 0 feet or 27 feet**

Unit 2 Lesson 32 • **121**

PRACTICE p. 32

ENRICHMENT p. 32

*available separately

---

❷ Teach

COOPERATIVE LEARNING **MANIPULATIVES** **Using the Student Pages** Have students work in groups to measure the length and width of the classroom or some other room or area of good size. They should use **measuring instruments with customary units of length***. Explain that groups should not share their results with other groups until all groups report. Then have each group report its measurements of length and width. Have a volunteer write these figures on the chalkboard. Then discuss page 120. Ask students to tell how they could have indicated the level of precision when reporting their own measurements of the classroom.

Have students complete the problems on page 121 independently. Invite students to discuss some of the problems, as needed. While the answer given for 27 is technically correct, it is an unreal situation. It is virtually impossible to measure a mile to such accuracy.

❸ Wrap-Up

In Closing To summarize the lesson, ask students to give different possible answers to problem 27, for example, 1 mile, 0 inches, or 63,360 inches. Ask them to explain which is easier to interpret.

ALTERNATIVE ASSESSMENT **Portfolio Assessment** Have students write a brief paragraph explaining the need for reporting with appropriate precision.

Assessment Criteria

Did the student . . .

✓ participate actively in the measuring activity?

✓ demonstrate understanding of the meaning of precision by correctly answering at least 75% of the problems on page 121?

✓ accurately explain the need for precision in reporting?

Homework Ask students to work with a family member to measure a region of their home and then report the measurement of that region with appropriate precision.

Reporting Metric Measurements

LESSON PLANNER

Objectives

▶ to teach the meaning of *precision* as it relates to reporting measurements

▶ to provide practice in computing perimeters and areas using a calculator

▶ to help students develop insight into the magnitude of errors in sums and products of imprecise measurements

Context of the Lesson This is the sixth of 11 lessons on operations with decimals. We do not expect mastery of the concept of precision. At this time students need only understand that the more decimal places used in reporting a measurement, the more precise the measurement is.

 MANIPULATIVES
none

Program Resources
Practice Master 33
Enrichment Master 33
For extra practice:
    CD-ROM* Lesson 33

❶ Warm-Up

 **Problem of the Day** Present the following problem: The approved weight of an official volleyball is a range from 9.17 ounces to 9.88 ounces. To the nearest tenth of an ounce, Ramona's volleyball weighs 9.1 ounces. Is her ball within the weight limits? (no)

Problem-Solving Strategies Ask students who have solved the Problem of the Day to share how they solved it and any strategies they used.

 Continue activities on estimating measurements. Focus attention on converting from one unit to another. Show an object and ask, "About how many meters long is this? How many centimeters is that? Let's measure to check."

❷ Teach

Using the Student Pages In going over the material on page 120 with the class, explain that whenever we affix

---

Reporting Metric Measurements

When we report a measurement, the number of decimal places we use gives an idea of how precise we think the measurement is.

Examples:

If we report:	We believe the true measure is
6 meters	between 5.5 meters and 6.5 meters.

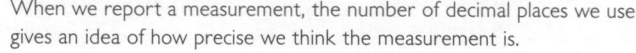

If we report:	We believe the true measure is
6.0 meters	between 5.95 meters and 6.05 meters.

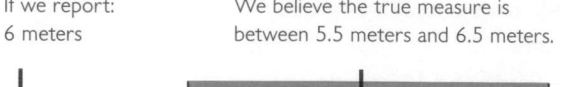

If we report:	We believe the true measure is
6.00 meters	between 5.995 meters and 6.005 meters.

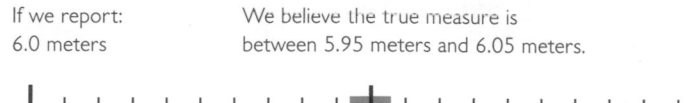

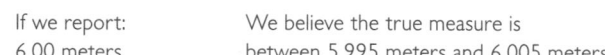

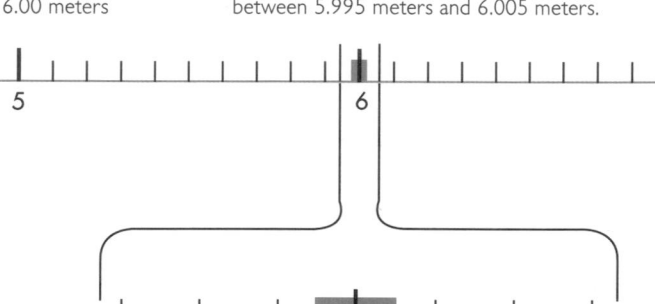

So when you are working with measurements, keep in mind that if you put 0s to the right of a decimal, then you are changing the meaning of that measurement.

What did the person who made the measurement believe was the true range of the measurement?

❶ 4 centimeters
between 3.5 cm and 4.5 cm

❷ 7.0 kilometers
between 6.95 km and 7.05 km

❸ 5.00 meters
between 4.995 m and 5.005 m

❹ 8 decimeters
between 7.5 dm and 8.5 dm

122 • Decimals and Exponents

 **teach it at this time?**

Precision is an important topic in the sequence of lessons on operations with decimals because an intelligent answer to a problem involving decimals must take into account how precise the numbers in the computation are.

Literature Connection For interesting information about determining weights and measurements, refer to *How Much and How Many?* by Jeanne Bendick.

RETEACHING

Reteaching or extensive extra teaching will not be necessary in this lesson, since reporting the precision of measurements is a difficult topic that students are not expected to master at this time. Rather, take advantage of opportunities as they arise in classroom measuring activities to discuss the precision of measurements made and how these should be reported.

*available separately

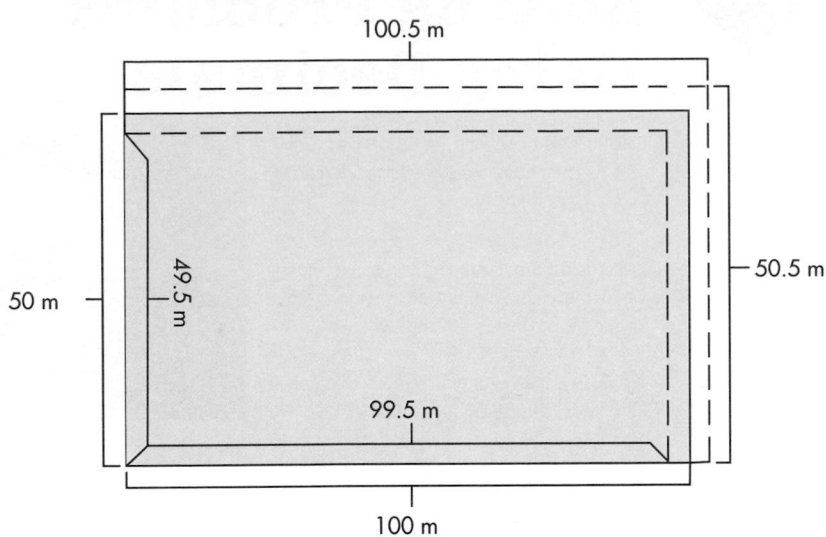

Hector measured the length of a rectangular field to be 100 m and the width to be 50 m.

Answer the following questions.

5 What are the perimeter and area of the field if Hector's measurements are exactly right?
P = 300 m; A = 5000 m²

6 If the true length and width of the field are 0.5 m greater than Hector's measurements, what is the true perimeter? What is the true area?
P = 302 m; A = 5075.25 m²

7 If the true length and width of the field are 0.5 m less than Hector's measurements, what is the true perimeter? What is the true area?
P = 298 m; A = 4925.25 m²

8 What are the greatest errors possible in Hector's figures for the perimeter and area of the field? **P = greatest possible error of 2 m; A = greatest possible error of 75.25 m²**

9 If Hector were measuring the area of the field to decide how much seed to buy and plant in the field, would he use the greatest possible area or the least possible area? **greatest**

10 If Hector were measuring the area of the field to see if it was large enough to use as a playing field for some game, would he use the greatest possible area or the least possible area? **least**

Unit 2 Lesson 33 • **123**

0s to the right of the decimal point (for example, to change 3 to 3.00), we are changing what we are indicating about the precision of the measurement. There is no problem, however, with writing 2 as 2.0 or 2.00 when using it to mean the number 2 in a calculation.

Work with the whole class or have students work in small groups to solve the problems on page 123. All should agree that the calculated perimeter and area for Hector's rectangular field are 300 m and 5000 m².

 Have students guess what the errors would be in the perimeter and area answers if the measurements were off by 0.5 m. Then have them calculate the greatest possible perimeter. This can be computed without a calculator, because the sum should be just 0.5 + 0.5 + 0.5 + 0.5, or 2 greater than the previous perimeter of 300. Therefore, the greatest possible perimeter is 302 m. The least possible perimeter is 2 less than 300, or 298 m. Then have students use **calculators*** to compute the greatest and least possible areas by multiplying 100.5 by 50.5 (5075.25) and 99.5 by 49.5 (4925.25). Guide them to notice the differences in the errors associated with each (75.25 vs. 74.75, respectively).

❸ Wrap-Up

In Closing Summarize the lesson by asking students to explain the meaning of the term *precision* as it applies to reporting a measurement. Have them also think of examples that show what differences knowing the precision of a measurement can make.

Informal Assessment Observe students as they work on the magnitude-of-error problems on page 123. Ask them to share their understanding of how an increase in the lengths of the sides of a figure affects the size of possible errors in measuring the perimeter and area of the figure.

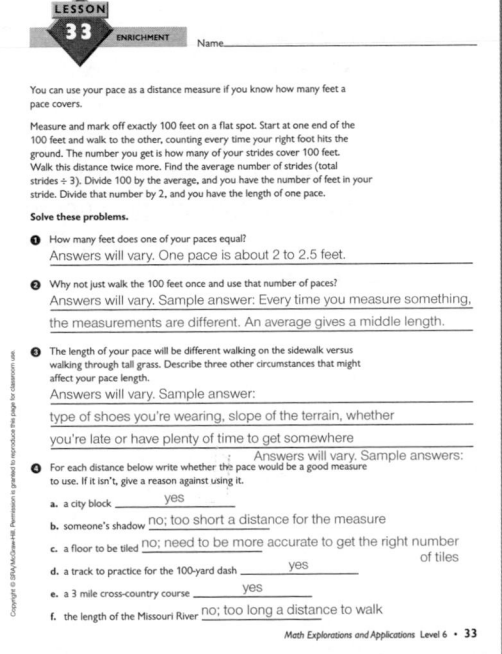

Assessment Criteria

Did the student . . .

✓ communicate an understanding of the concept of precision?

✓ explain how to find the measured perimeter and area of Hector's field?

✓ explain how to find the greatest possible errors in Hector's figures for the perimeter and area?

Homework Assign Practice Master 33 for further practice with precision.

PRACTICE p. 33

LESSON 33 PRACTICE Name_____

Your friend has made the following measurements and asks you to double-check them. Between what two measurements do you expect your measurement will be? **Answers will vary.**

1 5.6 miles — 5.55 miles and 5.65 miles

2 8.75 meters — 8.745 meters and 8.755 meters

3 10.00 kilometers — 9.995 kilometers and 10.005 kilometers

4 8.7 centimeters — 8.65 centimeters and 8.75 centimeters

5 48 miles — 47.5 miles and 48.5 miles

6 48.0 miles — 47.95 miles and 48.05 miles

7 26.000 meters — 25.9995 meters and 26.0005 meters

8 4 centimeters — 3.5 centimeters and 4.5 centimeters

Solve these problems.

Felicia measured a picture frame to be 60 centimeters wide and 50 centimeters high.

9 What are the perimeter and the area of the framed region if Felicia's measurements are exactly right? — 220 cm; 3000 cm²

10 If the true length and width are 0.5 centimeters less than Felicia's measurements, what are the true perimeter and true area? — 218 cm; 2945.25 cm²

11 If the true length and width are 0.5 centimeters greater than Felicia's measurements, what are the true perimeter and true area? — 222 cm; 3055.25 cm²

Math Explorations and Applications Level 6 • 33

ENRICHMENT p. 33

LESSON 33 ENRICHMENT Name_____

You can use your pace as a distance measure if you know how many feet a pace covers.

Measure and mark off exactly 100 feet on a flat spot. Start at one end of the 100 feet and walk to the other, counting every time your right foot hits the ground. The number you get is how many of your strides cover 100 feet. Walk this distance twice more. Find the average number of strides (total strides ÷ 3). Divide 100 by the average, and you have the number of feet in your stride. Divide that number by 2, and you have the length of one pace.

Solve these problems.

1 How many feet does one of your paces equal?
Answers will vary. One pace is about 2 to 2.5 feet.

2 Why not just walk the 100 feet once and use that number of paces?
Answers will vary. Sample answer: Every time you measure something, the measurements are different. An average gives a middle length.

3 The length of your pace will be different walking on the sidewalk versus walking through tall grass. Describe three other circumstances that might affect your pace length.
Answers will vary. Sample answer:
type of shoes you're wearing, slope of the terrain, whether you're late or have plenty of time to get somewhere

4 For each distance below write whether this pace would be a good measure to use. If it isn't, give a reason against using it. **Answers will vary. Sample answers:**

a. a city block — yes

b. someone's shadow — no; too short a distance for the measure

c. a floor to be tiled — no; need to be more accurate to get the right number of tiles

d. a track to practice for the 100-yard dash — yes

e. a 3 mile cross-country course — yes

f. the length of the Missouri River — no; too long a distance to walk

Math Explorations and Applications Level 6 • 33

*available separately

Solving Problems Using Decimals

LESSON PLANNER

Objectives

▶ to provide practice in multiplying decimals and in multiplying and dividing by powers of 10

▶ to provide applications of multiplying decimals

Context of the Lesson This is the seventh of 11 lessons on operations with decimals. The next lesson reviews division with a decimal divisor.

 MANIPULATIVES

Program Resources

Number Cubes (0–5 and 5–10)

Practice Master 34

Enrichment Master 34

The Cruncher*

For extra practice:
CD-ROM* Lesson 34

 ## ① **Warm-Up**

 Problem of the Day Present the following problem to the class: Elizabeth's father gave her $22.50 and her mother gave her $30 to go shopping. When she returned from shopping, Elizabeth had less than $5 left. What is the least she could have spent? ($47.51)

Problem-Solving Strategies Ask students who have solved the Problem of the Day to share how they solved it and any strategies they used.

MENTAL MATH Using exercise **a** as an example, demonstrate one way to add two-digit numbers using mental math. Then present the remaining exercises.

a. 46
    + 52
    ___
     98   is the answer

46 + 50 = 96
96 + 2 = 98

b. 75
    + 39
    ___
   (114)

75 + 30 = 105
105 + 9 = 114

(continued on page 125)

Solving Problems Using Decimals

Mr. Reilly is having carpet put in his living room. The room is 3.6 meters wide and 6.3 meters long.

The carpet he likes is 4.0 meters wide and costs $21.95 per running meter. He must buy a piece that is 4.0 meters wide, even though the room is not that wide.

① How many running meters of carpet must Mr. Reilly buy? **6.3**

② How much will he pay for the carpet? **$138.29**

The salesman tells Mr. Reilly that he can have the store install the carpet for $3.25 per square meter of the room. Included in this service is trimming the piece of carpet to fit and attaching the carpet to the floor.

③ How many square meters are in the room? **22.68**

④ How much will it cost if Mr. Reilly has the store install the carpet? **$73.71**

⑤ How much will it cost Mr. Reilly for the carpet and the installation? **$212.00**

Another carpeting store is having a sale on remnants, or pieces of carpeting that have already been cut. They are selling a piece of carpet that is 4.0 meters wide and 6.7 meters long for $19.95 per meter of length.

⑥ How much will this carpet remnant cost? **$133.67**

This store has an installation charge of $3.50 per square meter.

⑦ How much will it cost Mr. Reilly to have this store's employees install the carpet? **$79.38**

⑧ How much will it cost for the carpet and the installation from the second store? **$213.05**

⑨ Which store would charge less for the carpet and installation? **the first**

⑩ What factors besides cost might Mr. Reilly consider in deciding where to buy his carpet? **Answers will vary. Possible answers include the quality of carpet, quality of service, and delivery time.**

124 • Decimals and Exponents

 In conjunction with the Real-World Connection to the right, you may wish to have students form groups to figure out what it would cost to carpet the classroom. Each group can choose a particular carpet and padding. Groups can compare their findings.

 **Real-World Connection** Have students find out more about how carpet is sold in the area by looking at store ads or perhaps visiting a carpet store with an older family member. They can investigate price ranges, carpet pad and installation costs, and other things they need to know to make a purchase. They can also collect brochures and price lists. Have students share their findings with classmates.

*available separately

Hannah Reilly liked the carpet her father bought so much that now she wants to carpet her room. Her room is a rectangle 3.2 meters wide and 4.8 meters long.

The carpet she likes is 4 meters wide and costs $18.50 per running meter. Today only, there's a big sale. This carpet is selling for half its regular price. Installation is $2.50 per square meter of the room.

11 How many running meters of carpet does Hannah need? **4.8**

12 What will it cost to buy carpet for her room? **$44.40**

13 What is the area of the room in square meters? **15.36**

14 What will it cost to have the carpet installed? **$38.40**

15 What is the total cost to carpet Hannah's room? **$82.80**

Hannah would like to take a few days to think about the carpet and make sure it's what she wants. After the sale ends, the carpeting will be back to its regular price and installation will be $3.25 per square meter.

16 How much more will the carpeting cost after the sale ends? **$44.40**

17 How much more will the installation cost? **$11.52**

18 How much more will the total cost to carpet Hannah's room be if Hannah places her order after the sale ends? **$55.92**

Unit 2   Lesson 34 • **125**

Technology Connection Invite students to view the video *Math Mystery Theatre, Decimal Disagreement: The War of the Rose*, from EdCon/Imperial International (VHS, for grades 2–8) for further practice with multiplication of decimals.

Mental Math (continued)

c.
```
   75
   42
 + 36
 (153)
```
75 + 40 = 115
115 + 2 = 117
117 + 30 = 147
147 + 6 = 153

d.
```
   23
   16
 + 14
  (53)
```
23 + 10 = 33
33 + 6 = 39
39 + 10 = 49
49 + 4 = 53

e.
```
   52
   36
 + 19
 (107)
```
52 + 30 = 82
82 + 6 = 88
88 + 10 = 98
98 + 9 = 107

f.
```
   85
   51
 + 46
 (182)
```
85 + 50 = 135
135 + 1 = 136
136 + 40 = 176
176 + 6 = 182

❷ Teach

Using the Student Pages To provide practice multiplying decimals, demonstrate the "Make 25" game on page 127, so that students can play it after they finish pages 124–126.

Complete the problems on page 124 with the whole class, or have students work on them in groups and then gather as a class to discuss the results. Explain that the carpet at the first store comes in a roll 4 meters wide and costs $21.95 for each meter of length.

Have students do the problems on page 125 with partners or in small groups. When you review students' results, be sure that they have given their answers using the appropriate precision and have checked their answers for reasonableness. In discussing pages 124 and 125, you may wish to point out that some carpet will be wasted if Hannah and Mr. Reilly buy the amounts of carpeting mentioned in the problems. Ask students to determine how Hannah and her father could use the pieces cut from the width of the carpet to reduce the amount of carpet they need to buy (assuming that the direction the carpet runs doesn't matter).

Unit 2 Lesson 34 **125**

◆ LESSON 34 Solving Problems Using Decimals

Teach

Using the Student Pages Have students do the problems on page 126 on their own. Some of them may notice the patterns that emerge and quickly find answers to some problems based on previous answers. Some students may notice, when doing problems 28–30, that as more 3s are written in the factors, the product of 0.333 . . . times itself will get closer to 0.1111 . . . , which is an approximation for $\frac{1}{9}$. You may find it useful to talk about all the patterns on the page.

Students can play the "Make 25" game in pairs. This game provides practice with multiplying decimals. Play the game with two or three students as the rest of the class watches. Make sure students understand the rules and realize that the products should be calculated only if the players cannot tell by approximating or inspection which is closest to 25. This game focuses on multiplying decimals and approximating decimal products to decide which numbers to make, using the digits rolled. Students can use a blank **Cruncher*** spreadsheet to help them keep score. A copy of the "Make 25" game can also be found on page 18 of the Home Connections Blackline Masters.

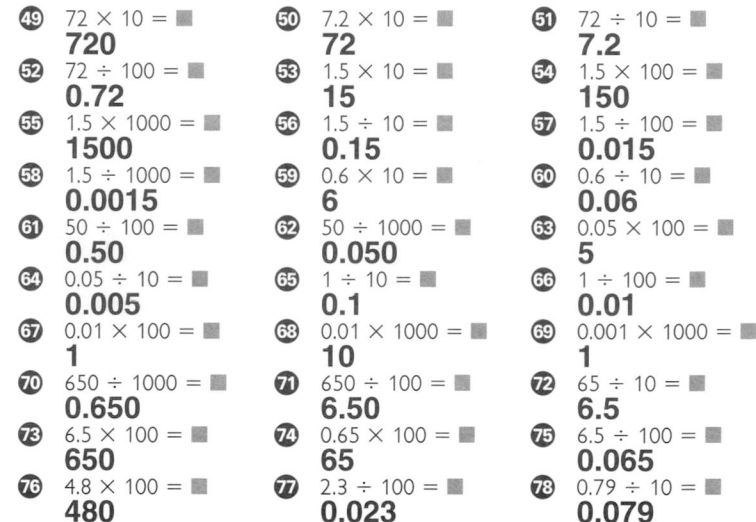

◆ LESSON 34 Solving Problems Using Decimals

Multiply. Look for patterns that will help you.

19 0.05 × 2 **0.10**	**20** 0.05 × 0.02 **0.0010**	**21** 0.05 × 0.2 **0.010**
22 0.5 × 0.2 **0.10**	**23** 0.5 × 2 **1.0**	**24** 5 × 0.2 **1.0**
25 5 × 2 **10**	**26** 0.3 × 4 **1.2**	**27** 0.3 × 14 **4.2**
28 0.3333 × 0.3333 **0.11108889**	**29** 0.33333 × 0.33333 **0.1111088889**	**30** 0.333333 × 0.333333 **0.111110888889**
31 2 × 3 **6**	**32** 21 × 31 **651**	**33** 2.1 × 3.1 **6.51**
34 2.01 × 3.1 **6.231**	**35** 2.01 × 3.01 **6.0501**	**36** 2.01 × 3.001 **6.03201**
37 2.001 × 3.001 **6.005001**	**38** 0.46 × 0.71 **0.3266**	**39** 0.85 × 2.6 **2.21**
40 9.4 × 2 **18.8**	**41** 9.4 × 0.2 **1.88**	**42** 9.4 × 0.02 **0.188**
43 9.4 × 1.02 **9.588**	**44** 0.94 × 1.02 **0.9588**	**45** 0.94 × 1.002 **0.94188**
46 1.8 × 8.1 **14.58**	**47** 2.7 × 7.2 **19.44**	**48** 3.6 × 0.63 **2.268**

Do these problems in your head. Watch the signs.

49 72 × 10 = ■ **720**	**50** 7.2 × 10 = ■ **72**	**51** 72 ÷ 10 = ■ **7.2**
52 72 ÷ 100 = ■ **0.72**	**53** 1.5 × 10 = ■ **15**	**54** 1.5 × 100 = ■ **150**
55 1.5 × 1000 = ■ **1500**	**56** 1.5 ÷ 10 = ■ **0.15**	**57** 1.5 ÷ 100 = ■ **0.015**
58 1.5 ÷ 1000 = ■ **0.0015**	**59** 0.6 × 10 = ■ **6**	**60** 0.6 ÷ 10 = ■ **0.06**
61 50 ÷ 100 = ■ **0.50**	**62** 50 ÷ 1000 = ■ **0.050**	**63** 0.05 × 100 = ■ **5**
64 0.05 ÷ 10 = ■ **0.005**	**65** 1 ÷ 10 = ■ **0.1**	**66** 1 ÷ 100 = ■ **0.01**
67 0.01 × 100 = ■ **1**	**68** 0.01 × 1000 = ■ **10**	**69** 0.001 × 1000 = ■ **1**
70 650 ÷ 1000 = ■ **0.650**	**71** 650 ÷ 100 = ■ **6.50**	**72** 65 ÷ 10 = ■ **6.5**
73 6.5 × 100 = ■ **650**	**74** 0.65 × 100 = ■ **65**	**75** 6.5 ÷ 100 = ■ **0.065**
76 4.8 × 100 = ■ **480**	**77** 2.3 ÷ 100 = ■ **0.023**	**78** 0.79 ÷ 10 = ■ **0.079**

126 • Decimals and Exponents

Literature Connection The tales of hidden treasures in *Gold and Silver, Silver and Gold* by Alvin Schwartz provide students with opportunities to determine the current value of the gold and silver discovered.

RETEACHING

No reteaching is necessary at this point. However, you may wish to pair students who have difficulty recognizing and using multiplication patterns with those who do not, to see if peer tutoring proves to be useful. You may want to assign Enrichment Master 34.

*available separately

Make 25 Game

COOPERATIVE LEARNING

GAME

Players:	Two or more
Materials:	Two 0–5 cubes, two 5–10 cubes, a calculator
Object:	To get the product closest to 25
Math Focus:	Multidigit multiplication with decimal numbers and mathematical reasoning

RULES

1. Take turns rolling all four cubes. If you roll a 10, roll that cube again.

2. Use each number once to make two two-digit numbers whose product is close to 25. You may make decimals. Do not use a calculator or pencil and paper in making these numbers.

3. The player with the product closest to 25 wins the round. Use a calculator or pencil and paper for checking products only if necessary.

SAMPLE GAME

Alicia rolled:

`0` `1` `5` `7`

Alicia made this problem:

5.1 × 7.0

Yan rolled:

`1` `5` `5` `2`

Yan made this problem:

5.1 × 5.2

Alicia and Yan knew that 5.1 × 7.0 is about 35 and that 5.1 × 5.2 is only a little more than 25. So they knew that Yan was the winner of the round. If the products had been closer, Alicia and Yan could have checked them on a calculator.

Suppose you roll 1, 3, 7, and 9. How would you decide which numbers to make? Record your ideas in your Math Journal.

Unit 2 Lesson 34 • **127**

---

③ Wrap-Up

5 MINUTES

In Closing To summarize the lesson, ask students to describe patterns they recognize among the computation problems on page 126.

Performance Assessment Ask students to do the following problems, solving as many as they can using mental math: 0.5 × 3, 0.5 × 0.3, 0.5 × 0.03, and 0.5 × 0.003. (1.5, 0.15, 0.015, 0.0015)

Assessment Criteria

Did the student . . .

✓ work with other students to correctly solve at least six of the eight problems on page 125?

✓ correctly answer at least 80% of the problems on page 126?

✓ understand the rules for and successfully play the "Make 25" game?

Homework Have students calculate what it would cost to carpet a room in their homes or at school using the kinds of carpeting that Mr. Reilly and Hannah chose.

LOOKING AHEAD You may wish to begin collecting for upcoming lessons suitable objects for weighing in class as well as the measuring tools for weighing them.

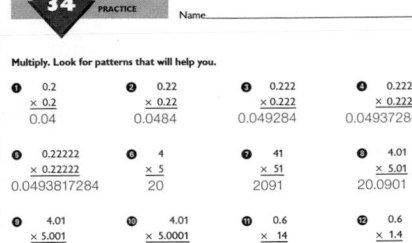
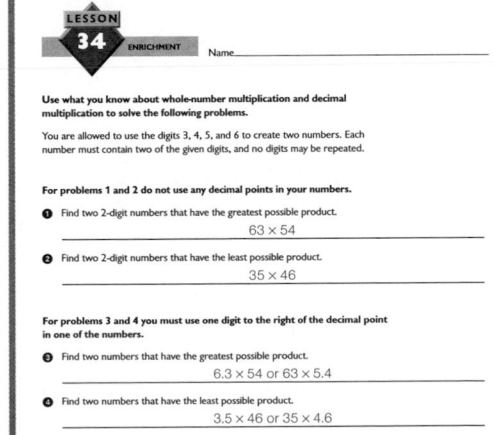

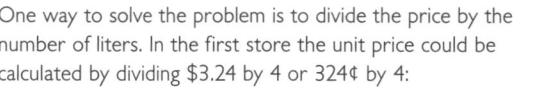

LESSON 35

Student Edition pages 128–129

Understanding Division by Decimals

LESSON PLANNER

Objectives

▶ to introduce the idea of division by a decimal and to begin to develop an algorithm

▶ to provide practice in approximating quotients for problems with decimal divisors

Context of the Lesson This is the eighth of 11 lessons on operations with decimals.

 MANIPULATIVES
none

Program Resources
Practice Master 35
Enrichment Master 35
For extra practice:
CD-ROM* Lesson 35

---

① Warm-Up ⏱ 5 MINUTES

 **Problem of the Day** Present the following problem to students: Juan has seven coins, which total 82¢. How many dimes does he have?
(3 dimes)

Problem-Solving Strategies Ask students who have solved the Problem of the Day to share how they solved it and any strategies they used.

 Tell students to solve these problems mentally:

a. 45 + 25 + 17 = 87
  Sample steps:
  45 + 20 = 65
  65 + 5 = 70
  70 + 10 = 80
  80 + 7 = 87

b. 67 + 52 + 32 = 151
  Sample steps:
  67 + 50 = 117
  117 + 2 = 119
  119 + 30 = 149
  149 + 2 = 151

c. 90 + 14 + 8 = 112
  Sample steps:
  90 + 14 = 104
  104 + 8 = 112

d. 96 + 214 + 108 = 418
  Sample steps:
  96 + 200 = 296
  296 + 4 = 300
  300 + 10 = 310
  310 + 108 = 418

Understanding Division by Decimals

Kyle and his family were comparing the price of a sports drink in two stores. In the first store they could get a 4-liter container for $3.24. The unit price listed was 81¢ per liter, or $0.81 per liter.

In the second store there was no unit price listed, but they could get a 3.80-liter container for only $3.12.

◆ Which sports drink was less expensive per liter?
4-L container

◆ How much less?
about 1¢ less per liter

One way to solve the problem is to divide the price by the number of liters. In the first store the unit price could be calculated by dividing $3.24 by 4 or 324¢ by 4:

$$4\overline{)324} \quad 81$$

So the sports drink costs 81¢ or $0.81 per liter at the first store. In the second store finding the unit price requires dividing 3.12 by 3.80:

$$3.80\overline{)3.12}$$

◆ Do you think the answer is greater than $1 or less than $1 per liter?
less than $1 per liter

Look at each of these division problems.

a. $3.80\overline{)3.12}$ b. $38.0\overline{)31.2}$ c. $380\overline{)312}$

d. $3800\overline{)3120}$ e. $0.380\overline{)0.312}$ f. $38,000\overline{)31,200}$

◆ Do you think they have the same answer? **yes**

◆ Estimate the answer. **Estimates will vary. The correct answer is about 0.821.**

Look at each of these division problems.

a. $4\overline{)32}$ b. $40\overline{)320}$ c. $400\overline{)3200}$

d. $0.4\overline{)3.2}$ e. $0.04\overline{)0.32}$ f. $4000\overline{)32,000}$

◆ What do you think is the relationship among their answers? **They are the same (for each, the answer is 8).**

Why teach it this way?

This lesson begins to develop an algorithm for dividing by a decimal and introduces a way to approximate answers so that when students actually do the division, they can tell if their quotients make sense.

 **Literature Connection** Have students read *Supergrandpa* by David M. Schwartz and use division to determine how many 10-kilometer races the Tour of Sweden equalled, as well as solve similar problems.

RETEACHING

Reteaching is not needed here because this is an introductory lesson and more practice will be given in the following lessons. Encourage all students to try the Enrichment Master 35 referenced for this lesson.

*available separately

If you multiply or divide both the divisor and the dividend of a division problem by the same number, the quotient will be unchanged.

So if you know that 32 ÷ 4 = 8, then:

320 ÷ 40 = 8   3200 ÷ 400 = 8   3.2 ÷ 0.4 = 8   0.32 ÷ 0.04 = 8

For each of the following problems, write three more problems that would have the same answer.

Answers are samples; student answers may vary.

① 0.42)8.71 **4.2)87.1,**
42)871, 420)8710

② 0.057)1.28 **57)1280,**
0.57)12.8, 5.7)128

③ 56.42)2.187
5.642)0.2187,
564.2)21.87, 5642)218.7

④ 56.4)66.14 **5.64)6.614,**
5640)6614, 564)661.4

⑤ 64.10)0.045 **64.1)0.0045,**
641)0.45, 0.641)0.00045

⑥ 0.14)82.6 **1.4)826,**
14)8260,
140)82,600

Approximate answers by short division if the decimal point of the divisor is between the first and second digit. If it is not, move it. Be sure also to move the point in the dividend the same number of places in the same direction.

Example:

0.42)8.71   It is hard to approximate because the decimal point isn't between the first and second digits.

0.4.2)8.7.1   Move the decimal point in both the divisor and dividend.

4)87.1   Round 4.2 to 4.

  21
4)87.1   Divide to get the approximation, which is about 21.

(The actual answer to 8.71 ÷ 0.42 is about 20.74.)

Decide which answer is closest to the correct answer.

⑦ 56.4)66.14   **a.** 0.117   **(b.)** 1.17   **c.** 11.7

⑧ 0.057)1.28   **a.** 0.225   **b.** 2.25   **(c.)** 22.5

⑨ 64.1)0.045   **a.** 0.07   **b.** 0.007   **(c.)** 0.0007

⑩ 0.29)10.73   **(a.)** 37   **b.** 370   **c.** 3700

⑪ 0.05)4.77   **a.** 9.54   **(b.)** 95.4   **c.** 954

⑫ 0.4)72.24   **a.** 1806   **(b.)** 180.6   **c.** 18.06

Unit 2   Lesson 35 • **129**

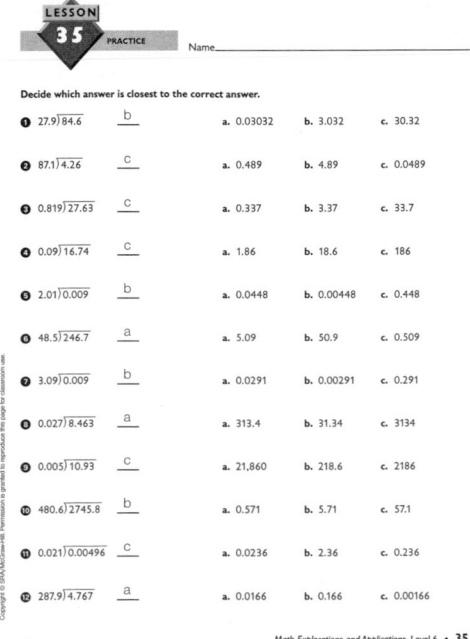
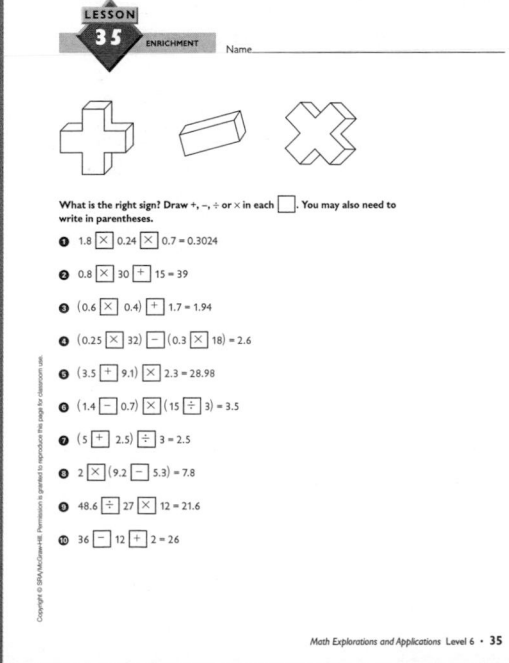
---

❷ Teach

Using the Student Pages Discuss the first problem on page 128 with the class. Here are two of the many possible solution methods: 1. Find the price of 3.80 liters at the price from the first store. 2. Find the price in cents per centiliter, and then convert to price per liter.

The first six division problems on page 128 all have the same answer; so do the second six. The essential point is that if students multiply or divide both divisor and dividend by any number, the quotient will be unchanged. For page 129, guide students to understand the ease with which they can estimate answers using short division when the divisor is between 1 and 10. Do one or two problems like 0.0597 ÷ 6.24 with the class. Because 6.24 rounds to 6, the nearest whole number, we can think: 0.0597 ÷ 6 = 0.0099. We could also think 0.06 ÷ 6 = 0.01. (The answer to 7 decimal places is 0.0095673.)

❸ Wrap-Up

In Closing Have students brainstorm ideas for why they would get the same answer if they move the decimal points in the dividend and the divisor the same number of places in the same direction.

Informal Assessment For the first set of problems on page 129, ask students to explain how they are able to move the decimal point and still get the same answer. For the second set, ask them to explain their strategy for finding the closest quotient.

Assessment Criteria

Did the student . . .

✓ demonstrate understanding of the concept of moving the decimal point when multiplying or dividing numbers with decimals?

✓ communicate strategies used to solve the problems in each set?

✓ correctly answer at least nine of the 12 problems?

Homework Have students determine which is the best buy on different brands and sizes of the same item. For example, have them figure out the price per pound for three different brands of the same item at a grocery store.

Dividing by Decimals

LESSON PLANNER

Objectives

▶ to introduce the algorithm for division by decimals

✓ to evaluate students' ability to divide with decimal numerals

▶ to provide practice in adding, subtracting, multiplying, and dividing decimals and in solving word problems that involve operations with decimals

Context of the Lesson This is the ninth of 11 lessons on operations with decimals. This lesson also contains Mastery Checkpoint 12 for assessing students' ability in division by decimals.

 MANIPULATIVES

graph paper
(optional)

Program Resources

Reteaching Master

Practice Master 36

Enrichment Master 36

Assessment Master

For extra practice:
CD-ROM* Lesson 36
Cumulative Review, page 560

① Warp-Up ⏱ 5 MINUTES

 **Problem of the Day** Present this problem orally to the class: A square has an area in square centimeters that is three times its perimeter in centimeters. What is the length of a side of the square? (12 cm)

Problem-Solving Strategies Ask students who have solved the Problem of the Day to share how they solved it and any strategies they used.

MENTAL MATH Ask students to show thumbs up if the answer is greater than 50 and thumbs down if it is not. Have students stand if the answer equals 50. Write the problems one at a time on the chalkboard to help students see the pattern.

a. 300 ÷ 2 (thumbs up)   **b.** 300 ÷ 3 (thumbs up)

c. 300 ÷ 4 (thumbs up)   **d.** 300 ÷ 5 (thumbs up)

e. 310 ÷ 5 (thumbs up)   **f.** 300 ÷ 6 (stand)

g. 350 ÷ 50 (thumbs down) **h.** 3500 ÷ 50 (thumbs up)

i. 3000 ÷ 50 (thumbs up)   **j.** 250 ÷ 50 (thumbs down)

Dividing by Decimals

In a new housing development there are 6.852 acres of land. If each lot in the development is about 0.37 of an acre, how many lots can there be?

Divide to find the answer.

6.852 ÷ 0.37 = ?

0.37)6.852 ⟶ 3.7)68.52   First approximate an answer.

4)68.52   Round 3.7 to 4.

17.
4)68.52   Do the short division. Stop when you get a reasonable approximation. The answer will be about 17.

Now do the division.

0.37)6.852   Move the decimal point in the divisor to the right of the last nonzero digit.

37)6.852   Move the decimal point in the dividend the same number of places in the same direction. Sometimes you will need to write extra 0s, but in this case you do not.

37)685.2   Now the problem is in a form with which you can work.

$$
\begin{array}{r}
18.5 \\
37\overline{)685.2} \\
-\,37 \\
\hline
315 \\
-\,296 \\
\hline
192 \\
-\,185 \\
\hline
7
\end{array}
$$

Divide. Carry out the division to as many places as you need. Place the decimal point in the quotient directly above the new place of the decimal point in the dividend.

The 6.852 acres of land will hold about 18 lots, each about 0.37 of an acre.

Why teach it this way?

Demonstrating two or more ways to divide decimals shows students that they have choices when computing with numbers and that often there is more than one "right way" to solve a problem.

Here is another method of dividing by a decimal with the same example.

Approximate the answer
by doing the short division. $0.37\overline{)6.852}$ ⟶ $3.7\overline{)68.52}$ ⟶ $4\overline{)68.52}^{\,17.}$

Now ignore the decimal point and divide.

Instead of $0.37\overline{)6.852}$, think
$$
\begin{array}{r}
185 \\
37\overline{)6852} \\
-\ 37 \\
\hline
315 \\
-\ 296 \\
\hline
192 \\
-\ 185 \\
\hline
7
\end{array}
$$
We know the answer is about 17, so we can carry out the division to as many places as we want.

Use the approximation (from the short division) to place the decimal point correctly in your quotient.

$$37\overline{)6852}^{\,18.5}$$

Divide. Round quotients to the nearest hundredth.

Remember: **To round to the nearest hundredth, you'll need to divide to thousandths. For example, if a quotient is 0.457, it rounds to 0.46.**

❶ 12 ÷ 0.4 **30**	❷ 999 ÷ 3.33 **300**	❸ 24.3 ÷ 0.27 **90**
❹ 125 ÷ 2.5 **50**	❺ 35 ÷ 7.2 **4.861 → 4.86**	❻ 0.384 ÷ 12 **0.032**
❼ 48 ÷ 0.16 **300**	❽ 81.54 ÷ 0.6 **135.9**	❾ 10.24 ÷ 12.8 **0.8**
❿ 8125 ÷ 1300 **6.25**	⓫ 12.47 ÷ 1.4 **8.907 → 8.91**	⓬ 16.18 ÷ 36 **0.449 → 0.45**
⓭ 300 ÷ 0.75 **400**	⓮ 2 ÷ 0.025 **80**	⓯ 28 ÷ 4.5 **6.222 → 6.22**
⓰ 512 ÷ 3.2 **160**	⓱ 200 ÷ 56 **3.571 → 3.57**	⓲ 21.6 ÷ 0.3 **72**
⓳ 75 ÷ 15 **5**	⓴ 560 ÷ 2.8 **200**	㉑ 9.7 ÷ 0.64 **15.165 → 15.16**

❷ Teach

Using the Student Pages Go over the example on page 130 and perhaps a few similar problems as well. Ask students to explain the steps they use. Point out that one way to divide by a decimal is to rewrite the divisor as a whole number by moving the decimal point to the right as many places as needed. As long as the dividend is changed in the same way, the quotient will not be affected. Discuss the last step in the first example, carrying out the division to as many places as needed. In this case, the answer was rounded down to a whole number. When dividing to find out, for example, how many tiles to purchase to cover a floor, round up to a whole number. When dividing to find an amount of money, it is customary to round to the nearest cent. It is not advisable to carry out division to more places than is warranted by the precision of the divisor and the dividend.

Go over the example at the top of page 131 with the class. It is not essential for students to be able to use this procedure, but many students will appreciate the simplicity of this method and should be allowed to use it.

Have students do problems 1–21 on their own.

GIFTED & TALENTED **Meeting Individual Needs**
    Create or challenge your more advanced students to make up problems similar to the Problem of the Day for classmates to solve. For example, "A square has an area in square centimeters that is twice its perimeter in centimeters. What is the length of a side of the square?" (8 cm)

Literature Connection
Have students read Thompson Yardley's *Buy Now, Pay Later,* which is about smart shopping. Ask them to create division problems related to the information in it.

◆ LESSON 36   Dividing by Decimals

Teach

Using the Student Pages You may wish to have students work in pairs or in small groups on the problems on pages 132–133. Encourage students to act out the situations or use drawings or models to help them work out the more difficult problems. For instance, some students will have an easier time with problem 23 if they draw a sketch of the fence on **graph paper**.

ESL **Meeting Individual Needs**

Because the application problems on pages 132 and 133 review operations other than division, you might want to pair ESL students with those more proficient in English to be sure they understand what information is given in the problem and what is being asked.

◆ LESSON 36   Dividing by Decimals

Solve these problems.

22 Melissa and Eric are making hand puppets for party favors. They use 0.25 meter of fabric for each puppet. They have four packages of fabric. Each package has 3 meters of fabric. How many hand puppets can they make? **48**

23 Barry is building a fence 15 meters long on one side of his yard. He plans to put a fence post every 1.5 meters. How many fence posts does he need? (Hint: There must be a post at each end.) **11**

24 Mikhail and his two brothers are evenly splitting the cost of a birthday gift for their mother. The gift cost $31.71, including tax. How much should each brother contribute? **$10.57**

25 Ms. Rasheed is knitting an afghan. She wants it to be 2 meters long. She can knit about 7.5 centimeters a day. About how many days will it take her to knit the afghan? (Hint: 7.5 centimeters = 0.075 meter) **about 27 days**

26 Mr. Sato spent $43.78 for groceries on Thursday and $26.39 for groceries on Saturday. Did he spend more than $100 for groceries in those two days? **no**

27 Dolores is in charge of collecting money for a class trip. The trip will cost $5.60 per student. So far, Dolores has collected $100.80. How many students have paid? **18**

28 Gong Li works part-time at the local nursery. She earns $7.50 an hour. She has forgotten how many hours she worked last week, but she knows that she earned $187.50. How many hours did she work? **25**

29 Mr. Rodriguez is a baker. He uses 0.4 kilogram of flour for each loaf of bread he makes. How many loaves of bread can he make from 100 kilograms of flour? **250**

132 • Decimals and Exponents

RETEACHING p. 11

LESSON 36 RETEACHING   Name_____

Example: 62.65 ÷ 8.95 = ?

Step 1 8.95⟌62.65.   Move the decimal point in the divisor to the right so that you are dividing by a whole number. Move the decimal point in the dividend the same number of places. Then place the decimal point in the quotient above the decimal point in the dividend.

Step 2 7.   895⟌6265.   Divide as you would in the division of whole numbers; so divide 895 into 6265.

Step 3 7.   895⟌6265.   Multiply 895 × 7. Then subtract. Carry out the division to as many places as you need.
        6265
           0

62.65 ÷ 8.95 = 7

Solve these problems.

❶ Marti's pay for the week was $152.00. If she earns $4.75 per hour, how many hours did Marti work?   **32**

❷ Each winter scarf requires 87.5 yards of yarn. How much yarn is required for 25 scarves?   **2187.5 yards**

❸ Mario has three pieces of wood, each 2.5 meters long. He needs two pieces, each 0.25 meters long, for a model he is making. How many models can he make from the wood he has?   **15**

❹ Elizabeth has $20.94. How many bags of apples can she buy for $1.59 each?   **13**

Math Explorations and Applications Level 6 • **11**

PRACTICE p. 36

LESSON 36 PRACTICE   Name_____

Divide. Round quotients to the nearest hundredth.

❶ 23⟌73 **3.17**   ❷ 18⟌1 **0.06**   ❸ 41⟌12 **0.29**   ❹ 22.5⟌56 **2.49**

❺ 69.1⟌15 **0.22**   ❻ 42.7⟌91 **2.13**   ❼ 5.03⟌27 **5.37**   ❽ 12.9⟌18 **1.40**

❾ 87.3⟌44.3 **0.51**   ❿ 3.01⟌37 **12.29**   ⓫ 0.95⟌39 **41.05**   ⓬ 0.87⟌62 **71.26**

⓭ 9.3⟌29 **3.12**   ⓮ 8.61⟌41 **4.76**   ⓯ 12.4⟌1.87 **0.15**   ⓰ 3.9⟌31 **7.95**

⓱ 3.01⟌8.9 **2.96**   ⓲ 0.46⟌22.55 **49.02**   ⓳ 1.01⟌28 **27.72**   ⓴ 3.09⟌72 **23.30**

㉑ 18.3⟌43.24 **2.36**   ㉒ 3.06⟌3 **0.98**   ㉓ 0.091⟌4 **43.96**   ㉔ 8.69⟌86.91 **10.00**

36 • *Math Explorations and Applications Level 6*

Watch the signs. Round quotients to the nearest hundredth.

30 43.78 + 26.39
70.17

31 43.78 − 26.39
17.39

32 5.7 × 1.3
7.41

33 4.2 ÷ 0.7
6

34 34.086 − 12.92
21.166 → 21.17

35 0.481 × 3.6
1.7316

36 5.7 ÷ 1.3
4.384 → 4.38

37 2.801 + 35.64
38.441 → 38.44

38 6.401 × 0.32
2.04832 → 2.05

39 1.024 ÷ 12.8
0.08

40 63 × 2.5
157.5

41 48 − 1.8
46.2

42 7.93 + 12.46
20.39

43 540 ÷ 12.6
42.857 → 42.86

44 54.2 − 36.4
17.8

Solve these problems.

45 The regular annual subscription rate for a weekly magazine is $57.00. The newsstand price is $1.50 per issue. How much will a yearly subscription save compared with the newsstand price? **$21.00 per year or about $0.40 per issue (assuming you were to purchase every issue at the newsstand)**

46 The regular annual subscription rate for a monthly magazine is $36.00. A three-year subscription is available for $116.00. When might it be worthwhile to subscribe for three years? **The three-year subscription is more expensive per year than the one-year subscription. It's only worthwhile if the three-year subscription is much more convenient than reordering each year, or if you feel the price will increase a lot within the three-year period.**

47 Marco used a calculator to multiply 34.5 by 74.1. His answer was 25,564.5. What, if anything, did Marco most likely do wrong? **He neglected to enter one of the decimal points.**

48 A one-bedroom apartment rents for $435 per month. How much is that per year? **$5220.00**

49 Kareem started a window-washing business. He estimates that to earn a good income, he needs to charge about $1.50 for each standard-sized window. On visiting the Crawford home, which has 30 windows, he told Mr. Crawford that he could wash all of the windows for $4.50. Does that seem to be a reasonable price? If not, what mistake do you think Kareem made? **It's much too low. Kareem meant $45.00 (30 × 1.50 = 45.00).**

Use the Cumulative Review on page 560 after this lesson.

Unit 2 Lesson 36 • **133**

LESSON **36** ENRICHMENT

Name _____

You would like to buy a portable cassette player and five tapes for it. You need to budget to save $65 to purchase the portable cassette player and $10.75 per tape. You have the following sources of income from which to save the money.

Weekly allowance: $5.00 (Usually $3.00 of this is needed for weekly expenses.)
Baby-sitting: You earn $2.50 per hour and average six hours of baby-sitting per week. Half of this money must remain in your savings account. The other half you may spend as you wish.
Extra chores at home: You have various chores that pay $3.50 each that you can do to earn extra money.

You may want to use **The Cruncher: I Want a Walkman™** project to help you plan a budget to purchase the cassette player.

Figure out a budget that will allow you to purchase the cassette player in each amount of time.

1 one month
  a. savings from allowance: _____ $8.00
  b. savings from baby-sitting: _____ $30.00
  c. savings from extra chores: _____ $80.75

2 two months
  a. savings from allowance: _____ $16.00
  b. savings from baby-sitting: _____ $60.00
  c. savings from extra chores: _____ $42.75

3 three months
  a. savings from allowance: _____ $24.00
  b. savings from baby-sitting: _____ $90.00
  c. savings from extra chores: _____ $4.75

4 Which plan would you prefer to use to buy the cassette player? ___ Answers will vary. ___
  Possible answer: two months

36 • Math Explorations and Applications Level 6

UNIT **2**

Mastery Checkpoint 12 Division with decimal divisors (Lesson 36)
Name _____
The student demonstrates mastery by correctly answering at least 12 of the 15 problems.

Divide. Round quotients to the nearest hundredth.

1 0.3)12 → 40

2 1.5)90 → 60

3 6)10.5 → 1.75

4 0.25)100 → 400

5 140)1008 → 7.2

6 4.3)116.1 → 27

7 0.55)110 → 200

8 2.22)1110 → 500

9 4.5)14.76 → 3.28

10 7.5)29.79 → 3.972 → 3.97

11 0.8)20.32 → 25.4

12 3.6)68.04 → 18.9

13 0.06)10 → 166.666 → 166.67

14 0.036)2.592 → 72

15 0.3)0.78 → 2.6

20 • Math Explorations and Applications Level 6

---

❸ Wrap-Up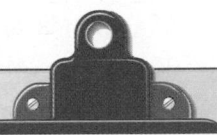

In Closing To summarize the lesson, ask students to explain the algorithm introduced for dividing by a decimal divisor.

Mastery Checkpoint 12

By this time most students should demonstrate mastery of division with decimals by getting correct answers to at least 17 of the 21 problems on page 131. Students who fall short of this objective can be given extra help. You may also wish to use Assessment Blackline Masters page 20 to check for mastery. The results of this assessment may be recorded on the Mastery Checkpoint Chart.

Assessment Criteria

Did the student . . .

✓ correctly answer at least 17 of the 21 problems on page 131 and 24 of the 28 problems on pages 132–133?

✓ choose the correct operation to use to solve the word problems on page 133?

Homework Assign Practice Master 36 for further practice with division of decimals.

LOOKING AHEAD Remember to gather suitable materials and tools for the activities in the following lesson.

Meeting Individual Needs

You may find it useful to use simpler numbers to show that changing the divisor and the dividend in the same way will not change the quotient. For example, show that 8 ÷ 4 = 80 ÷ 40. Also remind students that although the dividend is always changed in the same way as the divisor, the decimal point in the dividend will not always end up to the right of the last digit.

Unit 2 Lesson 36 **133**

LESSON 37

Student Edition pages 134–135

Arithmetic with Decimals

LESSON PLANNER

Objectives

▶ to provide real-life applications of decimal operations

▶ to apply arithmetic in a way that extends into a student investigation

Context of the Lesson This is the tenth of 11 lessons on operations with decimals. In this lesson students are introduced to applications involving all of the arithmetic operations with decimals they have learned so far.

 MANIPULATIVES

balance scale*
and gram
weights*

centimeter
ruler*

items to be
weighed, such
as paper clips,
paper, chalk

Program Resources

Practice Master 37

Enrichment Master 37

The Cruncher*

For extra practice:
CD-ROM* Lesson 37

① Wark-Up ⏱ 5 MINUTES

 Problem of the Day Present the following problem to the class: Jerome needs to use his calculator to divide 567 by 4. However, the 4 key doesn't work. Provide two ways for him to use his calculator to get the answer. (Many answers are possible; samples: divide 567 by 2 and then by 2 again; divide 567 by 8 and multiply that answer by 2.)

Problem-Solving Strategies Ask students who have solved the Problem of the Day to share how they solved it and any strategies they used.

MENTAL MATH Have students show thumbs up for yes or thumbs down for no as they answer the following questions: "Is $50.00 enough to buy . . ."

a. two pairs of shoes at $23.00 a pair? (yes)

b. bicycle handlebars for $35.00 plus a bell for $15.50? (no)

c. one shirt for $39.95 and two scarves for $12.50 each? (no)

d. dinner for $35.00 and a $5.50 tip? (yes)

e. a new videotape for $39.95 and a CD for $12.98? (no)

LESSON 37

Arithmetic with Decimals

Solve.

The floor of Alan's room is 3.6 meters long and 2.4 meters wide.

Alan wants to put tile on his floor. The chart shows the size and price of different square tiles he can buy.

Size (length of each side)	Price
0.1 meter	$0.10
0.2 meter	$0.36
0.3 meter	$0.81
0.4 meter	$1.35
0.5 meter	$2.00

❶ What is the area of Alan's room? **8.64 m²**

❷ What is the area of a 0.1-meter tile? **0.01 m²**

❸ How many 0.1-meter tiles would he need? **864**

❹ What is the area of a 0.2-meter tile? **0.04 m²**

❺ How many 0.2-meter tiles would he need? **216**

❻ Use a computer or other means to draw and complete the following chart. Which size of tile will be the least expensive for Alan? (He cannot cut the tiles, and he must cover the entire floor.) **the 0.4-meter tile**

Size of Tile	Area of Tile	Number of Tiles Needed	Price for Each Tile	Total Cost
0.1 meter	0.01 m²	864	$0.10	$86.40
0.2 meter	0.04 m²	216	$0.36	$77.76
0.3 meter	0.09 m²	96	$0.81	$77.76
0.4 meter	0.16 m²	54	$1.35	$72.90
0.5 meter				See margin.

Why teach it this way?

This lesson involves an application of decimal operations. It is useful for students to get hands-on experience with seeing how operations with decimals can be used to solve or be a part of the solution to real-life problems.

 **Literature Connection** Students can use the decimal measurements in *Amazing Biofacts* by Susan Goodman to make comparisons.

RETEACHING

Reteaching is not essential at this time. Continue to help students who are having difficulty with basic operations with decimals. You may want to assign Enrichment Master 37.

*available separately

"How thick is this piece of paper?" asked Inez. Here's how she solved the problem.

First she counted out 100 sheets of that kind of paper. Then she measured the thickness of the 100 sheets.

Inez found that 100 sheets are about 1.1 centimeters thick. Then she thought, "Since 100 sheets are about 1.1 centimeters thick, 1 sheet is about 0.011 centimeter thick. 0.011 centimeter is the same as 0.11 millimeter."

Answers to questions 7–12 will vary depending on the objects used. Calculations should follow the method shown above.

Solve these problems.

7 About how much does a paper clip weigh? (Hint: Weigh 100 paper clips.)

8 About how much does one facial tissue weigh? (Hint: Weigh a stack of tissues.)

9 About how much does one staple weigh? (Hint: Weigh a box of staples.)

Can you solve these problems without a hint?

10 About how much does one new piece of chalk weigh?

11 About how thick is the thickest paper you can find?

12 About how thick is the thinnest paper you can find?

To measure gold dust, the Egyptians used the amount that would fill a goose quill.

Unit 2   Lesson 37 • **135**

---

② Teach

Using the Student Pages Have students work in small groups to solve the problems on page 134. You may wish to draw a rectangle on the chalkboard to represent the floor of Alan's room. Label the length 3.6 meters and the width 2.4 meters. *Note*: Alan can't use 0.5-meter tiles because 0.5 is not a factor that can be multiplied by a whole number to obtain the length or width of the floor. Students can use a blank **Cruncher** spreadsheet to make a chart like the one on page 134.

 Go over the example on page 135. Then challenge students to solve one or more of the problems by making appropriate measurements or calculations. Let them work individually or in groups. Have **rulers***, **weights***, and a **balance scale*** available.

③ Wrap-Up

In Closing Have students write a short paragraph explaining the usefulness of extrapolating lesser values from greater ones, such as the paper clip problem. How could this be used in daily life?

 **Informal Assessment** Ask students to explain how they used operations with decimals to solve the problems to complete the table on page 134. Have them describe the method they used to answer problem 10, 11, or 12 on page 135.

Assessment Criteria

Did the student . . .

✓ communicate strategies used?

✓ correctly apply decimal operations to solve problems?

✓ contribute meaningfully to the group problem-solving effort?

Homework Have students formulate a new problem involving thickness and then solve it.

PRACTICE p. 37

37 PRACTICE Name_____

 Solve these problems.

1 Mr. Robbins's living room is 3.2 meters long and 4.4 meters wide. He wants to replace his carpet but isn't sure what he wants in place of it. He could have new carpeting installed for $12.95 a square meter. He might also refinish the floor and buy a rug. His third choice is to put wood tiles on the floor. The tiles are squares that are 0.2 meter on each side and cost $1.20 each.
   a. If carpeting is sold in whole square meters, how much would the carpeting cost? $194.25
   b. How much would the rug cost? can't tell
   c. How much would the wood tiles cost? $422.40

2 Ms. Maples bought 30 kilograms (30,000 grams) of sunflower seeds for $18.50. She will make up packages containing 150 grams of sunflower seeds and sell them for $0.35 a package.
   a. How many packages can she make? 200 packages
   b. How much money will she collect if she sells all the packages? $70.00
   c. What will her profit be? $51.50 (assuming it costs her nothing to make up the packages)

3 Elaine is crocheting a tablecloth. The tablecloth will be 1.8 meters (180 centimeters) long. She can crochet about 15 centimeters of the tablecloth in a day. About how many days will it take to crochet the tablecloth? about 12 days

4 Mary paid $7.50 for a box of used books. There were 23 books all together. About how much is that per book? about 33¢

5 Mia made $32.50 baby-sitting last week. She charges $2.50 an hour. How many hours did she baby-sit last week? 13 hours

6 Rex needs 1.2 meters of fabric to make two pairs of shorts. He has 22 meters of fabric. How many pairs of shorts can he make? 36 pairs of shorts

Math Explorations and Applications Level 6 • 37

ENRICHMENT p. 37

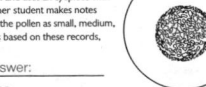
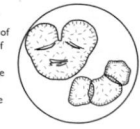

37 ENRICHMENT Name_____

Solve these problems.

1 You are hired to help inventory a hardware store. There are several bins of bolts to count. One way is to count the bolts one by one. Another way is to guess how many bolts are in the fullest bin and take a percentage of that number for the other bins. What's wrong with these two methods? Describe a better method.
Answers will vary. Possible answer: Count and weigh 100 bolts; then weigh all the bolts in a bin and divide by the weight for 100. Multiply by 100 to get the count.

2 Two students are looking at pollen grains under the microscope. One student draws a picture of each kind of grain and uses an eyepiece with a micrometer scale to measure size. The other student makes notes such as "looks like half a bagel," and classes the pollen as small, medium, and large. If you had to identify these spores based on these records, whose work would you rather use? Why?
Answers will vary. Possible answer: The first student because these records are more exact.

3 Which of the following methods is a better way to find the volume of a football? Carefully measure the dimensions of the two ends and of tiny cross sections of the rest of the ball, use volume formulas for each section, and add all the volumes. Or, put a bucket inside a large pan, fill the bucket to the brim, immerse the football in the water, and measure the water that overflows into the pan. Describe a case where the better method might not work very well.
Answers will vary. Possible answer: The water method is better because it's faster and probably very accurate. It wouldn't work well for something that absorbs water, like a sponge.

Math Explorations and Applications Level 6 • 37

Mid-Unit Review

The Mid-Unit Review pinpoints troublesome skill areas for students, allowing plenty of time for additional practice and reteaching before the unit ends. If students did not do well on the Mid-Unit Review and have completed additional practice, you may want to use the Mid-Unit Review provided on Assessment Blackline Masters pages 21–22.

Using the Student Pages Have students complete problems 1–45 on pages 136 and 137 on their own. Help students who need assistance with the reading in problems 38–45. You might treat this review as a formal assessment of students' skills and have students complete this review as a timed test. See suggestions for administering timed tests on page 49.

Mid-Unit Review

Add or subtract. Watch the signs.

1 $2.4 + 0.6$
3.0

2 $0.844 + 0.666$
1.510

3 $0.844 - 0.666$
0.178

Multiply.

4 2.7×10
27

5 0.46×1000
460

6 100×1.08
108

Divide.

7 $27 \div 100$
0.27

8 $14.5 \div 1000$
0.0145

9 $0.04 \div 10$
0.004

Complete.

10 $6 \text{ m} = \blacksquare \text{ cm}$
600

11 $300 \text{ mg} = \blacksquare \text{ g}$
0.3

12 $40 \text{ mL} = \blacksquare \text{ L}$
0.040

Choose the correct answer.

13 3.4×50
  (a.) 170
  b. 17
  c. 1.7

14 34×3.4
  (a.) 115.6
  b. 11.56
  c. 1.156

15 $4.2 \div 3$
  a. 140
  b. 14
  (c.) 1.4

16 2.3×5.08
  a. 116.84
  (b.) 11.684
  c. 1.1684

17 43.1×1.27
  a. 5.4737
  (b.) 54.737
  c. 547.37

18 $24.6 \div 0.03$
  a. 8.2
  b. 82
  (c.) 820

Solve.

19 6×2.7
16.2

20 0.203×0.06
0.01218

21 1.720×41
70.52

Between what two measures would you assume the true measure is if somebody reported each of the following measurements?

22 4 yards
3.5 yards and 4.5 yards

23 22.7 miles
22.65 miles and 22.75 miles

How would you report the measurement given below with the possible indicated error?

24 20 feet, possible error of $\frac{1}{2}$ foot
20 feet

25 2 miles, possible error of $\frac{1}{2}$ yard
3520 yards

For each of the following problems, write three more problems that would have the same answer.

Answers will vary. Sample responses are given.

㉖ 0.42)8.88   ㉗ 0.65)4.128   ㉘ 33.5)0.906

㉖ 42)88.8
42)888
0.042)0.888

㉗ 6.5)41.28
65)412.8
0.065)0.4128

㉘ 335)9.06
3.35)0.0906
0.335)0.00906

Divide. Round quotients to the nearest hundredth.

㉙ 0.38)77.52 **204**

㉚ 5.6)952 **170**

㉛ 0.012)64.8 **5400**

㉜ 0.28)4.97 **17.75**

㉝ 3.34)48.3 **14.461 → 14.46**

㉞ 0.07)98 **1400**

㉟ 4.5)58.5 **13**

㊱ 14.3)68.2 **4.769 → 4.77**

㊲ 0.23)75.21 **327**

Solve these problems.

㊳ Jessica went to the grocery store. She bought two containers of juice for $2.95 each, a box of cookies for $2.29, a loaf of bread for $1.39, and some vegetables for $3.25. She paid with a $10 bill and a $5 bill. How much change should she get from the cashier? **$2.17**

㊴ Ed's pet puppy, Alonzo, now weighs 5.80 kilograms. A year ago, Alonzo weighed in at 4.45 kilograms. How much weight did Alonzo gain? **1.35 kg**

㊵ Arthur is paid $635.85 a week. If he is paid the same amount every week, and then gets a bonus of one-week's salary, how much will he earn in a year? **$33,700.05**

㊶ Suki is collecting money for a class trip that will cost $7.25 per student. If she has collected $101.50 so far, how many students have paid? **14**

Mr. Rodriguez is having carpet installed in his den. The room is a rectangle 4.2 meters wide and 5.8 meters long. The carpet he has chosen is 4.5 meters wide and costs $25.95 per running meter. He has to buy a piece that is 4.5 meters wide even though the room is not that wide. Installation costs $3.50 per square meter of the room.

㊷ How many running meters of carpet must Mr. Rodriguez buy? **5.8**

㊸ How much will he pay for the carpet? **$150.51**

㊹ What is the area of the room? **24.36 m²**

㊺ How much will installation cost? **$85.26**

Unit 2 Mid-Unit Review • 137

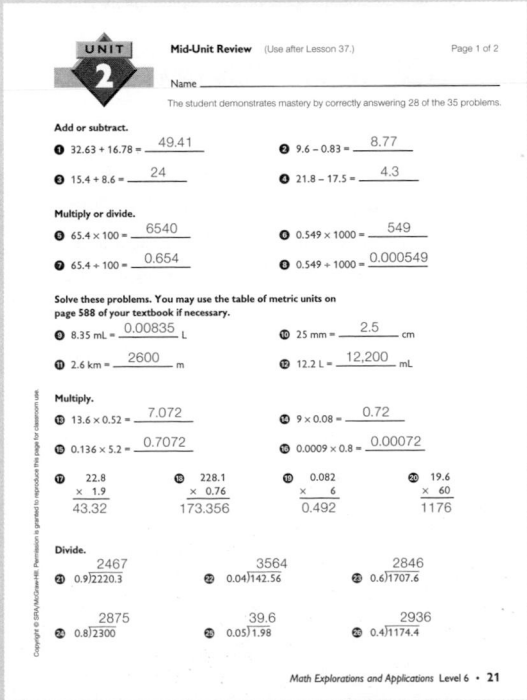

ASSESSMENT p. 21

UNIT 2 Mid-Unit Review (Use after Lesson 37.) Page 1 of 2

Name _____

The student demonstrates mastery by correctly answering 28 of the 35 problems.

Add or subtract.

❶ 32.63 + 16.78 = __49.41__   ❷ 9.6 − 0.83 = __8.77__

❸ 15.4 + 8.6 = __24__   ❹ 21.8 − 17.5 = __4.3__

Multiply or divide.

❺ 65.4 × 100 = __6540__   ❻ 0.549 × 1000 = __549__

❼ 65.4 ÷ 100 = __0.654__   ❽ 0.549 ÷ 1000 = __0.000549__

Solve these problems. You may use the table of metric units on page 588 of your textbook if necessary.

❾ 8.35 mL = __0.00835__ L   ❿ 25 mm = __2.5__ cm

⓫ 2.6 km = __2600__ m   ⓬ 12.2 L = __12,200__ mL

Multiply.

⓭ 13.6 × 0.52 = __7.072__   ⓮ 9 × 0.08 = __0.72__

⓯ 0.136 × 5.2 = __0.7072__   ⓰ 0.0009 × 0.8 = __0.00072__

⓱ 22.8 × 1.9 = 43.32   ⓲ 228.1 × 0.76 = 173.356   ⓳ 0.082 × 6 = 0.492   ⓴ 19.6 × 60 = 1176

Divide.

㉑ 0.9)2220.3 **2467**   ㉒ 0.04)142.56 **3564**   ㉓ 0.6)1707.6 **2846**

㉔ 0.8)2300 **2875**   ㉕ 0.05)1.98 **39.6**   ㉖ 0.4)1174.4 **2936**

Math Explorations and Applications Level 6 • 21

Home Connections You may want to send Home Connections Blackline Masters pages 44–45 home, which provide additional activities families can complete together. These activities apply the skills being presented in this unit.

Portfolio Assessment As students work through the second half of this unit, the Portfolio Assessment task provided on Assessment Blackline Masters page 87 can be used to evaluate students' ability to use decimals, exponents, and estimation skills in solving problems.

Performance Assessment The Performance Assessment Task 1 provided on Assessment Blackline Masters page 65 can be used at this time to evaluate students' proficiency with arithmetic involving decimals. You may want to administer this assessment with individual students or in small groups.

Unit Project This would be a good time to assign the "Planning a Trip" project on pages 172 and 173. Students can begin working on the project in cooperative groups in their free time as you work through the unit. This project is a good opportunity for students to apply the concepts of estimation and planning strategies to real-world problem solving.

LESSON 38

Student Edition pages 138–141

Keeping Sharp

LESSON PLANNER

Objectives

▶ to provide practice with facts and computation

▶ to help students develop an understanding of the relationship between a two-dimensional perspective and a three-dimensional figure

▶ to help students develop the broad ability to use mathematical common sense

Context of the Lesson This is the last of 11 lessons on operations with decimals. More work with decimals is provided in varying contexts throughout the year. This lesson also contains the second part of "The Efficiency Experts," a three-part Thinking Story.

MANIPULATIVES

stacking blocks or interlocking cubes*

toothpicks

Program Resources

Number Cubes

Practice Master 38

Enrichment Master 38

For career connections:
Careers and Math*

For extra practice:
CD-ROM* Lesson 38

① Warm-Up ⏱ 5 MINUTES

Problem of the Day Present the following problem to the class: Move two **toothpicks** to make seven squares.

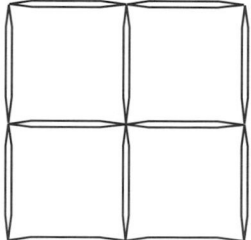

Possible answer:

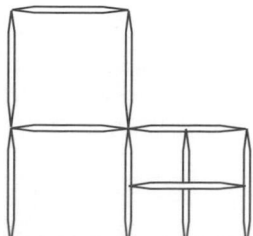

LESSON 38

Keeping Sharp

Solve. Do as many problems as you can without paper and pencil.

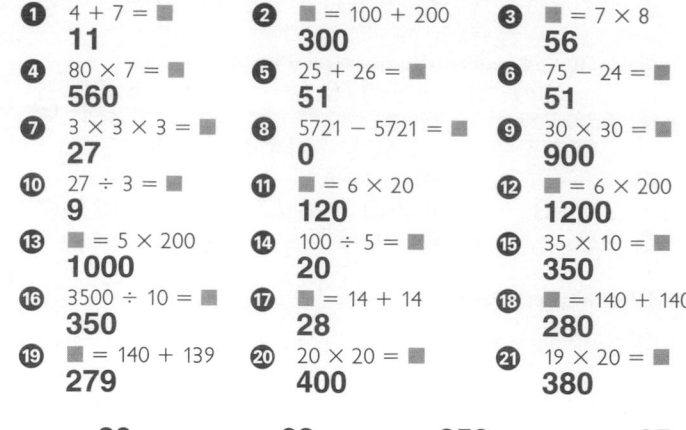

1. 4 + 7 = ■ **11**
2. ■ = 100 + 200 **300**
3. ■ = 7 × 8 **56**
4. 80 × 7 = ■ **560**
5. 25 + 26 = ■ **51**
6. 75 − 24 = ■ **51**
7. 3 × 3 × 3 = ■ **27**
8. 5721 − 5721 = ■ **0**
9. 30 × 30 = ■ **900**
10. 27 ÷ 3 = ■ **9**
11. ■ = 6 × 20 **120**
12. ■ = 6 × 200 **1200**
13. ■ = 5 × 200 **1000**
14. 100 ÷ 5 = ■ **20**
15. 35 × 10 = ■ **350**
16. 3500 ÷ 10 = ■ **350**
17. ■ = 14 + 14 **28**
18. ■ = 140 + 140 **280**
19. ■ = 140 + 139 **279**
20. 20 × 20 = ■ **400**
21. 19 × 20 = ■ **380**

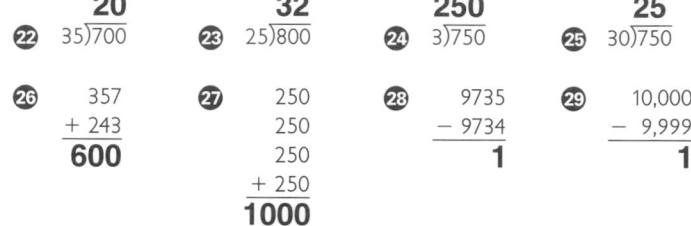

22. 35)700 **20**
23. 25)800 **32**
24. 3)750 **250**
25. 30)750 **25**

26.
```
  357
+ 243
-----
  600
```

27.
```
  250
  250
  250
+ 250
-----
 1000
```

28.
```
  9735
− 9734
------
     1
```

29.
```
 10,000
− 9,999
-------
      1
```

In each problem two of the answers are clearly wrong and one is correct. Choose the correct answer.

30. 1.578 + 2.397   (a.) 3.975   b. 39.75   c. 397.5

31. 10.632 − 2.977   a. 0.7385   b. 73.85   (c.) 7.655

32. 1.973 × 2.693   a. 53.13   (b.) 5.313   c. 0.5313

33. 16.31 ÷ 2.08   a. 0.7841   (b.) 7.841   c. 78.41

34. 10.25 × 12.55   (a.) 128.64   b. 1286.4   c. 12.864

35. 20.25 ÷ 4.45   a. 455.1   b. 45.51   (c.) 4.551

138 • Decimals and Exponents

Why teach it this way?

This lesson is one of several throughout the year entitled "Keeping Sharp." Practice in skills other than the ones being immediately taught helps students keep all their mathematical skills sharp.

 **COOPERATIVE LEARNING**

Work in groups on this problem.

From the views shown here, decide the maximum and minimum number of cubes that could be in the stack of cubes. Use blocks or number cubes to build a stack of cubes that has these views.

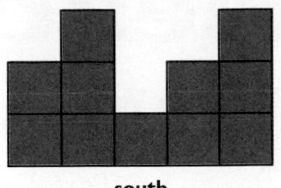
south

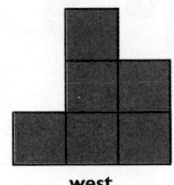
west

◆ How can you tell whether your stack has the maximum possible number of cubes? **You cannot add blocks without changing the views.**

◆ How can you tell whether your stack has the minimum possible number of cubes? **You cannot take away blocks without changing the views.**

Draw "maps" like these showing the maximum and minimum number of cubes in each stack if you were looking down from above.

maximum

N

1	1	1	1	1
2	3	1	2	3
2	2	1	2	2

W ... E

S

minimum

N

0	0	1	0	0
0	3	0	0	3
2	0	0	2	0

W ... E

S

Using cubes, make up your own stacks, and draw pictures of the south and west views. Work with your group to determine the minimum and maximum number of cubes that could be in a stack that makes those views.

After you have completed several examples, exchange them with other groups to see if they get different answers. Then try to decide who has the better answers.

Unit 2   Lesson 38   •   **139**

 **Technology Connection** Invite students to view the video *Math Mystery Theatre: Decimal Disaster, or The Case of the Maltese Fraction* from EdCon/Imperial International (VHS, for grades 2–8) for further practice with the addition and subtraction of decimals.

Problem-Solving Strategies Ask students who have solved the Problem of the Day to share how they solved it and any strategies they used.

MENTAL MATH Say a number between 1 and 99. Ask students to respond with a number that, when added to it, gives a sum of 100. Repeat with several numbers, beginning with easy numbers such as 50, 25, 75, 30, 90, and so on, and moving on to numbers such as 45, 61, 62, 93, and so on.

❷ Teach

Using the Student Pages Students should work independently on the problems on page 138. Then have students work in pairs to do page 139. Discuss the meaning of the different views presented and talk about why the two views could be formed by different numbers of blocks. Then have students build models using **blocks**, **interlocking cubes***, or Number Cubes. Have them start solving the problem about minimum and maximum numbers of blocks by first building one possible stack of blocks that gives the indicated views, and then adding or removing blocks in a way that preserves those views. As students place and remove blocks, they should begin to see how different numbers of blocks can present identical views from certain directions.

*available separately

◆ **LESSON 38** Keeping Sharp

Teach

Using the Thinking Story In this second segment of "The Efficiency Experts," the experts focus on devising a way for Mr. Schnitzel to save steps in waiting on customers in his butcher shop. Have students read the story and, to help them understand the problem, discuss or act out what Mr. Schnitzel usually did for each customer.

Answers to Thinking Story Questions:

1. About 40 meters, not counting any steps he has to take while inside the freezer room.

2. A large part of the travel can be eliminated simply by moving the cash register beside the counter (or perhaps putting it on the counter) and moving the wrapping table and the chopping block close to the freezer-room door.

3. Any plan that gets the total travel down to about 15 meters is good.

4. Answers will vary. The basic procedure is for students to divide the answer to problem 3 by 40 and multiply that by 3. For example, if according to a student's plan Mr. Schnitzel walks 20 instead of 40 meters per customer, he would walk $\frac{20}{40}$, or $\frac{1}{2}$, of 3 kilometers for the whole day. (1.5 km)

Ask students to record in their Math Journals some other time-saving ideas Marcus might come up with.

◆ **LESSON 38** Keeping Sharp

THINKING STORY

Efficiency Experts

Part 2

Mr. Schnitzel ran an old-fashioned butcher shop. He didn't sell meat already cut and wrapped in plastic. Instead, he asked customers what they wanted. Then he cut the meat for them. One day he went to the Efficiency Experts.

"Business is very good," Mr. Schnitzel said. "But I get tired running back and forth all day in my butcher shop. Could you help me find a way to operate my shop so that I won't have to walk so much?"

Marcus decided it was his turn to solve a problem. He drew a scale map of Mr. Schnitzel's shop. This is what it looked like:

Mr. Schnitzel's Butcher Shop

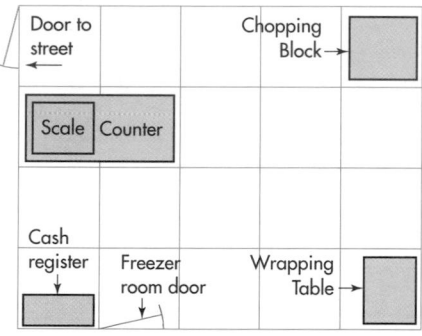

Scale: 1.5 cm = 1 m

Literature Connection Have students form groups to read *Take Me to Your Liter: Math and Science Jokes* by Charles Keller. Challenge them to make up two math jokes of their own.

RETEACHING

Many students may have difficulty visualizing the possibilities for the stacks on page 139. Have them start by visualizing an easier figure formed by fewer blocks. For example, use a figure that has a south view that shows three blocks on the bottom layer and a top layer with two blocks. The west view can show two rows of three blocks.

Marcus watched Mr. Schnitzel waiting on customers. He took careful notes. This is what Mr. Schnitzel usually did:

1. Stand at counter and find out what customer wants
2. Go into freezer room and get meat
3. Take meat to chopping block and cut piece off
4. Take meat to scale, weigh it, and show it to customer
5. Take meat to wrapping table and wrap it
6. Hand wrapped meat over counter and get money
7. Go to cash register and ring up money
8. Give customer change
9. Go to chopping block and pick up meat that is left
10. Carry meat back into freezer room
11. Return to counter and talk to next customer

"I can see why you get tired," Marcus said. "I think that by moving a few things around we can save you a lot of steps."

. . . to be continued

Work in groups. Discuss your answers and how you figured them out. Then compare your answers with those of other groups. Answers are in margin.

❶ About how far does Mr. Schnitzel have to walk each time he goes through the 11 steps of serving a customer? (Note: Marcus's map is marked off in 1-meter squares. Estimate instead of measuring each distance.)

❷ Design a better way of placing things in Mr. Schnitzel's butcher shop. Draw a scale map to show where things go. The following things can be moved: counter, scale, chopping block, cash register, and wrapping table. The following cannot be moved: the door to the street and the freezer room door.

❸ With your new plan how far will Mr. Schnitzel have to walk to serve a customer?

❹ If Mr. Schnitzel has to walk about 3 kilometers a day inside his shop now, about how far will he have to walk each day with your plan?

Unit 2   Lesson 38 • **141**

 **Wrap-Up** 5 MINUTES

In Closing To summarize the lesson, ask students to suggest ways to make the classroom more efficient.

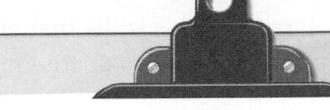 Have students time themselves on problems 1–29 on page 138 and also keep a record of the number of correct answers they get for problems 1–35.

Assessment Criteria

Did the student . . .

✓ correctly answer at least 28 of the 35 problems on page 138?

✓ figure out the minimum and maximum numbers of blocks in the figure on page 139 and in the stacks classmates built?

✓ contribute to the Thinking Story discussion?

✓ design a reasonable plan for Mr. Schnitzel in his or her answer to the Thinking Story problem?

Homework Ask students to make scale drawings of their kitchens at home. Then have them speak with family members to get ideas for making the kitchen more efficient. They can then create new scale drawings that illustrate some of these ideas.

LEARNING STYLES Meeting Individual Needs
For the activity on page 139, you may wish to pair visual learners with students who struggle with visualizing three-dimensional shapes. For the Thinking Story activity you may need to provide instruction in and pointers for making scale drawings.

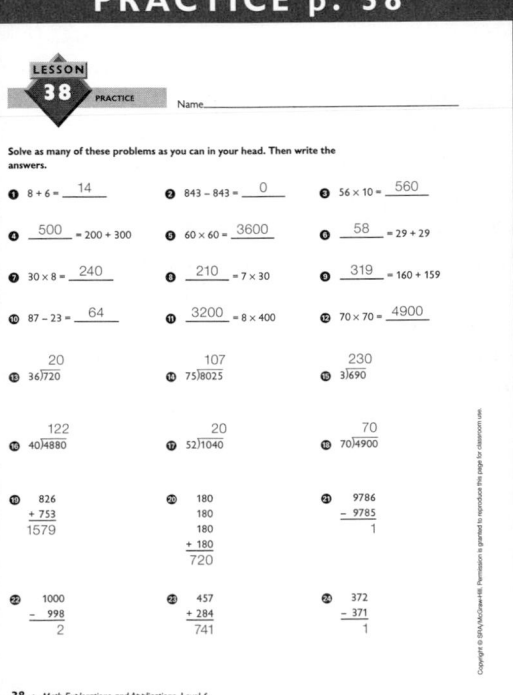
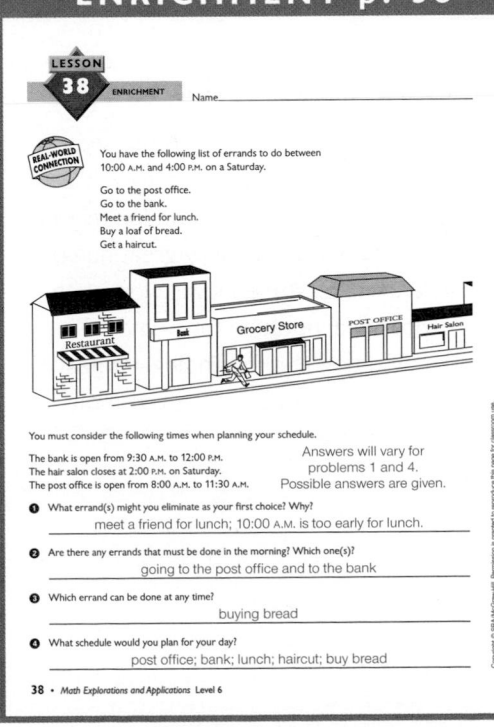

Unit 2 Lesson 38 **141**

Exponents

LESSON PLANNER

Objectives

▶ to introduce exponential notation

▶ to help students develop familiarity with the use of exponential notation in calculations

Context of the Lesson This is the first of seven lessons on exponential notation and operations with exponents.

 **MANIPULATIVES**
calculators*

Program Resources

Reteaching Master

Practice Master 39

Enrichment Master 39

For extra practice:
CD-ROM* Lesson 39

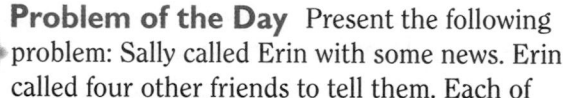

 Problem of the Day Present the following problem: Sally called Erin with some news. Erin called four other friends to tell them. Each of these friends called four of their friends. Then each of those people called four other people. If all the callers spread the word and no one was called twice, how many people heard whatever it was that Sally told Erin? (85, including Erin)

Problem-Solving Strategies Ask students who have solved the Problem of the Day to share how they solved it and any strategies they used.

MENTAL MATH Show students how to use mental math to do multidigit subtraction. One way is to make the number being subtracted into a multiple of 10, 100, or 1000. Remind students to add or subtract the same amount from the top number (minuend) as they do from the bottom number (subtrahend). Do the following problems with the class:

a. add 3 to each
$$\begin{array}{r} 532 \\ -397 \\ \hline 135 \end{array}$$
(535 – 400 = 135)

(continued on page 143)

Exponents

 Sometimes in solving problems we must repeatedly multiply by the same number.

If you know the edge of a cube is 4 centimeters long, you know there are $4 \times 4 \times 4$ cubic centimeters in the whole cube.

Suppose you have $500 in the bank and the bank pays 3% interest per year. To find the amount of money you have after one year, multiply $500 by 1.03. For each year that the money (the $500 and all the interest) stays in the bank, you find the amount of money you have at the end of the year by multiplying the amount at the beginning of the year by 1.03. To find how much money you have after four years, you can do this:

$$500 \times 1.03 \times 1.03 \times 1.03 \times 1.03$$

If you flip five coins (a penny, a nickel, a dime, a quarter, and a half dollar), there are many ways they could land. A few of the ways are shown in the chart. (**H** is for heads. **T** is for tails.)

	Penny	Nickel	Dime	Quarter	Half Dollar
First try	H	H	H	T	T
Second try	T	H	T	T	T
Third try	H	T	H	T	H
Fourth try	T	T	T	H	H
Fifth try	T	H	T	T	H
Sixth try	T	T	T	T	H

Since each coin must land in one of two possible ways, you can find out how many different ways the five coins could land by multiplying:
$2 \times 2 \times 2 \times 2 \times 2$.

Think about writing how to find the amount of money after eight years, or the number of different ways ten coins could land. Writing all of the factors could take a while.

Why teach it at this time?

As students work through this sequence of lessons on exponents, they will learn that using exponential notation makes it easier to work with very great numbers. In later units, students will work with exponential notation for prime factorization and for finding greatest common factors and least common denominators.

 **Technology Connection** Refer students to the software *Classroom Grade Level Math Programs* from Jostens Home Learning (Mac, IBM, for grades K–8) for more practice with exponents, exponential notation, simplifying, square roots, decimals, fractions, and more.

*available separately

To avoid writing so many factors, we write a small figure to the right of and slightly above the factor to show how many times that factor is used. The small figure is called an **exponent,** and the factor is called the **base.**

$4 \times 4 \times 4$ is written 4^3.

exponent
|
base ——— $4^3 = 4 \times 4 \times 4$

4^3 is read "4 to the third" or "4 cubed."

◆ Why might a number with an exponent of 3 be called "cubed"?

A number with an exponent of 3 tells how many cubes would be in a larger cube with that number of cubes on each side.

$1.03 \times 1.03 \times 1.03 \times 1.03$ is written 1.03^4.

exponent
|
base ——— $1.03^4 = 1.03 \times 1.03 \times 1.03 \times 1.03$

1.03^4 is read "1.03 to the fourth."

$500 \times 1.03 \times 1.03 \times 1.03 \times 1.03 = 500 \times 1.03^4$

$2 \times 2 \times 2 \times 2 \times 2$ is written 2^5.

exponent
|
base ——— $2^5 = 2 \times 2 \times 2 \times 2 \times 2$

2^5 is read "2 to the fifth."

When exponents are used to write numbers, we may say the number has been written in **exponential form.**

◆ Exponents are sometimes called powers. Can you see why 10, 100, 1000, and so on are called "powers of 10"? **These numbers can be written as 10 with an exponent.**

 **FANTASTIC FACT** If you flip 20 different coins, there are over 1,000,000 different ways for the coins to land.

Unit 2   Lesson 39 • **143**

Mental Math (continued)

b. add 5 to each
$$\begin{array}{r} 803 \\ -395 \\ \hline 408 \end{array}$$
$(808 - 400 = 408)$

c. add 2 to each
$$\begin{array}{r} 323 \\ -\ 98 \\ \hline 225 \end{array}$$
$(325 - 100 = 225)$

d. add 4 to each
$$\begin{array}{r} 456 \\ -196 \\ \hline 260 \end{array}$$
$(460 - 200 = 260)$

e. add 10 to each
$$\begin{array}{r} 642 \\ -490 \\ \hline 152 \end{array}$$
$(652 - 500 = 152)$

f. add 6 to each
$$\begin{array}{r} 9865 \\ -3994 \\ \hline 5871 \end{array}$$
$(9871 - 4000 = 5871)$

❷ Teach

Using the Student Pages Go over these pages with the class. Discuss the examples and the way we use exponents to avoid writing a factor many times. At this point it is not necessary for students to understand why the formulas for compound interest and for permutations of heads and tails are true. They should simply know that such formulas exist.

SPECIAL NEEDS **Meeting Individual Needs**

A common error students may make is to multiply the base by the exponent. Emphasize that 2^5 means that 2 is a factor five times. Students who have difficulty may be helped by individual tutoring in which they are asked to write out simple exponential forms in the long form. For example:

$2^5 = 2 \times 2 \times 2 \times 2 \times 2$

Then they may evaluate the exponential form by using simple arithmetic.

◆ LESSON 39 Exponents

Teach

Using the Student Pages Continue the discussion of exponential notation by considering the examples at the top of the page (4^3, 500×1.03^4; and 2^5) and the one in the middle (7×2^5). Students should be able to do the problems on this page with little direction from you. Remind them to use **calculators*** for the last set.

The word *biological* is used on page 145 to make sure that students give an answer of four for the number of grandparents, eight for the number of great-grandparents, and so on. Students should recognize a pattern in the answers to problems 32–39. For example, the number of ancestors two generations ago is $2^2 = 4$, the number of ancestors three generations ago is $2^3 = 8$, and so on. For problems 40 and 41, students will need to compute the approximate number of generations before calculating the number of ancestors. For example, to calculate the number of ancestors 500 years ago, divide 500 by 25 (the approximate number of years between generations), getting an answer of 20 generations. Calculate 2^{20}, getting an answer of 1,048,576 ancestors.

Answer to problem 42:

Students may be confused to discover that their computed number of ancestors living 750 years ago is greater than the total number of people on Earth at that time! In discussing how this can be, two points are particularly worth mentioning. First, as you go back a few generations, you are not likely to have nearly as many distinct ancestors as the mathematical procedure would suggest. For example, if your grandmother married her second cousin, then your grandparents had two great-grandparents in common. Second, these numbers suggest that if we go back far enough, most of us have some relatives in common not much more than 1000 years ago.

◆ LESSON 39 Exponents

To evaluate a number written in exponential form, simply do the indicated arithmetic.

Examples:

$$4^3 = 4 \times 4 \times 4 = 64$$

$$500 \times 1.03^4 = 500 \times 1.03 \times 1.03 \times 1.03 \times 1.03$$
$$= 562.754 \text{ or } 562.75$$

(Use a calculator to check this.)

$$2^5 = 2 \times 2 \times 2 \times 2 \times 2 = 32$$

Evaluate these numbers.

❶ 2^5	❷ 2^{10}	❸ 5^2	❹ 10^2	❺ 3^4
32	**1024**	**25**	**100**	**81**

❻ 4^3	❼ 1^{10}	❽ 1^{100}	❾ 12^3	❿ 6^3
64	**1**	**1**	**1728**	**216**

Write in exponential form. The first one has been done for you.

⓫ $5 \times 5 \times 5 \times 5 \times 5 \times 5 \times 5$ **5^7**

⓬ $3 \times 3 \times 3 \times 3 \times 3 \times 3 \times 3 \times 3$ **3^8**

⓭ $10 \times 10 \times 10 \times 10$ **10^4**

⓮ $12 \times 12 \times 12$ **12^3**

⓯ $7 \times 7 \times 7 \times 7 \times 7$ **7^5**

Evaluate each of these. You may find it easier to evaluate the exponential part first and then multiply by the other factor.

Example: $7 \times 2^5 = 7 \times 32$ and $7 \times 32 = 224$

⓰ 10×2^{10}	⓱ 7×5^2	⓲ 6×10^2	⓳ 7×3^4
10,240	**175**	**600**	**567**

⓴ 7×4^3	㉑ 10×1^{10}	㉒ 10×1^{100}	㉓ 4×10^3
448	**10**	**10**	**4000**

㉔ 5×10^3	㉕ 7×10^8	㉖ 6×10^4	㉗ 3×10^7
5000	**700,000,000**	**60,000**	**30,000,000**

Use a calculator to evaluate these.

㉘ 1.05^{10}	㉙ 1.06^{10}	㉚ 1.07^{10}	㉛ 1.08^{10}
1.6288946	**1.7908477**	**1.9671514**	**2.1589250**

144 • Decimals and Exponents

Literature Connection Invite students to read *The Rajah's Rice* by David Barry and use exponential notation to express the number of rice grains presented each day throughout the story.

---

*available separately

Use your calculator to help you answer the questions below. Before you calculate think about how using exponents can help you find answers.

You have two ancestors from one generation ago (your biological parents).

32 How many ancestors do you have from two generations ago (grandparents)? $2^2 = 4$

33 How many ancestors do you have from three generations ago (great-grandparents)? $2^3 = 8$

34 How many ancestors do you have from four generations ago? $2^4 = 16$

35 How many ancestors do you have from ten generations ago? $2^{10} = 1024$

36 How many ancestors do you have from 12 generations ago? $2^{12} = 4096$

37 How many ancestors do you have from 13 generations ago? $2^{13} = 8192$

38 How many ancestors do you have from 15 generations ago? $2^{15} = 32{,}768$

39 How many ancestors do you have from 18 generations ago? $2^{18} = 262{,}144$

If there are about 25 years between the births of parents and their children, your ancestors of ten generations ago were born about 250 years before you. So you had 1024 ancestors 250 years ago (not counting those from previous generations who were still alive).

40 How many ancestors did you have 500 years ago? **1,048,576**

41 How many ancestors did you have 750 years ago? If your calculator cannot display this number, try to find a way to use your calculator to help you find the answer using paper and pencil. **1,073,741,824**

42 Population experts estimate that there were fewer than 500,000,000 people on Earth until about 1600 A.D. Discuss this estimate in light of your answer to question 41. **See margin.**

Unit 2 Lesson 39 • **145**

3 Wrap-Up

In Closing Summarize the lesson by asking students to explain how to evaluate a number written in exponential form and expressions containing exponents.

Portfolio Assessment Have students research the number *googol*, which is 10^{100}. Make sure they include how this unusual number got its name. (It was coined by the American mathematician Edward Kasner's nine-year-old nephew, Milton Sirotta.) Have students place their reports in their portfolios.

Assessment Criteria

Did the student . . .

✓ explain how to evaluate numbers containing exponents?

✓ correctly answer at least 70% of the exercises?

✓ communicate strategies used to solve the problems on page 145?

Homework Assign Practice Master 39 for further practice with exponents.

Thinking is the basic skill in mathematics.

–Stephen S. Willoughby,
Teaching Mathematics: What Is Basic?

PRACTICE p. 39

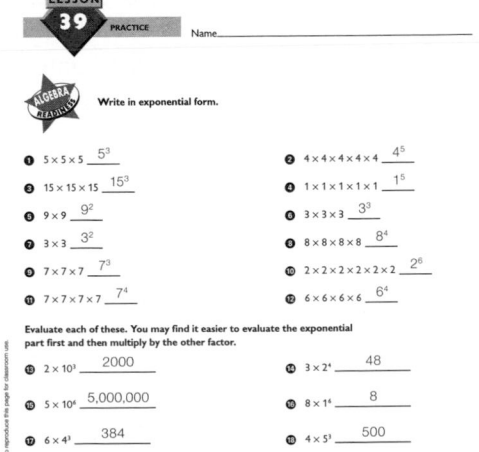

LESSON 39 PRACTICE Name_____

Write in exponential form.

1. $5 \times 5 \times 5$ __5^3__
2. $4 \times 4 \times 4 \times 4 \times 4$ __4^5__
3. $15 \times 15 \times 15$ __15^3__
4. $1 \times 1 \times 1 \times 1 \times 1$ __1^5__
5. 9×9 __9^2__
6. $3 \times 3 \times 3$ __3^3__
7. 3×3 __3^2__
8. $8 \times 8 \times 8 \times 8$ __8^4__
9. $7 \times 7 \times 7$ __7^3__
10. $2 \times 2 \times 2 \times 2 \times 2 \times 2$ __2^6__
11. $7 \times 7 \times 7 \times 7$ __7^4__
12. $6 \times 6 \times 6 \times 6$ __6^4__

Evaluate each of these. You may find it easier to evaluate the exponential part first and then multiply by the other factor.

13. 2×10^3 __2000__
14. 3×2^4 __48__
15. 5×10^6 __5,000,000__
16. 8×1^4 __8__
17. 6×4^3 __384__
18. 4×5^3 __500__
19. 3×9^2 __243__
20. 2×10^5 __200,000__
21. 3×2^5 __96__
22. 5×3^3 __135__
23. 4×5^2 __100__
24. 2×3^5 __486__

Math Explorations and Applications Level 6 • 39

ENRICHMENT p. 39

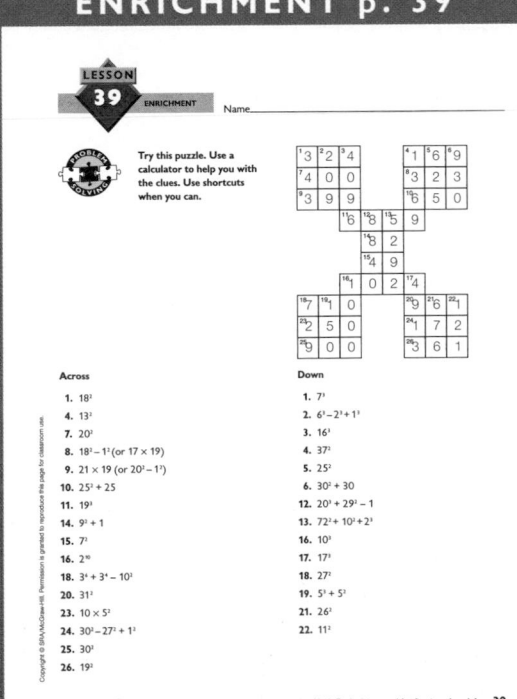

LESSON 39 ENRICHMENT Name_____

Try this puzzle. Use a calculator to help you with the clues. Use shortcuts when you can.

Across
1. 18^5
4. 13^2
7. 20^2
8. $18^2 - 1^1$ (or 17×19)
9. 21×19 (or $20^2 - 1^1$)
10. $25^1 + 25$
11. 19^3
14. $9^1 + 1$
15. 7^2
16. 2^{16}
18. $3^4 + 3^4 - 10^1$
20. 31^1
23. 10×5^1
24. $30^2 - 27^1 + 1^1$
25. 30^2
26. 19^2

Down
1. 7^3
2. $6^3 - 2^3 + 1^1$
3. 16^1
4. 37^2
5. 25^2
6. $30^1 + 30$
12. $20^1 + 29^2 - 1$
13. $72^2 + 10^1 + 2^3$
16. 10^1
17. 17^2
18. 27^1
19. $5^1 + 5^1$
21. 26^1
22. 11^1

Math Explorations and Applications Level 6 • 39

40 Counting Possibilities

Student Edition pages 146–147

Objective

▶ to introduce the principle of counting outcomes of independent events

Context of the Lesson This lesson is the second of seven lessons on exponential notation and operations with exponents.

 MANIPULATIVES
none

Program Resources
Practice Master 40
Enrichment Master 40
For extra practice:
CD-ROM* Lesson 40

❶ Warm-Up

 Problem of the Day Present the following problem: Alicia, Brett, Carla, and David are each presenting reports. In how many different orders could they give their presentations? (24)

Problem-Solving Strategies Ask students who have solved the Problem of the Day to share how they solved it and any strategies they used.

 Have students solve the following problems mentally.

a. $2 \times 437 \times 50 = (43,700)$ b. $113 \times 5 \times 20 = (11,300)$

c. $10 \times 105 \times 2 = (2100)$ d. $4 \times 79 \times 250 = (79,000)$

❷ Teach

Using the Student Pages Discuss the illustration on page 146. Try to be sure that everyone understands that there were two decisions to be made, one at the first split and the other at the second split, and that each had three possible outcomes. Have students draw maps or tree diagrams for several similar situations and decide how many final outcomes there are. Invite volunteers to attempt to generalize the counting principle.

Have students do the problems on page 147 independently or with a partner as needed. Be sure to discuss students' answers as a whole class.

146 Decimals and Exponents

LESSON

40 Counting Possibilities

Suppose you are walking down a path and you get to a place where the path splits into three paths. You must choose which of the three paths you will follow. You remember from the map that no matter which of the three paths you take, you will get to another place where the path splits into three. Then you will walk on to the end without further splits and without meeting any of the other paths. How many different places might you go?

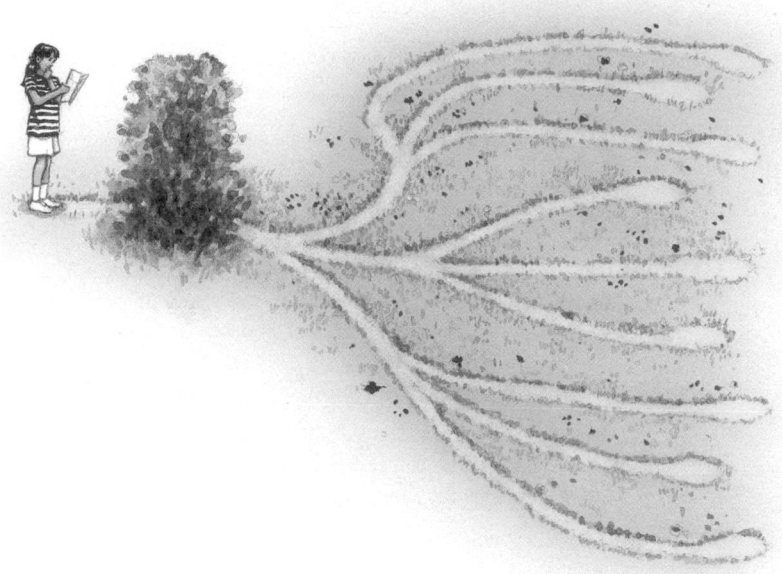

◆ Do you agree that you have 3 × 3, or nine different possible destinations?

◆ How could you express 3 × 3 using an exponent? **3^2**

◆ Suppose each of the nine destinations leads to yet another place where the road splits into three paths. How many possible final destinations are there? **27**

◆ How could you express this answer using an exponent? **3^3**

146 • Decimals and Exponents

Because this is an introductory lesson to concepts related to probability, which will be explored in greater depth later in the program, reteaching is not necessary at this time.

*available separately

Solve these problems.

1 If you know that a path splits into four paths, and then each of those splits into four paths, how many different destinations are possible? **16**

2 If a path splits into two paths and then each of those splits into three paths, how many possible destinations are there? **6**

3 Suppose you have four different colored shirts you can wear and three different colored slacks. How many different outfits are possible (assuming you don't care about color coordination)? **12**

4 The school lunch menu has two kinds of drinks and four kinds of fruit. How many different combinations of a drink and fruit are possible? **8**

5 If you roll a 0–5 number cube, how many possible numbers might appear? If you roll a 5–10 number cube, how many different numbers might appear? Suppose you roll both cubes together and record the number that each cube shows. How many possible number pairs are there with the 0–5 number written first? Some of those possible pairs are: (0,5), (0,6), (0,7), (0,8), (0,9), (0,10), (1,5), (1,6), and so on. How many of these are there all together? Try to explain how to get this result easily and why your procedure works. Discuss your procedure with other members of your class. **6; 6; 36**

6 Suppose you have two 0–5 cubes, one painted blue and one painted green. (The numbers are painted in white.) How many possible sets of rolls are there if the number on the blue cube is always listed first? **36**

7 If you roll a 0–5 number cube three times and keep track of the number showing each time, how many different ordered triples are possible? Those triples would include the following: (0,0,0), (0,0,1), (0,0,2), (0,0,3), (0,0,4), (0,0,5), (0,1,0), (0,1,1), (0,1,2), and so on. **216**

8 Can you think of a way to use exponents to show your answer and process for problem 7? Show it. $6 \times 6 \times 6 = 6^3 = 216$

Unit 2 Lesson 40 • **147**

PRACTICE p. 40

ENRICHMENT p. 40

---

❸ Wrap-Up  5 MINUTES

In Closing To summarize the lesson, have a student state the principle regarding successive choices. Ask how it could be applied to counting the number of possible outcomes when a coin is flipped five times. ($2 \times 2 \times 2 \times 2 \times 2 = 2^5 = 32$)

ALTERNATIVE ASSESSMENT **Portfolio Assessment** Ask students to write a paragraph describing what they learned about counting choices and how to find the number of ways the first five questions on a four option multiple-choice test could be answered. (1024)

Assessment Criteria

Did the student . . .

✓ complete the problems on page 147 correctly?

✓ express understanding of the principle of successive choices?

Homework Have students figure out how many times they would need to flip a coin to have more than 5000 possible outcomes.

 **GIFTED & TALENTED** **Meeting Individual Needs**
Challenge students to visit a local ice-cream store and figure out how many different two-scoop and three-scoop cones it is possible to create when a cone cannot have more than one scoop of the same flavor. Further challenge this group to figure out and apply a method for quickly solving problems like these.

 **SPECIAL NEEDS** **MANIPULATIVES** **Meeting Individual Needs**
Encourage students to draw diagrams, use manipulatives, or even model the situations in the problems to help them find the solutions.

Unit 2 Lesson 40 **147**

Student Edition pages 148–151

Writing Powers of 10

LESSON PLANNER

Objectives

▶ to demonstrate how to use powers of 10 to write numbers with only one nonzero digit

▶ to help students discover the ease of working with large numbers expressed in exponential form

▶ to help students develop the broad ability to use mathematical common sense

Context of the Lesson This is the third of seven lessons on exponential notation and operations with exponents. The next two lessons cover multiplication of numbers in exponential form. This lesson also contains the final installment of the three-part Thinking Story "The Efficiency Experts."

 MANIPULATIVES

Program Resources

Practice Master 41

Enrichment Master 41

For career connections:
  Careers and Math*

For extra practice:
  CD-ROM* Lesson 41
  Cumulative Review, page 561

① Warm-Up ⏱ 5 MINUTES

 **Problem of the Day** Present the following problem to the class: On the planet Yumongus, weight is measured in nirps, flots, and smeds. A nirp is ten times as heavy as a flot, which is ten times as heavy as a smed. If an inhabitant of the planet weighs 500 smeds, how heavy is the Yumongian in nirps? (5 nirps)

Problem-Solving Strategies Ask students who have solved the Problem of the Day to share how they solved it and any strategies they used.

Writing Powers of 10

If you are multiplying by the same factor several times, there is an easy way to indicate that.

$7 \times 10 \times 10 \times 10 \times 10 \times 10 \times 10 = 7{,}000{,}000$

$7 \times 10 \times 10 \times 10 \times 10 \times 10 \times 10 = 7 \times 10^6$

Sometimes it is convenient to write 7,000,000.

Sometimes it is convenient to write 7×10^6.

7×10^6 is read "7 times 10 to the sixth."

Write each of the following by using an exponent.
(We call this the *exponential form.*)

Examples:

$600{,}000 = 6 \times 10^5$

$60 = 6 \times 10$ or 6×10^1

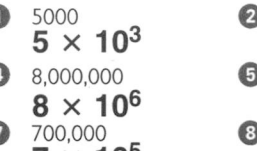

① 5000 5×10^3	**②** 200 2×10^2	**③** 40 4×10^1
④ 8,000,000 8×10^6	**⑤** 3,000,000,000 3×10^9	**⑥** 80 8×10^1
⑦ 700,000 7×10^5	**⑧** 40,000 4×10^4	**⑨** 800 8×10^2
⑩ 9,000,000 9×10^6	**⑪** 4000 4×10^3	**⑫** 3000 3×10^3
⑬ 600 6×10^2	**⑭** 400 4×10^2	**⑮** 30,000 3×10^4

Write in standard form.

⑯ 5×10^8 **500,000,000**	**⑰** 3×10^5 **300,000**	**⑱** 8×10^1 **80**	**⑲** 10^2 **100**
⑳ 4×10^7 **40,000,000**	**㉑** 2×10^2 **200**	**㉒** 5×10^2 **500**	**㉓** 10^3 **1000**
㉔ 8×10^6 **8,000,000**	**㉕** 7×10^4 **70,000**	**㉖** 8×10^3 **8000**	**㉗** 10^1 **10**
㉘ 9×10^3 **9000**	**㉙** 6×10^9 **6,000,000,000**	**㉚** 10^5 **100,000**	**㉛** 10^4 **10,000**

148 · Decimals and Exponents

Science Connection Ask students to examine the information in their planet chart. Have them write a summary of the data it shows about how planets orbit the sun and about the relationships among these planetary orbits.

SCIENCE CONNECTION

The chart below shows basic information about the known planets in our solar system. Using a computer or other means, draw the chart but use exponential notation to show the distances. Save your completed chart because you will need it in the next lesson.

5×10^7
25×10^6
—
35×10^6
368×10^6
745×10^6
1606×10^6
2667×10^6
2663×10^6

Our Solar System

Planet	Average Distance from the Sun (miles)	Closest Distance from Earth (miles)	Farthest Distance from Earth (miles)	
36×10^6 Mercury	36,000,000	50,000,000	136,000,000	136×10^6
672×10^5 Venus	67,200,000	25,000,000	161,000,000	161×10^6
929×10^5 Earth	92,900,000	—	—	—
142×10^6 Mars	142,000,000	35,000,000	248,000,000	248×10^6
484×10^6 Jupiter	484,000,000	368,000,000	600,000,000	6×10^8
887×10^6 Saturn	887,000,000	745,000,000	1,031,000,000	1031×10^6
178×10^7 Uranus	1,780,000,000	1,606,000,000	1,953,000,000	1953×10^6
28×10^8 Neptune	2,800,000,000	2,667,000,000	2,915,000,000	2915×10^6
367×10^7 Pluto	3,670,000,000	2,663,000,000	4,644,000,000	4644×10^6

Challenge question: How is it possible for Pluto sometimes to be farther from Earth than Neptune and at other times be closer to Earth than Neptune? **Their orbits are elliptical, not circular.**

FANTASTIC FACT

Our nearest star, other than the sun, is Proxima Centauri, which is just over 25,000,000,000,000 (25×10^{12}) miles away.

TECHNOLOGY CONNECTION

Technology Connection Refer students to the laser disc or software *Core Concepts in Math: Mastering Equations, Roots and Exponents,* from BFA/Systems Impact (Mac, IBM, for grades 5–9) for further practice with solving equations using exponents, combining like terms, and square root word problems.

MENTAL MATH

Write the following problems on the chalkboard. Ask students to use mental math to solve each problem and then discuss their strategies.

a.
$$723$$
$$-492$$
$$\overline{\;\;231\;\;}$$
(add 8 to each)
$$731$$
$$-500$$
$$\overline{\;\;231\;\;}$$

b.
$$523$$
$$-310$$
$$\overline{\;\;213\;\;}$$
(subtract 10 from each)
$$513$$
$$-300$$
$$\overline{\;\;213\;\;}$$

c.
$$848$$
$$-\;\,98$$
$$\overline{\;\;750\;\;}$$
(add 2 to each)
$$850$$
$$-100$$
$$\overline{\;\;750\;\;}$$

d.
$$353$$
$$-103$$
$$\overline{\;\;250\;\;}$$
(subtract 3 from each)
$$350$$
$$-100$$
$$\overline{\;\;250\;\;}$$

e.
$$498$$
$$-308$$
$$\overline{\;\;190\;\;}$$
(subtract 8 from each)
$$490$$
$$-300$$
$$\overline{\;\;190\;\;}$$

f.
$$948$$
$$-799$$
$$\overline{\;\;149\;\;}$$
(add 1 to each)
$$949$$
$$-800$$
$$\overline{\;\;149\;\;}$$

❷ Teach

ALGEBRA READINESS

Using the Student Pages Briefly discuss the material at the top of page 148. Explain that using a 10 with an exponent is a quick way of writing numbers with several 0s. Keep in mind that although the "shortcut" does not seem very useful for numbers with fewer than three 0s, understanding it helps to generalize rules that are applied later on. Point out to students that it is usually easier to think about and calculate mentally with a number like 3×10^9 than with 3,000,000,000. Explain that the exponent tells how many factors of 10 there are in a number; that is, how many zeros there are. If students have a strong grasp of this material, you may wish to introduce the use of 0 as an exponent, using as an example 4×10^0. To explain why this is the correct way to write 4, ask students to tell how many times 10 is used as a factor. (0) Then compare 4×10^0 and 4×10^1.

Go over the information in the table on page 149 with the class. You may wish to work through a few of the problems with the class before directing students to complete the page on their own or in pairs.

◆ LESSON 41 Writing Powers of 10

Teach

Using the Thinking Story In this final segment of "The Efficiency Experts," the experts focus on a way to save steps for the owner of a take-out restaurant who uses some of the same ingredients and procedures in the preparation of different dishes. Have students read the story in groups, look over the map of Ms. Hafiz's shop, and try to visualize her movements as she prepares the sandwiches. Each group should discuss the questions and try to agree on answers.

Answers to Thinking Story Questions:

1. The map does not show any place for customers to sit.

2. About 10 meters for a falafel and 14 meters for a hamburger. She sells two hamburgers for every falafel, so calculate the average of 10, 14, and 14 ($\frac{38}{3}$ or approximately 13 meters). Because she takes twice as many 14-m trips as 10-m trips, calculating the average of 10 and 14 would be incorrect.

3. Putting the salad table where the bread box is, the fryer in the salad table's place, and the bread box where the fryer is will save about 4 m on the average trip.

4. Check to see if students' final plans are realistic. For instance, objects must not be so close together that it is impossible to move between them. With the class, discuss which plan is best for making falafels, which is best for making hamburgers, and which is best on the average. Some students may suggest that Ms. Hafiz can save time, without rearranging anything, by changing the order in which she does things. For example, she could pick up bread on the way to the fryer or grill.

Ask students to explain why Ms. Hafiz's problem is more complicated than Mr. Schnitzel's.

◆ LESSON 41 Writing Powers of 10

Efficiency Experts

Part 3

After the Efficiency Experts helped Mr. Schnitzel, they had a visit from Ms. Hafiz. "I have a shop next door to Mr. Schnitzel's butcher shop," she said. "I hope you can save me steps the way you did for him. I brought you a map of my shop."

Ms. Hafiz's Shop

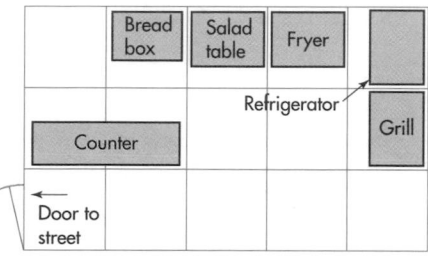

Scale: 1.5 cm = 1 m

"From this map I'd say you run a restaurant," Portia said.

"A take-out restaurant," explained Ms. Hafiz. "I make hamburgers and falafels that people pick up."

"What are falafels?" Manolita asked.

"They are like meatballs, but they are made from ground-up chickpeas," Ms. Hafiz said. "People in the Middle East put them in sandwiches. Americans call the sandwiches falafels. If you come to my shop, I'll give you one. They're very good!"

"But now I'll tell you how I make one. Suppose I am standing here at the counter," she said, pointing to the map.

150 · Decimals and Exponents

Literature Connection Have students read *The Westing Game* by Ellen Raskin. Ask them to use exponents to express the inheritance left by the millionaire.

"A customer orders a falafel. First I go to the fryer and put in three scoops of falafel dough. Then I go to the bread box and take out a piece of pita bread. It's round and hollow, so you can stuff things inside it. Then I go back to the fryer, take out the three falafels when they are done, and put them inside the pita bread. Next I go to the salad table. There I put salad and a special sauce into the pita bread. Then I go back to the counter. I put the whole thing inside a bag and give it to the customer."

"Falafels sound good," said Manolita. "Do you sell many?"

"Quite a few," said Ms. Hafiz. "But I sell twice as many hamburgers. I have to walk around even more to make a hamburger. First I am at the counter. Then I go to the refrigerator and take out a hamburger patty. Then I go to the grill and put it on. Then I go to the bread box and take out a bun. Then I go back to the grill, warm the bun, and put the hamburger on it. Next I go to the salad table and add lettuce, pickle, tomato, onion—whatever the customer wants. Finally I take it to the counter, put it in a bag, and give it to the customer."

"Your problem is more complicated than Mr. Schnitzel's," Manolita said. "But I'm sure we can solve it for you. In fact, I think I can see a way to save you a lot of steps. We need to switch around just three things in your shop."

. . . the end

Work in groups. Discuss how you figured out your answers. Compare your answers with those of other groups.
Answers are in margin.

① How could you tell from the map that Ms. Hafiz does not run a sit-down restaurant?

② About how far does Ms. Hafiz have to walk while making and serving a falafel? How far for a hamburger? Now figure the average distance she has to walk while serving a customer.

③ By moving only three things in Ms. Hafiz's shop, save her as many steps as possible. Draw a map to show your plan. On the average, how many meters will your plan save her?

④ By moving anything you want (except the door), design the best room plan you can for Ms. Hafiz.

Use the Cumulative Review on page 561 after this lesson.

Unit 2   Lesson 41 • **151**

❸ Wrap-Up

In Closing To summarize the lesson, ask students to write the number 100 using exponential notation. (1×10^2)

 **Portfolio Assessment** Ask students to include their chart of the solar system from page 149 in their Math Portfolios. Have them include an explanation of how to use exponents to express a number written in standard form.

Assessment Criteria

Did the student . . .

✓ correctly answer at least 25 of the 31 problems on page 148?

✓ demonstrate a clear understanding of how to write numbers in exponential form and how to write in standard form numbers using exponents?

✓ contribute to the Thinking Story discussion?

Homework Have students gather additional information about distances in space, using an almanac, encyclopedia, science text, or other source. Ask them to rewrite ten of these multidigit numbers using exponential form.

PRACTICE p. 41

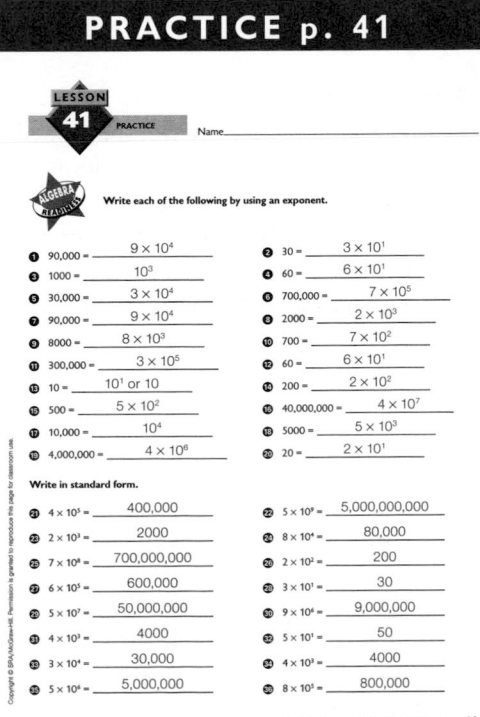

LESSON 41 PRACTICE Name_____

Write each of the following by using an exponent.

❶ 90,000 =	9×10^4	⓭ 30 =	3×10^1
❷ 1000 =	10^3	⓮ 60 =	6×10^1
❸ 30,000 =	3×10^4	⓯ 700,000 =	7×10^5
❹ 90,000 =	9×10^4	⓰ 2000 =	2×10^3
❺ 8000 =	8×10^3	⓱ 700 =	7×10^2
❻ 300,000 =	3×10^5	⓲ 60 =	6×10^1
❼ 10 =	10^1 or 10	⓳ 200 =	2×10^2
❽ 500 =	5×10^2	⓴ 40,000,000 =	4×10^7
❾ 10,000 =	10^4	5000 =	5×10^3
❿ 4,000,000 =	4×10^6	20 =	2×10^1

Write in standard form.

4 × 10⁵ =	400,000	5 × 10⁹ =	5,000,000,000
2 × 10³ =	2000	8 × 10⁴ =	80,000
7 × 10⁸ =	700,000,000	2 × 10² =	200
6 × 10⁵ =	600,000	3 × 10¹ =	30
5 × 10⁷ =	50,000,000	9 × 10⁶ =	9,000,000
4 × 10³ =	4000	5 × 10¹ =	50
3 × 10⁴ =	30,000	4 × 10³ =	4000
5 × 10⁶ =	5,000,000	8 × 10⁵ =	800,000

Math Explorations and Applications Level 6 • 41

ENRICHMENT p. 41

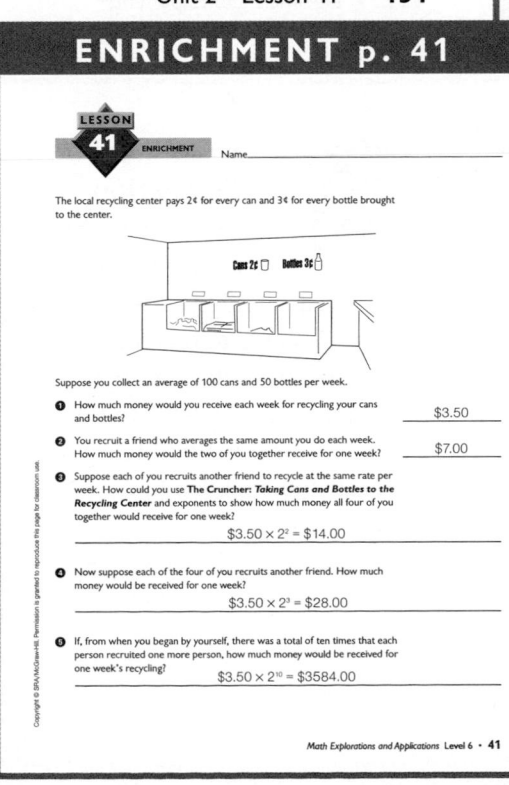

LESSON 41 ENRICHMENT Name_____

The local recycling center pays 2¢ for every can and 3¢ for every bottle brought to the center.

Cans 2¢ ☐   Bottles 3¢ ☐

Suppose you collect an average of 100 cans and 50 bottles per week.

❶ How much money would you receive each week for recycling your cans and bottles? **$3.50**

❷ You recruit a friend who averages the same amount you do each week. How much money would the two of you together receive for one week? **$7.00**

❸ Suppose each of you recruits another friend to recycle at the same rate per week. How could you use **The Cruncher: Taking Cans and Bottles to the Recycling Center** and exponents to show how much money all four of you together would receive for one week?
$3.50 \times 2^2 = \$14.00$

❹ Now suppose each of the four of you recruits another friend. How much money would be received for one week?
$3.50 \times 2^3 = \$28.00$

❺ If, from when you began by yourself, there was a total of ten times that each person recruited one more person, how much money would be received for one week's recycling?
$3.50 \times 2^{10} = \$3584.00$

Math Explorations and Applications Level 6 • 41

LESSON 42

Student Edition pages 152–153

Multiplying and Dividing Using Exponents

LESSON PLANNER

Objective

▶ to introduce multiplication and division with numbers in exponential form

Context of the Lesson This lesson is the fourth of seven lessons on exponential notation and operations with exponents.

 MANIPULATIVES

calculators*

Program Resources

Practice Master 42

Enrichment Master 42

For extra practice:
CD-ROM* Lesson 42

---

❶ Warm-Up

Problem of the Day Present the following problem: Teri just got a ten-day job. Which pay arrangement will pay her most: a flat rate of $800; $10 the first day and then $10 more each day than the previous day; or $1 the first day, $2 the second day, $4 the third, and so on, doubling each day? (The doubling rate pays most.)

Problem-Solving Strategies Ask students who have solved the Problem of the Day to share how they solved it and any strategies they used.

  Have students give each number in standard form.

a. 5^2 (25)   **b.** 4^3 (64)

c. 3^4 (81)   **d.** 10^6 (1,000,000)

e. 1^8 (1)   **f.** 2^4 (16)

g. 17^1 (17)   **h.** 20^2 (400)

❷ Teach

Using the Student Pages Go over the examples on page 152 with the class. As needed, review the meanings of *base* and *exponent*, reminding students that exponents tell how many times the base is used as a factor. Then emphasize that when multiplying numbers in exponential

152 Decimals and Exponents

LESSON 42

Multiplying and Dividing Using Exponents

$10^5 \times 10^2 = (10 \times 10 \times 10 \times 10 \times 10) \times (10 \times 10)$

◆ How many factors of 10 are in the product? Could you have gotten the answer by simply adding the original exponents? **7; yes**

Whenever we multiply two numbers written in exponential notation with the same base, the answer can be written with that base. To find the exponent of the answer, add the exponents of the factors.
So, $10^5 \times 10^2 = 10^{(5 + 2)} = 10^7$

$$10^7 \div 10^5 = \frac{(10 \times 10 \times 10 \times 10 \times 10 \times 10 \times 10)}{(10 \times 10 \times 10 \times 10 \times 10)}$$

◆ How many factors of 10 will be in the answer? **2**

Whenever we divide two numbers written in exponential notation with the same base, the answer can be written with that base. To find the exponent of the answer, take the exponent of the dividend (first number) minus the exponent of the divisor (second number).
So $10^7 \div 10^5 = 10^{(7 - 5)} = 10^2$

Use the chart you prepared on page 149. How long would it take a spaceship traveling at an average speed of 1000 miles per hour to travel from Earth to Jupiter? Assume that the spaceship travels the shortest possible distance.

We know that Jupiter's closest distance to Earth is 368×10^6 miles. The speed of the spaceship is 1×10^3 miles per hour.

Therefore, it will take at least $\frac{368 \times 10^6 \text{ miles}}{1 \times 10^3 \text{ miles per hour}} = 368 \times 10^3$ hours.

It will take the spaceship at least 368,000 hours to reach Jupiter.

 **Use a calculator to solve these problems.**

❶ Convert 368,000 hours into weeks, into months, and into years.
weeks: 2.19×10^3 = 2190; months: about 511; years: about 42

❷ Suppose the spaceship was traveling at an average speed of 2000 miles per hour. How many years would it take? **about 21 years**

152 • Decimals and Exponents

 **Literature Connection**
Have students read *Magnification* by Beth B. Norden and Lynette Ruschak, and use exponents to represent the magnification shown in the photographs. Ask students to think of applications for using multiplication with these numbers.

RETEACHING

Emphasize that exponents are not factors and that they are not multiplied. You may wish to have some students first write out all the factors and then either multiply them or divide them and compare their results with those obtained using exponents.

---

*available separately

Use a computer or other means to draw and complete the chart to show how many years it would take a spaceship to reach the planets under the conditions shown. The answers for Jupiter are already shown.

Number of Years for a Spaceship to Travel from Earth

Planet	Closest Distance from Earth (miles)	at 500 miles per hour	at 1000 miles per hour	at 10,000 miles per hour
Mercury	50×10^6	11.4	5.71	0.571
Venus	25×10^6	5.71	2.85	0.285
Earth	—	—	—	—
Mars	35×10^6	7.99	4.00	0.400
Jupiter	368×10^6	84.0	42.0	4.20
Saturn	745×10^6	170.1	85.0	8.50
Uranus	$1,606 \times 10^6$	366.7	183.3	18.33
Neptune	$2,667 \times 10^6$	608.9	304.5	30.45
Pluto	$2,663 \times 10^6$	608.0	304.0	30.40

Multiply or divide. Watch the signs. Leave answers in exponential form.

❸ $10^3 \times 10^6$
10^9

❹ $10^8 \div 10^5$
10^3

❺ $10^6 \div 10^2$
10^4

❻ $10^5 \times 10^3$
10^8

❼ $(4 \times 10^5) \times (3 \times 10^8)$
12×10^{13}

❽ $10^5 \times 10^4$
10^9

❾ $(15 \times 10^9) \div (5 \times 10^6)$
3×10^3

❿ $10^{12} \div 10^5$
10^7

⓫ $(2 \times 10^4) \times (3 \times 10^3)$
6×10^7

⓬ $10^{15} \div 10^{12}$
10^3

⓭ $(12 \times 10^6) \div (3 \times 10)$
4×10^5

⓮ $10^3 \times 10^8$
10^{11}

---

form with the same base, the sum of the exponents is the same as the number of factors in the product. Point out that when dividing, students can "cancel" or remove the number of factors in the divisor, and the number of factors left will be the difference between the exponents.

 Have students work on page 153 individually or in small groups, using a **calculator*** to complete the table. Students can compare answers when they finish. Because the spaceship would not travel in a straight line, times and distances will be slightly inaccurate, but the order of magnitude will give a good ballpark figure.

❸ Wrap-Up

In Closing To summarize the lesson, have students state a rule for multiplying two numbers in exponential form with the same base and one for dividing two numbers in exponential form with the same base.

 **Performance Assessment** Ask students to give the product of $7^5 \times 7^2$ (7^7) and the quotient of $8^6 \div 8^4$ (8^2).

Assessment Criteria

Did the student . . .

✓ successfully complete the problems on page 153?

✓ propose rules for the multiplying and dividing of numbers in exponential form?

✓ understand the rules when they were proposed?

Homework Have students make up a cross-number puzzle using as clues the multiplication and division of numbers that are written in exponential form and that have the same base.

Meeting Individual Needs

To help students clarify the meaning of the terms *exponent* and *base*, use the expressions "3 to the fourth power" and "4 to the third power." Ask students to compare the difference between the expressions. Focus on which number is the base and which is the exponent.

---

*available separately

LEVEL
43

Approximation with Exponents

Student Edition pages 154-157

LESSON PLANNER

Objectives

▶ to provide practice in computation with whole numbers, exponents, and negative numbers

▶ to teach how to use exponents in approximating

▶ to provide practice in using exponents to solve a series of imaginative but realistic problems

✓ to evaluate students' ability to multiply and divide numbers in exponential form

Context of the Lesson This is the fifth of seven lessons on exponential notation and operations with exponents. It provides Mastery Checkpoint 13 for assessing students' proficiency in multiplying and dividing numbers in exponential form.

 MANIPULATIVES

Program Resources

Practice Master 43

Enrichment Master 43

Assessment Master

For extra practice:
CD-ROM* Lesson 43

❶ Warm-Up ⏱ 5 MINUTES

 Problem of the Day Present the following problem to the class: If you add the square of Tanya's age to Steve's age, the sum is 60. But if you add the square of Steve's age to Tanya's age, the sum is 128. How old are Tanya and Steve? (7 and 11, respectively)

Problem-Solving Strategies Ask students who have solved the Problem of the Day to share how they solved it and any strategies they used.

MENTAL MATH Have students show thumbs down if the given answers are definitely wrong and thumbs up if the answers are possibly correct.

a. 430 + 430 = 860 (thumbs up)

b. 62 − 61 = 60 (thumbs down)

c. 333 + 333 = 999 (thumbs down)

(continued on page 155)

154 Decimals and Exponents

LESSON
43

Approximation with Exponents

Sometimes you need to approximate multidigit numbers. You can use exponential notation to help you approximate.

Example: $3748 \times 72,654$ is about $(4 \times 10^3) \times (7 \times 10^4)$
or about 28×10^7.

If you want, you can write this as 280,000,000. The precise answer is 272,307,192, so 280,000,000 is a good approximation.

Remember:

A. Round each number to a number with only one nonzero digit.

B. Think in exponential notation.

C. Multiply.

With a little practice you should be able to do this kind of problem without pencil and paper.

Answers shown are examples only. Accept all
Approximate. Use exponential notation. **reasonable estimates.**

❶ 348×657
21×10^4

❷ $26,437 \times 841$
24×10^6

❸ $5103 \times 89,248$
45×10^7

❹ 7499×8478
56×10^6 or 64×10^6 or 63×10^6

❺ $643,871 \times 869$
54×10^7

❻ $65,024 \times 76,503$
56×10^8 or 48×10^8 or 49×10^8

❼ 382×512
20×10^4 or 2×10^5

❽ $21,503 \times 498$
10×10^6 or 10^7

❾ 7047×6894
49×10^6

❿ 250×750
21×10^4 or 14×10^4 or 24×10^4

⓫ 921×584
54×10^4

⓬ 312×6928
21×10^5

Notice that for problems 4, 6, and 10, you probably rounded both numbers the same direction, even though both were about halfway between the two numbers with one nonzero digit. In such cases you will get more accurate answers if you round the two numbers in opposite directions.

154 • Decimals and Exponents

Why teach it this way?

The next lesson gives more practice in making approximations by putting numbers in exponential form. With this lesson and the next, students can begin to see how powerful a tool exponential notation can be.

154 Decimals and Exponents

*available separately

Midori lives in a city of 150,000 people. One day she wondered roughly how much time she would need to shake hands with everyone in her city.

Midori decided to find the answer to her question. She found that it took about 8 seconds to shake hands with ten people. She did this calculation:

$150,000 = 15 \times 10^4$ people

If it takes 8 seconds to shake hands with ten people, then it takes $8 \div 10$, or 0.8, second to shake hands with one person.

$0.8 \times 15 \times 10^4 = 12 \times 10^4$, or 120,000

So it would take about 12×10^4 seconds for Midori to shake hands with everyone in her city.

◆ How many minutes is that? **2000**

◆ How many hours is that? **33.3**

◆ How many days is that? **1.4 days**

Solve these problems.

⓭ Find out how many students there are at your school. How long would it take you to shake hands with all of them? (Hint: How long does it take you to shake hands with ten people?)

⓮ Find out about how many people live in your city, town, or village. How long would it take you to shake hands with all these people? (Hint: How long does it take you to shake hands with ten people?)

⓯ Find out about how many people live in your state. How long would it take you to shake their hands?

⓰ Find out about how many people live in the United States of America. How long would it take you to shake their hands?

⓱ Find out about how many people live in the world. How long would it take you to shake their hands? **Answers for questions 13–17 will vary depending on the populations used and the times for each student. Calculations should follow the method shown above.**

Unit 2   Lesson 43   •   **155**

Literature Connection Have students read *How Much Is a Million?* by David M. Schwartz. Students can use this book as a model for making up stories using exponents to express multidigit numbers.

Mental Math (continued)

d. $10 \times 25 = 2500$ (thumbs down)

e. $14 \times 10 = 144$ (thumbs down)

f. $10 \times 10 = 100$ (thumbs up)

g. $100 - 55 = 45$ (thumbs up)

h. $45 \div 5 = 9$ (thumbs up)

❷ Teach

Using the Student Pages Discuss the material at the top of page 154. Provide more examples if you wish. Point out that exponential notation is most useful for approximating answers to multiplication and division problems; addition and subtraction problems are not greatly simplified by using it. (In addition and subtraction problems, attention should be concentrated on the first one or two digits if both numbers have the same number of digits, or on the greater number if one has more digits than the other.)

Assign problems 1–12, keeping in mind that some of the answers will have several acceptable forms. Encourage students who express numbers written with exponents as the product of a number between 1 and 10 and a power of 10, such as writing 21×10^4 as 2.1×10^5. These students are using scientific notation, which is introduced in Lesson 45.

Go over with the class the first part of the story on page 155 about Midori and her interesting question to be sure that students understand how the calculations give her the answer to her question. After going over the discussion questions, have students work in small groups on problems 13–17.

For problem 16, using a population of about 270 million and 0.8 seconds per handshake, a reasonable answer is about 2.16×10^8 seconds, or about 6.8 years.

For problem 17, using a world population of about 5.8 billion and 0.8 seconds per handshake, a reasonable answer is about 4.64×10^9 seconds, or about 147 years.

◆ LESSON 43 Approximation with Exponents

Teach

Using the Student Pages Have students do the problems on page 156 on their own.

Assign the mixed word problems on page 157 for pairs of students to solve. Ask pairs to compare answers with other students, keeping in mind that some of the answers will have several acceptable forms. Invite students who finish early to create more coin problems similar to problem 61. Students can post their problems for others to see and try to solve.

◆ LESSON 43 Approximation with Exponents

Multiply or divide. Watch the signs.

18 $10^4 \times 10^3$
10^7

19 $(2 \times 10^4) \times (4 \times 10^3)$
8×10^7

20 $(8 \times 10^6) \times (5 \times 10^4)$
40×10^{10}

21 $10^8 \div 10^5$
10^3

22 $10^7 \div 10^4$
10^3

23 $(6 \times 10^5) \div (3 \times 10^3)$
2×10^2

24 $(9 \times 10^9) \times (8 \times 10^8)$
72×10^{17}

25 $(4 \times 10^4) \times (4 \times 10^4)$
16×10^8

26 $(16 \times 10^8) \div (4 \times 10^4)$
4×10^4

27 $(3 \times 10^5) \times 10^4$
3×10^9

28 $(2 \times 10^8) \div 10^6$
2×10^2

29 $(2 \times 10^3) \times 10^3$
2×10^6

30 $(10 \times 52) \times 10^2$
52×10^3

31 $(20 \times 10^4) \div 10^3$
20×10^1

32 $(2 \times 10^5) \div 10^3$
2×10^2

33 $(24 \times 10^8) \div (8 \times 10^5)$
3×10^3

34 $(48 \times 10^7) \div (6 \times 10^3)$
8×10^4

35 $(18 \times 10^6) \times (2 \times 10^4)$
36×10^{10}

36 $(20 \times 10^6) \times (2 \times 10^4)$
40×10^{10}

37 $(30 \times 10^6) \times (2 \times 10^4)$
60×10^{10}

38 $(40 \times 10^6) \times (2 \times 10^4)$
80×10^{10}

39 $(40 \times 10^6) \div (2 \times 10^4)$
20×10^2

40 $(4 \times 10^7) \div (2 \times 10^4)$
2×10^3

41 $(28 \times 10^7) \div (4 \times 10^4)$
7×10^3

42 $(63 \times 10^{11}) \div (7 \times 10^5)$
9×10^6

43 $10^8 \times 10^4$
10^{12}

44 $10^{12} \div 10^8$
10^4

45 $(7 \times 10^{12}) \div 10^8$
7×10^4

46 $(40 \times 10^6) \div (8 \times 10^4)$
5×10^2

47 $(4 \times 10^3) \times (6 \times 10^2)$
24×10^5

Add or subtract. Watch the signs.

48 605
+ 359
964

49 605
− 359
246

50 7005
− 2168
4837

51 7099
+ 1011
8110

52 250
145
+ 205
600

53 14
28
+ 95
137

54 368
420
+ 502
1290

55 132
407
+ 59
598

56 $(-10) + 5$ **−5** **57** $(-10) - 5$ **−15** **58** $5 - 10$ **−5** **59** $(-5) + 10$ **5**

156 · Decimals and Exponents

RETEACHING

Follow up individual tutoring or peer tutoring with exercises similar to those in the Mental Math section of this lesson. You present problems and answers to a group of students who show, by putting either thumbs up or thumbs down, whether the answer is possibly correct or whether it is obviously wrong. You can also use problems such as the following:
34×752 is about 24×10^3 (thumbs up)
and 460×978 is about 36×10^2 (thumbs down).

PRACTICE p. 43

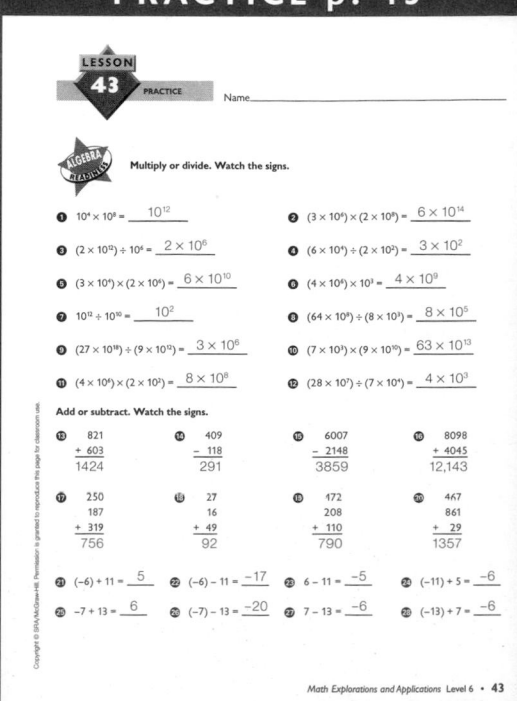

Solve these problems.

60 Sara used a calculator to add the following numbers: 345.60, 273.43, and 751.29. The answer the calculator showed was 75,748.03. What error did Sara most likely make? **She entered 75,129 instead of 751.29.**

61 When Sara asked for change for $1.00, she received 15 coins. Some were nickels and the rest were dimes. How many nickels and how many dimes did she receive? **10 nickels and 5 dimes**

62 Each year Earth travels about 2.92×10^8 miles as it revolves around the sun.
   a. About how many miles does it travel each day? (Assume that there are 365 days in one year.) **about 8×10^5 mi**

   b. Calculate the approximate average speed (in miles per hour) of Earth as it travels around the sun. **3.3×10^4 miles per hour**

63 An apartment rents for $634 per month. How much is that per year? **$7608**

64 The New City School System has 649 students in kindergarten through eighth grade. It is planning to spend $4,575,322 to operate this year.
   a. About how many students would you expect to find in each grade? **about 72 (70–75 is reasonable)**
   b. About how much money will New City spend for each student this year? **$7049.80 ($7000 and $7050 are reasonable estimates)**
   c. If ten students transfer out of the district, by how much do you think the operating expenses will change? Why? *
   d. There is a rule in New City that says a class can never have more than 25 students. About how many regular classroom teachers do you think there are in this school system? Explain your answers and tell your assumptions. **

65 A parking garage charges $3.00 for the first hour and $1.50 for each additional hour or part of an hour. How much will it cost to park there for 3 hours and 25 minutes? **$7.50**

66 Mrs. Moynihan's car gets about 24 miles to the gallon of gasoline. How many miles can she expect to go with 12.5 gallons of gasoline? **about 300**

*It will change very little because most big expenses are fixed. The school will still need the same number of teachers and staff and will still need to maintain the school building.

**27–30 teachers is reasonable. There is an average of about 72 students per grade. Each of the 9 grades will need three teachers and some may need four. Unit 2   Lesson 43 • 157

❸ Wrap-Up ⏱ 5 MINUTES

In Closing To summarize the lesson, ask students to explain what is meant by *exponential notation*.

✓ Mastery Checkpoint 13

By this time, most students should understand how to multiply and divide numbers in exponential form. You can assess this understanding by observing students during work on and discussion of problems 18–47 on page 156 or by assigning Assessment Blackline Masters page 23. The results of this assessment may be recorded on the Mastery Checkpoint Chart. Students who consistently have difficulty multiplying and dividing with exponents should be given extra help.

Assessment Criteria

Did the student . . .

✓ successfully solve the approximation problems on page 154?

✓ correctly answer at least 80% of the problems on page 156?

✓ work with a partner or group to successfully solve the word problems on pages 155 and 157?

Homework Have students figure out how long it would take to introduce themselves to everyone in the class or everyone in the school.

ENRICHMENT p. 43

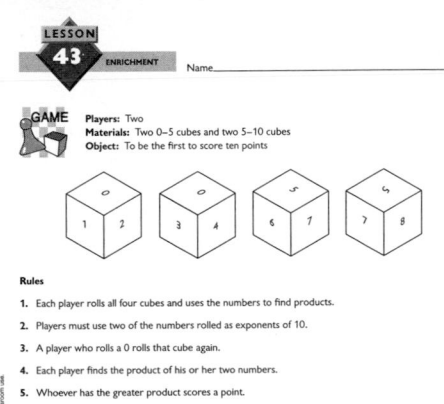

LESSON **43** ENRICHMENT   Name_____

GAME   Players: Two
Materials: Two 0–5 cubes and two 5–10 cubes
Object: To be the first to score ten points

Rules
1. Each player rolls all four cubes and uses the numbers to find products.
2. Players must use two of the numbers rolled as exponents of 10.
3. A player who rolls a 0 rolls that cube again.
4. Each player finds the product of his or her two numbers.
5. Whoever has the greater product scores a point.
6. Play the game until one player scores ten points. That player is the winner.
   Results of the game will vary.

Sample Game
- Player 1 rolls 4, 7, 9, and 10. She writes the numbers 4×10^9 and 7×10^{10}. Notice that two of the numbers must be used as exponents.
- Player 2 rolls 2, 6, 7, and 8. He writes the numbers 2×10^8 and 6×10^7.
- Both players find the products of their numbers.
- Player 1: $(4 \times 10^9) \times (7 \times 10^{10}) = 28 \times 10^{19}$
- Player 2: $(2 \times 10^8) \times (6 \times 10^7) = 12 \times 10^{15}$
- Player 1 scores one point for having the greater product.

Math Explorations and Applications Level 6 • 43

ASSESSMENT p. 23

UNIT **2**   Mastery Checkpoint 13   Multiplying and dividing with exponents
(Lesson 43)
Name_____
The student demonstrates mastery by correctly answering at least 24 of the 30 problems.

Multiply or divide.

1 $10^2 \times 10^5 = \underline{10^7}$ 　　　 **2** $(2 \times 10^3) \times (3 \times 10^2) = \underline{6 \times 10^5}$

3 $(7 \times 10^5) \times (6 \times 10^3) = \underline{42 \times 10^8}$ 　　 **4** $10^9 + 10^4 = \underline{10^5}$

5 $10^8 + 10^3 = \underline{10^5}$ 　　　 **6** $(15 \times 10^4) + (3 \times 10^2) = \underline{5 \times 10^2}$

7 $(8 \times 10^9) \times (7 \times 10^6) = \underline{56 \times 10^{15}}$ 　 **8** $(3 \times 10^3) \times (3 \times 10^3) = \underline{9 \times 10^6}$

9 $(25 \times 10^7) + (5 \times 10^3) = \underline{5 \times 10^4}$ 　 **10** $(2 \times 10^6) \times 10^3 = \underline{2 \times 10^9}$

11 $(3 \times 10^3) + 10^2 = \underline{3 \times 10^1}$ 　　 **12** $(2 \times 10^4) \times 10^2 = \underline{2 \times 10^6}$

13 $(30 \times 10^5) \times 10^3 = \underline{30 \times 10^8}$ 　 **14** $(30 \times 10^3) + 10^3 = \underline{30}$

15 $(4 \times 10^5) + 10^2 = \underline{4 \times 10^3}$ 　　 **16** $(21 \times 10^7) + (7 \times 10^2) = \underline{3 \times 10^5}$

17 $(42 \times 10^6) + (6 \times 10^3) = \underline{7 \times 10^3}$ 　 **18** $(24 \times 10^4) \times (2 \times 10^2) = \underline{48 \times 10^6}$

19 $(30 \times 10^5) \times (3 \times 10^5) = \underline{90 \times 10^{10}}$ 　 **20** $(20 \times 10^5) \times (3 \times 10^5) = \underline{60 \times 10^{10}}$

21 $(30 \times 10^3) \times (2 \times 10^2) = \underline{60 \times 10^5}$ 　 **22** $(30 \times 10^4) \times (2 \times 10^4) = \underline{15 \times 10^4}$

23 $(3 \times 10^4) \times (3 \times 10^5) = \underline{9 \times 10^9}$ 　　 **24** $(8 \times 10^9) + (4 \times 10^6) = \underline{2 \times 10^3}$

25 $(72 \times 10^{11}) + (8 \times 10^5) = \underline{9 \times 10^6}$ 　 **26** $10^9 \times 10^4 = \underline{10^{13}}$

27 $10^{11} \times 10^{10} = \underline{10^5}$ 　　　 **28** $(7 \times 10^{14}) + 10^6 = \underline{7 \times 10^8}$

29 $(50 \times 10^7) + (25 \times 10^3) = \underline{2 \times 10^4}$ 　 **30** $(30 \times 10^5) + (5 \times 10^1) = \underline{6 \times 10^4}$

Math Explorations and Applications Level 6 • 23

Student Edition pages 158–161

Interpreting Multidigit Numbers

LESSON PLANNER

Objective

▶ to provide practice in using exponents to solve problems involving multidigit numbers

Context of the Lesson This is the sixth of seven lessons on exponential notation and operations with exponents.

 **MANIPULATIVES**

calculator*

stopwatch* or clock with second hand

Program Resources

Number Cubes (0–5 and 5–10)

Practice Master 44

Enrichment Master 44

The Cruncher*

For extra practice: CD-ROM* Lesson 44

① Warm-Up

 **Problem of the Day** Present the following problem to the class: Jack and Jake are brothers. Both are older than 10 and younger than 32. The square of Jack's age is equal to the square of Jake's age with the digits reversed. How old are Jack and Jake? (either 12 and 21: 144 and 441; or 13 and 31: 169 and 961; if Jack and Jake are twins, their age could be 11: 121 or 22 : 484)

Problem-Solving Strategies Ask students who have solved the Problem of the Day to share how they solved it and any strategies they used.

MENTAL MATH Play a variation of "Cubo" (page 18) where students play a round or two in which they try to get 21 or close to it, and then use a roll of four number cubes to get, in turn, each of the numbers from 0 to 10. A copy of this game can also be found on page 9 of the Home Connections Blackline Masters.

Interpreting Multidigit Numbers

SOCIAL STUDIES CONNECTION

In 1960 the United States government had a total income of about $92,492,000,000. In that same year the government spent about $92,223,000,000. The population of the United States in 1960 was about 179,323,000 people.

◆ How does the government get income? **different kinds of taxes and fees**

◆ For what purposes does the government spend money? **running government, social services, defense, and so on**

When the government spends less money than it receives, we say it has a *surplus* for that period. When it spends more than it receives, we say it has a *deficit* for that period.

◆ In 1960 did the United States government have a surplus or a deficit? **surplus**

◆ How much was the surplus or deficit? **$269,000,000**

◆ If the surplus or deficit had been divided equally among all the people of the United States, estimate what each person's share would have been. Each person's share of the surplus or deficit is called the *per capita share*. **$1.50**

 **COOPERATIVE LEARNING** All students in a group should participate meaningfully in the work. From measuring, calculating, choosing the operation(s), recording, checking, and reporting their results to the class, each member of the group needs to play a significant role. As needed, guide groups to divide up the work so that all members are actively involved.

---

*available separately

Information about United States income, spending, and population for selected years is given in the chart below.

Use a calculator to complete the last two columns. Work out ways for doing the calculations even if your calculator can show only eight digits.

See answers in margin.

United States Income, Spending, and Population 1910–1994

Year	Income (dollars)	Spending (dollars)	Population	Surplus (+) or Deficit (−)	Per Capita Surplus (+) or Deficit (−)
1910	676,000,000	694,000,000	91,972,000	−18,000,000	−$0.19
1915	683,000,000	746,000,000	100,546,000	−63,000,000	−$0.63
1920	6,649,000,000	6,358,000,000	105,710,000	+291,000,000	+$2.75
1925	3,641,000,000	2,924,000,000	115,829,000	■	■
1930	4,058,000,000	3,320,000,000	122,775,000	■	■
1935	3,706,000,000	6,497,000,000	127,250,000	■	■
1940	6,361,000,000	9,456,000,000	131,669,000	■	■
1945	45,216,000,000	92,690,000,000	139,928,000	■	■
1950	39,485,000,000	42,597,000,000	151,325,000	■	■
1955	65,469,000,000	68,509,000,000	165,275,000	■	■
1960	92,492,000,000	92,223,000,000	179,323,000	■	■
1965	116,833,000,000	118,430,000,000	194,303,000	■	■
1970	193,743,000,000	196,588,000,000	203,302,000	■	■
1975	280,997,000,000	326,105,000,000	213,600,000	■	■
1980	520,050,000,000	579,011,000,000	226,545,805	■	■
1985	733,996,000,000	936,809,000,000	237,924,000	■	■
1990	1,031,462,000,000	1,251,850,000,000	248,709,873	■	■
1991	1,054,265,000,000	1,323,757,000,000	252,131,000	■	■
1992	1,090,453,000,000	1,380,794,000,000	255,028,000	■	■
1993	1,153,226,000,000	1,408,532,000,000	257,783,000	■	■
1994	1,257,187,000,000	1,460,557,000,000	260,341,000	■	■

Unit 2   Lesson 44   •   **159**

![Social Studies Connection] **Social Studies Connection** An interesting aspect of the figures in the chart on page 159 is population growth. Point out that between 1915 and 1975, the population more than doubled. Ask students to predict the population in the year 2035 if the trend in growth continues. (more than 400 million)

❷ Teach

Using the Student Pages This lesson focuses on government finances. In discussing this topic and in working on problems related to it, students will be exposed to very great numbers and should see that using exponential notation is a useful and efficient way to work with them.

Read page 158 with the class, stopping to discuss the questions. Be sure students understand the meaning of *per capita* share. Point out that each person in the country does not actually receive a share of the surplus or a bill for his or her share of the deficit.

COOPERATIVE LEARNING Read aloud the information at the top of page 159. Have students work in small groups, with **calculators***, to complete the last two columns of the table. Guide students to understand that to find the per capita information, they need to divide the surplus or deficit by the population. As needed, work through one or two items with the class.

Answers for last two columns of table:

Year	Surplus or Deficit	Per Capita Surplus or Deficit
1925	+$717,000,000	+$6.19
1930	+738,000,000	+6.01
1935	-2,791,000,000	-21.93
1940	-3,095,000,000	-23.51
1945	-47,474,000,000	-339.27
1950	-3,112,000,000	-20.57
1955	-3,040,000,000	18.39
1960	+269,000,000	+1.50
1965	-1,597,000,000	-8.22
1970	-2,845,000,000	-13.99
1975	-45,108,000,000	-211.18
1980	-58,961,000,000	-260.26
1985	-202,813,000,000	-852.43
1990	-220,388,000,000	-886.12
1991	-269,492,000,000	-1068.86
1992	-290,341,000,000	-1138.47
1993	-255,306,000,000	-990.39
1994	-203,370,000,000	-781.17

◆ LESSON 44 Interpreting Multidigit Numbers

Teach

Using the Student Pages Go over the top of page 160 with the class. Have students work in their groups to answer the questions. Students can use a blank **Cruncher*** spreadsheet to create a table like the one on page 159 to help them answer the questions.

For problem 6: For a family of four—$6488 share; remaining answers will vary. For a class of 25 students and 1 teacher, the share would be $42,172 and for a school of 500 students and 25 teachers the share would be $851,500.

Then have students work in their groups to solve the problems on page 161. The following information may be of use to students as they work.

For problem 9: A person's pulse rate changes with age and activity, but generally ranges from 50 to 120 beats per minute. Sixty heartbeats per minute is a reasonable figure to use in the problem, or students may find their own pulse rates by using a **stopwatch***.

For problem 10: Students can estimate the height of a stack of bills by measuring the thickness of a book, excluding the covers, and counting the number of separate pages (which will be half the total page count). Students should choose a book in which the paper quality is similar to that of a dollar bill. Estimates in the range of 100 to 130 dollars in a 1-cm stack are reasonable.

For problem 12: The approximate length of a dollar bill is 16.6 cm.

GIFTED & TALENTED **Meeting Individual Needs** Have students find out the current population of your city or town. Ask them to find out what the population was in 1915, 1920, 1925, and so on. Ask them to compare your town or city's population growth with that of the entire country. Challenge them to predict its population in the year 2078. Ask students to suggest factors that might affect the accuracy of their predictions.

◆ LESSON 44 Interpreting Multidigit Numbers

Check to be sure your answers make sense. Let's consider the year 1920 to see how you can easily check your answers.

In that year, income was about 6 billion 650 million dollars. Spending was about 6 billion 360 million dollars.

$$650 - 360 = 290$$

So the surplus should be about 290 million dollars. The answer 291 million dollars makes sense.

The surplus was about 3×10^8 dollars. The population was about 1×10^8.

$$\frac{3 \times 10^8}{1 \times 10^8} = \frac{3}{1} = 3$$

So the per capita surplus of $2.75 makes sense.

Discuss answers to these questions. You may need calculators for some of the questions.

1 In general, did the income of the United States government increase over the years shown in the chart? **yes**

2 Did spending increase? **yes**

3 Which increased more, income or spending? **spending**

4 Are there years that did not follow the general trend? **yes**

In 1960 the total deficit of the United States that had accumulated over the years was $290,862,000,000.

5 What was the per capita share of the deficit in 1960? **$1622.00**

6 What was the share of the deficit for a family of four people? For a class the size of yours? For a school the size of yours? **See comments in margin.**

In 1965 a newspaper reported that the accumulated deficit was about 323 million dollars when the real deficit was about 323 billion dollars.

7 What was the per capita share that year? **$1662.35**

8 What would it have been had the deficit really been 323 million dollars? How great a difference is that? **$1.66; $1660.69 per person**

Research: Find out what the current accumulated deficit or surplus is. Your librarian should be able to help. What is the per capita share? The share for a family of four? The share for your class? The share for your school?

Answers will depend on current deficit or surplus. Students may estimate the number of students in their school.

LOOKING AHEAD Lesson 45 involves scientific notation. If most of your students use the same type of calculator, become familiar with how it handles very great numbers and how to enter scientific notation, providing that the calculator has this feature.

Literature Connection You may find a number of applications for using exponents in *Math and Society* by Richard Gardner and Edward A. Shore. This book contains a number of interesting statistics about the world.

RETEACHING

No extra practice or reteaching is necessary at this time. You may want to assign Enrichment Master 44.

*available separately

Work in small groups of three or four. You may use a calculator. Give your best estimate of the answer. Then estimate the amount of error there is likely to be in your answer. **Answers are examples only.**

9 How many times will your heart beat in your lifetime? **Based on a pulse of 60 beats per minute over 75 years, the number of heartbeats would be $60 \times 60 \times 24 \times 365.25 \times 75 = 2,366,820,000$.**

10 Using $1 bills, how many dollars are in a stack that is 1 cm tall? **A reasonable estimate is 100 to 130 dollars in a 1-cm stack.**

11 How many dollars could be stacked in a pile that started on Earth and went to the moon? (Hint: The moon is about 384,400 kilometers from Earth. There are 1000 meters in a kilometer, and 100 centimeters in a meter.) **Based on an estimate of 115 dollars in one centimeter, a reasonable estimate would be between 3.6 trillion and 5.2 trillion.**

12 How many dollars would be needed to reach the moon if they could be placed end to end? **about 2.3 billion**

13 If you spent one dollar each minute, how many years would it take you to spend one million dollars? **about 2 years (1.9 years)**

14 If you spent one dollar each minute, how many years would it take you to spend one billion dollars? **about 1900 years**

15 If you counted 100 dollars every minute and kept counting without stopping, how many years would it take to count to one billion dollars? **about 19 years**

In your Math Journal record how you were able to solve problems in this lesson that used numbers with too many digits to display on your calculator.

---

③ Wrap-Up 5 MINUTES

In Closing Summarize the lesson by asking students to explain the value of using exponential notation when working with very great numbers. Ask them to suggest other data for which expressing figures using exponents would be very useful.

Informal Assessment Circulate around the classroom as the groups work together on the problems. Check to see that all students are participating meaningfully in the problem-solving process. Ask students to explain how they got some of their answers and how they plan to approach problems they have not yet begun. Ask them to explain in which problems exponential notation is helpful to them and in which problems it is not.

Assessment Criteria

Did the student . . .

✓ get reasonable answers to the problems?

✓ participate fully in the group activity?

✓ demonstrate understanding of the process the group used to solve problems and to check the reasonableness of the answers?

Homework Assign Practice Master 44 to provide further practice with interpreting data.

PRACTICE p. 44

ENRICHMENT p. 44

LESSON 45

Student Edition pages 162–163

Scientific Notation

LESSON PLANNER

Objectives

▶ to help students understand what scientific notation is

▶ to provide practice using scientific notation to write multidigit numbers

Context of the Lesson This lesson is the last of seven lessons on exponential notation and operations with exponents.

MANIPULATIVES **Program Resources**

calculators*   Reteaching Master

Practice Master 45

Enrichment Master 45

For extra practice:
CD-ROM* Lesson 45

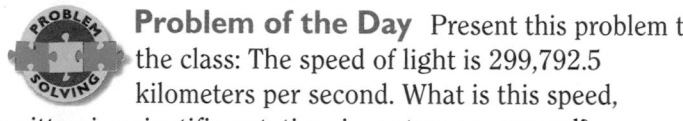

① Warf-Up ⏱

Problem of the Day Present this problem to the class: The speed of light is 299,792.5 kilometers per second. What is this speed, written in scientific notation, in meters per second?
(2.997925×10^8 meters per second)

Problem-Solving Strategies Ask students who have solved the Problem of the Day to share how they solved it and any strategies they used.

Ask students to tell how they would express each of the following using exponential form:

a. 4000 (4×10^3)   **b.** 50,000 (5×10^4)

c. 300 (3×10^2)   **d.** 80,000 (8×10^4)

② Teach

Using the Student Pages Go over the first part of page 162 and the examples with students. After students do problems 1–6 on their own, challenge them to work with a partner to figure out how to enter scientific notation on the **calculator*** if they can. Be prepared to provide assistance as needed. Tell students that the first factor is usually taken to be a number between 1 and 10.

162 Decimals and Exponents

EXPLORE

LESSON 45

Scientific Notation

You've learned the procedure for using exponents to express multidigit numbers. This procedure is often called **scientific notation**, since scientists often use multidigit numbers.

In scientific notation we place a decimal point after the first digit in a number. Then we show what power of 10 we would multiply by to move the decimal point to the "right place."

Examples:

$35 = 3.5 \times 10$ $35,897 = 3.5897 \times 10^4$

$400 = 4.00 \times 10^2 = 4 \times 10^2$ $30,000 = 3.0000 \times 10^4 = 3 \times 10^4$

Write these numbers using scientific notation.

① 2000   **②** 25,000   **③** 1,570,000
2.0×10^3 2.5×10^4 1.57×10^6

④ 26,987   **⑤** 293,000   **⑥** 10,900,000
2.6987×10^4 2.93×10^5 1.09×10^7

Scientific notation is also helpful in using a calculator. With scientific notation you can work with numbers that have a great many digits, even though most calculators show only eight-digit numbers. Use your calculator to multiply 35,897 by 42,683.

Some calculators will show an error message; others

◆ What happened? **will show 15.321916×10^8; still others will show different answers.**

Now use scientific notation and your calculator to multiply 35,897 by 42,683. We do it this way:

$(3.5897 \times 10^4) \times (4.2683 \times 10^4) = (3.5897 \times 4.2683) \times 10^8$

The answer is about 15.321916×10^8. We could now move the decimal point eight places to the right and find that the answer is about 1,532,191,600.

In doing any calculation, a calculator drops digits that don't fit, so the correct or complete answer is usually greater than the calculator display. (In this case the complete answer is 1,532,191,651.)

162 • Decimals and Exponents

Why teach it at this time?

Students have been learning about ways to express and work with very great numbers. Scientific notation is a useful application of exponents, one that allows for ease in operations with these great numbers, particularly those multidigit numbers that cannot easily be expressed as powers of 10.

RETEACHING p. 13

LESSON 45 RETEACHING

Name_____

To multiply or divide two numbers using scientific notation and a calculator, first write each number in scientific notation. Multiply or divide the number factors using the calculator. Use mental math to simplify the powers of 10.

Example 1: 23,400,000,000 × 18,590,000,000

To write a number in scientific notation, move the decimal point to the left until there is one digit to the left of the decimal point.

2 3 4 0 0 0 0 0 0 0 0
10 9 8 7 6 5 4 3 2 1

Write the number without the 0s. The number of places you move becomes your exponent. So, 23,400,000,000 = 2.34 × 10¹⁰.

Repeat.

1 8 5 9 0 0 0 0 0 0 0
10 9 8 7 6 5 4 3 2 1

18,590,000,000 = 1.859 × 10¹⁰

23,400,000,000 × 18,590,000,000 = (2.34 × 10¹⁰) × (1.859 × 10¹⁰)
= (2.34 × 1.859) × (10¹⁰ × 10¹⁰)
≈ 4.35006 × 10²⁰ To multiply numbers with exponents,
   = 4.35006 × 10²⁰   add the exponents.

Example 2: 693,000,000,000 ÷ 54,000

693,000,000,000 = 6.93 × 10¹¹   54,000 = 5.4 × 10⁴

693,000,000,000 ÷ 54,000 = (6.93 × 10¹¹) ÷ (5.4 × 10⁴)
= (6.93 ÷ 5.4) × (10¹¹ ÷ 10⁴)
= 1.283 × 10⁽¹¹⁻⁴⁾ = 1.283 × 10⁷ To divide numbers with exponents, subtract
   the exponents.

Use a calculator and scientific notation to get approximate answers.

① 539,000 × 876,000,000   _4.72164 × 10¹⁴_

② 24,790,000 × 79,000,000   _1.95841 × 10¹⁵_

③ 2,800,000 × 46,389,000,000   _1.298892 × 10¹⁷_

④ 53,900,000 ÷ 62,000   _8.693548 × 10²_

Math Explorations and Applications Level 6 • **13**

---

162 Decimals and Exponents

*available separately

Have students work in groups to do the problems on page 163, using **calculators***. Expect that scientific notation will be useful in most cases.

Note: The answers shown for page 163 are those that students will get if they use a calculator. Technically, these answers are more precise than warranted by the level of precision of the original numbers. Accept any reasonable answers.

C⦿PERATIVE LEARNING

Work in groups on these problems. Use a calculator and scientific notation. Find approximate answers to the following. Leave your answers in scientific notation.

7 $7342 \times 59{,}684$
4.38199928×10^8

8 $1440 \times 365{,}000$
5.256×10^8

9 $87{,}596 \times 4832$
4.23263872×10^8

10 $86{,}400 \times 36{,}500$
3.1536×10^9

11 $94{,}000 \times 83{,}000$
7.802×10^9

12 $200{,}792.5 \times 499.02$
1.00199473×10^8

13 How many minutes are there in a day? How many minutes are there in 1000 years if you assume each year has 365 days and ignore leap years?
1.44×10^3; 5.256×10^8

14 How many seconds are there in a day? How many seconds are there in 70 years (ignore leap years)? **8.64×10^4; 2.20752×10^9**

15 Light travels about 2.997925×10^5 km per second. Light from the sun takes about 499.02 seconds to reach Earth. About how many kilometers apart are the sun and Earth? (Note: At different times of the year, Earth is closer to or farther from the sun, so the above are average figures.)
1.496024534×10^8

We can divide numbers with many digits by using scientific notation and subtracting exponents. For example:

$536{,}498{,}327 \div 59{,}348$ is

$(5.36498327 \times 10^8) \div (5.9348 \times 10^4)$, or 0.9039871×10^4, or 9.039871×10^3, or 9039.871.

Work in groups. Use a calculator and scientific notation to get approximate answers to the following.

16 $835{,}492{,}643 \div 52{,}474$
$15{,}922.03$

17 $270{,}000{,}000 \div 500$
$540{,}000$

18 $67{,}000{,}000{,}000 \div 2{,}000{,}000$
$33{,}500$

19 $5{,}000{,}000{,}000 \div 250{,}000{,}000$
20

20 $540{,}000{,}000{,}000 \div 225{,}000{,}000$
2400

21 $490{,}000{,}000 \div 56{,}000{,}000$
8.75

22 $280{,}000{,}000 \div 3500$
$80{,}000$

23 $490{,}000{,}000 \div 56{,}000$
8750

FANTASTIC FACT

Light from Proxima Centauri, the nearest star to Earth other than the sun, takes $4\frac{1}{4}$ years to reach Earth.

Unit 2 Lesson 45 • **163**

❸ Wrap-Up

In Closing Have students brainstorm about why scientific notation would be useful for an astronomer. Tell them that the sun, the star that is closest to Earth, is 93 million miles away.

Informal Assessment Provide students with the population of a large city near you. Ask them to rewrite it using scientific notation. Then ask them to choose one of the first six problems on page 163 and explain how they used scientific notation to find the product.

Assessment Criteria

Did the student . . .

✓ demonstrate ability to write a number using scientific notation?

✓ demonstrate ability to multiply or divide two multidigit numbers using scientific notation?

Homework Have students find statistical data that are expressed using multidigit numbers, such as information on distances or prehistoric eras. They can look in the newspaper or in sources such as almanacs and encyclopedias. Ask them to record the data and then rewrite them using scientific notation.

PRACTICE p. 45

LESSON 45 PRACTICE Name_____

Use a calculator and scientific notation. Find approximate answers to the following. Leave your answers in scientific notation. Round your answers to have three nonzero digits. (For example, round 4.79263×10^7 to 4.79×10^7.)

1 $4392 \times 8756 = \underline{3.85 \times 10^7}$
2 $4{,}237{,}486 \div 9572 = \underline{4.43 \times 10^2}$

3 $89{,}070{,}486{,}872 \div 9300 = \underline{9.58 \times 10^6}$
4 $47{,}392 \times 63{,}471 = \underline{3.01 \times 10^9}$

5 $27{,}891 \times 56{,}913 = \underline{1.59 \times 10^9}$
6 $2{,}089{,}000 \div 2781 = \underline{7.51 \times 10^2}$

7 $43{,}891{,}000{,}000 \div 8912 = \underline{4.92 \times 10^6}$
8 $47{,}816 \times 29{,}387 = \underline{1.41 \times 10^9}$

9 $4591 \times 26{,}879 = \underline{1.23 \times 10^8}$
10 $2{,}081{,}470 \div 253 = \underline{8.23 \times 10^3}$

11 $40{,}789{,}000{,}000 \div 41{,}862 = \underline{9.74 \times 10^5}$
12 $75{,}096{,}000 \times 5{,}713{,}289 = \underline{4.29 \times 10^{14}}$

13 $437{,}691 \times 83{,}000{,}000 = \underline{3.63 \times 10^{13}}$
14 $7{,}124{,}000{,}000 \div 57{,}896 = \underline{1.23 \times 10^5}$

15 $79{,}751{,}000 \div 804 = \underline{9.92 \times 10^4}$
16 $27{,}000 \times 53{,}000 = \underline{1.43 \times 10^9}$

17 $412{,}819 \times 872{,}916 = \underline{3.60 \times 10^{11}}$
18 $7{,}893{,}416 \div 219 = \underline{3.60 \times 10^4}$

19 $512{,}000{,}000 \div 8769 = \underline{5.84 \times 10^4}$
20 $8979 \times 4{,}005{,}001 = \underline{3.60 \times 10^{10}}$

21 $58{,}000{,}000 \times 29{,}416 = \underline{1.71 \times 10^{12}}$
22 $8{,}297{,}418 \times 29{,}318 = \underline{2.83 \times 10^2}$

23 $12{,}000{,}800{,}000 \div 4989 = \underline{2.41 \times 10^6}$
24 $27{,}519{,}000 \times 42{,}716{,}000 = \underline{1.18 \times 10^{15}}$

Math Explorations and Applications Level 6 • 45

ENRICHMENT p. 45

LESSON 45 ENRICHMENT Name_____

If each boy in my family has three brothers and each girl has two sisters, how many children are in my family?
There are seven children in my family.

To find the answer to the riddle, shade each section that contains a number that is greater than 230,000.

9.5×10^4	2.4×10^7	4.5×10^6	8.1×10^5
4.2×10^3	3.7×10^3	2.3×10^4	6.2×10^7
6.8×10^2	9.4×10^4	3.5×10^5	2.2×10^3
	8.3×10^2	2.7×10^9	5.8×10^2	1.8×10^5
	7.1×10^6	2.2×10^5	3.9×10^4	7.2×10^2
	2.4×10^1	5.7×10^3	2.3×10^5	9.8×10^4

Math Explorations and Applications Level 6 • 45

*available separately

Unit 2 Review

Using the Student Pages Use this Unit Review as a preliminary unit test to indicate areas in which an individual student is having difficulty or in which the entire class may need help. If students do well on the Unit Review, you may wish to skip directly to the next unit. If not, you may want to spend a day or so helping students overcome their individual difficulties before they take the Unit Test.

Next to each instruction line is a list of the lessons in the unit covered in that set of problems. Students can refer to the specific lesson for additional instruction if they need help. You can also use this information to make additional assignments based on the previous lesson concepts.

Problems 1–6 If students miss more than one of these problems involving adding and subtracting decimals, check to determine the nature of the difficulty. Reteach these students using an appropriate strategy, and give them extra practice using the Unit 2 Practice. Your reteaching should focus on the need for lining up the decimal points and the fact that 0s can be written to the right of a decimal number without changing its value.

Problems 7–12 Students who miss more than one of these problems involving multiplying and dividing decimals by powers of 10 should be checked to determine the nature of the difficulty. Make sure students can determine how many places and in which direction to move the decimal point.

Problems 13–18 Students who miss more than one of these problems involving converting metric units should be checked to determine the nature of the difficulty. If the nature of the problem is not understanding the relations among the units, give extra help by having the students do actual measurements of weight, length, and volume.

Unit 2 Review

Lesson 27 Add or subtract. Watch the signs.

1 $2.34 + 5.18$ **7.52**   **2** $2.04 - 1.74$ **0.30**   **3** $29.6 + 53.8$ **83.4**

4 $51.8 - 2.34$ **49.46**   **5** $2.04 - 1.75$ **0.29**   **6** $1.07 + 6.35$ **7.42**

Lesson 29 Multiply or divide. Watch the signs.

7 0.932×100
93.2
8 $93.2 \div 10$
9.32
9 64.72×100
6472

10 $64.72 \div 100$
0.6472
11 $9.36 \div 1000$
0.00936
12 9.36×1000
9360

Lesson 29 Solve these problems. You may use the table of metric units on page 588 if necessary.

13 $33 \text{ mg} = \blacksquare \text{ g}$
0.033
14 $0.3 \text{ m} = \blacksquare \text{ cm}$
30
15 $7 \text{ L} = \blacksquare \text{ mL}$
7000

16 $750 \text{ mL} = \blacksquare \text{ L}$
0.750
17 $450 \text{ g} = \blacksquare \text{ kg}$
0.450
18 $250 \text{ m} = \blacksquare \text{ km}$
0.250

Lessons 30 and 31 Multiply.

19 22×1.23
27.06
20 2.2×12.3
27.06
21 37×0.09
3.33

22 0.37×0.09
0.0333
23 32×2.02
64.64
24 0.032×20.2
0.6464

Lessons 34 and 35 Divide.

25 $0.2\overline{)642}$ **3210**   **26** $0.07\overline{)4.963}$ **70.9**   **27** $0.12\overline{)2.448}$ **20.4**

Lessons 39 and 41 Write in standard form.

28 4×10^7
40,000,000
29 9×10^3
9000
30 5×10^6
5,000,000

Lessons 39 and 41 Write in exponential form.

31 $7,000,000$
7×10^6
32 4000
4×10^3
33 $80,000,000$
8×10^7

Lesson 42 Do the calculations and write your answers in exponential form.

34 $(9 \times 10^8) \times (8 \times 10^9)$
72×10^{17}
35 $(30 \times 10^5) \div (6 \times 10^3)$
5×10^2

36 $(3 \times 10^4) \times (3 \times 10^4)$
9×10^8
37 $(20 \times 10^7) \div (5 \times 10^3)$
4×10^4

RETEACHING

Students who have difficulty with this Unit Review should have further opportunity to review and to practice the skills before they proceed on with the next unit. For each set of problems there are specific suggestions for reteaching. These suggestions can be found in the margins.

Solve these problems.

Lessons 27, 28, 34, 36, 37, 40, and 44

38 Leote is a costume maker. She has 15 meters of fabric. She is cutting pieces 0.75 meter long to make vests for a play. How many vests will she be able to make? **20**

39 Matt usually earns $5.20 an hour. If he works on Saturday, he gets time and a half. That means he gets paid at 1.5 times the usual rate. How much does Matt earn per hour when he works on Saturday? **$7.80**

40 A stack of 100 sheets of notepaper is 1.05 centimeters thick. How thick is each sheet? **0.0105 cm (or 0.105 mm)**

41 There are about 500,000 oil wells in the United States. These oil wells produce about 3,000,000,000 barrels of oil each year. On the average, how many barrels of oil does each oil well produce in a year? **about 6000 (or 6 × 10³)**

42 Mrs. Azim's lawn is 20.2 meters wide and 30.5 meters long. She is buying fertilizer. Each bag will cover 400 square meters. How many bags does she need to buy? **2**

43 One Sunday Mr. Gartner's odometer read 64,287.3 miles. The following Sunday it read 64,542.8 miles. How far did Mr. Gartner drive during the preceding week? **255.5 miles**

44 Anna bought a carton of juice for $1.89, a loaf of bread for $1.59, and a can of soup for $0.99. How much change should she receive from a $5 bill? **53¢**

45 Kevin is making campaign signs for the student council election. He has four colors of markers and four colors of paper. How many different color combinations could he use if he uses one marker on each sign? **16**

Unit 2 Review • 165

Problems 19–24 Students who miss more than one of these problems involving multiplying decimals should be checked to determine the nature of the difficulty. Go over with students the procedure described in Lesson 30 for checking to see whether answers make sense.

Problems 25–27 Try to identify the trouble for students who miss more than one of these problems involving dividing by decimals, and reteach as necessary.

Problems 28–30 Students who miss more than one of these problems involving writing exponents in standard form should be reminded that the exponent of the 10 tells how many factors of 10 there are, and this in turn tells how many 0s must be annexed to the number.

Problems 31–33 Students who miss more than one of these problems involving writing numbers in exponential form should be reminded that the exponent of the 10 tells how many factors of 10 there are. To write a number in exponential form, we simply count the 0s, use that number as the exponent for 10, and multiply by the nonzero digits.

Problems 34–37 Students who miss more than one of these problems involving multiplying and dividing in exponential form should be reminded that these problems are done in two parts. First they should multiply or divide the "ordinary numbers," and then take care of the powers of 10 by adding exponents for multiplication or subtracting exponents for division problems.

Problems 38–45 Students who miss more than two of these word problems should be checked to see that they can read the problems with understanding. Encourage them to act out the problems or to draw pictures and to solve the problems with simpler numbers first.

Portfolio Assessment If you have not already assigned the Portfolio Assessment task provided on Assessment Blackline Masters page 87, it can be used at this time to evaluate students' ability to use decimals, exponents, and estimation skills in solving problems.

Performance Assessment The Performance Assessment Task 2 provided on Assessment Blackline Masters pages 66–67 can be used at this time to evaluate students' proficiency with decimals and exponents. You may want to administer this assessment with individual students or in small groups.

Unit Project If you have not already assigned the "Planning a Trip" project on pages 172 and 173, you may wish to do so at this time. This project is a good opportunity for students to apply the concepts of estimation and planning strategies to real-world problem solving.

PRACTICE p. 46

LESSON 46 PRACTICE Name_____

Add or subtract. Watch the signs.

| ❶ 7.9
 + 8.6
 16.5 | ❷ 16.3
 − 4.9
 11.4 | ❸ 10.0
 − 7.4
 2.6 | ❹ 7.09
 + 2.1
 9.19 |

Multiply or divide. Watch the signs.

❺ 14.3 ÷ 100 = __0.143__   ❻ 453 ÷ 10,000 = __0.0453__
❼ 526 × 10 = __5260__   ❽ 2 × 100 = __200__

Change each measurement to the indicated unit. You may use the table of metric units on page 588 in your book if necessary.

❾ 550 mg = __0.55__ g   ❿ 1.3 m = __130__ cm
⓫ 1.5 L = __1500__ mL   ⓬ 8000 m = __8__ km

Write in standard form.

⓭ 3 × 10⁴ __30,000__   ⓮ 5 × 10² __500__   ⓯ 7 × 10⁵ __700,000__

Write in exponential form.

⓰ 400,000,000 __4 × 10⁸__   ⓱ 50,000 __5 × 10⁴__   ⓲ 20 __2 × 10¹__

Solve these problems.

⓳ Sandi baby-sits on the weekend. If she charged $5.50 per hour and worked 6.5 hours, how much money did she earn? __$35.75__

⓴ Robert has to help with the chores around the house to earn his allowance. He gets $15 a week. How many weeks will it take him to earn $40.50? __2.7 weeks = 3 weeks__

㉑ Alicia plays bass guitar. Her lessons cost $20.50 each week. How much will one year of lessons cost? __$1066__

46 • Math Explorations and Applications Level 6

ENRICHMENT p. 46

LESSON 46 ENRICHMENT Name_____

Solve this puzzle. Use one square for the decimal point in your answers.

Across
1. 15.86 + 16.71
4. 2.3 × 4.1
7. number of inches in 1 yard + 1 inch
9. 31.2 − 7.7
10. 636 ÷ number of millimeters in a centimeter
11. 2.35 + 6.162
12. 4.2 − 2.3
13. 7.1 × 7
14. number of eggs in a dozen ÷ 10
15. 3.46 + 5.29
17. 25 − 4.47
19. 3.4 × 6.5

Down
1. 14 × 2.4
2. 0.3 × number of degrees in a right angle
3. 6.318 ÷ 1.2
4. 13.4 − 3.82
5. 1.37 + 2.915
6. 3.457 × number of centiliters in a liter
8. 5.229 − 3.8
16. 217.8 ÷ number of feet in a yard
18. 70 ÷ number of years in a century

46 • Math Explorations and Applications Level 6

LESSON 47 — Unit 2 Practice

Student Edition pages 166–169

Using the Student Pages The purpose of these pages is to provide additional practice for those students who demonstrated a need for it on the Unit Review. You may wish to assign only the specific exercises in this Unit Practice in which students need further reinforcement. Each instruction line gives the lessons in the unit it covers so that you or students can refer to the specific lesson for additional review and instruction.

Students who do not require additional practice on specific concepts may enjoy playing any of the games you have played so far, such as the "Make 25" game on page 127, which involves multiplying decimals and approximating. These students may also help by practicing flashcard drills and playing appropriate games with students who need remedial practice or by actually teaching certain procedures to other students.

You may want to use the Cumulative Review on page 562 after this lesson.

LESSON 47 — Unit 2 Practice

Lesson 27

Add or subtract. Watch the signs.

1. 2.5 + 1.5 **4.0** 2. 2.5 − 1.5 **1.0** 3. 4.0 − 1.5 **2.5**
4. 17.3 + 4.6 **21.9** 5. 1.73 + 0.46 **2.19** 6. 6.21 − 1.04 **5.17**
7. 3.05 − 1.7 **1.35** 8. 1.05 + 0.05 **1.10** 9. 4.75 + 3.25 **8.00**
10. 9 − 3.7 **5.3** 11. 9.6 − 3.85 **5.75** 12. 8 − 0.5 **7.5**
13. 8 + 0.5 **8.5** 14. 2.05 + 6.5 **8.55** 15. 10.0 − 7.5 **2.5**

Lesson 29

Multiply or divide. Watch the signs.

16. 18.3 × 10 **183** 17. 18.3 ÷ 10 **1.83** 18. 1.83 × 1000 **1830**
19. 183 ÷ 1000 **0.183** 20. 18.3 × 100 **1830** 21. 3.04 ÷ 10 **0.304**
22. 30.4 × 10 **304** 23. 30.4 ÷ 1000 24. 0.304 ÷ 10 **0.0304**
25. 0.304 × 100 **30.4** 26. 32.97 ÷ 100 27. 329.7 ÷ 10,000 **0.03297**
28. 3.297 × 100 **329.7** 29. 3.297 × 10,000 **32,970** 30. 329.7 ÷ 100 **3.297**

Lesson 29

Solve these problems. You may use the table of metric units on page 588 if necessary.

31. 600 mg = ■ g **0.6** 32. 36 cm = ■ m **0.36** 33. 50 mL = ■ L **0.050**
34. 2 g = ■ mg **2000** 35. 0.5 m = ■ cm **50** 36. 2 L = ■ mL **2000**
37. 3.5 kg = ■ g **3500** 38. 500 m = ■ km **0.5** 39. 1.2 L = ■ mL **1200**
40. 5000 mg = ■ g **5** 41. 50 cm = ■ m **0.50** 42. 50 dm = ■ m **5**
43. 50 m = ■ km **0.05** 44. 50 cm = ■ dm **5** 45. 50 km = ■ m **50,000**

Lessons 30 and 31

Multiply.

46. 2.34 × 518 **1212.12** 47. 2.34 × 5.18 **12.1212** 48. 23.4 × 51.8 **1212.12**
49. 1.2 × 12 **14.4** 50. 1.2 × 1.2 **1.44** 51. 55 × 0.22 **12.10**
52. 55 × 0.222 **12.21** 53. 5.5 × 0.22 **1.210** 54. 5.5 × 0.222 **1.2210**
55. 5.5 × 0.2222 56. 6.35 × 1.07 57. 635 × 10.7 **6794.5**
58. 6.35 × 10.7 **67.945** 59. 6.3 × 11 **69.3** 60. 6.3 × 0.11 **0.693**

23. **0.0304**, 26. **0.3297**, 55. **1.2221**, 56. **6.7945**

166 • Decimals and Exponents

Lessons 34 and 35

Divide.

61. $1.6\overline{)0.48}$ → **0.3**
62. $0.33\overline{)1.089}$ → **3.3**
63. $0.33\overline{)184.8}$ → **560.0**
64. $0.7\overline{)5.6}$ → **8.0**
65. $2.1\overline{)9.45}$ → **4.5**
66. $5.5\overline{)3.355}$ → **0.61**
67. $0.24\overline{)4.8}$ → **20.0**
68. $0.11\overline{)63.8}$ → **580.0**
69. $3.2\overline{)1.408}$ → **0.44**
70. $0.12\overline{)72}$ → **600.0**
71. $0.33\overline{)1.023}$ → **3.1**
72. $0.66\overline{)5.082}$ → **7.7**
73. $0.09\overline{)8.19}$ → **91.0**
74. $0.21\overline{)0.441}$ → **2.1**
75. $2.2\overline{)12.10}$ → **5.5**

Lessons 39 and 41

Write each in standard form.

76. 7×10^2 **700**
77. 10^3 **1000**
78. 2×10^1 **20**

79. 7×10^3 **7000**
80. 6×10^4 **60,000**
81. 5×10^3 **5000**

82. 8×10^5 **800,000**
83. 3×10^6 **3,000,000**
84. 8×10^2 **800**

85. 4×10^8 **400,000,000**
86. 8×10^1 **80**
87. 3×10^3 **3000**

Lessons 39 and 41

Write each in exponential form.

88. 5000 5×10^3
89. 3,000,000 3×10^6
90. 1300 13×10^2

91. 2,000,000 2×10^6
92. 16,000 16×10^3
93. 400,000 4×10^5

94. 10,000 1×10^4
95. 45,000,000 45×10^6
96. 20,000 2×10^4

97. 600 6×10^2
98. 2,000,000,000 2×10^9
99. 7,000,000 7×10^6

Lesson 42

Do the following calculations. Write your answers using exponents.

100. $10^3 \times 10^5$ → 10^8
101. $10^8 \div 10^3$ → 10^5
102. $(5 \times 10^4) \times (4 \times 10^3)$ → 20×10^7 or 2×10^8
103. $(5 \times 10^4) \times (7 \times 10^3)$ → 35×10^7
104. $(12 \times 10^4) \div (3 \times 10^2)$ → 4×10^2
105. $(3 \times 10^3) \times (1 \times 10^9)$ → 12×10^{12}
106. $(40 \times 10^4) \div (8 \times 10^3)$ → 5×10^1
107. $(4 \times 10^3) \div (8 \times 10^3)$ → 0.5×10^2 or 5×10^1
108. $(3 \times 10^4) \div (5 \times 10^2)$ → 0.6×10^2 or 6×10^1
109. $(24 \times 10^3) \div (6 \times 10^2)$ → 4×10^1
110. $(24 \times 10^6) \div (8 \times 10^3)$ → 3×10^3
111. $(6 \times 10^6) \times (5 \times 10^5)$ → 30×10^{11} or 3×10^{12}

Unit 2 Practice • **167**

Technology Connection You may want to refer students to the video *The Wonderful Problems of Fizz and Martina: Volume 3, Fizz & Martina Do Hollywood* from Tom Snyder Productions (VHS, for grades 3–6) for further practice with averaging, unit conversions, and graphing.

◆ **LESSON 47** Unit 2 Practice

◆ **LESSON 47** Unit 2 Practice

Lessons
27–29, 36,
37, and 40

Solve these problems.

112 Jing-wei's total bill at the grocery store was $14.32. She gave the clerk a
$20 bill. What was her change? **$5.68**

113 Ray bought an old encyclopedia at an auction for $7.75. He gave the seller
a $10 bill. What was his change? **$2.25**

114 The price of Elena's new desk was $148.98. The tax was $8.94. What
was the total cost? **$157.92**

115 The total cost of Elsie's new computer was $910.54. The price tag said
$859.00. How much tax did Elsie pay? **$51.54**

116 A stack of 100 sheets of paper has a thickness of 1.2 centimeters. How
thick is each sheet? **0.012 cm (or 0.12 mm)**

117 One hundred paper clips weigh about 55 grams. About how much does
one paper clip weigh? **about 0.55 g**

118 Leonard weighed ten 0–5 cubes. They weighed 49 grams. He said that
each one weighed 49 centigrams. Was he right? **no**

119 Patricia is choosing an outfit to wear to school. She is considering five
sweaters and three skirts, all of which match each other. How many
different outfits could she make from these clothes? **15**

120 Sonia ran 2200 meters.
  a. How many kilometers was that? **2.2**
  b. How many millimeters was that? **2,200,000**

121 Mr. Jones has five liters of cider. He is going to use glasses that hold about
450 milliliters. Does he have enough cider to serve eight people one glass
of cider each? **yes**

122 Tamara had 750 centimeters of model railroad track before her birthday.
She got another 250 centimeters of track for her birthday. How much
track does she have now? **1000 cm (or 10 m)**

123 Postcards cost $0.27 each, including tax. How many postcards can Gary
buy if he has $2.50? **9**

168 • Decimals and Exponents

RETEACHING

Students who have difficulty with this
Unit Practice should have further
opportunity to review and to practice
the skills before they proceed on with
the next unit. Beside each set of
problems is a reference to the lesson or
lessons from which the problems were
taken. You may want to review the
individual lessons with students who are
having difficulty with them.

Lessons 31, 34–36

Solve these problems.

124 Dennis bought a ham for $17.71. The ham weighed 2.3 kilograms. What was the price per kilogram? **$7.70**

125 Enrique will make eight birdhouses. It takes 0.75 meter of lumber for each birdhouse. How many meters of lumber does Enrique need to buy? **6**

126 Valerie plans to make ten loaves of bread. Each loaf requires 0.55 kilogram of flour. How many 2.0-kilogram bags of flour does Valerie need to buy? **3**

127 Mr. and Mrs. Newman want to buy carpet for their family room. The room is 5.5 meters long and 4.0 meters wide. The carpet they like is 4.0 meters wide and costs $26.50 per running meter. How much will it cost them to buy that carpet for the family room? **$145.75**

128 Marco and some friends are going to make aprons from 20 meters of fabric. Each apron requires 1.5 meters of fabric. How many aprons can they make? **13**

129 Jeff wants to make curtains for the four windows in his room. He needs 2.15 meters of fabric for each curtain. How many meters of fabric does he need to buy? (Remember: one window needs two curtains.) **17.2**

130 Jenna earns $5.75 an hour at her part-time job. Last week she worked 15 hours. How much did she earn? **$86.25**

131 The total amount of money paid for tickets to a circus was $62,155. The cost of one ticket was $15.50. How many people bought tickets to the circus? **4010**

132 One concession stand at the circus was selling popcorn for $2.25 per tub. The stand sold 247 tubs of popcorn, its only product. How much money did the stand take in? **$555.75**

Use the Cumulative Review on page 562 after this lesson.

Use the Cumulative Review on page 562 after this lesson.

Unit 2 Practice • **169**

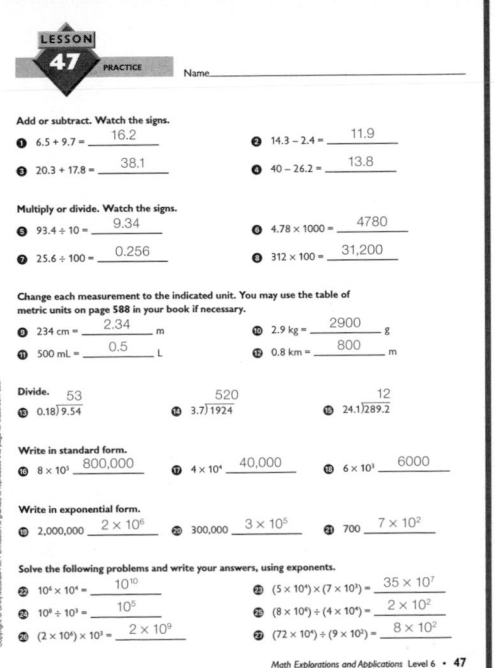

PRACTICE p. 47

LESSON 47 PRACTICE Name_____

Add or subtract. Watch the signs.

1 6.5 + 9.7 = ___16.2___ **2** 14.3 − 2.4 = ___11.9___

3 20.3 + 17.8 = ___38.1___ **4** 40 − 26.2 = ___13.8___

Multiply or divide. Watch the signs.

5 93.4 ÷ 10 = ___9.34___ **6** 4.78 × 1000 = ___4780___

7 25.6 ÷ 100 = ___0.256___ **8** 312 × 100 = ___31,200___

Change each measurement to the indicated unit. You may use the table of metric units on page 588 in your book if necessary.

9 234 cm = ___2.34___ m **10** 2.9 kg = ___2900___ g

11 500 mL = ___0.5___ L **12** 0.8 km = ___800___ m

Divide.

13 0.18)9.54 ___53___ **14** 3.7)1924 ___520___ **15** 24.1)289.2 ___12___

Write in standard form.

16 8 × 10⁵ = ___800,000___ **17** 4 × 10⁴ = ___40,000___ **18** 6 × 10³ = ___6000___

Write in exponential form.

19 2,000,000 ___2×10^6___ **20** 300,000 ___3×10^5___ **21** 700 ___7×10^2___

Solve the following problems and write your answers, using exponents.

22 10⁶ × 10⁴ = ___10^{10}___ **23** (5 × 10⁴) × (7 × 10³) = ___35×10^7___

24 10⁸ ÷ 10³ = ___10^5___ **25** (8 × 10⁴) ÷ (4 × 10²) = ___2×10^2___

26 (2 × 10⁶) × 10³ = ___2×10^9___ **27** (72 × 10⁴) ÷ (9 × 10²) = ___8×10^2___

Math Explorations and Applications Level 6 • 47

ENRICHMENT p. 47

LESSON 47 ENRICHMENT Name_____

In each of the following multiplication and division problems, the decimal points were omitted. You are given the answer to each problem. List all possible ways in which the decimal points could have been placed in the original numbers. (Hint: No original number had any 0s to the right of the decimal point.)

Problem	Answer	Possible original numbers:
1 324 × 56	18.144	32.4 × 0.56; 3.24 × 5.6; 0.324 × 56
2 57 × 148	4.36	57 × 1.48; 5.7 × 14.8; 0.57 × 148
3 3744 ÷ 16	2.34	37.44 ÷ 16; 3.744 ÷ 1.6; 0.3744 ÷ 0.16
4 147 ÷ 35	4.2	147 ÷ 35; 14.7 ÷ 3.5; 1.47 ÷ 0.35
5 22 × (35 × 6)	46.2	22 × (0.35 × 6); 2.2 × (3.5 × 6); 2.2 × (35 × 0.6); 0.22 × (35 × 6)

How many ways could the decimal points be placed in the problems below?

Problem	Answer	
6 1432 × (112 + 13)	179	___3___
7 (1250 ÷ 50) − 75	242.5	___2___
8 (111 × 46) − 1301	38.05	___3___
9 (573 + 27) ÷ (702 − 42)	212.77	___2___
10 (376 × 255) + (14 × 82)	1073.6	___6___

Math Explorations and Applications Level 6 • 47

Unit 2 Practice **169**

Using the Student Pages The Unit Test on Student Edition pages 170 and 171 provides an opportunity to formally evaluate your students' proficiency with concepts developed in this unit. It is similar in content and format to the Unit Review. Students who did well on the Unit Review may not need to take this test. Students who did not do well on the Unit Review should be provided with additional practice opportunities, such as the Unit Practice pages, before taking the Unit Test. As an alternative, you may wish to have these students take the Unit Test on Assessment Blackline Masters pages 24–25 or the Unit Test in standardized format, provided on Assessment Blackline Masters pages 101–107.

ASSESSMENT

UNIT
2

Unit Test

Add or subtract. Watch the signs.

1 $3.45 + 23.8$ **27.25**   **2** $7.09 - 3.24$ **3.85**   **3** $7.09 - 3.25$ **3.84**

4 $23.8 - 3.45$ **20.35**   **5** $31.7 + 42.8$ **74.5**   **6** $2.08 + 7.21$ **9.29**

Multiply or divide. Watch the signs.

7 0.679×10
6.79

8 $6.79 \div 100$
0.0679

9 34.92×1000
34,920

10 $34.92 \div 1000$
0.03492

11 $88.6 \div 100$
0.886

12 88.6×100
8860

Solve these problems. You may use the table of metric units on page 588 if necessary.

13 $123 \text{ mg} = \blacksquare \text{ g}$
0.123

14 $0.7 \text{ m} = \blacksquare \text{ cm}$
70

15 $9 \text{ L} = \blacksquare \text{ mL}$
9000

16 $350 \text{ mL} = \blacksquare \text{ L}$
0.350

17 $335 \text{ g} = \blacksquare \text{ kg}$
0.335

18 $150 \text{ m} = \blacksquare \text{ km}$
0.150

Multiply.

19 33×1.71
56.43

20 3.3×17.1
56.43

21 43×0.03
1.29

22 4.3×0.003
0.0129

23 0.042×30.1
1.2642

24 0.042×301
12.642

Divide.

25 $0.03\overline{)696}$ **23,200**   **26** $0.8\overline{)48.64}$ **60.8**   **27** $0.15\overline{)0.3075}$ **2.05**   **28** $0.19\overline{)6.27}$ **33**

Write in standard form.

29 10^6
1,000,000

30 6×10^4
60,000

31 3×10^5
300,000

32 5×10^3
5000

Write in exponential form.

33 500
5×10^2

34 6000
6×10^3

35 $800,000$
8×10^5

36 $90,000$
9×10^4

Write answers in exponential form.

37 $(8 \times 10^8) \times (3 \times 10^3)$
24×10^{11}

38 $(2 \times 10^5) \times (2 \times 10^5)$
4×10^{10}

39 $(6 \times 10^4) \div (2 \times 10^3)$
3×10^1

40 $(28 \times 10^3) \div (7 \times 10^3)$
4×10^0

170 • Decimals and Exponents

Solve these problems.

41 At the beginning of the day the odometer on the schoolbus showed 5016.3 kilometers. At the end of the day the odometer showed 5255.9 kilometers. How many kilometers did the bus go that day? **239.6**

42 Mr. Hughes has a 60-meter length of rope. He wants to cut it into pieces that are 3.5 meters long. How many 3.5-meter pieces can he make? **17**

43 Mrs. Rosen earns $10.40 an hour. How much does she earn for working eight hours? **$83.20**

44 A stack of 1000 sheets of paper is 11.0 centimeters thick. How thick is each sheet? **0.011 cm (or 0.11 mm)**

45 Shelly is buying lunch at school. She could get cheese, pepperoni, or mushroom pizza, and milk, orange juice, or apple juice. How many different combinations of pizza and drink could she get? **9**

46 Diego is training for a race. He knows the end of his street is about 150 meters from his house. If he runs to the end of his street and back twice a day for a week, how many meters will he have run? **4200**

47 If Diego runs 150 meters from his house to the end of his street and then back twice a day for a week, how many kilometers will he have run? **4.2**

48 Sandra bought a necklace that was on sale for $21.99. She paid $23.31. How much tax did she pay? **$1.32**

49 The Environmental Club was selling buttons for 75¢ each. They raised $82.50. How many buttons did they sell? **110**

50 Mr. Jackson's lawn is 15.3 meters wide and 24.2 meters long. He is buying grass seed. Each bag covers 400 square meters. How many bags does he need? **1**

Unit 2 Test • **171**

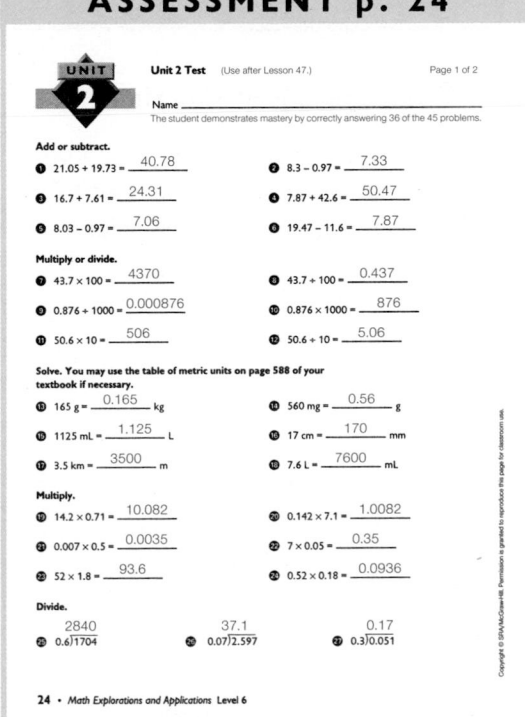

PRESENTING THE PROJECT

Project Objectives

▶ to learn planning strategies for a reasonably complicated project

▶ to learn to make assumptions to simplify planning

▶ to gain experience approximating costs for a reasonably complicated budget

Allow students to work in cooperative groups to read page 172 and to discuss the problems on page 173. Groups will need to make assumptions about the distance to be traveled, the meals to be eaten, and so on.

A reasonable estimate for costs might be $1200 to have the bus for three days, $170 for 200 excess miles (assuming the round-trip is 800 miles), $500 for hotel rooms (eight rooms for students and two rooms for adults), and $1518 for meals (33 dinners on Friday and 33 breakfasts, lunches, and dinners on Saturday and Sunday). This totals $3388, or about $117 for each of the 29 students.

Students can use the **Cruncher*** spreadsheet project *Plan a Trip* to help them calculate costs.

Consider having each student do some preliminary planning for a class trip and write a proposal that is to be judged in some predetermined manner. For example, you might have $500 budgeted for a trip. The trip must have educational value and must include the entire class. Proposals must include a statement telling the educational value of the trip and a preliminary budget.

Planning a Trip

The 15 boys and the 14 girls in the sixth grade class at Washington Street School were invited to attend the opening of a museum in our nation's capital, Washington, D.C.

Their community was an eight-hour drive from Washington. The museum opening was scheduled for Saturday morning at 9 A.M. Although the ceremony was expected to be over by noon, they wanted to spend the rest of Saturday visiting the White House, the Capitol, and other points of interest. They had to return home by 8 P.M. on Sunday.

Since they had to pay their own way, they investigated the cost of the trip. Then they had to decide how to get the needed money. Here's what they found.

A charter bus costs $400 per day, including 200 free miles. Each additional mile costs 85 cents.

A comfortable hotel, walking distance from the museum, was willing to give the class a special room rate of $50.00 per night. The rooms could hold four students or two adults comfortably.

The cost for meals was estimated to be $4.00 for breakfast, $7.00 for lunch, and $8.00 for dinner.

Besides the 29 children, their teacher, Ms. Jones, and three additional teacher's aides would make the trip.

172 • Decimals and Exponents

Why teach it at this time?

These pages provide an ongoing project that provides real applications for the mathematics covered in this unit.

The children decided that they would raise enough money to pay for transportation, room, and food for each child, for the teacher, and for the three aides. Other costs, such as souvenirs and snacks, would be paid by each individual person.

◆ Work in groups to estimate how much money needs to be raised.
 * See answer below.

◆ How much is the cost for each student? **about $117**

◆ If one boy in the class cannot make the trip, will the trip cost less? How much less? Will the cost per student be more or less? **yes; $46 (for meals); slightly more, since the transportation and hotel costs will remain unchanged and be divided among fewer people**

The class decided that it needed to raise $3400 for the trip.

◆ What is a fair way to raise money? **Possible suggestions are a bake sale, a raffle, a fair, car wash, odd jobs, and so on.**

Plan a trip for your class. Find out how much the trip would cost and develop plans to raise the needed money.

* Estimates will vary considerably because of different assumptions made by each group. See margin. Unit 2 Wrap-Up • **173**

What Is a Math Project? If this is the first time you have used math projects in your classroom, you may want to refer to pages 98–99 in this Teacher's Guide for more detailed information about effectively implementing and assessing projects.

Homework Many students may need to do some of the planning for the class trip at home, making phone calls, visiting prospective trip destinations, or writing to museums for information, and so on.

Wrapping Up the Project If the class actually takes a trip, students who planned it might make a final report, showing how actual expenses compared with the budgeted expenses.

Assessing the Project Written proposals can be assessed for good organization of ideas and for organization of the data in the budget. Do students present a budget in an organized table, or do they provide incomplete information in an unorganized manner?

SCIENCE CONNECTION **Science, Math & YOU** *Circling the Sun* is one of four units in a program published by SRA that provides a variety of hands-on projects that integrate real-world math and science. These projects can be used with small groups or with individual students. The four units in *Science, Math & YOU* are *Weather Counts, Life Adds Up, Motion Measures,* and *Circling the Sun.* Use projects from *Circling the Sun* with this unit to provide students with further practice in interpreting data.

COOPERATIVE LEARNING **Minds on Math** SRA's *Minds on Math* is a series of units covering Problem Solving, Data Collection, Number Sense, Measurement, Money, and Geometry and Spatial Relations. Each unit provides a series of open-ended projects for individual or small groups. These projects develop problem-solving and critical-thinking skills, utilize real-world materials, emphasize language, and integrate cross-curricular connections. Use projects from *Measuring Matters* to examine everyday experience involving measurements.

UNIT 3

Percents and Number Theory

REAL-LIFE APPLICATIONS

OVERVIEW

This unit begins with a review of the meaning of percent. Students learn to find a percent of a number, to use the percent key on a calculator, and to apply percents to situations that involve discounts, simple interest, and compound interest. Then students learn some divisibility rules and how to use those rules to check computations. Students are also introduced to prime and composite numbers.

Integrated Topics in This Unit Include:

♦ **reviewing the meaning of percent**

♦ **finding discounts**

♦ **finding percent using a calculator**

♦ **finding sales tax and discounts**

♦ **calculating interest**

♦ **applying percent**

♦ **using divisibility rules**

♦ **finding factors**

♦ **identifying prime and composite numbers**

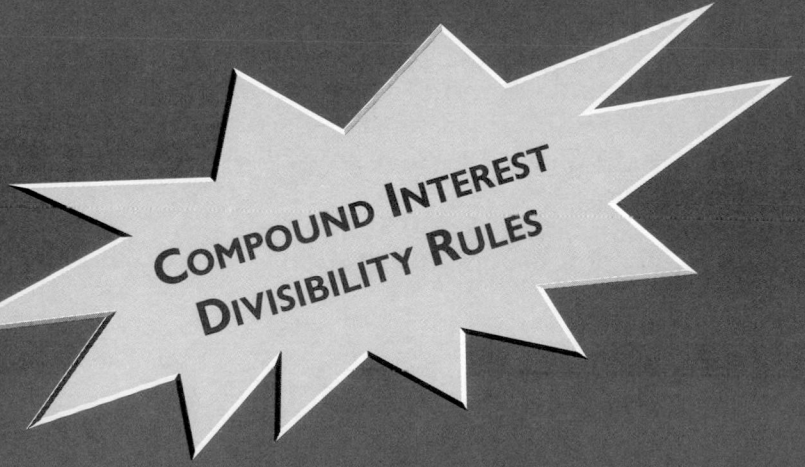

COMPOUND INTEREST
DIVISIBILITY RULES

" *Understanding multiple representations for numbers is a crucial precursor to solving many of the problems students encounter. Toward this end, students can represent fractions, decimals, and percents in a variety of meaningful situations, thereby learning to move flexibly among concrete, pictorial, and abstract representations.* "

—*NCTM Curriculum and Evaluation Standards for School Mathematics*

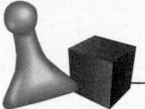

GAMES

Motivating Mixed Practice

Games provide **basic math skills** practice in cooperative groups. Playing the games also develops **mathematical reasoning.**

Tips	Lesson 48	page 178
5% Tax Game Mat	Lesson 48	page 178
Harder 5% Tax Game Mat	Lesson 48	page 178
$50 Price	Lesson 50	page 184
Discount Game Mat	Lesson 50	page 184
Harder Discount Game Mat	Lesson 50	page 184
Tiling	Lesson 59	page 216
Find the Treasure Game Mat	Lesson 60	page 220
Harder Find the Treasure Game Mat	Lesson 60	page 220

THINKING STORY

Integrated Problem Solving

Thinking Stories provide opportunities for students to work in **cooperative groups** and develop **logical reasoning** while they integrate **reading skills** with mathematics.

Competition

Part 1	Lesson 51	pages 188–189
Part 2	Lesson 56	pages 206–207
Part 3	Lesson 60	pages 220–221
Part 4	Lesson 61	pages 224–225

Story Summary "Competition" focuses on problems a business contends with when faced with competition. Continuing the saga of Mr. Muddle's T-shirt shop, the story examines Mr. Muddle's attempts to remain profitable after another T-shirt shop opens next door. Students will learn to evaluate these attempts, including his holding a discount sale, advertising his shop, and increasing business hours. Using arithmetic and percentage skills, students will calculate and compare the overhead costs and net profits of both T-shirt shops. In addition, students will be introduced to business tactics such as "buying out" a competitor.

PROJECT

Making Connections

The Unit Project makes real-world connections. Students work in **cooperative groups** to solve problems and to communicate their findings.

The project presented in the Unit Wrap-Up asks students to research information on savings accounts from neighborhood banks. The students should gather information on interest rates paid, any fees charged, and any available programs set up for young investors. Students can work on this project during their free time throughout the unit.

LESSON	PACING	OBJECTIVES	FEATURE	RESOURCES	NCTM STANDARD
48 Percents............ 176–179	1 day	to review finding the percent of a number	Game	Reteaching Master Practice Master 48 Enrichment Master 48	5, 7
49 Computing Percent Discounts 180–181	1 day	to review and practice calculating percent discounts		Reteaching Master Practice Master 49 Enrichment Master 49	5, 7
50 Percents on a Calculator............ 182–185	2 days	to provide practice in solving percent problems	Game	Reteaching Strategy Practice Master 50 Enrichment Master 50	1, 2, 3, 4, 5, 7
51 Sales Tax and Discounts 186–189	1 day	✓ to practice estimating answers to percent problems; to assess students' participation in Thinking Story discussions	Thinking Story	Reteaching Strategy Practice Master 51 Enrichment Master 51 Assessment Master	1, 2, 3, 4, 5, 7
52 Calculating Interest .. 190–191	1 day	to practice calculating interest		Reteaching Strategy Practice Master 52 Enrichment Master 52	2, 4, 5, 7
53 Compound Interest.. 192–195	1 day	to show how to find the value of interest plus principal		Reteaching Master Practice Master 53 Enrichment Master 53	2, 4, 5, 7
54 Reversing Percent Problems............ 196–199	1 day	to show how to solve problems that involve "undoing" the processes used in the percent problems		Reteaching Master Practice Master 54 Enrichment Master 54	1, 2, 3, 4, 5, 7
Mid-Unit Review..... 200–201				Assessment Master	
55 Applying Percents ... 202–203	1 day	✓ to evaluate students' proficiency in understanding and using percents		Reteaching Strategy Practice Master 55 Enrichment Master 55 Assessment Master	5, 7
56 Keeping Sharp 204–207	1 day	to practice computation and mental arithmetic	Thinking Story	Reteaching Strategy Practice Master 56 Enrichment Master 56	1, 2, 3, 4, 7, 9
57 Multiples of 9 208–209	1 day	to show how to check to see if a number is divisible by 9	ACT IT OUT	Reteaching Strategy Practice Master 57 Enrichment Master 57	6, 7
58 Finding Divisibility Rules 210–213	1 day	to develop divisibility rules for 2, 3, 4, 5, 6, 8, 9, and 10		Reteaching Strategy Practice Master 58 Enrichment Master 58	6, 7
59 Using Divisibility Rules 214–217	1 day	to provide realistic applications of divisibility rules	Game	Reteaching Strategy Practice Master 59 Enrichment Master 59	2, 4, 6
60 Factors 218–221	1 day	to review finding factors of numbers	Thinking Story Game	Reteaching Strategy Practice Master 60 Enrichment Master 60	1, 2, 3, 4, 6
61 Prime and Composite Numbers............ 222–225	1 day	to review the meaning of *prime number* and *composite number*	Thinking Story	Reteaching Master Practice Master 61 Enrichment Master 61	1, 2, 3, 4, 6

LESSON	PACING	OBJECTIVES	FEATURE	RESOURCES	NCTM STANDARD
62 **Checking Products** . . **226–227**	1 day	to learn a method for checking multiplication		Reteaching Strategy Practice Master 62 Enrichment Master 62	7
63 **Unit 3 Review** **228–229**		to review percents and number theory		Practice Master 63 Enrichment Master 63	
64 **Unit 3 Practice** **230–231**		to practice with percents and number theory		Practice Master 64 Enrichment Master 64	
Unit 3 Test **232–233**		to review percents and number theory		Assessment Masters	
Unit 3 Wrap-Up **234–235**			**Project**		

UNIT CONNECTIONS

INTERVENTION STRATEGIES

In this Teacher's Guide there will be specific strategies suggested for students with individual needs—ESL, Gifted and Talented, Special Needs, Learning Styles, and At Risk. These strategies will be given at the point of use. Here are the icons to look for and the types of strategies that will accompany them:

English as a Second Language
These strategies, designed for students who do not fluently speak the English language, will suggest meaningful ways to present the lesson concepts and vocabulary.

Gifted and Talented
Strategies to enrich and extend the lesson will offer further challenges to students who have easily mastered the concepts already presented.

Special Needs
Students who are physically challenged or who have learning disabilities may require alternative ways to complete activities, record answers, use manipulatives, and so on. The strategies labeled with this icon will offer appropriate methods of teaching lesson concepts to these students.

Learning Styles
Each student has his or her individual approach to learning. The strategies labeled with this icon suggest ways to present lesson concepts so that various learning modalities—such as tactile/kinesthetic, visual, and auditory—can be addressed.

At Risk
These strategies highlight the relevancy of the skills presented, making the connection between school and real life. They are directed toward students who appear to be at risk of dropping out of school before graduation.

TECHNOLOGY CONNECTIONS

The following materials, designed to reinforce and extend lesson concepts, will be referred to throughout this Teacher's Guide. It might be helpful to order the software, videos and laser discs or check them out of the school media center or local community library.

Look for this **Technology Connection** *icon*.

- *Core Concepts in Math: Mastering Decimals and Percents*, from BFA/Systems Impact, Mac, IBM, for grades 5–9 (software or laser disc)

- *Operation Neptune*, from The Learning Company, IBM, for grades 6–8 (software)

- *On Target Multiply and Divide*, from Gamco, Mac, for grades 2–8 (software)

- *Five in a Row*, from Critical Thinking Books & Software, Mac, IBM, for grades 2–12 (software)

- *Math Mystery Theatre: Great Numbers Bank Robbery*, from EdCon/Imperial International, VHS, for grades 2–8 (video)

- *Math Blaster Mystery: The Great Brain Robbery*, from Davidson, IBM, for grades 5–12 (software)

CROSS-CURRICULAR CONNECTIONS

This Teacher's Guide offers specific suggestions on ways to connect the math concept presented in this unit with other subjects students are studying. Students can connect math concepts with topics they already know about, and they can find examples of math in other subjects and in real-world situations. These strategies will be given at the point of use.

Look for these icons:

 Geography

 Health

 Social Studies

 Music

 Science

 Math

 Art

 Physical Education

 Language Arts

 Careers

LITERATURE CONNECTIONS

These books will be presented throughout the Teacher's Guide at the point where they could be used to introduce, reinforce, or extend specific lesson concepts. You may want to locate these books in your school or your local community library.

 *Look for this* **Literature Connection** *icon.*

- ♦ *Kid Power* by Susan Beth Pfeffer, F. Watts, 1977
- ♦ *263 Brain Busters: Just How Smart Are You, Anyway?* by Louis Phillips, Viking Kestrel, 1985
- ♦ *Kid's Money Book* by Patricia Byers, Julia Preston and Patricia Johnson, Liberty, 1983
- ♦ *50 Simple Things You Can Do to Save the Earth* by Earthworks Group, Andrews and McMeel, 1990
- ♦ *The Map with a Gap: Mathnet Casebook* by David D. Connell and Jim Thurmond, W.A. Freeman, 1994
- ♦ *If You Made a Million* by David M. Schwartz, Lothrop, Lee & Shepard Books, 1989
- ♦ *Inflation: When Prices Go Up, Up, Up* by David Adler, F. Watts, 1985
- ♦ *Calculator Riddles* by David A. Adler, Holiday House, 1995
- ♦ *The Meal a Mile Long* by Freida Hughes, Farrar, Straus & Giroux, 1989
- ♦ "Play with Your Triangle" in *Math Wizardry for Kids* by Margaret Kenda and Phyllis S. Williams, Barron's Educational Series, 1995

ASSESSMENT OPPORTUNITIES AT-A-GLANCE

LESSON	PORTFOLIO	PERFORMANCE	FORMAL	SELF	INFORMAL	CUMULATIVE REVIEW	MULTIPLE-CHOICE	MASTERY CHECKPOINTS	ANALYZING ANSWERS
48	✓								
49					✓				
50		✓							
51	✓		✓			✓		✓	
52	✓								
53		✓							
54		✓							
Mid-Unit Review	✓	✓	✓						
55			✓			✓		✓	
56					✓				
57					✓				
58		✓							
59	✓					✓			
60		✓							
61		✓							
62					✓				
63	✓	✓	✓						
64						✓			
Unit Test			✓				✓		

✔ ASSESSMENT OPTIONS

PORTFOLIO ASSESSMENT

Throughout this Teacher's Guide are suggested activities in which students draw pictures, make graphs, write about mathematics, and so on. Keep students' work to assess growth of understanding as the year progresses.

Lessons 48, 51, 52, Mid-Unit Review, 59, and 63

PERFORMANCE ASSESSMENT

Performance assessment items focus on evaluating how students think and work as they solve problems. Opportunities for performance assessment can be found throughout the unit. Rubrics and guides for grading can be found in the front of the Assessment Blackline Masters.

Lessons 50, 53, 54, Mid-Unit Review, 58, 60, 61, and 63

FORMAL ASSESSMENT

A Mid-Unit Review, Unit Review, and Unit Test help assess students' understanding of concepts, skills, and problem solving. The *Math Explorations and Applications* CD-ROM Test Generator can create additional unit tests at three ability levels. Also, Mastery Checkpoints are provided periodically throughout the unit.

Lesson 51, Mid-Unit Review, 55, 63, and Unit Test

CUMULATIVE REVIEW

Cumulative Reviews, covering material presented thus far in the year, are provided in the unit for use as either assessment or practice.

Lessons 51, 55, 59, and 64

INFORMAL ASSESSMENT

A variety of assessment suggestions are provided, including interviews, oral questions or presentation, debates, and so on. Also, each lesson includes Assessment Criteria, a list of questions about each student's progress, understanding, and participation.

Lessons 49, 56, 57, and 62

MULTIPLE-CHOICE TEST (STANDARDIZED FORMAT)

Each unit provides a unit test in standardized format, presenting students with an opportunity to practice taking a test in this format.

MASTERY CHECKPOINT

Mastery Checkpoints are provided throughout the unit to assess student proficiency in specific skills. Checkpoints reference appropriate Assessment Blackline Masters and other assessment options. Results of these evaluations can be recorded on the Mastery Checkpoint Chart.

Lessons 51 and 55

Look for these icons:

> **"** *Observing, questioning, and listening are the primary sources of evidence for assessment that is continual, recursive, and integrated with instruction.* **"**
>
> —*NCTM Assessment Standards*

 # MASTERY CHECKPOINTS

WHAT TO EXPECT FROM STUDENTS AS THEY COMPLETE THIS UNIT

⑭ THINKING STORY PARTICIPATION—LESSON 51

At this time you may want to begin a formal assessment of students' participation in the Thinking Story discussions. If students usually work in groups, observe them as they read and discuss the story. If they work individually, spot-check their answers to the story questions. If you read the stories as a class, observe how each student participates in class discussions. It may be helpful to use Assessment Blackline Master page 26. Results of this assessment may be recorded on the Mastery Checkpoint Chart.

⑮ PERCENT APPLICATIONS—LESSON 55

By this time most students should understand percents and be able to use them to solve problems. Assess their understanding and ability by observing them at work and by their results on the problems on page 202 or those on page 203. You may also wish to use Assessment Blackline Master page 28. Students who consistently have difficulty calculating or applying percent should be given extra help. Results of this assessment may be recorded on the Mastery Checkpoint Chart.

UNIT 3

PROGRAM RESOURCES

THESE ADDITIONAL COMPONENTS OF *MATH EXPLORATIONS AND APPLICATIONS* CAN BE PURCHASED SEPARATELY FROM **SRA/McGRAW-HILL.**

LESSON	BASIC MANIPULATIVE KIT	GAME MAT PACKAGE	TEACHER MANIPULATIVE KIT	INTERMEDIATE MANIPULATIVE KIT	INTERMEDIATE OVERHEAD MANIPULATIVE KIT	*THE CRUNCHER* SOFTWARE	*MATH EXPLORATIONS AND APPLICATIONS* CD-ROM
48	Number Cubes, Number Wheels	5% Tax and Harder 5% Tax Games		base-10 materials		spreadsheet	Lesson 48
49		play money			bills, coins	project	Lesson 49
50	Number Cubes, Number Wheels	Discount and Harder Discount Games				spreadsheet	Lesson 50
51		play money			bills, coins		Lesson 51
52						spreadsheet	Lesson 52
53						spreadsheet	Lesson 53
54							Lesson 54
55		play money			bills, coins		Lesson 55
56							Lesson 56
57							Lesson 57
58			Venn diagram mat				Lesson 58
59	Number Cubes						Lesson 59
60		Find the Treasure and Harder Find the Treasure Games					Lesson 60
61							Lesson 61
62							Lesson 62
63		play money		base-10 materials			Lesson 63
64						project	Lesson 64

Student Edition pages 174–175

Percents and Number Theory

INTRODUCING THE UNIT

Using the Student Pages Begin your discussion of the opening unit photo by asking students, "How does money make money?" Then read aloud the paragraph on the student page that highlights investing as a career. This helps make the connection between school and work and encourages students to explore how math is used in the real world.

ACTIVITY Point out to students that investors can make money from money if they make careful decisions about buying and selling stocks and bonds. Ask them to find the section of your local newspaper that lists the prices of stocks and bonds. Have them copy the listings for two or three particular stocks or bonds to discuss in class.

FYI Explain to students that the stock market as we know it today arose as trade and commerce expanded and grew more complex. The New York Stock Exchange, one of the largest markets in the world, got its start in 1792 with what was known as the Buttonwood Agreement. The United States Government had two years earlier issued $80,000,000 worth of bonds to pay the debt from the War of Independence. According to the agreement, people would be able to trade stock based on commonly recognized values. To this day, some stock markets still quote prices on the old system of pieces of eight. In the early days of the market, the basic unit of exchange was the dollar coin, for which change was made by cutting the coin into pieces. These pieces would be halves, quarters, eighths, or even sixteenths. Point out to students that as they look at the stock quotes in their local newspaper, many prices are still displayed using this fraction system, even though money is usually dealt with in decimals. Stress that the need for such markets becomes even greater as trade becomes more global. Stock markets are also crucial to our economic system, as buyers of stocks provide the money that companies need to succeed. The more companies that can find the money to stay in business, the more people are hired and the more powerful the economy becomes.

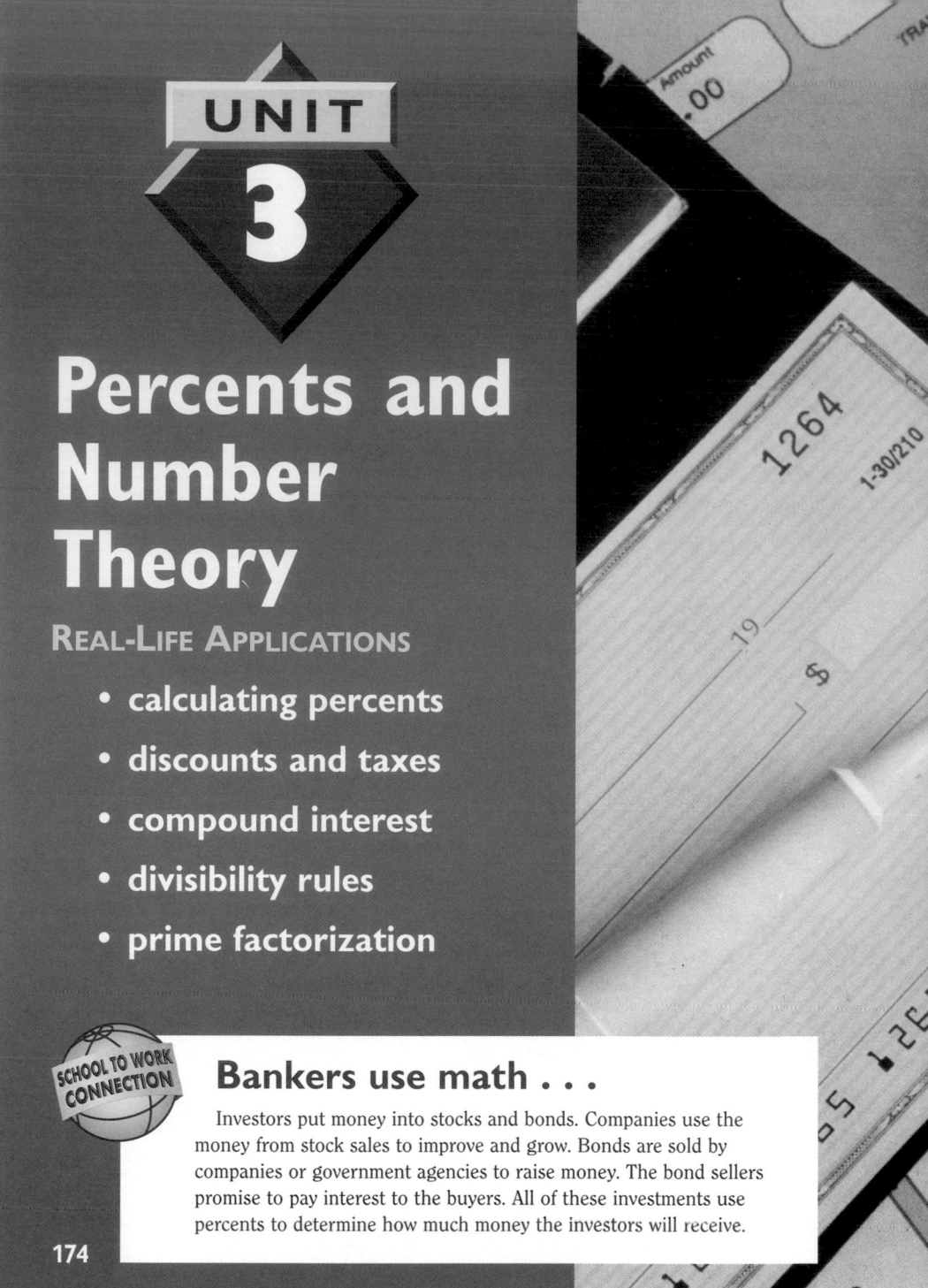

UNIT 3

Percents and Number Theory

REAL-LIFE APPLICATIONS

- calculating percents
- discounts and taxes
- compound interest
- divisibility rules
- prime factorization

Bankers use math . . .

Investors put money into stocks and bonds. Companies use the money from stock sales to improve and grow. Bonds are sold by companies or government agencies to raise money. The bond sellers promise to pay interest to the buyers. All of these investments use percents to determine how much money the investors will receive.

174

Thinklab™ 2

SRA's *Thinklab™ 2* provides a series of creative and logical problem-solving opportunities for individual students. The problems are designed to appeal to different cognitive abilities.

▶ Use Problems 46–50 and 71–75 with this unit to integrate object manipulation, creative insight, logical analysis, quantitative thinking, and brainstorming and to incorporate social interaction.

▶ Use Problems 51–60 with this unit to reinforce object manipulation (ways and means of dealing with specific data).

▶ Use Problems 61–70 with this unit to reinforce creative insight (extrapolating from, and beyond, given data).

Stress to students that math is central to investing. Returns are usually expressed using percentages. With good math skills an investor can tell how well a company has done in the past and estimate what its future might be. On a daily basis an investor must also be able to calculate losses and gains and try to understand patterns that arise over time. Some companies may fluctuate in value on a regular basis, while others seem only to rise or experience losses. These values can change over longer or shorter times, but understanding the meaning of these changes must come through understanding the numbers. Trends are often detected and explained using statistics. Explain that students interested in making money from money, whether as a career or as a personal investment, should pay special attention to their math homework. While other skills are also required to make sound investments—understanding the nature of supply and demand and learning to assess the needs of consumers, for example—math remains at the heart of sound investing.

Home Connections You may want to send Home Connections Blackline Masters pages 46–47 home to introduce this unit.

Unit Project This would be a good time to assign the "Birthday Present" project on pages 234 and 235. Students can begin working on the project in cooperative groups in their free time as you work through the unit. This project is a good opportunity for students to apply the concepts of percents, compound interest, and personal money management to real-world problem solving.

 *Cooperate 3*

Cooperate 3, published by SRA, provides a series of creative and logical problem-solving opportunities for cooperative groups. The problems are designed to provide practice in problem solving, communication, reasoning, and making connections. *Cooperate 3* presents the following cognitive strategies—perceiving spatial relations, ordering and sequencing, logical deduction, establishing and testing hypotheses, sequential exploration, identifying starting points, attending to detail, organizing information, and screening irrelevant

information. Each Problem Card emphasizes a principal strategy as well as reinforcing other strategies.

▶ Use Problem Cards 11–12 with this unit to emphasize ordering and sequencing.

▶ Use Problem Cards 13–14 with this unit to emphasize organizing information.

▶ Use Problem Card 15 with this unit to emphasize ordering and sequencing.

LESSON 48 Percents

Student Edition pages 176–179

LESSON PLANNER

Objectives

▶ to review the meaning of percent and finding the percent of a number

▶ to provide practice in mentally calculating the cost of items with tax

▶ to review and provide practice in approximating the product of two decimals

Context of the Lesson This is the first of eight lessons on percent. The first four lessons in the sequence mainly review material taught in the fifth grade. The next four lessons extend the applications of percent.

 MANIPULATIVES

base-10 materials*

Program Resources

"5% Tax" Game Mat

Number Cubes (0–5 and 5–10)

Number Wheels

Reteaching Master

Practice Master 48

Enrichment Master 48

The Cruncher*

For additional math integration:
  Math Throughout the Day*

For extra practice:
  CD-ROM* Lesson 48

Percents

You've probably seen **percents** in numbers you've read in newspapers and magazines and in signs. Percents are used to express store sales, tax rates, poll results, sports data, and other kinds of data.

Remember that percent (%) means "per hundred." So 5% means five per hundred or $\frac{5}{100}$. A 5% sales tax means you pay $5 of tax for every $100 worth of things you buy, or 5¢ per $1.00.

When you work with percents, it is sometimes useful to write them in decimal form. To change a percent to a decimal, you have to divide by 100. So you start with the percent and move the decimal point two places to the left.

Examples: Change 5% to a decimal.

5% ⟶ .05. ⟶ .05   5% = 0.05

Change 3.2% to a decimal.

3.2% ⟶ .03.2 ⟶ .032   3.2% = 0.032

To change a decimal to a percent, move the decimal point two places to the right.

Examples: Change 0.06 to a percent.

0.06 ⟶ 0.06. ⟶ 6%

Change 0.2 to a percent.

0.2 ⟶ 0.20. ⟶ 20%

Change each percent to a decimal.

❶ 3% **0.03**	❷ 8% **0.08**	❸ 7.2% **0.072**	❹ 1% **0.01**	❺ 10% **0.10**
❻ 100% **1.00**	❼ 50% **0.50**	❽ 25% **0.25**	❾ 0.1% **0.001**	❿ 20% **0.20**

Change each decimal to a percent.

⓫ 0.25 **25%**	⓬ 0.20 **20%**	⓭ 0.4 **40%**	⓮ 0.9 **90%**	⓯ 1 **100%**
⓰ 0.05 **5%**	⓱ 0.01 **1%**	⓲ 0.333 **33.3%**	⓳ 0.014 **1.4%**	⓴ 0.75 **75%**

176 • Percents and Number Theory

 # ❶ Warm-Up 5 MINUTES

Problem of the Day Present the following problem orally: Ed bought a car for $12,000. During each year the car loses 20% of the value it had at the beginning of the year. After how many full years will Ed's car have lost more than 50% of its original value? (after 4 years)

Problem-Solving Strategies Ask students who have solved the Problem of the Day to share how they solved it and any strategies they used.

Why teach it at this time?

This review of working with percents and decimals is in preparation for the work that takes up much of this unit and often involves multiplying with decimals. More practice with calculating and using percents is provided periodically throughout the year.

*available separately

We can find a percent of any number. For example, find 8% of 70.

One way to do this problem is to think "8% of $70 would be 8¢ per $1.00 or 8¢ for every $1.00. So 8% of $70 is 8¢ × 70, or 560¢, which is $5.60." So 8% of 70 is 5.6. Here is another way to do this.

Change the percent to a decimal.   8% = 0.08
            Multiply.   0.08 × 70 = 5.6
                        8% of 70 = 5.6

Find each amount.

㉑ 5% of 100 **5**   ㉒ 7% of 100 **7**   ㉓ 25% of 100 **25**

㉔ 5% of 8 **0.4**   ㉕ 7% of 63 **4.41**   ㉖ 12% of 4 **0.48**

㉗ 25% of 4 **1**   ㉘ 12.5% of 80 **10**   ㉙ 7% of 21 **1.47**

㉚ Kaya wants to buy a calculator. Its price is $19.99. If there is a 5% sales tax, how much will Kaya have to pay for the calculator (including the tax)? **$20.99**

㉛ How could you solve problem 30 without using pencil and paper or a calculator?

Round 19.99 to 20. Since 5% of 20 is 20 × 0.05, which is 1, the total cost is $19.99 + $1.00, or $20.99.

Suppose the sales tax is 5%. Figure out the total cost of these items. Try to do these in your head.

	Item	Price	Cost
㉜	Jeans	$29.99	▪$31.49
㉝	T-shirt	$8.99	▪$9.44
㉞	Calculator	$24.99	▪$26.24
㉟	Calendar	$1.99	▪$2.09
㊱	Notebook	$0.99	▪$1.04

Unit 3   Lesson 48 • **177**

MENTAL MATH Have students solve the following problems without pencil and paper. Students can show their answers on their Number Wheels by using the decimal point on the back of the wheels.

a. 8.5 ÷ 10 = (0.85)   **b.** 22 ÷ 100 = (0.22)

c. 20.3 ÷ 10 = (2.03)   **d.** 1.9 × 10 = (19)

e. 0.36 × 100 = (36)   **f.** 2.321 × 1000 = (2321)

g. 41.3 ÷ 100 = (0.413)   **h.** 0.621 × 10,000 = (6210)

❷ Teach

Using the Student Pages Before beginning work on pages 176–178, demonstrate the "Tips" game on page 179 and the "5% Tax" Game Mat, which provide practice calculating percents. Students can begin playing in pairs or small groups as they finish.

You may wish to begin a discussion of percents by asking for the meaning of a phrase such as "five percent" and for examples of everyday situations in which percents are used. Discuss with students how, to express a percent as a decimal, we divide by 100. Point out that to divide by 100, we move the decimal point two places to the left. You may wish to write on the chalkboard as an example:

5% of 70 = $\frac{5}{100}$ of 70 = $\frac{5}{100}$ × 70 = 0.05 × 70, which is 3.50.

After the discussion, have students solve problems 1–20 on their own. Provide help as needed. Have **base-10 materials*** available for students to use if they wish.

Next, review the two methods shown on page 177 for finding a percent of a number. Then have students solve problems 21–30 on their own. After going over the answers to these problems, discuss problem 31. Extend your discussion by asking students to explain why many stores tend to price things slightly less than a whole number of dollars. Two possible reasons are that it makes people perceive the price as a dollar less and that it gives the impression that the item is on sale. Have students save their answers to use when they complete page 183.

Then provide some additional practice calculating 5% of a number mentally and assign problems 32–36.

Students can use blank **Cruncher*** spreadsheets to help solve problems like those on pages 176 and 177.

◆ LESSON 48 Percents

Teach

Using the Student Pages Have students do the approximation problems on page 178 on their own.

 Introducing the "Tips" Game Have three students play five complete rounds of the "Tips" game on page 179 as the rest of the class watches. This game provides practice in calculating percents and in probabilistic thinking as students choose which tip to apply to each bill. Students can use a blank **Cruncher*** spreadsheet to help them keep score. A copy of this game can also be found on page 19 of the Home Connections Blackline Masters.

Introducing the "5% Tax" and "Harder 5% Tax" Game Mats Demonstrate this game by playing it with two students as the rest of the class watches. Complete instructions for playing can be found on the Game Mat. This game provides practice in calculating percents. Play long enough so that everyone understands the rules and techniques for doing the calculations mentally. When students demonstrate proficiency, have them turn to the harder version on the other side of the Game Mat. A copy of these Game Mats can also be found on pages 614–615 of this Teacher's Guide.

◆ LESSON 48 Percents

Working with percents often involves multiplying decimals. A common mistake people make when multiplying decimals is placing the decimal point in the wrong position. Avoid this error by thinking about whether the answer is reasonable.

In each problem two of the answers are clearly wrong and one is correct. Choose the correct answer.

		a.	**b.**	**c.**
37	4.02 × 22	a. 0.8844	b. 8.844	**c. 88.44**
38	33 × 0.07	a. 0.0231	b. 0.231	**c. 2.31**
39	0.63 × 2.1	**a. 1.323**	b. 13.23	c. 132.3
40	409 × 0.12	a. 4.908	**b. 49.08**	c. 490.8
41	7.11 × 1.13	a. 803.43	b. 80.343	**c. 8.0343**
42	32.2 × 10.9	a. 3520.7	**b. 350.98**	c. 35.207
43	2.11 × 8.6	a. 1814.6	b. 181.46	**c. 18.146**
44	2.9 × 2.9	**a. 8.41**	b. 84.1	c. 841
45	4.3 × 3.4	a. 0.1462	b. 1.462	**c. 14.62**
46	37 × 0.08	a. 296	**b. 2.96**	c. 29.6
47	25 × 1.04	a. 2.6	**b. 26**	c. 260
48	1.5 × 4.2	a. 630	b. 0.63	**c. 6.3**
49	12 × 4.8	**a. 57.6**	b. 5.76	c. 0.576
50	5.6 × 3.1	**a. 17.36**	b. 173.6	c. 1736
51	2.3 × 5.6	a. 0.1288	b. 1.288	**c. 12.88**
52	4.7 × 5.8	a. 272.6	**b. 27.26**	c. 2.726
53	4.8 × 6.7	a. 3216	b. 321.6	**c. 32.16**
54	4.56 × 2.3	**a. 10.488**	b. 104.88	c. 1048.8
55	3.16 × 3.3	a. 1.0428	**b. 10.428**	c. 104.28

 **Solve this problem.**

56 Ruth saw a sign that said, "Ice Show Tickets: $15.50." She said, "Oh, it will cost $3720 for the 24 students in our class to go to the ice show." Was Ruth right? **no (it will cost $372.00)**

 **Literature Connection** Invite students to read *Kid Power* by Susan Beth Pfeffer and have them determine Janie's earnings for different jobs.

LESSON 48 RETEACHING Name_____

One way to write a decimal as a percent is to change the decimal to a fraction, then write the percent.

Example 1:

Change 0.12 to a percent.

Recall that 0.12 is 12 hundredths, or $\frac{12}{100}$.

Write the fraction as a percent.

$\frac{12}{100}$ = 12%

Therefore, 0.12 = $\frac{12}{100}$ = 12%.

One way to write a percent as a decimal is to change the percent to a fraction, and then write the decimal equivalent.

Example 2:

Change 10% to a decimal.

Write the percent as a fraction. 10% = $\frac{10}{100}$

Write the fraction as a decimal. $\frac{10}{100}$ = 0.10

Therefore, 10% = $\frac{10}{100}$ = 0.10.

Change each percent to a decimal.

1 30% ___0.3___ **2** 4.6% ___0.046___ **3** 53% ___0.53___ **4** 1% ___0.01___

Change each decimal to a percent.

5 0.7 ___70%___ **6** 0.09 ___9%___ **7** 1 ___100%___ **8** 0.001 ___0.4%___

Find each amount.

9 15% of 80 ___12___ **10** 9% of 82 ___7.38___ **11** 50% of 90 ___45___

12 27% of 100 ___27___ **13** 4% of 89 ___3.56___ **14** 3% of 15 ___0.45___

15 30% of 90 ___27___ **16** 45% of 80 ___36___ **17** 18% of 40 ___7.2___

14 • *Math Explorations and Applications Level 6*

GAME

Tips Game

Players:	Two or more
Materials:	Two 0–5 cubes, two 5–10 cubes
Object:	To make the most money on tips
Math Focus:	Calculating percents, adding amounts of money, place value, and mathematical reasoning

RULES

1. Each player is waiting on customers in a restaurant and will get five tips. One tip will be 10%; three tips will be 15%; and one tip will be 20%.

2. Roll all four cubes. Find the bill for a customer by making an amount in dollars and cents. A 10 can be used anywhere in the amount, but it will have to be regrouped if it is not in the place for tens of dollars. For example, if you roll 10, 9, 5, and 5, you could make $109.55 (10, 9, 5, 5), $100.55 (9, 10, 5, 5), $96.05 (9, 5, 10, 5), or other amounts of money.

3. Decide which tip you'll get from this customer. Then calculate the tip. Keep a record of your tips.

4. After five rounds, add the tips. The player with the most money wins.

SAMPLE GAME

	Round 1	Round 2	Round 3	Round 4	Round 5
Ty rolled:	8 3 7 3	1 5 5 6	1 6 4 10	4 5 5 8	10 0 8 2
Ty made:	$87.33	$65.51	$106.41	$85.54	$108.20
Ty chose:	15%	15%	20%	10%	15%
Ty's tip:	$13.10	$9.83	$21.28	$8.55	$16.23
Isra rolled:	3 5 0 10	8 5 8 4	3 9 6 2	8 10 1 5	9 0 5 2
Isra made:	$105.30	$88.54	$96.32	$108.51	$95.20
Isra chose:	20%	15%	15%	15%	10%
Isra's tip:	$21.06	$13.28	$14.45	$16.28	$9.52

Ty's total was $68.99; Isra's total was $74.59. Isra was the winner.

Unit 3   Lesson 48 • **179**

PRACTICE p. 48

LESSON 48 PRACTICE   Name_____

Change each decimal to a percent.

1. 0.39 = 39%
2. 0.54 = 54%
3. 0.9 = 90%
4. 0.77 = 77%
5. 0.12 = 12%
6. 0.26 = 26%
7. 0.41 = 41%
8. 0.5 = 50%

Change each percent to a decimal.

9. 98% = 0.98
10. 36% = 0.36
11. 21% = 0.21
12. 0% = 0
13. 0.28% = 0.0028
14. 63% = 0.63
15. 10% = 0.1
16. 0.8% = 0.008

Find each amount.

17. 4% of 100 = 4
18. 7% of 200 = 14
19. 87% of 100 = 87
20. 7% of 20 = 1.4
21. 33% of 100 = 33
22. 25% of 80 = 20
23. 50% of 12 = 6
24. 10% of 99 = 9.9

Suppose the sales tax is 5%. Figure out the total cost of each item. Try to do the costs in your head.

Item	Price	Cost	Item	Price	Cost
lawn chair	$20.00	$21.00	T-shirt	$14.99	$15.74
comic book	$1.99	$2.09	baseball	$3.99	$4.19
pen	$0.80	$0.84	shirt	$23.00	$24.15

48 • Math Explorations and Applications Level 6

ENRICHMENT p. 48

LESSON 48 ENRICHMENT   Name_____

REAL-WORLD CONNECTION

Find out the number of points scored by each player on your favorite basketball team for each game of a given year's season.

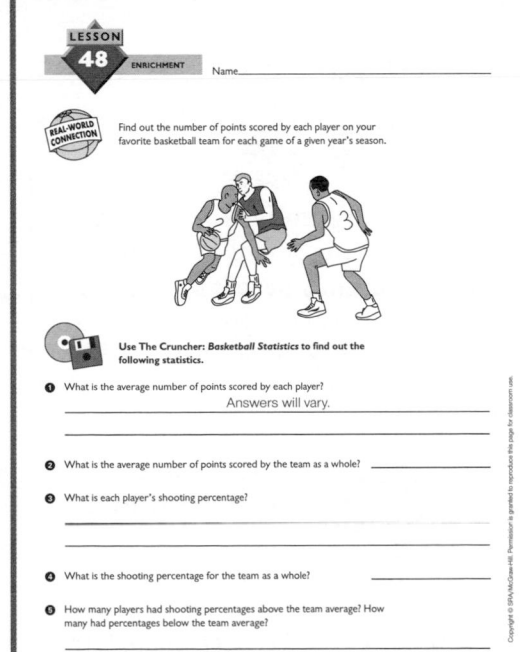

Use The Cruncher: Basketball Statistics to find out the following statistics.

1. What is the average number of points scored by each player?
   Answers will vary.

2. What is the average number of points scored by the team as a whole?

3. What is each player's shooting percentage?

4. What is the shooting percentage for the team as a whole?

5. How many players had shooting percentages above the team average? How many had percentages below the team average?

48 • Math Explorations and Applications Level 6

③ Wrap-Up

5 MINUTES

In Closing Summarize the lesson by asking students to explain how to express a decimal as a percent and a percent as a decimal. Have them explain a procedure for finding the percent of a number.

ALTERNATIVE ASSESSMENT

Portfolio Assessment Ask students to write a description of how and when they can use mental math to find the amount of tax on an item they purchase. Have them include an example or two with their explanation.

Assessment Criteria

Did the student . . .

✓ correctly answer at least 75% of the problems on pages 176–178?

✓ demonstrate an understanding of how to find a percent of a number by using multiplication of decimals?

✓ demonstrate understanding of how to find 5% of a number using mental math?

Homework Have students write and solve a word problem that involves computing a 7% sales tax.

GIFTED & TALENTED **Meeting Individual Needs**
Some students may be able to use their number sense to develop their own mental math strategies for quickly finding or estimating a greater range of percents of numbers. Encourage students to share their thinking and their strategies with classmates. Have them record their methods in their Math Journals.

Computing Percent Discounts

Computing Percent Discounts

LESSON PLANNER

Objective

▶ to review and practice calculating percent discounts

Context of the Lesson This is the second of eight lessons on percent.

 MANIPULATIVES

play money*
(optional)

Program Resources

Reteaching Master

Practice Master 49

Enrichment Master 49

The Cruncher*: *Mystery Population*

For extra practice:
CD-ROM* Lesson 49

---

① Wark-Up  5 MINUTES

 Problem of the Day Present the following problem: Aurora has read 42 books in the last year. She read five times as many mysteries as other books. How many mysteries did she read? (35)

Problem-Solving Strategies Ask students who have solved the Problem of the Day to share how they solved it and any strategies they used.

 Have students find each product or quotient using mental math.

a. 23.4 × 10 = (234)

b. 61 × 100 = (6100)

c. 4.3 × 1000 = (4300)

d. 23 ÷ 10 = (2.3)

e. 23.1 ÷ 10 = (2.31)

f. 14.22 ÷ 10 = (1.422)

g. 66.1 × 100 = (6610)

h. 26.2 ÷ 100 = (0.262)

② Teach

Using the Student Pages Discuss the material at the top of page 180. Do the first one or two problems with the class. Then use these points to review rounding:

▶ It is not necessary to report answers with more precision than the problems call for. On this page it would not make sense to give answers with more precision than to the nearest cent.

180 Percents and Number Theory

Sometimes stores give discounts. This means they reduce the price by some amount. Often the discount is stated as a percent.

The Bantam Department Store is having a sale. Athletic shoes are on sale for 20% off the regular price. Pat wants to buy a pair that usually costs $93.98. How much will the shoes cost?

We know that 20% of $93.98 is $18.796. The store rounds this to the next higher cent: $18.80.

$93.98	regular price
− $18.80	20% discount
$75.18	sale price

The tags on each item show the regular price and the discount. Give the sale price of each item.

 ❶ **Telescope** Regular Price: $250 Discount: 20%

$200.00

 ❸ **Radio** Regular Price: $4 Discount: 25%

$3.00

❷ **Tent** Regular Price: $125 Discount: 10%

$112.50

 ❹ **Camera** Regular Price: $106.95 Discount: 20%

$85.56

 ❺ **Tape Player** Regular Price: $89.95 Discount: 10%

$80.96

 ❻ **Chess Set** Regular Price: $19.95 Discount: 10%

$17.96

180 • Percents and Number Theory

 **LEARNING STYLES** **MANIPULATIVES**

Meeting Individual Needs Kinesthetic or interpersonal learners may benefit from acting out some of the problems, using **play money*** as needed.

 **LITERATURE CONNECTION**

Literature Connection For math puzzles requiring basic operations, refer students to *263 Brain Busters: Just How Smart Are You, Anyway?* by Louis Phillip.

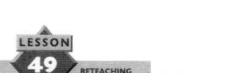
*available separately

⑦ Television Set
Regular Price: $259.86
Discount: 50%

$129.93

⑧ Guitar
Regular Price: $95.98
Discount: 50%

$47.99

⑨ Aquarium
Regular Price: $79.96
Discount: 25%

$59.97

⑩ Briefcase
Regular Price: $65.50
Discount: 15%

$55.68

⑪ Microscope
Regular Price: $125
Discount: $20

$105.00

⑫ Clock
Regular Price: $45
Discount: $10

$35.00

⑬ Skis
Regular Price: $200
Discount: 25%

$150.00

⑭ Toboggan
Regular Price: $90
Discount: 25%

$67.50

⑮ Drums
Regular Price: $160
Discount: 25%

$120.00

⑯ Flute
Regular Price: $195
Discount: 50%

$97.50

⑰ Coat
Regular Price: $105
Discount: 50%

$52.50

⑱ Headphones
Regular Price: $24
Discount: 50%

$12.00

PROBLEM SOLVING

Solve these problems.

⑲ There is a 25% discount on bongo drums at the Humdrum Music Shop. The regular price is $48. What is the sale price? **$36**

⑳ The tag on a cage at the Birds of a Feather store reads, "Regular price: $24. Discount: 175%." Is this possible? Explain. **No, because 175% is more than the total price of the birdcage.**

Unit 3   Lesson 49 • **181**

▶ Carry calculations to one place beyond the place you want to round to. If that digit is less than 5, drop it. If it is greater than 5, or if it is 5 and there are nonzero digits after it, round up. If the 5 is the last nonzero digit, we can round either way. However, for convenience students should round up in these problems. For example, $14.795 rounds up to $14.80, but $14.794 rounds down to $14.79.

Discuss how percent discounts can often be calculated mentally, as in problem 1. Discounts are sometimes given in the form of specified amounts rather than as percents, in which case all students need to do to find the sale price is subtract the amount of the discount from the original price. Have students do the problems on these pages on their own. In discussing problem 20, mention that this discount might be possible only if the owners of the store intend to pay the customer $18 for some reason, such as to take the birdcage away. Have students save their answers to use when they do page 183. Students can use the **Cruncher*** spreadsheet to help solve problems like those on pages 180 and 181.

❸ Wrap-Up ⏱ 5 MINUTES

In Closing Summarize the lesson by asking students to describe the procedure for finding the sale price of an item, given its original price and the percent of discount.

Informal Assessment Observe students as they work on the problems. Ask a student informally to explain the procedure he or she is using to find the sale price and to explain how he or she is rounding the answer.

Assessment Criteria

Did the student . . .

✓ correctly answer at least 75% of the problems?

✓ communicate procedures used to find sale prices?

✓ explain how rounding sale prices was done?

Homework Have students use store flyers and newspaper ads offering discounts to figure out the prices of items before and after the discounts.

Unit 3 Lesson 49   **181**

PRACTICE p. 49

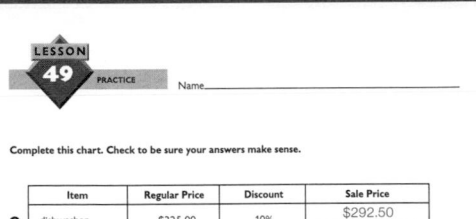

LESSON 49 PRACTICE   Name_____

Complete this chart. Check to be sure your answers make sense.

	Item	Regular Price	Discount	Sale Price
❶	dishwasher	$325.00	10%	$292.50
❷	used car	$9750.00	20%	$7800.00
❸	cassette tape	$8.39	45%	$4.61
❹	carton of eggs	$0.85	12.5%	$0.74
❺	microwave oven	$390.70	18%	$320.37
❻	pencil	$0.10	50%	$0.05
❼	used motorcycle	$920.00	80%	$184.00
❽	kitchen table	$256.20	33%	$171.66
❾	bread	$1.09	10%	$0.98
❿	doghouse	$29.99	24%	$22.79
⓫	piano	$1672.50	31%	$1154.03
⓬	fishing pole	$15.29	15%	$13.00
⓭	large eraser	$0.25	10%	$0.23
⓮	sleeping bag	$79.99	30%	$56.00
⓯	6-pack of cola	$1.89	13%	$1.64
⓰	painting set	$5.25	42%	$3.05
⓱	lamp	$46.50	62%	$17.67
⓲	ballpoint pen	$0.19	14%	$0.16
⓳	wagon	$57.20	20%	$45.76

Math Explorations and Applications Level 6 • 49

ENRICHMENT p. 49

LESSON 49 ENRICHMENT   Name_____

Two dogs named Maggie and Bridget both claim to have the best nose for a bargain. Here is a maze to test their claims. Each animal sniffs out a different path, as you can see in the drawing of the maze. Each animal claims to be the winner.

❶ Figure out the rule each animal used to pick a winning path, and write it here. Bridget sniffs out the cheapest path to take at each branch. Maggie snoops about for the cheapest overall path to the finish, which may mean taking fewer, more expensive paths.

❷ How much do Maggie and Bridget spend in the maze? Maggie spends $59.30. Bridget spends $279.10.

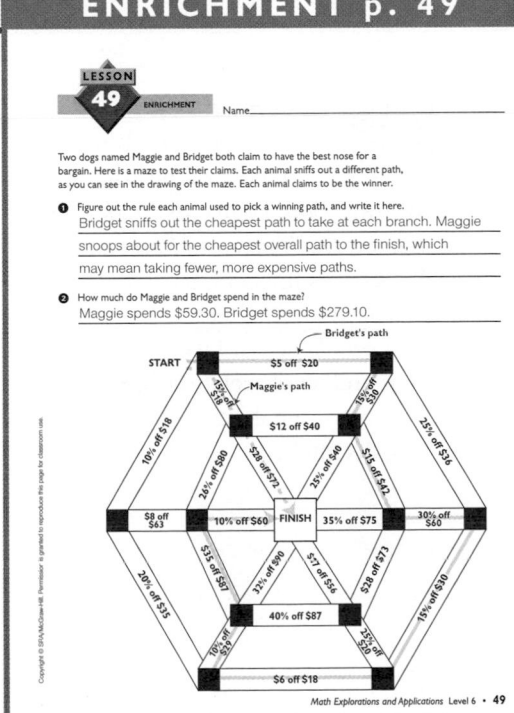

Math Explorations and Applications Level 6 • 49

*available separately

Percents on a Calculator

LESSON PLANNER

Objectives

▶ to review the use of the percent key on the calculator

▶ to provide practice in mentally calculating the price of an item on sale at a given percent discount

▶ to provide practice in solving percent problems

Context of the Lesson This is the third of eight lessons on percent.

 **MANIPULATIVES**

calculators*

Program Resources

"Discount" Game Mat

Number Cubes (0–5 and 5–10)

Number Wheels (optional)

Practice Master 50

Enrichment Master 50

The Cruncher*

For additional math integration:
Math Throughout the Day*

For extra practice:
CD-ROM* Lesson 50

Note: This lesson may take more than one day.

① Warm-Up ⏱

 **Problem of the Day** Present this problem: At Pat's Pants all jeans are immediately reduced by 10% of the suggested retail price when they arrive in the store. After seven days another 25% is taken off the price. After 14 days an additional 20% is taken off the price. After 21 days the price of the jeans is further reduced by 50%. If a pair of jeans originally costs $60, how much would the jeans cost after 42 days? ($16.20)

Problem-Solving Strategies Ask students who have solved the Problem of the Day to share how they solved it and any strategies they used.

 Have students compute the following percents mentally. Students can display their answers using Number Wheels.

a. 5% of $5.00 = ($0.25)   **b.** 6% of $8.00 = ($0.48)

c. 7% of $4.00 = ($0.28)   **d.** 8% of $8.00 = ($0.64)

(continued on page 183)

Percents on a Calculator

 Using a calculator can save you time when solving percent problems. You can do these problems on a calculator using a percent key, %, if your calculator has one. You use it like this, though your calculator may work slightly differently from the one in the examples.

Find the cost of a $56 item with a 4% sales tax.

What to Do:	What the Display Shows:
Clear the calculator. ──────▶	0
Push **5 6**. ──────▶	56
Push **+**. ──────▶	56
Push **4**. ──────▶	4
Push **%**. ──────▶	2.24

(The display now shows 4% of 56, which is 2.24. If you needed to know this number, you would write it down before going on to the next step.)

Push **=**. ──────▶ 58.24

The cost of the item, with tax, is $58.24.

◆ What answer do you get if you do the problems as 4% + 56? **56.04**

◆ What answer do you get if you find 56 × 4%? **2.24**

◆ What answer do you get if you find 4% × 56? **2.24**

◆ How can you find the cost of the item if your calculator doesn't have a percent key? **multiply 56 × 0.04 and add the result to 56**

◆ Think of a percent problem for which using mental arithmetic would be quicker than using a calculator. **Answers may vary. Possible answer: Find the cost of a $100 item with 5.75% sales tax.**

 **Technology Connection** Direct students to the laser disc or software *Core Concepts in Math: Mastering Decimals and Percents* from BFA/Systems Impact (Mac, IBM, for grades 5–9) for further practice with solving simple percent word problems, percent and whole relationships, converting decimals, and reading and writing decimals.

*available separately

Calculators can also be used to find percent discounts. Find the price of a
$7.43 item with a 15% discount.

What to Do: **What the Display Shows:**

Clear the calculator. ──────────────────▶ `0`

Push **7**. ──────────────────────────▶ `7`

Push **.**. ──────────────────────────▶ `7`

Push **4 3**. ──────────────────────▶ `7.43`

Push **–**. ──────────────────────────▶ `7.43`

Push **1 5**. ──────────────────────▶ `15`

Push **%**. ──────────────────────────▶ `1.1145`

Push **=**. ──────────────────────────▶ `6.3155`

The discounted price is $6.32. (You get that by rounding $6.3155 up to the
next cent. The amount of the discount, $1.1145, is rounded down to $1.11.)

Use a calculator to solve these problems.

1 5% of 100 **5**   **2** 7% of 100 **7**   **3** 25% of 100 **25**

4 5% of 8 **0.4**   **5** 7% of 63 **4.41**   **6** 12% of 4 **0.48**

7 25% of 4 **1**   **8** 12.5% of 80 **10**   **9** 7% of 21 **1.47**

Solve these problems.

10 Irma wants to buy a video game for $24.99. If there is a 5% sales tax,
how much will she have to pay for the game, including the tax? **$26.24**

11 Bob bought a $142 camera with a 10% discount. How much did he pay? **$127.80**

12 Marta will buy a printer for $395. If there is an 8% sales tax, how much
will she pay, including tax? **$426.60**

13 A speaker system is discounted 20%. The regular price is $200. If the
sales tax is 5%, what is the total cost of the system? **$168**

14 Mr. Montovano installed a new furnace that should reduce his monthly gas
bill by 15%. If the bill was $70, what should it be now? **$59.50**

15 Use a calculator to solve problems 1–19 on pages 180 and 181.

Unit 3   Lesson 50 • **183**

**Social Studies
Connection** Talk about
sales tax and why it exists.
Invite volunteers to find out more
about this tax—how it differs from
place to place, when it was first
introduced, how the money is used by
local governments. Ask researchers to
share their findings with the class.

Mental Math (continued)

e. 9% of $20.00 = ($1.80)   **f.** 10% of $30.00 = ($3.00)

g. 4% of $50.00 = ($2.00)   **h.** 5% of $10.00 = ($0.50)

i. 6% of $100.00 = ($6.00)   **j.** 4% of $1000.00 = ($40.00)

❷ Teach

Using the Student Pages You may wish to
demonstrate the "$50 Price" game on page 185 and the
"Discount" Game Mat, so that students who finish their
work on pages 182–184 early can practice calculating
percents by playing these games.

 Have students work in groups on the two examples
on pages 182–183, with at least one **calculator***
in each group. Discuss the results, emphasizing
these points:

▶ In the first example, when **%** is pushed, the calculator
described in this lesson displays 2.24, which is 4% of
56. Some other calculators would display 58.24 at
that point.

▶ In the second example, the displayed answer must
be rounded.

▶ For the fourth discussion question, some students may
recognize that they could also find the answer by
multiplying 56 by 1.04.

Have students use their calculators to do problems 1–15 on
page 183. They should compare their answers for problems
1–9 to those found when they did the same problems on
page 177. If there aren't enough calculators to go around,
have students estimate the answers mentally while waiting
their turns on the calculator. Or, have these students play
the "$50 Price" game and "Discount" Game Mat.

In problem 13, if students ask which should be calculated
first, the tax or the discount, explain to them that discount
is usually calculated first. (However, the order will not affect
the answer, as students will see in problem 16.)

> *Intelligent use of a calculator requires skill
> with the basic number facts, knowledge of the
> base ten system, and good number sense.
> These are all things that should be learned in
> school as a standard practice.*
>
> —Stephen S. Willoughby,
> *Mathematics Education for a Changing World*

◆ LESSON 50 Percents on a Calculator

Teach

Using the Student Pages Have students complete the problems on page 184 using a **calculator***. When all groups have finished, discuss the answers as a class. The problem in 16(b) is discussed in detail in Lesson 51. For problem 18, guide students to understand that the 5% discount was on $300 but the 5% tax was on the discounted price of $285, and that more is subtracted by the discount than is added by the tax. Encourage students to use trial and error to solve problems 21 and 22. Keep in mind that a method for solving such problems is presented later in the sequence of percent lessons, in Lesson 54.

Students can use a blank **Cruncher*** spreadsheet to help solve problems like those on page 184.

Introducing the "$50 Price" Game Demonstrate the "$50 Price" game on page 185 by having two students play it for the rest of the class. This game provides practice in mental arithmetic and in mathematical reasoning (deciding which numbers to make). Be sure that everyone understands that the expressions for the sale price need not be calculated unless it is impossible to tell by inspection or approximation which is closer to $50. Students can use calculators or paper and pencil to do any calculations.

Introducing the "Discount" and "Harder Discount" Game Mats Have two students play the "Discount" Game Mat as the rest of the class observes. This game provides practice in calculating percent discounts. Instructions for playing can be found on the Game Mat. Be sure that everyone understands the rules and the techniques for doing these calculations mentally. Invite students to play the harder version on the back of the Game Mat after they have played several rounds of the basic game. A copy of the "Discount" Game Mats can also be found on pages 608–609 of this Teacher's Guide.

◆ LESSON 50 Percents on a Calculator

COOPERATIVE LEARNING Work in groups and use a calculator to solve these problems.

16 A $56 jacket is on sale at a 20% discount. The sales tax is 4%.

  a. With the discount and tax, what is the cost of the jacket? **$46.59**

  b. Does it make a difference whether you add the tax first and then take the discount or take the discount first and then add the tax? **no**

17 A $129.98 bicycle is on sale at a 30% discount. The sales tax is 5%. How much will the bicycle cost with the discount and tax? **$95.54**

18 A $300 stereo is on sale at a 5% discount. The sales tax is 5%.

  a. What is the cost of the stereo? **$299.25**

  b. Since you subtract 5% and then add 5%, why isn't the answer $300? **What is being subtracted is 5% of $300, but only 5% of $285 is being added.**

19 A $600 stove is on sale at a 7% discount. The sales tax is 7%. How much will the stove cost? **$597.06**

20 A sign in Woolly's Clothing Store reads, "40% off the marked price of every item." Lisa buys four pairs of socks priced at $1.98 a pair, a shirt priced at $15.50, and another shirt priced at $19.98. She also buys two pairs of jeans priced at $16.50 and $24.98. If the sales tax is 5%, how much will Lisa's total be? **$53.47**

21 Malcolm's total bill for a set of three new CDs was $38.52. A 7% sales tax was included in the bill. How much of the $38.52 was for the CDs, and how much was for the tax? **$36.00 for the CDs; $2.52 for tax**

22 Fiona paid $20.98 for a double CD, including the 5% sales tax. What was the price of the CD without tax? (Hint: The tax was rounded to the nearest cent.) **$19.98**

184 • Percents and Number Theory

Literature Connection Invite students to read *Kid's Money Book* by Patricia Byers, Julia Preston, and Patricia Johnson. After students choose an idea and predict their earnings, have them determine what their percentage of the profits would be if two or three friends joined them in their enterprise.

*available separately

GAME

$50 Price Game

COOPERATIVE LEARNING

Players:	Two or more
Materials:	Two 0–5 cubes, two 5–10 cubes, a calculator for each player
Object:	To make the sale price closest to $50
Math Focus:	Mental arithmetic

RULES

1. Roll any cube and multiply the number rolled by 10 to find the percent discount. For example, if you roll a 2, the discount is 20%.

2. Roll the other three cubes and use two of the numbers rolled to make the regular price. (Try to get a sale price close to $50.)

3. Write the sale price. For example, if you roll 6, 9, and 4, you could make the regular price $64. The sale price would be 20% off $64. Another way to think of it is $64 − (20% of $64).

4. The player whose sale price is closest to $50 wins. Don't calculate the precise sale price unless you can't otherwise tell who wins.

SAMPLE GAME

Walter rolled a 0–5 cube: **1** The discount is 10%.	Luz rolled a 0–5 cube: **5** The discount is 50%.	Larry rolled a 5–10 cube: **9** The discount is 90%.
Walter rolled the other cubes: **2 5 6**	Luz rolled the other cubes: **9 7 0**	Larry rolled the other cubes: **10 4 4**
He wrote: 10% off $56	She wrote: 50% off $97	He wrote: 90% off $104

They knew that Larry's sale price wasn't at all close to $50, but they weren't sure whether Walter or Luz was closer to $50. They calculated the two sale prices. Walter's sale price was $50.40, and Luz's was $48.50. Walter was the winner.

---

③ Wrap-Up 🕐 5 MINUTES

In Closing Summarize the lesson by asking students to explain how they can use a calculator to solve percent problems involving discounts and sales tax.

Performance Assessment Tell students that a $40 watch is on sale at a discount of 20% and that the sales tax is 5%. Ask them to explain how they would use a calculator or mental math to find the total price of the watch.

Assessment Criteria

Did the student . . .

✓ communicate understanding of how to calculate the total price of an item with discount and sales tax?

✓ demonstrate ability to use a calculator to find discounted price and total price including sales tax?

Homework Have students play the "$50 Price" game with a family member for further practice with finding percents. A copy of this game can also be found on page 20 of the Home Connections Blackline Masters.

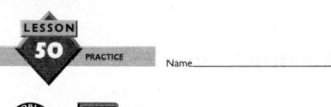

PRACTICE p. 50

LESSON 50 PRACTICE   Name_____

Use a calculator to solve these problems.

1. A $37.50 radio is on sale at a 20% discount. The sales tax is 5%. With the discount and tax, how much is the radio? — **$31.50**

2. A $55 calculator is on sale at a 15% discount. The sales tax is 6%. How much will the calculator cost with the discount and tax? — **$49.56**

3. A $350 television set is on sale at a 15% discount. The sales tax is 4%. How much will the television set cost? — **$309.40**

4. A $500 refrigerator is being sold at a 7% discount because it is scratched. The sales tax is 7%. How much will the refrigerator cost? — **$497.55**

5. Don bought a jacket that was on sale for $5 off and a pair of pants that cost $15. The sales tax was 4%. How much was his bill? — **can't tell**

6. Trudy bought a $7.50 book at a 10% discount, a $3.50 ring binder, and two packages of paper at $1.25 each. The sales tax was 4%. How much did everything cost? — **$13.26**

7. Mr. Miles paid a total of $420 for a microwave oven, including tax. The price of the oven itself was $400.
   a. How much was the tax? — **$20**
   b. What is the sales tax rate where Mr. Miles lives? — **5%**

8. A $118.95 bicycle is on sale for $20 off. There is no sales tax. How much will the bicycle cost? — **$98.95**

50 • Math Explorations and Applications Level 6

ENRICHMENT p. 50

LESSON 50 ENRICHMENT   Name_____

REAL-WORLD CONNECTION Li and Sara went out for lunch. The check for lunch is shown below.

When it came time to pay the check, Li said, "Let me use my calculator to figure the 15% tip."

She used her calculator to figure 15% × $14.00 and got $2.10.

Sara said, "I have an easy way to figure a 15% tip that does not require a calculator. Let me show you."

Sara first figured 10% of the check by simply moving the decimal point in the total amount one place to the left. $14.00 → $1.40

CHECK	
Chicken Salad	$5.50
Taco Salad	$4.50
Iced Tea	$1.00
Soda Pop	$1.00
Total	**$14.00**
Thank You	

She then figured an additional 5% of the check by taking half of her 10% amount. $\frac{1}{2}$ of $1.40 → $0.70

Sara said, "I can add $1.40 and $0.70 mentally to get $2.10."

Use Sara's method to find the 15% tip on each of the following checks.

	1. Amount: $25.00	2. Amount: $72.00	3. Amount: $130.00
10%:	$2.50	$7.20	$13.00
5%:	$1.25	$3.60	$6.50
Tip:	$3.75	$10.80	$19.50

50 • Math Explorations and Applications Level 6

Sales Tax and Discounts

LESSON PLANNER

Objectives

▶ to help students develop the broad ability to use mathematical common sense

▶ to provide practice in estimating answers to realistic percent problems

▶ to help students develop an understanding of adding and subtracting the same percent, and of the order of adding and subtracting a percent

✓ to assess students' participation in the Thinking Story discussions

Context of the Lesson This lesson, the fourth of eight lessons on percent, provides realistic applications of percent. Lessons on another common application of percent—interest—follow. This lesson also contains the first segment of "Competition," a four-part Thinking Story and includes a Mastery Checkpoint for students' participation in the discussion of this story.

 MANIPULATIVES

calculators*

play money*
(optional)

Program Resources

Practice Master 51

Enrichment Master 51

Assessment Master

For career connections:
  Careers and Math

For extra practice:
  CD-ROM* Lesson 51
  Cumulative Review, page 563

Sales Tax and Discounts

For each of the following problems, first estimate the total cost, and then do the calculation to see how close your estimate was.

1. Adam wants to buy a jacket that usually sells for $50. The store is having a 20% off sale on everything in the store. Sales tax is 5%. Adam has $43. Will he be able to buy the jacket? If not, how much more money does he need? If so, how much change will he receive?

2. Matthew wants to buy some shoes that usually cost $49.98. They are on sale for 20% off. Sales tax is 5%. He has $41. Will he be able to buy the shoes? If not, how much more money does he need? If so, how much change will he receive? **no; $0.98 more**

   yes; $1.00 in change

3. Rajiv is ordering a model kit from a catalogue. The regular price is $34.95, but he has a coupon for 10% off. Shipping costs $3.95, and there is no sales tax. Rajiv has $35.00 to spend on the order. Can he afford the model kit? If not, how much more money does he need? If so, how much money will he have left? **no; $0.41 more**

4. Alan plans to buy a football that has a list price of $29.99. Today it is on sale for 25% off. Sales tax is 4%. He has $23.50. Will he be able to buy the football? If not, how much more money does he need? If so, how much change will he receive? **yes; $0.10 in change**

5. Albert plans to buy a computer monitor for $500. He discovers that it is on sale this week for 20% off. He knows he will have to pay 7% sales tax. He has saved $400 to buy the monitor. How much more money will he need if he is going to buy the monitor this week? **$28**

6. Albert couldn't manage to buy the monitor when it was on sale for 20% off, but the next week the sale changed to a 25% off sale. Could he afford to buy it then? The sales tax is still 7%. **no**

7. Joan wants to buy a dress that usually sells for $30. Today the dress is on sale for 25% off. Sales tax is 4%. She has $25. Will she be able to buy the dress? If not, how much more money does she need? If so, how much change will she receive?

   yes; $1.60 in change

❶ Warm-Up ⏱ 5 MINUTES

Problem of the Day Present the following problem to the class: Patience pays off for customers at Jack's Jackets. Once a jacket has been in the store for one week, the price is reduced by 10%. After another week, the price is reduced again, this time by 20%. After the third week, the price of the jacket is further reduced by 50%. Fran bought a jacket that had been in the store for 24 days. She paid $72. What was its original price? ($200)

Problem-Solving Strategies Ask students who have solved the Problem of the Day to share how they solved it and any strategies they used.

Why teach it this way?

In this lesson students are asked to figure out for themselves the relationship among some real-life operations with percents. Challenging students in this way can bring out their creativity and enhance confidence in their math skills and problem-solving ability.

 **Technology Connection** Refer students to the software *Operation Neptune* from The Learning Company (IBM, for grades 6–8) for further practice with percents, estimation, decimals, fractions, mixed numbers, measurement, time, geometry, graphing, and statistics.

* The first store will always charge less because they are taking 5% off the original price and adding 5% to the lesser sales price. The

second store is still charging the original price.

When Adam went to the store to buy the $50 jacket that was on sale for 20% off, the sales clerk added the 5% tax first, and then deducted the 20% discount. Adam objected and said he would pay less sales tax if the discount were calculated first, and then the tax were added. The clerk said it would be cheaper the way he did it because Adam could get a bigger discount, since the discount was calculated on both the original price AND the tax. What do you think? Discuss this with your classmates and then calculate the final price both ways.

For the following exercises the original price, the discount rate, and the sales tax rate are given.

Determine the final price for each item if you add the tax first, and then deduct the discount. Figure out what the final price will be if you deduct the discount first and then add the tax.

	Original Price of Item	Discount Rate	Tax Rate	
8	$100.00	40%	4%	**$62.40**
9	$99.99	40%	4%	**$62.39**
10	$200.00	20%	2%	**$163.20**
11	$200.00	80%	4%	**$41.60**
12	$200.00	80%	8%	**$43.20**
13	$50.00	10%	4%	**$46.80**
14	$150.00	50%	5%	**$78.75**
15	$150.00	25%	10%	**$123.75**

Solve these problems.

16 Two furniture stores in a state with 5% sales tax are selling the same sofa with a regular price of $500. The first store is having a "5% off" sale, in which they reduce the price of all items by 5%, and customers pay tax on the discounted price. The second store is having a sale in which customers pay the regular price, but the store pays the sales tax for the customer.

  a. In which store would the sofa cost less? How much less?
  the first store; $1.25 less

  b. In which store would a $600 sofa cost less? How much less?
  the first store; $1.50 less

  c. Is there a rule you can use to tell in advance which store would charge less for a sofa with a given price? *****

MENTAL MATH Have students find the following percents without using pencil and paper:

  a. 50% of 50 = (25)   **b.** 75% of 24 = (18)

  c. 25% of 200 = (50)   **d.** $33\frac{1}{3}$% of 600 = (200)

  e. 100% of 77 = (77)   **f.** 90% of 50 = (45)

  g. 10% of 80 = (8)   **h.** 20% of 20 = (4)

❷ Teach

Using the Student Pages Before students begin working on these pages, discuss the problem at the top of page 187. Talk about the problem without doing any of the calculations. Help students understand that both procedures yield the same answer because subtracting 20% is the same as multiplying by 0.8, and adding 5% is the same as multiplying by 1.05, and multiplication is commutative. That is, the order of multiplying does not affect the result.

Then have students complete the problems on pages 186–187 on their own. Encourage them to use **calculators*** to check their answers.

Literature Connection Have students browse through *50 Simple Things You Can Do to Save the Earth* by the Earthworks Group. Ask them to express information from the bottom of one of the book's pages in terms of percent.

◆ LESSON 51 Sales Tax and Discounts

Teach

Using the Thinking Story In this, the first of four segments of "Competition," Mr. Muddle is concerned about his rising costs, dropping sales, and a new competitor, Mr. Sneaky. Have students read and discuss the story in small groups. Then discuss the questions as a class.

Answers to Thinking Story Questions:

1. He made about $650 in profit. Now he makes about $250 (if he sells 100 shirts). This is a decline of over 60%.

2. No. He sells about 100 and his competitor sells 50; the total is the same as it had been.

3. His competitor is taking away business.

4. Answers will vary, but some students may say that Mr. Sneaky's business is new, and as it becomes better known it may cut further into Mr. Muddle's business.

MATH JOURNAL Ask students to describe in their Math Journals the kind of person they think Mr. Muddle is, supporting their ideas with what they have read about him here and in previous Thinking Stories.

SPECIAL NEEDS **Meeting Individual Needs**
Check with students who are not participating in the Thinking Story discussions. If they are having difficulty reading, read the story and questions to them as they follow along with the text. If they are not able to work well with a certain group, consider changing groups or having students work individually. It is important to maintain a good classroom spirit around the Thinking Stories so that students feel comfortable presenting their own answers to the questions, even when they disagree with their classmates.

◆ LESSON 51 Sales Tax and Discounts

THINKING STORY # Competition

Part 1

❝ I don't know what's gone wrong with my store," said Mr. Muddle. "I used to sell about 150 T-shirts a week. But for the past few weeks I've been lucky to sell 100 a week."

"Have you raised your prices?" Portia asked.

"No," said Mr. Muddle. "I still charge just $9.00 for a T-shirt. That makes it hard to earn a living. I used to get T-shirts from the factory for $3.33 each. My other costs were about $800 a month. Now the T-shirts cost me $4.00 each, and my other costs are about $1000 a month."

"Maybe you don't advertise enough," said Manolita.

"I advertise as much as ever," Mr. Muddle said. "I don't think that's it. I think people just aren't buying T-shirts the way they used to. My friend Mr. Sneaky has started a T-shirt store right next to mine. He isn't doing very well either. In fact, he sells only about half as many T-shirts as I'm selling now."

. . . to be continued

188 • Percents and Number Theory

RETEACHING

 Some students may have more success with the concepts introduced on pages 186–187 if they can act out the problem situations using **play money***. For this approach, pair students who have command of the concepts with those who need reteaching.

PRACTICE p. 51

LESSON 51 PRACTICE Name_____

PROBLEM SOLVING For each of the following problems first estimate the cost to answer the question. Then do the calculation to see how reasonable your estimate was.

❶ Jules wants to buy a sweatshirt that usually sells for $24. Today the sweatshirt is on sale for 10% off. Sales tax is 6%. Jules has $25. Will he be able to buy the sweatshirt? If not, how much more money does he need? If so, how much change will he get? _____ yes; $2.10

❷ Keesha wants to buy a blouse that usually sells for $24. Today the blouse is on sale for 25% off. Sales tax is 7%. She has $15. Will she be able to buy the blouse? If **not**, how much more money does she need? If so, how much change will she get? _____ no; $4.28

❸ Brent wants to buy a portable CD player that costs $89.00. It is on sale today only for 20% off. Sales tax is 4%. If he has $80, can he buy the CD player? _____ yes

❹ Joanne wants to buy a dishwasher that usually costs $420. It is on sale for 30% off. Sales tax is 5%. Can she buy the dishwasher if she has $310? _____ yes

❺ Teresa wants to buy a sleeping bag that lists for $145.00. She has $116.00 saved for it, and she is waiting for a sale. How big a discount is necessary for her to be able to buy the sleeping bag? (She lives in New Hampshire, where there is no sales tax.) _____ 20%

❻ If Jorge has $52.00 and wants to buy CDs, how many can he buy at the regular price of $14.95 plus 7% sales tax? How many can he buy when the store has its two-for-$20 sale? _____ 3 CDs; 4 CDs

Math Explorations and Applications Level 6 • **51**

---

*available separately

Work in groups. Discuss your answers and how you figured them out. Then compare your answers with those of other groups. **Answers are in margin.**

1 About how much profit per week did Mr. Muddle make in the past? About how much profit is he making now? What percent decline is that?

2 Is Mr. Muddle right that people aren't buying as many T-shirts as they used to? Explain.

3 Why do you think Mr. Muddle is selling fewer T-shirts?

4 Would you expect business to get better or worse for Mr. Muddle in the next few months? Why?

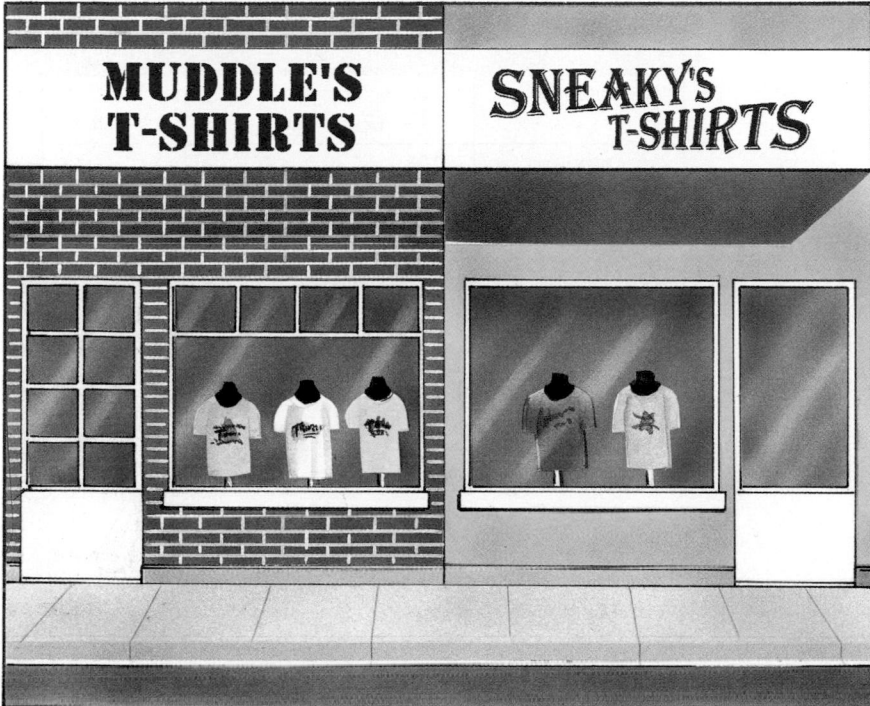

Use the Cumulative Review on page 563 after this lesson.

Unit 3 Lesson 51 • **189**

3 Wrap-Up

In Closing Ask students to state their conclusions regarding adding and subtracting the same percent or about the order of adding and subtracting a percent.

Mastery Checkpoint 14

At this time you may want to begin a formal assessment of students' participation in the Thinking Story discussions. If students usually work in groups, observe them as they read and discuss the story. If they work individually, spot-check their answers to the story questions. If you read the stories as a class, observe how each student participates in class discussions. It may be helpful to use Assessment Blackline Masters page 26. Results may be recorded on the Mastery Checkpoint Chart.

Portfolio Assessment Have students write a brief statement of their conclusions about the material in this lesson. Ask them to place it in their Math Portfolios as a record of ongoing learning.

Assessment Criteria

Did the student . . .

✓ correctly answer at least 13 of the 16 problems on pages 186–187?

✓ demonstrate understanding of the effects of adding and then subtracting a given percent?

✓ demonstrate understanding of how the order in which percent discounts and add-ons is calculated does not affect the results?

✓ participate in the discussion of the Thinking Story?

Homework Have students find out the kinds of discounts local merchants are currently giving on merchandise. Invite students to speak with two store owners to find out how the store owners determine their prices and discounts and about other decisions that affect customers. Have students share their findings with the class.

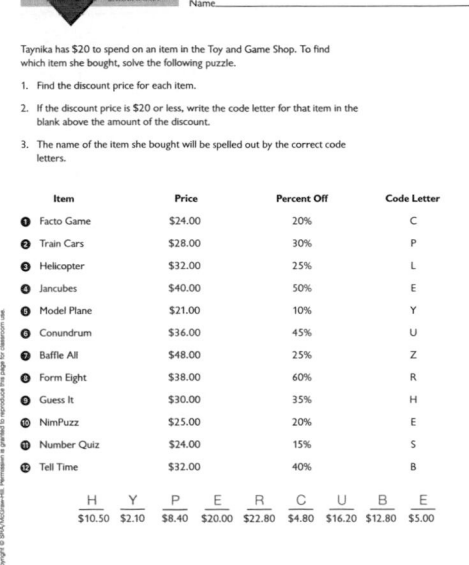

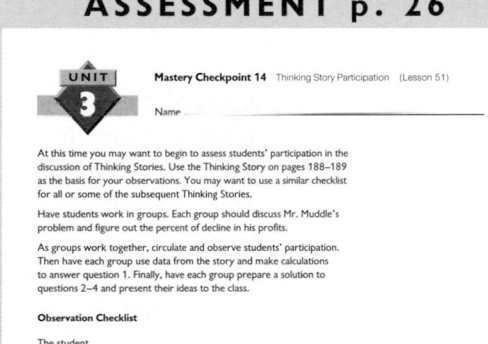

Unit 3 Lesson 51 **189**

Student Edition pages 190–191

Calculating Interest

LESSON PLANNER

Objectives

► to show how to calculate simple and compound interest

► to provide practice calculating interest

Context of the Lesson This is the fifth of eight lessons on percent. In this lesson students calculate interest using pencil and paper. In the next lesson they will use calculators to do similar problems and to figure interest that is compounded quarterly and monthly.

 MANIPULATIVES
none

Program Resources
Practice Master 52
Enrichment Master 52
The Cruncher*
For extra practice:
CD-ROM* Lesson 52

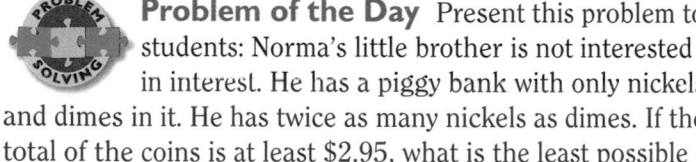 **Warm-Up** 5 MINUTES

 Problem of the Day Present this problem to students: Norma's little brother is not interested in interest. He has a piggy bank with only nickels and dimes in it. He has twice as many nickels as dimes. If the total of the coins is at least $2.95, what is the least possible number of each? (30 nickels and 15 dimes)

Problem-Solving Strategies Ask students who have solved the Problem of the Day to share how they solved it and any strategies they used.

MENTAL MATH Extend the exercises from the previous two lessons by presenting problems such as the following.

a. 20% off of $20.00 = ($4.00; cost is $16.00)

b. 4% off of $50.00 = ($2.00; cost is $48.00)

c. 5% off of $65.00 = ($3.25; cost is $61.75)

d. 6% off of $70.00 = ($4.20; cost is $65.80)

e. 7% off of $80.00 = ($5.60; cost is $74.40)

f. 8% off of $50.00 = ($4.00; cost is $46.00)

g. 9% off of $15.00 = ($1.35; cost is $13.65)

h. 10% off of $100.00 = ($10.00; cost is $90.00)

Calculating Interest

If you deposit money in a savings bank, the bank pays you for the use of your money. This payment is called *interest*. The money you deposit is called the *principal*. If the bank pays 5% interest per year, after one year you will have the amount of money you put in plus 5% more.

Example:

You deposit $70 in a bank that pays 6% interest. How much will you have after one year?

Find 6% of 70: $0.06 \times 70 = 4.2$
$70 + 4.2 = 74.20$
You will have $74.20 after one year.

How much will you have after five years?

Start with $70.00.

Time	Calculation	Amount
After one year	$0.06 \times 70 = 4.2$ $70 + 4.2 = 74.20$	$74.20
After two years	$0.06 \times 74.20 = 4.452$ $74.20 + 4.45 = 78.65$	$78.65
After three years	$0.06 \times 78.65 = 4.719$ $78.65 + 4.72 = 83.37$	$83.37
After four years	$0.06 \times 83.37 = 5.0022$ $83.37 + 5.00 = 88.37$	$88.37
After five years	$0.06 \times 88.37 = 5.3022$ $88.37 + 5.30 = 93.67$	$93.67

After five years if you haven't taken any money out of your account, you'll have $93.67.

Notice that the bank gives you interest on all the money you have in the bank, including last year's interest. This is called *compound interest* because you get interest on previous interest as well as on the money you deposited.

When a bank credits interest to your account only once a year, we say that the bank "compounds annually."

 **Literature Connection** Invite students to read *The Map with a Gap* by David D. Connell and Jim Thurmond. Have them determine a year's interest on Bronco's ninety-thousand dollar prize using different interest rates.

RETEACHING

Extra teaching on calculating interest is not essential at this time. If necessary, continue giving help on using percents, as in previous lessons. You may want to assign Enrichment Master 52.

*available separately

In each case calculate the amount of money you would have if interest is compounded annually.

	Principal	Rate of Interest	Number of Years	Amount	
1	$100	6%	1	■	**$106.00**
2	$100	8%	2	■	**$116.64**
3	$100	5%	5	■	**$127.63**
4	$200	7%	1	■	**$214.00**
5	$200	7%	5	■	**$280.51**
6	$ 50	6%	5	■	**$66.91**
7	$100	4%	5	■	**$121.67**
8	$100	3%	10	■	**$134.39**
9	$100	8%	10	■	**$215.89**
10	$100	7%	5	■	**$140.26**

11 Which would earn more interest, $1000 deposited for one year at 6% interest or $1000 deposited for two years at 3% interest? How much more? **two years at 3%; 90¢ more**

12 Which would earn more interest, $2000 deposited for three years at 2% interest or $2000 deposited for two years at 3% interest? How much more? **three years at 2%; 62¢ more**

13 Which would earn more interest, $100 deposited for two years at 10% interest or $200 deposited for one year at 5% interest? How much more? **$100; $11 more**

14 Which would earn more interest, $100 deposited for two years at 5% interest or $200 deposited for one year at 10% interest? How much more? **$200; $9.75 more**

Unit 3 Lesson 52 • **191**

PRACTICE p. 52

LESSON **52** PRACTICE Name _____

Use a calculator to solve these problems.

1 Ellis opened a savings account with $75 at a bank that pays 4% interest compounded annually. How much money will he have in the account after a year? After five years? After ten years? — $78.00; $91.25; $111.02

2 Which savings account will earn more interest, one that holds $1000 for 2 years at 3% annual interest or one that holds $2000 for 1 year at 3% annual interest? — 2 years at 3%

3 Kenna deposits $400 in the Pigg Economic Bank at 9% interest compounded annually. How long will it be until her money doubles? How much interest will she have earned in six years? — 9 years; $270.84

4 Ms. Wang wants to save $6000 for a down payment on a condominium. If she deposits $4000 in a money market fund that averages 8% interest compounded annually, how long will it be before she reaches her goal? — 6 years

5 Marco deposits $400 in a savings account that pays 5% interest compounded annually. On the other side of town, Toby deposits $500 in a bank that pays 4% interest compounded annually. Which person's account will reach $600 first, and about how long will it take? — Toby; 5 years

6 Mrs. Littman has $5500 in a savings account that pays 5% yearly interest. If the interest is mailed to her at the end of each year, how much will she receive in three years? — $825

52 • *Math Explorations and Applications Level 6*

ENRICHMENT p. 52

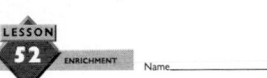

LESSON **52** ENRICHMENT Name _____

GAME **Players:** Two
Materials: One 0–5 Number Cube, ten money/savings cards, a calculator
Object: To have the higher total amount of interest

Answers will vary with each game.

Rules

1. The ten cards shown below give the amount of money deposited in savings institutions in ten states in 1993. Copy and cut out the cards, turn them over, and mix them up.

2. Taking turns, choose cards until each player has five. Turn the cards face up.

3. Roll the Number Cube to represent the percent of interest.

4. Decide to which state you will apply the interest amount. On a separate sheet of paper, record the number rolled as a percent of interest and the amount from the card.

5. Take turns rolling the cube until each state has an interest rate assigned.

6. Use a calculator to find the amount of interest each of your five states would have earned over three years if the deposit amount was compounded annually at the recorded percent of interest.

7. Total your interest amounts.

The person with the higher total amount of interest wins the game.

New Jersey $33,218,000,000	California $199,445,000,000	Ohio $30,808,000,000	Connecticut $34,227,000,000
New York $93,656,000,000	Pennsylvania $30,156,000,000	Massachusetts $45,664,000,000	
Texas $26,148,000,000	Illinois $35,773,000,000	Florida $25,721,000,000	

52 • *Math Explorations and Applications Level 6*

*available separately

---

2 Teach

Using the Student Pages Discuss the meaning of interest. Point out that in banking, *percent interest* is the interest paid per year and actually means "percent annual interest." Assume in all word problems dealing with bank interest that the deposits were made at the beginning of an interest period. Have students do problems 1–14 on page 191 on their own. Discuss the effects of doubling the money deposited (which doubles the final amount), doubling the interest rate (which more than doubles the interest paid if the interest has compounded), and doubling the number of years (which also more than doubles the total interest paid). Students can use a blank **Cruncher***
spreadsheet to explore the effects on the interest paid.

3 Wrap-Up

In Closing Summarize the lesson by asking students to explain what compound interest is and how percents are used to compute it.

Portfolio Assessment Ask students to explain in a short paragraph what compound interest is. Then have them explain how they would find the amount of money a person would have in a bank account after three years, if that person initially deposited $100 at 10% interest compounded annually. Challenge them to explain why the total will be more than $100 + $10 + $10 + $10. Students can put their paragraphs in their Math Portfolios.

Assessment Criteria

Did the student . . .

✓ demonstrate understanding of the concept of compound interest?

✓ demonstrate understanding of calculating the amount of money in an account that earns compound interest?

Homework Have students find the actual amounts of interest paid on savings accounts at their local bank. Have them contribute their findings to a class chart.

Unit 3 Lesson 52 **191**

Compound Interest

LESSON PLANNER

Objectives

▶ to show how to find the value of interest plus principal using a single calculation

▶ to show how to calculate the value of an account when interest is compounded quarterly or monthly

Context of the Lesson This is the sixth of eight lessons on percent.

 **MANIPULATIVES**

calculators*

Program Resources

Reteaching Master

Practice Master 53

Enrichment Master 53

The Cruncher*

For extra practice:
CD-ROM* Lesson 53

① Warm-Up

Problem of the Day Present this problem: Niko prepared for his appearance on a TV game show. He studied a total of 200 trivia facts over a five-day period. Each day he studied ten more facts than on the previous day. How many facts did Niko study on the first day? (20)

Problem-Solving Strategies Ask students who have solved the Problem of the Day to share how they solved it and any strategies they used.

 Continue the percent exercise from the previous lesson.

a. 20% off of $80.00 = ($16.00; cost is $64.00)

b. 50% off of $325.00 = ($162.50; cost is $162.50)

c. 12% off of $50.00 = ($6.00; cost is $44.00)

d. 40% off of $60.00 = ($24.00; cost is $36.00)

e. 75% off of $150.00 = ($112.50; cost is $37.50)

f. 65% off of $27.00 = ($17.55; cost is $9.45)

g. 15% off of $60.00 = ($9.00; cost is $51.00)

Compound Interest

Finding compound interest the way you did in Lesson 52 is straightforward but can take a long time. There is a quicker way.

Remember: 7% is the same as 0.07.
1 + 0.07 is the same as 1.07.

Multiplying a number by 1.07 is the same as taking the number once and adding 7% to it.

Example:
How much money will you have after one year if you deposit $200 in the bank at 7% interest?

Multiply 200 × 1.07.

$$
\begin{array}{r}
2\,00 \\
\times\ 1.07 \\
\hline
14\,00 \\
200 \\
\hline
2\,14.00
\end{array}
$$

After one year, you would have $214.00.

Example:
How much money would you have if you left $200 in the bank for five years at 7% interest?

Multiply 200 by 1.07 five times.

$$200 \times 1.07 \times 1.07 \times 1.07 \times 1.07 \times 1.07$$

To multiply this on a calculator, follow these steps (remember, your calculator may work slightly differently):

Push **on/c**, **2 0 0**, **×**, **1 . 0 7**, **=**, **=**, **=**, **=**, **=**.

After five years you would have $280.51.

Is this the same answer you got for problem 5 on page 191?

(Your answer may differ by 1¢ if you rounded after each year.)

Challenge: In your Math Journal describe how to calculate compound interest using exponents.

GIFTED & TALENTED **Meeting Individual Needs**

Challenge interested students to extend their calculations to see what difference various methods of compounding make over time, such as in 10 years, 20 years, or 30 years. Students can model this using **The Cruncher.***

192 Percents and Number Theory

*available separately

You can also do this problem on a calculator by adding 7% each year:

Push **2 0 0** **+** **7** **%** **=**
+ **7** **%** **=**
+ **7** **%** **=**
+ **7** **%** **=**
+ **7** **%** **=**

Again, the answer is $280.51.

Use a calculator to solve these problems.

❶ Ms. Morgan deposited $250 in the Last National Bank at 7% interest.

    a. How much money will she have after ten years? **$491.79**

    b. How long must Ms. Morgan leave her money in the bank to double the amount she deposited? **11 years**

❷ Jake deposited $1000 in the Last National Bank at 4.5% interest for 12 years. How much money did he have in the bank at the end of 12 years? **$1695.88**

❸ Mr. Pacheco's bank is now paying 5.1% interest per year.

    a. How long will it take him to double his money? **14 years**

    b. If Mr. Pacheco deposits $1000, how much will he have after nine years? **$1564.68**

❹ Mr. Nicolai put $80 in a bank at 4% interest for ten years. Mrs. Finnegan put $60 in a bank at 6% interest for ten years.

    a. At the end of ten years, who will have more money? **Mr. Nicolai**

    b. Who will have earned more interest? **Mrs. Finnegan**

Unit 3   Lesson 53 • **193**

❷ Teach

Using the Student Pages Go over the examples on page 192. Discuss how to implement this new, more efficient method using a **calculator***. When using the calculator's constant function, remember that the constant functions of different calculators may work differently. You may also wish to demonstrate or explain how to compute compound interest using the exponent key on a calculator.

Have students work individually or in small groups to solve the problems on page 193. If there are not enough calculators for all students, those who are waiting for them can try to solve problems using mental math until it is their turn to use the calculator. Students who are waiting may also wish to play the "Tips" game, "$50 Price" game, or the "5% Tax" or "Discount" Game Mats, all of which have been previously introduced.

Note that students have not learned a formal procedure for solving problems such as problem 3a. Suggest that they start with an amount and calculate the total amount after 1 year, 2 years, 3 years, and so on, at 5.1% interest.

Literature Connection Invite students to read *If You Made a Million* by David M. Schwartz. Have them calculate compound interest on a million dollars for five years at different rates of interest.

*available separately

◆ LESSON 53 Compound Interest

Teach

Using the Student Pages Go over the material at the top of pages 194–195, including the first discussion question. Then have students work on the problems on their own. When everyone has finished, discuss the questions at the bottom of each page. Show that even though problems 5d, 5e, and 8d involve the same principal, the same interest rate, and the same period of time, the amount at the end of the year is a little greater when compounding takes place more often.

Students can use a blank **Cruncher*** spreadsheet to explore the effects of interest rates and compounding periods on the total interest paid.

◆ LESSON 53 Compound Interest

Some banks pay interest four times a year instead of just once a year. Interest paid in this way is "compounded quarterly." For example, if a bank pays 8% annually, it might pay 2% every quarter.

◆ If a bank compounds the interest quarterly, how many times a year will the bank add interest to an account? **4**

Use a calculator, when it's helpful, to solve these problems.

5 The Trust-Us Bank advertises "6% interest compounded quarterly."

a. What is $\frac{1}{4}$ of 6%? **1.5%**

b. If you deposit $1000, how much will you have after one-quarter of a year? **$1015**

c. How many quarters are in one year? **4**

d. If you deposit $1000, how much will you have after one year (four quarters)? **$1061.36**

e. If you deposit $1000 in the Safe-Here Bank (which pays 6% interest once a year), how much will you have after one year? **$1060.00**

f. Compare your answers to d and e. How much more money do you get from the bank that compounds quarterly? **$1.36**

6 If two banks pay the same rate of interest, why does the bank that compounds quarterly pay more interest than the bank that compounds annually? **After the first quarter, interest is paid on the interest earned as well as on the principal.**

7 If a bank compounded interest semiannually (twice a year), would it pay more or less interest than a bank paying the same interest rate compounded quarterly? **less interest**

Real-World Connection Bring in, or ask students to find, information on interest-bearing investments other than savings accounts. Examples include certificates of deposit (CDs), bonds, and money market funds. Have students look at actual statements to see how interest is calculated.

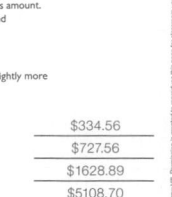

RETEACHING p. 16

Example 1:
You deposited $100.00 in an account that pays 5% interest at the end of each year. How much interest will you have at the end of six years?
After year 1, the amount at the beginning of each year is the same as the amount at the end of the previous year.
To find the total amount at the end of the year, multiply the amount at the beginning of the year by 1 + 5%, or 1.05. After one year the total will be 100 × 1.05 = 105.00.
After six years the total will be 100 × 1.05 × 1.05 × 1.05 × 1.05 × 1.05. We can think of this as 100 × (1.05)⁶.
You will have $134.01 at the end of six years.

Example 2:
Suppose that the $100.00 from example 1 still earns 5% interest, but the interest is compounded quarterly. Now how much money will you have at the end of six years?
Four quarters per year, for six years, means that 24 interest payments will be made. The interest rate at each payment is 5% ÷ 4 = 1.25%.
The total at the end of each quarter will be 1.0125 times the previous amount. Multiply 1.0125 times itself 24 times, and then multiply by 100, or find $100.00 × 1.0125²⁴.
= $100.00 × 1.34735105
= $134.74 to the nearest penny
Notice that earning interest more often than once a year gives you slightly more money at the end of the same time period.

Find each amount of money.

❶ Deposit of $250 at 6% annually for five years	$334.56
❷ Deposit of $575 at 4% annually for six years	$727.56
❸ Deposit of $1000 at 5% annually for ten years	$1628.89
❹ Deposit of $2500 at 6% for 12 years, compounded quarterly	$5108.70
❺ Deposit of $853 at 7% for eight years, compounded quarterly	$1486.11
❻ Deposit of $500 at 6% for five years, compounded monthly	$674.43

16 • Math Explorations and Applications Level 6

*available separately

Some banks pay interest every month instead of just once a year or once a quarter. Interest paid in this way is "compounded monthly."

◆ If a bank compounds the interest monthly, how many times a year will the bank add interest to an account? **12**

◆ If a bank pays 3% annual interest compounded monthly, what percent of the money deposited will be paid in interest each month? **0.25%**

Use a calculator, when it's helpful, to solve these problems.

(8) The Lock-Up Bank pays 6% interest compounded monthly.

a. If you have money in the Lock-Up Bank, what percent of that money will you earn in interest each month? **0.5%**

b. If you deposit $1000, how much will you have after one month? **$1005.00**

c. If you deposit $1000, how much will you have after one-quarter of a year (three months)? **$1015.08**

d. If you deposit $1000, how much will you have after one year (12 months)? **$1061.68**

e. Compare your answer for d with your answer for d in problem 5 on page 194. How much more money do you get in the bank that compounds monthly? **$0.32**

◆ Why does a bank that compounds monthly pay more interest than one that compounds quarterly? **After one month, interest is paid on the interest earned as well as on the principal.**

◆ Would a bank that compounds interest daily pay more interest on the same principal than one that compounds monthly? **yes, if the annual rate of interest is the same**

③ Wrap-Up

In Closing Summarize the lesson by asking students to explain how to find compound interest using a calculator.

Performance Assessment Ask students to suppose that they have just put $2000 in a savings account in a bank that pays 5% interest compounded quarterly. Ask them to describe the procedure for finding the amount of money they would have in the account at the end of one year.

Assessment Criteria

Did the student . . .

✓ demonstrate understanding of the procedure for finding compound interest?

✓ demonstrate understanding of how to use the calculator's constant function to find compound interest more quickly?

✓ communicate understanding of why money compounded more frequently increases at a faster rate than money compounded less frequently?

Homework Assign Practice Master 53 to provide further practice with compound interest.

PRACTICE p. 53

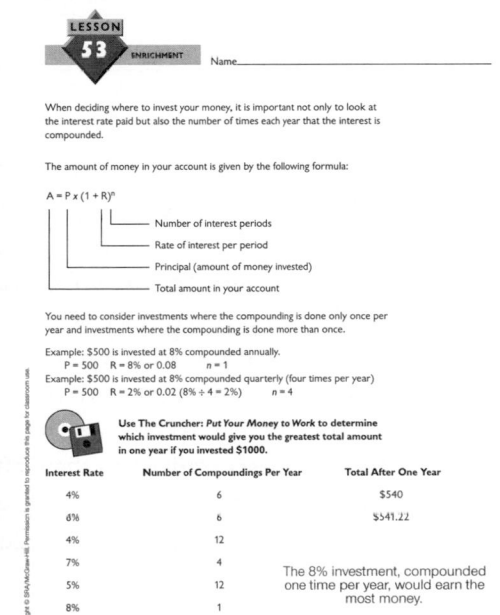

ENRICHMENT p. 53

Reversing Percent Problems

Reversing Percent Problems

LESSON PLANNER

Objective

▶ to show how to solve realistic problems that involve "undoing" the processes used in the percent problems presented in the previous lessons

Context of the Lesson This is the seventh of eight lessons on percent.

🖑 **MANIPULATIVES**

calculators*

Program Resources

Reteaching Master

Practice Master 54

Enrichment Master 54

For extra practice:
CD-ROM* Lesson 54

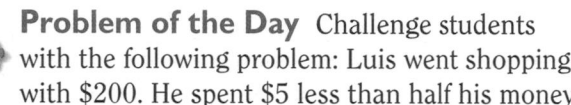

① Warm-Up ⏱ 5 MINUTES

 Problem of the Day Challenge students with the following problem: Luis went shopping with $200. He spent $5 less than half his money at the first store he visited. At the second store, he spent 60% of what he had left. Then he spent 50% of what remained plus $11 at a third store. With how much money did Luis end his shopping trip? ($10)

Problem-Solving Strategies Ask students who have solved the Problem of the Day to share how they solved it and any strategies they used.

MENTAL MATH Present the following problems for students to solve using mental math:

a. 50% of $40 = ($20)   b. 75% of $16 = ($12)

c. 20% of $10 = ($2)   d. 10% of $100 = ($10)

e. 70% of $1000 = ($700)   f. 40% of $25 = ($10)

g. 25% of $48 = ($12)   h. 30% of $50 = ($15)

You have learned how to find a fraction of a number when expressed as a percent. In this lesson you'll learn a way to find a number when you know a percent of it.

To do so, you'll "undo" a procedure that has taken place.

Examples:

Kimiko bought a golf club for $53.50, which included a 7% sales tax. What was the price of the club without the tax?

To do this, first look at how the cost with tax could have been calculated—by multiplying the price by 1.07.

price ——(× 1.07)——➤ cost with tax

To get the price from the cost with tax, you should be able to do the opposite (divide by 1.07).

price ◀——(÷ 1.07)—— cost with tax

(Notice that if you got the cost simply by adding on 7%, you wouldn't have known how to do the opposite.)

Divide 53.50 by 1.07. What is your answer for the price of the club? **$50.00**

Check to see if the answer is right.

What is 7% of 50? **3.5**

If the price was $50, the tax would be $3.50, and the cost with tax would be $53.50. So the answer is right.

196 • Percents and Number Theory

✦ **LEARNING STYLES** **Meeting Individual Needs**
Some students may find it helpful to act out the situations described in the problems as though they knew the answers. For example, a student doing the first problem on page 198 might begin by reasonably "assuming" that the price was $15. Then he or she should calculate the cost, with the tax, to see if the guess was correct. As needed, the student can make additional guesses, adjusting them after seeing the results of the previous guess. Once the student obtains the correct answer, he or she should work backward to get the original price.

*available separately

Mr. Wilcox bought a book during a sale at Medium-Rare Books. The book was on sale for 35% off its regular price. He paid $12.34 for it before tax. What was the original price of the book (the price before the discount)? Again, first look at how the discount price could have been calculated. It could have been done by multiplying the original price by (1 − 0.35), which is 0.65. This is similar to finding the cost of something with a 7% sales tax by multiplying by (1 + 0.07), or 1.07. You can also think of the discount price as paying $0.65 for each dollar of the original price.

original price   ×0.65   discount price

You can reverse this by dividing by 0.65.

original price   ÷0.65   discount price

Divide 12.34 by 0.65. Use a calculator.

What is your answer for the original price of the book?

about $18.98

Check to see that the answer makes sense:

What is 65% of 18.98? 12.337, or 12.34

So the answer makes sense.

Note that $18.99 \times 0.65 = 12.3435$ and $18.98 \times 0.65 = 12.337$. (Since both round to $12.34, the original price could have been $18.98 or $18.99.)

Another book was on sale for 20% off and cost $4.76 before tax. To find the original cost, find 1 − 0.20, which is 0.80, and divide 4.76 by 0.80.

The original price was $5.95.

② Teach

Using the Student Pages Go over the examples on pages 196–197 with the class. Emphasize that one reason for introducing the one-step multiplication is to make it easier to solve problems by working backward.

When discussing the first example on page 197, point out that multiplying by 0.65 is equivalent to subtracting 35%. Do several examples, as needed, to show that the answer is the same. For example: How much would you pay for a $40 snorkeling mask on sale at a 25% discount?

25% of 40 = 10; 40 − 10 = 30,

or (1 − 0.25) × 40 = 0.75 × 40 = 30.

These calculations show that multiplying by 0.75 is the same as subtracting 25%.

Physical Education Connection Invite students to formulate common sports problems using lesson concepts for classmates to solve. For example: A basketball player who makes about 75% of her free throws made 15 free throws. About how many did she attempt? (15 ÷ 0.75 = 20 attempts)

Science Connection Ask students to find out what it means when weather forecasters say that there is a 20% chance of rain. Guide students to understand that a 20% chance of rain means that under weather conditions like those being described, it rains 20% of the time.

◆ LESSON 54 Reversing Percent Problems

Teach

Using the Student Pages Have students work in groups, using **calculators***, to solve the problems on pages 198–199. When discussing solutions, invite volunteers to demonstrate how to solve the problems using paper and pencil. Challenge students to explain how to solve problem 8 using mental math. Also, ask students whether the answer to problem 8 would change if the stereo had a different price. (For any price over $100, a 20% discount is greater than a $20 discount)

◆ LESSON 54 Reversing Percent Problems

Use a calculator, if necessary, to solve these problems.

1 The sales tax in Stan's city is 4%. Suppose he paid $15.34 for a package of greeting cards, including tax. What was the price without tax? **$14.75**

2 Mr. Silvanos bought a sofa on sale for $520. That was 35% off the regular price. What was the regular price of the sofa? **$800**

3 Hannah wants to buy a pair of boots. The regular price of the boots is $125. The store is having a 20% discount sale, and the sales tax is 7%. How much will Hannah have to pay for the boots? **$107.00**

4 The Save-a-Lot Discount Store is having a 20% discount sale. In that city the sales tax is 7%. What was the original price of a camera for which a customer paid $64.20? Hint: Here is how the cost with tax could have been calculated:

original price $\xrightarrow{\times 0.80}$ discount price $\xrightarrow{\times 1.07}$ cost with tax

(Work backward to calculate the original price.) **$75.00**

5 Edward bought a sweater that was on sale for 30% off its regular price. With 6% sales tax, he paid $22.25. What was the original price of the sweater? **$29.99**

6 Tips at restaurants are usually calculated based on the total check, not including the tax. A check including 7% tax came to $25.68.

a. What was the total before the tax? **$24.00**

b. What would be a 15% tip on that total? **$3.60**

7 Lara bought a book marked $5.95 from a store that sells all books at 20% off. Tax was 6%. How much did she pay for the book? **$5.05**

8 Which costs less, a $200 stereo at 20% off or at $20 off? **a $200 stereo at 20% off**

198 • Percents and Number Theory

Literature Connection Invite students to read *Inflation: When Prices Go Up, Up, Up* by David Adler. Challenge them to determine the cost of an item minus the current year's inflation.

*available separately

9 Sook has $162.00 in the bank. His bank pays 5% interest, compounded annually. He has not deposited any money during the past year. How much money did he have in the bank one year ago? **$154.29**

10 Ted bought a wallet priced at $34.85 and a briefcase priced at $89.98. He had to pay a 6% sales tax. How much did he have to pay all together? **$132.32**

11 Marta wants to buy a shirt that is marked $24.98. The sales tax is 5%. Marta has $30.00. Does she have enough money to buy the shirt? **yes (the shirt costs $26.23)**

12 Anoki was buying a radio with a price tag that was unclear.

Regular Price....$40 Now $10 OFF

The clerk could not tell if it was supposed to be $10 off or 10% off, so she gave Anoki a choice.

a. Which should Anoki choose? **$10 off**

b. Why? **10% is only $4 off.**

13 Miriam wants to buy some apples. She can buy 50 kilograms of apples at the Farmer's Market for $0.70 a kilogram. She can buy 2.5 kilograms of apples at the City Market for $0.90 a kilogram. Where should she buy the apples? **not enough information given (it depends on how many she needs)**

14 Mr. and Mrs. Kramer have budgeted $800 for a new refrigerator. They have seen advertisements at the following prices and discounts: $899 and 10% off, $950 and 20% off, $999 and 25% off, and $1095 and 30% off. Which of these could fall within their budget? **$950 and 20% off, $999 and 25% off, and $1095 and 30% off**

Unit 3   Lesson 54 • **199**

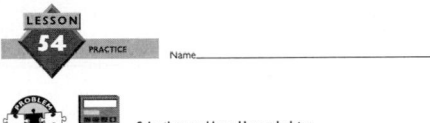

---

❸ Wrap-Up

In Closing Summarize the lesson by asking students how to work backward to solve problems that require them to find a number when they know a percent of it.

 **Performance Assessment** Tell students that with 6% sales tax, a shirt costs $26.50. Ask them to explain how to find the price of the shirt before the tax was added to it. ($25) Then tell them that with a 20% discount, a sweater sold for $64, before tax was added. Ask them to explain how to find the original price of the sweater. ($80)

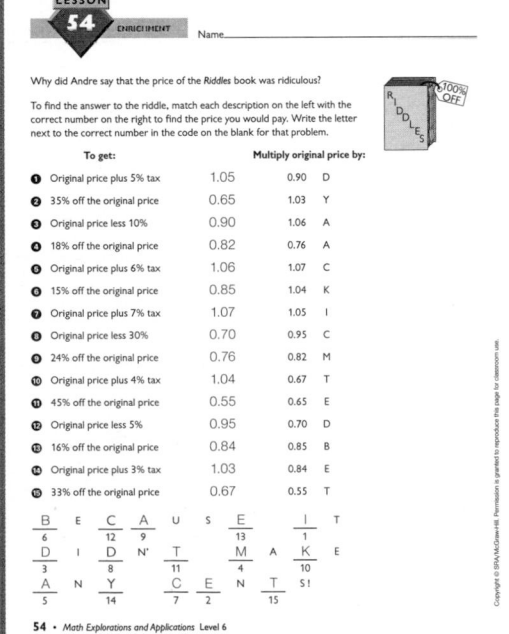

Assessment Criteria

Did the student . . .

✓ demonstrate understanding of how to work backward to find a number when a percent of it is known?

✓ understand that multiplying a number by $n\%$ gives the same result as subtracting $(100 - n)\%$ from the number?

Homework Give students total prices for several selected items, the percent of the discounts, and the sales tax. Have them find the original prices of the items. Alternatively, invite students to collect or create this data themselves, and challenge classmates to solve their problems.

Mid-Unit Review

Student Edition pages 200–201

The Mid-Unit Review pinpoints troublesome skill areas for students, allowing plenty of time for additional practice and reteaching before the unit ends. If students did not do well on the Mid-Unit Review and have completed additional practice, you may want to use the Mid-Unit Review provided on Assessment Blackline Masters page 27.

Using the Student Pages Have students complete problems 1–35 on pages 200 and 201 on their own. Help students who need assistance to fill in the charts for problems 19–26 and to do the reading in problems 27–35. You might treat this review as a formal assessment of students' skills and have students complete this review as a timed test. See suggestions for administering timed tests on page 49.

Mid-Unit Review

Change each percent to a decimal.

1 2%
0.02

2 64%
0.64

3 5.5%
0.055

4 0.3%
0.003

5 90%
0.90

Change each decimal to a percent.

6 0.35
35%

7 0.5
50%

8 0.006
0.6%

9 0.425
42.5%

10 0.60
60%

Find each amount.

11 8% of 100
8

12 8% of 50
4

13 12.5% of 40
5

14 25% of 200
50

Choose the correct answer. Watch the signs.

15 2.4 × 5
a.) 12
b. 1.2
c. 0.12

16 0.41 × 3.8
a. 0.1558
b.) 1.558
c. 15.58

17 3.2 × 6.5
a. 0.208
b. 2.08
c.) 20.8

18 1.56 × 7.3
a. 1.1388
b.) 11.388
c. 113.88

Determine the final price for each item.

	Original Price of Item	Discount Rate	Tax Rate	Final Price	
19	$100	20%	4%	■	**$83.20**
20	$100	30%	5%	■	**$73.50**
21	$200	25%	10%	■	**$165.00**
22	$300	50%	4%	■	**$156.00**

In each case calculate the amount of money you would have.

	Principal	Rate of Interest	Number of Years	Amount	
23	$100	5%	1	■	**$105.00**
24	$100	7%	2	■	**$114.49**
25	$200	4%	5	■	**$243.33**
26	$200	6%	10	■	**$358.17**

200 • Percents and Number Theory

Solve these problems.

27 There is a 25% discount on small trees at the Green Thumb nursery. The regular price is $96. What is the sale price? **$72.00**

28 Lorenzo wants to buy a personal stereo that lists for $120. If the sales tax is 6%, how much will he have to pay for it? **$127.20**

29 An $80 dictionary is on sale at a 10% discount. The sales tax is 7%. With the discount and the tax, what is the cost of the dictionary? **$77.04**

30 Erin wants to buy some CDs that regularly sell for $18 but now are on sale for 25% off. Sales tax is 5%. If Erin has $100 to spend, how many of the CDs can she afford to buy? **7**

31 Mr. Wang put $200 in a bank at 5% interest. How much money will he have after ten years? **$325.78**

32 Ms. Goldstein put $600 in the bank at 6% interest. How long must she leave the money in the account to double the amount she deposited? **12 years**

33 Jim wants to buy a jacket that usually sells for $175. Today the jacket is on sale for 20% off. Sales tax is 5%. He has $150. Will he be able to buy the jacket? If so, how much change will he get? If not, how much more money will he need? **yes; $3.00 in change**

34 The Safe Bank pays 5% interest compounded monthly. If you were to deposit $1000, how much money would you have after one month? After one year? **$1004.17; $1051.16**

35 The sales tax in Sam's city is 6%. Suppose he paid $79.50 for a baseball glove, including the tax. What is the price of the glove without the tax? **$75.00**

Home Connections You may want to send Home Connections Blackline Masters pages 48–49 home, which provide additional activities families can complete together. These activities apply the skills being presented in this unit.

Portfolio Assessment As students work through the second half of this unit, the Portfolio Assessment task provided on Assessment Blackline Masters page 88 can be used to evaluate students' ability to use their knowledge of factors and divisibility tests to solve problems.

Performance Assessment The Performance Assessment Task 1 provided on Assessment Blackline Masters page 68–69 can be used at this time to evaluate students' proficiency with percents. You may want to administer this assessment with individual students or in small groups.

Unit Project This would be a good time to assign the "Birthday Present" project on pages 234 and 235. Students can begin working on the project in cooperative groups in their free time as you work through the unit. This project is a good opportunity for students to apply the concepts of percents, compound interest, and personal money management to real-world problem solving.

ASSESSMENT p. 27

UNIT 3 **Mid-Unit Review** (Use after Lesson 54.)

Name _____

The student demonstrates mastery by correctly answering at least 16 of the 20 problems.

Write each of these as a percent.

1 0.27 _27%_   **2** 0.005 _0.5%_   **3** 0.09 _9%_

Give the decimal equivalent.

4 42% _0.42_   **5** 3.6% _0.036_   **6** 600% _6.0_

Find each amount.

7 10% of 30 _3_   **8** 20% of 500 _100_
9 5% of 50 _2.5_   **10** 30% of 100 _30_
11 25% of 280 _70_   **12** 125% of 50 _62.5_
13 8% of 160 _12.8_   **14** 12.5% of 32 _4_

Solve these problems.

15 Camden is buying a watch that costs $20. The sales tax is 6%. What is the total cost of the watch? _$21.20_

16 John deposited $120 in the bank. Interest is 7% compounded annually. How much will he have in his account at the end of one year? _$128.40_

17 The shoes that Jennifer bought cost $24. That price was after a 25% discount off the regular price. What was the regular price? _$32.00_

18 Ski-lift tickets at Bear Lake are discounted by 40% on Tuesday through Thursday. If lift tickets usually cost $26.00, how much do they cost on Wednesday? _$15.60_

19 If $1000 is deposited in a bank for five years at 5% interest, compounded annually, how much total interest will be earned by the end of five years? _$276.28_

20 Megan has $42.00. She wants to buy a sweater that costs $39.95. The sales tax rate is 8.5%. Does Megan have enough money for the sweater? _no_

Math Explorations and Applications Level 6 • **27**

LESSON 55 · Applying Percents

Student Edition pages 202–203

Applying Percents

LESSON PLANNER

Objectives

✓ to evaluate students' proficiency in understanding and using percents

▶ to provide practice in understanding and using percents

Context of the Lesson This is the last of eight lessons on percent. It provides Mastery Checkpoint 15 for assessing students' proficiency in applying their knowledge of percent.

 MANIPULATIVES

play money*
(optional)

Program Resources

Practice Master 55

Enrichment Master 55

Assessment Master

For extra practice:
CD-ROM* Lesson 55
Cumulative Review, page 564

① Warm-Up ⏱ 5 MINUTES

Problem of the Day Present the following problem: Herman surveyed students at his school about their favorite subject. He found that $12\frac{1}{2}$% chose science, 25% chose math, $12\frac{1}{2}$% chose language arts, 20% chose social studies, and the remaining 48 students chose music. How many students did Herman survey? (160)

Problem-Solving Strategies Ask students who have solved the Problem of the Day to share how they solved it and any strategies they used.

MENTAL MATH Have students find the following products mentally.

a. 20% of 20 = (4)   b. 25% of 40 = (10)

c. 75% of 16 = (12)   d. 50% of 150 = (75)

e. 125% of 20 = (25)   f. 30% of 160 = (48)

ESL · Meeting Individual Needs

As needed, partner ESL students with students who are more proficient in English to help them understand some of the key language in the word problems, such as *% off, on sale at, discount,* and *% raise.*

Applying Percents

Sometimes using the percent key or doing other computations on a calculator can speed up the problem-solving process, but sometimes it is quicker to solve problems mentally.

Use a calculator only if necessary to help you solve these problems.

❶ Toni wants to buy a backpack that is priced at $40. The sales tax is 5%. What will the total cost be? **$42**

❷ Which costs less, a $50 jacket at 10% off or at $10 off? **$10 off**

❸ A $100 chair is on sale at 15% off. The sales tax is 5%. Including the tax, will the chair cost more than $100? **no (the chair costs $89.25)**

❹ A dealer is offering a 10% discount on all used cars in stock. Will a car with a price of $5136 be on sale for less than $5000? **yes (the car will cost $4622.40)**

❺ Bill wants to buy a shirt that is on sale at 20% off the regular price of $30. There is a 5% sales tax. How much will Bill pay for the shirt, including tax? **$25.20**

❻ Eva's new suit is 35% wool. Is the suit more than one-half wool? **no**

❼ A weather report said there was a 20% chance of rain on Tuesday. According to the report, was there a greater chance of rain than of no rain? **no**

❽ Kristina's basketball team played ten games. The team won seven games and lost three. What percent of the games did the team win? **70%**

❾ Which would cost less, an item on sale at half price or at 20% off? **half price**

❿ A board game that normally sells for $20 is on sale at 25% off with 6% tax. What will the total cost of the game be? **$15.90**

⓫ Which would cost more, a $10 cassette tape at regular price, or a $15 CD that is on sale at 30% off? **a $15 CD on sale at 30% off**

⓬ The sale price of a hair dryer is $19.95. The regular price is $25.00. Is the discount more than 10%? **yes (the discount is 20.2%)**

202 • Percents and Number Theory

RETEACHING

 Students who still have difficulty with computing percent should be helped through teacher or peer tutoring. Problems can be acted out, perhaps using **play money***. Additionally, tutors can focus on high-interest topics such as sports statistics and clothes shopping.

PRACTICE p. 55

LESSON 55 PRACTICE

Name_____

Solve these problems. Use a calculator if necessary.

❶ Zelda wants to buy a portable compact disc player that is on sale for $59.98. The sales tax is 5%.
   a. What is the amount of sales tax? — $3.00
   b. What will the total cost be? — $62.98

❷ Which costs less, a $26 watch at 5% off or at $5 off? — $5 off

❸ Which costs less, a $100 watch at 5% off or at $5 off? — Both are the same.

❹ Which costs less, a $260 watch at 5% off or at $5 off? — 5% off

❺ A $600 sewing machine is on sale for 25% off. The sales tax is 5%. Will the sewing machine cost less than $500? — yes

❻ Luis wants to buy a guitar that is on sale at 20% off the regular price of $42.00. The sales tax is 6%. How much will he pay for the guitar? — $35.62

❼ About 5% of the people at the baseball game left before the end of the fifth inning. Was that less than half of the people at the game? — yes

❽ Joel's Little League team has won six games and lost nine.
   a. What percent of its games has the team won? — 40%
   b. What percent of its games has the team lost? — 60%

❾ Is the price of a bracelet on sale for 40% of the regular price less than it would be if it were on sale for 40% off the regular price? — yes

❿ Abby paid $30.24 for a blender that was on sale for 20% off. The sales tax was 5%. What was the regular price? — $36.00

Math Explorations and Applications Level 6 • 55

---

*available separately

⑬ Renee made 23 out of 25 free throw attempts in basketball. What percent of her shots did she make? **92%**

⑭ Calvin got two hits out of ten times at bat. What percent of his times at bat did he get a hit? **20%**

⑮ Which costs more, a $200 coat that is on sale for 25% off or a $200 coat that is on sale for $40 off? **$40 off**

⑯ Which costs more, a $40 book with a discount of $10 or a $40 book with a discount of 10%? **discount of 10%**

⑰ Which costs more, a $150 oven with a discount of $10 or a $150 oven with a discount of 10%? **discount of $10**

⑱ Richard's salary is $200 per week. He is going to get a 5% raise. How much will his salary be then? **$210 per week**

⑲ Ms. Morales's salary is $500 per week, but her employer takes out 20% for federal tax and 4% for state tax. How much will her take-home pay be if these are the only two deductions? **$380**

⑳ Mr. Patel has calculated that about 30% of his monthly pay is deducted for various taxes. His salary is $4000 per month. About how much money does he actually receive each month? **$2800**

㉑ A survey of 50 students found that 30 of those surveyed would like a greater variety of foods in the school cafeteria. What percent of the students want a greater variety? **60%**

㉒ Which costs less, a $50 painting with a discount of $15 or a $50 painting with a discount of 15%? **$50 painting with $15 discount**

How do you decide whether to use a calculator to help you solve problems using percents? Record your ideas in your Math Journal.

Use the Cumulative Review on page 564 after this lesson.

Unit 3   Lesson 55 • **203**

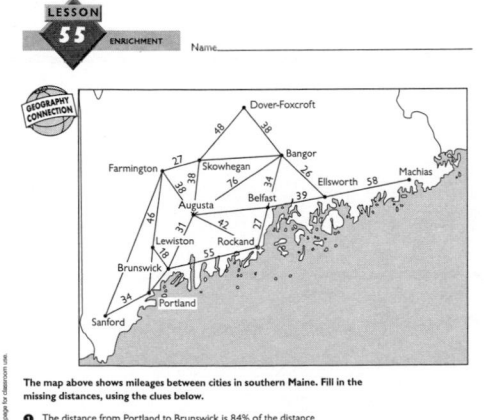
---

② Teach

Using the Student Pages Have students work on pages 202 and 203 independently. You can use the problems on either page as an assessment of students' ability to understand percents and to use them to solve problems. Observe students as they work, to see whether they understand what is being asked in the problems and whether they apply correct procedures for solving them.

③ Wrap-Up

In Closing To summarize the lesson, ask students to describe applications of percent in shopping and other activities in everyday life.

Mastery Checkpoint 15

By this time, most students should understand percents and be able to use them to solve problems. Assess their understanding and ability by observing them at work and by their results on the problems on page 202 or those on page 203. You may also wish to use Assessment Blackline Masters page 28. The results of this assessment may be recorded on the Mastery Checkpoint Chart. Students who consistently have difficulty calculating or applying percent should be given extra help.

Assessment Criteria

Did the student . . .

✓ correctly answer at least 9 of the 12 problems on page 202, or 8 of the 10 problems on page 203?

✓ demonstrate understanding of terms associated with percent, such as *sale, tax, discount,* and *raise?*

Homework Ask students to use real information from store flyers or newspaper ads about sales and discounts to formulate a few problems like the shopping problems on these pages.

Unit 3 Lesson 55   **203**

Keeping Sharp

LESSON PLANNER

Objectives

▶ to provide practice in computation and mental arithmetic

▶ to help students develop the broad ability to use mathematical common sense

Context of the Lesson
This lesson reviews computational skills and provides algebra readiness. It also contains the second part of "Competition," a four-part Thinking Story.

 MANIPULATIVES

calculators (optional)

Program Resources
Practice Master 56

Enrichment Master 56

For career connections:
Careers and Math*

For extra practice:
CD-ROM* Lesson 56

❶ Warm-Up

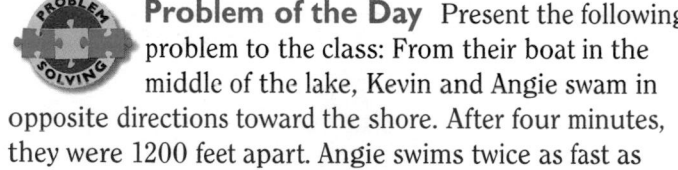

Problem of the Day Present the following problem to the class: From their boat in the middle of the lake, Kevin and Angie swam in opposite directions toward the shore. After four minutes, they were 1200 feet apart. Angie swims twice as fast as Kevin. How far did each swim? (Angie swam 800 ft; Kevin swam 400 ft.)

Problem-Solving Strategies Ask students who have solved the Problem of the Day to share how they solved it and any strategies they used.

 Ask students if $200 is enough money to purchase the following items. Students should indicate "yes" with thumbs up and "no" with thumbs down.

a. groceries for $87.40 plus dry cleaning for $32.50 (thumbs up)

b. two dozen T-shirts at $18.00 each (thumbs down)

c. three pairs of shoes at $24.50 per pair plus a dress for $39.95 (thumbs up)

(continued on page 205)

Keeping Sharp

Keep in shape by practicing your mental math skills and your basic computation facts. Look for shortcuts.

Solve these problems. Use paper and pencil only if necessary.

❶ 9 ÷ 3 **3**	❷ 90 ÷ 30 **3**	❸ 900 ÷ 300 **3**
❹ 900 ÷ 3 **300**	❺ 35 + 35 **70**	❻ 35 + 70 **105**
❼ 105 + 35 **140**	❽ 380 − 375 **5**	❾ 12 × 12 **144**
❿ 9 × 7 **63**	⓫ 4.98 + 3.02 **8.00**	⓬ 12.75 + 1.25 **14**
⓭ 135.2 − 1.2 **134.0**	⓮ 12 ÷ 3 **15**	⓯ 12 − 3 **9**
⓰ 12 × 3 **36**	⓱ 12 ÷ 3 **4**	⓲ 120 × 30 **3600**
⓳ 1200 ÷ 40 **30**	⓴ 1.97 × 10 **19.7**	㉑ 175 ÷ 25 **7**
㉒ 150 ÷ 75 **2**	㉓ 1500 ÷ 75 **20**	㉔ 9 × 8 **72**
㉕ 9 × 9 **81**	㉖ 9 × 10 **90**	㉗ 9 × 11 **99**
㉘ 9 × 12 **108**	㉙ 9 × 13 **117**	㉚ 9 × 14 **126**

 ALGEBRA READINESS

Solve for _n_. Use paper and pencil only if necessary.

㉛ 20 × n = 60 **3**	㉜ 200 × n = 600 **3**	㉝ 90 × n = 8100 **90**
㉞ 900 × n = 8100 **9**	㉟ 750 × n = 1500 **2**	㊱ 75 × n = 1500 **20**
㊲ 33 × n = 990 **30**	㊳ 30 × n = 990 **33**	㊴ 14 × n = 280 **20**
㊵ 140 × n = 28,000 **200**	㊶ 60 × n = 120 **2**	㊷ 6 × n = 1200 **200**

Solve these problems. Use paper and pencil only if necessary.

㊸ 350,000 + 349,999 **699,999**	㊹ 75 75 75 + 75 **300**	㊺ 42 × 15 **630**	㊻ 100,000 − 55,000 **45,000**
㊼ 325 + 399 **724**	㊽ 105 195 + 200 **500**	㊾ 420 × 15 **6300**	㊿ 40 25)1000

 FANTASTIC FACT

A bolt of lightning is as bright as one million 100-watt lightbulbs.

Why teach it at this time?

It is useful to periodically spend time sharpening math skills to prepare for solving equations and functions. Also, in everyday applications of computational skills students will save time (and make fewer errors) by solving problems mentally.

*available separately

Solve for n. Use paper and pencil only if necessary.

(51) $n = 50\%$ of 200 **100**

(52) $200 = n\%$ of 100 **200**

(53) $175 = n\%$ of 175 **100**

(54) $200 = 50\%$ of n **400**

(55) $150 = n\%$ of 75 **200**

(56) $15 = 300\%$ of n **5**

(57) $100 = n\%$ of 400 **25**

(58) $4 = n\%$ of 1 **400**

(59) $n = 25\%$ of 800 **200**

Solve these problems. Use pencil and paper when necessary.

(60) $100 \times 86 = ?$ **8600**

(61) $2 \times 86 = ?$ **172**

(62) $200 \times 86 = ?$ **17,200**

(63) $478{,}629 - 1 = ?$ **478,628**

(64) $478{,}629 - 478{,}628 = ?$ **1**

(65) $235{,}780 - 235{,}779 = ?$ **1**

(66) $25 + 25 + 25 + 25 = ?$ **100**

(67) $4 \times 25 = ?$ **100**

(68) $100 \div 4 = ?$ **25**

(69) $25 \times 8 = ?$ **200**

(70) $200 \div 25 = ?$ **8**

(71) $25 \times 400 =$ **10,000**

Solve for n.

(72) $n + n + n + n = 100$ **25**

(73) $4 \times n = 100$ **25**

(74) $4 \times n = 400$ **100**

(75) $n \times 4 = 400$ **100**

(76) $8 \times n = 800$ **100**

(77) $800 \div n = 8$ **100**

(78) $16 \div n = 8$ **2**

(79) $n - n = 1$ **impossible**

(80) $n - n = 0$ **any number**

(81) $40 \div 8 = n$ **5**

(82) $8 \times n = 40$ **5**

(83) $7 \times n = 14$ **2**

(84) $n = 14 \div 7$ **2**

(85) $n \times 0 = 12$ **impossible**

(86) $12 \div 0 = n$ **can't be done**

(87) $0 \times n = 0$ **any number**

(88) $0 \div 0 = n$ **can't be done**

(89) $7 \div 0 = n$ **can't be done**

(90) $n \div 7 = 0$ **0**

(91) $n \times 7 = 0$ **0**

(92) $0 \div 8 = n$ **0**

In each problem two of the answers are clearly wrong and one is correct. Choose the correct answer.

(93)	574 + 2651	**a.** 835	(**b.**) 3225	**c.** 2123
(94)	19,680 ÷ 492	(**a.**) 40	**b.** 400	**c.** 4000
(95)	72 × 53	**a.** 3426	(**b.**) 3816	**c.** 4936
(96)	24,386 − 17,591	**a.** 9765	**b.** 7695	(**c.**) 6795
(97)	807 × 93	**a.** 751	**b.** 7551	(**c.**) 75,051
(98)	43,380 ÷ 60	**a.** 72	(**b.**) 723	**c.** 7284

Real-World Connection

Ask students to obtain and examine brochures from mail order book, CD, and video clubs and look for similarities and differences in the deals offered. Have them work in groups to determine which clubs provide the best buys, which have hidden costs, which might make sense for them, which might not, and so on. Ask groups to share their findings with the class.

Mental Math (continued)

d. a new puppy for $123.00 plus a visit to the veterinarian for $62.50 (thumbs up)

e. dinner for four people at $27.30 each (thumbs up)

f. two plane tickets at $98.50 each (thumbs up)

2 Teach

Using the Student Pages Have students work on these pages independently. If they finish early, they can play any of the games introduced so far. Discuss the problems with the class. Problem 79 on page 205 cannot be answered, since whenever a number is subtracted from itself, the result is 0, not 1. For problem 80, n can be any number. For problem 85, point out that there is no number that when multiplied by 0 yields a product other than 0. Similarly, there is no answer to problem 86, since it would require that $0 \times n = 12$, an impossibility.

> ***Knowing the addition, subtraction, multiplication, and division facts "by heart" (or by mind) is at least as important as it ever was, and many other lower-order skills are still essential so that we can concentrate on the higher-order skills.***
>
> —Stephen S. Willoughby,
> *Mathematics Education for a Changing World*

◆ **LESSON 56** Keeping Sharp

Teach

Using the Thinking Story In this second
segment of "Competition," both Mr. Muddle
and Mr. Sneaky put their T-shirts on sale. The
focus is on how the consumer and the seller are affected by
a sale, and on how to determine the best buy among sale
items. Discuss the questions with the entire class. You may
need to spend more time on the second question than on
the others because several steps are needed for the solution.

Answers to Thinking Story Questions:

1. He sells T-shirts for $7.20 at 20% off, for $4.50 at 50% off,
   and for $2.70 at 70% off. Thus he gains $3.20 for 20%-off
   shirts and $0.50 for 50%-off shirts. He loses $1.30 for 70%-
   off shirts. Since he is apparently selling all the shirts at 70%
   off, he is losing money on every one.

2. Students can assume that Mr. Sneaky's shirts usually cost the
   same as Mr. Muddle's, or $9. Then 1-star shirts sell at 20%
   less than $9, or $7.20; 2-star shirts sell at 50% less than
   $18, or $9; and 3-star shirts sell at 70% less than $27, or
   $8.10. So the 1-star is the best buy at $7.20 and the 2-star is
   the worst buy at $9. The same relationships hold regardless
   of regular price. The 1-star shirts sell at 80% of 100% of the
   regular price, or 80%; 2-star shirts sell for 50% of 200% of
   the regular price, or 100%; and 3-star shirts sell at 30% of
   300% of the regular price, or 90%.

3. Mr. Sneaky's store will probably attract more customers at
   first, since he seems to have a greater variety of T-shirts and
   is giving bigger discounts on the 3-star shirts, which are
   supposedly of higher quality. However, wise shoppers will
   soon see that they get a better buy at Mr. Muddle's store.

Ask students to predict in their Math Journals
what will happen next in the ongoing competition
between Mr. Muddle and Mr. Sneaky.

◆ **LESSON 56** Keeping Sharp

THINKING STORY

Competition

Part 2

> **THIS WEEK ONLY.**
> **Every T-shirt**
> **20% TO 70% OFF!**

*You may want to refer to the first part of this Thinking
Story on pages 188-189.*

One day Mr. Muddle was walking past a clothing store. A
big sign in front said, "This week only. Everything 20%
to 70% off!" The store was crowded with customers
"There's an idea," said Mr. Muddle. "Maybe if I have a sale like
that, more people will buy my T-shirts."

So Mr. Muddle made up a bunch of stickers and put one on
each T-shirt. Some said "20% off;" some said "50% off;" and
some said "70% off." Since he sold only 1 kind of T-shirt, he
just mixed the stickers up and put one on each T-shirt. Then
he put a sign in his window. "This week only. Every T-shirt 20%
to 70% off!" As he had hoped, crowds flocked to his store to
buy T-shirts.

206 • Percents and Number Theory

**Literature
Connection**
Have students
read *Calculator Riddles*
by David A. Adler. Ask students to solve
the equations and then use a **calculator***
to find the answers to the riddles.

*available separately

"How is your sale going?" asked Mr. Sneaky. He was standing outside his own T-shirt store, unhappy because no one was in his store buying anything.

"The sale is going great," said Mr. Muddle. "I sold all the T-shirts that were 70% off in the first two hours. So I've had to keep changing the stickers on the other T-shirts to make more of them 70% off."

A week later a sign went up in the window of Mr. Sneaky's T-shirt store. It said, "This week only. 20% off on all one-star T-shirts. 50% off on all two-star T-shirts. 70% off on all three-star T-shirts."

Mr. Muddle went next door to see how his neighbor's sale was going. "I'm curious," said Mr. Muddle. "I have only one kind of T-shirt in my store, but you seem to have three. What's the difference between a one-star, a two-star, and a three-star T-shirt?"

"It's simple," said Mr. Sneaky. "They're all the same kind of shirt, but a one-star is the regular price with 20% taken off. A two-star is double the price with 50% taken off. For a three-star shirt I triple the price and then take 70% off."

. . . to be continued

Work in groups. Discuss your answers and how you figured them out. Then compare your answers with those of other groups. **Answers are in margin.**

❶ Remember that Mr. Muddle buys T-shirts for $4 each and usually sells them for $9 each. How much money does he gain or lose on each T-shirt in his special sale?

❷ Which is the best buy at Mr. Sneaky's sale, a one-star, a two-star, or a three-star T-shirt? Why?

❸ Whose sale is likely to attract more customers, Mr. Muddle's or Mr. Sneaky's? Why?

Unit 3 Lesson 56 • **207**

 **Wrap-Up** 5 MINUTES

In Closing To summarize the lesson, ask students to tell which of the two stores they would rather shop in, Mr. Muddle's or Mr. Sneaky's. Ask them to explain their choice.

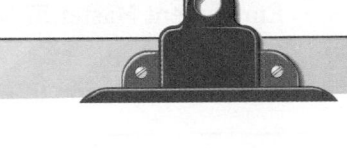 **Informal Assessment** Circulate through the class as students work on pages 204–205. Observe as they choose to use mental arithmetic or pencil and paper to solve the problems. If a choice is surprising to you, ask the student to explain his or her reasoning. Watch for students who are not using their number sense to figure out how problems can be solved mentally.

Assessment Criteria

Did the student . . .

✓ correctly answer at least 85% of the problems on pages 204–205?

✓ use mental arithmetic whenever possible to solve the problems?

✓ participate in the discussion of the Thinking Story?

Homework Challenge students to create a clever pricing system a T-shirt store might use to boost sales.

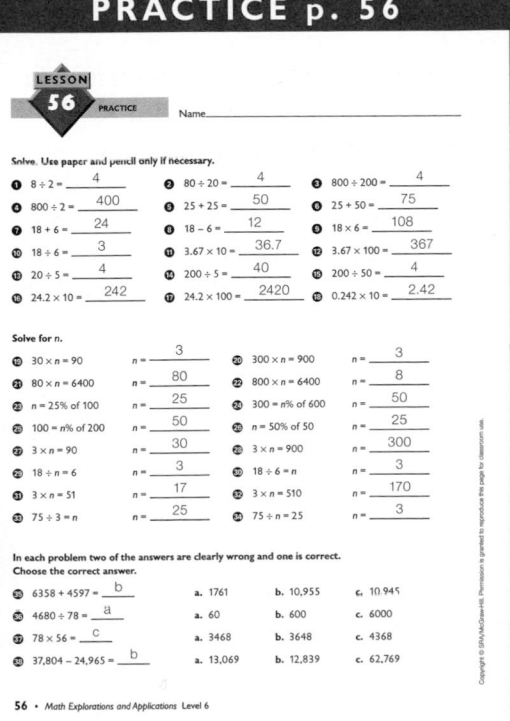

PRACTICE p. 56

ENRICHMENT p. 56

Student Edition pages 208–209
Multiples of 9

Multiples of 9

Tricky Nines

Try this activity with your friends.

Manolo said to Ken, "Choose any whole number from 1 to 10. Then multiply it by 9. Add the digits of your answer. The sum of the digits will be 9."

Ken chose the number 7. He multiplied it by 9, getting 63. He added 6 and 3 and got 9 as the sum, just as Manolo had said he would. "That's very good," said Ken, "but I bet you can't do it again."

Manolo thought he could. He repeated the instructions and again said that the sum of the digits would be 9.

◆ Was he right? Try all the numbers that Ken might have started with. **He was right.**

"That's not fair," said Ken. "The sum is always 9."

◆ Is Ken right? **yes**

"In fact," said Ken, "every multiple of 9 has a sum of digits equal to 9."

◆ Is he right? **no**

"I don't think that's true," Manolo argued. "What about 9 × 11?"

"Well," said Ken, "that's 99. And 9 + 9 = 18. If you add the digits of 18 you get 9. That's what I really meant."

◆ Is Ken right now? **yes (except for 0)**

208 • Percents and Number Theory

LESSON PLANNER

Objective

▶ to show how to check, without dividing, to see if a number is divisible by 9

Context of the Lesson This is the first of three lessons on divisibility rules.

 MANIPULATIVES   **Program Resources**

none   Practice Master 57

Enrichment Master 57

For extra practice:
    CD-ROM* Lesson 57

① Warm-Up ⏱

Problem of the Day Present the following problem: The computer club meets every third school day. The chess club meets every fourth school day. The cooking club meets every sixth school day. All three clubs meet today, Wednesday. What day of the week will it be the next time all three clubs meet on the same day, assuming school is in session Monday through Friday? (Friday)

Problem-Solving Strategies Ask students who have solved the Problem of the Day to share how they solved it and any strategies they used.

MENTAL MATH Write the following division problems on the chalkboard, asking students to show thumbs up if there is a remainder and thumbs down if there is not.

a. 330 ÷ 10 (thumbs down)   **b** 497 ÷ 7 (thumbs down)

c. 965 ÷ 10 (thumbs up)   **d.** 1427 ÷ 3 (thumbs up)

e. 2521 ÷ 5 (thumbs up)   **f.** 702 ÷ 9 (thumbs down)

g. 925 ÷ 5 (thumbs down)   **h.** 729 ÷ 2 (thumbs up)

Why teach it at this time?

Divisibility checks are useful in working with fractions and in other situations in which the factors of a number need to be determined. The check for 9 also provides an easy way to remember the multiplication facts for that number. Other divisibility rules are presented in the next lesson.

RETEACHING

Although divisibility rules presented in this lesson and in the next will help students in upcoming work with fractions, students are not expected to master them at this time. Students will have ample opportunities to become proficient with these rules during their work with fractions.

*available separately

For each problem multiply and then add the digits of the answer. If the sum is not a single-digit number, keep adding the digits until you get a single-digit number.

1 11 × 9 **99**   **2** 17 × 9 **153**   **3** 21 × 9 **189**
4 22 × 9 **198**   **5** 129 × 9 **1161**   **6** 131 × 9 **1179**

7 Is the final sum always 9? **yes**

8 Choose at least five different numbers and multiply each by 9. Try to find one for which Ken's rule doesn't work.
The rule works for all whole numbers except 0.
Manolo thinks that Ken's rule (page 208) also works backward. He says, "Suppose you keep adding the digits of a number until you have a one-digit sum. If that sum is 9, then your number is divisible by 9. If that sum is not 9, then your number is not divisible by 9."

Use a computer or other means to draw a chart, and complete the chart to see if Manolo's rule works.

Number	Final Sum of Digits	Remainder When Divided by 9	Does Rule Work?
351	9	0	yes
4122	9	0	yes
551	2	2	yes
2637	9	0	yes
442	1	1	yes

9 Choose at least five different numbers for which the final sum of digits is 9. Divide each by 9. Try to find a number for which Manolo's rule doesn't work. **There is no positive whole number that is not divisible by 9 for which the final sum of digits is 9.**

10 Choose at least five different numbers for which the final sum of digits is not 9. Divide each by 9. Try to find a number for which Manolo's rule doesn't work. **There is no positive whole number that Is divisible by 9 for which the final sum of digits is not 9.**

Unit 3   Lesson 57 • **209**

---

❷ Teach

Using the Student Pages Instead of reading about Manolo's trick, you may wish to try it on several members of the class until students understand how it works. Then extend the trick to include numbers greater than 10. Show that you must repeatedly add the digits until only a single digit remains. Challenge students to see if they can find exceptions to the rule for multiples of 9. (The only exception is 0.)

Next, ask students if they think the reverse is true, that when the final sum of the digits is 9, the number is divisible by 9. Have them check the examples 342 and 783 to see that the rule works in both cases.

Have students complete the problems on page 209 on their own. Before they begin, make sure all students understand that to be divisible by 9, a number must have a remainder of 0 when divided by 9. Commend students who notice that the final sum of digits for numbers not divisible by 9 (551 and 442) equals the remainder when the numbers are divided by 9. Encourage interested students to investigate whether this is true for other numbers. (It is.)

❸ Wrap-Up

In Closing Summarize the lesson by asking students to explain how they can tell if a number is divisible by 9.

Informal Assessment Write the number 3276 on the chalkboard. Ask students to tell whether the number is or is not divisible by 9 and to explain how they know. (Yes; the digits add up to 18, and 1 + 8 = 9.) Ask them to give a four-digit number that is not divisible by 9.

Assessment Criterion

Did the student . . .

✓ explain how to tell whether a number is divisible by 9 without actually dividing that number by 9?

Homework Invite students to try out the activity using the divisibility rule for 9 with a family member.

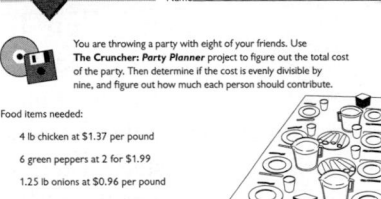
Unit 3 Lesson 57 **209**

Finding Divisibility Rules

LESSON PLANNER

Objectives

▶ to teach divisibility rules for 2, 3, 4, 5, 6, 8, 9, and 10

▶ to provide practice in division with divisors of 10 or less

Context of the Lesson This is the second of three lessons on divisibility rules. Students can use these rules to solve practical problems in the next lesson and these rules will be useful to them when they work with prime factorization and fractions.

 MANIPULATIVES

Venn Diagram Mat*

Program Resources

Practice Master 58

Enrichment Master 58

For extra practice:
CD-ROM* Lesson 58

1 Warm-Up ⏱ 5 MINUTES

 **Problem of the Day** Present the following problem: Place the numbers 1, 2, 3, 6, 9, 10, 11, and 16 in the diagram below.

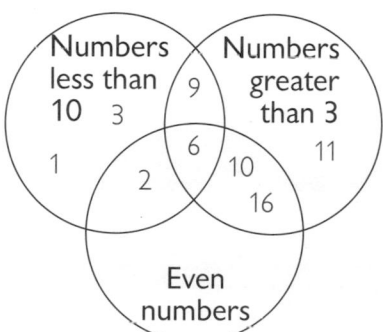

Problem-Solving Strategies Ask students who have solved the Problem of the Day to share how they solved it and any strategies they used.

Finding Divisibility Rules

Can 74 students in the sixth grade be divided equally into groups of three? Sometimes it's useful to check for divisibility without actually dividing.

1 Which of these numbers are divisible by 2?

(a.) 6   b. 7   (c.) 12   d. 15

(e.) 50   f. 53   g. 97   (h.) 100

i. 105   (j.) 1000   k. 10,467   (l.) 10,472

In your Math Journal, try to state a rule that will tell you whether a number is divisible by 2. (Hint: Does the last digit help?)

2 Which of these numbers are divisible by 5?

(a.) 10   (b.) 15   c. 18   (d.) 45

(e.) 145   (f.) 1000   g. 1013   (h.) 1035

Record each of these in your Math Journal.

◆ Write a rule that will tell you whether a number is divisible by 5.
If the last digit is 0 or 5, the number is divisible by 5.

◆ State a rule for deciding whether a number is divisible by 10.
If the last digit is 0, the number is divisible by 10.

◆ Find a rule for deciding whether a number is divisible by 3. (Hint: Think about the rule for 9. Try several numbers to see if your rule works.)
If the final sum of the digits is 3, 6, or 9, the number is divisible by 3.

3 Try your rule for deciding whether a number is divisible by 3 on each of these numbers. (In each case use the rule to see if the number is divisible by 3, and then divide to check.)

(a.) 12   (b.) 93   (c.) 126   (d.) 15   (e.) 24

f. 13   g. 23   h. 43   i. 26   (j.) 36

k. 46   (l.) 35,166   (m.) 8247   n. 8248   o. 8249

Record each of these in your Math Journal.

◆ Find a rule for deciding whether a number is divisible by 4. (Hint: Look at the last two digits.) **If the last two digits form a number divisible by 4, the number is divisible by 4.**

◆ Find a rule for deciding whether a number is divisible by 8. (Hint: Look at the last three digits.) **If the last three digits form a number divisible by 8, the number is divisible by 8.**

4 Can 74 students be divided equally into groups of 3? **no**

 **Literature Connection** Have students read *The Meal a Mile Long* by Frieda Hughes, which describes how a prisoner's last requested meal gives him freedom from his captors. Have students figure out how many 2-foot, 5-foot, and 10-foot sandwiches would fit on the table.

*available separately

5 On your paper draw two large circles that overlap like the ones shown here. Label one "Divisible by 2" and one "Divisible by 3." Then, decide whether each of the numbers shown below is divisible by 2, by 3, by both 2 and 3, or by neither 2 nor 3. If a number is divisible by 2 but not by 3, write it inside the "2" circle but *not* inside the "3" circle. If the number is divisible by 3 but not by 2, write it inside the "3" circle but *not* the "2" circle. If a number is divisible by both 2 and 3, write the number inside both circles where 12 has been written. If a number is not divisible by either 2 or 3, write the number outside the circles. The first five numbers have been written in the correct places.

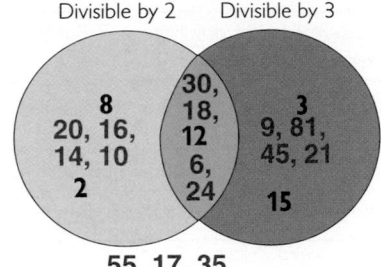

Divisible by 2   Divisible by 3

8
20, 16,
14, 10
2

30,
18,
12
6,
24

3
9, 81,
45, 21

15

55, 17, 35

Numbers to be checked for divisibility by 2 and by 3:

2	8	12	3	15	6	9	35	30	20
18	55	81	45	16	24	14	21	10	17

6 You have now placed all the numbers into one of the three sections made by the two circles or outside the circles. Are there any numbers inside only the "divisible by 2" section that are divisible by 6? **no**

7 Are there any numbers inside only the "divisible by 3" section that are divisible by 6? **no**

8 Where are all the numbers that are divisible by 6? Check to be sure you are correct. **in the intersection of both circles, where 12 has been written**

Record in your Math Journal a rule for deciding whether a number is divisible by 6.

Unit 3   Lesson 58 • **211**

Technology Connection Refer students to the software *On Target Multiply and Divide* from Gamco (Mac, for grades 2–8) for further practice with multiplication and division facts.

 Ask students to solve the following problems using mental math. Have them respond with thumbs up if there is a remainder, and thumbs down if there is not.

a. $2234 \div 2$ (thumbs down)

b. $639 \div 3$ (thumbs down)

c. $648 \div 4$ (thumbs down)

d. $4298 \div 9$ (thumbs up)

e. $423 \div 5$ (thumbs up)

f. $3020 \div 10$ (thumbs down)

g. $972 \div 9$ (thumbs down)

h. $240 \div 6$ (thumbs down)

❷ Teach

 **Using the Student Pages** Let students work individually or in small groups on the problems on page 210. Encourage them to try numbers other than those given to arrive at and check the different divisibility rules. Then, as a class, discuss the validity of the rules students derive. Here are some hints you can offer the students for checking divisibility by 4 and 8:

First, look at divisibility by 4. Check whether the last two digits form a number that is divisible by 4. That can be done by checking whether the two-digit number is divisible by 2 twice. These steps will tell you:

▶ Do the last two digits form an even number?

▶ If so, divide by 2.

▶ Is the result an even number?

▶ If so, the original number is divisible by four; otherwise it is not.

To check divisibility by 8, simply divide the last three digits by 2 twice. If the result is an even number, the original number is divisible by 8.

 Use a **Venn Diagram Mat*** to go over problem 5 on page 211 with students. Be sure they understand how to interpret what the circles show them about divisibility by carefully reviewing the placement of the first five numbers. You may wish to point out that overlapping circles, known as Venn diagrams (after John Venn, 1834–1923), are useful for showing relationships between sets. When students complete the page, ask volunteers to explain the placement of various numbers within the circles. You may wish to ask students to suggest other numbers that would fit within the different regions.

◆ LESSON 58 Finding Divisibility Rules

Teach

Using the Student Pages The table on page 212 summarizes the divisibility rules that the class should have developed so far. Although students should not memorize these or any other descriptions of the rules, they should become comfortable using the rules. Direct students' attention to the paragraph under the table. Explain that it is often important to know that a number is *not* divisible by another number.

Go over some examples with the class prior to assigning completion of the chart on page 213. For example, ask, "Which number should we check divisibility for first?" "Second?" "Third?" and so on. You might suggest first checking for divisibility by numbers that have a simple divisibility rule. For instance, offer the following procedure:

First look at the last digit. If it is 0, 2, 4, 6, or 8, the number is divisible by 2; if it is 0 or 5, the number is divisible by 5; and if it is 0, the number is divisible by 2, 5, and 10. You may want to check for divisibility by 4 or 8 next, or do this later. Next add the digits (repeat until the sum is a single-digit number). If the final sum is 9, the number is divisible by 9 and, of course, also divisible by 3; if it is 3 or 6, the number is divisible by 3 but not by 9. If the number is divisible by both 3 and 2, it is of course divisible by 6. If a number is not divisible by 2, it is not divisible by 4, 6, 8, or 10. A number that is not divisible by 4 is not divisible by 8. Finally, check for divisibility by 7 using short division.

GIFTED & TALENTED **Meeting Individual Needs**
Some students may be interested in learning why the divisibility rules work. Encourage them to research this. You may wish to point out that any number that divides exactly into two numbers also divides exactly into their sum. For instance, since 100 and 12 are both divisible by 4, we know 112 is divisible by 4, and since 1000 and 112 are both divisible by 8, we know that 1112 is divisible by 8.

◆ LESSON 58 Finding Divisibility Rules

Here are some rules for divisibility.

Divisor	Divisibility Rule
2	If a whole number ends with an **even** digit, it is divisible by 2.
3	If the sum of the digits is divisible by 3, the number is divisible by 3.
4	If the last two digits make a number divisible by 4, the number is divisible by 4.
5	If the number ends with 0 or 5, it is divisible by 5.
6	If the number is divisible by both 2 and 3, it is divisible by 6.
7	There are rules for divisibility by 7. But the simplest way to find out is simply to divide.
8	If the last three digits make a number divisible by 8, the number is divisible by 8.
9	If the sum of the digits is divisible by 9, the number is divisible by 9.
10	If the last digit is 0, the number is divisible by 10.

For each rule it is also true that if the condition does not hold, then the number is not divisible by that divisor. This is important, too.

Use the chart to help you solve the following problems.

9 Consider the number 7140.

a. Is 7140 divisible by 7? How can you check without dividing?
yes; 7 and 14 are divisible by 7

b. Is 7140 divisible by 8? How can you check without dividing?
no; 140 is not divisible by 8 (you must divide 140 by 8)

c. Is 7140 divisible by 9? How can you check without dividing?
no; the final sum of the digits is 3, not 9

d. Is 7140 divisible by 10? How can you check without dividing?
yes; the last digit is 0

e. How can the work you've done in checking for divisibility by 7, 8, 9, and 10 help you tell quickly whether 7140 is divisible by 2, 3, 5, and 6? **Since 7140 is divisible by 10, it's divisible by 2 and 5. Since 7140 is divisible by 9, it's divisible by 3. Any number divisible by 2 and 3 is divisible by 6.**

10 What is the least number greater than 0 that is divisible by
a. 2, 3, 6, and 7? **42 b.** 3, 6, 8, and 9? **72 c.** 4, 5, 8, and 10? **40**

11 In problem 10, did you need to use four division rules to check the answers? Explain. **No, because, for instance, every number divisible by 6 is divisible by 2 and 3, and every number divisible by 8 is divisible by 4.**

212 • Percents and Number Theory

Use a computer or other means to draw this chart. Then complete it by using a ✔ to tell whether each of the following numbers is divisible by 2, 3, 4, 5, 6, 7, 8, 9, and 10.   A ✔ indicates a "yes" answer.

	\multicolumn{9}{c}{Divisible By}								
	2	3	4	5	6	7	8	9	10
252	✔	✔	✔		✔	✔		✔	
315		✔		✔		✔		✔	
91						✔			
2520	✔	✔	✔	✔	✔	✔	✔	✔	✔
2521									
1024	✔		✔				✔		
97									
101									
105		✔		✔		✔			
729		✔						✔	
210	✔	✔		✔	✔	✔			✔
209									
2519									
2401						✔			

◆ Did you find that 2520 is divisible by all the numbers—2, 3, 4, 5, 6, 7, 8, 9, and 10? **yes**

◆ Since 2520 is divisible by 7, could 2521 also be divisible by 7? **no**

◆ What would the remainder be if 2521 were divided by 7? Divide to see if you're right. **1**

◆ Since 2520 is divisible by 2, 3, 4, 5, 6, 7, 8, 9, and 10, could 2521 be divisible by any of them? **no**

Record in your Math Journal the strategies you used for completing the chart. Did you need to use every divisibility rule for checking every number?

Unit 3   Lesson 58 • **213**

 **❸ Wrap-Up**

In Closing To summarize the lesson, ask students to tell what order they think works best for checking for divisibility by 2, 3, 4, 5, 6, 8, 9, and 10.

Performance Assessment Ask students to check the number 120 for divisibility by 2, 3, 4, 5, 6, 8, 9, and 10.

Assessment Criteria

Did the student. . . .

✓ participate in the effort to come up with divisibility rules?

✓ understand how to use the overlapping circles to show divisibility?

✓ demonstrate understanding of the given divisibility rules by correctly determining by which numbers the numbers on page 213 are exactly divisible?

Homework Ask students to list as many four-digit numbers as they can that are divisible by nine different one-digit numbers. (2520, 5040, 7560) Ask them to find the least three-digit number divisible by 1, 2, 3, 4, 5, 6, 8, 9, and 10. (360)

PRACTICE p. 58

ENRICHMENT p. 58

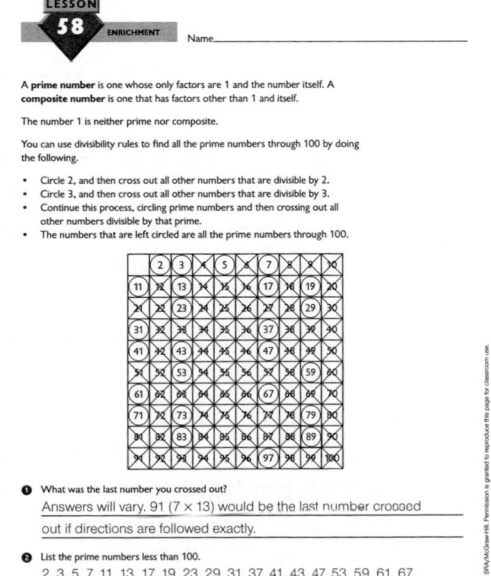
Unit 3 Lesson 58 **213**

LESSON 59 Using Divisibility Rules

LESSON 59 Using Divisibility Rules

LESSON PLANNER

Objective

▶ to provide realistic applications of divisibility rules

Context of the Lesson
This is the third of three lessons on divisibility rules.

 MANIPULATIVES

graph paper (optional)

cardboard rectangles (optional)

Program Resources

Number Cubes (0–5 and 5–10)

Practice Master 59

Enrichment Master 59

For extra practice:
CD-ROM* Lesson 59
Cumulative Review, page 565

① Warm-Up ⏱ 5 MINUTES

 Problem of the Day Present this problem: Using three straight cuts from the top, what is the greatest number of pieces you can make from a rectangular chocolate cake? How many pieces could you make if one or more of the cuts need not be from the top? (7 pieces; 8 pieces)

Problem-Solving Strategies Ask students who have solved the Problem of the Day to share how they solved it and any strategies they used.

MENTAL MATH Write the following division problems on the chalkboard, asking students to show thumbs up if there is a remainder and thumbs down if there is not:

a. 3078 ÷ 6 (thumbs down) **b.** 2006 ÷ 4 (thumbs up)

c. 1944 ÷ 2 (thumbs down) **d.** 3605 ÷ 9 (thumbs up)

e. 2086 ÷ 7 (thumbs down) **f.** 291 ÷ 3 (thumbs down)

g. 1901 ÷ 2 (thumbs up) **h.** 1944 ÷ 2 (thumbs down)

i. 2837 ÷ 4 (thumbs up) **j.** 2706 ÷ 6 (thumbs down)

k. 3062 ÷ 8 (thumbs up) **l.** 3040 ÷ 8 (thumbs down)

m. 957 ÷ 9 (thumbs up) **n.** 948 ÷ 4 (thumbs down)

Emily is packing small boxes of raisins in cartons. The top of each box is 3 centimeters wide and 5 centimeters long. She wants to pack the boxes so they stand up straight in the carton. She has cartons of several sizes from which to choose. She wants to choose a carton so that there won't be space on the sides and the boxes will fit nicely. All the cartons are the same height as the boxes of raisins. But the lengths and widths of the cartons are different. These are the sizes of the cartons:

10 centimeters by 10 centimeters   12 centimeters by 12 centimeters

15 centimeters by 15 centimeters   20 centimeters by 20 centimeters

Emily tried the smallest carton first.

"These don't fit evenly," Emily said.

Pablo was watching and decided to help. "You don't have to try every carton," he said. "Just think a little."

◆ Can you tell how Emily can figure out whether a certain carton will work? **Since the cartons have square bottoms, the length of a side must be divisible by both the length and width of the raisin boxes. Otherwise, there will be some space along the length or width (or both) of the carton.**

"I could have told you the 10-centimeter by 10-centimeter carton wouldn't work," said Pablo. "Since 10 is divisible by 5, you can put some boxes across the carton without leaving any space. But 10 is not divisible by 3, so you cannot fit all the rows of boxes without leaving space at the end."

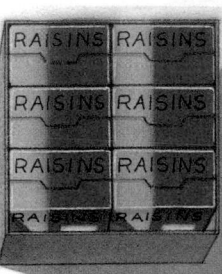

214 • Percents and Number Theory

Meeting Individual Needs

For students who are having trouble with the two-dimensional problems, you might begin with some that are one-dimensional. For example, can sticks that are each 6 centimeters long be placed in a straight line along a 27-cm track so that there is no space left over or between them? (no) From problems of this type, work up to the two-dimensional ones presented in the lesson. When a student does attempt the lesson problems, pair him or her with a student partner who understands the concepts well and is a good listener and explainer.

"I see," said Emily. "Then the 12-centimeter carton won't work either."

◆ Is Emily right? How do you know? **She is right because 12 is not divisible by 5.**

◆ Which size carton should she use? **The 15-cm × 15-cm carton, because 15 is divisible by 3 and 5.**

◆ Draw a picture to show how the boxes will fit in the carton you will use. Use graph paper if necessary. **Check students' drawings.**

◆ How many cartons would she need in order to pack 150 boxes? **10**

A week later Pablo was again watching Emily packing cartons. "You know," Emily said, "the boxes of raisins are bigger now. They are 4 centimeters by 6 centimeters instead of 3 centimeters by 5 centimeters."

◆ Which size carton should Emily use now? Draw a picture to show that you are right. **the 12-cm × 12-cm carton; check students' drawings**

◆ How many cartons would she need in order to pack 150 boxes? **25**

◆ Suppose the boxes were each 4 centimeters by 5 centimeters. Which size carton would Emily use? Draw a picture to show that you are right. **the 20-cm × 20-cm carton; check students' drawings**

◆ Could Emily pack these 4-centimeter by 5-centimeter boxes into a carton that was 12 centimeters by 15 centimeters? Draw a picture to show whether it would work. **yes (if she placed the boxes in the right direction); check students' drawings**

Emily bought a new batch of cartons in four different sizes:

12 centimeters by 12 centimeters

12 centimeters by 15 centimeters

12 centimeters by 20 centimeters

15 centimeters by 20 centimeters

For each size box, tell which of the new cartons Emily could use to pack the boxes exactly.
12 × 12, 12 × 15,

❶ 4 centimeters by 3 centimeters   ❷ 3 centimeters by 3 centimeters
12 × 20, 15 × 20   **12 × 12, 12 × 15**

❸ 3 centimeters by 5 centimeters   ❹ 5 centimeters by 6 centimeters
12 × 15, 12 × 20, 15 × 20   **12 × 15, 12 × 20**

❺ 6 centimeters by 10 centimeters   ❻ 4 centimeters by 6 centimeters
12 × 20   **12 × 12, 12 × 20**

❼ 5 centimeters by 10 centimeters   ❽ 4 centimeters by 5 centimeters
15 × 20   **12 × 15, 12 × 20, 15 × 20**

Unit 3 Lesson 59 • **215**

❷ Teach

Using the Student Pages You may wish to introduce the "Tiling" game on Teacher's Guide page 216 first, so that students can play it as they finish their work.

Read through the story on page 214 with the entire class. Be sure that all students understand Emily's situation before you discuss the question at the bottom of page 214. Continue reading the story with the class. Discuss the next two questions and assign students to do the fourth on their own. **Graph paper** may be helpful for this and the following questions. Have students work on the remaining questions and problems individually or in small groups.

GIFTED & TALENTED **Meeting Individual Needs**
Give students additional three-dimensional packing questions. For example: Could you pack 4-cm by 3-cm by 5-cm boxes into a carton that is a cube, 12 centimeters on a side, without leaving any space? (no) What about into a 12-cm by 12-cm by 15-cm carton? (yes) **How many will fit?** (36)

◆ LESSON 59 Using Divisibility Rules

Teach

![GAME] **Introducing the "Tiling" Game** Have two
students play the game as the others watch. This
game provides practice in finding common factors.
Students may play the game as they finish pages 216–217.
Be sure everyone understands the following rules:

Players: Two or more
Materials: Two 0–5 cubes and two 5–10 cubes
Object: To find the largest square tile that can be used to
cover a floor.

1. Each student rolls all four cubes and forms two two-digit
numbers. If a 10 is rolled, that cube should be rolled
again.

2. The two numbers are the length and width, in decimeters,
of a room the students must tile. Have students try to
find the largest square tile that can be used in covering
the floor.

3. The player who can use the largest tile is the winner.

Sample Round

Bill rolled: 1 9 5 2   and made 91 × 52.
                          He could use 13-dm × 13-dm tiles.

Tamara rolled: 4 2 5 5   and made 25 × 45.
                          She could use 5-dm × 5-dm tiles.

Andy rolled: 9 2 7 0   and made 90 × 72.
                          He could use 18-dm × 18-dm tiles.

Andy won this round.

Using the Student Pages Discuss the first paragraph
on page 216 and do the first few problems with the class.
Then assign the remaining problems. Have students work
independently on the problems on page 217.

◆ LESSON 59 Using Divisibility Rules

Imagine that you want to
cover a floor with square
tiles. You want to use the
largest tiles possible. They
can be any size, but they
must be square.

9 A floor is 40 decimeters by 30 decimeters.

   a. What is the largest square tile you could use to cover the floor? **10 dm × 10 dm**

   b. How many of those tiles will fit on the floor? **12**

10 A floor is 45 decimeters by 30 decimeters.

   a. What is the largest square tile you could use to cover the floor? **15 dm × 15 dm**

   b. How many of those tiles will fit on the floor? **6**

11 A floor is 64 decimeters by 48 decimeters.

   a. What is the largest square tile you could use to cover the floor? **16 dm × 16 dm**

   b. How many of those tiles will fit on the floor? **12**

12 A floor is 28 decimeters by 50 decimeters.

   a. What is the largest square tile you could use to cover the floor? **2 dm × 2 dm**

   b. How many of those tiles will fit on the floor? **350**

13 A floor is 35 decimeters by 50 decimeters.

   a. What is the largest square tile you could use to cover the floor? **5 dm × 5 dm**

   b. How many of those tiles will fit on the floor? **70**

14 A floor is 25 decimeters by 45 decimeters.

   a. What is the largest square tile you could use to cover the floor? **5 dm × 5 dm**

   b. How many of those tiles will fit on the floor? **45**

15 A floor is 24 decimeters by 48 decimeters.

   a. What is the largest square tile you could use to cover the floor? **24 dm × 24 dm**

   b. How many of those tiles will fit on the floor? **2**

16 A floor is 24 decimeters by 28 decimeters.

   a. What is the largest square tile you could use to cover the floor? **4 dm × 4 dm**

   b. How many of those tiles will fit on the floor? **42**

17 A floor is 16 decimeters by 27 decimeters.

   a. What is the largest square tile you could use to cover the floor? **1 dm × 1 dm**

   b. How many of those tiles will fit on the floor? **432**

216 • Percents and Number Theory

RETEACHING

 Students who have difficulty
with the material in this lesson
may benefit from work with
concrete objects, such as **cardboard
rectangles** that can be placed over
drawn squares. Have students work
through the problems in the lesson
using these materials. Demonstrate that
using divisibility checks often takes less
time than using trial and error.

Watch the signs.

⑱ 6 × 7 **42** ⑲ 8 × 6 **48** ⑳ 42 ÷ 6 **7** ㉑ 49 ÷ 7 **7**

㉒ 6 + 7 **13** ㉓ 6 + 9 **15** ㉔ 6 × 9 **54** ㉕ 36 ÷ 6 **6**

㉖ 19 − 9 **10** ㉗ 24 ÷ 4 **6** ㉘ 9 × 7 **63** ㉙ 9 × 9 **81**

㉚ 54 ÷ 9 **6** ㉛ 45 ÷ 5 **9** ㉜ 13 − 8 **5** ㉝ 18 − 9 **9**

㉞ 18 ÷ 9 **2** ㉟ 81 ÷ 9 **9** ㊱ 8 × 5 **40** ㊲ 40 ÷ 4 **10**

㊳ 15 − 7 **8** ㊴ 7 × 5 **35** ㊵ 36 ÷ 9 **4** ㊶ 8 × 3 **24**

㊷ 21 ÷ 3 **7** ㊸ 27 ÷ 3 **9** ㊹ 32 ÷ 4 **8** ㊺ 8 × 8 **64**

Add or subtract. Use shortcuts when you can.

㊻ 16,000 − 10,999 = **5,001**
㊼ 2987 + 1013 = **4000**
㊽ 992 + 992 = **1984**
㊾ 15,399 + 701 = **16,100**

㊿ 79,801 − 15,999 = **63,802**
(51) 9876 − 4321 = **5555**
(52) 1215 + 1812 = **3027**
(53) 17,890 − 599 = **17,291**

Multiply. Use shortcuts when you can.

(54) 37,037 × 3 = **111,111**
(55) 37,037 × 27 = **999,999**
(56) 598 × 50 = **29,900**
(57) 598 × 51 = **30,498**

(58) 101 × 66 = **6666**
(59) 10,101 × 66 = **666,666**
(60) 4444 × 500 = **2,222,000**
(61) 673 × 123 = **82,779**

Divide.

(62) 12)1440 **120**
(63) 33)2541 **77**
(64) 56)13,104 **234**
(65) 28)19,740 **705**

(66) 42)6762 **161**
(67) 37)49,284 **1332**
(68) 24)720 **30**
(69) 16)4096 **256**

Use the Cumulative Review on page 565 after this lesson.

❸ Wrap-Up (5 MINUTES)

In Closing Summarize the lesson by asking students to explain how they were able to use their understanding of divisibility rules to solve Emily's problems and the tiling problems.

ALTERNATIVE ASSESSMENT

Portfolio Assessment For their Math Portfolios, have students write an explanation of how they used their knowledge of divisibility to solve one of the spatial problems presented in the lesson. Tell them to include a description of how they might be able to use divisibility rules to solve real-life problems. Ask them to describe what they found easiest and most difficult about the process of solving the problems in the lesson.

Assessment Criteria

Did the student . . .

- ✓ demonstrate understanding of divisibility rules for 2, 3, 4, 5, 9, and 10?
- ✓ apply understanding of divisibility rules to solve the spatial problems on pages 214–216?
- ✓ correctly answer at least 75% of the problems on page 217?

Homework Have students play the "Tiling" game with a family member to practice using divisibility rules.

PRACTICE p. 59

LESSON 59 PRACTICE Name__________

In each problem small boxes are to be placed in a larger box so that there won't be any space left and the boxes will fit neatly. Choose the large box that will do the best-fitting job.

❶ 4 cm by 6 cm __b__ **a.** 20 cm by 25 cm **b.** 16 cm by 24 cm **c.** 15 cm by 24 cm

❷ 5 cm by 6 cm __a__ **a.** 30 cm by 25 cm **b.** 32 cm by 35 cm **c.** 35 cm by 40 cm

❸ 3 cm by 4 cm __c__ **a.** 18 cm by 25 cm **b.** 16 cm by 23 cm **c.** 27 cm by 64 cm

❹ 5 cm by 15 cm __a__ **a.** 10 cm by 45 cm **b.** 15 cm by 56 cm **c.** 34 cm by 75 cm

❺ 9 cm by 12 cm __c__ **a.** 81 cm by 45 cm **b.** 50 cm by 108 cm **c.** 72 cm by 144 cm

❻ 8 cm by 12 cm __b__ **a.** 24 cm by 35 cm **b.** 56 cm by 36 cm **c.** 102 cm by 136 cm

❼ 15 cm by 12 cm __a__ **a.** 84 cm by 75 cm **b.** 100 cm by 29 cm **c.** 150 cm by 86 cm

❽ 7 cm by 9 cm __b__ **a.** 105 cm by 84 cm **b.** 63 cm by 108 cm **c.** 56 cm by 64 cm

Math Explorations and Applications Level 6 • **59**

ENRICHMENT p. 59

LESSON 59 ENRICHMENT Name__________

Find hardcover books that have more than 200 pages. For each book, record the title and the total number of pages in the first two columns of the chart below. Count every page, even those that are not numbered, but don't count the covers or the end sheets. Remember that a page is one side of one of the sheets of paper that make up the book. Then complete the chart by marking whether the total number of pages is divisible by each number written across the top of the chart.

Title	Total Number of Pages	Numbers by Which Total Is Divisible: 2, 3, 4, 5, 6, 7, 8, 9, 10, 16, 20, 32, 50, 64
		Answers will vary.

Do you see any patterns in the completed chart? __________

Math Explorations and Applications Level 6 • **59**

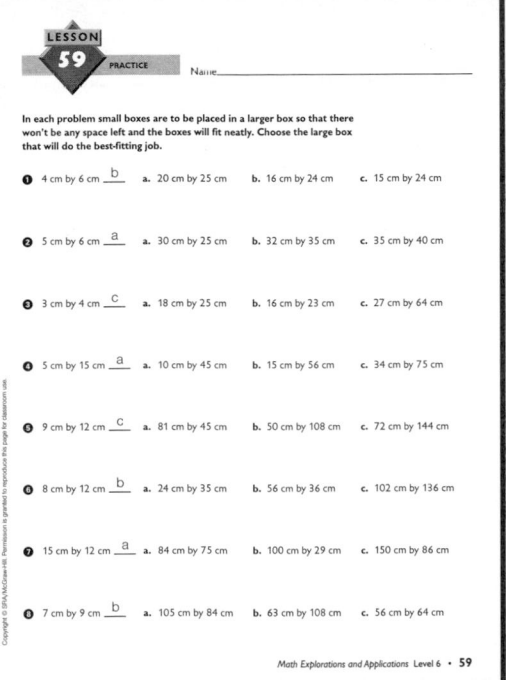

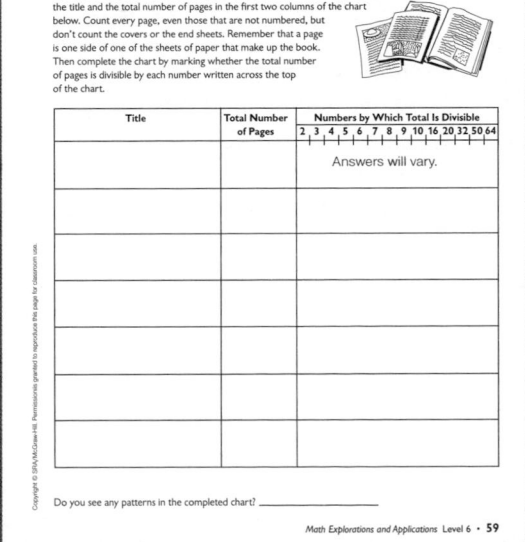

Student Edition pages 218–221

Factors

LESSON PLANNER

Objectives

▶ to review the meaning of *factor* and to provide practice finding factors of numbers

▶ to help students develop the broad ability to use mathematical common sense

Context of the Lesson
This lesson is the first of two lessons on factorization. The next lesson covers prime and composite numbers. Students will use this knowledge in the next unit to express answers to fraction problems in simplest form. This lesson also contains part three of "Competition," a four-part Thinking Story.

 MANIPULATIVES
none

Program Resources
"Find the Treasure" Game Mat
"Harder Find the Treasure" Game Mat
Practice Master 60
Enrichment Master 60
For career connections:
  Careers and Math*
For additional math integration:
  Math Throughout the Day*
For extra practice:
  CD-ROM* Lesson 60

① Warm-Up ⏱ 5 MINUTES

 **Problem of the Day** Present the following problem to the class: To celebrate its 50th anniversary today, Muddle's Department Store is giving away gifts to its customers. Every customer who comes into the store will receive a free calculator. Every second person will receive a watch. Every fourth customer will receive a CD, and every fifth one will receive perfume. Every 15th customer will receive a sweater. Which lucky customer will be the first to receive all five gifts? (60th customer)

Problem-Solving Strategies Ask students who have solved the Problem of the Day to share how they solved it and any strategies they used.

Factors

You've learned divisibility rules for several numbers. In this lesson you'll learn about **factors** of a given number, those whole numbers that can be multiplied by a whole number to equal the given number.

We say that 6 is *divisible* by 2 because there is no remainder when we divide 6 by 2.

We also say:

2 is a *divisor* of 6.

2 is a *factor* of 6.

6 is a *multiple* of 2.

We say that 72 is divisible by 12 because there is no remainder when we divide 72 by 12.

We also say:

12 is a *divisor* of 72.

12 is a *factor* of 72.

72 is a *multiple* of 12.

Suppose we want to find all the factors of 72. We can simply test each number, starting with 1, to see if it is a factor of 72.

1 is a factor (72 ÷ 1 = 72, so 1 × 72 = 72)

2 is a factor (72 ÷ 2 = 36, so 2 × 36 = 72)

3 is a factor (72 ÷ 3 = 24, so 3 × 24 = 72)

4 is a factor (72 ÷ 4 = 18, so 4 × 18 = 72)

5 is not a factor (72 ÷ 5 has remainder 2)

6 is a factor (72 ÷ 6 = 12, so 6 × 12 = 72)

7 is not a factor (72 ÷ 7 has remainder 2)

8 is a factor (72 ÷ 8 = 9, so 8 × 9 = 72)

9 is a factor (72 ÷ 9 = 8, so 9 × 8 = 72)

10 is not a factor (72 ÷ 10 has remainder 2)

11 is not a factor (72 ÷ 11 has remainder 6)

12 is a factor (72 ÷ 12 = 6, so 12 × 6 = 72)

218 • Percents and Number Theory

 **Literature Connection** Have students read "Play with Your Triangle" in *Math Wizardry for Kids* by Margaret Kenda and Phyllis S. Williams to learn about Fibonacci numbers and some of the many unusual features of these numbers.

---

*available separately

The next number we test that is a factor of 72 will be 18. Since we already know that $4 \times 18 = 72$, 18×4 must be 72. Similarly, since $3 \times 24 = 72$, $24 \times 3 = 72$, and 24 is a factor of 72.

Notice that the factors come naturally in pairs; 8 is paired with 9 because $8 \times 9 = 72$, 1 is paired with 72, 2 is paired with 36, 3 with 24, and so on. As soon as you start repeating pairs, you know that you have all the possible factors and you don't have to continue.

Another way to think about the factors of 72 is to picture all of the rectangles with side lengths in whole units that could be made within an **area** of 72 square units.

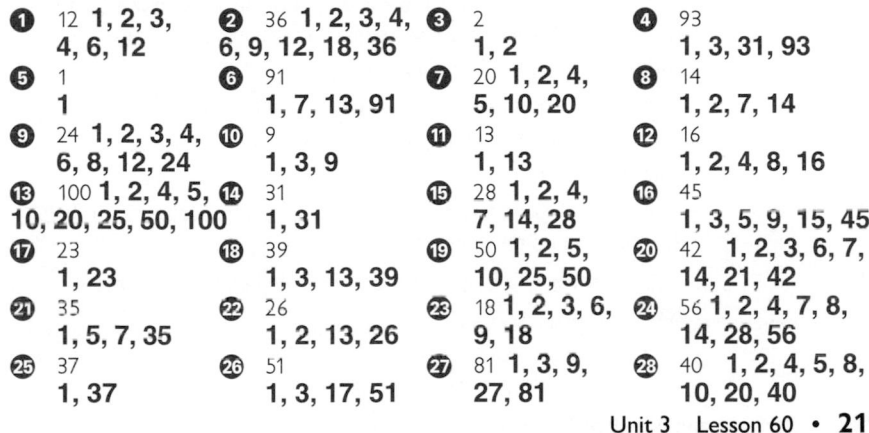

Any number that is the length of a side of one of these rectangles is a factor of 72. The factors of 72 are 1, 2, 3, 4, 6, 8, 9, 12, 18, 24, 36, and 72.

For each number list all the factors.

1 12 **1, 2, 3, 4, 6, 12**

2 36 **1, 2, 3, 4, 6, 9, 12, 18, 36**

3 2 **1, 2**

4 93 **1, 3, 31, 93**

5 1 **1**

6 91 **1, 7, 13, 91**

7 20 **1, 2, 4, 5, 10, 20**

8 14 **1, 2, 7, 14**

9 24 **1, 2, 3, 4, 6, 8, 12, 24**

10 9 **1, 3, 9**

11 13 **1, 13**

12 16 **1, 2, 4, 8, 16**

13 100 **1, 2, 4, 5, 10, 20, 25, 50, 100**

14 31 **1, 31**

15 28 **1, 2, 4, 7, 14, 28**

16 45 **1, 3, 5, 9, 15, 45**

17 23 **1, 23**

18 39 **1, 3, 13, 39**

19 50 **1, 2, 5, 10, 25, 50**

20 42 **1, 2, 3, 6, 7, 14, 21, 42**

21 35 **1, 5, 7, 35**

22 26 **1, 2, 13, 26**

23 18 **1, 2, 3, 6, 9, 18**

24 56 **1, 2, 4, 7, 8, 14, 28, 56**

25 37 **1, 37**

26 51 **1, 3, 17, 51**

27 81 **1, 3, 9, 27, 81**

28 40 **1, 2, 4, 5, 8, 10, 20, 40**

Unit 3 Lesson 60 • **219**

Technology Connection Refer students to the software *Five in a Row* from Critical Thinking Books and Software (Mac, IBM, for grades 2–12) for further practice with multiplication rules, division rules, and factors.

 Provide practice with divisibility rules by asking students to show thumbs up if there is a remainder and thumbs down if there is none.

a. $80 \div 4$ (thumbs down)

b. $3500 \div 7$ (thumbs down)

c. $4605 \div 9$ (thumbs up)

d. $1746 \div 6$ (thumbs down)

e. $29 \div 3$ (thumbs up)

f. $180 \div 6$ (thumbs down)

g. $3473 \div 2$ (thumbs up)

h. $2472 \div 8$ (thumbs down)

❷ Teach

Using the Student Pages Review the meaning of *factor* by using page 218 to go over the factors of 72 with the class. Then ask students to find the factors of 48. Note that 1 and the number itself are always factors. You may wish to point out that it may be easier to find all the factors of a number by pairing them off as they are listed in increasing order, for example, (1, 48), (2, 24), (3, 16), and so on. Point out that students can tell that they have listed all the factors of a number when, for the first time, the second factor in a pair is smaller than the first—(8, 6), for example. After this discussion, have students do the problems on page 219. Guide them to try to list factors in increasing order, or to list factors in pairs.

> *Most people who find themselves in a situation that requires mathematics either don't recognize that good decisions depend on mathematical thought or don't make the best decisions because they are unable or unwilling to think mathematically.*
>
> —Stephen S. Willoughby, *Mathematics Education for a Changing World*

◆ **LESSON 60 Factors**

Teach

Using the Thinking Story In this third segment of "Competition," Mr. Muddle learns from College of Canine Knowledge owner Mr. Breezy about a free way to advertise his T-shirt business. Have students think about the suggestion Mr. Breezy makes.

Answers to Thinking Story Questions:

1. Each business owner advertises another's business by allowing that person to place a sign on the wall. This costs participants very little, and works because the businesses are not in competition with one another.

2. Possible answers: the costs of producing the posters, and the time and expense of travel to stores to place the posters.

3. It does not make sense for Mr. Muddle and Mr. Sneaky to trade ads because the two stores compete for the same business and they could take business away from each other. Mr. Muddle should trade ads with people who are not his competitors.

Ask students to write descriptions in their Math Journals of the different kinds of advertising available to store owners and to explain why they think some might work better than others. Ask them to explain why they would or would not use Mr. Breezy's approach if they were in Mr. Muddle's situation.

Introducing the "Find the Treasure" and "Harder Find the Treasure" Game Mats
Introduce this game by playing it with a student as the rest of the class watches. This game provides practice with following directions and basic number operations. Play long enough so that everyone understands the rules. After students play the game a few times, have them try the "Harder Find the Treasure" Game Mat. Complete directions are provided on the Game Mats. A copy of these Game Mats can also be found on pages 612–613 in this Teacher's Guide.

◆ **LESSON 60 Factors**

THINKING STORY Competition

Part 3

You may want to refer to the earlier parts of this Thinking Story on pages 188-189 and 206-207.

Mr. Muddle was still looking for ways to sell more T-shirts. "You need to advertise," Mr. Breezy told him. "Then more people will know about your store and come buy from you. That's how people learn about my dog training school."

"Do you advertise on television?" Mr. Muddle asked.

"No, that costs too much for a small business like mine," said Mr. Breezy. "Here's how I advertise and it costs practically nothing." He pointed to a sign on the wall of his office.

"But that's an ad for Raul's Garage," said Mr. Muddle.

"Exactly. And Raul has an ad in his garage for my dog training school."

"And here's an ad on your wall for Spiffy Dry Cleaners. I'll bet they have an ad on their wall. . . ."

"For Breezy's College of Canine Knowledge. Right. Now you get the idea."

220 • Percents and Number Theory

Invite students to share what they know about advertising practices in other countries or in different parts of this country. Have them speculate about the reasons for differences among or similarities to advertising in your area.

RETEACHING

Reteaching is not necessary at this time. However, you may need to emphasize the distinction between factors and multiples.

Mr. Muddle thanked Mr. Breezy for the idea. Then he went back to his store and made a poster that looked like this:

> # MUDDLE'S T-SHIRTS
> They fit you
> from head to toe.
> Come to my store at
> ## 511 Elm Street

He took the sign with him and went next door to Sneaky's T-Shirts. "I've got a wonderful deal for you, Mr. Sneaky," he said. "You'll be able to advertise for free, I'll be able to advertise for free, and we'll both make more money."

. . . to be continued

Work in groups. Discuss your answers and how you figured them out. Then compare your answers with those of other groups. **Answers are in margin.**

❶ Explain how Mr. Breezy's way of advertising works. Why do the other merchants agree to it?

❷ Mr. Breezy said his way of advertising costs "practically nothing." What costs would you count?

❸ Does it make sense for Mr. Muddle to trade ads with Mr. Sneaky? What is it that Mr. Muddle has failed to understand about Mr. Breezy's way of advertising?

Unit 3   Lesson 60 • **221**

---

❸ Wrap-Up

In Closing To summarize the lesson, ask students to explain what a factor is and how to find all the factors of a number.

 **Performance Assessment** Ask students to list all the factors of 80 and describe the method they used to make their list. (1, 2, 4, 5, 8, 10, 16, 20, 40, 80)

Assessment Criteria

Did the student . . .

✓ express understanding of the meaning of *factor*?

✓ correctly list all the factors for 25 of the 28 numbers on page 219?

✓ contribute to the Thinking Story discussion?

✓ demonstrate understanding of Mr. Muddle's error in approaching Mr. Sneaky in the Thinking Story?

Homework Invite students to write their own ad for Mr. Muddle's or Mr. Breezy's business.

ESL   Meeting Individual Needs
You may wish to help ESL students distinguish the mathematical definition of *factor* from other meanings of the term that might be more familiar to them. Work with them to list alternative meanings of the word, using a dictionary when needed, and discuss how the different definitions are related.

PRACTICE p. 60

LESSON 60 PRACTICE Name_____

For each number list all the factors.

❶ 8	1, 2, 4, 8	❷ 5	1, 5
❸ 45	1, 3, 5, 9, 15, 45	❹ 80	1, 2, 4, 5, 8, 10, 16, 20, 40, 80
❺ 24	1, 2, 3, 4, 6, 8, 12, 24	❻ 49	1, 7, 49
❼ 11	1, 11	❽ 20	1, 2, 4, 5, 10, 20
❾ 32	1, 2, 4, 8, 16, 32	❿ 37	1, 37
⓫ 56	1, 2, 4, 7, 8, 14, 28, 56	⓬ 60	1, 2, 3, 4, 5, 6, 10, 12, 15, 20, 30, 60
⓭ 42	1, 2, 3, 6, 7, 14, 21, 42	⓮ 55	1, 5, 11, 55
⓯ 18	1, 2, 3, 6, 9, 18	⓰ 30	1, 2, 3, 5, 6, 10, 15, 30
⓱ 36	1, 2, 3, 4, 6, 9, 12, 18, 36	⓲ 16	1, 2, 4, 8, 16
⓳ 27	1, 3, 9, 27	⓴ 99	1, 3, 9, 11, 33, 99
㉑ 52	1, 2, 4, 13, 26, 52	㉒ 44	1, 2, 4, 11, 22, 44
㉓ 75	1, 3, 5, 15, 25, 75	㉔ 81	1, 3, 9, 27, 81

60 • *Math Explorations and Applications* Level 6

ENRICHMENT p. 60

LESSON 60 ENRICHMENT Name_____

A **perfect number** is one for which the sum of all of its factors, other than itself, is exactly equal to the number.
The number 6 is a perfect number. 1 + 2 + 3 = 6

6

A **deficient number** is one for which the sum of all of its factors, other than itself, is less than the number.
The number 8 is a deficient number. 1 + 2 + 4 < 8

8

An **abundant number** is one for which the sum of all of its factors, other than itself, is greater than the number.
The number 12 is an abundant number. 1 + 2 + 3 + 4 + 6 > 12

12

❶ Find the numbers from 2 through 30 that are perfect numbers.
6, 28

❷ Find the numbers from 2 through 30 that are deficient numbers.
2, 3, 4, 5, 7, 8, 9, 10, 11, 13, 14, 15, 16, 17, 19, 21, 22, 23, 25, 26, 27, 29

❸ Find the numbers from 2 through 30 that are abundant numbers.
12, 18, 20, 24, 30

60 • *Math Explorations and Applications* Level 6

LESSON 61

Prime and Composite Numbers

Student Edition pages 222–225

LESSON PLANNER

Objectives

▶ to review the meaning of *prime number* and *composite number*

▶ to provide practice in finding prime factors

▶ to help students develop the broad ability to use mathematical common sense

Context of the Lesson This lesson, the second of two lessons on factorization, contains the last part of "Competition," a four-part Thinking Story.

 MANIPULATIVES

Program Resources

Reteaching Master

Practice Master 61

Enrichment Master 61

For career connections:
  Careers and Math

For extra practice:
  CD-ROM* Lesson 61

 Warm-Up

5 MINUTES

 **Problem of the Day** Present the following problem to the class: A number is called an abundant number if the sum of its factors other than the number itself is greater than the number. What are the first five abundant numbers? (12, 18, 20, 24, 30)

Problem-Solving Strategies Ask students who have solved the Problem of the Day to share how they solved it and any strategies they used.

MENTAL MATH Present the following problems and have students indicate thumbs down for answers that are obviously wrong and thumbs up for answers that are possibly right.

a. 10 x 10 = 1000 (thumbs down)

b. 2500 − 500 = 1500 (thumbs down)

c. 81 ÷ 9 = 9 (thumbs up)

d. 0.23 + 0.23 = 4.6 (thumbs down)

(continued on page 223)

LESSON 61

Prime and Composite Numbers

You may have noticed in the previous lesson that some numbers have many factors and some have only two. We can classify whole numbers according to how many factors they have.

A **prime number** has exactly two factors, 1 and itself.

A **composite number** has more than two factors.

The number 1 is neither prime nor composite since it has only one factor. It is the only whole number that is neither prime nor composite.

For each number write *P* on your paper if the number is prime, *C* if it is composite, or *N* if it is neither.

1	1	N	**2**	2	P	**3**	3	P
4	4	C	**5**	5	P	**6**	6	C
7	7	P	**8**	8	C	**9**	9	C
10	10	C	**11**	11	P	**12**	12	C
13	13	P	**14**	14	C	**15**	15	C
16	18	C	**17**	19	P	**18**	20	C
19	22	C	**20**	28	C	**21**	29	P
22	30	C	**23**	99	C	**24**	101	P
25	105	C	**26**	1001	C	**27**	89	P
28	124	C	**29**	252	C	**30**	2520	C

31 What are the prime numbers that are less than 20?
2, 3, 5, 7, 11, 13, 17, 19

Every whole number except 1 can be factored into prime numbers in exactly one way (except for the order of the factors). We call this prime factorization. For example, $28 = 2 \times 2 \times 7$. Of course, $28 = 7 \times 2 \times 2$ and $28 = 2 \times 7 \times 2$, but we do not consider these different prime factorizations of 28, because all that is changed is the order of the factors. Usually, we write factors in increasing order and use exponents if we can.

$$28 = 2^2 \times 7$$

To find the prime factors of a number, factor it into any two factors and continue factoring until all factors are prime.

 In the group discussions about these particular Thinking Story questions, which involve logical reasoning rather than computation, students should make every effort to listen carefully and considerately to all ideas members suggest and to be open to new ideas. Encourage students to behave in a supportive manner whenever working cooperatively with classmates.

*available separately

Example:
Show the prime factorization of 2156.
Find any factor of 2156. Since 56 is divisible by 4, 2156 is divisible by 4.

$$2156 = 4 \times 539$$

Next, find factors of 4 and 539. Continue finding factors until all factors left are prime.

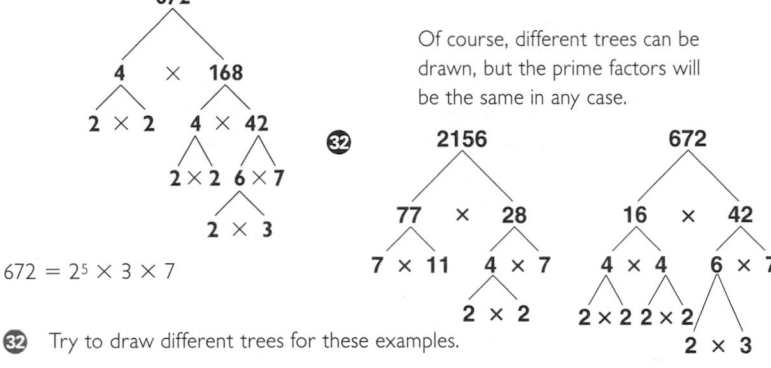

Note that the factors appear at the ends of the branches of the "tree."

$2156 = 2 \times 2 \times 7 \times 7 \times 11 = 2^2 \times 7^2 \times 11$

We can use these steps for any number.

Show the prime factorization of 672.

Of course, different trees can be drawn, but the prime factors will be the same in any case.

$672 = 2^5 \times 3 \times 7$

32 Try to draw different trees for these examples.

33 Show the prime factorization of 53. **53**

34 Show the prime factorization for each of the numbers in problems 2–30 on page 222. **Be sure to check students' answers carefully.**

The largest living thing on Earth is believed to be the "General Sherman" sequoia tree located in Sequoia National Park, California. It is 275 feet tall and weighs over 1400 tons (as much as the weight of nine blue whales or 360 elephants).

Unit 3   Lesson 61 • **223**

Technology Connection Invite students to view the video *Math Mystery Theatre: Great Numbers Bank Robbery* from EdCon/Imperial International (VHS, for grades 2–8) for further practice with prime and composite numbers, and prime factorization.

Mental Math (continued)

e. 1746 ÷ 6 = 291 (thumbs up)

f. 20 × 20 = 400 (thumbs up)

g. 13.33 + 13.33 = 13.3333 (thumbs down)

h. 21 ÷ 7 = 3 (thumbs up)

❷ Teach

Using the Student Pages Before students begin page 222, go over the definitions of prime and composite numbers presented at the top of the page. Provide additional examples of each. If a student wonders how to categorize 0, explain that normally only positive whole numbers are considered as prime or composite. If we have to choose, 0 must be a composite number, since any number times 0 equals 0, and thus it has more than two factors.

When discussing the tree diagrams on page 223, guide students to understand that although several different "trees" are possible for a given composite number, its prime factors are always the same. As needed, show this by starting the first tree with 2 x 1078, rather than 4 x 539. Have students do problems 1–31 on page 222 and 32–34 on page 223 on their own. You may choose to have students complete problem 34 on page 223 for homework.

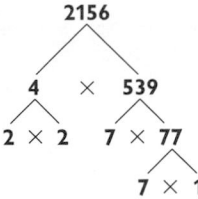

SPECIAL NEEDS **Meeting Individual Needs**
Help students who have difficulty finding prime factors by reviewing the following rules, which should be applied in sequence: (1) If the last digit is 0, keep dividing by 10 until the last digit is not 0 (each factor of 10 should be further factored to 5 x 2); (2) If the number is even, keep dividing by 2 until an odd quotient results; (3) If the sum of the digits is 3 or 6, divide once by 3; if it is 9, divide twice by 3. Then work the sum of the digits of the resulting number; (4) If the ones digit is 5, keep dividing by 5 until the ones digit is not 5; (5) Try dividing by prime numbers starting with 7, then 11, 13, 17, and so on. Have students practice solving problems and compare their problem-solving strategies.

◆ LESSON 61 Prime and Composite Numbers

Teach

Using the Thinking Story In this last segment of "Competition," Mr. Muddle is at his wit's end. He cannot think of any way to compete with Mr. Sneaky. Then Mr. Sneaky changes his business and Mr. Muddle, without the competition, can go on selling T-shirts at a profit and without any gimmicks.

Answers to Thinking Story Questions:

1. The store's employees and those few people who like to shop at late hours gained. All the other customers lost because the cost of keeping the stores open at night caused the price of T-shirts to increase. Local examples of this "open all night" phenomenon might be pointed out.

2. Mr. Sneaky would not go out of business but would in fact be better off: he would have made money from selling all his T-shirts and could have bought more to restock his store.

3. Students should not be expected to know what is actually involved in buying and selling a business. However, they should understand that Mr. Muddle would have to pay Mr. Sneaky for his store and stock plus enough extra to get Mr. Sneaky to agree to give up his business.

4. Mr. Sneaky changed to another business and so ceased being Mr. Muddle's competitor.

5. The story suggests that neither Mr. Muddle nor Mr. Sneaky was selling enough T-shirts to make a sufficient profit, and one or both would have eventually gone out of business. Mr. Sneaky may have quit first because he had higher costs, was less tolerant of being poor, or realized that selling discount CDs was more profitable.

Ask students to write in their Math Journals any ideas Mr. Muddle might have tried to win business back from Mr. Sneaky.

Competition
Part 4

You may want to refer to the earlier parts of this Thinking Story on pages 188–189, 206–207, and 220–221.

Mr. Muddle tried still another way to sell more T-shirts. He tried keeping his store open all night. But that didn't work. He had to pay a helper because he couldn't stay awake all night to look after the store. Soon Mr. Sneaky started keeping his T-shirt store open all night too. Neither of them sold any more T-shirts because nobody came to buy T-shirts in the middle of the night. It cost so much to stay open all night that they both had to raise the prices of their T-shirts.

"I give up," Mr. Muddle said. "No matter what I do to sell more T-shirts, Mr. Sneaky does it too. Things always end up as bad as before."

"Why don't you buy out Mr. Sneaky's business?" Loretta the Letter Carrier asked. "Then you would be the only person left selling T-shirts. You would be sure to get more business."

Mr. Muddle thought that was a brilliant idea. He called in his friends Ferdie, Portia, Manolita, Marcus, and Willy. He told them of his plan. "I'll give you money. I want you to go next door to Mr. Sneaky's store. Keep buying T-shirts until his T-shirts are all gone. Then I'll be the only person in town selling T-shirts."

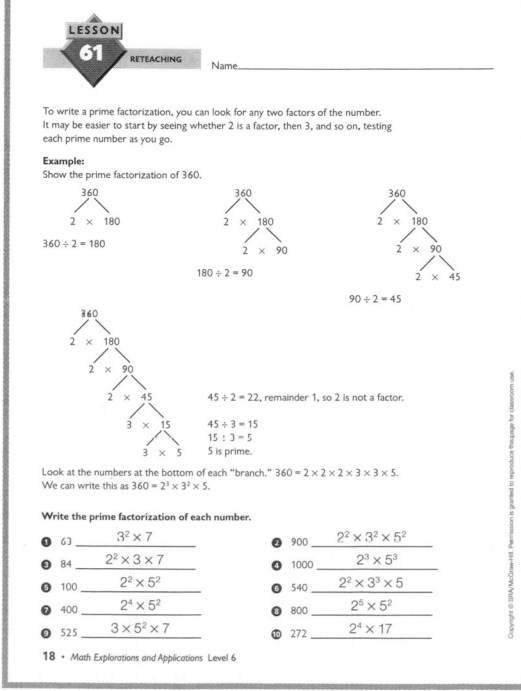

"I'm sorry, Mr. Muddle," said Willy. "Your plan won't work."

"Nothing works," Mr. Muddle said sadly. "Mr. Sneaky is sure to win, no matter what I do. He copies all my ideas. He has a bigger store, a newer store. He has more T-shirts, brighter lights, and an expensive sign in front. I guess I'll just do the best I can and be poor."

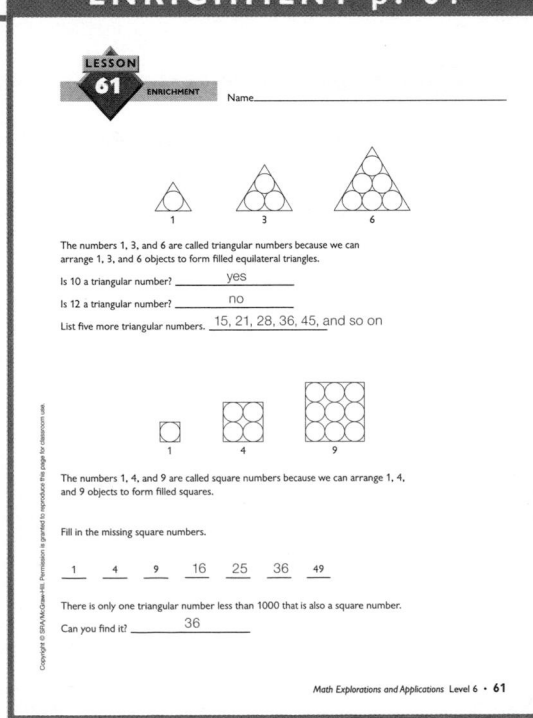

So Mr. Muddle quit having sales. He quit staying open all night. He charged $9 for each T-shirt, the same as before. He sold only 70 or 80 of them a week. He was so poor that he started buttering his bread on the edge because it took less butter than on the flat side. But suddenly, after a few months, he started selling more and more T-shirts. He went next door to see if Mr. Sneaky was also doing better. But the sign above Mr. Sneaky's store no longer said, "Sneaky's T-shirts." It said, "Sneaky's Discount CDs. 20% off on all one-star CDs. 50% off on all two-star CDs. 70% off on all three-star CDs."

. . . the end

Work in groups. Discuss your answers and how you figured them out. Then compare your answers with those of other groups. **Answers are in margin.**

1 Who gained and who lost from having the T-shirt stores open all night? Explain.

2 Why wouldn't Mr. Muddle's plan for buying out Mr. Sneaky's business work?

3 What would you need to do in order to buy out the business of someone like Mr. Sneaky?

4 Why did business suddenly get much better for Mr. Muddle?

5 Why do you think Mr. Sneaky changed businesses?

Unit 3   Lesson 61 • **225**

---

③ Wrap-Up

In Closing To summarize the lesson, ask students to describe what a composite number is and to explain why 0 might be considered one.

Performance Assessment Ask students to decide whether 141 is a prime or composite number and to tell how they know. (It is composite because it is divisible by 3.)

Assessment Criteria

Did the student . . .

✓ correctly answer at least 90% of the problems on page 222?

✓ demonstrate an understanding of how to find the prime factors of a number?

✓ express understanding of the distinction between prime and composite numbers?

✓ participate meaningfully in group discussions about the last segment of "Competition?"

Homework Have students complete the prime factorizations from page 223 begun in class.

GIFTED & TALENTED **Meeting Individual Needs**
Present the following problem: The sum of the ages of the three Hurni sisters is 46. Margaret, the oldest, is twice the age of Rose, the youngest. Nancy is the middle sister. Three years ago, all their ages were prime numbers. How old was each of the sisters three years ago? (Rose: 7; Nancy: 13; Margaret: 17)

PRACTICE p. 61

LESSON 61 PRACTICE Name_____

Show the prime factorization of each number. The first one has been done for you. "Trees" shown are examples only.

1 812
4 — 203
2 2   7 29
$2^2 \times 7 \times 29$

2 230
23 — 10
5 2
$2 \times 5 \times 23$

3 14
2 7
2×7

4 891
9 — 99
3 3 9 11
3 3
$3^4 \times 11$

5 502
2 251
2×251

6 612
4 — 153
2 2 9 17
3 3
$2^2 \times 3^2 \times 17$

7 720
10 — 72
2 5 8 9
2 4 3 3
2 2
$2^4 \times 3^2 \times 5$

8 420
10 — 42
2 5 6 7
2 3
$2^2 \times 3 \times 5 \times 7$

9 2160
9 — 240
3 3 2 120
2 60
6 10
2 3 2 5
$2^4 \times 3^3 \times 5$

Math Explorations and Applications Level 6 • 61

ENRICHMENT p. 61

LESSON 61 ENRICHMENT Name_____

The numbers 1, 3, and 6 are called triangular numbers because we can arrange 1, 3, and 6 objects to form filled equilateral triangles.

Is 10 a triangular number? **yes**

Is 12 a triangular number? **no**

List five more triangular numbers. **15, 21, 28, 36, 45, and so on**

The numbers 1, 4, and 9 are called square numbers because we can arrange 1, 4, and 9 objects to form filled squares.

Fill in the missing square numbers.

1   4   9   **16**   **25**   36   49

There is only one triangular number less than 1000 that is also a square number.

Can you find it? **36**

Math Explorations and Applications Level 6 • 61

Unit 3 Lesson 61 **225**

Checking Products

LESSON PLANNER

Objective
▶ to learn a method for checking multiplication

Context of the Lesson Students can work on this lesson while others are getting extra teaching or practice on the divisibility rules and factoring.

 MANIPULATIVES
none

Program Resources
Practice Master 62
Enrichment Master 62
For extra practice:
CD-ROM* Lesson 62

❶ Warm-Up

Problem of the Day Present the following problem: Alex opened his social studies textbook. When Elena asked him to what pages his book was opened, he answered that the product of the facing pages was 59,780. To what pages did Alex open his book? (244–245)

Problem-Solving Strategies Ask students who have solved the Problem of the Day to share how they solved it and any strategies they used.

 Have students tell which of the following numbers are divisible by all three of the numbers 4, 5, and 6:

a. 30 (no) **b.** 324 (no) **c.** 660 (yes) **d.** 1030 (no)

e. 80 (no) **f.** 2160 (yes) **g.** 4290 (no) **h.** 540 (yes)

❷ Teach

Using the Student Pages Go over the procedure for checking multiplication by adding the digits, multiplying sums, and comparing the final single-digit numbers. Emphasize that while this method can identify an incorrect product, it cannot assure that an answer is correct. Have students work on these pages independently and then compare and check answers as a class. Note that the examples on page 227 show that the test fails to detect when the correct digits are transposed, a common error. In fact,

---

Checking Products

In this unit you have learned some rules for divisibility. These rules tell you whether a number is divisible by any of the numbers from 1 to 10 and can help you check your answers to some problems.

There is a method for checking multiplication in which you add digits.

First add the digits of each factor. Multiply the sums. Then add the digits of the product. That sum should be the same as the sum of the digits of the product of the two factors. When we say add the digits, we mean to go on adding until we arrive at a one-digit number.

Examples:

$314 \times 256 = ?$ Check the multiplication with the rule.

```
    2 5 6      Add the digits of the factors.
  × 3 1 4      2 + 5 + 6 = 13    1 + 3 = 4
    1 0 2 4    3 + 1 + 4 = 8
    2 5 6      Multiply the sums.    8 × 4 = 32
    7 6 8      Add the digits.       3 + 2 = 5
  8 0,3 8 4    Add the digits of the product of the multiplication.
               8 + 0 + 3 + 8 + 4 = 23    2 + 3 = 5
```

Both numbers are the same. We can be pretty sure the answer is correct.

$654 \times 9876 = ?$

```
      9 8 7 6      9 + 8 + 7 + 6 = 30    3 + 0 = 3
    ×   6 5 4      6 + 5 + 4 = 15        1 + 5 = 6
      3 9 5 0 4    6 × 3 = 18            1 + 8 = 9
      4 9 3 8 0
      5 9 2 5 6
    6,4 5 8,9 0 4  6 + 4 + 5 + 8 + 9 + 0 + 4 = 36    3 + 6 = 9
```

Both numbers are the same. We can be pretty sure the answer is correct.

Joanna calculated 213×65 as 14,845. She wanted to check her answer.

$213 \times 65 = 14,845$
$2 + 1 + 3 = 6$
$6 + 5 = 11$ $1 + 1 = 2$
$6 \times 2 = 12$ $1 + 2 = 3$
$1 + 4 + 8 + 4 + 5 = 22$ $2 + 2 = 4$

The two numbers are not the same. Joanna must have made a mistake in her calculation.

Why teach it at this time?

In addition to the rules for divisibility the students have been learning in previous lessons, this lesson provides another strategy for checking answers.

RETEACHING

Reteaching is not necessary at this time. You may want to assign Enrichment Master 62.

*available separately

Use the rule to see which of these answers are wrong.

Answers not marked passed the check but may not be right.

① 317 × 714 = 226,338

② 87 × 65 = 5565

③ 518 × 273 = 141,414

④ 145 × 325 = 47,125

⑤ 87 × 56 = 4972 **wrong**

⑥ 92 × 29 = 2668

⑦ 23 × 578 = 13,294

⑧ 69 × 57 = 3933

⑨ 519 × 127 = 65,713 **wrong**

⑩ 73 × 84 = 6432 **wrong**

⑪ 258 × 963 = 248,854 **wrong**

⑫ 518 × 309 = 160,062

⑬ 951 × 753 = 716,103

⑭ 48 × 307 = 14,736

If you don't get the same sums, you know the answer is wrong. Sometimes, however, the sums will be the same even though the answer is wrong.

Example: 73 × 84 = 6123

To check this problem, you would do these calculations:

7 + 3 = 10	1 + 0 = 1
8 + 4 = 12	1 + 2 = 3
3 × 1 = **3**	
6 + 1 + 2 + 3 = 12	1 + 2 = **3**

It seems that the answer is correct, but it isn't. The correct answer is 6132.

Example: 564 × 88 = 48,732

To check, you would do this:

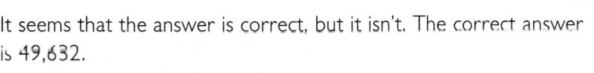

5 + 6 + 4 = 15	1 + 5 = 6
8 + 8 = 16	1 + 6 = 7
6 × 7 = 42	4 + 2 = **6**
4 + 8 + 7 + 3 + 2 = 24	2 + 4 = **6**

It seems that the answer is correct, but it isn't. The correct answer is 49,632.

Remember: If the rule says the answer is wrong, then the answer is wrong, if the rule doesn't say the answer is wrong, it may be right or wrong.

Unit 3 Lesson 62 • **227**

the answer in problem 2 is incorrect (it should be 5655) but passes the check.

Invite students to find out if this method for checking multiplication can be modified to check answers to additions or subtractions. (It can, as long as the same operation is used on the final sum of digits as in the problem. The final sum of digits of that result will be the same as the final sum of digits of the answer to the problem, if the answer is correct.) Keep in mind that in order to apply this method to a subtraction problem, it may be necessary to add 9 to the final sum of the first number before subtracting the final sum of the second number. For example, show students how to check the following problem:

$$102 \qquad - \qquad 67 \qquad = \qquad 35$$

102	67	35
↓	↓	↓
1 + 0 + 2 = <u>3</u>	6 + 7 = 13	3 + 5 = $\boxed{8}$
	1 + 3 = ④	

(<u>3</u> - ④ is negative, so use 3 + 9 instead)

$$3 + 9 = \triangle{12} \qquad \triangle{12} - ④ = \boxed{8} \qquad \boxed{8} = \boxed{8}$$

❸ Wrap-Up

In Closing To summarize the lesson, ask students to explain the procedure for and limits of checking multiplication by adding digits.

Informal Assessment Write the problem 215 × 166 = 35,690 on the chalkboard. Have students use the rule to tell whether that product is correct. (the product is possibly correct)

Assessment Criterion

Did the student . . .

✓ demonstrate understanding of the method for checking multiplication by adding digits?

Homework Ask students to explain the method for checking multiplication to a family member and to try a few examples. Challenge them to try out the method to check sums and differences as well.

PRACTICE p. 62

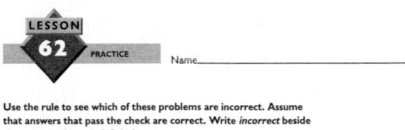

LESSON 62 PRACTICE   Name_____

Use the rule to see which of these problems are incorrect. Assume that answers that pass the check are correct. Write *incorrect* beside the answers that are definitely wrong.

① 47 × 986 = 46,332 <u>incorrect</u>

② 2176 × 53 = 115,328 <u>correct</u>

③ 89 × 512 = 46,568 <u>incorrect</u>

④ 118 × 207 = 255,266 <u>incorrect</u>

⑤ 417 × 591 = 246,447 <u>correct</u>

⑥ 179 × 814 = 144,706 <u>incorrect</u>

⑦ 861 × 432 = 361,942 <u>incorrect</u>

⑧ 276 × 614 = 169,464 <u>correct</u>

⑨ 537 × 186 = 99,882 <u>correct</u>

⑩ 781 × 486 = 379,566 <u>correct</u>

⑪ 29 × 84 = 2436 <u>correct</u>

⑫ 524 × 697 = 365,228 <u>correct</u>

⑬ 76 × 53 = 4128 <u>incorrect</u>

⑭ 256 × 643 = 154,608 <u>incorrect</u>

⑮ 126 × 91 = 11,466 <u>correct</u>

⑯ 702 × 891 = 624,482 <u>incorrect</u>

⑰ 874 × 190 = 166,060 <u>correct</u>

⑱ 532 × 114 = 60,648 <u>correct</u>

⑲ 243 × 115 = 27,955 <u>incorrect</u>

⑳ 289 × 755 = 208,195 <u>incorrect</u>

62 • *Math Explorations and Applications Level 6*

ENRICHMENT p. 62

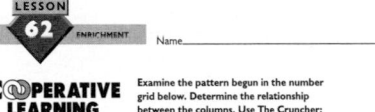

LESSON 62 ENRICHMENT   Name_____

COOPERATIVE LEARNING

Examine the pattern begun in the number grid below. Determine the relationship between the columns. Use The Cruncher: Number Patterns to complete the grid. Then play the game below with the completed grid.

Column	1	2	3	4	5	6	7	8	9	10
Row 1	0	1	2	3	4	5	6	7	8	9
2	1	3	5	7	9	11	13	15	17	19
3	2	5	8	11	14	17	20	23	26	29
4	3	7	11	15	19	23	27	31	35	39
5	4	9	14	19	24	29	34	39	44	49
6	5	11	17	23	29	35	41	47	53	59
7	6	13	20	27	34	41	48	55	62	69
8	7	15	23	31	39	47	55	63	71	79
9	8	17	26	35	44	53	62	71	80	89
10	9	19	29	39	49	59	69	79	89	99

Players: Two
Materials: Two 0–5 cubes, two 5–10 cubes, grid
Object: To be the first to score 20 points

Rules

1. Take turns rolling all four cubes.

2. Choose one of the numbers rolled as the row and another of the numbers as the column. Write down the number shown on the completed grid.

3. The player whose number is closer to 25 scores one point. If both numbers are equally close, then neither player scores.

4. Continue rolling and comparing numbers until one player reaches 20 points. The first player to score 20 points is the winner.

62 • *Math Explorations and Applications Level 6*

LESSON 63 — Unit 3 Review

Student Edition pages 228–229

Using the Student Pages Use this Unit Review as a preliminary unit test to indicate areas in which an individual student is having difficulty or in which the entire class may need help. If students do well on the Unit Review, you may wish to skip directly to the next unit. If not, you may want to spend a day or so helping students overcome their individual difficulties before they take the Unit Test.

Next to each instruction line is a list of the lessons in the unit covered in that set of problems. Students can refer to the specific lesson for additional instruction if they need help. You can also use this information to make additional assignments based on the previous lesson concepts.

Problems 1–6 Students who miss more than three of these problems involving operations with decimals should be checked to determine the nature of their difficulty.

Problems 7–14 Students who miss these problems may have a hard time remembering which way to move the decimal point with these problems involving changing percents to decimals. Recalling an easily remembered example, such as 1/2 = 0.50 = 50%, often helps.

Problems 15–22 Refer students who miss more than one of these decimal to percent problems to the strategy used in problems 7–14.

LESSON 63 — Unit 3 Review

Lessons 48 and 56

Solve these problems. Watch the signs.

1 234 + 518
752

2 2.34 × 51.8
121.212

3 48.23 − 17.005
31.225

4 2.96 + 53.8
56.76

5 4.8 − 1.6
3.2

6 48 ÷ 1.6
30

Lesson 48

Give the decimal equivalent.

7 53%
0.53

8 6%
0.06

9 101%
1.01

10 53.7%
0.537

11 61%
0.61

12 6.1%
0.061

13 200%
2.00

14 0.9%
0.009

Lessons 48

Write each of these as a percent.

15 0.27
27%

16 0.86
86%

17 0.04
4%

18 0.925
92.5%

19 2.34
234%

20 0.003
0.3%

21 0.815
81.5%

22 10.3
1030%

Lessons 48

Find each amount.

23 5% of 100
5

24 20% of 60
12

25 12.5% of 30
3.75

26 10% of 80
8

27 25% of 200
50

28 5% of 9
0.45

Solve these problems.

29 The tax in Lester's city is 7%. With tax, how much will he pay for a television set that is marked $200.00? **$214.00**

Lessons 49 and 55

30 Armando wants to buy a CD cabinet that is marked $120. The sales tax is 6%. How much will the cabinet cost? **$127.20**

31 Grace is buying ice skates on sale. The original price was $110.00. There is a 20% discount. What is the sale price? **$88.00**

32 Which costs more, a $150 VCR on sale at 20% off or on sale for $20 off? **$20 off**

33 Reggie is buying a desk chair on sale. The original price was $300. The discount is 30%. How many **$90.00** dollars will the discount be?

228 • Percents and Number Theory

Lessons 60 and 61

Show the prime factorization of each of these numbers. If the number is prime, just write the number with a *P* next to it. Use exponents if you wish.

34 4
2^2

35 252
$2^2 \times 3^2 \times 7$

36 2500
$2^2 \times 5^4$

37 300
$2^2 \times 3 \times 5^2$

38 5
P

39 1260
$2^2 \times 3^2 \times 5 \times 7$

40 1024
2^{10}

41 240
$2^4 \times 3 \times 5$

Solve these problems.

Lessons 49, 52–54, and 59

42 A comic book set priced at $15 is on sale at a 40% discount. What is the sale price of the comics? **$9.00**

43 Which is a better buy, a $79.98 bicycle on sale at 50% off or on sale at half price? **Both discounts are the same.**

44 Ingrid deposited $70 in the bank at 4% interest per year. How much money will she have after one year? **$72.80**

45 Curtis deposited some money in the bank last year at 5% interest. After one year the bank said he had $147. How much did he deposit last year? **$140.00**

46 What is the largest size square tile you can use to cover the floor in a room that is 48 decimeters long and 36 decimeters wide? **12 dm × 12 dm**

47 Mario bought a sweatshirt at a 20% discount. The sales tax was 5%. How much did Mario pay? **not enough information given**

48 Fran has $25 to spend on a computer game. The game she wants costs $28.95 but is on sale at 20% off. Can she afford that game? **yes**

49 Which will earn more interest in three years, $500 invested at 5% compounded quarterly or $500 invested at 5% compounded monthly? **5% compounded monthly**

50 With 6% tax, a pair of shoes costs $42.35. What was the price before tax? **$39.95**

Unit 3 Review • **229**

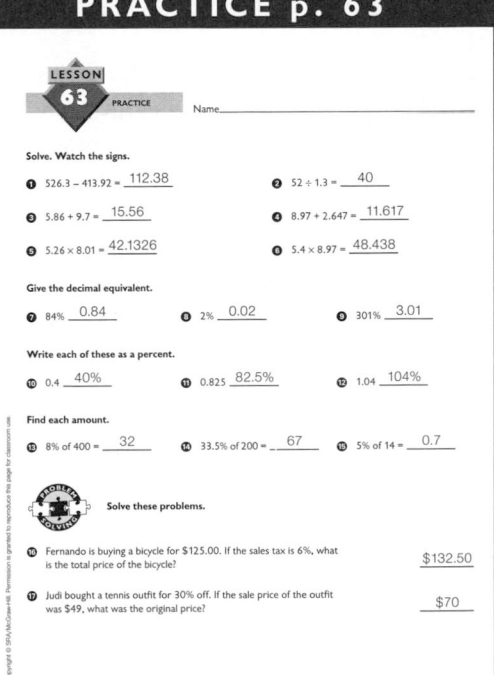
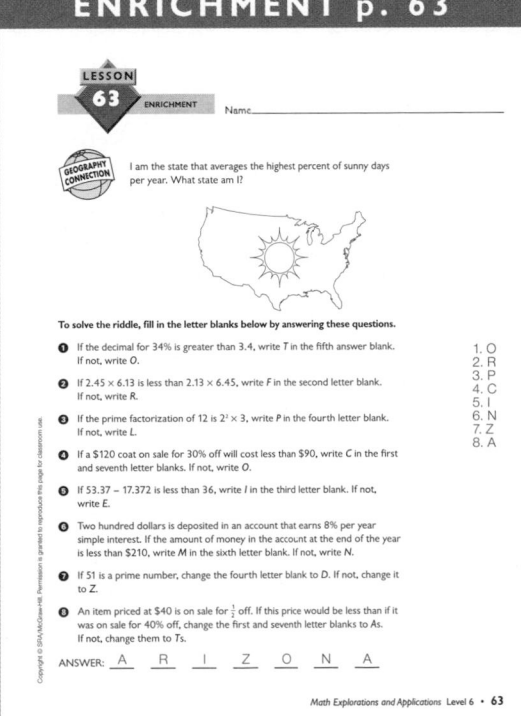

 **Problems 23–28** Students who miss more than one of these percent problems should be assessed to determine the nature of their difficulty. Refer to the strategy mentioned for problems 7–14, or work with **play money*** or **base-10 materials*** to illustrate the concepts. Remind students that they can think of fraction equivalents or they can change the percent to a decimal and multiply. Invite students to play the "Tips" game (page 179) as well.

 Problems 29–33 Students who miss more than one of these word problems should be assessed to determine the nature of their difficulty. To give students more experience with this type of problem, invite them to look at newspaper advertisements of discount sales to try to figure out what each ad means. You may also wish to have them play the "5% Tax" Game Mat.

Problems 34–41 Students who miss more than two of these factorization problems should be assessed to see what the difficulty is. You may wish to go through one or two of these problems so that students understand what is being asked.

Problems 42–50 Students who miss more than two of these word problems should get special help. Invite them to reread the problem carefully and to draw pictures to illustrate the problem. Have them use simpler numbers at first.

 **Portfolio Assessment** If you have not already assigned the Portfolio Assessment task provided on Assessment Blackline Masters page 88, it can be used at this time to evaluate students' ability to use their knowledge of factors and divisibility tests to solve problems.

 **Performance Assessment** The Performance Assessment Task 2 provided on Assessment Blackline Masters page 70 can be used at this time to evaluate students' proficiency with finding factors.

Unit Project If you have not already assigned the "Birthday Present" project on pages 234 and 235, you may wish to do so at this time. This project is a good opportunity for students to apply the concepts of percents, compound interest, and personal money management to real-world problem solving.

*available separately

LESSON 64

Unit 3 Practice

Student Edition pages 230–231

Using the Student Pages The purpose of these pages is to provide additional practice for those students who demonstrated a need for it on the Unit Review. You may wish to assign only the specific exercises in this Unit Practice in which students need further reinforcement. Each instruction line gives the lessons in the unit it covers so that you or students can refer to the specific lesson for additional review and instruction.

Students who do not require additional practice on specific concepts may enjoy playing any of the games you have played so far, such as the "Tips" game on page 179, which reinforces finding percents and using probabilistic thinking. These students may also help by practicing flashcard drills and playing appropriate games with students who need remedial practice or by actually teaching certain procedures to other students.

Students can use **The Cruncher*:** *Mystery Population* spreadsheet to create a table to help them solve problems 100–104.

You may want to use the Cumulative Review on page 566 after this lesson.

LESSON 64

Unit 3 Practice

Lessons 48 and 56

Watch the signs.

1 0.2 + 0.143 **0.343** **2** 0.2 − 0.143 **0.057** **3** 0.2 × 0.143 **0.0286**

4 0.6 + 0.571 **1.171** **5** 0.6 − 0.571 **0.029** **6** 0.6 × 0.571 **0.3426**

7 0.375 + 0.25 **0.625** **8** 0.375 − 0.25 **0.125** **9** 0.375 × 0.25 **0.09375**

10 0.5 × 0.3 **0.15** **11** 0.5 + 0.3 **0.8** **12** 0.5 − 0.3 **0.2**

13 0.625 − 0.333 **0.292** **14** 0.625 × 0.333 **0.208125** **15** 0.625 + 0.333 **0.958**

16 0.333 × 9 **2.997** **17** 9 × 0.667 **6.003** **18** 0.286 × 21 **6.006**

19 21 × 0.571 **11.991** **20** 21 × 0.714 **14.994** **21** 6 × 0.667 **4.002**

Lesson 48

Write each of these as a decimal.

22 1% **0.01** **23** 5% **0.05** **24** 10% **0.10** **25** 75% **0.75**

26 2.5% **0.025** **27** 6.2% **0.062** **28** 1.1% **0.011** **29** 35% **0.35**

30 0.6% **0.006** **31** 0.02% **0.0002** **32** 0.12% **0.0012** **33** 12% **0.12**

34 42% **0.42** **35** 8.5% **0.085** **36** 28.7% **0.287** **37** 0.9% **0.009**

Lesson 48

Write each of these as a percent.

38 0.1 **10%** **39** 0.15 **15%** **40** 0.0045 **0.45%** **41** 0.09 **9%**

42 0.01 **1%** **43** 0.35 **35%** **44** 1.0 **100%** **45** 0.086 **8.6%**

46 0.05 **5%** **47** 0.005 **0.5%** **48** 0.65 **65%** **49** 2.4 **240%**

50 0.07 **7%** **51** 0.025 **2.5%** **52** 0.605 **60.5%** **53** 0.75 **75%**

Lesson 48

Find each amount.

54 5% of 100 **5** **55** 5% of 500 **25** **56** 12% of 100 **12**

57 12% of 60 **7.2** **58** 3% of 200 **6** **59** 3% of 20 **0.6**

60 12.5% of 100 **12.5** **61** 12.5% of 50 **6.25** **62** 60% of 80 **48**

63 60% of 40 **24** **64** 75% of 100 **75** **65** 75% of 200 **150**

Solve this problem.

66 Mr. Archer invests $3000 at 4% interest compounded annually. Mrs. Butler invests $3000 at 4% interest compounded quarterly. At the end of one year, how much more interest will Mrs. Butler have earned than Mr. Archer? **$1.81**

Lesson 53

Technology Connection Refer students to the software *Math Blaster Mystery: The Great Brain Robbery* from Davidson (IBM, for grades 5–12) for further review of computation, estimation, decimals, integers, calculator skills, and word problems.

RETEACHING

Students who have difficulty with this Unit Practice should have further opportunity to review and to practice the skills before they proceed on with the next unit. Beside each set of problems is a reference to the lesson or lessons from which the problems were taken. You may want to review the individual lessons with students who are having difficulty with them.

*available separately

Lessons 60 and 61 Show the prime factorization of each number. If the number is prime, write the number with a *P* next to it. Use exponents if you wish.

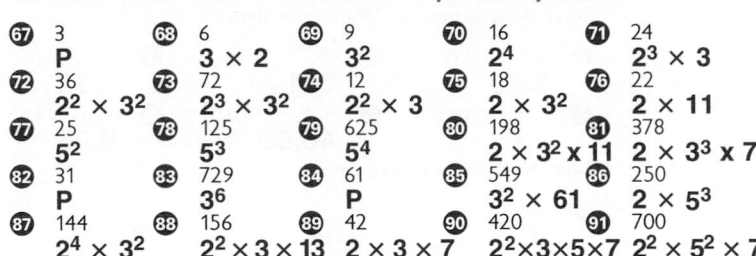

67 3 P	**68** 6 3×2	**69** 9 3^2	**70** 16 2^4	**71** 24 $2^3 \times 3$
72 36 $2^2 \times 3^2$	**73** 72 $2^3 \times 3^2$	**74** 12 $2^2 \times 3$	**75** 18 2×3^2	**76** 22 2×11
77 25 5^2	**78** 125 5^3	**79** 625 5^4	**80** 198 $2 \times 3^2 \times 11$	**81** 378 $2 \times 3^3 \times 7$
82 31 P	**83** 729 3^6	**84** 61 P	**85** 549 $3^2 \times 61$	**86** 250 2×5^3
87 144 $2^4 \times 3^2$	**88** 156 $2^2 \times 3 \times 13$	**89** 42 $2 \times 3 \times 7$	**90** 420 $2^2 \times 3 \times 5 \times 7$	**91** 700 $2^2 \times 5^2 \times 7$

Lesson 49 Find the cost, with tax, of each item.

92 $30 clock with 5% sales tax **$31.50**

93 $400 television with 7% sales tax **$428.00**

94 $750 sofa with 6% sales tax **$795.00**

95 $10 football with 6% sales tax **$10.60**

96 $15 mouse pad with 5% sales tax **$15.75**

97 $25 video game with 7% sales tax **$26.75**

98 $5.50 book with 5% sales tax **$5.78**

99 $77.98 bicycle with 6% sales tax **$82.66**

Lesson 49 Find the discount price of each item.

	Item	Regular Price	Discount	
100	basketball	$10.00	10%	**$9.00**
101	notebook	$1.25	20%	**$1.00**
102	guitar	$96.00	25%	**$72.00**
103	CD player	$124.50	$30	**$94.50**
104	book	$4.75	30%	**$3.33 or $3.32**

Lessons 52 and 53

105 Mr. Redwing put $500 in the bank at 7% interest, compounded annually. Use a calculator. How much will he have at the end of

a. one year?   **b.** three years?   **c.** five years?
$535.00   **$612.52**   **$701.28**

Use the Cumulative Review on page 566 after this lesson.

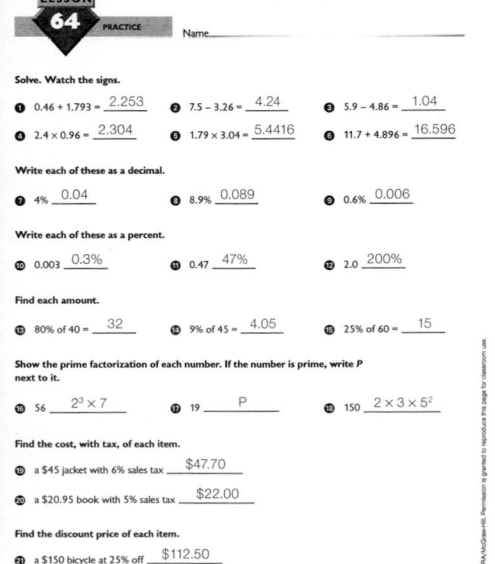

PRACTICE p. 64

LESSON 64 PRACTICE   Name_____

Solve. Watch the signs.

1 0.46 + 1.793 = _2.253_   **2** 7.5 − 3.26 = _4.24_   **3** 5.9 − 4.86 = _1.04_

4 2.4 × 0.96 = _2.304_   **5** 1.79 × 3.04 = _5.4416_   **6** 11.7 + 4.896 = _16.596_

Write each of these as a decimal.

7 4% _0.04_   **8** 8.9% _0.089_   **9** 0.6% _0.006_

Write each of these as a percent.

10 0.003 _0.3%_   **11** 0.47 _47%_   **12** 2.0 _200%_

Find each amount.

13 80% of 40 = _32_   **14** 9% of 45 = _4.05_   **15** 25% of 60 = _15_

Show the prime factorization of each number. If the number is prime, write P next to it.

16 56 _$2^3 \times 7$_   **17** 19 _P_   **18** 150 _$2 \times 3 \times 5^2$_

Find the cost, with tax, of each item.

19 a $45 jacket with 6% sales tax _$47.70_

20 a $20.95 book with 5% sales tax _$22.00_

Find the discount price of each item.

21 a $150 bicycle at 25% off _$112.50_

22 a $75 pair of skates at 15% off _$63.75_

64 • *Math Explorations and Applications Level 6*

ENRICHMENT p. 64

LESSON 64 ENRICHMENT   Name_____

This pie chart (also called a circle graph) shows the share of U.S. households of different income levels in 1993.

39% <$30,000
>$100,000 18%
43% $30–$100,000

1 The total number of households in the United States was 91,947,410 in 1993. About how many households had incomes less than $30,000? _35,859,489_

2 About how many middle-income households were there in 1993? _39,537,386_

3 In the year 2005 the number of U.S. households will be about 104,000,000. The projected number of households at each income level is: 12,480,000 at $100,000 or more; 40,560,000 between $30,000 and $100,000; and 50,960,000 at less than $30,000. What percentages do these represent? _12%, 39%, 49%_

4 In the circle below draw a pie chart of the number of households in each income level in the year 2005.

39% $30,000–$100,000
49% <$30,000
12% >$100,000

Students' drawings need not be exact.

64 • *Math Explorations and Applications Level 6*

Using the Student Pages The Unit Test on Student Edition pages 232 and 233 provides an opportunity to formally evaluate your students' proficiency with concepts developed in this unit. It is similar in content and format to the Unit Review. Students who did well on the Unit Review may not need to take this test. Students who did not do well on the Unit Review should be provided with additional practice opportunities, such as the Unit Practice pages, before taking the Unit Test. As an alternative, you may wish to have these students take the Unit Test on Assessment Blackline Masters pages 29–30 or the Unit Test in standardized format, provided on Assessment Blackline Masters pages 108–113.

UNIT
3
ASSESSMENT

Unit Test

Solve these problems. Watch the signs.

❶ 4.87 + 3.19 **8.06**   ❷ 612 − 351 **261**   ❸ 2.4 × 1.8 **4.32**

❹ 64.8 ÷ 0.48 **135**   ❺ 5.19 + 43.8 **48.99**   ❻ 12.7 − 4.65 **8.05**

Give the decimal equivalent.

❼ 35% **0.35**   ❽ 9% **0.09**   ❾ 125% **1.25**   ❿ 28.3% **0.283**

⓫ 16% **0.16**   ⓬ 9.3% **0.093**   ⓭ 300% **3.00**   ⓮ 0.6% **0.006**

Write each of these as a percent.

⓯ 0.19 **19%**   ⓰ 0.37 **37%**   ⓱ 0.06 **6%**   ⓲ 0.741 **74.1%**

⓳ 2.79 **279%**   ⓴ 0.005 **0.5%**   ㉑ 0.732 **73.2%**   ㉒ 6.5 **650%**

Find each amount.

㉓ 5% of 200 **10**   ㉔ 20% of 40 **8**   ㉕ 12.5% of 40 **5**

㉖ 10% of 60 **6**   ㉗ 25% of 100 **25**   ㉘ 5% of 6 **0.3**

Solve these problems.

㉙ The tax in Mrs. Turner's city is 6%. With tax, how much will she pay for a dryer that is marked $400.00? **$424.00**

㉚ Alfred wants to buy a fax machine that is on sale for $150. The tax is 5%. How much will the fax machine cost? **$157.50**

㉛ Mr. Becker is buying a boat on sale. The original price was $3400.00. There is a 10% discount. What is the sale price? **$3060.00**

㉜ Rudy is buying a CD player on sale. The original price was $130. The discount is 20%. How much less will he pay? **$26.00**

㉝ Which costs more, a $40 jacket on sale at 10% off or on sale at $10 off? **10% off**

㉞ With 5% tax, a picture frame costs $7.88. What was the cost before tax? **$7.50**

232 • Percents and Number Theory

Show the prime factorization of each of these numbers. If the number is prime, just write the number with a *P* next to it. Use exponents if you wish.

35 6
2 × 3

36 101
P

37 243
3⁵

38 160
2⁵ × 5

39 7
P

40 120
2³ × 3 × 5

41 900
2² × 3² × 5²

42 1000
2³ × 5³

Solve these problems.

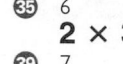

43 A $50 sweatshirt was on sale at 20% off. The tax was 5%. Bridget paid for the sweatshirt. How much change did she receive? **not enough information given**

44 Jacob has $12. He finds a baseball cap regularly $16.50 on sale for 20% off. Can he afford the cap? **no**

45 Which earns more interest over two years, $300 invested at 4% compounded monthly or $300 invested at 4% compounded quarterly? **compounded monthly**

46 A book priced at $12 is on sale at a 50% discount. How much will the book cost on sale? **$6.00**

47 Which is a better buy, a $150.00 bicycle on sale at 50% off or on sale at $50 off? **50% off**

48 Belva deposited $70 in the bank at 4% interest per year. How much money will she have after one year? **$72.80**

49 Mrs. Kito deposited some money in the bank last year at 6% interest. After one year the bank said she had $212. How much did she deposit last year? **$200.00**

50 What is the largest size square tile you can use to cover the floor in a room that is 36 decimeters long and 24 decimeters wide? **12 dm × 12 dm**

Unit 3 Test • **233**

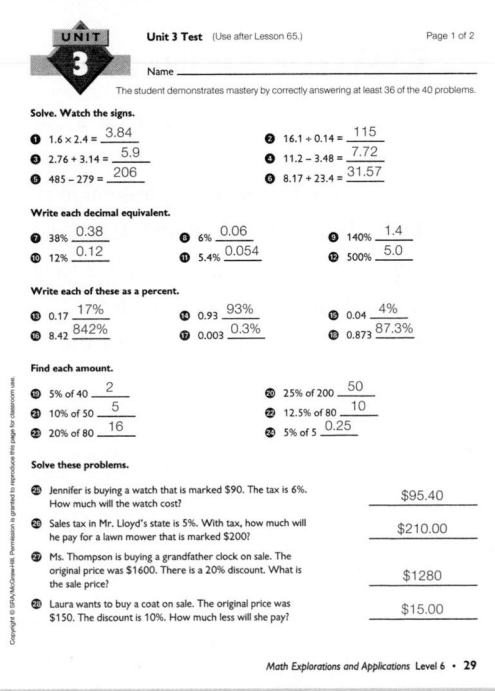

ASSESSMENT p. 29

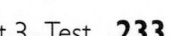

Wrap-Up

PRESENTING THE PROJECT

Project Objectives

▶ to introduce notions of thrift and personal money management

▶ to introduce the notion of compound interest and show how it allows savings to grow over time

▶ to provide a real application for the use of percents

 To begin the project, have students complete the first part of page 234 individually. Then discuss the reasons for saving money as a whole class. Although there are many reasons for saving and spending that must be acknowledged, the notions that saving money gives us security and independence should be acknowledged. The main focus of page 235 is not to practice computation but to show how compound interest allows money to grow, so the use of **calculators*** would be appropriate. Students may also use a blank **Cruncher*** spreadsheet.

Have students complete the problems on page 235. This may be done in cooperative groups or by individual students. Getting information from local banks is best done as a longer term project. As part of that project, consider asking a local banker to visit your class, or arrange for the class to visit one or more local banks.

Answers to chart on page 235:

Year	5%	10%
3	$115.76	$133.10
4	$121.55	$146.41
5	$127.63	$161.05
6	$134.01	$177.16
7	$140.71	$194.87
8	$147.75	$214.36
9	$155.13	$235.79
10	$162.89	$259.37
11	$171.03	$285.31
12	$179.59	$313.84
13	$188.56	$345.23
14	$197.99	$379.75
15	$207.89	$417.72

A Birthday Present

Suppose you received a birthday present of $100.

What are some things you could do with that amount of money?

◆ If you placed the money in a bank account at 5% annual interest, how much would your investment be worth in one year? **$105.00**

◆ If you asked the bank to send you the interest at the end of the year, how much will be sent to you? How much will still be in your bank account? **$5.00; $100.00**

◆ Suppose you kept the $100 in the bank. How much money will be sent to you at the end of the second year? How much will still be in your bank account? **$5.00; $100.00**

Think about it. If you have $100, you can spend it on something you want, or if you invest it at 5%, you can get $5 a year for the rest of your life and still have the $100.

◆ What are some reasons for saving your money instead of spending it?

Answers will fall into two categories, those focusing on saving toward near-term purchases and those taking a lon range view of saving money as providing security and independence.

◆ What are some reasons for spending your money instead of saving it?

Answers will vary (an item is on sale, you need an item now, prices may go up, and so on).

A Savings Plan

Suppose you decided to put your $100 in the bank or in another investment for a long time and let the money grow. At 5% annual interest, how much will your investment be worth at the end of each year? At 10% annual interest, how much will it be worth?

234 • Percents and Number Theory

Why teach it at this time?

Sixth grade is not too early for students to begin thinking about personal money management or learning the value of thrift. Besides these objectives, these pages allow students to tackle a longer-range project that provides a real application of percents, one of the major mathematical topics in this unit.

*available separately

To find out, use a calculator or computer to extend this chart for at least ten years.

$100 Initial Investment
Value at End of Each Year (Dollars) See margin.

Years	5%	10%
1	$105.00	$110.00
2	$110.25	$121.00

Study the completed chart. You may need to extend the chart to answer some questions.

How long would it take to double your original investment if you earn 5% per year? **between 14 and 15 years**

How long will it take to double your original investment if you earn 10% per year? **between 7 and 8 years**

If you let the initial $100 grow, how much will you have after 40 years? First estimate; then calculate the amounts. **$704.00**

Get information from banks in your neighborhood. How much interest does each pay on savings accounts? What fees, if any, does each charge? Organize your information so that it is easy to compare banks. Are you able to find a bank that offers a good savings program for sixth graders?

What Is a Math Project? If this is the first time you have used math projects in your classroom, you may want to refer to pages 98–99 in this Teacher's Guide for more detailed information about effectively implementing and assessing projects.

Homework Consider having students write reports that compare the services offered by two banks that are appropriate for sixth-grade students.

Wrapping Up the Project Have a final discussion that focuses on which local bank is most sensitive to the needs of sixth-grade students.

Assessing the Project This project offers an opportunity to note those students who are able to intelligently discuss interest rates and growth of money without having to use paper and pencil or a calculator to make calculations or approximate calculations.

C⊕⊕PERATIVE LEARNING **Minds on Math** SRA's *Minds on Math* is a series of units covering problem solving, data collection, number sense, measurement, money, and geometry and spatial relations. Each unit provides a series of open-ended projects for individuals or small groups. These projects develop problem-solving and critical-thinking skills, utilize real-world materials, emphasize language, and integrate cross-curricular connections. Use projects from *Money Problems* to explore budgets, banking, how to plan purchases, how to plan events, and other aspects of using money in the real world.

C⊕⊕PERATIVE LEARNING **Math CrossSections** SRA's *Math CrossSections* is a set of eight units that provide real-world math projects related to famous places in the United States. These open-ended projects focus on problem solving and reinforce reading, research, and study skills. The eight units are:

The White House (Washington, D.C.)
747 DFW (Texas)
California's Giant Sequoias (California)
Pencil Making (Tennessee)
Barging Through the Locks (Michigan)
Atlanta's Olympic Stadium (Georgia)
Madison Square Garden (New York)
The Denver Mint (Colorado)

Use projects from *747 DFW* to give students an opportunity to solve problems based on real-life data and to use their skills with percents and approximation.

Perhaps you have less than 45 minutes to devote to each lesson. Perhaps you have a slower-than-average class that needs extra time on various lessons. Or, perhaps you simply feel comfortable proceeding at a more leisurely pace. Whatever the reason, a few tips will help you trim the program with the fewest consequences.

Because each unit should take up about one-sixth of the school year, you can use the units somewhat as mileposts. From time to time, after each unit or halfway though each unit, do a rough calculation to see whether your pace will allow you to finish the program. If it appears that you won't finish, check the suggestions given below; but don't speed up at the expense of students' understanding. If you are moving at an appropriate pace and yet won't finish the program, that is all right. The students will be ready for seventh-grade mathematics.

MORE THAN 100 DAYS LEFT AFTER UNIT 3

If more than 100 days remain, you'll probably be able to finish the Level 6 program, so you won't need to significantly modify the lesson plans for the rest of the year.

80–100 DAYS LEFT AFTER UNIT 3

If, after you finish Unit 3, 80–100 days remain in the school year, go though the lesson list below and decide which lessons or portions of lessons to omit. The lessons listed may be omitted without creating undue difficulty for students when they enter the seventh grade. Any of these lessons may be omitted,

but if you have to skip only a few lessons, try to choose lessons from later in the year rather than earlier. This will minimize disruption of the lesson continuity. Whenever possible, do the Mental Math exercises of the lessons you omit.

Unit 4

Lesson 80	Adding and Subtracting Mixed Numbers
Lesson 81	Using Mixed Numbers

Unit 5

Lesson 116	Graphing Nonlinear Functions
Lesson 117	More Nonlinear Functions
Lesson 118	Graphing a Perimeter Function
Lesson 119	Determining the Function Rule
Lesson 120	Finding Circumference

Unit 6

Lesson 143	Angles and Rotation
Lesson 144	Measuring Angles
Lesson 145	Corresponding Angles and Vertical Angles
Lesson 146	Straight and Supplementary Angles
Lesson 147	Angles of Polygons
Lesson 148	Points, Lines, and Planes
Lesson 150	Compass Constructions
Lesson 151	Circle Graphs

If you omit any material from a unit, be sure to modify the Unit Review and Unit Test to take into account the deleted material.

FEWER THAN 80 DAYS LEFT AFTER UNIT 3

If, after you finish Unit 3, fewer than 80 days remain in the school year, omit the items listed below.

Unit 4

Lesson 80   Adding and Subtracting Mixed Numbers
Lesson 81   Using Mixed Numbers

Unit 5

Lesson 116   Graphing Nonlinear Functions
Lesson 117   More Nonlinear Functions
Lesson 118   Graphing a Perimeter Function
Lesson 119   Determining the Function Rule
Lesson 120   Finding Circumference

Unit 6

All Lessons

Allow plenty of time for remediation outlined in Lesson 122 (if you stopped at the end of Unit V) or Lesson 153 (if you stopped at the end of Unit VI). Depending on how much remediation you foresee, you'll spend from three days to two weeks on this. Be sure you go through the final review and diagnostic test early enough to leave as much time as you think you'll need for remediation.

IF YOU ADMINISTER STANDARDIZED TESTS

You might want to review the test that you will be administering to your students at this time. Note any topics that will be assessed that you have not covered in your mathematics curriculum. You might want to introduce a series of lessons earlier to accommodate your testing schedule.

UNIT 4

Fractions and Mixed Numbers

UNDERSTANDING PARTS AND PROPORTIONS

OVERVIEW

This unit begins with a review of some fraction topics, leading to work with mixed numbers. Function concepts and notation are reviewed, and the concept of a multiplicative inverse is introduced. Students practice finding probabilities and relate probabilities to fractions, decimals, and percents. Students also review ratios, rates, and mean, median, and mode. At the end of the unit, students learn to solve proportions and to use proportions to solve problems about similar figures.

Integrated Topics in This Unit Include:

- ◆ **finding a fraction of a whole number and of a fraction**
- ◆ **finding equivalent fractions, including decimal equivalents**
- ◆ **multiplying fractions**
- ◆ **finding probability**
- ◆ **expressing improper fractions and mixed numbers**

> INVERSE FUNCTIONS
> PROPORTIONS

- ◆ **finding decimal equivalents and approximations of fractions and mixed numbers**
- ◆ **adding and subtracting fractions and mixed numbers**
- ◆ **dividing fractions**
- ◆ **completing a distance matrix for a map**
- ◆ **finding averages and rates**
- ◆ **finding mean, median, and mode and choosing an appropriate average**
- ◆ **solving proportions**

"The use of concise symbols and language to represent numbers is a significant historical and practical development. In the middle school years, students come to recognize that numbers have multiple representations, so the development of concepts for fractions, ratios, decimals, and percents and the idea of multiple representations of these numbers need special attention and emphasis."

—NCTM Curriculum and Evaluation Standards for School Mathematics

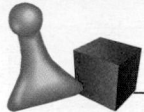 ## GAMES

Motivating Mixed Practice

Games provide **basic math skills** practice in cooperative groups. Playing the games also develops **mathematical reasoning.**

Fractions of 60	Lesson 65	page 240
Up to 1	Lesson 67	page 245
Equivalence 2 Game Mat	Lesson 67	page 246
Equivalence 1 Game Mat	Lesson 68	page 249
Greatest Common Factor	Lesson 69	page 252
Cosmic Cafe Game Mat	Lesson 71	page 260
Circo 11	Lesson 73	page 265
Harder Cosmic Cafe Game Mat	Lesson 74	page 268
Roll a 15	Lesson 75	page 272
Routes Game Mat	Lesson 75	page 272
Harder Routes Game Mat	Lesson 75	page 272
Anything But 10	Lesson 76	page 275
Fringo Factory Game Mat	Lesson 78	page 281
Harder Fringo Factory Game Mat	Lesson 78	Page 281
Up to 2	Lesson 79	page 283
Make 1	Lesson 80	page 288
Make 2	Lesson 82	page 296
Pentathlon Game Mat	Lesson 88	page 316
Inverso	Lesson 94	page 335

 ## THINKING STORY

Integrated Problem Solving

Thinking Stories provide opportunities for students to work in **cooperative groups** and develop **logical reasoning** while they integrate **reading skills** with mathematics.

Energy Savers

Part 1	Lesson 67	pages 246–247
Part 2	Lesson 70	pages 256–257
Part 3	Lesson 74	pages 268–269
Part 4	Lesson 79	pages 284–285

Story Summary "Energy Savers" examines energy conservation methods, telling the story of a group of students who enlist their neighbors in an effort to save energy. As the story develops, students will examine the particulars of carpooling, stopping and starting automobiles less, and insulating houses. They will solve problems using skills with mapping, computing with fractions, and calculating percents.

PROJECT

Making Connections

The Unit Project makes real-world connections. Students work in **cooperative groups** to problem solve and to communicate their findings.

The project presented in the Unit Wrap-Up asks students to gather newspaper advertisements and then work in groups to determine which ads are fair and which are not fair. They should assemble three scrap albums: one for the fair ads, one for those that are not fair, and one for those for which they are unsure. Students may work on this project in their free time throughout the unit.

LESSON	PACING	PRIMARY OBJECTIVES	FEATURE	RESOURCES	NCTM STANDARD
65 Fractions of Whole Numbers............238–241	1 day	to review and practice finding fractions of whole numbers	Game	Reteaching Master Practice Master 65 Enrichment Master 65	5, 6, 7
66 Multiplying Fractions............242–243	1 day	to review and practice finding a fraction of a fraction		Reteaching Strategy Practice Master 66 Enrichment Master 66	6, 7
67 Decimal Equivalents of Fractions..........244–247	1 day	to practice comparing decimals and fractions	Thinking Story Game	Reteaching Master Practice Master 67 Enrichment Master 67	1, 2, 3, 4, 5, 6
68 Equivalent Fractions............248–249	1 day	to review and provide practice in finding equivalent fractions	Game	Reteaching Master Practice Master 68 Enrichment Master 68	5
69 Reducing Fractions .. 250–253	1 day	to practice reducing fractions	Game	Reteaching Master Practice Master 69 Enrichment Master 69	6
70 Multiplying and Reducing Fractions............254–257	1 day	to demonstrate methods for multiplying fractions efficiently	Thinking Story	Reteaching Strategy Practice Master 70 Enrichment Master 70	1, 2, 3, 4, 5, 6
71 Comparing Fractions............258–261	1 day	to demonstrate ways to compare fractions	Game	Reteaching Master Practice Master 71 Enrichment Master 71	3, 6
72 Adding and Subtracting Fractions............262–263	1 day	to review and practice adding and subtracting fractions		Reteaching Master Practice Master 72 Enrichment Master 72	6, 7
73 Adding and Subtracting Special Fractions.....264–265	1 day	✓ to evaluate students' ability to add and subtract fractions	Game	Reteaching Strategy Practice Master 73 Enrichment Master 73 Assessment Master	1, 2, 3, 4, 7
74 Least Common Multiples of 3 or More Numbers ...266–269	1 day	to demonstrate finding the least common multiple of three or more numbers	Thinking Story Game	Reteaching Strategy Practice Master 74 Enrichment Master 74	1, 2, 3, 4, 5, 6, 7
75 Probability...........270–273	1 day	to help students to apply knowledge of probability	Game	Reteaching Master Practice Master 75 Enrichment Master 75	4, 6, 11
76 Analyzing Probability...........274–277	2 days	to practice using fractions, decimals, and percents in probabilities	Game	Reteaching Strategy Practice Master 76 Enrichment Master 76	5, 6, 8, 9, 11
77 Practice with Fractions and Decimals 278–279	1 day	to show the relationship between operations with fractions and operations with decimals		Reteaching Strategy Practice Master 77 Enrichment Master 77	5, 6, 7
78 Improper Fractions and Mixed Numbers 280–281	1 day	to show how to express the improper fractions as mixed numbers	Game	Reteaching Strategy Practice Master 78 Enrichment Master 78	2, 4, 5
79 Practice with Decimal Equivalents 282–285	1 day	to practice converting fractions to decimals and comparing fractions and decimals	Thinking Story Game	Reteaching Strategy Practice Master 79 Enrichment Master 79	2, 4, 5, 6, 7
80 Adding and Subtracting Mixed Numbers 286–289	1 day	✓ to evaluate students' ability to add and subtract mixed numbers	Game	Reteaching Master Practice Master 80 Enrichment Master 80 Assessment Master	1, 2, 3, 4, 6

	LESSON	PACING	PRIMARY OBJECTIVES	FEATURE	RESOURCES	NCTM STANDARD
81	**Using Mixed Numbers**............290–291	1 day	to practice converting fractions to decimals		Reteaching Strategy Practice Master 81 Enrichment Master 81	1, 2, 3, 4, 7
	Mid-Unit Review.....292–293			♟	Assessment Master	
82	**Keeping Sharp**.......294–297	1 day	to have students analyze information and then make decisions based on their analyses	**Game**	Reteaching Strategy Practice Master 82 Enrichment Master 82	1, 2, 3, 4, 5, 6, 7
83	**Division by Fractions**............298–301	2 days	to illustrate the meaning of division by a fraction by presenting a practical problem	**ACT IT OUT**	Reteaching Strategy Practice Master 83 Enrichment Master 83	4, 6
84	**Functions** 302–303	1 day	to review the concept of functions and introduce multiplicative inverses		Reteaching Strategy Practice Master 84 Enrichment Master 84	6, 8, 9
85	**Dividing Fractions** ...304–307	1 day	to demonstrate how to divide by fractions ✓ to assess student's understanding of multiplying and dividing by fractions	♟	Reteaching Master Practice Master 85 Enrichment Master 85 Assessment Master	6, 7
86	**Using Maps and Charts**...........308–309	1 day	to practice calculating distances		Reteaching Strategy Practice Master 86 Enrichment Master 86	2, 4, 5
87	**Ratios** 310–313	1 day	to practice solving problems that involve ratios		Reteaching Strategy Practice Master 87 Enrichment Master 87	2, 4, 5, 6, 7
88	**Averages and Rates** 314–317	2 days	✓ to practice solving problems that involve ratios and rates	♟ **Game**	Reteaching Master Practice Master 88 Enrichment Master 88 Assessment Masters	1, 2, 3, 4 6, 10
89	**Mean, Median, and Mode** 318–321	1 day	to present methods of finding the mean, median, and mode of data		Reteaching Master Practice Master 89 Enrichment Master 89	1, 2, 3, 4, 10
90	**Choosing an Appropriate Average**...............322–323	1 day	to involve students in a discussion of which concept of average is most useful in a given situation		Reteaching Strategy Practice Master 90 Enrichment Master 90	1, 2, 3, 4, 10
91	**Solving Proportions**..........324–327	1 day	to show several methods for solving problems involving proportions		Reteaching Master Practice Master 91 Enrichment Master 91	1, 2, 3, 4, 6
92	**Similar Figures**.......328–329	1 day	to relate similar figures and proportions		Reteaching Strategy Practice Master 92 Enrichment Master 92	1, 2, 3, 4, 6, 12
93	**Unit 4 Review**........330–331		to review fractions and mixed numbers		Practice Master 93 Enrichment Master 93	
94	**Unit 4 Practice**......332–335		to practice with fractions and mixed numbers	**Game**	Practice Master 94 Enrichment Master 94	
	Unit 4 Test 336–337		to review fractions and mixed numbers	♟	Assessment Masters	
	Unit 4 Wrap-Up.....338–339			**Project**		

UNIT CONNECTIONS

INTERVENTION STRATEGIES

In this Teacher's Guide there will be specific strategies suggested for students with individual needs—ESL, Gifted and Talented, Special Needs, Learning Styles, and At Risk. These strategies will be given at the point of use. Here are the icons to look for and the types of strategies that will accompany them:

English as a Second Language
These strategies, designed for students who do not fluently speak the English language, will suggest meaningful ways to present the lesson concepts and vocabulary.

Gifted and Talented
Strategies to enrich and extend the lesson will offer further challenges to students who have easily mastered the concepts already presented.

Special Needs
Students who are physically challenged or who have learning disabilities may require alternative ways to complete activities, record answers, use manipulatives, and so on. The strategies labeled with this icon will offer appropriate methods of teaching lesson concepts to these students.

Learning Styles
Each student has his or her individual approach to learning. The strategies labeled with this icon suggest ways to present lesson concepts so that various learning modalities—such as tactile/kinesthetic, visual, and auditory—can be addressed.

At Risk
These strategies highlight the relevancy of the skills presented, making the connection between school and real life. They are directed toward students who appear to be at risk of dropping out of school before graduation.

TECHNOLOGY CONNECTIONS

The following materials, designed to reinforce and extend lesson concepts, will be referred to throughout this Teacher's Guide. It might be helpful to order the software, videos, and laser discs or to check it out of the school media center or local community library. If the school does not provide Internet access, consider visiting a local library, college, or business specializing in Internet services. Some students may be able to access the Internet at home.

Look for this **Technology Connection** *icon.*

♦ *Modumath: Arithmetic, Multiplying Fractions,* from VTAE, VHS, IBM, for grades 6–12 (video, software, or laser disc)

♦ *Modumath: Arithmetic, Renaming Fractions,* from VTAE, VHS, IBM, for grades 6–12 (video, software, or laser disc)

♦ *NumberMaze,* from Great Wave, Mac, IBM, for grades K–6 (software)

♦ *Math Ace,* from Magic Quest, IBM, for grades 3–12 (software)

♦ *Core Concepts in Math: Mastering Fractions,* from BFA/Systems Impact, Mac, IBM, for grades 5–9 (software or laser disc)

♦ *Mathematics Curriculum and Teaching Program,* from National Council of Mathematics, Inc., Mac, IBM, for grades K–10 (video, software, and printed materials)

♦ *In the Neighborhood,* from Critical Thinking Software & Books, Mac, IBM, for grades 2–12 (software)

♦ *Modumath: Arithmetic, Changing Fractions to Decimals,* from VTAE, VHS, IBM, for grades 6–12 (video, software, or laser disc)

♦ *Prevocational Math Series,* from Shopware, Mac, IBM, for grades 3–8 (software)

♦ *Spotlight: Fractions and Decimals,* from Scholastic, Mac, for grades 1–10 (software)

♦ *Brain Teasers,* from the Eisenhower National Clearinghouse for Mathematics and Science, http://www.hmco.com/school/math/brain/(Internet)

CROSS-CURRICULAR CONNECTIONS

This Teacher's Guide offers specific suggestions on ways to connect the math concepts presented in this unit with other subjects students are studying. Students can connect math concepts with topics they already know and can find examples of math in other subjects and in real-world situations. These strategies will be given at the point of use.

Look for these icons:

 Geography

 Health

 Social Studies

 Music

 Science

 Math

 Art

 Physical Education

 Language Arts

 Careers

LITERATURE CONNECTIONS

These books will be presented throughout the Teacher's Guide at the point where they could be used to introduce, reinforce, or extend specific lesson concepts. You may want to locate these books in your school or your local community library.

 *Look for this* **Literature Connection** *icon.*

- *Math Curse* by Jon Sciezka, Viking 1995
- *The Phantom Tollbooth* by Norman Juster, Knopf, 1961
- *The Bunyans* by Audrey Wood, Blue Sky Press/Scholastic, 1996
- *Math for Smarty Pants* by Marilyn Burns, Little, Brown, 1982
- *Sideways Arithmetic from Wayside School* by Louis Sachar, Scholastic, 1989
- *The Children's Space Atlas* by Robin Kerrod, Millbrook Press, 1992
- *Dominoes: Basic Rules and Variations* by Reiner Maler, Sterling Pub. Co., 1995
- *Math Fun: Test Your Luck* by Rose Wyler and Mary Etling, J. Messner, 1992
- *Do You Wanna Bet?* by Jean Cushman, Clarion Books, 1991
- *Our Solar System* by Seymour Simon, Morrow Junior Books, 1992
- *The Story of the New York Stock Exchange* by Zachary Kent, Childrens Press, 1990
- *Ed Emberly's Picture Pie* by Ed Emberly, Little, Brown, 1984
- *All About Sam* by Lois Lowry, Dell Publishing, 1988
- *The Science Chef* by Joan D'Amico and Karen Eich Drummond, J. Wiley, 1995
- *Math-A-Magic Number Tricks for Magicians* by Laurence B. White, Jr. and Ray Brokel, A. Whitman, 1990
- *Woodsong* by Gary Paulsen, Bradbury Press, 1990
- *Gulliver's Travels* by Jonathan Swift
- *The Hoboken Chicken Emergency* by D. Manus Pinkwater, Prentice Hall Books for Young Readers, 1997
- *Bingo Brown and the Language of Love* by Betsy Byars, Viking Kestrel, 1989

ASSESSMENT OPPORTUNITIES AT-A-GLANCE

LESSON	PORTFOLIO	PERFORMANCE	FORMAL	SELF	INFORMAL	CUMULATIVE REVIEW	MULTIPLE-CHOICE	MASTERY CHECKPOINTS	ANALYZING ANSWERS
65					✓				
66		✓							
67		✓							
68					✓	✓			
69		✓							
70					✓				✓
71		✓							
72					✓	✓			✓
73			✓					✓	
74		✓							
75	✓								
76					✓	✓			✓
77		✓							
78					✓				
79					✓				
80			✓	✓				✓	
81		✓				✓			
Mid-Unit Review	✓	✓	✓						
82					✓				
83					✓				✓
84		✓							
85		✓	✓					✓	
86	✓					✓			
87					✓				
88		✓	✓					✓	
89		✓							
90		✓				✓			
91		✓							
92					✓				
93	✓	✓	✓						
94						✓			
Unit Test			✓				✓		

ASSESSMENT OPTIONS

PORTFOLIO ASSESSMENT

Throughout this Teacher's Guide are suggested activities in which students draw pictures, make graphs, write about mathematics, and so on. Keep students' work to assess growth of understanding as the year progresses.

Lessons 75, Mid-Unit Review 86, and 93

PERFORMANCE ASSESSMENT

Performance assessment items focus on evaluating how students think and work as they solve problems. Opportunities for performance assessment can be found throughout the unit. Rubrics and guides for grading can be found in the front of the Assessment Blackline Masters.

Lessons 66, 67, 69, 71, 74, 77, 81, Mid-Unit Review, 84, 85, 88, 89, 90, 91, and 93

FORMAL ASSESSMENT

A Mid-Unit Review, Unit Review, and Unit Test help assess students' understanding of concepts, skills, and problem solving. The *Math Explorations and Applications* CD-ROM Test Generator can create additional unit tests at three ability levels. Also, Mastery Checkpoints are provided periodically throughout the unit.

Lessons 73, 80, Mid-Unit Review, 85, 88, 93, and Unit Test

SELF ASSESSMENT

Throughout the program students are given the opportunity to check their own math skills.

Lesson 80

INFORMAL ASSESSMENT

A variety of assessment suggestions are provided, including interviews, oral questions or presentation, debates, and so on. Also, each lesson includes Assessment Criteria, a list of questions about each student's progress, understanding, and participation.

Lessons 65, 68, 70, 72, 76, 78, 79, 82, 83, 87, and 92

CUMULATIVE REVIEW

Cumulative Reviews, covering material presented thus far in the year, are provided in the unit for use as either assessment or practice.

Lessons 68, 72, 76, 81, 86, 90, and 94

MULTIPLE-CHOICE TEST (STANDARDIZED FORMAT)

Each unit provides a unit test in standardized format, presenting students with an opportunity to practice taking a test in this format.

MASTERY CHECKPOINT

Mastery Checkpoints are provided throughout the unit to assess student proficiency in specific skills. Checkpoints reference appropriate Assessment Blackline Masters and other assessment options. Results of these evaluations can be recorded on the Mastery Checkpoint Chart.

Lessons 73, 80, 85, and 88

ANALYZING ANSWERS

Analyzing answers items suggest possible sources of student error and offer teaching strategies for addressing difficulties.

Lessons 70, 72, 76, and 83

Look for these icons:

> **"**Assessment is the process of gathering evidence about a student's knowledge of, ability to use, and disposition toward, mathematics and of making inferences from that evidence for a variety of purposes. **"**
>
> —NCTM Assessment Standards

MASTERY CHECKPOINTS

WHAT TO EXPECT FROM STUDENTS AS THEY COMPLETE THIS UNIT

⓰ ADDING AND SUBTRACTING FRACTIONS—LESSON 73

Most students should demonstrate mastery of adding and subtracting fractions with unlike denominators by correctly answering at least 80% of the problems on page 264 or on Assessment Blackline Master page 31 in a reasonable amount of time. Results of this assessment may be recorded on the Mastery Checkpoint Chart.

⓱ ADDING AND SUBTRACTING MIXED NUMBERS—LESSON 80

At this time most of the students should demonstrate mastery of changing improper fractions to mixed numbers, rewriting mixed numbers as improper fractions, and adding and subtracting mixed numbers by correctly answering at least 80% of the problems on page 288 or on Assessment Blackline Master page 32. Results of this assessment may be recorded on the Mastery Checkpoint Chart.

⓲ MULTIPLICATION AND DIVISION OF FRACTIONS AND MIXED NUMBERS— LESSON 85

At this time most students should be able to multiply and divide fractions and mixed numbers. This ability may be assessed by observing students as they work on Assessment Blackline Master page 34 or on a similar set of problems. Results of this assessment may be recorded on the Mastery Checkpoint Chart.

⓳ UNDERSTANDING RATES, RATIOS, AND AVERAGES—LESSON 88

At this time most students should demonstrate mastery of finding the mean of a set of data and solving problems involving ratios and rates by correctly answering at least 80% of the problems on pages 316–317 or on Assessment Blackline Masters pages 35–36 in a reasonable amount of time. Results of this assessment may be recorded on the Mastery Checkpoint Chart.

UNIT 4

PROGRAM RESOURCES

THESE ADDITIONAL COMPONENTS OF *MATH EXPLORATIONS AND APPLICATIONS* CAN BE PURCHASED SEPARATELY FROM **SRA/McGraw-Hill.**

LESSON	BASIC MANIPULATIVE KIT	GAME MAT PACKAGE	TEACHER MANIPULATIVE KIT	INTERMEDIATE MANIPULATIVE KIT	INTERMEDIATE OVERHEAD MANIPULATIVE KIT	*THE CRUNCHER* SOFTWARE	*MATH EXPLORATIONS AND APPLICATIONS* CD-ROM
65	Number Cubes						Lesson 65
66							Lesson 66
67	Number Cubes	Equivalence 2 Game, play money			bills, coins	spreadsheet	Lesson 67
68		Equivalence 1 Game					Lesson 68
69	Number Cubes						Lesson 69
70			scale	tape measure			Lesson 70
71		Cosmic Cafe Game					Lesson 71
72				fraction tower cubes	fraction tiles		Lesson 72
73	Number Cubes			fraction tower cubes	fraction tiles		Lesson 73
74		Harder Cosmic Cafe Game		fraction tower cubes	fraction tiles	spreadsheet	Lesson 74
75	Number Cubes	Routes and Harder Routes					Lesson 75
76	Number Cubes					spreadsheet	Lesson 76
77							Lesson 77
78		Fringo Factory Game					Lesson 78
79	Number Cubes			fraction tower cubes	fraction tiles	spreadsheet	Lesson 79
80	Number Cubes			fraction tower cubes	fraction tiles		Lesson 80
81						project	Lesson 81
82	Number Cubes					spreadsheet	Lesson 82
83				fraction tower cubes	fraction tiles		Lesson 83
84							Lesson 84
85						spreadsheet	Lesson 85
86						spreadsheet	Lesson 86
87						spreadsheet	Lesson 87
88		Pentathlon Game				spreadsheet	Lesson 88
89							Lesson 89
90							Lesson 90
91						spreadsheet	Lesson 91
92							Lesson 92
93							Lesson 93
94							Lesson 94

Fractions and Mixed Numbers

INTRODUCING THE UNIT

Using the Student Pages Begin your discussion of the opening unit photo by asking students, "What must firefighters know about proportions and fractions?" Then read aloud the paragraph on the student page that highlights firefighting as a career. This helps make the connection between school and work and encourages students to explore how math is used in the real world.

ACTIVITY Explain to students that firefighters must assess the intensity of a fire in order to determine the right amounts of water pressure needed to extinguish it. Ask students to find out how many fire stations there are in their community. Then ask them to find out the number and types of firefighting equipment each station has. Suggest that while they are gathering this information they also learn the number of fires that were put out during the previous month.

FYI Point out to students that communities have not always had organized firefighters. From ancient times through the Middle Ages, most Western cities and towns depended on civilians to put out fires as they arose. Because most structures were built of highly flammable materials, and because open fire was commonly used for household purposes such as lighting, heating, and cooking, fires were regarded as a fact of life. The first organized system for fighting fires was probably the humble bucket brigade, in which buckets of water were passed from hand to hand by a line of people stretching from a water source to the fire. Stress that it was not until the development of the water pump in the seventeenth century that cities got the upper hand on fighting their fires.

The next best thing to fighting fires was fire insurance, which was first sold in ancient Rome. Insured houses would receive an iron symbol stamped in their walls that would serve as proof when a claim was made. In the United States volunteer firefighting units were established as early as the colonial era, but it was not until a century or so later that designated firefighters would be trained in their trade and use specialized equipment such as wagons for ladders and mobile water tanks.

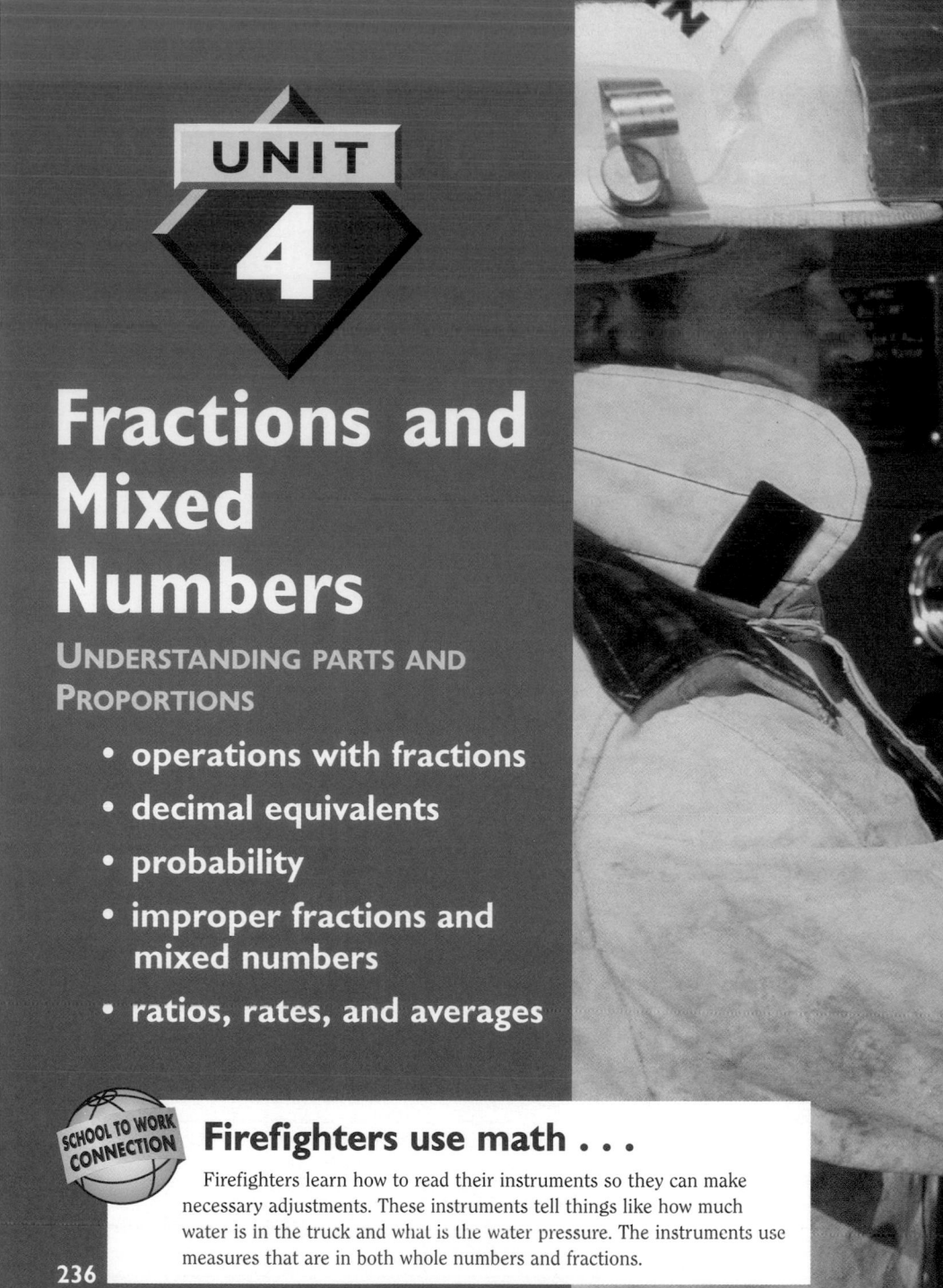

Fractions and Mixed Numbers

UNDERSTANDING PARTS AND PROPORTIONS

- **operations with fractions**
- **decimal equivalents**
- **probability**
- **improper fractions and mixed numbers**
- **ratios, rates, and averages**

Firefighters use math . . .

Firefighters learn how to read their instruments so they can make necessary adjustments. These instruments tell things like how much water is in the truck and what is the water pressure. The instruments use measures that are in both whole numbers and fractions.

236

Thinklab™ 2

SRA's *Thinklab™ 2* provides a series of creative and logical problem-solving opportunities for individual students. The problems are designed to appeal to different cognitive abilities.

▶ Use Problems 76–85 with this unit to reinforce logical analysis (absorbing multiple data, testing hypotheses, and planning a set of operations).

▶ Use Problems 86–95 with this unit to reinforce quantitative thinking (interpreting and synthesizing data).

▶ Use Problems 96–100 with this unit to integrate object manipulation, creative insight, logical analysis, quantitative thinking, and brainstorming and to incorporate social interaction.

Technology has always been key to firefighting: the ability to deliver large amounts of water (and these days sometimes chemicals) to the fire makes the critical difference. Fast response times are also a key ingredient in fighting fires, which is why even early fire wagons were painted red, warning passersby to get out of the way.

Point out to students that nothing could be more pressured and rushed than fighting a fire, and yet a firefighter must be able to gauge quickly and accurately how much water to throw where. This means being able to read complex gauges and meters that tell exactly how much pressure is available for a given hose and calculating what will be needed to reach the fire. Stress that this also means figuring out how much hose to assign to a particular place, or, on the fire chief's level, how many trucks to assign to a fire. Students contemplating a career in firefighting should know that in most communities they will have to pass a highly competitive test of both endurance and mental competence. While it can be a difficult field to enter, firefighting can be both exciting and rewarding.

Home Connections You may want to send Home Connections Blackline Masters pages 50–51 home to introduce this unit.

Unit Project This would be a good time to assign the "Fair Advertising" project on pages 338 and 339. Students can begin working on the project in cooperative groups in their free time as you work through the unit. This project is a good opportunity for students to practice analyzing advertising for fairness.

237

Cooperate 3

Cooperate 3, published by SRA, provides a series of creative and logical problem-solving opportunities for cooperative groups. The problems are designed to provide practice in problem solving, communication, reasoning, and making connections. *Cooperate 3* presents the following cognitive strategies—perceiving spatial relations, ordering and sequencing, logical deduction, establishing and testing hypotheses, sequential exploration, identifying starting points, attending to detail, organizing information, and screening irrelevant information. Each Problem Card emphasizes a principal strategy as well as reinforcing other strategies.

▶ Use Problem Card 16 with this unit to emphasize ordering and sequencing.

▶ Use Problem Cards 17–18 with this unit to emphasize logical deduction.

▶ Use Problem Cards 19–20 with this unit to emphasize organizing information.

Student Edition pages 238–241

LESSON 65

Fractions of Whole Numbers

LESSON PLANNER

Objectives

▶ to review the meaning of *fractions*

▶ to review the use of the word *of* as it relates to multiplication of fractions

▶ to review and provide practice in finding fractions of whole numbers

Context of the Lesson
This is the first of 20 lessons on fractions.

MANIPULATIVES

Program Resources
Number Cubes (0–5)
Reteaching Master
Practice Master 65
Enrichment Master 65

For extra practice:
CD-ROM* Lesson 65

❶ Warm-Up

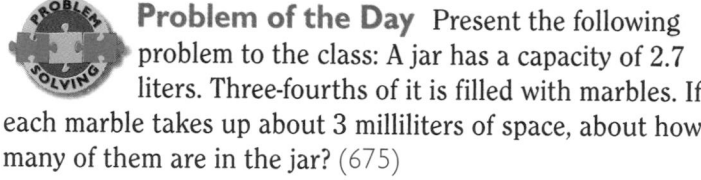

⏱ 5 MINUTES

Problem of the Day Present the following problem to the class: A jar has a capacity of 2.7 liters. Three-fourths of it is filled with marbles. If each marble takes up about 3 milliliters of space, about how many of them are in the jar? (675)

Problem-Solving Strategies Ask students who have solved the Problem of the Day to share how they solved it and any strategies they used.

MENTAL MATH Ask students to use mental math to find the following products.

a. $\frac{1}{2}$ of 12 (6)   b. $\frac{2}{3}$ of 15 (10)

c. $\frac{1}{4}$ of 60 (15)   d. $\frac{3}{5}$ of 500 (300)

e. $\frac{3}{4}$ of 400 (300)   f. $\frac{1}{3}$ of 1200 (400)

LESSON 65

Fractions of Whole Numbers

We can use fractions to describe how much of something we are taking.

To take $\frac{3}{5}$ of a pizza, we divide the pizza into 5 equal parts and take 3 of them.

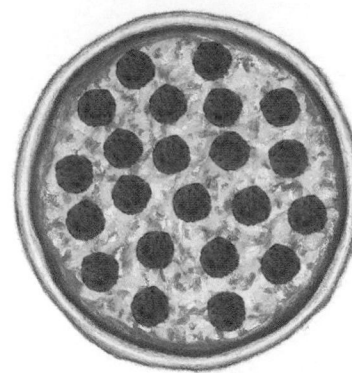
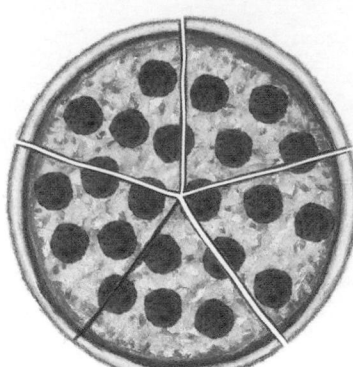

Remember: **The denominator (bottom number) of a fraction tells how many equal parts there are.**

$\frac{3}{5}$ —— numerator
—— denominator

The numerator (top number) tells how many of these parts to take.

To find a fraction of a number, you can divide the number into as many equal parts as the denominator tells you, and then take as many as the numerator says.

For example, to find $\frac{3}{5}$ of 60, divide 60 into 5 equal parts.

Since $60 \div 5 = 12$, each part will be 12.

Then take 3 of those parts.

$3 \times 12 = 36$

So $\frac{3}{5}$ of 60 = 36.

238 • Fractions and Mixed Numbers

Literature Connection Have students read *Math Curse* by Jon Scieszka. Ask them to find all the occasions the main character has to use fractions during his day of math problems.

*available separately

PRACTICE

One way to find $\frac{3}{5}$ of 60 is to divide 60 by 5 and then multiply by 3. What would happen if you multiplied by 3 and then divided by 5?

$60 \times 3 = 180$ $180 \div 5 = 36$

◆   Is this the same answer as before? **yes**

◆   Try this method with other problems. Do you get the same answer, whether you divide first then multiply, or multiply first then divide?
Yes, you would get the same answer. This will always work.

Notice that in order to find $\frac{3}{5}$ of a number, you always multiply by 3 at some time. Because taking a fraction of a number always involves multiplying, we call the "of" operation "multiplication." So $\frac{2}{3}$ of 60 and $\frac{2}{3} \times 60$ mean the same thing.

With multiplication of whole numbers, as you know, the order in which you multiply doesn't change the product. The same thing is true for fractions and whole numbers.

$$\tfrac{3}{4} \text{ of } 60 = \tfrac{3}{4} \times 60 = 60 \times \tfrac{3}{4}$$

Solve for _n_ in the following.

1. $\frac{2}{5}$ of $60 = n$ **24**
2. $\frac{2}{5} \times 60 = n$ **24**
3. $60 \times \frac{2}{5} = n$ **24**
4. $n = \frac{3}{4}$ of 60 **45**
5. $n = \frac{3}{4} \times 60$ **45**
6. $n = 60 \times \frac{3}{4}$ **45**
7. $\frac{1}{2}$ of $n = 60$ **120**
8. $\frac{1}{2}$ of $30 = n$ **15**
9. $\frac{2}{3} \times 90 = n$ **60**
10. $120 \times \frac{4}{5} = n$ **96**
11. $360 \times \frac{1}{12} = n$ **30**
12. $\frac{0}{3}$ of $30 = n$ **0**
13. $\frac{n}{4} \times 20 = 5$ **1**
14. $\frac{n}{4}$ of $20 = 10$ **2**
15. $20 \times \frac{n}{4} = 15$ **3**
16. $\frac{2}{3} \times 6 = n$ **4**
17. $\frac{2}{3} \times 12 = n$ **8**
18. $\frac{2}{3} \times n = 12$ **18**
19. $\frac{1}{4} \times 8 = n$ **2**
20. $\frac{n}{4} \times 8 = 8$ **4**
21. $\frac{1}{2} \times 50 = n$ **25**
22. $\frac{1}{5} \times 50 = n$ **10**
23. $\frac{2}{5} \times 50 = n$ **20**
24. $\frac{n}{5} \times 50 = 40$ **4**

Solve these problems.

25. A pair of jeans is on sale for $\frac{2}{3}$ of the regular price. If the regular price is $36, what is the sale price?   **$24**

26. A newspaper reported that $\frac{3}{4}$ of the town's residents who were surveyed approved of the mayor's job performance. If 200 residents were surveyed, how many approved of the mayor's job performance?   **150**

27. A math teacher announced that $\frac{3}{5}$ of the class earned an "A" or a "B" on the last math test. If the class has 25 students, how many had an A or a B?   **15**

Unit 4   Lesson 65   •   **239**

❷ Teach

Using the Student Pages   You may wish to demonstrate the "Fractions of 60" game on page 241, which provides practice with fractions of whole numbers. Students can play it as they finish pages 238–240.

You may wish to begin pages 238 and 239, which review material studied in previous grades, by asking a volunteer to explain how to find $\frac{3}{5}$ of 60. Guide the student to see that instead of dividing 60 into five equal parts and then taking three of them, he or she could have gotten the same answer by dividing three 60s by 5.

Go over the information at the top of page 239 with the class, and provide examples to demonstrate that multiplying by a fraction is commutative (the order of the factors does not change the product). Then assign the problems on the page for independent work. When you go over students' answers, pay particular attention to problems 13–15, which may confuse students. You may wish to state these problems aloud. For example, for problem 14 you might ask, "What number of fourths of 20 is 10?" or "How many fourths of 20 equals 10?" For problem 15 you might ask, "The product of 20 and some number divided by 4 equals 15. What is the number?"

Technology Connection   For further practice multiplying a fraction or mixed number and a whole number, multiplying combinations of fractions and mixed numbers, and solving word problems, refer students to the software, video, and laser disc _Modumath: Arithmetic, Multiplying Fractions_ (IBM/VHS, for grades 6–12).

Unit 4 Lesson 65   **239**

◆ LESSON 65 Fractions of Whole Numbers

Teach

Using the Student Pages Have students work in pairs on the word problems on page 240. You may wish to do the first problem with the whole class. Be sure students understand why a majority vote must be more than precisely half of the votes.

Introducing the "Fractions of 60" Game Have students play the "Fractions of 60" game in pairs or in small groups. If students have developed variations of this game, which they have played in earlier grades, invite them to teach the variations to others. This game involves finding fractions of whole numbers and using division, multiplication, and addition.

GIFTED & TALENTED Meeting Individual Needs Challenge your more advanced students to play "Fractions of 2520," choosing any two of two 0–5 and two 5–10 Number Cubes to roll. Challenge them to figure out what is special about the number 2520. (It is the least number divisible by every whole number from 1 to 10.)

◆ LESSON 65 Fractions of Whole Numbers

Solve these problems.

SOCIAL STUDIES CONNECTION

28 In order to win an election with two candidates, one must win a majority of the votes cast. A majority is any number greater than $\frac{1}{2}$ of those voting. If 200 votes are cast in an election with two candidates, what is the fewest number of votes a candidate can receive to win the election? **101**

29 Why do we not agree that a candidate will win if she or he receives exactly half of the votes cast? **The other candidate has received the same number of votes.**

30 If there are more than two candidates, we sometimes declare the winner to be the candidate who received the most votes, even if that is not a majority. We say such a candidate received a plurality of the votes.

  a. If there are 300 votes cast and there are three candidates, what is the fewest number of votes a candidate might receive and still win? **101**

  b. Would a candidate who won 101 votes in such an election necessarily win? Explain. **No, unless the other candidates received exactly 100 and 99 votes.**

31 The President of the United States is chosen by the Electoral College, which has 538 members. How many votes must a candidate get in the Electoral College to have a majority? **270**

32 If a candidate fails to get a majority in the Electoral College, the outcome is decided in the House of Representatives, but each of the 50 states gets only one vote and the candidate must get a majority to win. If no candidate wins in the Electoral College, how many votes are required in order to win in the House of Representatives? **26**

33 In order to pass in Congress, a bill must receive a majority vote in the House of Representatives and in the Senate.

  a. How many of the 435 votes in the House of Representatives must a bill receive in order to pass? **218**

  b. How many of the 100 votes in the Senate must a bill receive in order to pass? **51**

34 In order to override a veto (or rejection) by the President, a bill must receive a $\frac{2}{3}$ vote in the House and in the Senate.

  a. How many votes are needed in the House of Representatives to override a veto? **290**

  b. How many votes are needed in the Senate to override a veto? **67**

240 • Fractions and Mixed Numbers

SOCIAL STUDIES CONNECTION

Social Studies Connection Invite interested students to do research to find out more about the history and workings of the Electoral College. Ask them to find the difference between "popular vote" and "electoral vote." Have them research the election of 1888 between Grover Cleveland and Benjamin Harrison. Although Cleveland received more popular votes, he received fewer electoral votes and hence lost the election.

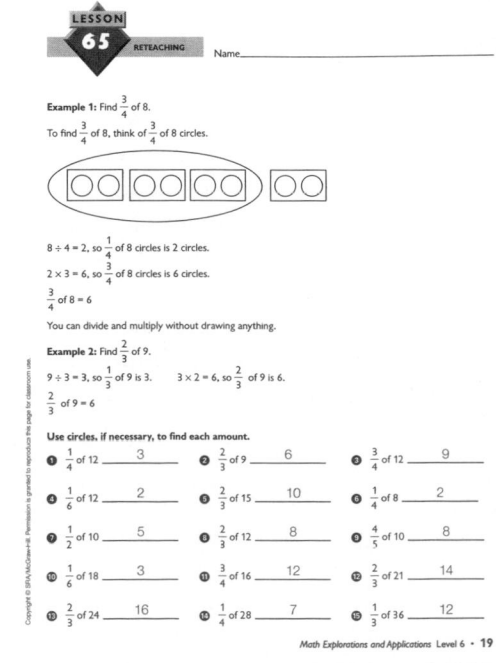

Fractions of 60 Game

COOPERATIVE LEARNING

GAME

Players:	Two or more
Materials:	Two 0–5 cubes
Object:	To score a total of 150 or more
Math Focus:	Finding fractions of numbers and adding

RULES

1. Take turns rolling both cubes. Combine the numbers rolled to make a fraction no greater than 1.

2. Find that fraction of 60 and write the answer.

If you rolled:	You would take:	Your answer would be:
2 3	$\frac{2}{3}$ of 60	40
0 4	$\frac{0}{4}$ of 60	0
2 2	$\frac{2}{2}$ of 60	60

3. Add the answer to your last score.
4. If you roll a 0, your score for that turn is 0.
5. If you roll 0 and 0, roll both cubes again.
6. The first player whose score totals 150 or more is the winner.

OTHER WAYS TO PLAY THIS GAME

1. Try to score a different total.
2. Change the game to "Fractions of 120."

MATH JOURNAL

Suppose this game were played with a 5–10 cube. Which rolls would give answers that are not whole numbers? Record your answers in your Math Journal.

Unit 4   Lesson 65 • **241**

---

③ Wrap-Up

5 MINUTES

In Closing To summarize the lesson, ask students to explain and demonstrate a procedure for finding a fraction of a whole number.

ALTERNATIVE ASSESSMENT

Informal Assessment Circulate about the room and observe students as they work on the numerical problems and word problems on pages 239 and 240 and as they play the game. If you notice students making errors, ask them whether they can see the mistakes you catch and are then able to correct them.

Assessment Criteria

Did the student . . .

✓ demonstrate understanding of how to multiply fractions and whole numbers by correctly answering at least 80% of the computation problems and word problems?

✓ demonstrate understanding that multiplication of fractions, as with whole numbers, is commutative?

✓ successfully play the "Fractions of 60" game?

Homework Ask students to play "Fractions of 60" with a family member for further practice with multiplication by a fraction. A copy of this game can also be found on page 21 of the Home Connections Blackline Masters.

PRACTICE p. 65

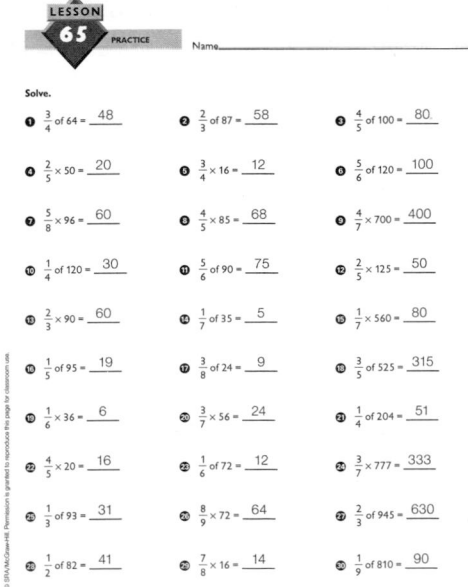

LESSON 65 PRACTICE Name_____

Solve.

1. $\frac{3}{4}$ of 64 = __48__
2. $\frac{2}{5} \times 50$ = __20__
3. $\frac{5}{8} \times 96$ = __60__
4. $\frac{1}{4}$ of 120 = __30__
5. $\frac{2}{3} \times 90$ = __60__
6. $\frac{1}{5}$ of 95 = __19__
7. $\frac{1}{6} \times 36$ = __6__
8. $\frac{4}{5} \times 20$ = __16__
9. $\frac{1}{3}$ of 93 = __31__
10. $\frac{1}{2}$ of 82 = __41__

11. $\frac{2}{3}$ of 87 = __58__
12. $\frac{3}{4} \times 16$ = __12__
13. $\frac{4}{5} \times 85$ = __68__
14. $\frac{5}{6}$ of 90 = __75__
15. $\frac{1}{7}$ of 35 = __5__
16. $\frac{3}{8}$ of 24 = __9__
17. $\frac{3}{7} \times 56$ = __24__
18. $\frac{1}{6}$ of 72 = __12__
19. $\frac{8}{9} \times 72$ = __64__
20. $\frac{7}{8} \times 16$ = __14__

21. $\frac{4}{5}$ of 100 = __80__
22. $\frac{5}{6}$ of 120 = __100__
23. $\frac{4}{7} \times 700$ = __400__
24. $\frac{2}{5} \times 125$ = __50__
25. $\frac{1}{7} \times 560$ = __80__
26. $\frac{3}{5}$ of 525 = __315__
27. $\frac{1}{4}$ of 204 = __51__
28. $\frac{3}{7} \times 777$ = __333__
29. $\frac{2}{3} \times 945$ = __630__
30. $\frac{1}{9}$ of 810 = __90__

Math Explorations and Applications Level 6 • 65

ENRICHMENT p. 65

LESSON 65 ENRICHMENT Name_____

PROBLEM SOLVING

Solve these problems.

Three leopards in the jungle were arguing about which of them had the greatest number of spots.

Leon said, "I have $\frac{1}{2}$ the number of spots of my great-grandfather, the king of all leopards."

Lori said, "I have $\frac{3}{4}$ the number of spots of my great-grandmother, the queen of all leopards and $\frac{3}{4}$ is more than $\frac{1}{2}$."

Lianna said, "I have $\frac{4}{5}$ the number of spots of my great-uncle, brother to the king and queen of all leopards, and $\frac{4}{5}$ is more than $\frac{1}{2}$ and $\frac{3}{4}$."

Oswald, the wise old owl, said, "The fraction of spots that you have means nothing until we know how many spots your relatives had."

The number of spots for Leon's great-grandfather, Lori's great-grandmother, and Lianna's great-uncle are: 100, 140, and 180, but we do not know who had how many spots.

1. How could Leon have the most spots?
Leon could never have the most spots.

2. How could Lori have the most spots? List as many ways as you can.
if Lori's great-grandmother had 140 spots, Leon's great-grandfather had 180 spots, and Lianna's great-uncle had 100 spots; or if Lori's great-grandmother had 180 spots

3. How could Lianna have the most spots? List as many ways as you can.
if Lianna's great-uncle had 140 spots, Leon's great-grandfather had 180 spots, and Lori's great-grandmother had 100 spots; or if Lianna's great-uncle had 180 spots

Math Explorations and Applications Level 6 • 65

Multiplying Fractions

LESSON PLANNER

Objective

▶ to review and practice finding a fraction of a fraction

Context of the Lesson
This is the second of 20 lessons on fractions.

MANIPULATIVES
none

Program Resources
Practice Master 66
Enrichment Master 66
For extra practice:
CD-ROM* Lesson 66

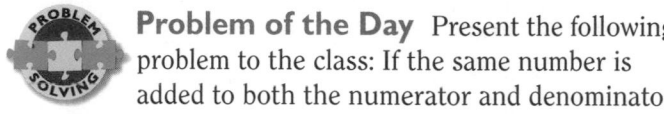

① Warm-Up

Problem of the Day Present the following problem to the class: If the same number is added to both the numerator and denominator of a fraction between 0 and 1, will the new fraction be greater than, equal to, or less than the original fraction? Explain your answer. (greater than; the value of the fraction will increase if the digits increase, but the difference between them remains the same; for example, if you add 8 to both the 3 and the 4 in $\frac{3}{4}$, you get $\frac{11}{12}$; $\frac{11}{12} > \frac{3}{4}$)

Problem-Solving Strategies Ask students who have solved the Problem of the Day to share how they solved it and any strategies they used.

MENTAL MATH Have students indicate whether the answer is less than 1 (thumbs down), greater than 1 (thumbs up), or equal to 1 (stand).

a. $\frac{3}{4} + \frac{1}{2}$ (thumbs up)

b. $\frac{1}{3} + \frac{2}{3}$ (stand)

c. $\frac{1}{2} + \frac{1}{2}$ (stand)

d. $\frac{1}{5} + \frac{1}{2}$ (thumbs down)

e. $\frac{1}{5} + \frac{3}{5}$ (thumbs down)

f. $\frac{1}{4} + \frac{4}{4}$ (thumbs up)

g. $\frac{1}{8} + \frac{4}{8}$ (thumbs down)

h. $\frac{3}{4} + \frac{3}{4}$ (thumbs up)

i. $\frac{5}{10} + \frac{5}{10}$ (stand)

j. $\frac{1}{4} + \frac{3}{4}$ (stand)

Multiplying Fractions

Sometimes we need to find a fraction of a fraction. This example helps show how we can do that. Using a piece of paper as a pizza, act out this story.

Find $\frac{2}{3}$ of $\frac{4}{7}$ of a pizza.

Divide the pizza into 7 equal pieces and separate 4 of them. That is $\frac{4}{7}$ of the pizza.

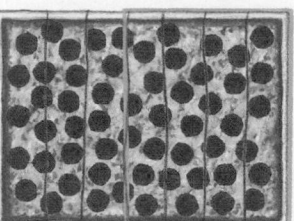

To take $\frac{2}{3}$ of that, cut each of the 7 pieces into 3 equal pieces. Then from each of the $\frac{4}{7}$ that we separated, take 2 of these smaller pieces. So all together we take 8 of the smaller pieces.

In effect, we have cut the pizza into 3 × 7, or 21, equal pieces. Then we took 2 × 4, or 8, of those pieces.

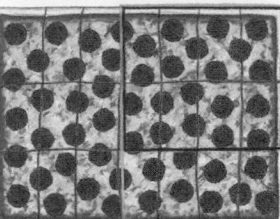

$$\frac{2}{3} \text{ of } \frac{4}{7} = \frac{2 \times 4}{3 \times 7} = \frac{8}{21}$$

Notice that $\frac{2}{3}$ of $\frac{4}{7} = \frac{2 \times 4}{3 \times 7}$. So it is reasonable to write $\frac{2}{3} \times \frac{4}{7}$ for $\frac{2}{3}$ of $\frac{4}{7}$. We can use this rule for multiplying fractions: To multiply two fractions, multiply their numerators to get the numerator of the answer and multiply denominators to get the denominator of the answer.

Solve these problems. Be careful.

❶ $\frac{1}{2}$ of $\frac{1}{4}$ **$\frac{1}{8}$**   ❷ $\frac{1}{2}$ of $\frac{1}{3}$ **$\frac{1}{6}$**   ❸ $\frac{1}{3}$ of $\frac{1}{2}$ **$\frac{1}{6}$**   ❹ $\frac{1}{2}$ of $\frac{2}{3}$ **$\frac{2}{6}$ (or $\frac{1}{3}$)**

❺ $\frac{1}{2}$ of $\frac{3}{5}$ **$\frac{3}{10}$**   ❻ $\frac{2}{5}$ of $\frac{3}{4}$ **$\frac{6}{20}$ (or $\frac{3}{10}$)**   ❼ $\frac{3}{7} \times \frac{3}{4}$ **$\frac{9}{28}$**   ❽ $\frac{4}{5} \times \frac{2}{3}$ **$\frac{8}{15}$**

❾ $\frac{5}{6} \times \frac{5}{9}$ **$\frac{25}{54}$**   ❿ $\frac{2}{3} \times \frac{1}{5}$ **$\frac{2}{15}$**   ⓫ $\frac{3}{8} \times \frac{1}{2}$ **$\frac{3}{16}$**   ⓬ $\frac{2}{5} \times \frac{1}{7}$ **$\frac{2}{35}$**

GIFTED & TALENTED Meeting Individual Needs

Present the following problem: Benny has had a long career in baseball. He spent $\frac{1}{12}$ of it playing in the A minor league and $\frac{1}{6}$ of it in the AAA minor league. Then he spent $\frac{1}{5}$ of his career in the major leagues. Following that, he spent $\frac{1}{3}$ of his career as a manager. Finally, during the last 13 years of his career, he was both an executive and a scout for the organization. How long was Benny's career in baseball? (60 years)

RETEACHING

Use drawings to reteach fractions-of-fractions concepts. For example, to take $\frac{2}{3}$ of $\frac{3}{5}$, draw a rectangle divided into fifths. Shade in three fifths. Then, divide the shaded part into thirds, or show that the three fifths is already divided into three parts. Show that $\frac{2}{3}$ of $\frac{3}{5}$ is actually $\frac{2}{5}$.

*available separately

Solve.

13 $\frac{1}{3}$ of 30 **10** **14** $\frac{1}{4}$ of 60 **15** **15** $\frac{1}{2}$ of 100 **50** **16** $\frac{1}{5}$ of 100 **20**

17 $\frac{2}{3}$ of 75 **50** **18** $\frac{3}{4}$ of 80 **60** **19** $\frac{2}{5}$ of 40 **16** **20** $\frac{4}{5}$ of 40 **32**

21 $\frac{1}{3}$ of 24 **8** **22** $\frac{2}{3}$ of 24 **16** **23** $\frac{1}{7}$ of 35 **5** **24** $\frac{1}{8}$ of 40 **5**

25 $\frac{4}{5}$ of 30 **24** **26** $\frac{3}{5}$ of 80 **48** **27** $\frac{1}{2}$ of 36 **18** **28** $\frac{2}{3}$ of 120 **80**

Solve these problems.

29 If you roll a 0–5 cube many times, about what fraction of the time would you expect to roll a 0? $\frac{1}{6}$

30 If you roll a 0–5 cube many times, about what fraction of the time would you expect to roll a 3? $\frac{1}{6}$

31 If you roll a 0–5 cube 60 times, about how many times would you expect a 0 to come up? Try it to see if you get about the number of 0s you expected. **about 10**

32 If you roll a 0–5 cube many times, about what fraction of the time would you expect to roll an odd number (1, 3, or 5)? $\frac{3}{6}$ **(or** $\frac{1}{2}$**)**

33 If you roll a 0–5 cube 60 times, about how many times would you expect to roll an odd number? Try it to see. **about 30**

34 If you roll a 0–5 cube many times, about what fraction of the time would you expect to roll a number less than 5? $\frac{5}{6}$

35 Two-thirds of the 600 students at Ford High School play some kind of team sport. Of those who do, $\frac{1}{10}$ play football.

   a. What fraction of the students at Ford High School play football? $\frac{2}{30}$ **(or** $\frac{1}{15}$**)**

   b. How many students at Ford play football? **40**

36 A grove in Florida has 400 trees. Of those trees, $\frac{1}{4}$ are grapefruit trees and $\frac{3}{4}$ are orange trees. A recent frost damaged $\frac{1}{2}$ of the orange trees but no grapefruit trees.

   a. What fraction of the total trees did the frost damage? $\frac{3}{0}$

   b. How many trees were damaged? **150**

A banyan tree in India has the widest spread of any plant on Earth. Its branches cover an area as large as four football fields.

Unit 4 Lesson 66 • **243**

---

② Teach

Using the Student Pages Go over pages 242–243 with the class. Have students recreate the story while you are discussing it, using a sheet of paper for the pizza. They can either make lines for the cuts and shade parts of the "pizza" or actually cut their "pizzas."

Before students do problems 1–36 on their own, you may wish to go over one or two of the word problems with the entire class. If students do not remember probability from earlier grades, address it informally at this time by asking students to consider how many ways the number cube could come up and how many would be the desired outcome. Point out that the results of problems 31 and 33 will be slightly off for some students, exactly on target for some, and way off for others. During the discussion of the problems, look at the results of the entire class for both of these problems.

③ Wrap-Up

In Closing Summarize the lesson by asking students to explain how to use a rule to find a fraction of a fraction.

Performance Assessment Ask students to find $\frac{1}{3}$ of $\frac{2}{5}$, and have them explain the procedure they use.

Assessment Criteria

Did the student . . .

✓ demonstrate understanding of the algorithm for multiplying fractions?

✓ correctly answer at least 75% of the problems on pages 242–243?

Homework Assign Practice Master 66 for further practice with multiplying fractions.

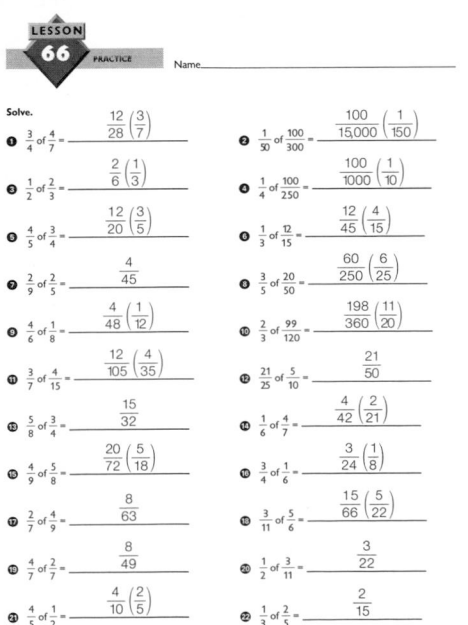

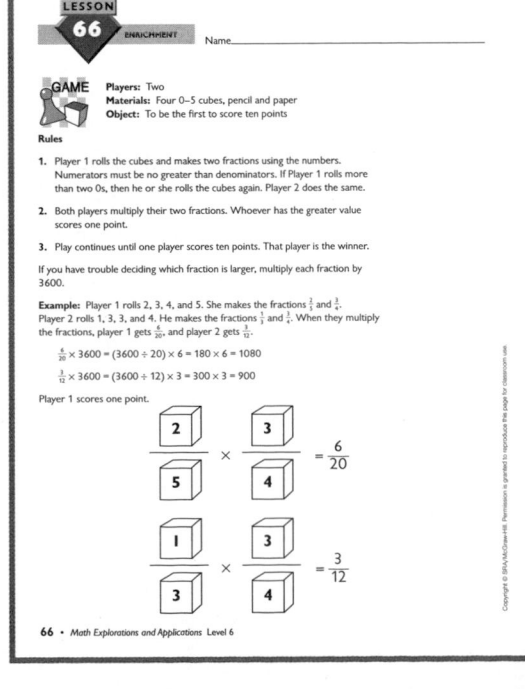

Unit 4 Lesson 66 **243**

Decimal Equivalents of Fractions

LESSON PLANNER

Objectives

▶ to review the meaning of and provide practice for finding decimal equivalents or approximations of fractions

▶ to provide practice in comparing decimals and fractions

▶ to help students develop the broad ability to use mathematical common sense

Context of the Lesson This is the third of 20 lessons on fractions. This lesson also contains the first part of "Energy Savers," a four-part Thinking Story.

MANIPULATIVES

meterstick (optional)

play money* (optional)

Program Resources

"Equivalence 2" Game Mat

Number Cubes (0–5)

Reteaching Master

Practice Master 67

Enrichment Master 67

The Cruncher*

For career connections:
  Careers and Math*

For additional math integration:
  Math Throughout the Day*

For extra practice:
  CD-ROM* Lesson 67

1 Warm-Up

Problem of the Day Present the following problem to the class: Which numbers between 1 and 100 have exactly five factors? (16 and 81— only perfect squares can have an odd number of factors.)

Problem-Solving Strategies Ask students who have solved the Problem of the Day to share how they solved it and any strategies they used.

Decimal Equivalents of Fractions

We can find $\frac{3}{100}$ of a meter by dividing a meter into 100 parts and taking 3 of them. We also know that this is 0.03 meter. So $\frac{3}{100}$ or 0.03 is the number that we get when we divide 3 by 100.

We know that $\frac{3}{8}$ can mean to divide something into 8 equal parts and take 3 of those parts.

The fraction $\frac{3}{8}$ can also represent a number.

Think of the bar of a fraction as meaning "divided by." To write a fraction as a decimal, find the numerator divided by the denominator.

If we want to write the number $\frac{3}{8}$ as a decimal, we can divide 3 by 8.

$$\begin{array}{r} 0.\ 3\ 7\ 5 \\ 8\overline{)3.{}^30{}^60{}^40} \end{array}$$

We can write: $\frac{3}{8} = 3 \div 8 = 0.375$.

We call 0.375 the **decimal equivalent** of $\frac{3}{8}$.

Try to find a decimal equivalent of $\frac{2}{11}$ (divide 2 by 11).

$$\begin{array}{r} 0.\ 1\ 8\ 1\ 8 \\ 11\overline{)2.0{}^90{}^20{}^90} \end{array}$$

We can carry this division on and on. So we can approximate $\frac{2}{11}$ with a decimal to as many places as we wish, but it has no decimal equivalent. For example, we would say that to the nearest thousandth, $\frac{2}{11}$ is about 0.182. Notice that to round to the nearest thousandth, we must carry the division out to the ten thousandths place.

For each fraction write the decimal equivalent or an approximation rounded to the nearest thousandth.

❶ $\frac{1}{2}$ 0.5   ❷ $\frac{1}{4}$ 0.25   ❸ $\frac{3}{4}$ 0.75   ❹ $\frac{1}{3}$ 0.333   ❺ $\frac{2}{3}$ 0.667

❻ $\frac{1}{5}$ 0.2   ❼ $\frac{2}{5}$ 0.4   ❽ $\frac{3}{5}$ 0.6   ❾ $\frac{4}{5}$ 0.8   ❿ $\frac{1}{6}$ 0.167

⓫ $\frac{2}{6}$ 0.333   ⓬ $\frac{1}{7}$ 0.143   ⓭ $\frac{1}{8}$ 0.125   ⓮ $\frac{2}{8}$ 0.25   ⓯ $\frac{3}{8}$ 0.375

Why teach it at this time?

Decimal equivalents of fractions are useful when it is not possible to easily compare two fractions or a decimal and a fraction. Finding decimal equivalents or approximations helps students develop a sense of the relative magnitudes of fractions and will provide a check as students work with equivalent fractions in the next several lessons.

*available separately

Up to 1 Game

Players:	Two or more
Materials:	Four 0–5 cubes
Object:	To be the last player to get to 1
Math Focus:	Comparing and ordering fractions and decimals, finding decimal equivalents of common fractions, and mathematical reasoning

RULES

1. Take turns rolling all four cubes.

2. On your turn use any two of the numbers you roll to make a fraction or a decimal less than 1. (For example, if you roll 2, 3, 2 and 1, you could make $\frac{1}{3}$, $\frac{2}{3}$, $\frac{1}{2}$, or any of these decimals: .12, .21, .22, .23, .32, .13, and .31.)

3. Keep a record of the amount you make on each turn. If you make a fraction, write the decimal equivalent or an approximation.

4. On each turn you must write an amount greater than the amount you made on your previous turn.

5. On any turn if you cannot write an amount less than 1 but greater than your previous turn, then you are out. The last player to go out wins.

SAMPLE GAME

	Hilda's Record		Ben's Record	
Turns	Numbers Rolled	Amount Made	Numbers Rolled	Amount Made
1	2 3 3 4	0.23	3 2 5 2	0.22
2	1 2 0 5	0.25	1 3 0 5	0.333 ($\frac{1}{3}$)
3	1 2 2 5	0.10 ($\frac{2}{5}$)	1 0 4 5	0.41
4	2 2 0 3	0.667 ($\frac{2}{3}$)	3 0 3 5	0.50
5	2 2 0 5	can't go	5 5 2 3	0.52

Ben won.

Literature Connection In *The Phantom Tollbooth* by Norman Juster, students can read about several situations in which the relationships between fractions and decimals are explained.

 **MENTAL MATH** Ask students to find the answers to the following problems quickly without using pencil and paper:

a. $\frac{1}{2}$ of 10 = (5) **b.** $\frac{1}{3}$ of 24 = (8)

c. $\frac{1}{4}$ of 20 = (5) **d.** $\frac{1}{6}$ of 18 = (3)

e. $\frac{1}{5}$ of 10 = (2) **f.** $\frac{2}{5}$ of 10 = (4)

g. $\frac{3}{5}$ of 10 = (6) **h.** $\frac{4}{5}$ of 10 = (8)

i. $\frac{2}{3}$ of 12 = (8) **j.** $\frac{2}{5}$ of 100 = (40)

❷ Teach

Using the Student Pages Introduce the "Up to 1" game on page 245, which provides practice comparing fractions and decimals, before beginning the work on page 244. As students finish page 244 they can play the game. You may also wish to introduce the "Equivalence 2" Game Mat, which provides practice recognizing fraction and decimal equivalents, at this time.

Go over the examples on page 244. When dividing 2 by 11, carry out the division further until students see the repetition and are convinced that the process can go on indefinitely. You may wish to mention that symbols such as a line or a dot above the repeating portion of the decimal are used to show that those digits repeat continuously, but it is not necessary to bring this up at this point. Do one or two of the problems on the page with the class and then have students do the rest on their own. When discussing the problems, keep in mind that students may write correct answers in different forms. For example, for problem 1 they may write 0.5, 0.50, or 0.500, which are all equivalent and correct responses. Encourage students to use a 0 in the ones place, since this makes it easier to notice where the decimal point is.

GAME **Introducing the "Up to 1" Game** The "Up to 1" game provides practice in comparing and ordering fractions and decimals. Demonstrate how to play this game with two students as the class watches. First show how to play with four 0–5 cubes and then how to play with two 0–5 cubes and two 5–10 cubes. Have students play this game in pairs or small groups. The game can also be played as a solitaire game: Each student takes as many turns as he or she can before going out. See who in the class gets the most turns. A copy of this game can also be found on page 22 of the Home Connections Blackline Masters.

Students can use a blank **Cruncher*** spreadsheet to help them keep track of their scores.

Teach

Using the Thinking Story Part 1 of "Energy Savers" focuses on planning routes to make the most of a car pool, and on examining whether the pick-up and drop-off locations of the participants warrant a car pool. Have students read and discuss the story, examine the map, and answer the questions in small groups. Ask them to help each other understand routes on the grid. Then discuss the questions as a class.

Answers to Thinking Story Questions:

1. | | |
   |---|---|
   | Pick up Loretta | 6.2 km |
   | Pick up Ms. Eng | 0.8 km |
   | Drop off Loretta at post office | 0.4 km |
   | Pick up Mr. Breezy | 0.6 km |
   | Drop off Ms. Eng at thumbtack factory | 7.2 km |
   | Drop off Mr. Breezy at dog school | 0.4 km |
   | Go to Mr. Muddle's store | 5.0 km |
   | Total | 20.6 km |

2. If each person drove, Mr. Breezy would drive 6.8 km; Ms. Eng, 8.2 km; Loretta, 0.4 km; and Mr. Muddle, 4.2 km. The total would be 19.6 km, considerably less than the distance Mr. Muddle would drive by the shortest possible car pool route.

3. The car pool members do not all live or work in the same part of town. A car pool would be practical if the participants lived close together and worked close together, or if their homes and workplaces lay along a simple route that did not require zigzagging or doubling back.

 After students discuss their answers to the questions about Mr. Muddle's car pool, have them write in their Math Journals what the Energy Savers could do to help Mr. Muddle solve his time problem and to help their neighbors conserve energy.

Introducing the "Equivalence 2" Game Mat The "Equivalence 2" Game Mat provides practice in recognizing fraction and decimal equivalents and in mathematical reasoning. Introduce this game by having the class watch as two students play for a while—long enough so that everyone understands the rules. Have students play in groups of two or three. Complete directions are on the Game Mat. A copy of this can also be found on page 611 of this Teacher's Guide.

THINKING STORY

Energy Savers
Part 1

"For an Energy Savers Club project we're trying to get people to save energy," Manolita said. "Will you help us, Mr. Muddle?"

"I'm always glad to do my part," said Mr. Muddle. "Last year you had me save empty bottles. Then no one ever came to pick them up. If I save energy for you this year, I hope someone will come around to collect it."

"That's not how it works," Marcus said.

"I was just joking," Mr. Muddle said. "I know you save energy by using less electricity or heating fuel or gas."

"We'd like you to save gas by starting a car pool," Willy said.

"I like that idea," said Mr. Muddle. "I'll get to ride to work with my neighbors. And we'll save money as well as energy. Each day one person drives all the others to work. That way only one car is being driven instead of three or four or five."

Mr. Muddle said that he would start a car pool right away. The next day the Energy Savers checked back to see how it was working. "I enjoyed driving Ms. Eng and Mr. Breezy and Loretta the Letter Carrier to work," said Mr. Muddle.

"But it was a lot of driving. I drove about 50 kilometers, and it took almost two hours. I'll have to close my store early in order to drive each person home from work."

RETEACHING p. 20

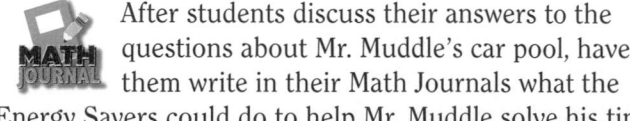

LESSON 67 RETEACHING Name_____

Fractions and decimals are two different ways of expressing the same number.
To change a fraction to a decimal, divide the numerator by the denominator.

Example 1:
Write $\frac{1}{16}$ as a decimal equivalent.

Divide 1 by 16.

$$16\overline{)1.0000} = 0.0625$$

Add 0s as needed in order to divide. Four 0s are needed here. Divide until the remainder is 0.

$\frac{1}{16} = 0.0625$

Example 2:
Write $\frac{5}{9}$ as a decimal equivalent.

Divide 5 by 9.

$$9\overline{)5.0000} = 0.5555$$

Add 0s as needed in order to divide. The remainder is not 0, and one or more digits in the quotient repeat themselves in exactly the same order.

This quotient can be rounded to the nearest thousandth.
The ten-thousandths place is 5, and the place value after it is not zero. Round the answer up.

$\frac{5}{9}$ is about 0.556.

Rewrite each fraction as a decimal equivalent or an approximation to the nearest thousandth.

1. $\frac{3}{8}$ _0.375_
2. $\frac{4}{7}$ _0.571_
3. $\frac{3}{5}$ _0.6_
4. $\frac{5}{6}$ _0.833_
5. $\frac{3}{20}$ _0.15_
6. $\frac{4}{11}$ _0.364_
7. $\frac{11}{25}$ _0.44_
8. $\frac{7}{15}$ _0.467_
9. $\frac{15}{64}$ _0.234_
10. $\frac{5}{8}$ _0.625_
11. $\frac{2}{9}$ _0.222_
12. $\frac{9}{40}$ _0.225_

20 • Math Explorations and Applications Level 6

"Let's draw a map of your route," said Marcus. "Maybe we can find a way to make the drive shorter."

. . . to be continued

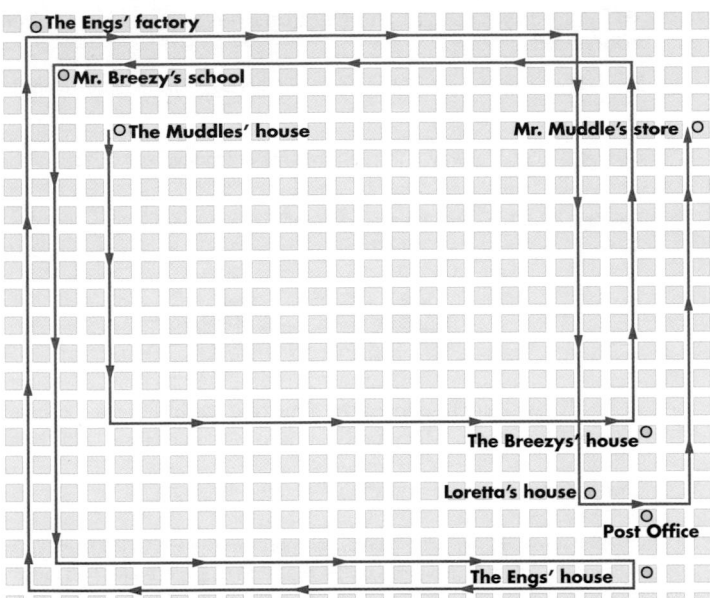

Mr. Muddle's Car Pool Route

5 blocks = 1 kilometer

Work in groups. Discuss your answers and how you figured them out. Compare your answers with other groups. Answers are in margin.

❶ The map shows the route that Mr. Muddle took. Plan the shortest route you can for Mr. Muddle that will get everyone to work. List the stops in order and the distances between stops. What is the total distance?

❷ Suppose each person drives to work by the shortest route. What is the total number of kilometers that everyone would drive? Compare this distance with your answer for problem 1.

❸ What is wrong with the car pool Mr. Muddle set up? What would be a better kind of car pool for people who want to save gas?

Unit 4   Lesson 67 • **247**

---

❸ Wrap-Up

 5 MINUTES

In Closing To summarize the lesson, ask students to explain why it could be useful to know how to express a fraction as a decimal.

 **Performance Assessment** Have students express the fractions $\frac{5}{8}$ and $\frac{3}{7}$ as decimals.

Assessment Criteria

Did the student . . .

✓ correctly answer at least 12 of the 15 problems on page 244?

✓ demonstrate an understanding of how to express fractions as decimals when playing the "Up to 1" game?

✓ participate in the discussion about car pooling in the Thinking Story?

Homework Ask students to interview someone they know who has taken part in a car pool. Have them find out why the person joined the car pool and how the route was planned.

SPECIAL NEEDS **MANIPULATIVES** **Meeting Individual Needs**
Students who have difficulty understanding fraction-decimal equivalents may benefit from extra teaching using concrete materials such as **play money***, a **meterstick,** or strips of cardboard. Guide students to use these materials to show, for instance, that a quarter of a meter is the same length as 0.25 meter and that a quarter (of a dollar) is the same as $0.25. Repeat for several different fractions.

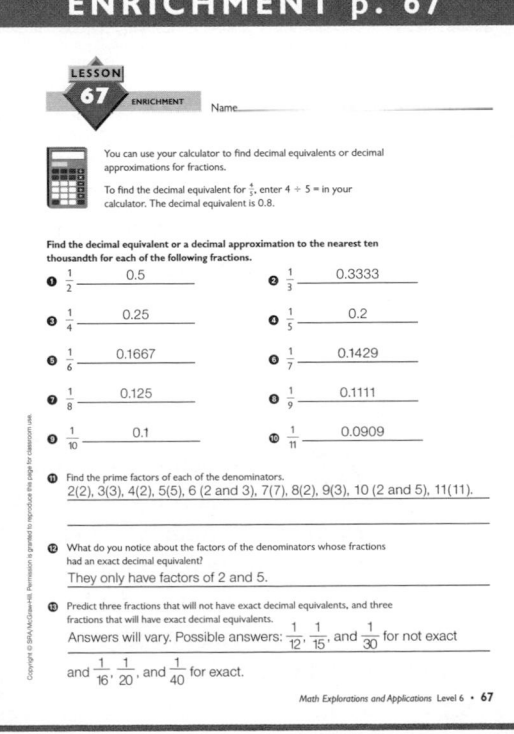

Equivalent Fractions

LESSON PLANNER

Objective

▶ to review and provide practice in finding equivalent fractions

Context of the Lesson This is the fourth of 20 lessons on fractions.

 **MANIPULATIVES**
none

Program Resources

"Equivalence 1" Game Mat

Reteaching Master

Practice Master 68

Enrichment Master 68

For additional math integration:
  Math Throughout the Day*

For extra practice:
  CD-ROM* Lesson 68
  Cumulative Review, page 567

① Warm-Up

 Problem of the Day Challenge students with the following problem: Use six different digits to make a fraction equivalent to $\frac{1}{2}$. (some possible answers: $\frac{267}{534}$, $\frac{364}{728}$, $\frac{436}{872}$)

Problem-Solving Strategies Ask students who have solved the Problem of the Day to share how they solved it and any strategies they used.

MENTAL MATH Have students respond with a fraction or decimal equivalent to each of the following numbers:

a. $\frac{1}{4}$ (0.25)   b. 0.63 $\left(\frac{63}{100}\right)$

c. 0.3 $\left(\frac{3}{10}\right)$ d. $\frac{1}{5}$ (0.2)

e. $\frac{2}{5}$ (0.4)   f. $\frac{9}{10}$ (0.9)

② Teach

Using the Student Pages To provide practice with equivalent fractions, you may wish to introduce the "Equivalence 1" Game Mat first so that students can play as they finish their work.

Equivalent Fractions

A given number can be written as a fraction in many different ways.

◆ Find the decimal equivalent of $\frac{1}{2}$. **0.5**

◆ Find the decimal equivalent of $\frac{2}{4}$. **0.5**

◆ What do you notice? **The fractions have the same decimal equivalent.**

We call two different ways of writing a number as a fraction **equivalent fractions**.

Examples:

Change $\frac{2}{3}$ to an equivalent fraction that has a denominator of 18.

Divide each of the three original parts into six equal parts. Now we have 18 equal parts. We must take 12 of those to be equivalent to the original two parts.

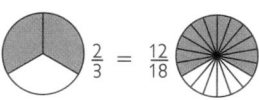 $\frac{2}{3} = \frac{12}{18}$

Notice that we could have found the same result by multiplying the numerator and the denominator by 6, which is equivalent to multiplying the fraction by $\frac{6}{6}$, or 1.

Change $\frac{4}{5}$ to an equivalent fraction that has a numerator of 8.

In order to get 8 equal blue pieces, we must divide each of the blue pieces into two equal parts. We must also divide the remaining piece into two equal parts so that all parts are equal. This gives us 10 equal parts.

$\frac{4}{5} = \frac{8}{10}$

We could also multiply $\frac{4}{5}$ by $\frac{2}{2}$. We get $\frac{4}{5} \times \frac{2}{2} = \frac{8}{10}$

Multiplying or dividing the numerator and denominator of a fraction by the same amount produces an equivalent fraction.

Why teach it at this time?

Finding and writing equivalent fractions is a necessary prerequisite for finding sums and differences of fractions and mixed numbers with different denominators.

 **Literature Connection** Have students read about Paul Bunyan's family in *The Bunyans* by Audrey Wood. Invite them to create fractions that compare such things as students' heights with estimated heights of the Bunyan family members.

LESSON
68 RETEACHING   Name

Find the equivalent fraction.
$\frac{3}{4} = \frac{?}{20}$
You know both denominators.

Think: 20 ÷ 4 = 5
Multiply: $\frac{3}{4} \times \frac{5}{5}$. Since $\frac{5}{5}$ = 1, this is the same as multiplying by 1.

$\frac{3}{4} \times \frac{5}{5} = \frac{15}{20}$
? = 15

Complete to write an equivalent fraction.

❶ $\frac{3}{4} = \frac{?}{12}$ 9	❷ $\frac{4}{5} = \frac{8}{?}$ 10	❸ $\frac{5}{6} = \frac{?}{30}$ 25
❹ $\frac{2}{3} = \frac{16}{?}$ 24	❺ $\frac{3}{4} = \frac{15}{?}$ 20	❻ $\frac{2}{3} = \frac{18}{?}$ 27
❼ $\frac{4}{5} = \frac{?}{30}$ 24	❽ $\frac{1}{6} = \frac{7}{?}$ 42	❾ $\frac{5}{6} = \frac{35}{?}$ 42
❿ $\frac{3}{8} = \frac{15}{?}$ 40	⓫ $\frac{1}{8} = \frac{?}{40}$ 5	⓬ $\frac{5}{8} = \frac{45}{?}$ 72
⓭ $\frac{7}{8} = \frac{49}{?}$ 56	⓮ $\frac{4}{9} = \frac{16}{?}$ 36	⓯ $\frac{7}{9} = \frac{?}{72}$ 56
⓰ $\frac{3}{4} = \frac{?}{40}$ 30	⓱ $\frac{5}{9} = \frac{25}{?}$ 45	⓲ $\frac{6}{7} = \frac{42}{?}$ 49
⓳ $\frac{4}{5} = \frac{?}{80}$ 64	⓴ $\frac{3}{5} = \frac{90}{?}$ 150	㉑ $\frac{4}{7} = \frac{28}{?}$ 49
㉒ $\frac{1}{2} = \frac{20}{?}$ 40	㉓ $\frac{5}{6} = \frac{?}{300}$ 250	㉔ $\frac{2}{3} = \frac{?}{90}$ 60

Math Explorations and Applications Level 6 • **21**

*available separately

Complete to write an equivalent fraction.

① $\frac{2}{3} = \frac{?}{12}$ **8** ② $\frac{3}{4} = \frac{?}{12}$ **9** ③ $\frac{1}{6} = \frac{2}{?}$ **12** ④ $\frac{5}{6} = \frac{?}{12}$ **10**

⑤ $\frac{1}{4} = \frac{5}{?}$ **20** ⑥ $\frac{3}{4} = \frac{?}{20}$ **15** ⑦ $\frac{1}{2} = \frac{?}{20}$ **10** ⑧ $\frac{1}{5} = \frac{?}{20}$ **4**

⑨ $\frac{2}{5} = \frac{?}{20}$ **8** ⑩ $\frac{3}{5} = \frac{12}{?}$ **20** ⑪ $\frac{4}{5} = \frac{16}{?}$ **20** ⑫ $\frac{3}{10} = \frac{?}{20}$ **6**

⑬ $\frac{3}{4} = \frac{12}{?}$ **16** ⑭ $\frac{2}{5} = \frac{6}{?}$ **15** ⑮ $\frac{1}{3} = \frac{?}{18}$ **6** ⑯ $\frac{3}{10} = \frac{?}{100}$ **30**

To produce an equivalent fraction with a denominator less than the original denominator, we can divide the numerator and denominator by the same number. We call this *reducing the fraction*. A fraction is in reduced form if it cannot be further reduced.

Example: Change $\frac{15}{18}$ to an equivalent fraction with a denominator of 6.

$$\frac{15}{18} = \frac{?}{6}$$ We divide 18 by 3 to get 6, so we divide 15 by 3 to get 5.

$$\frac{15}{18} = \frac{3 \times 5}{3 \times 6} = \frac{3}{3} \times \frac{5}{6}$$

Since $\frac{3}{3} = 1$, we can say $\frac{15}{18} = \frac{5}{6}$.

To reduce a fraction, find a number that is a factor of both the numerator and denominator.

Example: Reduce $\frac{8}{12}$.

Since we can multiply the numerator and denominator by the same number, we can also divide the numerator and denominator by the same number without changing the fraction's numerical value. $\frac{8}{12} = \frac{8 \div 4}{12 \div 4} = \frac{2}{3}$.

Complete to write an equivalent reduced fraction.

⑰ $\frac{12}{16} = \frac{?}{4}$ **3** ⑱ $\frac{12}{18} = \frac{2}{?}$ **3** ⑲ $\frac{6}{10} = \frac{?}{5}$ **3** ⑳ $\frac{5}{15} = \frac{?}{3}$ **1**

㉑ $\frac{16}{20} = \frac{?}{10}$ **8** ㉒ $\frac{10}{12} = \frac{5}{?}$ **6** ㉓ $\frac{15}{25} = \frac{?}{5}$ **3** ㉔ $\frac{16}{24} = \frac{4}{?}$ **6**

㉕ $\frac{12}{20} = \frac{?}{?}$ **3 6 / 5, 10** ㉖ $\frac{6}{14} = \frac{?}{?}$ **3 / 7** ㉗ $\frac{0}{18} = \frac{?}{?}$ **4 / 9** ㉘ $\frac{4}{20} = \frac{?}{?}$ **1 2 / 5, 10**

㉙ $\frac{18}{24} = \frac{?}{?}$ **3 6 9 / 4, 8, 12** ㉚ $\frac{8}{20} = \frac{?}{?}$ **2 4 / 5, 10** ㉛ $\frac{6}{15} = \frac{?}{?}$ **2 / 5** ㉜ $\frac{10}{20} = \frac{?}{?}$ **1 2 5 / 2, 4, 10**

Accept any of the given answers for problems 25, 28, 29, 30, and 32.

Use the Cumulative Review on page 567 after this lesson.

Unit 4 Lesson 68 • **249**

PRACTICE p. 68

ENRICHMENT p. 68

Go over the material preceding the problems and then have students do the problems on their own. Guide students to understand that if the denominator of a fraction is multiplied by some number, we will have increased the number of pieces of which we are finding the fractions. Therefore, to keep the fraction at the same value, we must multiply the numerator by the same number.

 Introducing the "Equivalence 1" Game Mat Demonstrate "Equivalence 1" for the class. This Game Mat provides practice in finding equivalent fractions and using mathematical reasoning. Point out that the game is like "Equivalence 2," which was introduced in Lesson 67.

❸ Wrap-Up

In Closing Summarize the lesson by asking students to explain how to write a new fraction that is equivalent to another fraction.

 **Informal Assessment** Observe students as they work on the problems. Ask questions such as, "What will you multiply the numerator and denominator of this fraction by in order to write a new fraction equivalent to it?" or "What will you divide the numerator and denominator of this fraction by in order to write an equivalent fraction in reduced form?"

Assessment Criteria

Did the student . . .

✓ demonstrate understanding of how to find an equivalent new fraction when given only the numerator or the denominator of that new fraction?

✓ demonstrate understanding of how to write a reduced version of a given fraction?

✓ correctly complete at least 75% of the problems?

Homework Have students play the "Equivalence 1" game at home with family members to practice finding equivalent fractions. A copy of this game can also be found on page 610 of this Teacher's Guide.

Unit 4 Lesson 68 **249**

LESSON 69
Reducing Fractions

LESSON PLANNER

Objectives

▶ to teach how to use factoring to completely reduce fractions

▶ to teach how to find the greatest common factor of two numbers

▶ to provide practice in reducing fractions

Context of the Lesson This is the fifth of 20 lessons on fractions.

 MANIPULATIVES
none

Program Resources

Number Cubes (0–5 and 5–10)

Reteaching Master

Practice Master 69

Enrichment Master 69

For extra practice:
CD-ROM* Lesson 69

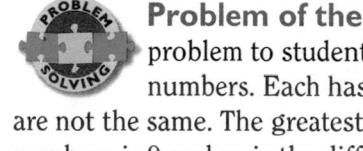 # ① Warm-Up

 Problem of the Day Present the following problem to students: There are two mystery numbers. Each has two digits, the sums of which are not the same. The greatest common factor of the two numbers is 9 and so is the difference between the numbers. What are the numbers? (99 and 90)

Problem-Solving Strategies Ask students who have solved the Problem of the Day to share how they solved it and any strategies they used.

MENTAL MATH Ask students to provide a decimal or fraction equivalent or approximately equivalent to each of the following.

a. $\frac{3}{4}$ (0.75) b. $\frac{1}{2}$ (0.5)

c. $\frac{1}{3}$ (0.33) d. $\frac{3}{5}$ (0.6)

e. 0.2 ($\frac{2}{10}$ or $\frac{1}{5}$) f. 0.03 ($\frac{3}{100}$)

g. 7.4 ($7\frac{4}{10}$ or $7\frac{2}{5}$) h. 0.83 ($\frac{83}{100}$ or $\frac{5}{6}$)

i. $\frac{7}{10}$ (0.7) j. $\frac{23}{100}$ (0.23)

LESSON 69
Reducing Fractions

Alexis needs to divide 126 by 189. "That looks hard," she says. "There must be something I can do to make this easier."

She decides to write the problem as a fraction:

$$\frac{126}{189}$$

She notices that the sum of the digits of 126 is 9 and the sum of the digits of 189 is 18. That tells her that 126 and 189 are both divisible by 9. So she rewrites the fraction.

$$\frac{126}{189} = \frac{9 \times 14}{9 \times 21}$$

Then she rewrites it again:

$$\frac{9}{9} \times \frac{14}{21}$$

"I see," says Alexis. "That's the same as $\frac{9}{9}$ of $\frac{14}{21}$, or just $\frac{14}{21}$. So:

$$\frac{126}{189} = \frac{9}{9} \times \frac{14}{21} = \frac{14}{21}$$

"I wonder if there's a way to make this fraction even simpler."

◆ Do you see a way to make the problem still easier? Is there some number that is a factor of both 14 and 21? **Both 14 and 21 are divisible by 7, so the fraction can be rewritten as $\frac{7 \times 2}{7 \times 3}$, or $\frac{2}{3}$.** This fraction reduces to $\frac{2}{3}$. Divide 2 by 3. Find the answer to at least seven decimal places. Now divide 126 by 189.

◆ Are both answers the same? **yes**

In most cases it is easier to work with $\frac{2}{3}$ than $\frac{126}{189}$.

Factoring numbers is useful when rewriting fractions as equivalent fractions in reduced form.

◆ Why might this process be called "reducing fractions"? **We are reducing the values of the numerator and denominator.** When we have reduced a fraction as much as we can, we say we have completely reduced it. Remember, the reduced fraction still stands for the same number as the original fraction.

250 • Fractions and Mixed Numbers

Technology Connection The video, laser disc, or software *Modumath: Arithmetic, Renaming Fractions* from VTAE (VHS, IBM, for grades 6–12) provides further practice with expressing fractions in highest and lowest terms, reducing fractions to lowest terms, and fractions equal to 1 or 0.

---

*available separately

To reduce a fraction completely, decide what factors the numerator and denominator have in common and divide the numerator and denominator by those factors. Here are two ways you might keep your records for reducing $\frac{336}{840}$.

A. $\frac{336}{840} = \frac{4 \times 84}{4 \times 210} = \frac{2 \times 42}{2 \times 105} = \frac{3 \times 14}{3 \times 35} = \frac{7 \times 2}{7 \times 5} = \frac{2}{5}$

B.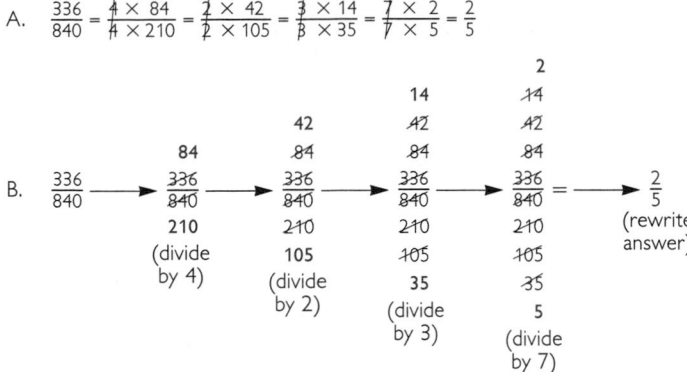

The second method is messier, but it does not require rewriting the problem each time. You may use either method, or a different one if you prefer.

The order in which you find the factors is not important.

◆ Is there a way to reduce $\frac{336}{840}$ using fewer steps? If so, how?
We could divide by greater numbers, such as 12 or 18.

Reduce each fraction completely.

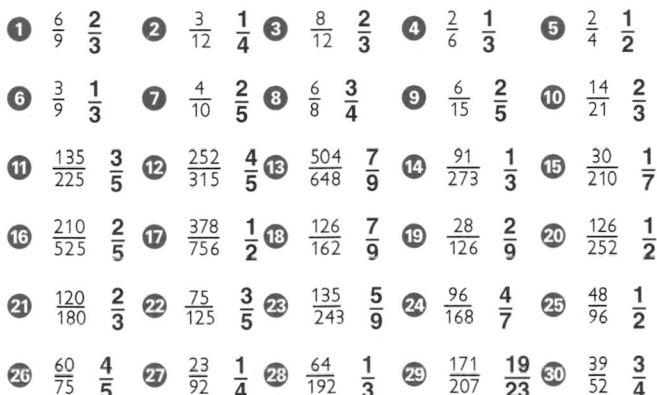

1. $\frac{6}{9}$ $\frac{2}{3}$ 2. $\frac{3}{12}$ $\frac{1}{4}$ 3. $\frac{8}{12}$ $\frac{2}{3}$ 4. $\frac{2}{6}$ $\frac{1}{3}$ 5. $\frac{2}{4}$ $\frac{1}{2}$

6. $\frac{3}{9}$ $\frac{1}{3}$ 7. $\frac{4}{10}$ $\frac{2}{5}$ 8. $\frac{6}{8}$ $\frac{3}{4}$ 9. $\frac{6}{15}$ $\frac{2}{5}$ 10. $\frac{14}{21}$ $\frac{2}{3}$

11. $\frac{135}{225}$ $\frac{3}{5}$ 12. $\frac{252}{315}$ $\frac{4}{5}$ 13. $\frac{504}{648}$ $\frac{7}{9}$ 14. $\frac{91}{273}$ $\frac{1}{3}$ 15. $\frac{30}{210}$ $\frac{1}{7}$

16. $\frac{210}{525}$ $\frac{2}{5}$ 17. $\frac{378}{756}$ $\frac{1}{2}$ 18. $\frac{126}{162}$ $\frac{7}{9}$ 19. $\frac{28}{126}$ $\frac{2}{9}$ 20. $\frac{126}{252}$ $\frac{1}{2}$

21. $\frac{120}{180}$ $\frac{2}{3}$ 22. $\frac{75}{125}$ $\frac{3}{5}$ 23. $\frac{135}{243}$ $\frac{5}{9}$ 24. $\frac{96}{168}$ $\frac{4}{7}$ 25. $\frac{48}{96}$ $\frac{1}{2}$

26. $\frac{60}{75}$ $\frac{4}{5}$ 27. $\frac{23}{92}$ $\frac{1}{4}$ 28. $\frac{64}{192}$ $\frac{1}{3}$ 29. $\frac{171}{207}$ $\frac{19}{23}$ 30. $\frac{39}{52}$ $\frac{3}{4}$

Unit 4 Lesson 69 • **251**

❷ Teach

Using the Student Pages You may wish to demonstrate the "Greatest Common Factor" game, which provides practice finding common factors, before beginning work on pages 250–252 so that students who finish early can immediately begin playing the game in pairs or small groups.

Read page 250 to the class. Stop to discuss the bulleted questions.

Go over the two methods for reducing fractions given at the top of page 251. Do a few examples with the class. Be sure students understand that when they use method B, they do not rewrite the problem each time; they simply continue dividing the new numerators and denominators. You might not want to introduce further shortcuts at this time, because they might obscure the essence of the procedure. Have students complete the problems on their own after going over a few examples with the class.

Literature Connection Invite students to read *Math for Smarty Pants* by Marilyn Burns, which has some easy-to-follow explanations about different ways to calculate answers.

◆ **LESSON 69 Reducing Fractions**

Teach

Using the Student Pages Go over page 252 with the class. Students may use either method shown on the page for finding the greatest common factor. Have them do problems 31–36 on their own. You might want students to notice the similarities between finding the greatest common factor and reducing a fraction.

GAME **Introducing the "Greatest Common Factor" Game** Demonstrate the "Greatest Common Factor" game on page 253 by having two students play a few rounds in front of the class. Be sure that the players remember to roll again if they roll two 0s. This game provides practice in finding common factors and using mathematical reasoning to form numbers with great common factors. It is similar to the "Tiling" game, which was introduced in Lesson 59.

SPECIAL NEEDS **Meeting Individual Needs**
For students having difficulty understanding why $\frac{126}{189} = \frac{9 \times 14}{9 \times 21} = \frac{14}{21}$, you may find it helpful to use easier fractions and then relate the two problems. For example, use the same approach with $\frac{6}{15} : \frac{6}{15} = \frac{3 \times 2}{3 \times 5} = \frac{2}{5}$, pointing out that 3 is a factor of both 6 and 15, just as 9 is a factor of 126 and 189.
Alternately, show $\frac{6}{15}$ visually by dividing a circle into 15 equal parts and shading 6 of them. Point out to students that because 3 is a factor of both 6 and 15, we can group the small parts into sets of 3. Then we would have 2 sets of 3 that are shaded out of a total of 5 sets, or $\frac{2}{5}$. As a result $\frac{6}{15} = \frac{2}{5}$.

◆ **LESSON 69 Reducing Fractions**

When reducing fractions, the greater the factor we start with, the fewer steps it takes. For example, we can reduce $\frac{16}{24}$ as follows:

A. $\frac{16}{24} = \frac{\cancel{2} \times 8}{\cancel{2} \times 12} = \frac{\cancel{2} \times 4}{\cancel{2} \times 6} = \frac{\cancel{2} \times 2}{\cancel{2} \times 3} = \frac{2}{3}$

Or we could reduce it like this:

B. $\frac{16}{24} = \frac{\cancel{8} \times 2}{\cancel{8} \times 3} = \frac{2}{3}$

Instead of just finding a common factor of two numbers, we often want to find the **greatest common factor.** If you know the greatest common factor of the numerator and denominator of a fraction, you can completely reduce it by just dividing by that one number.

To find the greatest common factor of two numbers, you can simply look at all the factors and choose the greatest one they have in common.

Example: Find the greatest common factor of 60 and 84.

A. List all the factors of each number.

B. Then look for the greatest factor they have in common.

60	84
1 × 60	1 × 84
2 × 30	2 × 42
3 × 20	3 × 28
4 × 15	4 × 21
5 × ⑫	6 × 14
6 × 10	7 × ⑫

The greatest common factor of 60 and 84 is 12.

Another way to find the greatest common factor is to completely factor each number. Let's try this with the same problem. Find the greatest common factor of 60 and 84.

Write $60 = 2^2 \times 3 \times 5$

And $84 = 2^2 \times 3 \times 7$

So the greatest common factor is $2^2 \times 3$, or 12.

Find the greatest common factor of each pair of numbers.

㉛ 12 and 18 **6** ㉜ 72 and 120 **24** ㉝ 126 and 162 **18**

㉞ 9 and 24 **3** ㉟ 252 and 315 **63** ㊱ 14 and 42 **14**

252 · Fractions and Mixed Numbers

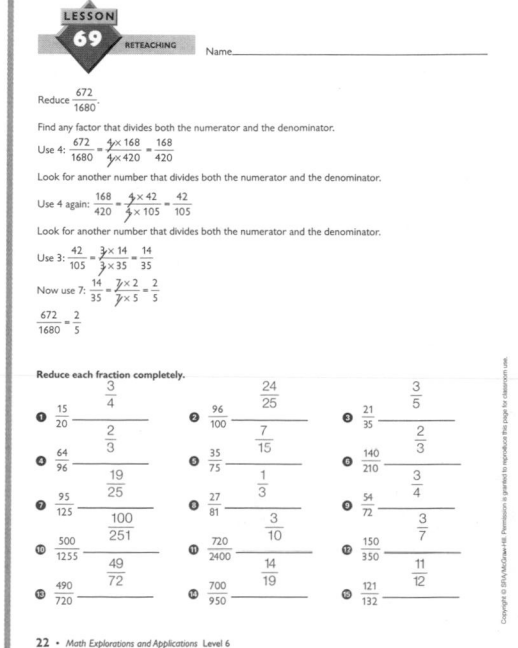

Greatest Common Factor Game

COOPERATIVE LEARNING

GAME

Players:	Two or more
Materials:	Two 0–5 cubes, two 5–10 cubes
Object:	To get the highest total score
Math Focus:	Finding greatest common factors

RULES

1. Decide in advance how many turns each player will take (usually from five to ten turns).

2. Take turns rolling all four cubes and use them to form two two-digit numbers. If you roll a 10, one of the numbers will have three digits. For example, a 10 and a 4 might be used to form 104 and 410. If you roll 10 and 10, you could form one four-digit number, 1010, or two three-digit numbers. If you roll 0 and 0, roll again.

3. Find the greatest common factor of the two numbers, and add that to your score.

4. Continue until each player has taken the agreed-upon number of turns.

5. The player with the greatest total wins.

SAMPLE GAME

	Round	Numbers Rolled	Numbers Made	Greatest Common Factor	Score
Hasin's Record	1	1 5 5 8	51, 85	17	17
	2	3 4 7 9	34, 79	1	18
	3	2 4 8 9	42, 98	14	32
Lisa's Record	1	7 7 2 4	42, 77	7	7
	2	2 2 5 8	28, 52	4	11
	3	3 3 5 5	53, 53	53	64

Lisa won because her total score (64) was higher.

Unit 4 Lesson 69 • **253**

3 Wrap-Up ⏱ 5 MINUTES

In Closing Summarize the lesson by asking students to explain how to find the greatest common factor of a pair of numbers, and then by asking them how that helps them reduce a fraction to its lowest terms.

Performance Assessment Write the fraction $\frac{48}{216}$ on the chalkboard. Ask students to (a) give the greatest common factor of the two numbers, and (b) reduce the fraction completely. $(24; \frac{2}{9})$

Assessment Criteria

Did the student . . .

✓ demonstrate understanding of how to reduce a fraction?

✓ demonstrate understanding of how to find the greatest common factor of two numbers?

✓ correctly answer at least 75% of the exercises?

Homework Have students play the "Greatest Common Factor" game at home for further practice finding common factors. A copy of this game can also be found on page 23 of the Home Connections Blackline Masters.

PRACTICE p. 69

LESSON 69 PRACTICE Name_____

Reduce each fraction completely.

1. $\frac{2}{6} = \frac{1}{3}$
2. $\frac{3}{6} = \frac{1}{2}$
3. $\frac{3}{9} = \frac{1}{3}$
4. $\frac{2}{10} = \frac{1}{5}$
5. $\frac{13}{52} = \frac{1}{4}$
6. $\frac{24}{120} = \frac{1}{5}$
7. $\frac{90}{240} = \frac{3}{8}$
8. $\frac{84}{720} = \frac{7}{60}$
9. $\frac{48}{240} = \frac{1}{5}$
10. $\frac{50}{120} = \frac{5}{12}$
11. $\frac{224}{432} = \frac{14}{27}$
12. $\frac{490}{756} = \frac{35}{54}$
13. $\frac{6}{9} = \frac{2}{3}$
14. $\frac{2}{8} = \frac{1}{4}$
15. $\frac{4}{8} = \frac{1}{2}$
16. $\frac{6}{18} = \frac{1}{3}$
17. $\frac{7}{42} = \frac{1}{6}$
18. $\frac{6}{24} = \frac{1}{4}$
19. $\frac{68}{432} = \frac{17}{108}$
20. $\frac{175}{525} = \frac{1}{3}$
21. $\frac{80}{216} = \frac{10}{27}$
22. $\frac{90}{720} = \frac{1}{8}$
23. $\frac{250}{525} = \frac{10}{21}$
24. $\frac{48}{162} = \frac{8}{27}$

Math Explorations and Applications Level 6 • **69**

ENRICHMENT p. 69

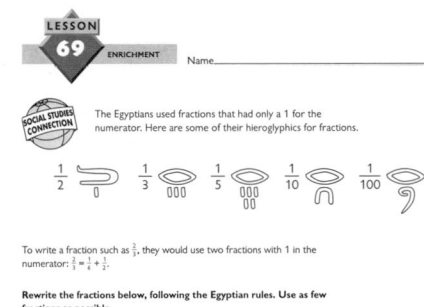

LESSON 69 ENRICHMENT Name_____

SOCIAL STUDIES CONNECTION The Egyptians used fractions that had only a 1 for the numerator. Here are some of their hieroglyphics for fractions.

$\frac{1}{2}$ $\frac{1}{3}$ $\frac{1}{5}$ $\frac{1}{10}$ $\frac{1}{100}$

To write a fraction such as $\frac{3}{4}$, they would use two fractions with 1 in the numerator: $\frac{3}{4} = \frac{1}{4} + \frac{1}{2}$.

Rewrite the fractions below, following the Egyptian rules. Use as few fractions as possible.

1. $\frac{3}{4}$ $\frac{1}{4} + \frac{1}{2}$
2. $\frac{7}{9}$ $\frac{1}{9} + \frac{1}{6} + \frac{1}{2}$
3. $\frac{3}{16}$ $\frac{1}{16} + \frac{1}{8}$
4. $\frac{23}{100}$ $\frac{1}{5} + \frac{1}{50} + \frac{1}{100}$
5. $\frac{12}{30}$ $\frac{1}{3} + \frac{1}{15}$
6. $\frac{5}{36}$ $\frac{1}{9} + \frac{1}{36}$
7. $\frac{4}{7}$ $\frac{1}{2} + \frac{1}{14}$
8. $\frac{8}{49}$ $\frac{1}{7} + \frac{1}{49}$
9. $\frac{64}{1024}$ $\frac{1}{16}$
10. $\frac{24}{512}$ $\frac{1}{32} + \frac{1}{64}$

Math Explorations and Applications Level 6 • **69**

Multiplying and Reducing Fractions

Multiplying and Reducing Fractions

When multiplying fractions, you can sometimes use common factors to help simplify the computations. For example: If you are multiplying $\frac{16}{24}$ by $\frac{9}{10}$, you could start by multiplying the numerators, getting 144. Then multiply the denominators to get 240. The answer is $\frac{144}{240}$. The numbers 144 and 240 both have a factor of 48, so this is equal to

$$\frac{144}{240} = \frac{48 \times 3}{48 \times 5} = \frac{3}{5}$$

However, you could have started with the original problem and found common factors in the numerators and denominators. You can divide by the common factors before you multiply. To multiply $\frac{16}{24} \times \frac{9}{10}$, you might start by noticing there is a factor of 8 in both 16 and 24:

A. $\frac{2 \, \cancel{16}}{3 \, \cancel{24}} \times \frac{9}{10}$

Next, you might see that there is a factor of 3 in both 9 and 3:

B. $\frac{2 \, \cancel{16}}{1 \, \cancel{3} \cancel{24}} \times \frac{\cancel{9} \, 3}{10}$

Finally, there is a factor of 2 in both 2 and 10:

C. $\frac{1 \, \cancel{2} \cancel{16}}{1 \, \cancel{3} \cancel{24}} \times \frac{\cancel{9} \, 3}{\cancel{10} \, 5}$

Now, since $1 \times 3 = 3$, and $1 \times 5 = 5$, the final answer is $\frac{3}{5}$. Notice that this was easier than multiplying all the numbers together and then looking for common factors in the numerator and denominator at the end.

Solve the following multiplication problems. Reduce answers completely.

❶ $\frac{2}{3} \times \frac{6}{11} = ?$ **$\frac{4}{11}$**   ❷ $\frac{8}{18} \times \frac{3}{8} = ?$ **$\frac{1}{6}$**   ❸ $\frac{5}{6} \times \frac{9}{10} = ?$ **$\frac{3}{4}$**

❹ $\frac{9}{16} \times \frac{12}{27} = ?$ **$\frac{1}{4}$**   ❺ $\frac{4}{14} \times \frac{21}{24} = ?$ **$\frac{1}{4}$**   ❻ $\frac{3}{4} \times \frac{6}{7} = ?$ **$\frac{9}{14}$**

❼ $\frac{8}{25} \times \frac{35}{48} = ?$ **$\frac{7}{30}$**   ❽ $\frac{5}{27} \times \frac{36}{50} = ?$ **$\frac{2}{15}$**   ❾ $\frac{7}{12} \times \frac{18}{25} = ?$ **$\frac{21}{50}$**

❿ $\frac{12}{75} \times \frac{15}{64} = ?$ **$\frac{3}{80}$**   ⓫ $\frac{3}{7} \times \frac{5}{11} = ?$ **$\frac{15}{77}$**   ⓬ $\frac{4}{9} \times \frac{6}{16} = ?$ **$\frac{1}{6}$**

⓭ $\frac{120}{225} \times \frac{105}{112} = ?$ **$\frac{1}{2}$**   ⓮ $\frac{3}{7} \times \frac{35}{45} = ?$ **$\frac{1}{3}$**   ⓯ $\frac{6}{11} \times \frac{3}{5} = ?$ **$\frac{18}{55}$**

⓰ $\frac{2}{3} \times \frac{3}{4} = ?$ **$\frac{1}{2}$**   ⓱ $\frac{3}{7} \times \frac{4}{9} = ?$ **$\frac{4}{21}$**   ⓲ $\frac{20}{33} \times \frac{12}{25} = ?$ **$\frac{16}{55}$**

LESSON PLANNER

Objectives

▶ to demonstrate methods for multiplying fractions efficiently

▶ to provide practice with basic arithmetic facts, multidigit computation, and word problems

▶ to help students develop the broad ability to use mathematical common sense

Context of the Lesson This lesson, the sixth of 20 lessons on fractions, also provides practice in basic mathematical skills and contains Part 2 of "Energy Savers," a four-part Thinking Story.

 MANIPULATIVES

metersticks, tape measure*, or yardsticks scale* or other weighing device

Program Resources

Practice Master 70

Enrichment Master 70

For career connections: Careers and Math*

For extra practice: CD-ROM* Lesson 70

---

❶ Warm-Up ⏱ 5 MINUTES

 **Problem of the Day** Present the following problem to the class: The sum of the digits on a digital clock face is 19. The number of hours shown is $\frac{1}{7}$ the number of minutes. What time is it? (8:56)

Problem-Solving Strategies Ask students who have solved the Problem of the Day to share how they solved it and any strategies they used.

  Show students five different objects in the classroom. Present appropriate measuring tools in either metric or customary units as a reference (**metersticks, tape measures*, yardsticks, scales***, and so on), and ask students to estimate either the length or weight of each object. If possible, use the same units for each object. Then have a volunteer find the actual measurement of each object before you present the next object and invite estimates.

Why teach it this way?

Canceling prior to multiplying fractions is an efficient technique because it can reduce the magnitude of the numbers students actually multiply, and therefore cut down on multiplication errors.

Watch the signs.

19 72 + 9 = ■ **81**　　**20** 72 ÷ 9 = ■ **8**　　**21** 72 − 9 = ■ **63**

22 72 × 9 = ■ **648**　　**23** 8 × 7 = ■ **56**　　**24** 54 ÷ 6 = ■ **9**

25 17 − 8 = ■ **9**　　**26** 9 × 4 = ■ **36**　　**27** 8 + 8 = ■ **16**

28 8 × 8 = ■ **64**　　**29** 0 × 7 = ■ **0**　　**30** 7 + 0 = ■ **7**

31 43 − 9 = ■ **34**　　**32** 43 + 9 = ■ **52**　　**33** 52 ÷ 4 = ■ **13**

34　437　　**35**　437　　**36**　649　　**37**　173
　　　− 286　　　　+ 286　　　× 100　　　× 200
　　　151　　　　**723**　　　**64,900**　　**34,600**

　　　357　　　　**839**　　　**863**　　　**123**
38 9)3213　　**39** 6)5034　　**40** 5)4315　　**41** 7)861

Solve these problems.

42 At the beginning of the week the odometer on Maureen's bicycle showed 9743.2 kilometers. At the end of the week the odometer showed 0027.5 kilometers.
　a. What do you think happened? **The odometer started again (turned over).**
　b. How far do you think the bicycle went that week? **284.3 km**

43 A theater group is presenting four shows this season. Tickets cost $16.50 each. A season ticket good for all four shows costs $55. How much would you save on each show by buying a season ticket? **$2.75**

44 A taxi in the Take-You Taxi Company can carry four passengers plus the driver. How many Take-You taxis will be needed to take 15 people from the PTA meeting to the football game? **4**

❷Teach

Using the Student Pages Go through the worked example on the top of page 254 with the class. Do another similar problem (such as $\frac{15}{24} \times \frac{4}{5} = \frac{1}{2}$) if necessary. Then have students complete pages 254 and 255 independently.

Technology Connection Refer students to the software *NumberMaze* from Great Ware (Mac, IBM, for grades K–6) for further practice doing multidigit multiplication and division, and translating word problems into math equations.

◆ **LESSON 70** Multiplying and
Reducing Fractions

Teach

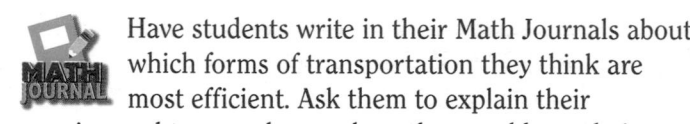

Using the Thinking Story Part 2 of
"Energy Savers" focuses on estimating the
gasoline savings that would result from a plan
based on a single piece of information—the amount of gas a
car uses when it stops and starts—and the importance of
examining all the consequences of a plan.

Answers to Thinking Story Questions:

1. He is assuming that every car stops at all 1000 stop signs
   every day. This is very unlikely: If it took only one minute
   between stops, passing all the stop signs would take 1000
   minutes, or almost 17 hours, of driving; drivers would have
   to pass through each intersection in town two or more
   times a day, since stop signs are usually placed in twos or
   fours to an intersection; and drivers would have to travel at
   least 1000 blocks, which amounts to about 200 km of city
   driving.

2. Mr. Harper was pointing out the safety hazards that would
   result from removing stop signs. Often a plan with positive
   effects on one measure (for instance, energy consumption)
   has negative effects on another (for instance, safety).

3. Cars with larger gas tanks tend to be larger cars and
   probably burn more gas in stopping and starting than
   smaller cars, so it is possible that cars with different-sized gas
   tanks use about $\frac{1}{100}$, or some other common fraction, of a
   tankful of gas at each stop and start.

4. Expressed as a fraction of a tankful, the amount of gas used
   in starting and stopping is about the same for all cars; one
   figure can be used to describe the rate of gas consumption
   for many different cars.

Have students write in their Math Journals about
which forms of transportation they think are
most efficient. Ask them to explain their
reasoning and to speculate on how they could use their
mathematical skills to test their ideas.

◆ **LESSON 70** Multiplying and Reducing Fractions

THINKING STORY

Energy Savers
Part 2

*You may want to refer to the first part of this
Thinking Story on pages 246–247.*

Marcus told the Energy Savers about his idea for a new
way to save energy. "Get rid of stop signs. I heard on the
radio that every time a car stops and starts up again, it
uses $\frac{1}{100}$ of a tank of gas."

"Great idea!" said Ferdie. "Let's take down all the stop signs in
town. That way we'll save more energy than any other group.
There must be 1000 stop signs. That's ten tanks of gas. And there
must be about 3000 cars. By taking down the stop signs we'll
save 30,000 tanks of gas a day!"

The club adviser, Mr. Harper, said, "You'd better figure in the
extra gas that ambulances and tow trucks will use. After all,
won't they be on the road more often if we follow your plan?"

"Wait a minute," said Portia. "I think Marcus has his facts
wrong. Some cars are little and have little tiny gas tanks. Some
cars are big and have great big gas tanks. How can you say every
car uses up $\frac{1}{100}$ of a tank of gas when it stops and starts? It

256 • Fractions and Mixed Numbers

**Literature
Connection** Have
students work in
groups to do some of
the brain teasers and puzzles in
*Sideways Arithmetic from Wayside
School* by Louis Sachar.

doesn't make any sense. That's like saying you use $\frac{1}{100}$ of a tube of toothpaste each time you brush your teeth, when toothpaste tubes are all different sizes."

. . . to be continued

Work in groups. Discuss your answers and how you figured them out. Then compare your answers with those of other groups. Answers are in margin.

❶ Suppose there are 1000 stop signs and 3000 cars in town. Is Ferdie right that stopping at stop signs uses up 30,000 tanks of gas a day? What would drivers have to do in order for that to be true?

❷ What do you think Mr. Harper was trying to get the club members to see about their plan?

❸ How could it be possible that cars with different-sized gas tanks all use about $\frac{1}{100}$ tank of gas when they stop and start? Hint: Big cars and small cars are all built so that they can go about the same distance on a tank of gas.

❹ Why does it make sense to give the amount of gas used as a fraction of a tank rather than as a number of gallons?

Unit 4   Lesson 70 • **257**

---

❸ Wrap-Up

In Closing Invite students to suggest ways for drivers to cut down on gasoline consumption.

Students who get products that are not in simplest form are not finding all the common factors in the first stage of the multiplication process. Emphasize the usefulness of (1) looking for the greatest common factor; and/or (2) making sure that there are no more common factors in numerators and denominators before completing the multiplication.

Informal Assessment Observe as students reduce and multiply fractions. Check to see that they are finding the common factors of numerators and denominators and not of two numerators or two denominators. Check that their answers are written in simplest form. If they are not, ask students to look back and see where more reducing was possible.

Assessment Criteria

Did the student . . .

✓ correctly answer at least 14 of the 18 problems on page 254 and 21 of the 26 problems on page 255?

✓ demonstrate an understanding of how to reduce two fractions before multiplying them?

✓ understand the weaknesses in Ferdie's energy-saving plan in the Thinking Story?

Homework Have students collect articles about ways people are conserving gasoline or otherwise conserving energy. Then make a class display of the findings.

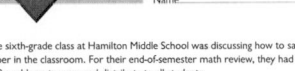

Student Edition pages 258–261

Comparing Fractions

Comparing Fractions

LESSON PLANNER

Objectives

▶ to demonstrate several different ways to compare two fractions

▶ to demonstrate why the "cross-multiply" technique works and to help students remember why it does

Context of the Lesson This is the seventh of 20 lessons on fractions.

MANIPULATIVES

calculators*

Program Resources

"Cosmic Cafe" Game Mat

Reteaching Master

Practice Master 71

Enrichment Master 71

For additional math integration:
Math Throughout the Day*

For extra practice:
CD-ROM* Lesson 71

① Warm-Up ⏱ 5 MINUTES

Problem of the Day Present the following problem to the class: The consecutive whole numbers 2 and 3 are prime numbers. Is there another pair of consecutive prime numbers? Explain. (No; one of the pair will be an even number and every even number greater than 2 is a composite number.)

Problem-Solving Strategies Ask students who have solved the Problem of the Day to share how they solved it and any strategies they used.

MENTAL MATH Ask students to show thumbs up if there is a remainder and thumbs down if there is none.

a. $666 \div 2$ (thumbs down)

b. $3000 \div 8$ (thumbs down)

c. $405 \div 9$ (thumbs down)

d. $637 \div 5$ (thumbs up)

e. $4020 \div 10$ (thumbs down)

f. $623 \div 6$ (thumbs up)

g. $752 \div 2$ (thumbs down)

(continued on page 259)

258 Fractions and Mixed Numbers

There are several ways to compare two fractions with different denominators to see which is greater.

One method is to use a calculator, convert each fraction to an equivalent or approximate decimal, and compare the decimals. For example, to decide which is greater, $\frac{3}{7}$ or $\frac{4}{9}$, you can find a decimal approximation of each.

$$\frac{3}{7} = 3 \div 7, \text{ which is about } 0.4285714$$

$$\frac{4}{9} = 4 \div 9, \text{ which is about } 0.4444444$$

The greater decimal is 0.4444444, so $\frac{4}{9}$ must be the greater fraction.

A second method of comparing $\frac{3}{7}$ and $\frac{4}{9}$ is to rewrite both fractions as equivalent fractions with the same denominator. We say that a number that is a multiple of both original denominators is a **common denominator.** The product of the two original denominators will always be a common denominator.

We can use a common denominator of 63 to compare $\frac{3}{7}$ with $\frac{4}{9}$.

$$\frac{3}{7} \times \frac{9}{9} = \frac{27}{63}$$
$$\frac{4}{9} \times \frac{7}{7} = \frac{28}{63}$$

◆ Which is greater, $\frac{27}{63}$ or $\frac{28}{63}$? **$\frac{28}{63}$**

Notice that if you use the product of the denominators as the common denominator, each new fraction will have the product of its numerator and the other fraction's denominator as its new numerator. In this example the numerator of the first fraction is 3×9, and the numerator of the second fraction is 4×7. Since the denominators are the same, this product tells which fraction is greater.

So, a third way to decide which is greater, $\frac{3}{7}$ or $\frac{4}{9}$, is to find the two products, 3×9 and 4×7. Whichever numerator appears in the greater product is the numerator of the greater fraction.

Sometimes you can compare fractions in other ways as well.

Example: Compare $\frac{7}{12}$ and $\frac{13}{30}$.
Notice that $\frac{7}{12}$ is slightly greater than $\frac{1}{2}$, since $\frac{1}{2} = \frac{6}{12}$ and $\frac{7}{12}$ is greater than $\frac{6}{12}$.
Also notice that $\frac{13}{30}$ is slightly less than $\frac{1}{2}$, since $\frac{1}{2} = \frac{15}{30}$ and $\frac{13}{30}$ is less than $\frac{15}{30}$.

◆ Which is greater, $\frac{7}{12}$ or $\frac{13}{30}$? **$\frac{7}{12}$**

258 • Fractions and Mixed Numbers

Why teach it this way?

A least common denominator is a special kind of least common multiple. Finding least common denominators simplifies the addition and subtraction of fractions, though it is not essential.

*available separately

Once we know which fraction is greater, we can write the fractions with a <, >, or = symbol between them to show whether the first fraction is less than, greater than, or equal to the second. Remember, the point of the symbol points towards the lesser number.

So, for our example, you would write $\frac{3}{7} < \frac{4}{9}$, since $\frac{3}{7}$ is less than $\frac{4}{9}$.

Write each of the following fraction pairs with a <, >, or = symbol between them.

1 $\frac{1}{3} \blacksquare \frac{1}{2}$ **<**   **2** $\frac{4}{7} \blacksquare \frac{5}{9}$ **>**   **3** $\frac{1}{6} \blacksquare \frac{2}{11}$ **<**   **4** $\frac{7}{13} \blacksquare \frac{8}{13}$ **<**

5 $\frac{73}{87} \blacksquare \frac{74}{87}$ **<**   **6** $\frac{1}{2} \blacksquare \frac{1}{3}$ **>**   **7** $\frac{5}{7} \blacksquare \frac{5}{8}$ **>**   **8** $\frac{12}{17} \blacksquare \frac{12}{18}$ **>**

9 $\frac{13}{27} \blacksquare \frac{1}{2}$ **<**   **10** $\frac{14}{27} \blacksquare \frac{1}{2}$ **>**   **11** $\frac{17}{36} \blacksquare \frac{1}{2}$ **<**   **12** $\frac{18}{36} \blacksquare \frac{1}{2}$ **=**

13 $\frac{19}{36} \blacksquare \frac{1}{2}$ **>**   **14** $\frac{5}{9} \blacksquare \frac{7}{12}$ **<**   **15** $\frac{21}{36} \blacksquare \frac{7}{12}$ **=**   **16** $\frac{4}{7} \blacksquare \frac{1}{2}$ **>**

17 $\frac{5}{11} \blacksquare \frac{1}{2}$ **<**   **18** $\frac{4}{7} \blacksquare \frac{5}{11}$ **>**   **19** $\frac{10}{19} \blacksquare \frac{9}{20}$ **>**   **20** $\frac{11}{12} \blacksquare \frac{13}{14}$ **<**

21 Arrange the following fractions in order from least to greatest:

$\frac{1}{8}, \frac{3}{5}, \frac{4}{10}, \frac{5}{6}, \frac{2}{3}, \frac{17}{20}$ **$\frac{1}{8}, \frac{4}{10}, \frac{3}{5}, \frac{2}{3}, \frac{5}{6}, \frac{17}{20}$**

22 There is a puzzle about a man with three sons. He died and left $\frac{1}{2}$ of what he owned to his eldest son, $\frac{1}{4}$ of what he owned to the middle son, and $\frac{1}{6}$ of what he owned to the youngest son. But the man owned only 11 cows. He had no other property. How could the sons divide the cows without killing them?

A wise man with a cow came along. He added his cow to the herd. Then he gave the eldest son $\frac{1}{2}$ of the 12 cows. To the middle son he gave $\frac{1}{4}$ of the 12 cows. And he gave the youngest son $\frac{1}{6}$ of the 12 cows. Then he went away with his own cow.

a. Why did this work?   **$\frac{1}{2} + \frac{1}{4} + \frac{1}{6} = \frac{11}{12}$, not 1**

b. Did the wise man carry out the dead father's instructions?   **No, because the sons got $\frac{6}{11}, \frac{3}{11}$, and $\frac{2}{11}$ rather than $\frac{6}{12}, \frac{3}{12}$, and $\frac{2}{12}$ as listed in the will.**

Unit 4 Lesson 71 • **259**

Technology Connection Refer students to the software *Math Ace* from Magic Quest (IBM, for grades 3–12) for practice with fractions, geometry, basic computation, exponents, real-world problems, and algebra.

*available separately

Mental Math (continued)

h. 518 ÷ 6 (thumbs up)

i. 633 ÷ 3 (thumbs down)

❷ Teach

Using the Student Pages To provide practice with least common multiples, you may wish to demonstrate the "Cosmic Cafe" Game Mat first, so that students who finish early can play it.

Before discussing pages 258 and 259, ask students to tell which is greater, $\frac{3}{7}$ or $\frac{4}{9}$. Encourage them to use any method they wish to decide and to explain their methods. Go over page 258 with the class. Be sure to discuss the three methods described. As needed, discuss another example or two, such as $\frac{5}{8}$ and $\frac{3}{5}$, for which the greater fraction is not easily identifiable.

Have students do the problems on page 259 without calculators in order to practice using one of the other methods, but allow them to check their answers with a **calculator***.

Problem 22 on page 259 is difficult and is best attempted after an initial class discussion by students working in cooperative groups.

ESL Meeting Individual Needs
Be sure that students understand the distinctions among denominators, common denominators, and least common denominators, and among multiples, common multiples, and least common multiples. You may wish to have ESL students record this information, along with examples, in their Math Journals.

◆ LESSON 71 Comparing Fractions

Teach

Using the Student Pages Discuss the material at the top of page 260. Guide students to understand that they can always find a common denominator by multiplying the denominators of the two fractions to be compared. Go over the three discussion questions with the class that show that there are often lesser common denominators that can be used.

Discuss the two methods presented on page 261 for finding the least common multiple of two numbers. Present additional opportunities for students to use both methods. Point out that the method of using prime factors is usually more efficient, although it may at first seem complicated. For students having difficulty with method 2, start by checking to see whether they can find prime factors. Next, list the prime factors in ascending order and use the greater exponent for each factor. For example, to find the least common multiple of 192 and 288, factor: $192 = 2^6 \times 3^1$ and $288 = 2^5 \times 3^2$. So the least common multiple is $2^6 \times 3^2$, or 576. Use 2^6, not 2^5, because 6 is greater than 5. Similarly, use 3^2, not 3^1, because 2 is greater than 1. Have students do problems 23–40 on their own. Encourage students to use both methods for each problem to see that they yield the same result.

Introducing the "Cosmic Cafe" Game Mat Students should play the "Cosmic Cafe" Game Mat to practice finding least common multiples. Complete instructions for playing can be found on the Game Mat. Be sure that students understand the rules and that it is clear that the player who does not reach STOP is the winner. A copy of this game can also be found on page 604 of this Teacher's Guide.

SPECIAL NEEDS
Meeting Individual Needs
For students still having difficulty with the procedures for finding least common multiples, you may wish to direct students to use the first method because it is so straightforward—the student simply lists the multiples of each number, looks for common ones, and then chooses the least of them.

◆ LESSON 71 Comparing Fractions

When fractions have different denominators, we can compare them by rewriting each as an equivalent fraction with a common denominator. Then we compare the numerators.

To compare $\frac{5}{12}$ and $\frac{7}{18}$ you could use 12×18, which is 216, as a common denominator:

$$\frac{5}{12} = \frac{5 \times 18}{12 \times 18} = \frac{90}{216}$$

$$\frac{7}{18} = \frac{7 \times 12}{18 \times 12} = \frac{84}{216}$$

Since $\frac{90}{216} > \frac{84}{216}$, then $\frac{5}{12} > \frac{7}{18}$.

However, there are lesser denominators that could have been used. For example, 36 is a multiple of both 12 and 18. We could have written:

$$\frac{5}{12} = \frac{5 \times 3}{12 \times 3} = \frac{15}{36}$$

$$\frac{7}{18} = \frac{7 \times 2}{18 \times 2} = \frac{14}{36}$$

Again, since $\frac{15}{36} > \frac{14}{36}$, then $\frac{5}{12} > \frac{7}{18}$.

The number 216 is one common multiple of 12 and 18 (216 is a multiple of 12, since $216 = 18 \times 12$ and a multiple of 18, since $216 = 12 \times 18$). Here are some other common multiples of 12 and 18:

108   ($108 = 9 \times 12$ and $108 = 6 \times 18$)

72   ($72 = 6 \times 12$ and $72 = 4 \times 18$)

36   ($36 = 3 \times 12$ and $36 = 2 \times 18$)

◆ Can you find a common multiple of 12 and 18 that is greater than 216? Name one. **Examples are 432, 648, 864.**

◆ Can you find a common multiple of 12 and 18 that is between 36 and 216 other than those listed? Name two. **144 and 180**

◆ Can you find a common multiple of 12 and 18 that is less than 36? **If 0 and negative numbers are excluded, there is no common multiple of 12 and 18 that is less than 36.**

Literature Connection Have students read *The Children's Space Atlas* by Robin Kerrod. Students can use information in this book to make fractions that compare planets.

LESSON 71 RETEACHING Name_____

To find the least common multiple of two numbers, you can use an "upside-down dividing" method.

Example:
Find the least common multiple of 24 and 30.

2 | 24   30   Use an upside-down division symbol.
      12   15   Divide by a common factor. Write each quotient.

2 | 24   30   Repeat the procedure with another divisor.
3 | 12   15
      4   5

When the only common factor of the two quotients is 1, find the least common multiple by multiplying the numbers around the division symbols as shown.

2 | 24   30
×
3 | 12   15
×
      4 × 5
$2 \times 3 \times 4 \times 5 = 120$
The least common multiple of 24 and 30 is 120.

Find the least common multiple of each pair of numbers.

❶ 8 and 12 __24__   ❷ 20 and 35 __140__   ❸ 48 and 18 __144__

❹ 20 and 16 __80__   ❺ 32 and 40 __160__   ❻ 8 and 50 __200__

❼ 20 and 36 __180__   ❽ 45 and 48 __720__   ❾ 50 and 35 __350__

❿ 9 and 12 __36__   ⓫ 16 and 30 __240__   ⓬ 15 and 24 __120__

⓭ 36 and 40 __360__   ⓮ 15 and 18 __90__   ⓯ 42 and 56 __168__

Math Explorations and Applications Level 6 · 23

The **least common multiple** of two numbers is the lowest number (except 0) that is a multiple of both numbers.

Here are two methods for finding the least common multiple of two numbers. The examples show how to find the least common multiple of 6 and 8.

Method 1

List the multiples of each number and choose the lowest common multiple. You don't need to go beyond the product of the two numbers. List a few multiples of one number and then a few of the other number until you find the least common multiple.

Multiples of 8: 8, 16, 24, 32, 40, 48

Multiples of 6: 6, 12, 18, 24

Method 2

List the prime factors of each number. The least common multiple must have each of these factors used as many times as it appears in the number in which it occurs most often.

$$6 = 2 \times 3 \qquad 8 = 2 \times 2 \times 2$$

$$2 \times 2 \times 2 \times 3 = 8 \times 3 = 24$$

Using either method, we find the least common multiple of 6 and 8 is 24.

Find the least common multiple of each pair of numbers.

㉓ 3 and 4 **12**   ㉔ 4 and 6 **12**   ㉕ 4 and 10 **20**

㉖ 3 and 5 **15**   ㉗ 9 and 12 **36**   ㉘ 2 and 8 **8**

㉙ 4 and 12 **12**   ㉚ 6 and 12 **12**   ㉛ 10 and 12 **60**

㉜ 10 and 20 **20**   ㉝ 10 and 15 **30**   ㉞ 15 and 20 **60**

㉟ 15 and 18 **90**   ㊱ 18 and 20 **180**   ㊲ 16 and 30 **240**

㊳ 15 and 24 **120**   ㊴ 6 and 15 **30**   ㊵ 14 and 21 **42**

Unit 4   Lesson 71 • **261**

 **In Closing** To summarize the lesson, ask students to explain different methods of comparing two fractions and ask for opinions as to which method they prefer. Ask them to explain how they think they would compare more than two fractions. Students can include all their responses in their Math Journals.

Performance Assessment Ask students to tell which fraction is greater, $\frac{4}{9}$ or $\frac{12}{25}$. Then ask them to give the least common multiple of 6 and 10. Be sure students explain their reasoning.

Assessment Criteria

Did the student . . .

✓ use more than one method of comparing fractions?

✓ successfully complete at least 16 of the 20 comparison problems on page 259?

✓ demonstrate understanding of how to use both methods presented for finding the least common multiple of two numbers?

Homework Have students complete Practice Master 71 for further practice comparing fractions and finding least common multiples.

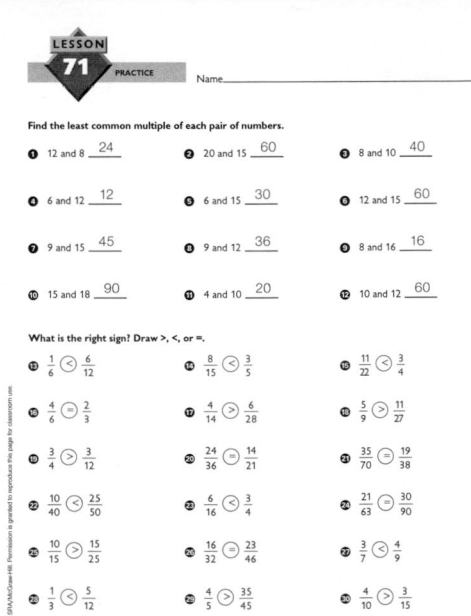

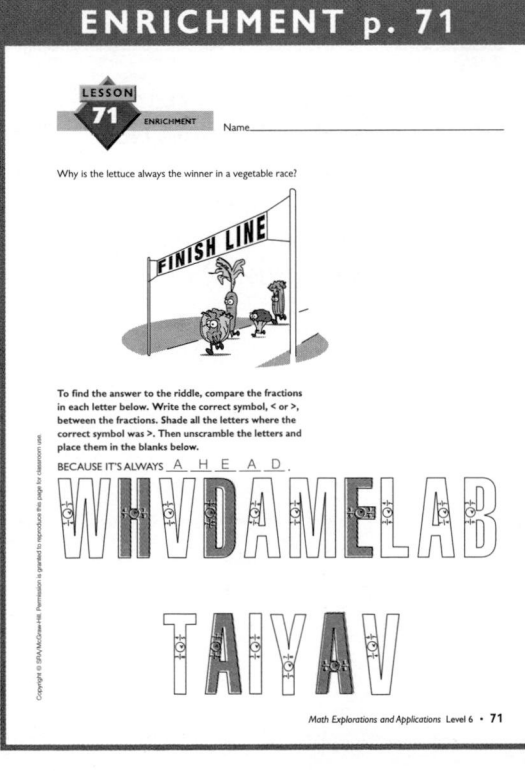

Unit 4 Lesson 71 **261**

LESSON 72

Student Edition pages 262–263

Adding and Subtracting Fractions

LESSON PLANNER

Objective

▶ to review and provide practice in adding and subtracting fractions

Context of the Lesson This is the eighth of 20 lessons on fractions. Adding and subtracting fractions was covered in the fourth- and fifth-grade programs.

MANIPULATIVES
fraction models*
(optional)

Program Resources
Reteaching Master
Practice Master 72
Enrichment Master 72

For extra practice:
CD-ROM* Lesson 72
Cumulative Review, page 568

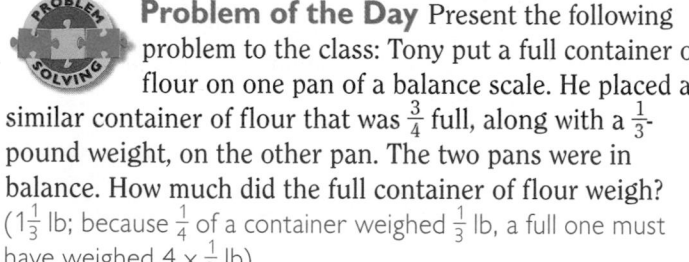

① Warm-Up

Problem of the Day Present the following problem to the class: Tony put a full container of flour on one pan of a balance scale. He placed a similar container of flour that was $\frac{3}{4}$ full, along with a $\frac{1}{3}$-pound weight, on the other pan. The two pans were in balance. How much did the full container of flour weigh? ($1\frac{1}{3}$ lb; because $\frac{1}{4}$ of a container weighed $\frac{1}{3}$ lb, a full one must have weighed $4 \times \frac{1}{3}$ lb)

Problem-Solving Strategies Ask students who have solved the Problem of the Day to share how they solved it and any strategies they used.

MENTAL MATH Challenge students to provide the numerator that will make each fraction equivalent to the first fraction.

a. $\frac{1}{2}, \frac{(2)}{4}, \frac{(3)}{6}, \frac{(4)}{8}, \frac{(5)}{10}, \frac{(6)}{12}, \frac{(7)}{14}$

b. $\frac{1}{3}, \frac{(2)}{6}, \frac{(3)}{9}, \frac{(4)}{12}, \frac{(5)}{15}, \frac{(6)}{18}, \frac{(7)}{21}$

c. $\frac{1}{4}, \frac{(2)}{8}, \frac{(4)}{16}, \frac{(5)}{20}, \frac{(3)}{12}, \frac{(6)}{24}, \frac{(7)}{28}$

d. $\frac{2}{3}, \frac{(4)}{6}, \frac{(6)}{9}, \frac{(10)}{15}, \frac{(12)}{18}, \frac{(8)}{12}, \frac{(14)}{21}$

e. $\frac{3}{4}, \frac{(6)}{8}, \frac{(9)}{12}, \frac{(12)}{16}, \frac{(15)}{20}, \frac{(21)}{28}, \frac{(24)}{32}, \frac{(18)}{24}$

f. $\frac{2}{5}, \frac{(4)}{10}, \frac{(8)}{20}, \frac{(6)}{15}, \frac{(10)}{25}, \frac{(14)}{35}, \frac{(12)}{30}$

LESSON 72

Adding and Subtracting Fractions

A clothing pattern calls for $\frac{1}{3}$ of a yard of cloth. A second pattern calls for $\frac{3}{5}$ of a yard of the same cloth.

◆ Will 1 yard of cloth be enough for both patterns?

To find out, add $\frac{1}{3}$ and $\frac{3}{5}$.

Example: $\frac{3}{5} + \frac{1}{3} = ?$

$$\begin{array}{r} \frac{3}{5} \\ + \frac{1}{3} \end{array}$$

We can't add because the denominators aren't the same.

$$\frac{3}{5} = \frac{?}{15}$$
$$\frac{1}{3} = \frac{?}{15}$$

Find a common denominator. We'll use 15.

$$\frac{3}{5} = \frac{9}{15}$$ Change $\frac{3}{5}$ to $\frac{9}{15}$.
$$\frac{1}{3} = \frac{5}{15}$$ Change $\frac{1}{3}$ to $\frac{5}{15}$.

$$\begin{array}{r} \frac{3}{5} \\ + \frac{1}{3} \end{array} \rightarrow \begin{array}{r} \frac{9}{15} \\ + \frac{5}{15} \\ \hline \frac{14}{15} \end{array}$$

Now we can add the fractions.

Since $\frac{14}{15}$ of a yard is less than 1 yard, 1 yard of cloth is enough.

Add.

① $\frac{1}{3} + \frac{1}{6}$ $\frac{3}{6}$ (or $\frac{1}{2}$) ② $\frac{1}{2} + \frac{2}{3}$ $\frac{7}{6}$ ③ $\frac{3}{5} + \frac{3}{10}$ $\frac{9}{10}$ ④ $\frac{1}{2} + \frac{1}{3}$ $\frac{5}{6}$

⑤ $\frac{2}{3} + \frac{4}{9}$ $\frac{10}{9}$ ⑥ $\frac{1}{8} + \frac{3}{4}$ $\frac{7}{8}$ ⑦ $\frac{3}{7} + \frac{1}{6}$ $\frac{25}{42}$ ⑧ $\frac{3}{5} + \frac{1}{4}$ $\frac{17}{20}$

⑨ $\frac{5}{8} + \frac{3}{4}$ $\frac{11}{8}$ ⑩ $\frac{7}{8} + \frac{1}{2}$ $\frac{11}{8}$ ⑪ $\frac{1}{9} + \frac{1}{3}$ $\frac{4}{9}$ ⑫ $\frac{3}{8} + \frac{1}{2}$ $\frac{7}{8}$

⑬ $\frac{5}{12} + \frac{1}{4}$ $\frac{8}{12}$ (or $\frac{3}{4}$) ⑭ $\frac{5}{8} + \frac{1}{4}$ $\frac{7}{8}$ ⑮ $\frac{2}{7} + \frac{1}{4}$ $\frac{15}{28}$ ⑯ $\frac{1}{6} + \frac{1}{3}$ $\frac{3}{6}$ (or $\frac{1}{2}$)

262 • Fractions and Mixed Numbers

Literature Connection Students can play fraction dominoes using page 68 of *Dominoes: Basic Rules and Fractions* by Reiner Måler.

RETEACHING p. 24

LESSON 72 RETEACHING

Name_____

Example 1:
$\frac{2}{3} + \frac{1}{4} = ?$

Find a number that is a multiple of both 3 and 4 to use as a common denominator.

$\frac{2}{3} + \frac{1}{4} = \left(\frac{2}{3} \times \frac{4}{4}\right) + \left(\frac{1}{4} \times \frac{3}{3}\right)$

$= \frac{8}{12} + \frac{3}{12}$

$= \frac{8+3}{12}$

$= \frac{11}{12}$

Example 2:
$\frac{5}{8} - \frac{1}{3} = ?$

Use the common denominator 24.

$\frac{5}{8} - \frac{1}{3} = \left(\frac{5}{8} \times \frac{3}{3}\right) - \left(\frac{1}{3} \times \frac{8}{8}\right)$

$= \frac{15}{24} - \frac{8}{24}$

$= \frac{15-8}{24}$

$= \frac{7}{24}$

Add or subtract. Watch the signs.

❶ $\frac{2}{3} + \frac{1}{6}$ $\frac{5}{6}$ ❷ $\frac{5}{6} - \frac{1}{3}$ $\frac{3}{6}$ ($\frac{1}{2}$) ❸ $\frac{7}{12} - \frac{1}{8}$ $\frac{11}{24}$

❹ $\frac{3}{8} + \frac{5}{6}$ $\frac{29}{24}$ ($1\frac{5}{24}$) ❺ $\frac{2}{3} - \frac{1}{12}$ $\frac{7}{12}$ ❻ $\frac{5}{6} + \frac{1}{8}$ $\frac{35}{24}$ ($1\frac{11}{24}$)

❼ $\frac{3}{4} + \frac{9}{10}$ $\frac{33}{20}$ ($1\frac{13}{20}$) ❽ $\frac{11}{12} - \frac{3}{8}$ $\frac{13}{24}$ ❾ $\frac{7}{10} + \frac{1}{12}$ $\frac{47}{60}$

❿ $\frac{5}{12} + \frac{4}{15}$ $\frac{41}{60}$ ⓫ $\frac{1}{18} + \frac{2}{5}$ $\frac{41}{90}$ ⓬ $\frac{7}{10} - \frac{1}{3}$ $\frac{11}{30}$

⓭ $\frac{8}{9} - \frac{1}{2}$ $\frac{13}{18}$ ⓮ $\frac{5}{8} + \frac{1}{4}$ $\frac{7}{8}$ ⓯ $\frac{11}{15} - \frac{1}{12}$ $\frac{29}{60}$

24 • Math Explorations and Applications Level 6

*available separately

When you subtract fractions, many of the steps are the same as when you add fractions.

Example: $\frac{3}{5} - \frac{1}{3} = ?$

$\begin{array}{r}\frac{3}{5}\\[-2pt]-\ \frac{1}{3}\end{array}$ We can't subtract because the denominators aren't the same.

$\frac{3}{5} = \frac{?}{15}$ Find a common denominator. We'll use 15.

$\frac{1}{3} = \frac{?}{15}$

$\frac{3}{5} = \frac{9}{15}$ Change $\frac{3}{5}$ to $\frac{9}{15}$.

$\frac{1}{3} = \frac{5}{15}$ Change $\frac{1}{3}$ to $\frac{5}{15}$.

$\begin{array}{r}\frac{3}{5}\ \rightarrow\ \frac{9}{15}\\[2pt]-\ \frac{1}{3}\ -\ \frac{5}{15}\\[2pt]\hline \frac{4}{15}\end{array}$ Now we can subtract the fractions.

Subtract.

17. $\frac{1}{3} - \frac{1}{6}$ $\frac{1}{6}$ 18. $\frac{2}{3} - \frac{1}{2}$ $\frac{1}{6}$ 19. $\frac{3}{5} - \frac{3}{10}$ $\frac{3}{10}$ 20. $\frac{5}{6} - \frac{7}{12}$ $\frac{3}{12}$ (or $\frac{1}{4}$)

21. $\frac{2}{3} - \frac{4}{9}$ $\frac{2}{9}$ 22. $\frac{3}{4} - \frac{1}{8}$ $\frac{5}{8}$ 23. $\frac{3}{7} - \frac{1}{6}$ $\frac{11}{42}$ 24. $\frac{3}{4} - \frac{3}{8}$ $\frac{3}{8}$

25. $\frac{3}{4} - \frac{5}{8}$ $\frac{1}{8}$ 26. $\frac{7}{8} - \frac{1}{2}$ $\frac{3}{8}$ 27. $\frac{1}{3} - \frac{1}{9}$ $\frac{2}{9}$ 28. $\frac{3}{7} - \frac{2}{7}$ $\frac{1}{7}$

Add or subtract. Watch the signs.   30. $\frac{5}{10}$ (or $\frac{1}{2}$)

29. $\frac{2}{3} + \frac{7}{9}$ $\frac{13}{9}$ 30. $\frac{2}{5} + \frac{1}{10}$ 31. $\frac{7}{8} - \frac{3}{4}$ $\frac{1}{8}$ 32. $\frac{3}{5} + \frac{1}{4}$ $\frac{17}{20}$

33. $\frac{7}{9} - \frac{2}{3}$ $\frac{1}{9}$ 34. $\frac{5}{6} - \frac{1}{2}$ $\frac{2}{6}$ (or $\frac{1}{3}$) 35. $\frac{3}{7} + \frac{1}{3}$ $\frac{16}{21}$ 36. $\frac{1}{4} + \frac{1}{8}$ $\frac{3}{8}$

37. $\frac{5}{6} + \frac{1}{2}$ $\frac{8}{6}$ 38. $\frac{2}{5} - \frac{1}{10}$ $\frac{3}{10}$ 39. $\frac{5}{9} - \frac{1}{3}$ $\frac{2}{9}$ 40. $\frac{1}{3} - \frac{1}{9}$ $\frac{2}{9}$

Use the Cumulative Review on page 568 after this lesson.

Unit 4 Lesson 72 • **263**

---

❷ Teach

Using the Student Pages Before going over the examples, ask students to explain how to add two fractions with the same denominator, for example, $\frac{2}{5} + \frac{1}{5}$. Once students recall how to add fractions with the same denominator, ask them to think about and explain how to subtract two fractions with the same denominator. Then go over the examples. At this time, focus on finding any common denominator. To a problem like $\frac{2}{3} + \frac{1}{6}$, accept such answers as $\frac{10}{12}$ or $\frac{15}{18}$, as well as $\frac{5}{6}$. Remind students that finding a common denominator is necessary for adding and subtracting fractions. Have students do the problems on their own.

❸ Wrap-Up

In Closing Summarize the lesson by asking students to explain how to add or subtract two fractions with unlike denominators.

 Students who do not correctly rewrite fractions with common denominators need more work with the concept of equivalent fractions. Those who add or subtract the denominators and numerators do not understand the algorithm for addition and subtraction of fractions and would benefit from review, perhaps including manipulation of **fraction models***.

 **Informal Assessment** Circulate and observe students to check that they are correctly expressing the fractions with their common denominators.

Assessment Criteria

Did the student . . .

✓ demonstrate understanding of what common denominators are?

✓ correctly rewrite pairs of fractions to have common denominators?

✓ correctly answer at least 75% of the problems?

Homework Have students make up three addition and three subtraction problems involving fractions without common denominators. They should solve the problems on a different sheet of paper, so they can exchange problems with other students to solve.

PRACTICE p. 72

LESSON **72** PRACTICE   Name_____

Add.

1. $\frac{3}{7} + \frac{2}{9} =$ $\frac{41}{63}$ 2. $\frac{1}{3} + \frac{8}{9} =$ $\frac{11}{9} \left(1\frac{2}{9}\right)$

3. $\frac{2}{3} + \frac{3}{10} =$ $\frac{29}{30}$ 4. $\frac{3}{10} + \frac{3}{5} =$ $\frac{9}{10}$

5. $\frac{4}{11} + \frac{3}{22} =$ $\frac{1}{2}$ 6. $\frac{2}{5} + \frac{7}{10} =$ $\frac{11}{10} \left(1\frac{1}{10}\right)$

7. $\frac{5}{9} + \frac{1}{5} =$ $\frac{34}{45}$ 8. $\frac{1}{2} + \frac{1}{4} =$ $\frac{3}{4}$

9. $\frac{3}{7} + \frac{1}{4} =$ $\frac{19}{28}$ 10. $\frac{3}{5} + \frac{1}{10} =$ $\frac{7}{10}$

Subtract.

11. $\frac{1}{2} - \frac{1}{4} =$ $\frac{1}{4}$ 12. $\frac{3}{7} - \frac{5}{14} =$ $\frac{1}{14}$

13. $\frac{2}{5} - \frac{3}{10} =$ $\frac{1}{10}$ 14. $\frac{4}{11} - \frac{3}{22} =$ $\frac{5}{22}$

15. $\frac{8}{9} - \frac{7}{12} =$ $\frac{1}{72}$ 16. $\frac{4}{5} - \frac{3}{10} =$ $\frac{1}{2}$

17. $\frac{3}{7} - \frac{1}{5} =$ $\frac{8}{35}$ 18. $\frac{2}{3} - \frac{2}{7} =$ $\frac{8}{21}$

19. $\frac{5}{9} - \frac{2}{9} =$ $\frac{1}{3}$ 20. $\frac{5}{9} - \frac{1}{7} =$ $\frac{26}{63}$

72 • Math Explorations and Applications Level 6

ENRICHMENT p. 72

LESSON **72** ENRICHMENT   Name_____

Here is another way you can do a fraction addition or subtraction problem. There are four steps. Three are multiplication. The fourth is addition or subtraction.

$\frac{3}{5} + \frac{1}{4} = ?$

The steps, as numbered below, are shown on the right.

1. Diagonally multiply a denominator and a numerator.
2. Diagonally multiply the other denominator and the other numerator.
3. Add or subtract the numbers you got in steps 1 and 2. This will be the numerator of the answer.
4. Multiply the two denominators. This will be the denominator of the answer.

Try this method on the problems below.

1. $\frac{2}{3} + \frac{1}{9} =$ $\frac{7}{9}$ 2. $\frac{3}{4} - \frac{2}{7} =$ $\frac{13}{28}$

3. $\frac{5}{8} - \frac{2}{9} =$ $\frac{9}{40}$ 4. $\frac{2}{3} + \frac{3}{5} =$ $\frac{19}{15}$ or $1\frac{4}{15}$

5. $\frac{3}{8} + \frac{2}{9} =$ $\frac{43}{72}$ 6. $\frac{6}{7} - \frac{4}{5} =$ $\frac{2}{35}$

7. Why does this method work?
You are really converting both fractions to a common denominator, which is the product of the two denominators in the problem.

72 • Math Explorations and Applications Level 6

---

*available separately

LESSON 73

Adding and Subtracting Special Fractions

Student Edition pages 264–265

LESSON PLANNER

Objectives

▶ to provide practice with addition and subtraction of fractions when one denominator is a factor of the other

✓ to evaluate students' ability to add and subtract fractions with unlike denominators

▶ to provide practice in adding and subtracting fractions

Context of the Lesson This is the ninth of 20 lessons on fractions. A Mastery Checkpoint is provided in this lesson for assessing students' ability to add and subtract fractions with unlike denominators.

 MANIPULATIVES

fraction models*
(optional)

Program Resources

Number Cubes (0–5)

Practice Master 73

Enrichment Master 73

Assessment Master

For extra practice:
CD-ROM* Lesson 73

1 Warm-Up
 5 MINUTES

Problem of the Day Present this problem to students: In the restored seaport village of Whalewatch, a guided path goes from the visitor center to the lighthouse. It is $\frac{3}{4}$ mile from the visitor center to the ship chandlery. It is $\frac{1}{3}$ mile farther to the cooper's shop and $\frac{1}{2}$ mile from the cooper's shop to the sailmaker's. From there, it is $\frac{3}{8}$ mile to the lighthouse. Juan started to walk back from the lighthouse at the same time Willy started out from the visitor center. Each walked for 1 mile. Who was closer to the cooper's shop at that point? How much closer? (Willy; $\frac{1}{24}$ mile closer)

Problem-Solving Strategies Ask students who have solved the Problem of the Day to share how they solved it and any strategies they used.

 Have students provide the numerator that will make each fraction equivalent to the first fraction:

(continued on page 265)

LESSON 73

Adding and Subtracting Special Fractions

When you add or subtract fractions, quite often the denominator of one fraction will be a factor of the denominator of the other. In these cases you can use the greater denominator as a common denominator. You will save work by doing that.

Example: $\frac{2}{3} + \frac{1}{6} = ?$

Since 3 is a factor of 6, you can use 6 as a common denominator.

$$\frac{2}{3} \qquad \frac{2}{3} = \frac{?}{6} \qquad \frac{2}{3} = \frac{4}{6} \qquad \frac{4}{6}$$
$$+\frac{1}{6} \rightarrow \frac{1}{6} = \frac{?}{6} \rightarrow \frac{1}{6} = \frac{1}{6} \rightarrow +\frac{1}{6}$$
$$\overline{\frac{5}{6}}$$

Add or subtract. For many of these, the denominator of one of the fractions can be used as a common denominator. Reduce answers if possible. $\frac{2}{6}$ (or $\frac{1}{3}$)

❶ $\frac{2}{3} - \frac{1}{6}$ $\frac{3}{6}$(or$\frac{1}{2}$) ❷ $\frac{2}{3} - \frac{4}{7}$ $\frac{2}{21}$ ❸ $\frac{1}{2} - \frac{1}{3}$ $\frac{1}{6}$ ❹ $\frac{1}{2} - \frac{1}{6}$

❺ $\frac{1}{4} + \frac{1}{2}$ $\frac{3}{4}$ ❻ $\frac{1}{6} + \frac{1}{3}$ $\frac{3}{6}$(or$\frac{1}{2}$)❼ $\frac{1}{7} + \frac{3}{14}$ $\frac{5}{14}$ ❽ $\frac{1}{2} - \frac{3}{8}$ $\frac{1}{8}$

❾ $\frac{1}{2} - \frac{1}{4}$ $\frac{1}{4}$ ❿ $\frac{1}{2} + \frac{1}{3}$ $\frac{5}{6}$ ⓫ $\frac{3}{8} - \frac{1}{4}$ $\frac{1}{8}$ ⓬ $\frac{3}{4} - \frac{3}{8}$ $\frac{3}{8}$

 **Solve this problem.**

⓭ Leona baked a cheesecake and cut it into twelfths. She, Henry, and Nita each ate one piece. Then five more pieces were eaten at supper.

  a. How much of the cheesecake did Leona, Henry, and Nita eat? $\frac{3}{12}$ (or $\frac{1}{4}$)

  b. How much of the cheesecake was eaten at supper? $\frac{5}{12}$

  c. How much of the cheesecake was left after supper? $\frac{4}{12}$ (or $\frac{1}{3}$)

RETEACHING

 Students who incorrectly express equivalent fractions can work with **fraction models*** to see and manipulate physical examples of equivalences. Working with a partner, they can use the models to do the Mental Math exercises for this lesson.

PRACTICE p. 73

LESSON 73 PRACTICE Name_____

Add.

❶ $\frac{3}{7} + \frac{4}{9} =$ $\frac{55}{63}$ ❷ $\frac{3}{4} + \frac{1}{6} =$ $\frac{11}{12}$

❸ $\frac{1}{6} + \frac{3}{8} =$ $\frac{13}{24}$ ❹ $\frac{3}{10} + \frac{1}{4} =$ $\frac{11}{20}$

❺ $\frac{1}{8} + \frac{2}{7} =$ $\frac{23}{56}$ ❻ $\frac{7}{9} + \frac{2}{3} =$ $\frac{13}{9}\left(1\frac{4}{9}\right)$

❼ $\frac{2}{5} + \frac{5}{6} =$ $\frac{37}{30}\left(1\frac{7}{30}\right)$ ❽ $\frac{2}{3} + \frac{3}{5} =$ $\frac{19}{15}\left(1\frac{4}{15}\right)$

❾ $\frac{7}{9} + \frac{2}{5} =$ $\frac{53}{45}\left(1\frac{8}{45}\right)$ ❿ $\frac{3}{8} + \frac{1}{2} =$ $\frac{7}{8}$

Subtract.

⓫ $\frac{1}{2} - \frac{5}{12} =$ $\frac{1}{12}$ ⓬ $\frac{6}{7} - \frac{6}{25} =$ $\frac{108}{175}$

⓭ $\frac{2}{7} - \frac{1}{11} =$ $\frac{15}{77}$ ⓮ $\frac{5}{6} - \frac{7}{30} =$ $\frac{3}{5}$

⓯ $\frac{5}{6} - \frac{4}{5} =$ $\frac{1}{30}$ ⓰ $\frac{4}{5} - \frac{2}{5} =$ $\frac{2}{5}$

⓱ $\frac{7}{9} - \frac{5}{9} =$ $\frac{2}{9}$ ⓲ $\frac{8}{9} - \frac{7}{8} =$ $\frac{1}{72}$

⓳ $\frac{7}{8} - \frac{1}{24} =$ $\frac{5}{6}$ ⓴ $\frac{7}{10} - \frac{3}{5} =$ $\frac{1}{10}$

Circo 11 Game

Players: Two
Materials: Two 0–5 cubes, paper, two pencils or pens of different colors
Object: To win more circles
Math Focus: Mental addition of common fractions, using fractions, and mathematical reasoning

RULES

1. Make one game board for both players by drawing 11 circles on a sheet of paper. Put a dot at about the center of each circle. (The circles don't need to be perfectly drawn.) Each player uses a different color pencil or pen.

2. Take turns rolling both cubes and making a fraction equal to 1 or less. (If you roll a 0, roll that cube again.) For example, if you roll a 2 and a 3, you make the fraction $\frac{2}{3}$. Then capture that fraction of a circle by using your pen or pencil to mark off a pie-shaped part of any circle and write the fraction in that part. (The part does not have to be drawn to the exact size, but the closer the better.)

3. On a turn you may capture parts in more than one circle. The fractions for the parts you capture must all have the same denominator. For example, if you make the fraction $\frac{3}{5}$, you may take $\frac{1}{5}$ of one circle and $\frac{2}{5}$ of another or $\frac{1}{5}$ of each of three circles. But you may not take $\frac{1}{2}$ of one circle and $\frac{1}{10}$ of another.

4. Whenever you think you have captured more than $\frac{1}{2}$ of a circle, you may win the circle by proving that your parts make up more than $\frac{1}{2}$ of the circle. This may be done by approximation or by finding an exact sum (mentally, with paper and pencil, or with a calculator).

5. If $\frac{1}{2}$ of a circle is captured by one player and the other $\frac{1}{2}$ is captured by the other player, neither player wins the circle.

6. The player who has captured more circles is the winner.

Unit 4 Lesson 73 • **265**

Mental Math (continued)

a. $\frac{3}{5}, \frac{(6)}{10}, \frac{(12)}{20}, \frac{(9)}{15}, \frac{(15)}{25}, \frac{(21)}{35}$

b. $\frac{2}{6}, \frac{(4)}{12}, \frac{(8)}{24}, \frac{(10)}{30}, \frac{(14)}{42}, \frac{(12)}{36}$

c. $\frac{3}{7}, \frac{(6)}{14}, \frac{(9)}{21}, \frac{(12)}{28}, \frac{(15)}{35}, \frac{(21)}{49}$

d. $\frac{3}{4}, \frac{(6)}{8}, \frac{(12)}{16}, \frac{(9)}{12}, \frac{(18)}{24}$

❷ Teach

Using the Student Pages Before beginning work on page 264, you may wish to introduce the "Circo 11" game so that students can play when they have completed all of the problems. After reviewing the material at the top of page 264, have students complete the problems.

 **Introducing the "Circo 11" Game**
Demonstrate the "Circo 11" game on page 265, which provides practice with adding fractions and with mathematical reasoning (deciding which circles to capture). Make it clear that the circles and fractions do not have to be exactly drawn, as long as they are labeled.

❸ Wrap-Up 5 MINUTES

In Closing Summarize the lesson by asking students to explain how to add or subtract these three pairs of fractions:

a. $\frac{50}{100} + \frac{2}{50} = \left(\frac{54}{100}\right)$
b. $\frac{3}{16} + \frac{1}{4} = \left(\frac{7}{16}\right)$
c. $\frac{5}{18} + \frac{2}{3} = \left(\frac{17}{18}\right)$

Mastery Checkpoint 16

Most students should demonstrate mastery of adding and subtracting fractions with unlike denominators by correctly answering at least 80% of the problems on page 264 or on Assessment Blackline Masters page 31 in a reasonable amount of time. Results of this assessment can be recorded on the Mastery Checkpoint Chart.

ENRICHMENT p. 73

ASSESSMENT p. 31

Assessment Criteria

Did the student . . .

✓ demonstrate understanding of adding and subtracting fractions with unlike denominators?

✓ correctly solve 80% of the problems on page 264?

Homework Have students play the "Circo 11" game with a family member for further practice adding and subtracting fractions. A copy of this game can also be found on page 24 of the Home Connections Blackline Masters.

Least Common Multiples of Three or More Numbers

A band director wants the band to be able to march in rows of 6, 8, or 9, with no one left over. What's the least number of band members she'll need? To find out, find the least common multiple.

The least common multiple of three or more numbers can be found in the same ways it is found for two numbers.

Example: Find the least common multiple of 6, 8, and 9.

Method 1

List the multiples of each number and choose the least common multiple. Again, list a few multiples of each number at a time. Stop when you find the least common multiple.

Multiples of 9: 9, 18, 27, 36, 45, 54, 63, 72, 81, 90
Multiples of 8: 8, 16, 24, 32, 40, 48, 56, 64, 72, 80, 88
Multiples of 6: 6, 12, 18, 24, 30, 36, 42, 48, 54, 60, 66, 72

The band leader will need 72 members.

Method 2

List the prime factors of each number and find the product of the greatest power of each prime factor.

$6 = 2 \times 3$ $8 = 2^3$ $9 = 3^2$

The least common multiple of 6, 8, and 9 is $2^3 \times 3^2$, or 72.

The band must have at least 72 members.

Notice that the second method is much easier for finding the least common multiple of three or more numbers.

Find the least common multiple of each set of numbers.

❶ 3, 6, and 9 **18**   **❷** 7, 14, and 21 **42**   **❸** 4, 6, 9, and 12 **36**

❹ 4, 8, and 16 **16**   **❺** 3, 5, and 7 **105**   **❻** 1, 2, 3, and 4 **12**

❼ 2, 3, and 5 **30**   **❽** 8, 12, and 24 **24**   **❾** 2, 3, 4, and 6 **12**

❿ 6, 5, and 10 **30**   **⓫** 4, 12, and 5 **60**   **⓬** 3, 5, 6, and 15 **30**

Student Edition pages 266–269

Least Common Multiples of Three or More Numbers

LESSON PLANNER

Objectives

▶ to demonstrate and provide practice in finding the least common multiple of three or more numbers

▶ to help students develop the broad ability to use mathematical common sense

Context of the Lesson This lesson, the tenth of 20 lessons on fractions, contains Part 3 of "Energy Savers," a four-part Thinking Story.

 MANIPULATIVES

fraction models*
  (optional)

Program Resources

"Harder Cosmic Cafe" Game Mat

Practice Master 74

Enrichment Master 74

The Cruncher*

For career connections:
  Careers and Math*

For additional math integration:
  Math Throughout the Day*

For extra practice:
  CD-ROM* Lesson 74

❶ Warm-Up ⏱ 5 MINUTES

Problem of the Day Present the following problem to the class: Ask students how they could determine which is larger—$\frac{1}{2}$ of a small rectangular pizza or $\frac{1}{3}$ of a large one? (Find the actual area of both pizzas, and then find the area of $\frac{1}{2}$ of the small pizza and $\frac{1}{3}$ of the large, and compare.)

Problem-Solving Strategies Ask students who have solved the Problem of the Day to share how they solved it and any strategies they used.

Finding the least common multiple can be helpful if you ever need to add three or more fractions with different denominators.

Example: $\frac{2}{5} + \frac{1}{4} + \frac{3}{10} = ?$

The least common multiple of 5, 4, and 10 is 20.

$$\frac{2}{5} \quad\quad \frac{2}{5} = \frac{?}{20} \quad\quad \frac{2}{5} = \frac{8}{20} \quad\quad \frac{8}{20}$$
$$\frac{1}{4} \longrightarrow \frac{1}{4} = \frac{?}{20} \longrightarrow \frac{1}{4} = \frac{5}{20} \longrightarrow \frac{5}{20}$$
$$+\frac{3}{10} \quad\quad \frac{3}{10} = \frac{?}{20} \quad\quad \frac{3}{10} = \frac{6}{20} \quad\quad +\frac{6}{20}$$
$$\frac{19}{20}$$

Now try these. Use your answers to problems 1–12 on page 266.

13 $\frac{1}{3} + \frac{1}{6} + \frac{1}{9}$ **$\frac{11}{18}$** 14 $\frac{1}{6} + \frac{1}{5} + \frac{3}{10}$ **$\frac{20}{30}$ (or $\frac{2}{3}$)** 15 $\frac{1}{4} + \frac{5}{12} + \frac{1}{5}$ **$\frac{52}{60}$ (or $\frac{13}{15}$)**

16 $\frac{3}{16} + \frac{1}{4} + \frac{3}{8}$ **$\frac{13}{16}$** 17 $\frac{1}{3} + \frac{1}{5} + \frac{1}{7}$ **$\frac{71}{105}$** 18 $\frac{7}{24} + \frac{1}{12} + \frac{1}{8}$ **$\frac{12}{24}$ (or $\frac{1}{2}$)**

Compare. Write >, <, or =.

19 $\frac{3}{5} \blacksquare \frac{5}{8}$ **<**   20 $\frac{2}{3} \blacksquare \frac{4}{7}$ **>**   21 $\frac{5}{6} \blacksquare \frac{7}{8}$ **<**

22 $\frac{1}{3} \blacksquare \frac{10}{18}$ **<**   23 $\frac{3}{8} \blacksquare \frac{5}{12}$ **<**   24 $\frac{3}{4} \blacksquare \frac{18}{24}$ **=**

Solve these problems.

25 A band director wants his band to march in rows of 4, 5, or 6. What's the least number of members needed? **60**

26 A band director with fewer than 50 band members finds that if she arranges her band in rows of 2, 3, or 4, there is one person left over, but if she arranges her band in rows of 5, there is no one left over. How many people are in the band? **25**

27 The band in problem 26 grows to between 50 and 100 members, and the director finds that she has the same problem as before. If she arranges the band in rows of 2, 3, or 4, one person is left over, but if she puts members in rows of 5, no one is left over. How many people are in the band now? **85**

Unit 4 Lesson 74 • **267**

Technology Connection Refer students to the laser disc or software *Core Concepts in Math: Mastering Fractions* from BFA/Systems Impact (Mac, IBM, for grades 5–9) for further practice with adding, subtracting, and multiplying fractions, working with common and mixed numbers, fractions on a number line, and simplifying.

*available separately

 MENTAL MATH Have students show thumbs up if the sum is more than 1, show thumbs down if it is less than 1, or stand if it is equal to 1.

a. $\frac{1}{3} + \frac{1}{3}$ (thumbs down)   b. $\frac{1}{2} + \frac{1}{2}$ (stand)

c. $\frac{1}{8} + \frac{3}{8}$ (thumbs down)   d. $\frac{4}{7} + \frac{3}{7}$ (stand)

e. $\frac{3}{4} + \frac{6}{8}$ (thumbs up)   f. $\frac{1}{4} + \frac{2}{3}$ (thumbs down)

g. $\frac{3}{4} + \frac{3}{4}$ (thumbs up)   h. $\frac{1}{2} + \frac{3}{4}$ (thumbs up)

❷ Teach

Using the Student Pages You may wish to demonstrate the "Harder Cosmic Cafe" Game Mat, which provides practice with common multiples, before beginning work on pages 266–269 so that students who finish early can play.

Go through one or two examples like the ones on page 266 and 267, using both methods for each example. Guide students to see that the second method requires less work in some cases. As needed, review the meaning of prime numbers, and remind students as they work on page 267 that the inequality arrows always point to the lesser number. Have students solve the problems on both pages on their own.

Students can use a blank **Cruncher*** spreadsheet to help them solve the problems on page 266.

  **Meeting Individual Needs** Kinesthetic learners may benefit from working with manipulatives, such as **fraction cubes*** or **fraction strips**, to understand the concept of using common multiples to compare or add fractions that have different denominators.

◆ **LESSON 74 Least Common Multiples of Three or More Numbers**

Teach

Using the Thinking Story In Part 3 of "Energy Savers," the focus is on conducting tests and making estimates systematically. Marcus's mother helps him to figure out the actual effects of stop signs on gasoline use by driving her car the same distance on the highway and in town and comparing the amount of gas she uses. Plan to spend the most time on the third problem during the class discussion.

Answers to Thinking Story Questions:

1. He should divide by 100, not multiply.

2. She used about 10 liters. She used 21 liters driving around town compared with 11 liters driving the same distance without stopping: the difference of 10 liters is a result of the starting and stopping.

3. $\frac{1}{1000}$ was used. If 10 liters of gasoline were used in 200 stops, that is $\frac{1}{20}$ of a liter per stop. The gas tank holds 50 liters, and $\frac{1}{20}$ of a liter equals $\frac{1}{1000}$ of 50. An alternative way for students to arrive at this figure is to note that if $\frac{1}{20}$ of a liter is used for each stop, it would take 20 stops to use a liter and therefore 50 × 20, or 1000, stops to use a tankful: So one stop would equal $\frac{1}{1000}$ of a tankful.

4. She would use about 36 liters. If each stop uses $\frac{1}{20}$ of a liter, two stops a day would use $\frac{1}{10}$ of a liter. In a year, $\frac{1}{10}$ of a liter × 360 days, or 36 liters, would be used.

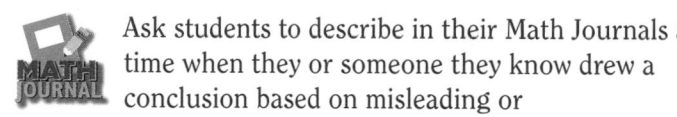 Ask students to describe in their Math Journals a time when they or someone they know drew a conclusion based on misleading or misinterpreted information.

Introducing the "Harder Cosmic Cafe" Game Mat This game provides practice in finding the least common multiple of three numbers. The rules are the same as for the "Cosmic Cafe" game introduced in Lesson 71. Complete directions are on the Game Mat. Have students play the game in pairs or small groups. Keep in mind that this game lends itself to a solitaire variation in which a player can try to beat a score of 5.

◆ **LESSON 74 Least Common Multiples of Three or More Numbers**

THINKING STORY

Energy Savers

Part 3

You may want to refer to the earlier parts of this Thinking Story on pages 246–247 and 256–257.

The Energy Savers had another meeting. "I have important news," Manolita said. "Mr. Dill wants to have a stop sign put up by his house on Pickle Street. He says it's for safety. But everyone knows it's just to keep people from driving past his house. Just think how much gas will be wasted if people have to stop every time they pass his house."

"Right," said Ferdie. "Every car that stops will use up $\frac{1}{100}$ of a tank of gas. We can count the number of cars that go past Mr. Dill's house and multiply by 100. Then we'll know how many tanks of gas that stop sign will waste."

"We must be sure we have our facts right," Mr. Harper warned. "Marcus says that a car uses $\frac{1}{100}$ of a tank of gas when it stops and starts. He says he heard it on the radio. But he can't remember who said it or what the proof was."

268 • Fractions and Mixed Numbers

RETEACHING

Present the following sequence of steps for adding three or more fractions: (1) Look at the denominators to check whether they are different; (2) find a common multiple of the denominators; (3) write equivalent fractions with a common denominator; and (4) add the numerators. Have students work in pairs to solve problems using these steps.

Marcus's mother said she would help him get some proof. One day she had to drive along a highway where there were no stop signs. To make a good test she drove slowly, the same speed that she would have driven in town. Her trip was 126 kilometers. She used 11 liters of gas. For the next few days she did all her driving in town. She counted the number of times she had to stop and start. As soon as she had driven 126 kilometers, she stopped to get gas. She found it had taken 21 liters of gas to drive 126 kilometers in town. In that distance she had made 200 stops.

When Marcus's mother reported these facts to Marcus, he did some figuring. "I hope the gas tank of your car holds about 5 liters," he said.

"Oh, no," she said. "It holds 50 liters. I don't know of any car that holds only 5 liters."

"Then either the person on the radio said the wrong thing or I heard it wrong," Marcus said sadly.

. . . to be continued

Work in groups. Discuss your answers and how you figured them out. Then compare your answers with those of other groups. Answers are in margin.

1 What's wrong with Ferdie's way of figuring out how many tanks of gas the stop sign will waste?

2 While driving 126 kilometers around town, how much gas did Marcus's mother use stopping and starting? (Hint: How much gas did she use to go the same distance without any stops?)

3 From problem 2 you should know how much gas Marcus's mother used in making about 200 stops and starts. About how much of a tank of gas was used for each stop and start, $\frac{1}{10}$, $\frac{1}{100}$, $\frac{1}{1000}$ or even less?

4 Marcus's mother has to drive past Mr. Dill's house twice a day. About how much extra gas would she use in a year to stop at his stop sign?

Unit 4   Lesson 74 • **269**

❸ Wrap-Up ⏱ 5 MINUTES

In Closing To summarize the lesson, ask students to describe the easiest way to determine the *least common multiple* for three or more numbers.

Performance Assessment Ask students to give the least common multiple of 4, 5, and 10. (20)

Assessment Criteria

Did the student . . .

✓ demonstrate an understanding of the concept of least common multiples?

✓ correctly answer at least 10 of the 12 problems on page 266?

✓ demonstrate an understanding of how to use the concept of least common multiples to add and compare fractions with different denominators?

✓ contribute to the Thinking Story discussion?

Homework Have students play the "Harder Cosmic Cafe" Game Mat with a family member for further practice finding common multiples. A copy of this can also be found on page 605 of this Teacher's Guide.

GIFTED & TALENTED **Meeting Individual Needs**
   Ask students to find the number that is halfway between $\frac{7}{10}$ and $\frac{13}{14}$. ($\frac{57}{70}$) Ask them to try to discover a procedure that will work for any similar question.

PRACTICE p. 74

LESSON 74 PRACTICE   Name_____

Find the least common multiple of each set of numbers.

1 6, 8, and 12 ___24___
2 8, 12, and 15 ___120___
3 4, 9, and 12 ___36___
4 10, 12, and 15 ___60___
5 5, 10, and 15 ___30___
6 8, 12, and 20 ___120___
7 6, 8, and 10 ___120___
8 6, 9, and 21 ___126___
9 9, 12, and 15 ___180___
10 4, 9, and 21 ___252___
11 4, 5, and 9 ___180___
12 6, 10, and 15 ___30___

Add.

13 $\frac{1}{6} + \frac{1}{8} + \frac{1}{12} = \frac{3}{8}$

14 $\frac{3}{8} + \frac{1}{12} + \frac{4}{15} = \frac{29}{40}$

15 $\frac{1}{4} + \frac{2}{9} + \frac{5}{12} = \frac{8}{9}$

16 $\frac{2}{9} + \frac{1}{12} + \frac{4}{15} = \frac{103}{180}$

17 $\frac{1}{5} + \frac{3}{10} + \frac{4}{15} = \frac{23}{30}$

18 $\frac{3}{8} + \frac{5}{12} + \frac{3}{20} = \frac{113}{120}$

19 $\frac{1}{6} + \frac{3}{8} + \frac{3}{10} = \frac{101}{120}$

20 $\frac{1}{6} + \frac{2}{9} + \frac{4}{21} = \frac{73}{126}$

21 $\frac{1}{7} + \frac{3}{14} + \frac{5}{42} = \frac{10}{21}$

22 $\frac{3}{4} + \frac{4}{9} + \frac{1}{21} = \frac{229}{252}$

23 $\frac{1}{4} + \frac{2}{5} + \frac{4}{9} = \frac{197}{180} \left(1\frac{17}{180}\right)$

24 $\frac{1}{6} + \frac{3}{10} + \frac{4}{15} = \frac{11}{15}$

25 $\frac{1}{5} + \frac{1}{7} + \frac{1}{9} = \frac{143}{315}$

26 $\frac{2}{5} + \frac{2}{7} + \frac{2}{9} = \frac{286}{315}$

74 • *Math Explorations and Applications Level 6*

ENRICHMENT p. 74

LESSON 74 ENRICHMENT   Name _____

You can use the method below to find the least common multiple of several numbers. This method is especially helpful when you are using three or more numbers.

Find the least common multiple of 8, 12, and 24.

Divide each of the three numbers by the smallest prime that is a factor of at least one number (in this case, 2).

Write the quotients below. Continue to divide by 2 until no more quotients are divisible by 2. (For any quotients that are not divisible by 2, simply repeat them.)

When 2 cannot be used anymore, divide by the next largest prime that will divide at least one of the quotients (in this case, 3).

Continue the process until the last row has all 1s.

The product of the prime numbers you divided by is the least common multiple.

```
2 | 8    12    24
2 | 4    6     12
2 | 2    3 (Repeat)  6
3 | 1 (Repeat)  3    3
    1    1     1
```
└→ LCM = 2 × 2 × 2 × 3 = 24

Try this method below.

1 Find the least common multiple of 12, 15, and 18. ___180___
2 Find the least common multiple of 8, 12, 18, and 28. ___504___
3 Find the least common multiple of 12, 15, and 20. ___60___
4 Find the least common multiple of 30, 36, and 48. ___720___
5 Find the least common multiple of 15, 24, and 60. ___120___
6 Find the least common multiple of 25, 30, and 35. ___1050___
7 Find the least common multiple of 100, 150, and 200. ___600___
8 Find the least common multiple of 28, 32, and 40. ___1120___

74 • *Math Explorations and Applications Level 6*

Unit 4 Lesson 74 **269**

Probability

Probability

LESSON PLANNER

Objectives

▶ to provide practice finding probabilities of chance events

▶ to help students to apply knowledge of probability in analyzing a game

Context of the Lesson This is the 11th of 20 lessons on fractions. Students have worked with probability concepts since the first grade.

 **MANIPULATIVES**
none

Program Resources
"Routes" Game Mat
Harder "Routes" Game Mat
Number Cubes (0–5 and 5–10)
Reteaching Master
Practice Master 75
Enrichment Master 75
For additional math integration:
    Math Throughout the Day*
For extra practice:
    CD-ROM* Lesson 75

In this lesson you'll learn about the concept of probability, or chance, and how to find the probabilities of simple events.

◆ If you were to roll a 0–5 cube a great many times, about what fraction of the time would you expect to roll a 0? $\frac{1}{6}$

◆ What fraction of the time would you expect to roll a 3? $\frac{1}{6}$

◆ What fraction of the time would you expect to roll a 5? $\frac{1}{6}$

If, in the long run, we expect something to happen $\frac{1}{6}$ of the time, we say that the **probability** of that event happening is $\frac{1}{6}$. When we roll a fair 0–5 cube, any one of the six numbers is equally likely to come up. We think of these numbers as six equally likely events, and we say that the probability of each is $\frac{1}{6}$.

Answer the following questions.

1 If you roll a 0–5 cube, what is the probability of getting a 5? $\frac{1}{6}$

2 If you roll a 0–5 cube, what is the probability of getting a 2? $\frac{1}{6}$

3 If you roll a 0–5 cube, what is the probability of getting a 2 or a 5? $\frac{2}{6}$ (or $\frac{1}{3}$)

4 If you roll a 0–5 cube, what is the probability of getting a 0, 2, or 4? $\frac{3}{6}$ (or $\frac{1}{2}$)

5 If you roll a 0–5 cube, what is the probability of getting a 1, 3, or 5? $\frac{3}{6}$ (or $\frac{1}{2}$)

6 If you roll a 0–5 cube, what is the probability of getting a 0, 1, 2, 3, 4, or 5? $\frac{6}{6}$ (or 1)

7 If you roll a 0–5 cube, what is the probability of getting a 4 or less? $\frac{5}{6}$

8 If you roll a 0–5 cube, what is the probability of getting a 5 or greater? $\frac{1}{6}$

9 If you roll a 0–5 cube, what is the probability of getting a 6? $\frac{0}{6}$ (or 0)

10 If something is sure to happen (as in problem 6), what is its probability? **1**

11 If something cannot happen (such as getting a 6 when you roll a 0–5 cube), what is its probability? **0**

1 Warm-Up ⏱ 5 MINUTES

 **Problem of the Day** Challenge students with the following problem: Carla heard that there is a terrific bookstore somewhere along the road between Sunset and Happy Valley. If Sunset and Happy Valley are 60 miles apart, what is the probability that the store is within 10 miles of either town? ($\frac{1}{3}$)

Problem-Solving Strategies Ask students who have solved the Problem of the Day to share how they solved it and any strategies they used.

 MENTAL MATH Have students show thumbs up if the answer is greater than 1, thumbs down if the answer is less than 1, or stand up if it is equal to 1:

a. $\frac{4}{21} + \frac{10}{21}$ (thumbs down)   **b.** $\frac{2}{5} + \frac{4}{6}$ (thumbs up)

c. $\frac{7}{12} + \frac{5}{12}$ (stand)   **d.** $\frac{3}{8} + \frac{2}{3}$ (thumbs up)

e. $\frac{1}{8} + \frac{3}{8}$ (thumbs down)   **f.** $\frac{1}{2} + \frac{1}{2}$ (stand)

(continued on page 271)

 **Physical Education Connection** Ask students to think about the sports they play or watch. Have them suggest ways that coaches use the concept of probability to make coaching decisions, such as whom to foul at the end of a close basketball game, whether to pass or run in a football game, or what pitch to throw to a batter in a crucial situation in a baseball game. If possible, invite a coach at the school to lead a discussion on the usefulness of knowing probabilities in making strategy choices.

*available separately

If you know the probability of an event, then you can estimate how many times that event will occur in 10 tries, 20 tries, 30 tries, and so on. Your estimate should be reasonably close to the actual results.

Answer the following questions.

12 If you flip a coin, what is the probability of it landing on heads? $\frac{1}{2}$

13 If you flip a coin ten times, about how many times would you expect it to land on heads? **5**

14 If you flip a coin 50 times, about how many times would you expect it to land on heads? **25**

15 If you roll a 0–5 cube 120 times, about how many times would you expect to roll

   a. a 5? **20**   **b.** a 6? **never**   **c.** a 0? **20**

16 Sheila rolls a 0–5 cube 90 times. About how many times would you expect her to roll a 3 or a 5? **30**

17 If you roll a 0–5 cube many times, about what fraction of the time would you expect not to roll a 3? (Hint: It is the same fraction of the time that you would expect to roll a 0, 1, 2, 4, or 5.) $\frac{5}{6}$

18 Austin rolls a 0–5 cube 120 times. About how many times would you expect that he will roll a number other than 3? **100**

19 If you roll a 5–10 cube many times, about what fraction of the time would you expect to roll something other than 5 or 10? $\frac{4}{6}$ **(or $\frac{2}{3}$)**

20 Jessica rolls a 5–10 cube 90 times. About how many times would you expect her to roll 6, 7, 8, or 9? **60**

More than 5,000,000 students participate in high school sports. However, only one in 50 makes a college team, and one in 1000 makes it to the pros. There are fewer than 3500 people in the United States who play professional sports for a living.

Mental Math (continued)

g. $\frac{1}{4} + \frac{1}{2}$ (thumbs down)   **h.** $\frac{3}{4} + \frac{1}{8}$ (thumbs down)

i. $\frac{5}{8} + \frac{4}{8}$ (thumbs up)   **j.** $\frac{1}{3} + \frac{2}{5}$ (thumbs down)

k. $\frac{3}{4} + \frac{1}{4}$ (stand)   **l.** $\frac{2}{3} + \frac{5}{9}$ (thumbs up)

❷ Teach

Using the Student Pages You may also wish to demonstrate the "Routes" Game Mat, which provides practice with probability, so that students can play it as they finish the problems on pages 271 and 273.

Hold up a 0–5 Number Cube as you begin the discussion questions. After the questions, discuss the meaning of the term *probability*. Inform students of two definitions of the probability of an event: the fraction of the times, in the long run, that an event will probably occur, and the number of favorable possibilities divided by the total number of equally likely possibilities. For example, there are three favorable possibilities (0, 2, and 4) and six total possibilities (0, 1, 2, 3, 4, and 5) for rolling an even number.

Ask students "If you know the probability that an event will happen, how can you find the probability that the event will not happen?" (Subtract from 1 the probability that the event will happen.)

Have students complete the rest of pages 270 and 271 individually or in small groups.

Literature Connection *Math Fun: Test Your Luck* by Rose Wyler and Mary Etling explores probability through puzzles, information, and activities.

Technology Connection The software, video, and printed curriculum materials *Mathematics Curriculum and Teaching Program* from the National Council of Mathematics, Inc. (Apple, Mac, IBM, for grades K–10) provide further practice with probability, estimation, geometry, problem solving, algebra, logic, number properties, and visual imagery.

◆ LESSON 75 Probability

Teach

Using the Student Pages Have students play the "Roll a 15" game on page 272, which uses intuitive notions of probability. Allow just enough time for students to become familiar with the game (students may remember the game from previous grades) so they can answer the questions about the game on these pages. Another variation of the game students might try is to keep the scores secret until all the players have had their turns.

The questions on pages 272-273 help students formally analyze the "Roll a 15" game. Have them work on all of the problems, in groups if you wish, then discuss the answers with the entire class. For problem 25, students should see that there are six equally likely cases (0, 1, 2, 3, 4, 5) and that three of these cases (1, 2, 3) make the score closer, one (5) makes it worse, and two (0 and 4) leave it as close as it was to 15. Point out that as the first player, Olga would presumably roll a 0–5 cube with a score of 13. On the other hand, the second player might use a different strategy based on what the first player's score was. Show how a similar analysis yields the answers for problems 26–30. You may wish to point out that the strategies would be different if the second player didn't know the first player's score.

Introducing the "Routes" and "Harder Routes" Game Mats Demonstrate the "Routes" Game Mat by playing it with three students as the rest of the class watches. This game involves reading a network diagram and using probabilistic thinking in deciding which route to take. Complete instructions for playing are on the Game Mat. Students can play the harder version on the back of the Game Mat if they wish. This game can be played in pairs or small groups. A copy of these Game Mats can also be found on pages 626-627 of this Teacher's Guide.

◆ LESSON 75 Probability

Roll a 15 Game

COOPERATIVE LEARNING

Players:	Two
Materials:	Two 0–5 cubes, two 5–10 cubes
Object:	To get the sum closer to 15
Math Focus:	Addition and subtraction, mathematical reasoning

RULES

1. Roll the cubes one at a time.
2. Add the numbers as you roll. The sum of all the cubes you roll should be as close to 15 as possible.
3. You may stop after two, three, or four rolls.
4. The player with the sum closer to 15 wins the round. (The best score is 15; the next best scores are 14 and 16; and so on.)

Answer these questions about the "Roll a 15" game.

21 Kevin went first. He rolled a 10 and then a 4. What should Kevin do now? **Kevin should stop. He has three chances of getting a worse score (by rolling 3, 4, or 5); two chances of staying even (0 or 2); and one chance of getting a better score (1).**

22 Sara went first. She rolled a 9 and a 3. What should Sara do now? **She should roll a 0–5 cube.**

23 Lauren went first. Her score was 16. Kevin went second. First he rolled an 8. Then he rolled a 6. What should Kevin do now? **Kevin should probably stop for reasons similar to those given in the first question.**

24 Lauren went first. Her score was 17. Kevin went second. First he rolled a 9. Then he rolled a 4. What should Kevin do now? **Kevin should roll a 0–5 cube.**

272 · Fractions and Mixed Numbers

RETEACHING p. 25

LESSON **75** RETEACHING   Name_____

If you roll a 5–10 number cube, what are the possible outcomes?

Each outcome is equally likely to happen, and there are six possible outcomes. The probability of rolling any one number is $\frac{1}{6}$.

Example:

Find the probability of rolling an odd number.

The odd numbers are 5, 7, and 9, so there are three ways to roll an odd number.

$$\frac{1}{6} + \frac{1}{6} + \frac{1}{6} = \frac{3}{6}$$ The probability is $\frac{3}{6}$ or $\frac{1}{2}$.

If you roll a number cube 100 times, you will roll an odd number about $\frac{1}{2} \times 100$, or 50, times. If you roll a 5–10 number cube 120 times, about how many times will you roll

1 a 5? __20__		**2** a 6? __20__
3 a 7? __20__		**4** an 8? __20__
5 a 9? __20__		**6** a 10? __20__
7 a 5 or a 6? __40__		**8** a number less than 8? __60__
9 a number greater than 8? __40__		**10** a number greater than 4? __120__
11 an 11? __0__		**12** an even number? __60__

Math Explorations and Applications Level 6 · **25**

Answer these questions about the "Roll a 15" game.

25 Olga is the first player in the game. She has already rolled a 6 and 7, so her score is 13 so far. If she now rolls a 0–5 cube, what is the probability that her score will

    a. get closer to 15? $\frac{3}{6}$ (or $\frac{1}{2}$)

    b. get further from 15? $\frac{1}{6}$

    c. stay the same distance from 15? $\frac{2}{6}$ (or $\frac{1}{3}$)

26 What would the three probabilities (a, b, and c in problem 25) be if her score was 12 after rolling two 5–10 cubes?   **a.** $\frac{5}{6}$; **b.** $\frac{0}{6}$; **c.** $\frac{1}{6}$

27 What would the three probabilities (a, b, and c in problem 25) be if her score was 14 after rolling two 5–10 cubes?   **a.** $\frac{1}{6}$; **b.** $\frac{3}{6}$ **(or $\frac{1}{2}$)**; **c.** $\frac{2}{6}$ **(or $\frac{1}{3}$)**

28 Find the sum of the three probabilities in problems 24, 25, and 26. **1; 1; 1**

    a. Is the sum the same for each problem?   **yes**

    b. Will the sum be the same for every possible score?   **yes**

29 Pierre is the second player. Olga, the first player, has a score of 15. Pierre's first roll was 7 and his second roll is 4. What is the probability that he will win?   **0, but he may tie.**

30 Pierre is the second player again. This time Lori is the first player. She stops with a score of 13. Pierre's first roll is 5 (on the 5–10 cube), and his second roll is 7. On his next roll he rolls a 0. On his last roll what is the probability that his score will

    a. win? $\frac{3}{6}$

    b. tie? $\frac{2}{6}$ (or $\frac{1}{3}$)

    c. lose? $\frac{1}{6}$

    d. remain the same? $\frac{1}{6}$

Unit 4   Lesson 75 • **273**

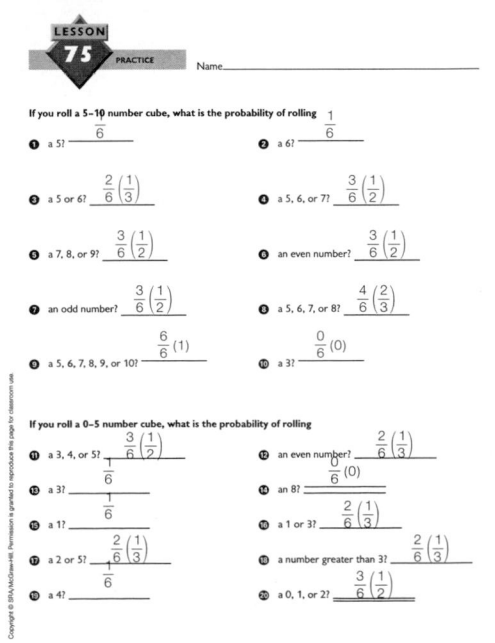
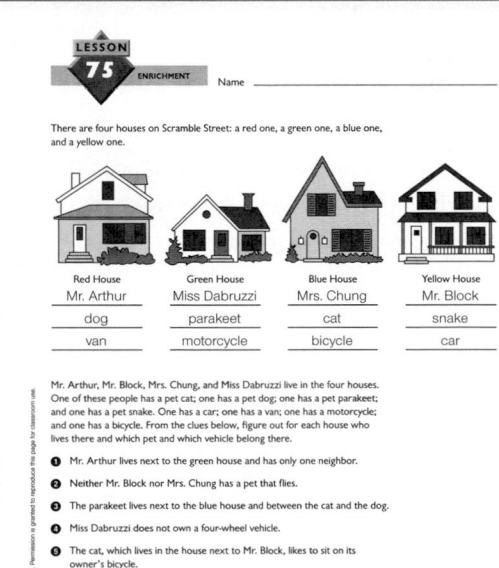
---

③ Wrap-Up

In Closing   Summarize the lesson by asking students to explain how they can use probability to make predictions.

 **Portfolio Assessment**   Have students write a brief explanation of how they were able to use their knowledge of probability to predict the chances of getting certain rolls in the "Roll a 15" game.

Assessment Criteria

Did the student . . .

✓ demonstrate understanding of the concept of probability by correctly answering 75% of the questions on pages 270 and 271?

✓ exhibit understanding of the winning strategies and probabilities for the "Roll a 15" game?

Homework   Invite students to make up a probability problem based on something in their own lives. For example, a student could predict the probability of having a peanut butter sandwich for lunch. If he or she usually has one three times a week at school, the probability of having a peanut butter sandwich for a particular day picked at random would be $\frac{3}{5}$.

Meeting Individual Needs

    Kinesthetic learners who have difficulty with the work on page 270 should roll a Number Cube, count the number of rolls and the number of favorable rolls, and then divide. Have them use this method until they understand the concept more fully and compute the probability more automatically.

Student Edition pages 274–277

Analyzing Probability

LESSON PLANNER

Objectives

▶ to show how probability can be used to help choose strategies in games and in other situations

▶ to provide practice in using fractions, decimals, and percents in recording and interpreting data involving probabilities

Context of the Lesson This is the 12th of 20 lessons on fractions.

 **MANIPULATIVES**
calculators*

Program Resources
Number Cubes (0–5 and 5–10)
Practice Master 76
Enrichment Master 76
The Cruncher*

For extra practice:
CD-ROM* Lesson 76
Cumulative Review, page 569

Note: This lesson may take more than one day.

① Warm-Up ⏱ 5 MINUTES

 **Problem of the Day** Present the following problem to students: In Lisa's sock drawer there are 12 black socks, 12 green socks, and 12 yellow socks. It is dark in her room early in the morning, and Lisa reaches into the drawer for socks without being able to see them. What is the minimum number of socks she must take out to make certain that she will have at least one matched pair? (4)

Problem-Solving Strategies Ask students who have solved the Problem of the Day to share how they solved it and any strategies they used.

 MENTAL MATH Does the answer make sense? Students should show thumbs up if the answer is reasonable and thumbs down if the answer is definitely wrong.

a. 30 × 2 = 60 (thumbs up)

b. 41.2 + 2 = 41.4 (thumbs down)

c. 300 ÷ 30 = 3 (thumbs down)

d. 621 ÷ 9 = 69 (thumbs up)

(continued on page 275)

Analyzing Probability
Anything but 10 Game

COOPERATIVE LEARNING

Players:	Two or more
Materials:	One 0–5 cube, one 5–10 cube
Object:	To be the first to score 100 or more
Math Focus:	Addition facts, adding, and mathematical reasoning

RULES

1. Roll both cubes. Find the sum of the two numbers you rolled.

2. If the sum is not 10, you get the number of points you rolled. You may roll again, or you may stop and add those points to your score. Continue rolling until you roll a sum of 10 or choose to stop.

3. When you roll a sum of 10, you lose your turn, and you lose any points you may have earned on that turn.

4. The first player to score 100 or over is the winner.

SAMPLE GAME

Turn	Ernie's Roll	Sum	Score	Pearl's Roll	Sum	Score
1	7, 5	12		9, 4	13	
	5, 4	9		6, 2	8	21
	10, 5	15	36	Pearl stopped.		
	Ernie stopped.					
2	8, 3	11		10, 4	14	
	6, 4	10	36	7, 1	8	43
	Ernie lost his turn.			Pearl stopped.		

After two turns Pearl was ahead.

Why teach it at this time?

This lesson continues and extends the study of probability. It introduces the distinction between experimental and theoretical probability.

*available separately

For the "Anything But 10 Game," you want to know the probability of getting a 10 when you roll both cubes.

When you roll the two cubes, there are 11 possible sums: 5, 6, 7, 8, 9, 10, 11, 12, 13, 14, and 15. You may have noticed that you get a sum of 10 more often than some other sums, such as 5 or 15.

Think of it this way: The 0–5 cube can land 0, 1, 2, 3, 4, or 5. If the cube is fair, each of these numbers is equally likely to come up.

The 5–10 cube can land 5, 6, 7, 8, 9, or 10, and each of these numbers is equally likely.

Since neither cube knows what the other is doing, the results of one cube will not affect the other.

If the 0–5 cube lands 0, the 5–10 cube is equally likely to land 5, 6, 7, 8, 9, or 10. If the 0–5 cube lands 1, the 5–10 cube is equally likely to land 5, 6, 7, 8, 9, or 10. The same is true if the 0–5 cube lands 2, or 3, and so on.

Solve the following problems.

1 There are 36 equally likely cases that can come up when you roll a 0–5 cube and a 5–10 cube. One case would be (0, 5); another would be (0, 6); and so on. See if you can list them all. Hint: Make an addition table for addends 0–5 and 5–10. **See chart in margin.**

2 How many cases in problem 1 had a sum of 10? **6**

3 What is the probability of getting a sum of 10 if you roll a 0–5 and a 5–10 cube? $\dfrac{6}{36}$ **(or** $\dfrac{1}{6}$**)**

4 What percent of the time would you expect to roll a sum of 10 if you rolled a 0–5 cube and 5–10 cube many times? **about** $16\dfrac{2}{3}$**%**

5 How many cases in problem 1 had a sum of

   a. 9? **5**   **b.** 11? **5**   **c.** 8? **4**   **d.** 12? **4**   **e.** 7? **3**
   f. 13? **3**   **g.** 6? **2**   **h.** 14? **2**   **i.** 5? **1**   **j.** 15? **1**

6 Are the probabilities of the 11 events (sums) equal? **no**

Unit 4 Lesson 76 • **275**

Literature Connection For more exploration of probability, guide students to read *Do You Wanna Bet?* by Dean Cushman.

*available separately

Mental Math (continued)

e. $\dfrac{3}{4} + \dfrac{1}{4} = 1\dfrac{1}{4}$ (thumbs down)

f. $\dfrac{1}{4} + \dfrac{1}{4} = \dfrac{1}{2}$ (thumbs up)

g. 320 ÷ 0.32 = 100 (thumbs down)

h. 32.10 ÷ 100 = 3210 (thumbs down)

i. $\dfrac{1}{8} + \dfrac{7}{8} = 1$ (thumbs up)

j. 62.5 × 100 = 6250 (thumbs up)

k. 700 ÷ 70 = 10 (thumbs up)

l. 700 ÷ 700 = 1 (thumbs up)

m. 14.2 + 14.02 = 28.4 (thumbs down)

n. 98.1 × 10 = 9.81 (thumbs down)

o. $\dfrac{1}{8} + \dfrac{1}{8} = \dfrac{1}{4}$ (thumbs up)

p. 30 × 30 = 90 (thumbs down)

❷ Teach

 Using the Student Pages The "Anything but 10" game on page 274 can be demonstrated by having two students play it in front of the class. This game provides more practice with using probability to develop strategies. Guide players to think about the probability of getting a sum of 10 with the two Number Cubes. A copy of this game can also be found on page 26 of the Home Connections Blackline Masters.

Discuss page 275 and do problem 1 with the class. Students can use a blank **Cruncher*** spreadsheet to create the table. Everyone should then have a table that looks something like this:

5–10 Cube

		5	6	7	8	9	10
	0	(0, 5)	(0, 6)	(0, 7)	(0, 8)	(0, 9)	(0, 10)
	1	(1, 5)	(1, 6)	(1, 7)	(1, 8)	(1, 9)	(1, 10)
0–5 Cube	2	(2, 5)	(2, 6)	(2, 7)	(2, 8)	(2, 9)	(2, 10)
	3	(3, 5)	(3, 6)	(3, 7)	(3, 8)	(3, 9)	(3, 10)
	4	(4, 5)	(4, 6)	(4, 7)	(4, 8)	(4, 9)	(4, 10)
	5	(5, 5)	(5, 6)	(5, 7)	(5, 8)	(5, 9)	(5, 10)

This table may make it easier for students to answer problems 3 and 4. For problem 5, some students will notice that sums occur in diagonals from the lower left to the upper right in the table.

Unit 4 Lesson 76 **275**

◆ LESSON 76 Analyzing Probability

Teach

Using the Student Pages You may find it necessary to spend extra time on pages 276–277. On these pages students will compare predicted values with outcomes in an actual experiment. Have them work in pairs or in groups of three on the activity in problem 7. If they work in groups of three, one person should be in charge of keeping a running total of the number of rolls. Point out that they will find it very easy to calculate if they stop at 100 rolls, as *percent* means "per hundred." They should pause to count the number of rolls when they sense that the number is approaching 100.

Students can use a blank **Cruncher*** spreadsheet to create a table like the one on page 276.

Have students work individually on problem 8. As they do, check their results for part *a* to see that everyone knows how to find the percents by using the data in the table. In part *b* students use their own data. Students should work in groups and use **calculators*** for problems 9–12. They should continue to use the chart they started in problem 7.

Work with the entire class on problem 14. Make a chart on the chalkboard like the one on page 276. Use the combined data that students have gathered. Have students copy the chart and work in groups to calculate actual percents for the entire class.

◆ LESSON 76 Analyzing Probability

COOPERATIVE LEARNING

7 Work in pairs or in groups of three. Use a computer or other means to make a chart like the one shown, but fill in only the Sum column (at the left). One person rolls a 0–5 cube and a 5–10 cube and calls out the sum. Another person keeps a tally to see how many times each sum is rolled. Roll the cubes exactly 100 times. (When you think you're getting close to 100 times, stop and count.) Write the total number of times you rolled each sum. Are your results similar to those shown in the Tally column on this chart?

Sum	Tally of How Many Times the Sum Was Rolled	Number of Times Sum Was Rolled	Percent of Times Sum Was Rolled	Probability of Rolling That Sum	Expected Percent of Times the Sum Would Be Rolled
5	III	3	3%	$\frac{1}{36}$	2.778
6	‖‖‖ I	6	6%	$\frac{2}{36}$	5.556%
7	‖‖‖ III	8	8%	$\frac{3}{36}$	8.333%
8	‖‖‖ ‖‖‖ IIII	14	14%	$\frac{4}{36}$	11.111%
9	‖‖‖ ‖‖‖ I	11	11%	$\frac{5}{36}$	13.889%
10	‖‖‖ ‖‖‖ IIII	14	14%	$\frac{6}{36}$	16.667%
11	‖‖‖ ‖‖‖ II	12	12%	$\frac{5}{36}$	13.889%
12	‖‖‖ ‖‖‖ II	12	12%	$\frac{4}{36}$	11.111%
13	‖‖‖ ‖‖‖	10	10%	$\frac{3}{36}$	8.333%
14	‖‖‖ I	6	6%	$\frac{2}{36}$	5.556%
15	IIII	4	4%	$\frac{1}{36}$	2.778%
Total		100			

8 Remember that *percent* means "per hundred." If you rolled a 5 three times in 100 tries, those three rolls represent 3% of the tries.

a. What percent of the times was each sum rolled in the experiment shown above? **See chart.**

b. In your experiment what percent of the time was each sum rolled? (Fill in the Percent column on your chart.) **Answers will vary according to individual student outcomes. Answers should be close to numbers listed above.**

276 • Fractions and Mixed Numbers

Technology Connection Refer students to the software *In the Neighborhood* from Critical Thinking Software & Books (Apple, Mac, and IBM: for grades 2–12) for further practice with probability, logical thinking, problem solving, and mental computation.

RETEACHING

Students having difficulty with problem 1 on page 275 may benefit by seeing actual Number Cubes. Place a 0–5 cube and a 5–10 cube in front of them with the 0 and 5 face up. Record (0, 5). Then change the 5 on the 5–10 cube to 6 and record (0, 6). Repeat for the numerals 7–10. Then change the 0 to 1 on the 0–5 cube, and change the 10 on the 5–10 cube to a 5. Continue until all 36 possibilities are recorded. Once students get the idea that different sums have different probabilities of occurring, select a few of the problems on these pages to go over individually. Extensive reteaching, however, is not essential.

*available separately

⑨ In problem 1 on page 275 you listed all of the 36 equally likely results of rolling a 0–5 and 5–10 cube. From that list or table, find the probability of each sum. Record your answers in the column of your chart labelled "Probability of Rolling That Sum." **See chart on previous page.**

Example: Your list should show that you can get a sum of 8 in four ways: (0, 8), (1, 7), (2, 6), and (3, 5). The probability of getting an 8 is $\frac{4}{36}$, or $\frac{1}{9}$.

⑩ Change each probability to a decimal (rounded to the nearest hundred thousandth). For example, $\frac{1}{9}$ would be 0.11111. Then change each decimal to a percent. For example, 0.11111 becomes 11.111%. Write these percents in the Expected Percent column of the chart you made. **See chart on previous page.**

⑪ What is the sum of the numbers in the Probability column of the chart you made? $\frac{36}{36} = 1$

Compare these expected percents with the percents you got when you did the experiment. **Answers will vary according to individual student outcomes.**

⑫ What is the sum of the numbers in the Expected Percent column of the chart you made? Convert the percent to a number. **100.001; 1.00001**

⑬ Why might your answers to problems 11 and 12 be different? **Rounding the percents created some error.**

⑭ Combine everyone's results for the experiment.

　a. Find the total number of times each sum was rolled (for the whole class).
Answers will vary according to individual student outcomes.

　b. Calculate the percent of times each sum was rolled.

　c. Compare these percents with the expected percents.

　d. Are the class percents closer to the expected percents than yours were?

Results should be closer to the expected results than the individual student results.

⑮ Suppose a class of 24 students did this experiment: Each group of two students rolled the cube 1000 times.

　a. How many total rolls would the class have? **1200**

　b. How many times would you expect a 7 to be rolled? **about 100**

　c. How many times would you expect a 10 to be rolled? **about 200**

　d. How many times would you expect a 15 to be rolled? **about 33**

Use the Cumulative Review on page 569 after this lesson.

Unit 4　Lesson 76　•　**277**

---

③ Wrap-Up

In Closing Summarize the lesson by asking students to explain why different sums have different probabilities of occurring. Ask them to explain differences between individual and class results.

 Some students will have individual experimental percents that are closer to the expected percents than are those of the class. In general, however, class results should be closer than individual results, because they are based on more trials. Guide students to understand that as the number of trials increases, experimental percents should get closer to the predicted percents.

 **Informal Assessment** Observe students as they play the "Anything But 10" game and work together on finding the experimental probabilities. Observe whether students are playing the game correctly and that they are working cooperatively on the experiment and on filling in the chart correctly.

Assessment Criteria

Did the student . . .

✓ demonstrate understanding of the rules of the "Anything But 10" game and use his or her knowledge of probability to apply appropriate strategies to playing the game?

✓ demonstrate ability to express a probability as a fraction, a decimal, and a percent?

✓ express understanding of the difference between experimental and theoretical probability, and of the relationship between the accuracy of results and the number of trials?

Homework Have students repeat the experiment on page 276 with a family member.

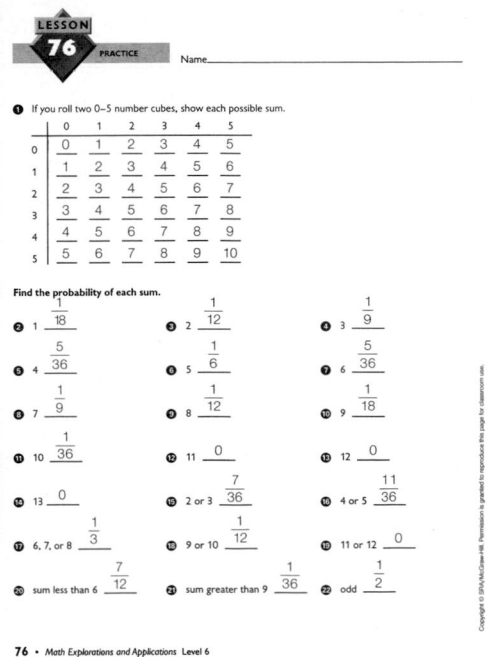
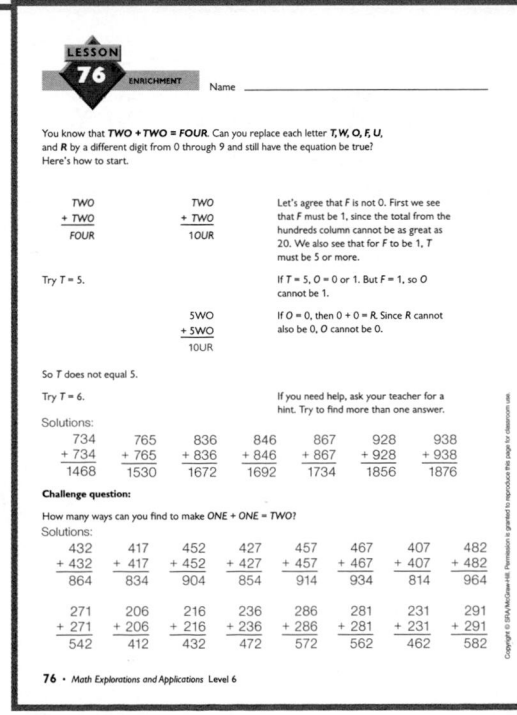

Practice with Fractions and Decimals

Student Edition pages 278–279

Practice with Fractions and Decimals

Keep in shape by practicing adding, subtracting, and multiplying fractions and decimals and by practicing expressing fractions as decimals.

Solve these problems. Watch the signs. Reduce your answers.

1. $\frac{1}{4} + \frac{1}{2}$ $\frac{3}{4}$ **2.** $\frac{2}{7} + \frac{3}{7}$ $\frac{5}{7}$ **3.** $\frac{3}{5} + \frac{2}{5}$ 1

4. $\frac{1}{2} - \frac{1}{4}$ $\frac{1}{4}$ **5.** $\frac{3}{7} - \frac{2}{7}$ $\frac{1}{7}$ **6.** $\frac{3}{5} - \frac{2}{5}$ $\frac{1}{5}$

7. $\frac{1}{2} \times \frac{1}{4}$ $\frac{1}{8}$ **8.** $\frac{3}{5} \times \frac{2}{5}$ $\frac{6}{25}$ **9.** $\frac{1}{4} + \frac{1}{6}$ $\frac{5}{12}$

10. $\frac{1}{4} - \frac{1}{6}$ $\frac{1}{12}$ **11.** $\frac{3}{4} - \frac{2}{3}$ $\frac{1}{12}$ **12.** $\frac{3}{4} \times \frac{2}{3}$ $\frac{1}{2}$

13. $\frac{1}{3} - \frac{2}{9}$ $\frac{1}{9}$ **14.** $\frac{1}{3} + \frac{2}{9}$ $\frac{5}{9}$ **15.** $\frac{1}{2} \times \frac{2}{3}$ $\frac{1}{3}$

Solve these problems. Watch the signs.

16. $0.25 + 0.5$ **0.75**   **17.** $0.29 + 0.43$ **0.72**   **18.** $0.60 + 0.40$ **1.00**

19. $0.5 - 0.25$ **0.25**   **20.** $0.43 - 0.29$ **0.14**   **21.** $0.60 - 0.40$ **0.20**

22. 0.5×0.25 **0.125**   **23.** 0.6×0.4 **0.24**   **24.** $0.25 + 0.17$ **0.42**

25. $0.25 - 0.17$ **0.08**   **26.** $0.75 - 0.67$ **0.08**   **27.** 0.75×0.67 **0.5025**

28. $0.33 - 0.22$ **0.11**   **29.** $0.33 + 0.22$ **0.55**   **30.** 0.5×0.67 **0.335**

31. Write the decimal equivalent, or a decimal approximation to the nearest hundredth, for each of your answers in problems 1–15. **See below.**

32. Compare your decimal answers to problem 31 with the decimal answers to problems 16–30. Are the answers equal or approximately equal? **yes**

33. Compare problems 1–15 with problems 16–30. Are the decimals in problems 16–30 equivalent to or approximations of the fractions in problems 1–15? **yes**

Answers for problem 31:

1. 0.75	2. 0.71	3. 1.00	4. 0.25	5. 0.14
6. 0.20	7. 0.125	8. 0.24	9. 0.42	10. 0.08
11. 0.08	12. 0.50	13. 0.11	14. 0.56	15. 0.33

$\frac{1}{2} + \frac{1}{2} = 1$ $0.5 + 0.5 = 1.0$
$\frac{1}{2} \times \frac{1}{2} = \frac{1}{4}$ $0.5 \times 0.5 = 0.25$

278 • Fractions and Mixed Numbers

LESSON PLANNER

Objectives

▶ to provide practice in adding, subtracting, and multiplying fractions

▶ to provide practice in adding, subtracting, and multiplying decimals

▶ to show the relationship between operations with fractions and operations with decimals

▶ to provide practice with division

Context of the Lesson This is the 13th of 20 lessons on fractions.

 **MANIPULATIVES**   **Program Resources**

calculators*   Practice Master 77

Enrichment Master 77

For extra practice:
CD-ROM* Lesson 77

① Warm-Up  5 MINUTES

Problem of the Day Present the following problem: In two years Jerome will be twice as old as he was five years ago. How old is he now? (12 years old)

Problem-Solving Strategies Ask students who have solved the Problem of the Day to share how they solved it and any strategies they used.

 **MENTAL MATH** Ask students to show thumbs up if the answer is greater than 1 or thumbs down if the answer is less than 1. Students should stand if the answer is equal to 1.

a. $\frac{2}{7} + \frac{3}{7}$ (thumbs down)   **b.** $\frac{1}{4} + \frac{1}{2}$ (thumbs down)

c. $0.25 + \frac{3}{4}$ (stand)   **d.** $0.33 + \frac{1}{3}$ (thumbs down)

e. $\frac{1}{4} + \frac{1}{6}$ (thumbs down)   **f.** $\frac{3}{5} + \frac{2}{5}$ (stand)

g. $0.75 + \frac{1}{2}$ (thumbs up)   **h.** $0.50 + \frac{2}{3}$ (thumbs up)

i. $0.20 + \frac{2}{5}$ (thumbs down)   **j.** $\frac{1}{8} + \frac{2}{4}$ (thumbs down)

Literature Connection You may wish to use information from the planets chart in *Our Solar System* by Seymour Simon to give students practice in comparing the use of fractions and decimals.

RETEACHING

Provide extra help for students who have difficulty with page 278 by referring to appropriate previous lessons. Some students may have greater success with the missing digit problems by making up some of their own for partners to solve. The pair can solve each other's problems, explaining and comparing their thinking as they work. Invite pairs to share their strategies with the class both for formulating and for solving these kinds of problems.

*available separately

Find the missing digits.

34
```
       3 2 4.6
  2 ■)5 6 8 0.0
     4 6
     1 0 8
       9 2
     1 6 0
     1 3 8
```

35
```
       4 0.4 1
  17)6 8 7.0 0
     6 8
       7 0
       6 8
         2 0
         1 7
           3
```

36
```
       3 7.1 6
  24)8 9 2.0 0
     7 2
     1 7 2
     1 ■ 8  6
       4 0
       2 4
       1 6 0
       1 4 4
         1 6
```

37
```
        2
      1 ■ 3
  45)5 5 3 5
     4 5
     1 0 3
       9 0
       1 3 5
       1 3 5
```

38
```
        0
      2 ■.7 8
  41)8 5 2.0 0
     8 2
       3 2 0
       2 8 7
         3 3 0
         3 2 8
           2
```

39
```
       3
     3 1.0 6
  ■1)9 6 3.0 0
     9 3
       3 3
       3 1
         2 0 0
         1 8 6
           1 4
```

40
```
     1 1.7 6
  63)7 4 1.0 0
     6 3
     1 1 1
       6 3
       4 8 0
       4 4 1
         3 9 0
         3 7 8
         1 ■ 2
```

41
```
        9 9
  22)2 1 7 8
     1 9 8
       1 9 8
       1 9 8
```

42
```
     6 5.7 5
  12)7 8 9.0 0
     7 2
     6 9
     6 0
       9 0
       8 4
         6 0
         6 0
```

43
```
       3 3
  24)7 9 2
     7 2
     7 2
     7 2
```

44
```
       5 9
  34)2 0 0 6
     1 7 0
     3 0 6
     3 0 6
```

45
```
     1 0 3
  12)1 2 3 6
     1 2 3
       ■ 6
       3 6
```

❷ Teach

Using the Student Pages Have students work individually without calculators on problems 1–30 on page 278. They may work in groups, using **calculators***, for problems 31–33.

When everyone has finished, briefly discuss the answers to problems 32 and 33. Make it clear that problems 1–15 are essentially the same as problems 16–30, although approximation may make answers differ slightly. For example, problem 2 has an answer of $\frac{5}{7}$, which to the nearest hundredth is 0.71, whereas the answer to problem 17 is 0.72.

Have students find the missing digits on page 279 independently.

❸ Wrap-Up 5 MINUTES

In Closing Summarize the lesson by asking students to explain how to check their answers to a problem involving fractions by using decimals.

Performance Assessment Ask each student to demonstrate how to solve the following kinds of problems:

a. $\frac{1}{8} + \frac{1}{7} = \left(\frac{15}{56}\right)$

b. $0.75 \times 0.3 = (0.225)$

c. $\frac{6}{11} \times \frac{2}{9} = \left(\frac{4}{33}\right)$

d. $\frac{2}{3} - \frac{1}{2} = \left(\frac{1}{6}\right)$

Assessment Criteria

Did the student . . .

✓ demonstrate understanding of the algorithms for adding, subtracting, and multiplying fractions and decimals?

✓ accurately demonstrate or express how to find a missing digit in a division problem?

✓ correctly answer at least 75% of the problems?

Homework Have students express in a brief paragraph how to find the missing digits in a division problem.

PRACTICE p. 77

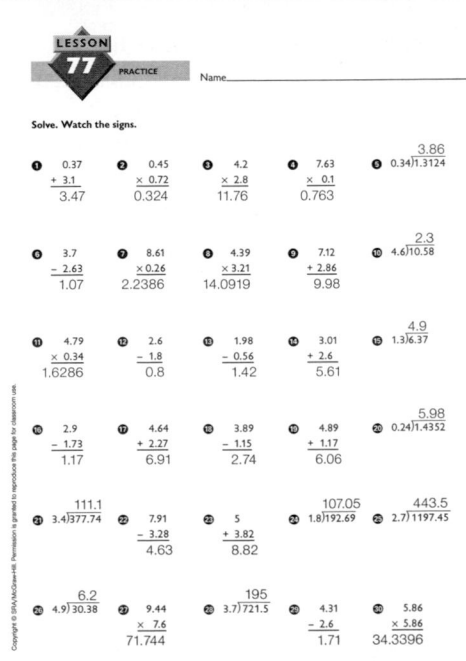

LESSON 77 PRACTICE Name_____

Solve. Watch the signs.

1. 0.37 + 3.1 = 3.47
2. 0.45 × 0.72 = 0.324
3. 4.2 × 2.8 = 11.76
4. 7.63 × 0.1 = 0.763
5. 0.34)1.3124 = 3.86

6. 3.7 − 2.63 = 1.07
7. 8.61 × 0.26 = 2.2386
8. 4.39 × 3.21 = 14.0919
9. 7.12 + 2.86 = 9.98
10. 4.6)10.58 = 2.3

11. 4.79 × 0.34 = 1.6286
12. 2.6 − 1.8 = 0.8
13. 1.98 − 0.56 = 1.42
14. 3.01 + 2.6 = 5.61
15. 1.3)6.37 = 4.9

16. 2.9 − 1.73 = 1.17
17. 4.64 + 2.27 = 6.91
18. 3.89 − 1.15 = 2.74
19. 4.89 + 1.17 = 6.06
20. 0.24)1.4352 = 5.98

21. 3.4)377.74 = 111.1
22. 7.91 − 3.28 = 4.63
23. 5 + 3.82 = 8.82
24. 1.8)192.69 = 107.05
25. 2.7)1197.45 = 443.5

26. 4.9)30.38 = 6.2
27. 9.44 × 7.6 = 71.744
28. 3.7)721.5 = 195
29. 4.31 − 2.6 = 1.71
30. 5.86 × 5.86 = 34.3396

Math Explorations and Applications Level 6 • 77

ENRICHMENT p. 77

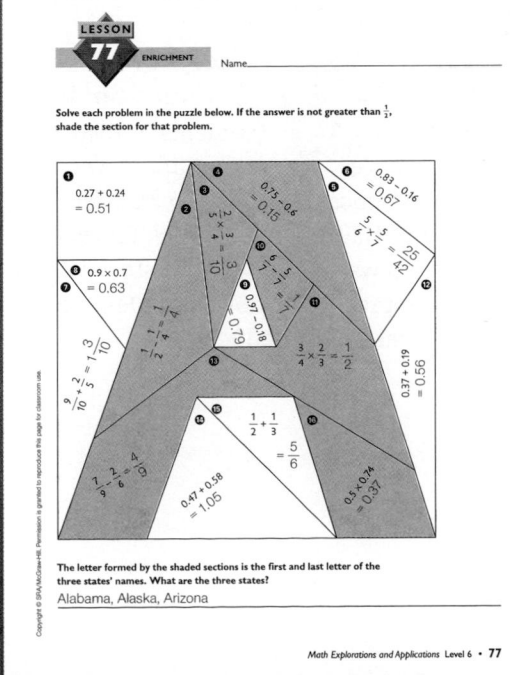

LESSON 77 ENRICHMENT Name_____

Solve each problem in the puzzle below. If the answer is not greater than $\frac{1}{3}$, shade the section for that problem.

0.27 + 0.24 = 0.51
0.75 − 0.6 = 0.15
0.83 − 0.16 = 0.67
$\frac{5}{7} + \frac{5}{7} = \frac{25}{42}$
0.9 × 0.7 = 0.63
0.97 − 0.18 = 0.79
$\frac{3}{4} \times \frac{2}{3} = \frac{1}{2}$
0.37 + 0.19 = 0.56
$\frac{9}{10} \times \frac{2}{5} = \frac{3}{10}$
$\frac{1}{1} - \frac{1}{4} = \frac{4}{5}$
$\frac{1}{2} + \frac{1}{3}$
$\frac{5}{6}$
$\frac{7}{9} \times \frac{2}{3} = \frac{4}{9}$
0.47 + 0.58 = 1.05
0.5 × 0.74 = 0.37

The letter formed by the shaded sections is the first and last letter of the three states' names. What are the three states?
Alabama, Alaska, Arizona

Math Explorations and Applications Level 6 • 77

*available separately

Improper Fractions and Mixed Numbers

Student Edition pages 280–281

Objectives

▶ to show how to express improper fractions as mixed numbers

▶ to show how to find decimal equivalents or approximations of mixed numbers

Context of the Lesson This is the 14th of 20 lessons on fractions.

 **MANIPULATIVES**   **Program Resources**

"Fringo Factory" Game Mat

Practice Master 78

Enrichment Master 78

For additional math integration:
  Math Throughout the Day*

For extra practice:
  CD-ROM* Lesson 78

1 Warm-Up

Problem of the Day Challenge students with the following problem: Use five 2s and the +, −, ×, and ÷ symbols to make the whole numbers 1 through 5. You can also use parentheses. (Some possible answers for 1: $(2 + 2) \div 2 - \frac{2}{2}$, for 2: $(2 \times 2 \times \frac{2}{2}) - 2$; for 3: $\frac{2}{2} + (2 \times \frac{2}{2})$; for 4: $\frac{(2 + 2 + 2 + 2)}{2}$ for 5: $2 + 2 + 2 - (\frac{2}{2})$)

Problem-Solving Strategies Ask students who have solved the Problem of the Day to share how they solved it and any strategies they used.

 For each problem, students should tell whether the sum is greater (thumbs up) or less (thumbs down) than 1. Students should stand if the sum equals 1.

a. $\frac{1}{2} + \frac{2}{3}$ (thumbs up)

b. $\frac{1}{3} + \frac{5}{2}$ (thumbs up)

c. $0.25 + \frac{2}{3}$ (thumbs down)

d. $0.5 + \frac{1}{2}$ (stand)

e. $0.4 + \frac{1}{2}$ (thumbs down)

f. $\frac{3}{8} + \frac{2}{16}$ (thumbs down)

g. $\frac{3}{4} + \frac{5}{6}$ (thumbs up)

h. $0.2 + \frac{2}{5}$ (thumbs down)

(continued on page 281)

280 Fractions and Mixed Numbers

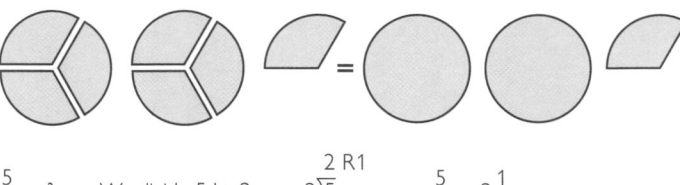

Improper Fractions and Mixed Numbers

Some fractions have numerators that are greater than or equal to the denominators, such as $\frac{7}{3}$, $\frac{5}{2}$, $\frac{9}{7}$, and $\frac{6}{6}$. A fraction like this is called an **improper fraction.** Sometimes it is convenient to work with improper fractions. And sometimes we change them to mixed numbers or whole numbers by dividing.

Example:

$\frac{7}{3} = ?$ To evaluate $\frac{7}{3}$, we divide 7 by 3. $3\overline{)7}$ 2 R1

$\frac{7}{3} = 2$ wholes and a remaining $\frac{1}{3}$

$\frac{7}{3} = 2\frac{1}{3}$

We write $2\frac{1}{3}$ and say "two and a third" or "two and one-third."

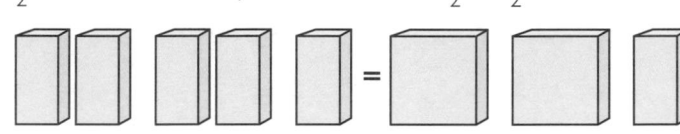

$\frac{5}{2} = ?$ We divide 5 by 2. $2\overline{)5}$ 2 R1 $\frac{5}{2} = 2\frac{1}{2}$

$\frac{9}{7} = ?$ We divide 9 by 7. $7\overline{)9}$ 1 R2 $\frac{9}{7} = 1\frac{2}{7}$

$\frac{6}{6} = ?$ We divide 6 by 6. $6\overline{)6}$ 1 $\frac{6}{6} = 1$

(Of course, you don't have to divide to see that $\frac{6}{6} = 1$.)

280 • Fractions and Mixed Numbers

Literature Connection Invite students to read *The Story of the New York Stock Exchange* by Zachary Kent. Have them use stock tables in the newspaper to convert stock values to improper fractions and then into decimal equivalents.

For students who have difficulty rewriting improper fractions as mixed numbers, show that, for example, $\frac{7}{3}$ can be thought of as $\frac{3}{3} + \frac{3}{3} + \frac{1}{3}$, or $2\frac{1}{3}$. Show this with pictures or with objects, as needed. Point out that division is a quick way to determine how many wholes there are in the improper fraction. The quotient becomes the whole number part of the mixed number, and the remainder the numerator of the fractional part.

*available separately

To find the decimal equivalent or a decimal approximation of an improper fraction, we carry the division beyond the decimal point.

Examples:
$$\frac{5}{2} \quad 2)\overline{5.0} \quad \frac{2.5}{}$$

$$\frac{5}{2} = 2.5$$

$$\frac{7}{3} \quad 3)\overline{7.000} \quad \frac{2.333}{}$$

$\frac{7}{3}$ is equal to 2.33, to the nearest hundredth.

You can convert a mixed number to a decimal by converting the fractional part.

Examples:
$2\frac{1}{2}$ $\frac{1}{2} = 0.5$

$2\frac{1}{2} = 2.5$

$2\frac{1}{3}$ $\frac{1}{3}$ is about 0.33.

$2\frac{1}{3}$ is about 2.33.

Change each improper fraction to a mixed or whole number.

1. $\frac{4}{3}$ $1\frac{1}{3}$
2. $\frac{7}{5}$ $1\frac{2}{5}$
3. $\frac{10}{8}$ $1\frac{1}{4}$
4. $\frac{25}{5}$ 5
5. $\frac{10}{10}$ 1

6. $\frac{7}{2}$ $3\frac{1}{2}$
7. $\frac{24}{7}$ $3\frac{3}{7}$
8. $\frac{9}{4}$ $2\frac{1}{4}$
9. $\frac{26}{5}$ $5\frac{1}{5}$
10. $\frac{10}{6}$ $1\frac{2}{3}$

11. $\frac{8}{5}$ $1\frac{3}{5}$
12. $\frac{10}{3}$ $3\frac{1}{3}$
13. $\frac{6}{2}$ 3
14. $\frac{8}{3}$ $2\frac{2}{3}$
15. $\frac{5}{4}$ $1\frac{1}{4}$

Find the decimal equivalent or an approximation to the nearest hundredth.

16. $1\frac{1}{2}$ **1.5**
17. $6\frac{1}{5}$ **6.2**
18. $\frac{9}{10}$ **0.9**
19. $\frac{11}{9}$ **1.22**
20. $\frac{8}{5}$ **1.6**

21. $\frac{5}{2}$ **2.5**
22. $\frac{10}{8}$ **1.25**
23. $\frac{10}{9}$ **1.11**
24. $1\frac{1}{9}$ **1.11**
25. $\frac{8}{6}$ **1.33**

26. $\frac{4}{3}$ **1.33**
27. $\frac{8}{9}$ **0.89**
28. $\frac{1}{9}$ **0.11**
29. $1\frac{2}{9}$ **1.22**
30. $\frac{1}{7}$ **0.14**

31. $1\frac{2}{3}$ **1.67**
32. $\frac{9}{8}$ **1.125**
33. $\frac{2}{9}$ **0.22**
34. $\frac{8}{4}$ **2**
35. $1\frac{1}{7}$ **1.14**

Unit 4 Lesson 78 • **281**

LESSON 78 PRACTICE   Name_____

Change each improper fraction to a mixed or whole number.

1. $\frac{11}{6} = 1\frac{5}{6}$
2. $\frac{23}{9} = 2\frac{5}{9}$
3. $\frac{26}{21} = 1\frac{5}{21}$

4. $\frac{29}{12} = 2\frac{5}{12}$
5. $\frac{21}{8} = 2\frac{5}{8}$
6. $\frac{38}{7} = 5\frac{3}{7}$

7. $\frac{31}{6} = 5\frac{1}{6}$
8. $\frac{9}{4} = 2\frac{1}{4}$
9. $\frac{17}{5} = 3\frac{2}{5}$

10. $\frac{7}{6} = 1\frac{1}{6}$
11. $\frac{7}{4} = 1\frac{3}{4}$
12. $\frac{24}{6} = 4$

13. $\frac{31}{8} = 3\frac{7}{8}$
14. $\frac{15}{9} = 1\frac{2}{3}$
15. $\frac{32}{7} = 4\frac{4}{7}$

Change each mixed number to an improper fraction.

16. $8\frac{7}{8} = \frac{71}{8}$
17. $2\frac{3}{8} = \frac{19}{8}$
18. $7\frac{3}{4} = \frac{31}{4}$

19. $5\frac{3}{5} = \frac{28}{5}$
20. $2\frac{1}{4} = \frac{9}{4}$
21. $4\frac{5}{12} = \frac{53}{12}$

22. $3\frac{4}{5} = \frac{19}{5}$
23. $1\frac{5}{8} = \frac{13}{8}$
24. $4\frac{2}{9} = \frac{38}{9}$

25. $1\frac{1}{6} = \frac{7}{6}$
26. $2\frac{2}{3} = \frac{8}{3}$
27. $9\frac{1}{9} = \frac{82}{9}$

28. $2\frac{3}{7} = \frac{17}{7}$
29. $3\frac{1}{5} = \frac{16}{5}$
30. $4\frac{3}{8} = \frac{35}{8}$

78 • *Math Explorations and Applications* Level 6

LESSON 78 ENRICHMENT   Name_____

Players: Two or more
Materials: Fraction cards (below)
Object: To be the first to score ten points

Rules

1. Copy and cut out the 24 fraction cards below, shuffle them, and put them face down in a pile.

2. On a sheet of paper each player should draw three squares in a row.

3. One player draws a card, and each player writes the fraction in one of the squares. The next player draws a card, and each player writes that fraction in an empty square. A third card is drawn and players write that fraction in the remaining square.

4. After all three squares are filled, use a calculator, if necessary, to check the order. A player scores one point if two fractions next to each other are in order from least to greatest and two points if all three fractions are in order.

5. Repeat the game until someone wins by scoring ten points. When all the fraction cards have been used, shuffle them again.

(Hint: You may find it helpful to change the improper fractions to mixed numbers before you try to order them.)

$\frac{9}{4}$	$\frac{7}{3}$	$\frac{12}{5}$	$\frac{6}{2}$	$\frac{18}{7}$	$\frac{5}{4}$
$\frac{24}{9}$	$\frac{17}{8}$	$\frac{10}{4}$	$\frac{22}{7}$	$\frac{13}{5}$	$\frac{9}{6}$
$\frac{11}{4}$	$\frac{16}{5}$	$\frac{19}{6}$	$\frac{16}{9}$	$\frac{9}{7}$	$\frac{25}{9}$
$\frac{11}{6}$	$\frac{14}{7}$	$\frac{17}{9}$	$\frac{22}{6}$	$\frac{14}{9}$	$\frac{8}{5}$

Example:
The fractions are $\frac{8}{5}$, $\frac{11}{8}$, and $\frac{15}{6}$.

Jillian writes them in the following order: $\frac{11}{8}, \frac{8}{5}, \frac{15}{6}$

Jillian gets two points.

$\frac{11}{8} = 1.37$ $\frac{8}{5} = 1.6$ $\frac{15}{6} = 2.5$

78 • *Math Explorations and Applications* Level 6

Mental Math (continued)

i. 0.8 + 0.8 (thumbs up)
j. $\frac{1}{10}$ + 0.9 (stand)
k. $\frac{1}{25}$ + 0.04 (thumbs down)
l. 0.32 + $\frac{2}{3}$ (thumbs down)

❷ Teach

Using the Student Pages Before beginning these pages, you may wish to demonstrate the "Fringo Factory" Game Mat, which provides practice with mixed numbers, so that as students complete the problems, they can play the game.

When discussing page 281 guide students to recall that fractions indicate division, pointing out that $\frac{7}{3} = 7 \div 3$. Tell students that to find decimal equivalents of improper fractions, we divide. Have students complete the problems on page 281 on their own. For problem 32, have students give the exact decimal equivalent, since $\frac{1}{8}$ is a common fraction.

 **Introducing the "Fringo Factory" Game Mat** Demonstrate this Game Mat by having two students play in front of the class. This Game Mat provides practice in writing improper fractions as mixed numbers, and in mathematical reasoning (deciding which space to cover and which cubes to roll). A copy of this game can also be found on page 616 of this Teacher's Guide.

❸ Wrap-Up

In Closing Write the number $\frac{11}{4}$ on the chalkboard. Ask students to express the fraction both as a mixed number and as a decimal. ($2\frac{3}{4}$; 2.75)

 **Informal Assessment** Point out errors as students work on page 281, and see if students know how to correct them.

Assessment Criteria

Did the student . . .

✓ demonstrate understanding of the procedures for rewriting an improper fraction as a mixed number and as a decimal?

✓ correctly answer at least 75% of the problems on page 281?

Homework Have students find five examples of mixed numbers, improper fractions, or decimals greater than 1 in newspapers or magazines and express the numbers in different forms. For example, for "$2\frac{1}{2}$ million copies," they might write "2.5 million copies."

Unit 4 Lesson 78   **281**

Student Edition pages 282–285

LESSON 79
Practice with Decimal Equivalents

LESSON PLANNER

Objectives

▶ to provide practice in converting fractions to decimals and in judging the relative magnitude of fractions and decimals

▶ to help students develop the broad ability to use mathematical common sense

Context of the Lesson This is the 15th of 20 lessons on fractions. This lesson contains part 4 of "Energy Savers," a four-part Thinking Story.

 MANIPULATIVES

decimal number line (optional)

fraction models* (optional)

Program Resources

Number Cubes (0–5 and 5–10)

Practice Master 79

Enrichment Master 79

The Cruncher*

For career connections:
  Careers and Math*

For extra practice:
  CD-ROM* Lesson 79

❶ Warp-Up

⏱ 5 MINUTES

Problem of the Day Present the following problem to the class: Use the numbers 1, 3, and 5 no more than once each to write as many fractions as you can that are less than $\frac{1}{2}$. $\left(\frac{1}{3}, \frac{1}{5}, \frac{1}{35}, \frac{1}{53}, \frac{3}{15}, \frac{3}{51}, \frac{5}{13}, \frac{5}{31}\right)$

Problem-Solving Strategies Ask students who have solved the Problem of the Day to share how they solved it and any strategies they used.

 **MENTAL MATH** Provide practice with fractions and decimals by asking students to show thumbs up if the answer is greater than 1, show thumbs down if it is less than 1, and stand if it is equal to 1.

a. $\frac{2}{5} + \frac{5}{10}$ (thumbs down)

b. $1.50 - \frac{1}{2}$ (stand)

c. $\frac{6}{5} - \frac{1}{5}$ (stand)

d. $2 - \frac{1}{4}$ (thumbs up)

(continued on page 283)

282 Fractions and Mixed Numbers

LESSON 79 GAME
Practice with Decimal Equivalents

COOPERATIVE LEARNING

Make 2 Game

Players:	Two or more
Materials:	Two 0–5 cubes, two 5–10 cubes
Object:	To make a greater number on each turn, but to be the last player to go past 2
Math Focus:	Comparing and ordering fractions, finding decimal equivalents of proper and improper fractions, and mathematical reasoning

RULES

1. Take turns rolling all four cubes.

2. Use any two of the numbers you roll to make a fraction or a decimal of 2 or less than 2. (For example, if you roll 3, 3, 5, and 10, you could make $\frac{3}{3}, \frac{3}{5}, \frac{3}{10}, \frac{5}{3}, \frac{5}{10}, \frac{10}{5}$, or any of these decimals: .103, .105, .310, .33, .35, .510, .53, 1.03, 1.05. Notice that you may place the point between the 1 and the 0 if you roll a 10.)

3. Keep a record of the number you make on each turn. Write the number as a decimal. If you make a fraction, write the decimal equivalent or an approximation. You may round approximations to the nearest thousandth. (For example, if you make $\frac{2}{3}$, you may write 0.667.) Use the chart on page 283.

4. On each turn you must write a number greater than the number you made on your previous turn, but you cannot make a number greater than 2.

5. On any turn if you cannot write 2 or a number less than 2 but greater than your previous turn, then you are out.

6. The last player to go out wins.

282 • Fractions and Mixed Numbers

 **Literature Connection** Have students read *Ed Emberly's Picture Pie* by Ed Emberly. Students can represent the finished projects with an improper fraction and find the decimal equivalent.

---

282 Fractions and Mixed Numbers

*available separately

Table of Decimal Approximations or Equivalents of Fractions

Numerator

		1	2	3	4	5	6	7	8	9	10
Denominator	**1**	1	2	3	4	5	6	7	8	9	10
	2	0.5	1	1.5	2	2.5	3	3.5	4	4.5	5
	3	0.333	0.667	1	1.333	1.667	2	2.333	2.667	3	3.333
	4	0.25	0.5	0.75	1	1.25	1.5	1.75	2	2.25	2.5
	5	0.2	0.4	0.6	0.8	1	1.2	1.4	1.6	1.8	2
	6	0.167	0.333	0.5	0.667	0.833	1	1.167	1.333	1.5	1.667
	7	0.143	0.286	0.429	0.571	0.714	0.857	1	1.143	1.286	1.429
	8	0.125	0.25	0.375	0.5	0.625	0.75	0.875	1	1.125	1.25
	9	0.111	0.222	0.333	0.444	0.556	0.667	0.778	0.889	1	1.111
	10	0.1	0.2	0.3	0.4	0.5	0.6	0.7	0.8	0.9	1

for reference when playing the "Up to 2" Game

In your Math Journal write about the strategies you used in playing this game.

Answer the following questions about the "Up to 2" Game.

❶ Is it always possible to make a number less than or equal to 2? **yes**

❷ Is it always possible to make a number greater than 1 but not greater than 2? **no**

❸ If this game were played with four 0–5 cubes, instead of two of each kind, would you be more or less likely to get a roll that you could use to make a number between 1 and 2? **less likely**

❹ If this game were played with four 5–10 cubes instead of two of each kind, would you be more or less likely to get a roll that you could use to make a number between 1 and 2? **more likely**

❺ Give an example of a roll of four 0–5 cubes that you could not use to make a number greater than 1 but not greater than 2. **possible answer: 5, 5, 2, 2**

Unit 4   Lesson 79 • **283**

Mental Math (continued)

e. $0.8 - \frac{8}{10}$ (thumbs down)

f. $1.3 - \frac{1}{2}$ (thumbs down)

g. $3.5 - 0.75$ (thumbs up)

h. $0.75 + 0.35$ (thumbs up)

❷ Teach

 **Using the Student Pages** Introduce the "Up to 2" game on page 282 by first reminding students of the "Up to 1" game they played previously in Lesson 67, and then showing that this game is similar. This game provides practice in comparing and ordering fractions and decimals. However, in this game two 0–5 cubes and two 5–10 cubes are used and players go up to 2 rather than 1. Play one or two games with the class; then let students play in groups of two or three. Show students how to use the chart of decimal equivalents on page 283 for reference. Students can also use a blank **Cruncher*** spreadsheet to help them calculate and record their score. When students have finished playing the game, have them answer the questions on page 283.

 **Technology Connection** Refer students to the video, laser disc or software *Modumath: Arithmetic, Changing Fractions to Decimals* from VTAE (VHS, IBM, for grades 6–12) for further practice with changing a fraction or mixed number to a decimal and changing a decimal to a fraction or mixed number.

◆ **LESSON 79 Practice with Decimal Equivalents**

Teach

Using the Thinking Story In this last installment of "Energy Savers," the focus is on using systematic methods and common sense to make estimates. The story involves the extra amount of heating fuel used when mail slots are left open.

Answers to Thinking Story Questions:

1. It would cost $25 to $50 more per year.

2. Estimates will vary, but the following should be considered: "almost every day" might mean 100 out of 150 days because on some days no ads will be delivered or the ads will go all the way through the slot; sometimes the ads will be removed immediately, and at other times they may stay in place a day or longer. A reasonable estimate of the average time mail slots are open might be 4 hours, or $\frac{1}{6}$ of a day. Over 100 days this would amount to 400 hours, or the equivalent of about 17 full days.

3. If the average heating bill is $500 per year, and the furnace is on for 150 days during that time, the average daily cost is $3.33. The mail slot is open an average of 17 full days (see problem 2) and the normal heating cost for those days would be 17 × $3.33, or about $57. If having the mail slot open increases heating costs by 10 percent, the cost of ads in the slot is about 0.10 × $57, or $5.70 a year; if the increase is 5 percent, the extra cost is 0.05 × $57, or about $2.85 a year.

4. What saves energy in the winter is turning down the thermostat so that the furnace runs less. If the mail slot is open, the furnace has to run more, using more energy, as it heats the cold air that comes in.

Have students think about Ferdie, recalling his actions and ideas in the four segments of this Thinking Story about saving energy. Ask them to write a description of this character in their Math Journals.

◆ **LESSON 79 Practice with Decimal Equivalents**

Energy Savers
Part 4

You may want to refer to earlier parts of this Thinking Story on pages 246–247, 256–257, and 268–269.

"Help me think of new ways to save energy," Manolita told her parents.

"You could ask people to insulate their houses," her mother said.

"Someone has already thought of that," Manolita said.

"Then you could ask people to keep their houses cooler in winter," her father said. "That can save a lot of energy."

"Someone has already thought of that too," Manolita said.

"Speaking of cooler houses," said her mother, "does anyone feel a cold draft in here?"

They all felt the draft. Manolita looked around to find where it was coming from. She found that the cold air was coming in through the mail slot. It was being held open by an ad someone had stuck in it.

284 • Fractions and Mixed Numbers

"That happens almost every day," Manolita's mother said. "There ought to be a law. It would be easy enough for people to push the ads all the way through the slot. Then it wouldn't stay open."

Manolita's parents got out some books on heating. They did some figuring. They showed that an open mail slot could increase heating costs by five to ten percent.

"I wish you'd stop thinking about that old mail slot and help me think of ways to save energy," Manolita said.

the end

Work in groups. Discuss how you figured your answers and compare them with those of other groups. *Answers are in margin.*

❶ The average heating bill in Manolita's town is $500 a year. If her parents figured correctly, how much extra would it cost if a mail slot were open all the time?

❷ Where Manolita lives, people use their furnaces about 150 days a year. Of course, no one's mail slot is likely to be open all that time. Estimate how much time during those 150 days a mail slot might be open. Figure that ads are placed in it almost every day.

❸ Using what you know from questions 1 and 2, estimate how much it costs people to have ads stuck in their mail slots. Be prepared to explain your estimate.

❹ When Ferdie heard about this he said, "I think open mail slots should save energy. After all, they make the house cooler. Everybody says that keeping your house cooler in winter saves energy." Do you agree? Why or why not?

Unit 4   Lesson 79 • **285**

---

❸ Wrap-Up

In Closing To summarize the lesson, ask students to explain their strategy for playing the "Up to 2" game.

 **Informal Assessment** Circulate through the class as students play the game to see the strategies they use and to see whether they correctly write the equivalent number for each decimal or fraction they make.

Assessment Criteria

Did the student . . .

✓ understand how to express a fraction as a decimal and a decimal as a fraction?

✓ demonstrate an understanding of the relative size of fractions and decimals?

✓ participate in the group discussions of the Thinking Story?

Homework For further practice with ordering fractions and decimals, have students play the "Up to 2" game with a family member, using two sets of six slips of paper numbered 0–5, and two sets of six slips of paper numbered 5–10 in place of Number Cubes if necessary. A copy of this game can also be found on page 27 of the Home Connections Blackline Masters.

 **Meeting Individual Needs** Students who still have difficulty comparing and ordering fractions and decimals may benefit from using **fraction models*** and a **decimal number line**. Have students use these materials when playing the "Up to 1" and "Up to 2" games.

PRACTICE p. 79

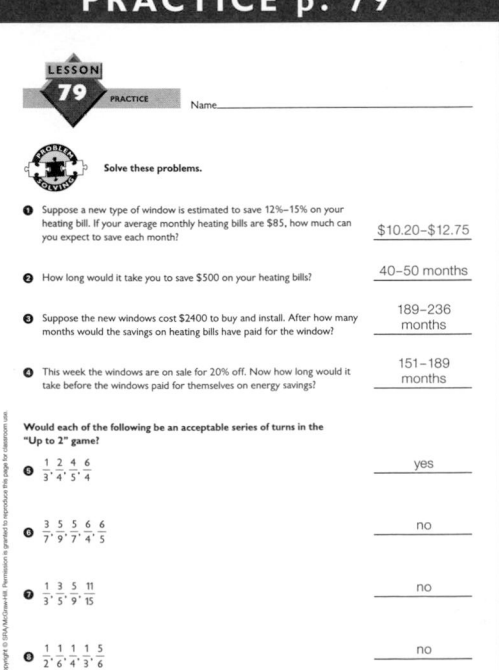

LESSON **79** PRACTICE   Name _____

Solve these problems.

❶ Suppose a new type of window is estimated to save 12%–15% on your heating bill. If your average monthly heating bills are $85, how much can you expect to save each month? $10.20–$12.75

❷ How long would it take you to save $500 on your heating bills?   40–50 months

❸ Suppose the new windows cost $2400 to buy and install. After how many months would the savings on heating bills have paid for the window?   189–236 months

❹ This week the windows are on sale for 20% off. Now how long would it take before the windows paid for themselves on energy savings?   151–189 months

Would each of the following be an acceptable series of turns in the "Up to 2" game?

❺ $\frac{1}{3}, \frac{2}{4}, \frac{4}{5}, \frac{6}{4}$ yes

❻ $\frac{3}{7}, \frac{5}{9}, \frac{5}{7}, \frac{6}{4}, \frac{6}{5}$ no

❼ $\frac{1}{3}, \frac{3}{5}, \frac{5}{9}, \frac{11}{15}$ no

❽ $\frac{1}{2}, \frac{1}{6}, \frac{1}{4}, \frac{1}{3}, \frac{5}{6}$ no

Math Explorations and Applications Level 6 • 79

ENRICHMENT p. 79

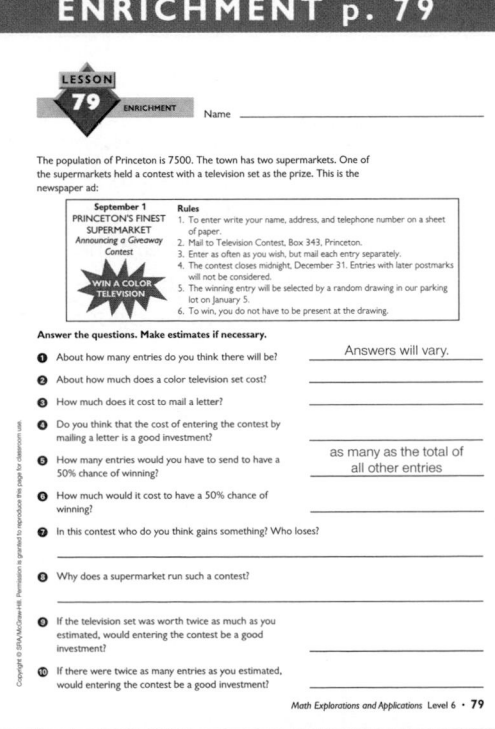

LESSON **79** ENRICHMENT   Name _____

The population of Princeton is 7500. The town has two supermarkets. One of the supermarkets held a contest with a television set as the prize. This is the newspaper ad:

September 1
PRINCETON'S FINEST SUPERMARKET
Announcing a Giveaway Contest
WIN A COLOR TELEVISION

Rules
1. To enter write your name, address, and telephone number on a sheet of paper.
2. Mail to Television Contest, Box 343, Princeton.
3. Enter as often as you wish, but mail each entry separately.
4. The contest closes midnight, December 31. Entries with later postmarks will not be considered.
5. The winning entry will be selected by a random drawing in our parking lot on January 5.
6. To win, you do not have to be present at the drawing.

Answer the questions. Make estimates if necessary.

❶ About how many entries do you think there will be?   Answers will vary.

❷ About how much does a color television set cost?   _____

❸ How much does it cost to mail a letter?   _____

❹ Do you think that the cost of entering the contest by mailing a letter is a good investment?   _____

❺ How many entries would you have to send to have a 50% chance of winning?   as many as the total of all other entries

❻ How much would it cost to have a 50% chance of winning?   _____

❼ In this contest who do you think gains something? Who loses?   _____

❽ Why does a supermarket run such a contest?   _____

❾ If the television set was worth twice as much as you estimated, would entering the contest be a good investment?   _____

❿ If there were twice as many entries as you estimated, would entering the contest be a good investment?   _____

Math Explorations and Applications Level 6 • 79

*available separately

Adding and Subtracting Mixed Numbers

LESSON PLANNER

Objectives

▶ to review addition and subtraction of mixed numbers

✓ to evaluate students' ability to add and subtract mixed numbers

Context of the Lesson This is the 16th of 20 lessons on fractions. Although this subject was introduced formally toward the end of the fifth-grade program, be prepared to provide extra teaching and practice for those who still have difficulty. A Mastery Checkpoint for assessing addition and subtraction of mixed numbers is provided in this lesson.

 MANIPULATIVES

fraction models*
(optional)

Program Resources

Number Cubes (0–5 and 5–10)

Reteaching Master

Practice Master 80

Enrichment Master 80

Assessment Master

For extra practice:
CD-ROM* Lesson 80

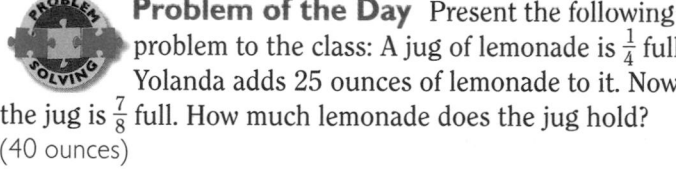

 **Problem of the Day** Present the following problem to the class: A jug of lemonade is $\frac{1}{4}$ full. Yolanda adds 25 ounces of lemonade to it. Now the jug is $\frac{7}{8}$ full. How much lemonade does the jug hold? (40 ounces)

Problem-Solving Strategies Ask students who have solved the Problem of the Day to share how they solved it and any strategies they used.

MENTAL MATH For each problem, challenge students to tell whether the sum or difference is greater (thumbs up) or less (thumbs down) than 2. Students should stand if the sum or difference equals 2.

a. $\frac{3}{4} + \frac{3}{4}$ (thumbs down)

b. 0.50 + 1.75 (thumbs up)

c. 0.3 + $1\frac{1}{2}$ (thumbs down)

(continued on page 287)

Adding and Subtracting Mixed Numbers

Ms. Owens is planning to drive from Miller's Creek to Rattlesnake Bluff by way of Green Valley. She knows it will take about $2\frac{3}{4}$ hours to drive from Miller's Creek to Green Valley and about $3\frac{1}{2}$ hours to drive from Green Valley to Rattlesnake Bluff. About how long will the entire trip from Miller's Creek to Rattlesnake Bluff take?

To find the answer, add $2\frac{3}{4}$ and $3\frac{1}{2}$. Here's how.

First estimate the answer. Since the sum of the two fractions is a little more than 1, the answer will be a little more than 6.

$$\begin{array}{r} 2\frac{3}{4} \\ + 3\frac{1}{2} \end{array}$$
Add the fraction parts. We can't add because the denominators are different.

$2\frac{3}{4} = 2\frac{?}{4} = \mathbf{2\frac{3}{4}}$ Find a common denominator.

$3\frac{1}{2} = 3\frac{?}{4} = \mathbf{3\frac{2}{4}}$ We'll use 4. The fraction $\frac{1}{2} = \frac{2}{4}$.

$$\begin{array}{r} 2\frac{3}{4} \\ + 3\frac{1}{2} \end{array} \longrightarrow \begin{array}{r} 2\frac{3}{4} \\ + 3\frac{2}{4} \\ \hline \mathbf{5\frac{5}{4}} \end{array}$$
Add the fraction parts. Add the whole numbers. $\frac{5}{4}$ is an improper fraction.

$\frac{5}{4} = 1\frac{1}{4}$ so $5\frac{5}{4} = 5 + 1\frac{1}{4}$

$5\frac{5}{4} = 6\frac{1}{4}$ Rewrite the answer.

Check: $6\frac{1}{4}$ is a little more than 6, so it checks with our estimate.

It will take about $6\frac{1}{4}$ hours to drive from Miller's Creek to Rattlesnake Bluff by way of Green Valley.

 **Literature Connection** Invite students to read *All About Sam* by Lois Lowry. Have them compare their ages to Sam's at different parts of the story as he goes from birth to age four.

*available separately

Dan drove from Miller's Creek to Rattlesnake Bluff on the interstate highway in $4\frac{1}{2}$ hours. How much less than $6\frac{1}{4}$ hours was that?

To find out, subtract $4\frac{1}{2}$ from $6\frac{1}{4}$. Here's how.

First estimate the answer. Since $\frac{1}{2}$ is more than $\frac{1}{4}$, the answer should be a little less than 2.

$$\begin{array}{r} 6\frac{1}{4} \\ -\ 4\frac{1}{2} \end{array}$$

Subtract the fraction parts. We can't because the denominators are different.

$6\frac{1}{4} = 6\frac{?}{4} = 6\frac{1}{4}$ Find a common denominator.

$4\frac{1}{2} = 4\frac{?}{4} = 4\frac{2}{4}$ We'll use 4. The fraction $\frac{1}{2} = \frac{2}{4}$.

$$\begin{array}{r} 6\frac{1}{4} \\ -\ 4\frac{2}{4} \end{array}$$

We still can't subtract the fractions, because $\frac{1}{4}$ is less than $\frac{2}{4}$. Sometimes, we have to rename a mixed number twice.

$6\frac{1}{4} = 5\frac{5}{4}$ Rename 1 as $\frac{4}{4}$. Decrease the whole number by 1. Increase the fraction part by $\frac{4}{4}$. Rewrite $6\frac{1}{4}$ as $5\frac{5}{4}$.

$$\begin{array}{rr} 6\frac{1}{4} & 5\frac{5}{4} \\ -\ 4\frac{1}{2} & -\ 4\frac{2}{4} \\ \hline & 1\frac{3}{4} \end{array}$$

Now subtract the fraction parts. Subtract the whole numbers.

Check: This is a little less than 2, so it checks with our estimate.

It took about $1\frac{3}{4}$ hours less to drive from Miller's Creek to Rattlesnake Bluff on the interstate than it did by way of Green Valley.

Mental Math (continued)

d.   0.75 + 0.75 (thumbs down)

e. $\frac{10}{10} - \frac{10}{15}$ (thumbs down)

f.   1.2 + 0.8 (stand)

g.   0.64 + 0.46 (thumbs down)

h.   2.29 − .29 (stand)

i.   3.14 − 1.13 (thumbs up)

❷ Teach

Using the Student Pages You may wish to introduce the "Make 1" game before starting the problems on pages 286–288 so that students can play the game, which provides practice with fraction operations, as they finish the problems.

You may wish to have students keep their books closed while you read aloud the problem on page 286 about Ms. Owens's trip. Draw a picture to represent the situation on the chalkboard, and ask a volunteer to explain how to get the answer. Then, with the class, develop a procedure similar to the one presented on the page. Next, with students' books still closed, read aloud the problem at the top of page 287. Again, try to develop a procedure with the class for subtracting mixed numbers that is similar to the one shown on the page.

SPECIAL NEEDS   **Meeting Individual Needs**

You can provide guided practice in adding and subtracting mixed numbers by presenting steps like these:

Problem	Common Denominator	Numerator
$41\frac{2}{3}$	$41\frac{\ }{12}$	$41\frac{8}{12}$
$+27\frac{3}{4}$	$+27\frac{\ }{12}$	$+27\frac{9}{12}$

Add	Make Proper	
$41\frac{8}{12}$	$41\frac{8}{12}$	
$+27\frac{9}{12}$	$+27\frac{9}{12}$	
$68\frac{17}{12}$	$68\frac{17}{12}$	$69\frac{5}{12}$

This procedure actually requires rewriting the problem only once, so the final procedure looks like this:

$41\frac{2}{3}$	$41\frac{8}{12}$
$+27\frac{3}{4}$	$+27\frac{9}{12}$
	$68\frac{17}{12}$ $69\frac{5}{12}$

For subtracting, an extra step may be needed between the third and fourth steps:

$$\begin{array}{r} 40\frac{20}{12} \\ -27\frac{9}{12} \end{array}$$

◆ LESSON 80 Adding and Subtracting Mixed Numbers

Teach

Using the Student Pages Have students do the problems on page 288 on their own. Use the page as an assessment tool. For students who would benefit from a better understanding of adding and subtracting common fractions, playing "Circo 11" (page 265) with a student who has mastered the skill may help. Some students may experience difficulty rewriting mixed numbers with regrouping for subtraction, such as when subtracting $4\frac{1}{2}$ from $8\frac{1}{3}$ in problem 46. Pay particular attention to these cases. As needed, try using **fraction models*** or geometric figures to help these students understand why $8\frac{1}{3}$ and $7\frac{4}{3}$ have the same value.

Introducing the "Make 1" Game
Demonstrate the "Make 1" game by playing it with a student while the class watches. This game provides extensive practice with mental arithmetic involving fractions. Once everyone understands the rules, have students play in pairs or small groups.

◆ LESSON 80 Adding and Subtracting Mixed Numbers

Change each improper fraction to a mixed number with a proper fraction or a whole number.

❶ $\frac{6}{5}$ $1\frac{1}{5}$ ❷ $\frac{9}{7}$ $1\frac{2}{7}$ ❸ $\frac{4}{3}$ $2\frac{1}{3}$ ❹ $\frac{3}{2}$ $3\frac{1}{2}$ ❺ $\frac{10}{5}$ 2

❻ $1\frac{5}{4}$ $2\frac{1}{4}$ ❼ $3\frac{6}{6}$ 4 ❽ $2\frac{7}{5}$ $3\frac{2}{5}$ ❾ $5\frac{4}{3}$ $6\frac{1}{3}$ ❿ $2\frac{9}{4}$ $4\frac{1}{4}$

⓫ $3\frac{5}{2}$ $5\frac{1}{2}$ ⓬ $2\frac{9}{2}$ $6\frac{1}{2}$ ⓭ $\frac{10}{2}$ 5 ⓮ $1\frac{10}{9}$ $2\frac{1}{9}$ ⓯ $4\frac{4}{3}$ $5\frac{1}{3}$

⓰ $4\frac{5}{3}$ $5\frac{2}{3}$ ⓱ $2\frac{10}{7}$ $3\frac{3}{7}$ ⓲ $5\frac{11}{8}$ $6\frac{3}{8}$ ⓳ $6\frac{6}{6}$ 7 ⓴ $7\frac{10}{10}$ 8

Rewrite each mixed number as an improper fraction.

㉑ $3\frac{1}{2}$ $\frac{7}{2}$ ㉒ $4\frac{3}{8}$ $\frac{35}{8}$ ㉓ $2\frac{2}{3}$ $\frac{8}{3}$ ㉔ $2\frac{1}{2}$ $\frac{5}{2}$ ㉕ $4\frac{1}{3}$ $\frac{13}{3}$

㉖ $2\frac{7}{8}$ $\frac{23}{8}$ ㉗ $3\frac{4}{7}$ $\frac{25}{7}$ ㉘ $2\frac{1}{5}$ $\frac{11}{5}$ ㉙ $4\frac{7}{10}$ $\frac{47}{10}$ ㉚ $3\frac{7}{12}$ $\frac{43}{12}$

㉛ $5\frac{3}{10}$ $\frac{53}{10}$ ㉜ $2\frac{1}{8}$ $\frac{17}{8}$ ㉝ $4\frac{1}{12}$ $\frac{49}{12}$ ㉞ $3\frac{8}{9}$ $\frac{35}{9}$ ㉟ $6\frac{1}{4}$ $\frac{25}{4}$

㊱ $4\frac{2}{5}$ $\frac{22}{5}$ ㊲ $5\frac{1}{3}$ $\frac{16}{3}$ ㊳ $3\frac{3}{8}$ $\frac{27}{8}$ ㊴ $6\frac{2}{7}$ $\frac{44}{7}$ ㊵ $2\frac{1}{6}$ $\frac{13}{6}$

Add or subtract.

㊶ $2\frac{5}{8} + 3\frac{4}{8}$ $6\frac{1}{8}$ ㊷ $3\frac{2}{7} - 1\frac{4}{7}$ $1\frac{5}{7}$ ㊸ $5\frac{3}{5} - 2\frac{2}{5}$ $3\frac{1}{5}$ ㊹ $5\frac{3}{5} + 2\frac{2}{5}$ 8

㊺ $8\frac{1}{3} + 4\frac{1}{2}$ $12\frac{5}{6}$ ㊻ $8\frac{1}{3} - 4\frac{1}{2}$ $3\frac{5}{6}$ ㊼ $3\frac{1}{2} + 2\frac{3}{4}$ $6\frac{1}{4}$ ㊽ $3\frac{1}{2} - \frac{3}{4}$ $2\frac{3}{4}$

㊾ $5\frac{1}{3} - 1\frac{1}{2}$ $3\frac{5}{6}$ ㊿ $12\frac{1}{3} - 5\frac{1}{2}$ $6\frac{5}{6}$ ⓝ $4\frac{2}{3} - 1\frac{3}{4}$ $2\frac{11}{12}$ ⓞ $14\frac{2}{3} - 11\frac{3}{4}$ $2\frac{11}{12}$

Solve this problem.

㊾ Ms. Owens discovered another route from Miller's Creek to Rattlesnake Bluff. This route goes through Orange Park. It took her $2\frac{1}{2}$ hours to drive from Miller's Creek to Orange Park and $3\frac{1}{4}$ hours to drive from Orange Park to Rattlesnake Bluff.

a. How long did it take Ms. Owens to go from Miller's Creek to Rattlesnake Bluff on this route? $5\frac{3}{4}$ **hours**

b. How much less time would it take to go from Miller's Creek to Rattlesnake Bluff through Orange Park than through Green Valley? $\frac{1}{2}$ $(\frac{2}{4})$ **hour**

288 • Fractions and Mixed Numbers

*available separately

Make 1 Game

COOPERATIVE LEARNING

Players:	Two or more
Materials:	Two 0–5 cubes, two 5–10 cubes
Object:	To make a problem with the answer closest to 1
Math Focus:	Mental arithmetic and addition and subtraction of fractions

RULES

1. Take turns rolling all four cubes.

2. Make two fractions. The fractions can be proper, improper, or both.

3. Make an addition or subtraction problem with the fractions that gives an answer close to 1. Don't calculate the answer yet.

4. The player whose problem has an answer closest to 1 wins the round. You don't need to calculate the answers unless you can't tell by looking.

SAMPLE GAME

Tomás rolled:

Jackie rolled:

Tomás made:

$\frac{5}{5} - \frac{0}{9}$

Jackie made:

$\frac{6}{5} - \frac{1}{8}$

(Tomás knew that he couldn't use 0 in the denominator of a fraction.)

Tomás won this round. Both players knew that Tomás had 1 exactly and that Jackie had more than 1.

Describe in your Math Journal your strategies for playing this game.

Unit 4 Lesson 80 • **289**

---

③ Wrap-Up ⏱ 5 MINUTES

In Closing Summarize the lesson by presenting students with the following word problem: Ishmael took a boat trip to Palm Island that took him $20\frac{1}{4}$ hours. If he had flown, it would have taken him $2\frac{1}{2}$ hours. How much longer did the boat ride take? ($17\frac{3}{4}$ hours)

SELF ASSESSMENT Encourage students to keep a record of their scores on problems 41–52 on page 288. They can compare their results with those they get on future sets of problems involving addition and subtraction of mixed numbers.

✓ Mastery Checkpoint 17

At this time most students should demonstrate mastery of changing improper fractions to mixed numbers, rewriting mixed numbers as improper fractions, and adding and subtracting mixed numbers by correctly answering at least 80% of the problems on page 288 or on Assessment Blackline Masters page 32 in a reasonable amount of time. Results of this assessment may be recorded on the Mastery Checkpoint Chart.

Assessment Criteria

Did the student . . .

✓ continue to demonstrate an ability to express an improper fraction as a mixed number?

✓ show that he or she understands the procedure for adding or subtracting mixed numbers?

✓ demonstrate ability to correctly rewrite a mixed number as a mixed number with an improper fraction as necessary for subtraction?

Homework Invite students to play the "Make 1" game with a family member, for further practice working with fractions. A copy of this game can also be found on page 28 of the Home Connections Blackline Masters.

Using Mixed Numbers

LESSON PLANNER

Objective

▶ to provide practice in solving practical problems that involve fractions and mixed numbers

Context of the Lesson This is the 17th of 20 lessons on fractions.

 MANIPULATIVES

Program Resources

Practice Master 81

Enrichment Master 81

The Cruncher*: *Recipe Converter*

For extra practice:
CD-ROM* Lesson 81
Cumulative Review, page 570

❶ Warm-Up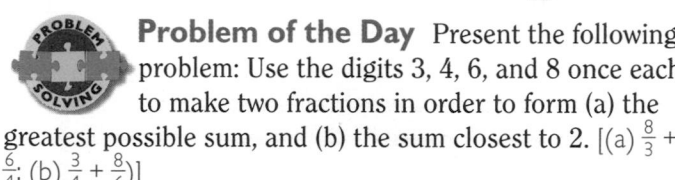

 Problem of the Day Present the following problem: Use the digits 3, 4, 6, and 8 once each to make two fractions in order to form (a) the greatest possible sum, and (b) the sum closest to 2. [(a) $\frac{8}{3}$ + $\frac{6}{4}$; (b) $\frac{3}{4}$ + $\frac{8}{6}$)]

Problem-Solving Strategies Ask students who have solved the Problem of the Day to share how they solved it and any strategies they used.

 For each problem, students should tell whether the sum or difference is greater (thumbs up) or less (thumbs down) than 2. If the sum or difference equals 2, they should stand.

a. $\frac{3}{6}$ + 0.5 (thumbs down)   b. $\frac{15}{5}$ − $\frac{5}{5}$ (stand)

c. $\frac{4}{3}$ + $\frac{4}{3}$ (thumbs up)   d. 0.4 + $1\frac{6}{10}$ (stand)

e. $3\frac{1}{3}$ − 0.33 (thumbs up)   f. 1.25 + 1.75 (thumbs up)

g. 3.8 − 1.5 (thumbs up)   h. $\frac{1}{4}$ + 0.25 (thumbs down)

i. $3\frac{1}{8}$ − $1\frac{8}{8}$ (thumbs down)   j. 0.5 + $1\frac{5}{10}$ (stand)

Literature Connection Use *The Science Chef* by Joan D'Amico and Karen Eich Drummond to have students determine the amount of ingredients needed to make enough of one of the recipes to serve the entire class.

Using Mixed Numbers

There are times in real life that you'll need to apply what you've learned about computing with fractions and mixed numbers. Following recipes is one common application.

Solve these problems.

❶ Cesar wants to make about 200 cookies. The recipe will make about 100 cookies, so he decides to double it. The recipe calls for these ingredients:

$1\frac{1}{2}$ cups of butter **3 c**	$\frac{3}{4}$ teaspoon of grated orange rind **$1\frac{1}{2}$ tsp**	
1 cup of sugar **2 c**	$\frac{3}{8}$ teaspoon of nutmeg **$\frac{3}{4}$ tsp**	
$\frac{3}{4}$ teaspoon of salt **$1\frac{1}{2}$ tsp**	3 cups of flour **6 c**	
2 teaspoons of vanilla extract **4 tsp**		

The recipe says to bake the cookies in a preheated oven for 12 minutes at 375°.

a. How much of each ingredient should Cesar use in the doubled recipe? **See recipe above.**

b. About how long should he bake the cookies? **12 minutes**

c. At what temperature should he bake the cookies? **375°**

❷ Ruth was making a cake that called for $2\frac{1}{4}$ cups of flour and $1\frac{1}{3}$ cups of sugar. She confused the two amounts. By mistake she poured $1\frac{1}{3}$ cups of flour into a bowl and began to mix in the sugar. After mixing in 1 cup of sugar she thought, "My, this is going to be a sweet cake." Then she realized what she had done.

a. How much more flour should she add? **$\frac{11}{12}$ c**

b. How much more sugar should she add? **$\frac{1}{3}$ c**

c. Suppose she had put in $1\frac{1}{3}$ cups of flour and $2\frac{1}{4}$ cups of sugar and had decided that she had to double the recipe to make it work out. Then, how much more sugar and how much more flour would she add? **$\frac{5}{12}$ c sugar, $3\frac{1}{6}$ c flour**

d. How could Ruth measure about $\frac{1}{6}$ cup if she has measuring cups marked $\frac{1}{2}$ cup, $\frac{1}{3}$ cup, and $\frac{1}{4}$ cup?
Measure $\frac{1}{2}$ cup and then empty out $\frac{1}{3}$ cup.

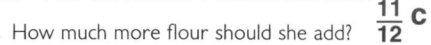 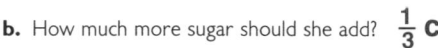

Physical Education Connection Many running tracks are $\frac{1}{4}$ of a mile long. Invite students who are interested in track and field to create a poster showing a track with all the races in a track meet and their distances. They might also include a table showing what fraction of a mile each race is and the metric equivalent of each distance.

RETEACHING

Arrange for students who are having difficulty reading and understanding the problems to work with classmates who have mastered this material. Pair ESL students with fluent English-speaking students, who can help them interpret the problem situations.

Solve these problems.

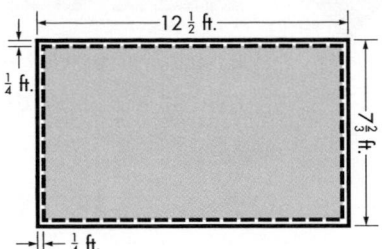
— 12½ ft. —
¼ ft.
7⅔ ft.
¼ ft.

❸ A rug is 12½ feet long and 7⅔ feet wide. The owner wants to put a rubber pad under the rug. The pad should be ¼ foot from the edge of the rug.

   a. How wide should the pad be? **7⅙ ft**

   b. How long should the pad be? **12 ft**

❹ If it takes 2½ hours to mow your lawn and 1¾ hours to do your homework, how long will it take to do both? **4¼ h**

❺ Woody can run 1½ miles in ten minutes.

   a. At that rate, how long will it take him to run 6 miles? **40 min**

   b. Do you think he could run 6 miles at that rate? Why or why not?
   For example: No, because he would become tired.

❻ A recipe calls for ⅔ cup of butter.

   a. You have two sticks of butter, each of which is labeled ½ cup. Do you have enough butter? **yes**

   b. If you use one whole stick, how much more butter will you need (in cups)? **⅙ c**

   c. If you use one whole stick, what fraction of the other stick will you have to use? **⅓**

❼ Trina has a recipe for making 36 blueberry muffins. She wants to make only ⅓ of that amount. Some of the ingredients are 6 cups of unbleached flour, 9 tablespoons of honey, 1½ cups of vegetable oil, 2¼ teaspoons of cinnamon, and 3 cups of blueberries. The recipe says to bake the muffins for 25 minutes at 400°F.

   a. About how many muffins does Trina want to make? **12**

   b. How many teaspoons of cinnamon should she use? **¾ tsp**

   c. At what temperature should she bake the muffins? **400°F**

   d. About how long should she bake the muffins? **25 minutes**

❼ Kevin is making waffles. His recipe calls for 4 cups of flour, but he only has 3 cups, so he is adjusting the recipe. If the original recipe made two dozen waffles, how many waffles can Kevin make? **18**

Use the Cumulative Review on page 570 after this lesson.

Unit 4   Lesson 81 • **291**

PRACTICE p. 81

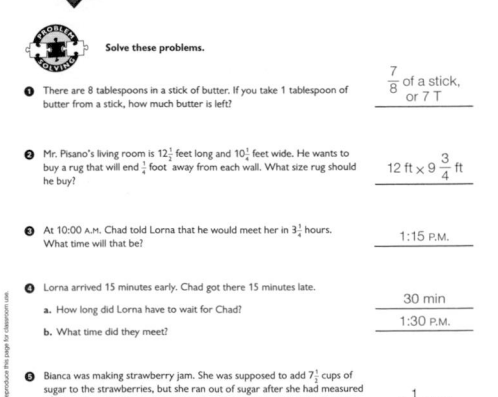

LESSON 81 PRACTICE   Name_____

Solve these problems.

❶ There are 8 tablespoons in a stick of butter. If you take 1 tablespoon of butter from a stick, how much butter is left? — ⅞ of a stick, or 7 T

❷ Mr. Pisano's living room is 12½ feet long and 10½ feet wide. He wants to buy a rug that will end ¾ foot away from each wall. What size rug should he buy? — 12 ft × 9¾ ft

❸ At 10:00 A.M. Chad told Lorna that he would meet her in 3¼ hours. What time will that be? — 1:15 P.M.

❹ Lorna arrived 15 minutes early. Chad got there 15 minutes late.
   a. How long did Lorna have to wait for Chad? — 30 min
   b. What time did they meet? — 1:30 P.M.

❺ Bianca was making strawberry jam. She was supposed to add 7¼ cups of sugar to the strawberries, but she ran out of sugar after she had measured 5¼ cups. She opened a new bag of sugar. How many more cups of sugar did she need to add to the strawberries? — 2¼ cups

❻ Drew did his homework from 6:00 P.M. to 7:30 P.M. and then worked on a model airplane until he went to bed.
   a. How many hours did Drew do homework? — 1½ hours
   b. How many hours did Drew work on his model airplane? — can't tell

Math Explorations and Applications Level 6 • **81**

ENRICHMENT p. 81

LESSON 81 ENRICHMENT   Name_____

You work at the local lumber yard. The most common sizes that people want 1¼-in. dowels cut to are 2½ ft and 3¼ ft. The store manager asks you to decide what length of dowel will accommodate cuts of either length, with no waste. You need a plan to figure out the correct length.

❶ Suppose the dowel is 5 ft long.
   a. Can 2½ ft-lengths be cut with no waste? — yes
   b. Can 3¼ ft-lengths be cut with no waste? — no

❷ Suppose the dowel is 7 ft long.
   a. Can 2½ ft-lengths be cut with no waste? — no
   b. Can 3¼ ft-lengths be cut with no waste? — yes

❸ How might you use the lengths tried in questions 1 and 2 to help you find a logical way to solve this problem? — Continue checking multiples of 2½ and 3¼ until you find one that is the same. 17½ ft, 35 ft, and so on

❹ What length will work?

❺ What is the shortest length that can accommodate cuts of 3¼ feet and 4½ feet with no waste? — 31½ ft

Math Explorations and Applications Level 6 • **81**

---

❷ Teach

Using the Student Pages Have students solve the problems on these pages on their own. If they have difficulty with problem 6c, provide the following explanation: One stick is ½ c of butter and ⅔ c is needed. Therefore, ⅔ c – ½ c, or ⅙ c, of butter needs to be taken from the second stick. Because each stick is ½, or 3/6 of a cup, then ⅓ of the second stick is needed. Students can use **The Cruncher***: *Recipe Converter* spreadsheet to help solve the recipe conversion problems. Discuss all the problems once students have finished. Students who finish early may play any of the games introduced in this unit.

❸ Wrap-Up ⏱ 5 MINUTES

In Closing Summarize the lesson by asking students to describe why it would be important to apply their understanding of fractions and mixed numbers when following recipes. Ask them to suggest other applications of these kinds of computations.

Performance Assessment Tell students that a rectangular room measures 8½ feet by 14 feet, and that a rug 6 feet by 11¾ feet is going to be put into the room. Ask them to draw a sketch of the room and the rug, labeling the dimensions and area of the regions of the floor *not* covered by the rug. (48.5 square feet will not be covered by the rug.)

Assessment Criteria

Did the student . . .

✓ demonstrate understanding of how to add and subtract mixed numbers and fractions, particularly where renaming is concerned?

✓ choose the right operations to solve the problems, and describe why he or she chose those operations?

✓ demonstrate ability to explain all the procedures he or she followed?

Homework Have students select a recipe and determine the measurements needed to make only a fraction of the amount the recipe is for, to make more than the recipe indicates, or both.

UNIT 4 Mid-Unit Review

Student Edition pages 292–293

The Mid-Unit Review pinpoints troublesome skill areas for students, allowing plenty of time for additional practice and reteaching before the unit ends. If students did not do well on the Mid-Unit Review and have completed additional practice, you may want to use the Mid-Unit Review provided on Assessment Blackline Masters page 33.

Using the Student Pages Have students complete problems 1–70 on pages 292 and 293 on their own. You might treat this review as a formal assessment of students' skills, and have students complete this review as a timed test. See suggestions for administering timed tests on page 49.

ASSESSMENT

UNIT 4 Mid-Unit Review

Solve for n in the following.

❶ $\frac{1}{2}$ of 18 = n **9**   ❷ $\frac{2}{3}$ of 24 = n **16**   ❸ $n = \frac{2}{5}$ of 40 **16**

Solve these problems.

❹ $\frac{1}{3}$ of 42 **14**   ❺ $\frac{2}{3}$ of 60 **40**   ❻ $\frac{1}{4}$ of 80 **20**

❼ $\frac{2}{3} \times \frac{4}{11}$ **$\frac{8}{33}$**   ❽ $\frac{2}{9} \times \frac{7}{8}$ **$\frac{7}{36}$**   ❾ $\frac{21}{44} \times \frac{3}{7}$ **$\frac{9}{44}$**

For each fraction find the decimal equivalent or an approximation rounded to the nearest thousandth.

❿ $\frac{1}{4}$ **0.25**   ⓫ $\frac{5}{6}$ **0.833**   ⓬ $\frac{5}{8}$ **0.625**   ⓭ $\frac{4}{5}$ **0.8**   ⓮ $\frac{2}{7}$ **0.286**

⓯ $\frac{10}{6}$ **1.667** ⓰ $\frac{4}{9}$ **0.444**   ⓱ $1\frac{1}{3}$ **1.333**   ⓲ $1\frac{3}{5}$ **1.6**   ⓳ $\frac{10}{8}$ **1.25**

Complete to write an equivalent fraction in simpler form.

⓴ $\frac{10}{14} = \frac{?}{7}$ **5**   ㉑ $\frac{12}{18} = \frac{?}{3}$ **2**   ㉒ $\frac{8}{10} = \frac{4}{?}$ **5**   ㉓ $\frac{8}{20} = \frac{2}{?}$ **5**

Reduce each fraction completely.

㉔ $\frac{2}{6}$ **$\frac{1}{3}$**   ㉕ $\frac{9}{12}$ **$\frac{3}{4}$**   ㉖ $\frac{50}{175}$ **$\frac{2}{7}$**   ㉗ $\frac{20}{80}$ **$\frac{1}{4}$**   ㉘ $\frac{9}{45}$ **$\frac{1}{5}$**

Find the greatest common factor of each pair of numbers.

㉙ 12 and 20 **4**   ㉚ 9 and 15 **3**   ㉛ 24 and 132 **12**

Copy each pair of fractions but insert <, >, or =.

㉜ $\frac{1}{3} \blacksquare \frac{2}{5}$ **<**   ㉝ $\frac{5}{6} \blacksquare \frac{7}{8}$ **<**   ㉞ $\frac{5}{12} \blacksquare \frac{9}{24}$ **>**

Find the least common multiple of each set of numbers.

㉟ 2 and 5 **10**   ㊱ 4 and 16 **16**   ㊲ 5 and 10 **10**   ㊳ 6 and 15 **30**

㊴ 2, 4, and 8 **8** ㊵ 3, 5, and 9 **45** ㊶ 3, 4, and 14 **84** ㊷ 6, 4, and 9 **36**

292 • Fractions and Mixed Numbers

Add or subtract. Reduce answers if possible.

$\frac{11}{9}$ (or $1\frac{2}{9}$) **43** $\frac{2}{3} + \frac{5}{9}$ **44** $\frac{1}{5} + \frac{3}{4}$ $\frac{19}{20}$ **45** $\frac{9}{10} - \frac{3}{5}$ $\frac{3}{10}$ **46** $\frac{1}{4} - \frac{1}{8}$ $\frac{1}{8}$

47 $\frac{2}{3} - \frac{1}{2}$ $\frac{1}{6}$ **48** $\frac{3}{4} - \frac{3}{8}$ $\frac{3}{8}$ **49** $\frac{2}{7} + \frac{5}{14}$ $\frac{9}{14}$ **50** $\frac{4}{5} + \frac{1}{10}$ $\frac{9}{10}$

51 $2\frac{1}{3} + \frac{3}{4}$ $3\frac{1}{12}$ **52** $4\frac{1}{4} - 2\frac{7}{8}$ $1\frac{3}{8}$ **53** $10\frac{1}{5} - 1\frac{1}{2}$ $8\frac{7}{10}$ **54** $2\frac{2}{3} + 5\frac{2}{3}$ $8\frac{1}{3}$

Change each improper fraction to a mixed or whole number.

55 $\frac{5}{4}$ $1\frac{1}{4}$ **56** $\frac{27}{5}$ $5\frac{2}{5}$ **57** $\frac{15}{2}$ $7\frac{1}{2}$ **58** $\frac{10}{3}$ $3\frac{1}{3}$ **59** $\frac{12}{6}$ 2

Change each mixed number to an improper fraction.

60 $2\frac{1}{3}$ $\frac{7}{3}$ **61** $3\frac{2}{7}$ $\frac{23}{7}$ **62** $1\frac{4}{5}$ $\frac{9}{5}$ **63** $4\frac{3}{4}$ $\frac{19}{4}$ **64** $3\frac{1}{8}$ $\frac{25}{8}$

Solve these problems.

65 If you roll a 0–5 cube many times, about what fraction of the time would you expect to roll a 4? $\frac{1}{6}$

66 If you roll a 0–5 cube, what is the probability of getting an even number? $\frac{3}{6}$ (or $\frac{1}{2}$)

67 If you roll a 0–5 cube, what is the probability of getting a 1 or a 5? $\frac{2}{6}$ (or $\frac{1}{3}$)

68 If you roll a 0–5 cube 150 times, about how many times would you expect to roll a 0?   **about 25**

69 If you roll a 0–5 cube many times, about what fraction of the time would you expect to roll either a 2 or a 4? About what fraction of the time would you expect not to roll a 0 or a 5?   **about** $\frac{1}{3}$; **about** $\frac{2}{3}$

70 If it takes $\frac{3}{4}$ of an hour to write an essay and $\frac{1}{2}$ an hour to edit it, how long will it take to write and edit the essay? At those rates of writing and editing, how long would it take to write and edit three essays?   **about $1\frac{1}{4}$ hours; about $3\frac{3}{4}$ hours**

Home Connections You may want to send Home Connections Blackline Masters pages 52–53 home, which provide additional activities families can complete together. These activities apply the skills being presented in this unit.

Portfolio Assessment As students work through the second half of this unit, the Portfolio Assessment task provided on Assessment Blackline Masters page 89 can be used to evaluate students' ability to use ratios to solve problems.

Performance Assessment The Performance Assessment Task 1 provided on Assessment Blackline Masters page 71–73 can be used at this time to evaluate students' proficiency with fractions. You may want to administer this assessment with individual students or in small groups.

Unit Project This would be a good time to assign the "Fair Advertising" project on pages 338 and 339. Students can begin working on the project in cooperative groups in their free time as you work through the unit. This project is a good opportunity for students to practice analyzing advertising for fairness.

ASSESSMENT p. 33

Student Edition pages 294–297

Keeping Sharp

Keeping Sharp

Mrs. Norton needs to rent a car. She will use it for two days and will drive between 100 and 200 miles. She has a choice of three companies.

Sure Thing Auto Rental charges $18.95 per day plus 15¢ per mile. Cheap Auto Rental Company charges $23.95 per day plus 12¢ per mile. Comfo-Car Rental Company charges $34.95 per day with 200 free miles plus 12¢ per mile over 200.

Solve these problems.

❶ Which automobile company will be least expensive? **Sure Thing**

❷ If Mrs. Norton drives less than 100 miles, which company will be least expensive? **Sure Thing**

❸ If Mrs. Norton drives 300 miles, which company will be least expensive? **Comfo-Car**

LESSON PLANNER

Objectives

▶ to have students analyze consumer information and then make decisions based on their analyses

▶ to provide practice in converting fractions to decimals, adding decimals, and judging the relative magnitudes of fractions and decimals

▶ to provide practice in using a calculator

Context of the Lesson This lesson constitutes a pause in the 20-lesson sequence on fractions.

 **MANIPULATIVES**
none

Program Resources
Number Cubes (0–5 and 5–10)
Practice Master 82
Enrichment Master 82
The Cruncher*
For extra practice:
CD-ROM* Lesson 82

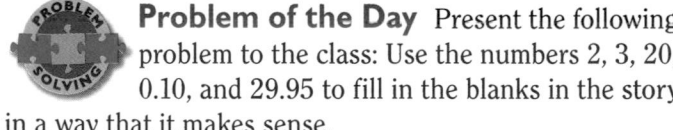
❶ Warm-Up
5 MINUTES

 Problem of the Day Present the following problem to the class: Use the numbers 2, 3, 20, 0.10, and 29.95 to fill in the blanks in the story in a way that it makes sense.

Sally bought _____ shirts at $_____ each. She paid with _____ $_____ bills, and her change was $_____.
(2, 29.95, 3, 20, 0.10)

Problem-Solving Strategies Ask students who have solved the Problem of the Day to share how they solved it and any strategies they used.

MENTAL MATH Ask students to brainstorm a list of 10 things that weigh about as much as a kilogram and 10 that weigh about as much as 10 kilograms.

COOPERATIVE LEARNING As you circulate to observe groups working together on the problems on page 297, check to see that all members are participating actively, that they are communicating with one another in a productive way, that they are recording their strategies and results, and that they have a plan for presenting their findings.

*available separately

While planning to open a checking account, Joshua learned the rates charged by two local banks. The 8th National Bank charged $3.00 per month plus 10¢ for each check written. The 9th National Bank charged 25¢ for each check but did not have a monthly charge. Joshua plans to write between five and ten checks each month.

4 Which bank is likely to be less expensive for Joshua? **9th National**

5 If Joshua really does write between five and ten checks per month, can he be sure that the bank you answered in problem 4 will always be less expensive? **yes**

6 How many checks would Joshua have to write for the other bank to be less expensive? **more than 20**

Joshua's older sister Andrea lives in another city. She knows she wants to open a checking account with 10th Federal Bank since it has branches near her home and office, but she is choosing between three kinds of accounts.

The Basic account costs $4.00 per month with five free checks and costs 50¢ for each additional check.

The Standard account has no fees per check and no monthly charge, as long as the balance in the account is at least $750; if the balance is less than $750, there is an $8.50 charge that month.

The Super account has no fees per check and no monthly charge, as long as the balance in the account is at least $2000; if the balance is less than $2000, there is a $12.50 charge that month. The Super account pays 2% annual interest. (The Basic and Standard accounts do not pay interest.)

Andrea writes 25 to 30 checks per month.

7 How much will the Basic account cost her per month if she continues to write 25 to 30 checks? **between $14.00 and $16.50**

8 If Andrea cannot be sure of keeping more than $500 in her account, which account would be least expensive? **Standard**

9 If Andrea keeps about $2500 in her account for a year, how much interest would she earn with a Super account? **about $50.00**

10 Suppose Andrea plans to keep over $2000 in her account but knows there will be one or two months when her balance falls to around $1500. Which account would have the lowest net cost? **Super (the interest compensates for the fees)**

Unit 4   Lesson 82   •   **295**

Technology Connection Refer students to the software *Prevocational Math Series* from Shopware (Apple, Mac, IBM for grades 3–8) for further practice with basic consumer math skills (story scenarios demonstrate how math can be used at home, on the job, or while shopping).

❷ Teach

Using the Student Pages To provide practice with fractions and decimals, you may wish to introduce the "Make 2" game on page 296 first so that students who finish pages 294–295 early can begin playing.

Students may solve the problems on page 294 in several ways, and will benefit from discussing their strategies and solutions with others. Here is one approach.

If Mrs. Norton travels 200 miles, she would pay the following:

Sure Thing: ($18.95 × 2) + ($0.15 × 200) = $67.90

Cheap: ($23.95 × 2) + ($0.12 × 200) = $71.90

Comfo-Car: ($34.95 × 2) = $69.90

Clearly, Sure Thing has the cheapest rates if Mrs. Norton drives 200 miles. Students can explore how rates compare if she were to drive 175 miles, 150 miles, or 110 miles. One way to do this is to make function tables for the companies whose rates vary with mileage driven, and then graph both sets of data on the same graph in order to see the point at which one company becomes less expensive than the other. Ask students to explain what the point at the intersection of the two lines shows. You may find it useful to review or provide practice in graphing ordered pairs.

Assign the problems on page 295. Again, some students may find making function tables a useful way to compare the data and identify the cheaper bank in the first set of problems. You may wish to point out that the problems Joshua, Andrea, and Mrs. Norton have to solve are common everyday problems that people tackle using their math problem-solving strategies.

Students can use blank **Cruncher*** spreadsheets to help compare the car rental costs and the bank fees on these pages.

◆ LESSON 82 Keeping Sharp

Teach

Introducing the "Make 2" Game Have students play the "Make 2" game after completing page 295, and again after completing page 297. Demonstrate this game by playing it with a student as the rest of the class watches. Try to be sure that everyone sees the difference between this game and the "Make 1" game, which was introduced earlier. This game involves using mathematical reasoning to choose which numbers to make, finding decimal equivalents of fractions, and adding decimals. Students can use a blank **Cruncher*** spreadsheet to help them record their scores. A copy of this game can also be found on page 29 of the Home Connections Blackline Masters.

COOPERATIVE LEARNING Have students work in small groups to solve the problems on page 297. As students work, walk around the room, looking in on each group and offering help as needed. Guide students to check their answers for reasonableness.

AT RISK Meeting Individual Needs

You may wish to present your at-risk students with a problem to solve that is more in tune with their interests than car rental or banking issues. For example, you can provide or have students gather take-out menus from pizza restaurants to have these students plan the most reasonable purchases to make for a class party. They can choose among different sizes and prices of pizza, a variety of toppings with different costs, and a variety of sizes and prices of soft drinks.

◆ LESSON 82 Keeping Sharp   COOPERATIVE LEARNING

Make 2 Game

GAME

Players:	Two
Materials:	Two 0–5 cubes, two 5–10 cubes
Object:	To get closer to 2 without going over
Math Focus:	Finding decimal equivalents of common fractions, adding common fractions and decimal equivalents, and mathematical reasoning

RULES

1. The first player chooses a starting number in decimal form between 0.50 and 1.50.

2. The second player rolls all four cubes, uses any two of the numbers rolled to make a fraction or a decimal, and adds this amount to the first player's starting number. The second player gets the score.

3. The players reverse roles and repeat steps 1 and 2.

4. The player who makes an amount closer to 2 without going over is the winner of the round.

SAMPLE GAME

Eduardo and Polly were playing.

Round 1:	Eduardo chose 1.47.	Polly rolled 2, 4, 5, and 10. She made 0.52.
	Polly chose 1.25.	Eduardo rolled 2, 3, 8, and 10. He made $\frac{2}{3}$, which is about 0.67.

Polly won this round because 1.47 + 0.52 is closer to 2 than 1.25 + 0.67.

In your Math Journal explain the strategies you used when playing the game. Did it make a difference what number the first player chose?

296 • Fractions and Mixed Numbers

Literature Connection Have students read some of the math tricks in *Math-a-Magic Number Tricks for Magicians* by Laurence B. White, Jr. and Ray Broekel.

RETEACHING

Aside from continuing any extra help begun in previous lessons, no reteaching is necessary at this time. You may want to assign Enrichment Master 82.

*available separately

COOPERATIVE LEARNING Work in groups and use a calculator to solve the following problems. Discuss in your group whether your solutions make sense.

11 There are 307 sixth-grade students in the South Prauline School. By contract no more than 25 students can be put in one classroom with one teacher. How many teachers and classrooms will be needed for the sixth grade? If students are divided as equally as possible among the teachers, how many students will each teacher have? **13 teachers and classrooms will be needed. Five teachers will each have 23 students, and eight teachers will each have 24 students**

12 There are 2056 students who attend the South Prauline School. A total of 1239 students walk to school or are brought by public transportation or by their parents. The others must be brought to school by school buses. If each school bus is allowed to carry no more than 40 students, what is the minimum number of bus trips necessary? Is it possible that more bus trips will be necessary? **At least 21 bus trips, each with about 39 students, are needed. More trips may be necessary if the students live over a wide area.**

13 The North Prauline School has only 79 sixth-grade students. By contract only 25 students can be assigned to one classroom with one teacher, as in the South Prauline School. How many teachers and classrooms are needed for the North Prauline sixth grade? If students are divided as equally as possible, how many students will each teacher have? **Four teachers and classrooms will be needed. Three teachers will have 20 students and one teacher will have 19 students.**

14 Of the 517 students who attend the North Prauline School, 284 are brought on school buses. If school buses are allowed to transport no more than 40 students, what is the minimum number of bus trips needed? **8**

15 All of the sixth-grade students from both North Prauline School and South Prauline School are going on a field trip, along with their teachers and four parents per class. No more than 40 people can ride each bus.

   a. How many buses are needed to transport everyone going on the field trip from North Prauline School? **3**

   b. How many buses are needed to transport everyone going on the trip from South Prauline School? **10**

   c. If buses can carry some people from each school, how many buses are needed to transport everyone going on the field trip? **12**

Unit 4   Lesson 82 • **297**

❸ Wrap-Up ⏱ 5 MINUTES

In Closing To summarize the lesson, ask students how they think their school or school system assigns numbers of students to teachers.

Informal Assessment Observe students as they work on the rental car and banking problems to see whether they are following an organized, logical plan to solve the problems, and whether they are being thorough enough in their efforts to address all contingencies.

Assessment Criteria

Did the student . . .

✓ work out reasonable solutions to the problems on pages 294–295 in an organized manner?

✓ use charts or graphs appropriately to solve the problems?

✓ work cooperatively with others on the problems on page 297?

Homework Ask students to design what they believe is an ideal teacher-to-student ratio and write an explanation of why their choice works better than others.

Division by Fractions

LESSON PLANNER

Objective

▶ to illustrate the meaning of division by a fraction by presenting a practical problem

Context of the Lesson This is the 18th of 20 lessons on fractions.

 MANIPULATIVES

fraction models*

Program Resources

Practice Master 83

Enrichment Master 83

For extra practice:
CD-ROM* Lesson 83

Note: This lesson may take more than one day.

① Warm-Up ⏱ 5 MINUTES

 **Problem of the Day** Present the following problem to students: Patty had a 12-foot board from which she sawed 1-foot shelves. Each cut she made took her $2\frac{1}{4}$ minutes. She spent $13\frac{1}{2}$ minutes sawing. How many shelves did she make? (6)

Problem-Solving Strategies Ask students who have solved the Problem of the Day to share how they solved it and any strategies they used.

 MENTAL MATH Present the problems shown below. Ask students to stand if the sum or difference is equal to 2, to show thumbs up if it is greater than 2, or to show thumbs down if it is less than 2.

a. $\frac{3}{4} + \frac{5}{4}$ (stand)

b. $0.75 + \frac{5}{4}$ (stand)

c. $\frac{2}{3} + \frac{1}{2}$ (thumbs down)

d. $\frac{2}{3} + \frac{6}{3}$ (thumbs up)

e. $2.31 - \frac{1}{8}$ (thumbs up)

f. $2.31 - \frac{1}{2}$ (thumbs down)

g. $1\frac{3}{5} + \frac{2}{5}$ (stand)

h. $4\frac{3}{5} - 2\frac{3}{5}$ (stand)

Division by Fractions

ACT IT OUT

A Material Problem with Fractions

Mr. Alekos has $32\frac{1}{2}$ yards of material from which to make suits. Each suit requires $1\frac{2}{3}$ yards of material. How many suits can Mr. Alekos make from $32\frac{1}{2}$ yards of material?

◆ Estimate an answer to this problem. Can you narrow the range of possible answers? **Answers will vary. Possible answer: The answer is between 32 ÷ 2, or 16 and 33 ÷ 1.5, or 22.**

Work in groups. Find at least three different ways to solve this problem.

◆ Does each way of solving the problem give you the same answer? How can you check to be sure your answer is right? **Answers are in margin**

Why teach it this way?

The multiplicity of methods introduced here is presented to spark students' interest and may stimulate their critical thinking processes. It is not essential that students fully understand all of the approaches presented. This lesson also helps students develop an understanding of division by fractions. It prepares them for upcoming lessons in which they will use a procedure for dividing fractions that involves multiplicative inverses.

*available separately

There are many ways to find out how many suits Mr. Alekos can make. Here are five different ways.

A. By multiplying

$1\frac{2}{3}$ yards for one suit

5 yards for three suits (we multiplied by 3)

30 yards for 18 suits (we multiplied by 6)

$31\frac{2}{3}$ yards for 19 suits (we added 1 suit)

This leaves $\frac{1}{3} + \frac{1}{2}$, or $\frac{5}{6}$, of a yard of material. It is not enough for another suit.

Mr. Alekos can make 19 suits.

B. By adding

$1\frac{2}{3} + 1\frac{2}{3} + 1\frac{2}{3}$ and so on until the total passes $32\frac{1}{2}$. Then count how many times you wrote $1\frac{2}{3}$ before the total passed $32\frac{1}{2}$.

The answer is 19.

Mr. Alekos can make 19 suits.

C. By changing the numbers to decimals and dividing

$1\frac{2}{3}$ is about 1.667.

$32\frac{1}{2}$ is the same as 32.5.

$$1.667)\overline{32.500}$$

$$\begin{array}{r} 19 \\ 1667)\overline{32500} \\ \underline{1667} \\ 15830 \\ \underline{15003} \\ 827 \end{array}$$

Mr. Alekos can make 19 suits.

(If you used a calculator, you could divide 32.5 by 1.6666667. You would get 19.499999, which would tell you that Mr. Alekos can make 19 suits.)

This lesson provides an opportunity for students to work cooperatively to solve an unfamiliar, challenging, and perhaps frustrating problem. Before students begin, you may wish to encourage them to try to be good communicators and listeners, open to different ideas and approaches. Guide them to plan how to undertake the task in an organized way as a group, and how to record and then present their methods and findings in an effective manner.

② Teach

ACT IT OUT

Using the Student Pages Without having students open their texts, explain the problem Mr. Alekos had with the material. Write the key information on the chalkboard and ask the question, "How many suits can Mr. Alekos make?" Have students work in small groups to try to devise different ways to solve the problem. Observe groups to see how many solution methods they can find. You may wish to explain to students that they will have a few minutes the next day to explore the problem in preparation for a class discussion. As students finish, invite them to play any of the games introduced in the unit so far.

On the second day of the lesson, give groups a few minutes to work on other solutions for Mr. Alekos. Then have each group report its ideas to the class.

Answers to Second Discussion Question:

All viable methods should produce the answer that he can make 19 suits and have some material left over. This answer can be checked using multiplication. $19 \times 1\frac{2}{3} = 31\frac{2}{3}$ and $20 \times 1\frac{2}{3} = 33\frac{1}{3}$.

Bring up and discuss any of the five methods shown on pages 299 and 300 that have not already been presented and discussed by any of the groups. Note that Method C is particularly useful if students have calculators.

There are many other ways to solve the problem. For instance, students might convert from yards to feet and find $97\frac{1}{2} \div 5$.

◆ LESSON 83   Division by Fractions

Teach

Using the Student Pages Have students work in pairs to solve the equations and word problems on page 301 using any of the methods introduced in the lesson. Some students may find working with **fraction models*** useful. Others may benefit by acting out some of the situations. Encourage all reasonable approaches. Guide students to share unusual solution methods.

◆ LESSON 83   Division by Fractions

D. By intelligent guessing and multiplying

$$1\tfrac{2}{3} \times n = 32\tfrac{1}{2}$$

Let's change $1\tfrac{2}{3}$ and $32\tfrac{1}{2}$ to improper fractions.

$$\tfrac{5}{3} \times n = \tfrac{65}{2}$$

$13 \times 5 = 65$ What can you multiply 3 by to get 2?

This is hard. Maybe you could multiply by an extra 3 in the numerator to get rid of the 3 in the $\tfrac{5}{3}$.

$$\tfrac{5}{3} \times \tfrac{13 \times 3}{?} = \tfrac{65 \times 3}{3 \times ?} = \tfrac{65}{2}$$

What number would you like the ? to stand for? You might choose 2 because $\tfrac{65 \times 3}{3 \times 2}$ is equivalent to $\tfrac{65}{2}$.

Try $\tfrac{13 \times 3}{2}$ for n.

$$\tfrac{5}{3} \times \tfrac{13 \times 3}{2} = \tfrac{65 \times 3}{3 \times 2} = \tfrac{65}{2}$$

$\tfrac{13 \times 3}{2}$ was the right number for n, but that was hard.

$$\tfrac{13 \times 3}{2} = \tfrac{39}{2} = 19\tfrac{1}{2}$$

So Mr. Alekos can make 19 suits (and have material left over for $\tfrac{1}{2}$ suit).

E. By dividing the fractions (after converting to mixed numbers)

$$\tfrac{65}{2} \div \tfrac{5}{3}$$

How can you do this? Find a common denominator. Since 6 is a multiple of both 2 and 3, rewrite the fractions as $\tfrac{195}{6} \div \tfrac{10}{6}$. Now both fractions have the same denominator.

You can think of the problem as 195 of something (sixths) divided by 10 of the same thing (sixths).

$195 \div 10 = 19.5$, or $19\tfrac{1}{2}$

So Mr. Alekos can make 19 suits (with material left over for $\tfrac{1}{2}$ suit).

300 • Fractions and Mixed Numbers

Literature Connection Have students read *Woodsong* by Gary Paulsen. Ask them to figure out how many half-mile segments are in the 1100-mile Iditarod.

RETEACHING

Reteaching is not recommended at this time unless students still need help with addition, subtraction, and multiplication of fractions. Refer to suggestions in the appropriate preceding lessons if necessary.

*available separately

Divide the following fractions. Give your answer as a fraction or whole number.

❶ $\frac{24}{37} \div \frac{8}{37}$ **3** **❷** $\frac{8}{37} \div \frac{24}{37}$ **$\frac{1}{3}$** **❸** $\frac{3}{11} \div \frac{6}{11}$ **$\frac{1}{2}$**

❹ $\frac{5}{7} \div \frac{3}{4}$ **$\frac{20}{21}$** **❺** $\frac{3}{8} \div \frac{4}{9}$ **$\frac{27}{32}$** **❻** $\frac{42}{5} \div \frac{14}{5}$ **3**

❼ $\frac{8}{9} \div \frac{4}{3}$ **$\frac{2}{3}$** **❽** $\frac{4}{3} \div \frac{8}{9}$ **$\frac{3}{2}$** **❾** $\frac{3}{4} \div \frac{8}{9}$ **$\frac{27}{32}$**

Solve the following problems.

❿ Ms. Wilkins needs $4\frac{2}{3}$ yards of material to make one pair of curtains. She has $43\frac{1}{6}$ yards of material. How many pairs of curtains can she make? Will she have any material left over? How much?   **9; yes; $1\frac{1}{6}$ yd.**

⓫ Two schools are going to have a long-distance relay race. Each team must run $16\frac{1}{2}$ miles. Each runner will run only $\frac{3}{4}$ of a mile before handing off the baton to the next runner. How many runners will each school need on its relay team? **22**

⓬ Jeremy was serving pizzas at the school picnic. Each student was supposed to get $\frac{3}{8}$ of a pizza. Jeremy had $5\frac{1}{2}$ pizzas to serve. How many students did he serve? Was there any pizza left over? How much? **14; yes, $\frac{1}{4}$ of a pizza**

⓭ Giorgio ran $14\frac{1}{2}$ laps around the track. His younger brother, Sam, ran $5\frac{1}{4}$ laps. "I ran three times as far as you," said Giorgio. "No, you didn't," said Sam, "$5\frac{1}{4} \times 3$ is $15\frac{3}{4}$ laps. You only ran $14\frac{1}{2}$ laps." Who's right? Exactly how many times Sam's distance did Giorgio run? **Sam; $2\frac{16}{21}$**

⓮ Donna knows it takes her about $\frac{1}{4}$ hour to walk a mile.

    a. How many hours will it take her to walk $1\frac{1}{2}$ miles? **$\frac{3}{8}$ hour**

    b. About how many minutes is that?
    about 22–23 minutes

Unit 4 Lesson 83 • **301**

---

❸ Wrap-Up

5 MINUTES

In Closing To summarize the lesson, ask students to evaluate the usefulness of the different methods given for solving Mr. Alekos's problem.

Be sure that students correctly interpret their answers. A student who says that in problem 10 there will be $\frac{1}{4}$ yard of material left over may have found an answer of $9\frac{1}{4}$ and assumed that the $\frac{1}{4}$ had to do with yards rather than pairs of curtains. To make $\frac{1}{4}$ of a pair of curtains requires $1\frac{1}{6}$ yards of material.

Informal Assessment Observe students as they work in groups to solve the problem facing Mr. Alekos as well as the problems on page 301. Check to see that all students are participating in a meaningful way, that they are listening and are supportive of the ideas of others, and that they are showing an open-mindedness when faced with more than one method for solving an unfamiliar kind of problem.

Assessment Criteria

Did the student . . .

✓ actively participate in the problem-solving process?

✓ listen to and respect the problem-solving ideas of classmates?

Homework Have students play the "Make 2" game on page 296 with a family member to practice adding and converting between fractions and decimals. A copy of this game can also be found on page 29 of the Home Connections Blackline Masters.

Functions

ALGEBRA READINESS

In each case tell what number *n* stands for or what number the ? stands for. Watch which way each arrow goes.

① 7 → (×5) → n **35**   ② 5 → (+4) → n **9**

③ 18 → (−9) → n **9**   ④ 18 → (÷9) → n **2**

⑤ 10 → (+?) → 14 **4**   ⑥ 10 → (×?) → 30 **3**

⑦ 15 → (×$\frac{2}{3}$) → n **10**   ⑧ 10 → (×$\frac{3}{2}$) → n **15**

⑨ n ← (×$\frac{3}{4}$) ← 8 **6**   ⑩ 6 → (×$\frac{4}{3}$) → n **8**

⑪ n → (×$\frac{1}{2}$) → 7 **14**   ⑫ n ← (×2) ← 7 **14**

⑬ n → (×$\frac{3}{5}$) → 9 **15**   ⑭ n ← (×$\frac{5}{3}$) ← 9 **15**

⑮ 28 → (×$\frac{4}{7}$) → n **16**   ⑯ 28 ← (×?) ← 16 **$\frac{7}{4}$**

⑰ n → (×3) → 21 **7**   ⑱ 7 ← (×$\frac{1}{3}$) ← n **21**

If you multiply 15 by $\frac{2}{3}$, you will get 10. What can you multiply 10 by to get 15? **$\frac{3}{2}$**

Do you see a relationship between $\frac{2}{3}$ and $\frac{3}{2}$?

We can show this with arrows:

10 (×$\frac{2}{3}$) (×$\frac{3}{2}$) 15

LESSON PLANNER

Objectives

▶ to review the concept of functions and the notation for working with functions

▶ to help students develop the concept of the multiplicative inverse and to show how it can be used to "undo" multiplication

▶ to introduce the relationship between multiplicative inverses and division

Context of the Lesson This is the 19th of 20 lessons on fractions. The arrow notation for functions should be familiar to students who have worked with this program. Extensive work with functions and graphing is provided in Unit 5.

 MANIPULATIVES   **Program Resources**

none   Practice Master 84

Enrichment Master 84

For extra practice:
CD-ROM* Lesson 84

① Warm-Up ⏱ 5 MINUTES

 **Problem of the Day** Present the following puzzler to the class: Five robots can put together five space shuttle parts in five minutes. If they are able to continue working at that rate, how many parts could they put together in five hours? (300)

Problem-Solving Strategies Ask students who have solved the Problem of the Day to share how they solved it and any strategies they used.

 MENTAL MATH Use these problems to review arithmetic strategies:

a. 144   142
   +298   +300
   (442)   442

b.   49   48
   + 99   +100
   (148)   148

c. 608   609
   −199   −200
   (409)   409
   (add 1)

d. 555   556
   −499   −500
   (56)   56
   (add 1)

Why teach it at this time?

The work with inverse functions in this lesson prepares students to learn about using the multiplicative inverse to divide by fractions in Lesson 85.

LITERATURE CONNECTION

Literature Connection Invite students to use arrow notation to represent Gulliver's age throughout the first chapter of Jonathan Swift's *Gulliver's Travels*.

RETEACHING

A complete review and extension of functions and graphing is given in the following unit. At this time, the only reteaching necessary is to help students who have difficulty understanding the arrow notation for function machines. You may wish to draw a "function machine" for students who need help visualizing the meaning of input and output.

*available separately

What number does the ? stand for? What number does *n* stand for? Find ? and *n*.

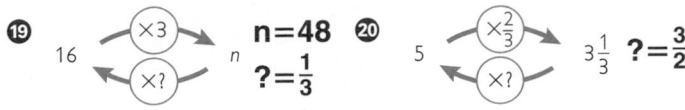

19 16 $\times 3$ / $\times ?$ → *n* **n=48** **?=$\frac{1}{3}$**

20 5 $\times \frac{2}{3}$ / $\times ?$ → $3\frac{1}{3}$ **?=$\frac{3}{2}$**

21 16 $\times 3$ / $\div ?$ → *n* **n=48** **?=3**

22 30 $\times \frac{2}{3}$ / $\times ?$ → 20 **?=$\frac{3}{2}$**

23 56 $\div 7$ / $\times ?$ → *n* **n=8** **?=7**

24 36 $\times ?$ / $\times \frac{3}{2}$ → *n* **?=$\frac{2}{3}$** **n=24**

25 56 $\times \frac{1}{7}$ / $\times ?$ → *n* **n=8** **?=7**

26 48 $\times ?$ / $\times \frac{4}{3}$ → *n* **?=$\frac{3}{4}$** **n=36**

27 7 $\times \frac{2}{3}$ / $\times ?$ → $4\frac{2}{3}$ **?=$\frac{3}{2}$**

28 24 $\times \frac{3}{8}$ / $\times ?$ → 9 **?=$\frac{8}{3}$**

29 20 $\times \frac{2}{5}$ / $\times ?$ → *n* **n=8** **?=$\frac{5}{2}$**

30 5 $\times \frac{3}{4}$ / $\times ?$ → *n* **n=$\frac{15}{4}$** **?=$\frac{4}{3}$**

For problems 35–38, solve for ? only.

31 *x* $\times \frac{2}{3}$ / $\times ?$ → *y* $\frac{3}{2}$

32 *x* $\times \frac{3}{5}$ / $\times ?$ → *y* $\frac{5}{3}$

33 *x* $\times 4$ / $\times ?$ → *y* $\frac{1}{4}$

34 *x* $\times 1\frac{1}{2}$ / $\times ?$ → *y* $\frac{2}{3}$

Unit 4 Lesson 84 • **303**

---

② Teach

Using the Student Pages Do several examples together with the class to review arrow notation. Explain how to solve for what is missing. You may wish to provide a few more examples. Be sure to vary whether the input, output, or function rule is missing. When students appear to understand the function notation, go over the example at the bottom of page 302, focusing on the inverse relationship between the two function rules.

For problems 24 and 26 on page 303, encourage students to start with the first number and work backward. For problems 31–34, emphasize that students are not expected to solve for both *x* and *y*. Suggest that they choose any non-zero number for *x*, find out what *y* must be, and then decide what ? stands for.

③ Wrap-Up 🕔 5 MINUTES

In Closing Summarize the lesson by asking students to explain with examples how to follow function notation to determine the missing number.

ALTERNATIVE ASSESSMENT **Performance Assessment** Write three functions on the chalkboard: one missing the input number, one the output number, and one the function rule. Ask students to solve them. Observe students as they work, asking questions to assess their understanding.

Assessment Criteria

Did the student . . .

✓ demonstrate understanding of function notation?

✓ demonstrate ability to use the given information to solve for the missing input numbers, output numbers, and function rules?

✓ express ability to find multiplicative inverses?

ART CONNECTION **Homework** Students might enjoy "inventing" their own unique function machines and sharing their drawings with classmates. Remind them that each machine needs a place where the data is input, a place where the data gets something done to it, and a place where the output data gets "cranked out."

PRACTICE p. 84

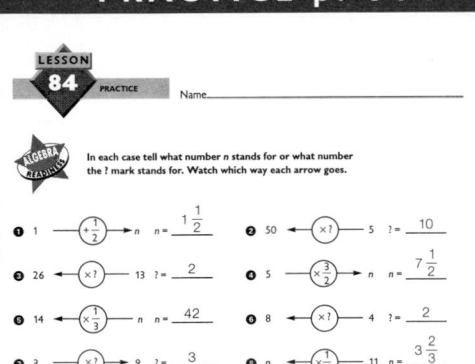

ENRICHMENT p. 84

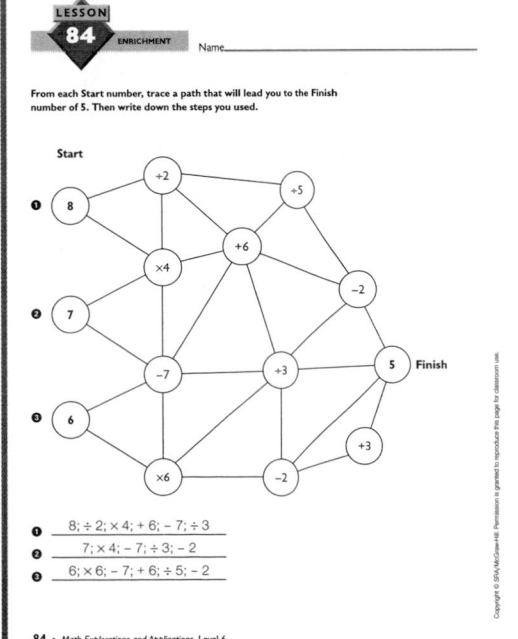

LESSON 85

Dividing Fractions

LESSON 85

Dividing
Fractions

LESSON PLANNER

Objectives

✓ to demonstrate how to divide by fractions by inverting and multiplying

▶ to provide practice in dividing by fractions

Context of the Lesson This is the last of 20 lessons on fractions. This lesson contains Mastery Checkpoint 18 for assessing students' proficiency in multiplying and dividing fractions.

 **MANIPULATIVES**

newspaper (financial section)

Program Resources

Reteaching Master

Practice Master 85

Enrichment Master 85

Assessment Master

The Cruncher*

For extra practice:
CD-ROM* Lesson 85

---

❶ Warm-Up ⏱ 5 MINUTES

 Problem of the Day Present the following problem: Angela went to three stores on a shopping trip. She spent $10 less than half her money at the first store she went to. She spent $\frac{3}{5}$ of what she had left at the next store. At the third store, she spent $5 more than half of the money she had left. If she had $12 left after all the shopping, with how much money did she begin her trip? ($150)

Problem-Solving Strategies Ask students who have solved the Problem of the Day to share how they solved it and any strategies they used.

MENTAL MATH Present the following problems for students to solve mentally.

a. $\frac{1}{2} \times 3000 = $ (1500)

b. $200 - 50\frac{1}{2} = (149\frac{1}{2})$

c. $100 \div \frac{1}{2} = (200)$

d. $\frac{3}{4} \times 6000 = (4500)$

e. $4000 \div \frac{1}{4} = (16,000)$

f. $20\frac{3}{4} + 10\frac{1}{2} = (31\frac{1}{4})$

Dividing Fractions

You found this pattern in problem 31 of the previous lesson.

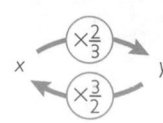

If you multiply any number by $\frac{2}{3}$ and then multiply the product by $\frac{3}{2}$, you get back the number with which you started. Try it with a few numbers.

The fraction $\frac{3}{2}$ is called the **reciprocal** or **multiplicative inverse** of $\frac{2}{3}$.

And $\frac{2}{3}$ is the reciprocal of $\frac{3}{2}$.

When a fraction and its reciprocal are multiplied, their product is 1.

We find the reciprocal by switching the numerator and the denominator.

Multiplying by the reciprocal of a number does the opposite of multiplying by the number.

Dividing by a number also does the opposite of multiplying by the number.

◆ Why might the reciprocal be called the multiplicative inverse?
Multiplying by the reciprocal is the inverse function of multiplying by the number. To divide by a number, you can multiply by its reciprocal.

Example: $24 \div \frac{2}{3} = ?$

Instead of dividing by $\frac{2}{3}$, multiply by $\frac{3}{2}$.

$24 \times \frac{3}{2} = 36$

36 should be the answer to $24 \div \frac{2}{3}$.

Since multiplication and division are inverse operations, you can check that answer by multiplying $\frac{2}{3} \times 36$ to see if you get 24.

304 • Fractions and Mixed Numbers

CULTURAL DIVERSITY Display currency from several countries, and invite students to bring in examples of currency from other countries for students to examine and compare with American money. Ask students to look for and describe what features all or most coins or bills have in common and to note the ways in which the currency differs.

Example: Kurt used $1\frac{1}{2}$ cups of sugar to make a pitcher of lemonade. The pitcher holds $8\frac{1}{3}$ glasses of lemonade. How much sugar is there in each glass (if the sugar is evenly distributed)?

$$1\frac{1}{2} \div 8\frac{1}{3} = ?$$

First estimate the answer. If we had 1 cup of sugar and 9 glasses, it would be about $\frac{1}{9}$ cup per glass. If there had been 2 cups of sugar and 8 glasses, it would be about $\frac{1}{4}$ cup per glass. The answer should be between these numbers.

We can find the precise answer by changing to improper fractions and dividing:

$$\frac{3}{2} \div \frac{25}{3} = \frac{3}{2} \times \frac{3}{25} = \frac{9}{50}$$

Each glass contains $\frac{9}{50}$ of a cup of sugar. You can see that this answer makes sense by converting it and the estimate to decimals and comparing them.

Example: Kurt is sharing the lemonade with 4 of his friends. If they all share the lemonade equally, how many glasses will each person receive?

$$8\frac{1}{3} \div 5 = ?$$

First, estimate the answer. If the pitcher held only 5 glasses, each person would get 1 glass, and if it held 10 glasses, each person would get 2 glasses. The answer must be between 1 and 2.

To find the exact amount, change to improper fractions and divide:

$$8\frac{1}{3} \div 5 = \frac{25}{3} \div \frac{5}{1} = {}^{5}\frac{\cancel{25}}{3} \times \frac{1}{\cancel{5}\,1} = \frac{5}{3}$$

The answer is $\frac{5}{3}$ or $1\frac{2}{3}$. Each person can have $1\frac{2}{3}$ glasses of lemonade.

This agrees with our estimate.

Unit 4 Lesson 85 • **305**

②Teach

Using the Student Pages Discuss pages 304 and 305 with the class, perhaps giving a few examples to show that either multiplying by the multiplicative inverse or dividing will "undo" multiplication. Then go over the examples, which show the entire procedure for dividing by multiplying by the multiplicative inverse.

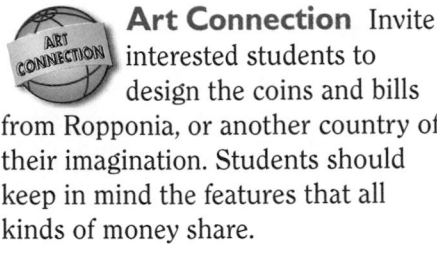 **Art Connection** Invite interested students to design the coins and bills from Ropponia, or another country of their imagination. Students should keep in mind the features that all kinds of money share.

◆ LESSON 85 Dividing Fractions

Teach

Using the Student Pages Have students solve problems 1–24 on page 306 on their own, guiding them to refer to the example at the top of the page or to those on the preceding two pages. Have them work on problem 25 in small groups. When groups have finished, discuss this problem. Emphasize that improper fractions are acceptable answers.

Social Studies Connection Discuss the information presented on page 307 about currency exchange. Invite students who have traveled to other countries or are otherwise familiar with other currencies to share some of their experiences exchanging money. You may wish to bring in copies of recent currency exchange rates for students to examine in addition to the one in today's **newspaper**. Ask them to describe what they see. Then explain or have a volunteer explain how to read the tables. Discuss the changes in values. Ask students to guess why the rates change. Have students work in pairs on the problems.

Students can use a blank **Cruncher*** spreadsheet to help them calculate currency equivalents.

SPECIAL NEEDS

Meeting Individual Needs
For students who have difficulty finding the multiplicative inverse of the divisor, show them how to write the divisor as a fraction and then how to "turn it upside down," or invert it. Then provide practice writing inverses. If students have difficulty remembering which number to invert, guide them to think of function machines. Point out that it is the function rule that is changed, not the input.

◆ LESSON 85 Dividing Fractions

Remember: To divide by a number you can multiply by its reciprocal.

Examples:

$$\frac{3}{7} \div \frac{5}{9} = \frac{3}{7} \times \frac{9}{5} = \frac{27}{35}$$

⑪ $\frac{9}{8}$ (or $1\frac{1}{8}$)

$$32\frac{1}{2} \div 1\frac{2}{3} = \frac{65}{2} \div \frac{5}{3} = \frac{65}{2} \times \frac{3}{5}$$

⑬ $\frac{3}{2}$ (or $1\frac{1}{2}$)

⑲ $\frac{5}{2}$ (or $2\frac{1}{2}$)

$$= \frac{13}{2} \times \frac{3}{1} = \frac{39}{2} = 19\frac{1}{2}$$

㉒ $\frac{8}{5}$ (or $1\frac{3}{5}$)

Divide. Reduce when possible.

① $12 \div \frac{2}{3}$ **18** ② $16 \div \frac{4}{5}$ **20** ③ $\frac{3}{7} \div \frac{3}{7}$ **1** ④ $\frac{6}{7} \div \frac{3}{7}$ **2**

⑤ $\frac{5}{12} \div \frac{10}{3}$ $\frac{1}{8}$ ⑥ $100 \div 25$ **4** ⑦ $12 \div 25$ $\frac{12}{25}$ ⑧ $\frac{3}{5} \div 7$ $\frac{3}{35}$

⑨ $\frac{1}{4} \div \frac{1}{2}$ $\frac{1}{2}$ ⑩ $\frac{1}{2} \div \frac{1}{4}$ **2** ⑪ $\frac{3}{8} \div \frac{1}{3}$ ⑫ $\frac{3}{8} \div 3$ $\frac{1}{8}$

⑬ $\frac{1}{2} \div \frac{1}{3}$ ⑭ $\frac{2}{5} \div \frac{3}{7}$ $\frac{14}{15}$ ⑮ $\frac{5}{8} \div \frac{5}{4}$ $\frac{1}{2}$ ⑯ $\frac{9}{4} \div \frac{3}{2}$ $\frac{3}{2}$ (or $1\frac{1}{2}$)

⑰ $\frac{12}{5} \div \frac{3}{5}$ **4** ⑱ $\frac{4}{7} \div \frac{2}{7}$ **2** ⑲ $\frac{5}{6} \div \frac{1}{3}$ ⑳ $\frac{1}{3} \div \frac{5}{6}$ $\frac{2}{5}$

㉑ $2\frac{1}{2} \div 4$ $\frac{5}{8}$ ㉒ $4 \div 2\frac{1}{2}$ ㉓ $\frac{5}{6} \div 2$ $\frac{5}{12}$ ㉔ $\frac{3}{5} \div \frac{2}{3}$ $\frac{9}{10}$

㉕ Use a calculator to solve problems 8, 9, 10, 12, 15, and 16 again. Compare your calculator answers with your fraction answers by changing the fraction answers to decimals. **8. 0.0857142; 9. 0.5; 10. 2; 12. 0.125;**
15. 0.5; 16. 1.5

For example, here's how you would solve problem 8. **The two answers should not differ except perhaps in the last decimal place.**

$$\frac{3}{5} \div 7 = 0.6 \div 7$$

Push ▣ 6 ⫶ 7 ═ ──➤ 0.0857142

Let's say your answer to $\frac{3}{5} \div 7$ was $\frac{3}{35}$ when you solved it with paper and pencil.

Find a decimal approximation for $\frac{3}{35}$ by dividing: $3 \div 35$.

Push 3 ⫶ 3 5 ═ ──➤ 0.0857142

Both methods give the same answer.

RETEACHING p. 27

LESSON 85 RETEACHING Name_____

Example:

Divide.

$\frac{3}{4} \div \frac{1}{8}$

$\frac{3}{4} \div \frac{1}{8} = \frac{3}{4} \times \frac{8}{1}$

To divide by a number is the same as to multiply by the reciprocal of the number.
The reciprocal of $\frac{1}{8}$ is $\frac{8}{1}$.

$\frac{3}{\cancel{4}} \times \frac{\cancel{8}^2}{1}$

Simplify before multiplying by dividing the numerator and the denominator by 4.

$\frac{3}{1} \times \frac{2}{1} = \frac{6}{1}$

Multiply the numerators. $3 \times 2 = 6$
Multiply the denominators. $1 \times 1 = 1$

$\frac{6}{1} = 6$ Simplify

Divide.

① $\frac{1}{2} \div \frac{3}{4}$ __$\frac{2}{3}$__ ② $4 \div \frac{2}{3}$ __6__ ③ $6 \div \frac{2}{3}$ __9__

④ $\frac{3}{4} \div \frac{7}{8}$ __$\frac{6}{7}$__ ⑤ $\frac{2}{3} \div \frac{1}{2}$ __$1\frac{1}{3}$__ ⑥ $\frac{1}{2} \div \frac{2}{3}$ __$\frac{3}{4}$__

⑦ $\frac{7}{8} \div \frac{1}{2}$ __$1\frac{3}{4}$__ ⑧ $\frac{3}{4} \div \frac{1}{3}$ __$2\frac{1}{4}$__ ⑨ $\frac{3}{4} \div \frac{1}{4}$ __$\frac{3}{16}$__

⑩ $5 \div \frac{3}{4}$ __$6\frac{2}{3}$__ ⑪ $\frac{1}{3} \div \frac{1}{4}$ __$1\frac{1}{3}$__ ⑫ $\frac{1}{2} \div \frac{1}{4}$ __2__

⑬ $5 \div \frac{2}{3}$ __$7\frac{1}{2}$__ ⑭ $4 \div \frac{1}{2}$ __8__ ⑮ $\frac{5}{6} \div \frac{1}{3}$ __$2\frac{1}{2}$__

Math Explorations and Applications Level 6 • **27**

PRACTICE p. 85

LESSON 85 PRACTICE Name_____

Multiply. Reduce when possible.

① $1\frac{1}{2} \times 2\frac{1}{3}$ __$3\frac{1}{2}$__ ② $3\frac{5}{8} \times \frac{2}{3}$ __$2\frac{5}{12}$__ ③ $\frac{7}{6} \times \frac{3}{2}$ __$\frac{3}{4}$__

④ $\frac{5}{4} \times \frac{4}{25}$ __$\frac{2}{5}$__ ⑤ $\frac{3}{2} \times \frac{1}{3}$ __$\frac{1}{2}$__ ⑥ $\frac{7}{8} \times \frac{5}{4}$ __$1\frac{3}{32}$__

⑦ $3\frac{1}{4} \times 1\frac{1}{3}$ __$4\frac{1}{3}$__ ⑧ $6\frac{1}{7} \times \frac{1}{2}$ __$3\frac{1}{14}$__ ⑨ $\frac{3}{4} \times \frac{6}{7}$ __$\frac{9}{14}$__

Divide. Reduce when possible.

⑩ $\frac{2}{3} \div 2$ __$\frac{1}{3}$__ ⑪ $\frac{2}{3} \div \frac{2}{3}$ __1__ ⑫ $\frac{6}{7} \times \frac{1}{4}$ __$\frac{1}{7}$__

⑬ $\frac{3}{8} \div \frac{1}{2}$ __$\frac{1}{2}$__ ⑭ $1\frac{1}{2} \div \frac{2}{3}$ __$\frac{11}{16}$__ ⑮ $2\frac{1}{6} \div 1\frac{1}{3}$ __$1\frac{5}{8}$__

⑯ $6\frac{1}{2} \div \frac{3}{4}$ __$8\frac{2}{3}$__ ⑰ $\frac{9}{2} \div \frac{3}{8}$ __12__ ⑱ $\frac{3}{4} \div \frac{2}{3}$ __$1\frac{1}{8}$__

Multiply or divide. Reduce when possible.

⑲ $\frac{6}{4} \times \frac{5}{3}$ __$2\frac{1}{2}$__ ⑳ $\frac{6}{4} \div \frac{5}{3}$ __$\frac{9}{10}$__ ㉑ $1\frac{2}{3} \times 2\frac{1}{3}$ __$3\frac{8}{9}$__

㉒ $1\frac{2}{3} \div 2\frac{1}{3}$ __$\frac{5}{7}$__ ㉓ $\frac{3}{5} \div \frac{6}{7}$ __$\frac{7}{10}$__ ㉔ $\frac{3}{5} \times \frac{6}{7}$ __$\frac{18}{35}$__

㉕ $\frac{3}{7} \div \frac{2}{3}$ __$\frac{6}{7}$__ ㉖ $\frac{3}{7} \times 2$ __$\frac{6}{7}$__ ㉗ $\frac{3}{7} \times \frac{1}{2}$ __$\frac{3}{14}$__

Math Explorations and Applications Level 6 • **85**

SOCIAL STUDIES CONNECTION

How much is one dollar worth?

In the United States our basic unit of money, or currency, is the dollar. Other countries have different units of currency. Some of these units are shown in the chart.

Country	Currency
Mexico	peso
China	yuan
Japan	yen
Ecuador	sucre
Canada	dollar
India	rupee
United Kingdom	pound
Zambia	kwacha

The value of each currency changes as a result of changes in the economies of the different countries. For example, on April 30, 1970 the value of the British pound was 2.39 U.S. dollars. Twenty-four years later, on April 30, 1994, its value was 1.53 U.S. dollars.

26 Using the business section of a newspaper, find the value of each of these currencies today. **Answers will vary.**

At currency exchange locations, people can change one currency for another of the same value.

Suppose you are calculating currency values for Ropponia, Tropponia, and Dopponia. The units of currency in these imaginary countries are the ropple, the tropple, and the dopple.

One ropple is worth $\frac{5}{8}$ of one tropple.

One tropple is worth $\frac{4}{10}$ of one dopple.

One dopple is worth $2\frac{1}{2}$ tropples.

Answer these questions. Be sure your answers make sense.

27 How many ropples can you get for one dopple? **4**

28 How many dopples can you get for one ropple? $\frac{1}{4}$

29 Did you need all of the information you were given? **No; the second and third sentences mean the same thing.**

Unit 4 Lesson 85 • **307**

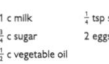
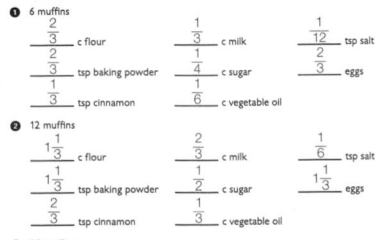

---

③ Wrap-Up  5 MINUTES

In Closing To summarize the lesson, ask students to explain what happens when they multiply a number by its multiplicative inverse.

ALTERNATIVE ASSESSMENT

Performance Assessment Have students divide 16 by $\frac{2}{3}$ and divide $\frac{4}{5}$ by $\frac{1}{2}$, and explain the procedure they used.

Mastery Checkpoint 18

At about this time most students should be able to multiply and divide fractions and mixed numbers. This ability may be assessed by observing students as they work on Assessment Blackline Masters page 34 or on a similar set of problems. Results of this assessment may be recorded on the Mastery Checkpoint Chart.

Assessment Criteria

Did the student . . .

✓ demonstrate ability in multiplying and dividing fractions and mixed numbers?

✓ demonstrate understanding of the concept of reciprocals?

✓ successfully complete the exercise set on page 306 by correctly answering at least 18 of the first 24 problems?

✓ correctly use division of fractions to solve the currency problems on page 307?

Homework Assign Practice Master 85 for further practice with dividing by fractions.

GIFTED & TALENTED Meeting Individual Needs
Invite students to create their own imaginary money system of various denominations, and then formulate problems about this money for classmates to solve.

Using Maps and Charts

LESSON PLANNER

Objectives

▶ to provide practice in calculating distances from others given on a map

▶ to provide practice in completing a matrix that shows distances between cities

Context of the Lesson This lesson contains information that will be used in the following lesson on ratios.

 MANIPULATIVES
none

Program Resources
Practice Master 86
Enrichment Master 86
The Cruncher*
For extra practice:
CD-ROM* Lesson 86
Cumulative Review, page 571

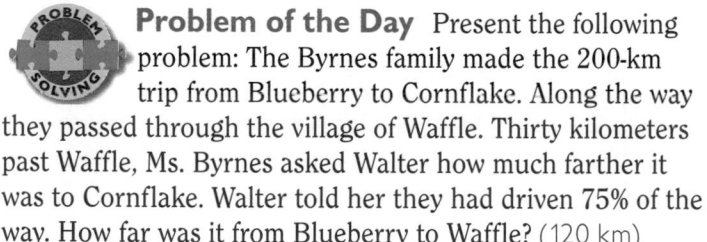 **① Warm-Up** 5 MINUTES

 Problem of the Day Present the following problem: The Byrnes family made the 200-km trip from Blueberry to Cornflake. Along the way they passed through the village of Waffle. Thirty kilometers past Waffle, Ms. Byrnes asked Walter how much farther it was to Cornflake. Walter told her they had driven 75% of the way. How far was it from Blueberry to Waffle? (120 km)

Problem-Solving Strategies Ask students who have solved the Problem of the Day to share how they solved it and any strategies they used.

MENTAL MATH Provide practice with breaking up large arithmetic problems into smaller ones:

a.
```
   66
 + 41
 (107)
```
(Think: 66 + 40 = 106, 106 + 1 = 107)

b.
```
   232      (add 2)      234
 −  98                  −100
 (134)                   134
```

(continued on page 309)

Using Maps and Charts

 GEOGRAPHY CONNECTION

The Rough-Ride Railroad Company runs a train line between East Village and West Village. Look at this map. It shows the stations on the line and the distances, in kilometers, between some of them.

How many kilometers is it from

① East Village to Granitetown? **13**

② East Village to Junction City? **17**

③ Granitetown to Middledorf? **15**

④ Middledorf to Princeton? **15**

⑤ Burgerville to Junction City? **14**

⑥ Princeton to West Village? **7**

⑦ Princeton to Princeton? **0**

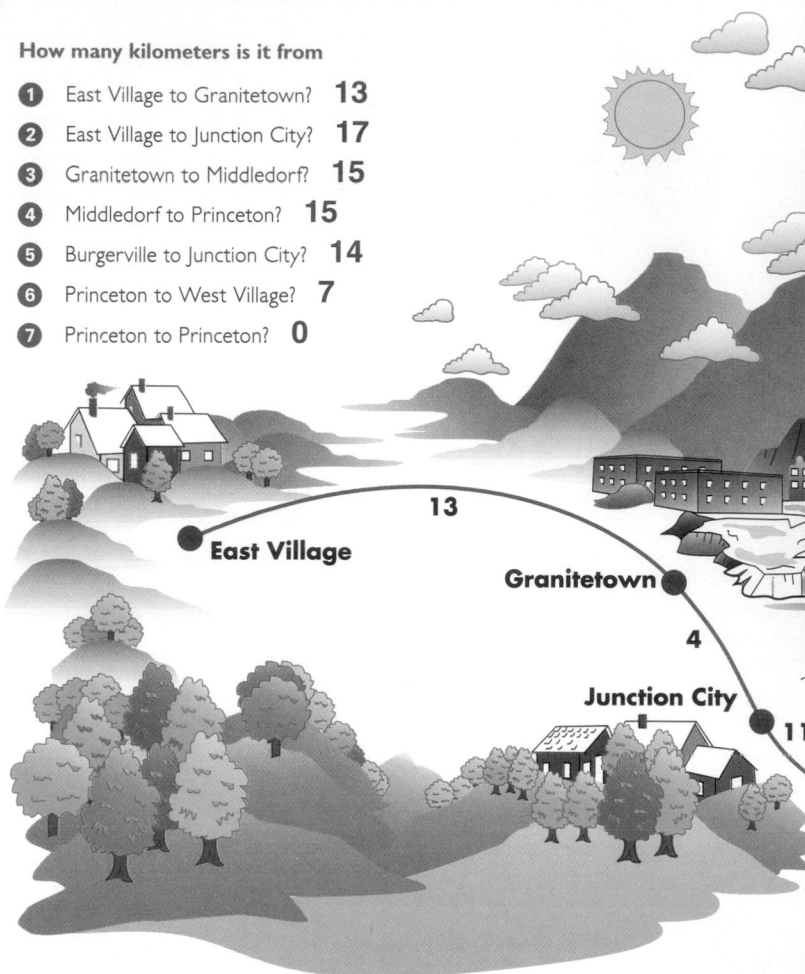

RETEACHING

No reteaching is necessary at this point. However, you may wish to pair students who have difficulty reading maps or charts with students who are proficient.

*available separately

Use a computer or other means to draw a chart, and complete the chart to make a record of the distances between all the stations.

	East Village	Granitetown	Junction City	Middledorf	Burgerville	Princeton	West Village
East Village	0	13	17	28	31	43	50
Granitetown	13	0	4	15	18	30	37
Junction City	17	4	0	11	14	26	33
Middledorf	28	15	11	0	3	15	22
Burgerville	31	18	14	3	0	12	19
Princeton	43	30	26	15	12	0	7
West Village	50	37	33	22	19	7	0

Save your chart. You will need it for an upcoming lesson.

Answer the following questions.

8 What do the 0s mean in the chart? **They mean zero distance.**

9 Do you need to calculate every distance in the chart? **no**

10 What shortcuts did you use in completing the chart? **Answers may vary. One possibility is that you can use the fact that the distance between, say, East Village and Middledorf is the same as the distance between Middledorf and East Village.**

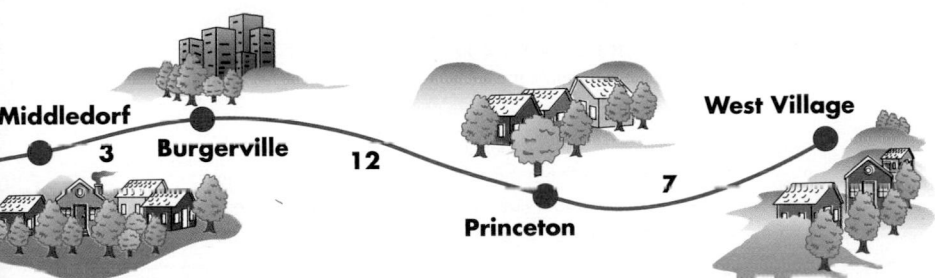
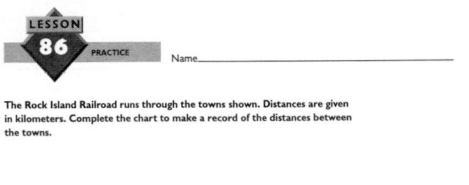

Use the Cumulative Review on page 571 after this lesson.

Unit 4   Lesson 86   • **309**

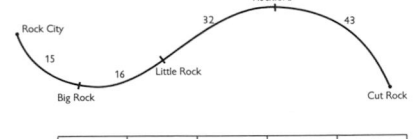

*available separately

Mental Math (continued)

c. $\begin{array}{r} 423 \\ + 37 \\ \hline (460) \end{array}$

$(423 + 30 = 453, 453 + 7 = 460)$

❷ Teach

Using the Student Pages Make sure students understand how to read the map on pages 308–309. Do one or two problems as a class, and then have students complete the rest on their own. Students can use a blank **Cruncher*** spreadsheet to create a chart like the one on page 309.

Discuss the distance chart. Have a volunteer explain the meaning of the numbers already filled in. Ask students to tell what information in the table can be filled in based on the given data. For example, if it is 43 km from East Village to Princeton, then it is 43 km from Princeton to East Village. Next discuss the advantages of using information displayed in a chart. Have students copy and complete this one and answer the questions on page 309.

❸ Wrap-Up

In Closing Summarize the lesson by presenting another map that shows distances between locations. Ask students to identify the distances between some of the places on the map.

Portfolio Assessment Ask students to brainstorm ways of inferring information not on the chart from the information given on the chart. Have students write a brief summary of these methods. Invite them to put this summary in their Math Portfolios.

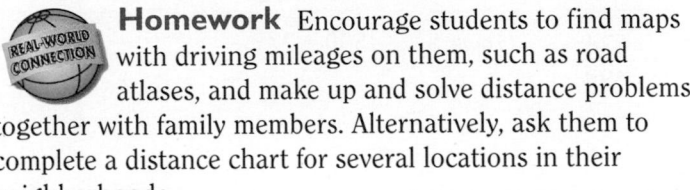

Assessment Criteria

Did the student . . .

✓ understand how to read the map?

✓ understand how to interpret and complete the distance chart?

Homework Encourage students to find maps with driving mileages on them, such as road atlases, and make up and solve distance problems together with family members. Alternatively, ask them to complete a distance chart for several locations in their neighborhoods.

Unit 4 Lesson 86   **309**

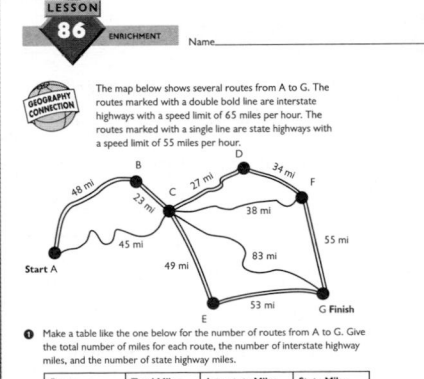

LESSON 87 Ratios

Student Edition pages 310–313

LESSON PLANNER

Objectives

▶ to review the concept of ratio as a way of comparing two numbers

▶ to provide practice in solving problems that involve ratios

▶ to provide practice in using timetables and fare schedules

Context of the Lesson
This is the first of six lessons on averages, rates, ratios, and proportions. The focus in this lesson is on the meaning of ratio and on understanding when and how to find and interpret ratios to solve problems.

✋ MANIPULATIVES	Program Resources
none	Practice Master 87
	Enrichment Master 87
	The Cruncher*
	For extra practice:
	CD-ROM* Lesson 87

---

❶ Warm-Up ⏱ 5 MINUTES

Problem of the Day Present the following problem: The third digit of a three digit number is one fourth of the first digit and twice the second digit. What is the number? (812)

Problem-Solving Strategies Ask students who have solved the Problem of the Day to share how they solved it and any strategies they used.

Write the following problems on the chalkboard. Have students use mental math to find each sum or difference. Invite volunteers to explain the steps they used to find the solutions.

a.　43　　(*Think 46 – 30 = 16*)
　　　−27
　　　(16)

b.　526　　(*Think 527 – 500 = 27*)
　　　−499
　　　(27)

(continued on page 311)

℞ Ratios

We usually compare numbers in one of these ways:

    A. We find the difference between the numbers.

    B. We find the quotient (or **ratio**) of the numbers.

    C. We simply report the numbers.

Suppose Penny rode 9 kilometers and Ross rode 6 kilometers.

A.   To find the difference, subtract 6 from 9. Using the difference we could say:

    "Penny rode 3 kilometers farther than Ross," or "Ross rode 3 kilometers less than Penny."

◆   Based on these statements alone, can you tell how far Ross and Penny rode? **no**

B.   To find the ratio, express the distances as a fraction. The ratio of Penny's distance to Ross's distance is $\frac{9}{6}$, which reduces to $\frac{3}{2}$, or $1\frac{1}{2}$. The ratio of Ross's distance to Penny's distance is $\frac{6}{9}$, which reduces to $\frac{2}{3}$. Using the ratio, we could say:

    "Penny rode $1\frac{1}{2}$ times as far as Ross," or "Ross rode $\frac{2}{3}$ as far as Penny."

◆   Based on these statements alone, can you tell how far Ross and Penny rode? **no**

C.   We may simply report the numbers and not find the difference or ratio. Then we would simply say:

    "Penny rode 9 kilometers, and Ross rode 6 kilometers."

◆   Based on this statement alone, can you tell how far Ross and Penny rode? **yes**

Notice that in the last statement we do not lose information. But the other two statements organize the information to emphasize certain points and may be more useful for some purposes.

How we choose to compare numbers depends on the kind of information we are trying to stress and how the information will be used. But just giving a number or numbers is not enough. You must use a sentence or phrase to show the meaning.

⬛ Why teach it at this time?

Students should begin to recognize that ratios are fractions, and that they are often a useful way of presenting information. The next several lessons involve calculating with ratios to find averages and proportions, which relate to the previous work with fractions. The next unit deals with yet another way to report information—displaying it in a graph.

 **C(O)OPERATIVE LEARNING**

Work in groups to consider the following statements. Think of ways in which you could report the information. Discuss which ways would be most useful. **Answers will vary. Possible answers are given.**

1 Emma bought a stamp for 25¢ and sold it for 50¢.
She made 25¢ or doubled her money.

2 Jan bought a lot of stamps for 25¢ each and sold them for 50¢ each. **She doubled her money or sold stamps for twice as much as she paid.**

3 It costs Mr. McLaren 20¢ per kilometer to drive his small car and 40¢ per kilometer to drive his van.
It costs twice as much to drive his van as his car.

4 Hal is 150 centimeters tall, and Lena is 143 centimeters tall.
Simply report both heights.

Read each of the following. Think of ways to report the information. Give the advantages of reporting it as a difference, as a ratio, or simply as numbers: **Accept all reasonably defended answers.**

5 Mary is 7 years old. Her sister is 14 years old. Mary was born in 1992. She'd like to know what year her sister was born. **Her sister was born in 1985. Mary is looking for a year, so a number is more useful than a ratio or a difference.**

6 A small container of milk holds one quart. A large container holds 4 quarts. We know that one quart will serve four people. **A large container contains four times as much milk as a small container. Using this ratio, you can determine how many people any amount of milk will serve.**

7 José walked 6 miles in two hours. **This information could be reported as raw data or as a ratio (3 miles in one hour) to predict something about José.**

8 Abigail walked 10 miles and Sam walked 7 miles.
A difference (3 miles) is the most useful way to compare how far Abigail and Sam walked.

9 Rachel made a shade of orange by mixing $\frac{1}{2}$ can of yellow paint with $\frac{1}{4}$ can of red paint. She wants to keep track of how much she used of each color so that she can make the shade again. **The information should be reported as a ratio so that the shade can be made from other amounts of paint.**

10 Tickets to a Saturday evening performance of a play cost $22.50. Tickets to a Sunday afternoon performance cost $19.00.
The information could be reported as a difference to show how much more expensive Saturday would be.

Unit 4   Lesson 87   •   **311**

Mental Math (continued)

c.
$$224 + 562 \atop (786)$$
$$224 + 500 \atop 724$$
$$724 + 60 \atop 784$$
$$784 + 2 \atop 786$$

d.
$$627 + 469 \atop (1096)$$
$$469 + 600 \atop 1069$$
$$1069 + 20 \atop 1089$$
$$1089 + 7 \atop 1096$$

e.
$$723 - 485 \atop (238)$$ (add 15)

f.
$$1328 - 514 \atop (814)$$ (subtract 14)

g.
$$867 - 290 \atop (577)$$ (add 10)

h.
$$1247 + 905 \atop (2152)$$

i.
$$723 + 298 \atop (1021)$$

j.
$$479 + 351 \atop (830)$$

② Teach

Using the Student Pages Discuss the material on page 310 with the class. Then have students work in small groups on problems 1–4 on page 311. Encourage them to offer and defend different answers. Afterward, bring all groups together to debate the different ways to report the information.

Have students work on problems 5–10 in small groups, as they did for problems 1–4. Instruct group members to accept all reasonably defended ways to report the information. Encourage them to try to come to a consensus regarding which ways make the most sense. Note that the statement for problem 7 cannot be reported as a difference.

◆ LESSON 87   Ratios

Teach

Using the Student Pages Begin working on pages 312 and 313 by asking a few direct questions to be sure that students interpret the information in the table correctly. For example, ask "What time does the Chug-Chug local leave the Middledorf station?" (8:48 A.M.) You may wish to point out that timetables for commuter trains show departure times. Tell students that trains generally arrive in the station a minute or two before the departure time, passengers board and get off, and then the trains leave the station. (Students need not take this into account when solving the problems.) Have students work on the problems on page 312 individually or in pairs. Discuss answers as a whole class.

When discussing problem 15 on page 313, ask students to tell whether fares appear to be greater for greater distances. You may wish to have them estimate how much the company charged for each kilometer a person traveled and check each estimate with the class. Next, discuss the rise in fares and the structure of the schedule of fares. Ask a volunteer to explain how the two fares already entered in the schedule were calculated, why they are placed where they are, and why some of the boxes are crossed out. Have students complete the table on their own. Students may use a blank **Cruncher*** spreadsheet to help them create and complete the table. Remind them of the change in the rate per kilometer.

◆ LESSON 87   Ratios

The Rough-Ride Railroad Company runs two trains a day from East Village to West Village. Here is the timetable for the two trains.

Rough-Ride Railroad Company Timetable

Station		Chug-Chug Local	East-West Express
East Village	Departs	8:00 A.M.	1:00 P.M.
Granitetown	Departs	8:21 A.M.	—
Junction City	Departs	8:27 A.M.	—
Middledorf	Departs	8:48 A.M.	—
Burgerville	Departs	9:04 A.M.	—
Princeton	Departs	9:16 A.M.	—
West Village	Arrives	9:30 A.M.	2:00 P.M.

11 About how many minutes does it take the Chug-Chug Local to go from

    a. East Village to Granitetown? **21**

    b. East Village to Middledorf? **48**

    c. East Village to Princeton? **76**

    d. Junction City to Middledorf? **21**

    e. Middledorf to West Village? **42**

    f. Princeton to West Village? **14**

12 About how many hours does it take to go from East Village to West Village on

    a. the Chug-Chug Local? **$1\frac{1}{2}$**

    b. the East-West Express? **1**

13 Why do you think the East-West Express is quicker? **It doesn't stop between East Village and West Village.**

14 It is 50 kilometers from East Village to West Village. Between those two stations what is the average speed

    a. of the East-West Express? **50 km/h**

    b. of the Chug-Chug Local? **$33\frac{1}{3}$ km/h**

312 • Fractions and Mixed Numbers

Literature Connection Have students read *The Hoboken Chicken Emergency* by D. Manus Pinkwater. Ask them to create a ratio to compare an average chicken's weight to that of Arthur's chicken, and to find other opportunities to apply ratio to the events in the story.

RETEACHING

To help students understand that a ratio is a way to compare two numbers by division, provide additional examples with simpler numbers. Emphasize that a rate is a way of comparing measurements with different units. Again, provide a few more examples. Then show that rates are calculated by dividing the first number by the second.

*available separately

Here are some of the fares that the Rough-Ride Railroad Company charged last year:

East Village to Middledorf $4.20

East Village to Princeton $6.45

Middledorf to Burgerville $0.45

Granitetown to Junction City .. $0.60

15 How do you think the fares were calculated? (Hint: Look at the chart of distances you made when you worked on page 309.) **The company charged $0.15 per kilometer.**

This year the Rough-Ride Railroad Company is charging $0.24 per kilometer. A worker at the company began to make a chart showing the fare between any two stations.

16 Why are some of the boxes on the chart crossed out? **There is no fare because there is no distance.**

17 Use a computer or other means to draw the chart below, and complete the chart.

Rough-Ride Railroad Company Schedule of Fares

	East Village	Granitetown	Junction City	Middledorf	Burgerville	Princeton	West Village
East Village		$3.12	$4.08	$6.72	$7.44	$10.32	$12.00
Granitetown	$3.12		$0.96	$3.60	$4.32	$7.20	$8.88
Junction City	$4.08	$0.96		$2.64	$3.36	$6.24	$7.92
Middledorf	$6.72	$3.60	$2.64		$0.72	$3.60	$5.28
Burgerville	$7.44	$4.32	$3.36	$0.72		$2.88	$4.56
Princeton	$10.32	$7.20	$6.24	$3.60	$2.88		$1.68
West Village	$12.00	$8.88	$7.92	$5.28	$4.56	$1.68	

Unit 4 Lesson 87 • **313**

---

③ Wrap-Up

In Closing To summarize the lesson, ask students to give an example of when it would be useful to use a ratio to present information.

Informal Assessment Circulate and observe students as they work on reporting the information, interpreting the railroad timetable, and completing the fare schedule. Be sure students are correctly using the data presented and the information from the chart of distances they made in the previous lesson about the Rough-Ride Railroad.

Assessment Criteria

Did the student . . .

✓ demonstrate understanding of the different ways to compare numbers and report information?

✓ demonstrate ability to interpret and use a timetable?

✓ correctly apply information to complete the schedule of fares?

Homework Have students make up a timetable for trains traveling from West Village to East Village.

Meeting Individual Needs

Work with students who have difficulty understanding the timetable, using the map of the train line on pages 308–309. Have them trace the route of the train with a finger on the map. Begin by explaining that as the train leaves East Village, the time is 8:00 A.M., according to the timetable. Work through a few of the timetable problems in this fashion.

Unit 4 Lesson 87 **313**

Averages and Rates

LESSON PLANNER

Objectives

▶ to review the meaning of *average* and how to calculate an average

▶ to review the concept of rate

✓ to provide practice in solving problems that involve ratios and rates

Context of the Lesson This is the second of six lessons on averages, rates, ratios, and proportions. Averages were introduced formally in the fourth-grade program. This lesson includes a Mastery Checkpoint to assess students' understanding of ratios and rates.

 MANIPULATIVES
calculators*

Program Resources
"Pentathlon" Game Mat
Reteaching Master
Practice Master 88
Enrichment Master 88
Assessment Masters
The Cruncher*

For additional math integration:
Math Throughout the Day*

For extra practice:
CD-ROM* Lesson 88

Note: This lesson may take more than one day.

① Wark-Up ⏱

 Problem of the Day Present the following problem: Aaron drove the 50 km from Highmount to Low Valley at an average speed of 30 kmph. How long did it take him to get to Low Valley? (1 hour and 40 minutes.)

Problem-Solving Strategies Ask students who have solved the Problem of the Day to share how they solved it and any strategies they used.

MENTAL MATH Ask students if $300 is enough money to buy the following items. Students should show thumbs up if $300 is enough and thumbs down if it is not.

a. a stereo set for $249.50 plus a CD for $12.50 (thumbs up)

b. three shirts at $40.00 each, three ties at $12.50 each, and two pairs of pants at $50.95 each (thumbs up)

(continued on page 315)

Averages and Rates

Sometimes when we describe numerical data, it is useful to use one number, called the average, to describe the data. Finding averages helps us to understand the data and to make predictions based on the data.

People talk about and use averages often.

◆ What do you think **average** means? **See margin.**

The following example shows one way to calculate an average.

Example: Find the average of 21, 23, 27, 29, and 26.

Add the numbers: $21 + 23 + 27 + 29 + 26 = 126$

Divide by how many numbers there were: $126 \div 5 = 25.2$

25.2 is the average of 21, 23, 27, 29, and 26.

This average is called the **mean.**

Sometimes an average gives useful information, but sometimes it doesn't. Sometimes an average is useful for one application but not for another.

Since an average is a ratio, an average of whole numbers is not necessarily a whole number.

Find the averages.

① 13, 15, 16, 18 **15.5**   ② 13, 14, 14, 14, 15 **14**

③ 13, 15, 17, 19, 21 **17**   ④ 13, 17, 19, 15, 14 **15.6**

⑤ 13, 13, 14, 14 **13.5**   ⑥ 13, 13, 13, 13, 13 **13**

⑦ 5, 5, 5, 10, 10, 15, 15, 15 **10**   ⑧ 5, 10, 10, 10, 10, 10, 10, 15 **10**

 **Solve these problems.**

⑨ Sasha is measuring the heights of two groups of plants. The five plants in one group have heights of 6.2 cm, 5.7 cm, 6.2 cm, 5.3 cm, and 5.6 cm. What is the average height of the plants in this group? **5.8 cm**

⑩ The five plants in Sasha's other group have heights of 5.2 cm, 5.8 cm, 5.3 cm, 5.3 cm, and 5.4 cm. What is the average height of the plants in this group? **5.4 cm**

Why teach it this way?

The definition of *average* given on the page is an operational one, telling students to follow the steps and that the result is the average. At this time concentrate on the steps rather than on a more elaborate definition. Throughout the Level 6 program, students will work with averages in different contexts and will gradually develop a solid understanding of the different meanings of the term.

*available separately

Rates are special kinds of ratios that are used to report certain kinds of information. So we often talk about average rates.

Example: Leroy rode his bicycle 24 kilometers in two hours. On the average how fast did he ride?

We can set up a ratio to compare the distance Leroy rode and the time it took.

$$\frac{24 \text{ kilometers}}{2 \text{ hours}}$$

Since $\frac{24}{2} = 12$, we can say that Leroy's average speed was 12 kilometers per hour.

We can check this by asking ourselves, "If Leroy rode steadily at 12 kilometers per hour for two hours, how far would he go?"

$$12 \times 2 = 24$$

Leroy would go 24 kilometers in two hours. This checks with the original information.

COOPERATIVE LEARNING   Use a calculator and work in groups. Check your answers to see that they make sense.

11 A 7.5-kilogram bag of flour costs $3.78, and a 5.0-kilogram bag of the same flour costs $3.02.

   a. How much does the flour cost per kilogram in a 7.5-kilogram bag?   **50.4¢/kg**

   b. How much does the flour cost per kilogram in a 5.0-kilogram bag?   **60.4¢/kg**

   c. Which bag costs less per kilogram?   **7.5-kg bag**

12 Brittany can run 100 meters in 14.6 seconds. Do you think she can run 10,000 meters in 1460 seconds?   **no**

13 Mrs. Flores paddled a canoe 32 kilometers in about four hours. About what was her average speed?   **about 8 km/h**

14 Matthew read a 100-page book in 40 minutes. About how many pages did he read per minute?   **about $2\frac{1}{2}$**

15 An airplane flight between two cities covers about 1400 miles and takes about three hours.

   a. What is the airplane's average speed in miles per hour?
   about 467 mph

   b. What is the airplane's average speed in miles per minute?
   about 7.8 miles per minute

Unit 4   Lesson 88 • **315**

Literature Connection Invite students to read *Bingo Brown and the Language of Love* by Betsy Byars. Have students determine the average cost of Bingo Brown's long-distance calls totaling $54.29.

Mental Math (continued)

   c. four car tires at $75.50 each (thumbs down)

   d. ten silk blouses at $25.00 each (thumbs up)

   e. an upholstered chair for $125.99 plus matching draperies for $219.00 (thumbs down)

   f. a painting for $199.00 plus a frame for $54.50 (thumbs up)

   g. two lawn mowers at $150.95 each (thumbs down)

   h. twelve pairs of pants at $25.00 each (thumbs up)

❷ Teach

Using the Student Pages Before beginning page 315, introduce the "Pentathlon" Game Mat, which provides practice with averages. Read page 314 with the class. Ask students for examples of how they have seen or heard the word *average* used. After doing the discussion question, go through the steps outlined on the page for calculating the average of a set of numbers.

Note: Average is used in different ways in different contexts. As used in this lesson, *average* is also known as the arithmetic mean. The *median* and the *mode* are discussed in the following lesson.

Answer to Discussion Question (page 314):

Among the many answers you'll get, expect some similar to the following:

• something that is as much like the others as possible in its group

• a middle number

• the number you get when you even out all the numbers so that they are the same

 Discuss page 315 with the class. Then have students work in groups to figure out reasonable answers to problems 11–15 using **calculators***. Students can use a blank **Cruncher*** spreadsheet to help them solve these problems and those on pages 316–317. Bring the groups together for a class discussion when they finish.

◆ LESSON 88 Averages and Rates

Teach

Using the Student Pages Have students do the problems on these pages on their own or with partners. Use the pages as an assessment. Encourage students to check their answers to see that they make sense.

GIFTED & TALENTED Meeting Individual Needs
Challenge students to think of data for which the mean may not be the most effective measure to describe the average of those data. To help them get started, you might ask students to consider whether the mean shoe size would be a useful piece of information for the owner of a shoe store to know, and then have students explain their answers. (Mode would be a better choice when deciding what sizes to order.)

GAME Using the "Pentathlon" Game Mat
Demonstrate the "Pentathlon" Game Mat by playing it with a student as the rest of the class watches. This game provides practice with using statistics and averaging. Complete directions are found on the Game Mat. A copy of this Game Mat can also be found on page 622 of this Teacher's Guide.

◆ LESSON 88 Averages and Rates

Solve these problems.

16 Mrs. Collins drove about 500 kilometers in eight hours and used 54 liters of gasoline.

  a. About what was her average speed? **about 62.5 km/h**

  b. On the average about how many kilometers did Mrs. Collins drive for each liter of gasoline? **about 9.3**

  c. If she continued at that average speed, how far could she have gone in 12 hours? **about 750 km**

  d. About how much gasoline would she use to drive 800 kilometers if she was using gasoline at the same rate? **Accept any answer between 80 and 90 liters.**

17 A 5-kilogram bag of Fancy Feline cat food costs $6.98 at one store. At another store a 6-kilogram bag of the same cat food costs $5.98. Which store has the better buy? **the second store**

18 Liza played three games of miniature golf. Her scores were 78, 82, and 74. What was her average score for the three games? **78**

19 Sidney keeps a record of the time he spends doing homework. Last week he spent two hours on Monday, $1\frac{1}{2}$ hours on Tuesday, two hours on Wednesday, one hour on Thursday, and one hour on Friday. What was the average time per day he spent on homework for that five-day period? **$1\frac{1}{2}$ h**

20 Sidney has a math test on Friday. He wants to study a total of at least two hours spread evenly over the next four nights.

  a. How many hours should he study each night? **at least $\frac{1}{2}$ hour**

  b. How many minutes is that? **30 minutes**

21 Sidney has been helping his younger brother practice basic math facts using flashcards. He can correctly answer 15 questions in 60 seconds. On the average how many seconds does it take him to answer each question?

4 seconds

316 · Fractions and Mixed Numbers

RETEACHING p. 28

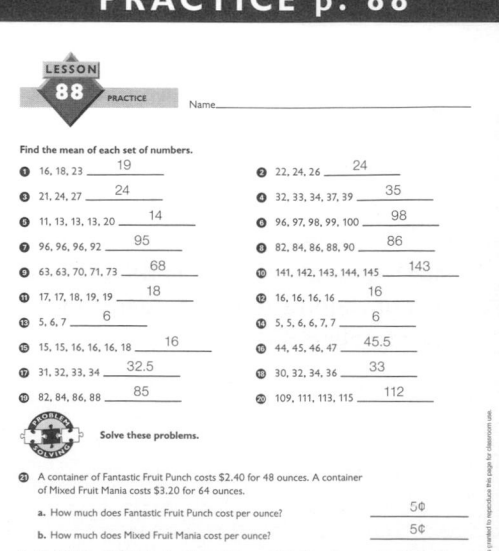

LESSON 88 RETEACHING Name_____

To find an average rate, think about the units that the answer should have. Divide the number of the first unit by the number of the second unit.

Example:

Mr. Mills drove about 240 kilometers in three hours. At what average speed was Mr. Mills driving?

The average speed will be in kilometers per hour, so divide the number of kilometers driven by the number of hours the trip took.

$\frac{240 \text{ kilometers}}{3 \text{ hours}} = \frac{240}{3}$ kilometers per hour   Write the division problem.

$240 \div 3$ = 80 kilometers per hour   Divide.

Solve these problems.

1 Monica drove 82 miles in four hours. What was her average driving speed? _20.5 miles per hour_

2 James spent $15.50 for 5 kilograms of potatoes. What was the price per kilogram? _$3.10_

3 A bottle of perfume costs $45.90 for 5 ounces. What was the price per ounce? _$9.18_

4 Lucy read 595 pages over 20 hours. What was her average rate of reading for this book? _29.75 pages per hour_

5 A plant grew 48 inches in height over 16 days. What was the average rate of growth for the plant? _3 inches per day_

6 Jana found notebooks on sale at $14.95 for 5, while Dan found them on sale at $16.00 for 6. Who found the better buy? _Dan_

7 Anthony drove for 4 hours at 40 miles per hour. He has to drive a total of 500 miles.
  a. How far has he traveled? _160 miles_
  b. At what average rate should he drive for the rest of the trip if he wants to take 12 hours for the trip? _42.5 miles per hour_

8 Marissa scored 78, 92, 88, and 96 on four math tests. What must the score be on the fifth test if she wants a 90 average? _96_

28 · Math Explorations and Applications Level 6

PRACTICE p. 88

LESSON 88 PRACTICE Name_____

Find the mean of each set of numbers.

1 16, 18, 23 _19_
2 22, 24, 26 _24_
3 21, 24, 27 _24_
4 32, 33, 34, 37, 39 _35_
5 11, 13, 13, 13, 20 _14_
6 96, 97, 98, 99, 100 _98_
7 96, 96, 96, 92 _95_
8 82, 84, 86, 88, 90 _86_
9 63, 63, 70, 71, 73 _68_
10 141, 142, 143, 144, 145 _143_
11 17, 17, 18, 19, 19 _18_
12 16, 16, 16, 16, 16 _16_
13 5, 6, 7 _6_
14 5, 5, 6, 7, 7 _6_
15 15, 15, 16, 16, 16, 18 _16_
16 44, 45, 46, 47 _45.5_
17 31, 32, 33, 34 _32.5_
18 30, 32, 34, 36 _33_
19 82, 84, 86, 88 _85_
20 109, 111, 113, 115 _112_

PROBLEM SOLVING Solve these problems.

21 A container of Fantastic Fruit Punch costs $2.40 for 48 ounces. A container of Mixed Fruit Mania costs $3.20 for 64 ounces.
  a. How much does Fantastic Fruit Punch cost per ounce? _5¢_
  b. How much does Mixed Fruit Mania cost per ounce? _5¢_

22 Mr. Affelt drove 165 miles in about 3 hours. His car used 7.4 gallons of gas.
  a. What was Mr. Affelt's average speed? _about 55 miles per hour_
  b. About how many miles did Mr. Affelt drive for each gallon of gas? _22.3 miles_
  c. Mr. Affelt needs to drive another 250 miles. If he continues at about the same speed, how long will it take him? _about $4\frac{1}{2}$ hours_

23 David's scores on his first four science tests were 94, 87, 90, and 89. What was his average score? _90_

88 · Math Explorations and Applications Level 6

---

22 A loaf of Farmer Brown whole grain bread costs $0.85, and a loaf of Super A bread costs $0.83. Farmer Brown bread weighs 500 grams, and Super A bread weighs 300 grams.

   a. How much does Farmer Brown bread cost per gram? **0.17¢ ($0.0017)**

   b. How much does Super A bread cost per gram? **0.277¢ ($0.00277)**

23 Mr. Mikami is driving from Southville to Northfield, a distance of 540 kilometers. He wants to make the trip in ten hours.

   a. About how many kilometers per hour must he average? **54**

   b. After four hours of driving, Mr. Mikami had traveled 200 kilometers. What was his average speed for the first four hours? **about 50 km/h**

   c. He still wants to make the trip last ten hours. About what speed should he average for the rest of the trip? **about 57 km/h**

24 Jennifer took five spelling tests and got these scores: 80, 86, 88, 82, 80.

   a. What was her average score for the five tests? **83.2**

   b. Jennifer then got 100s on three tests. What was her average after the eight tests? **89.5**

   c. Does the average fairly represent Jennifer's performance in spelling? **Answers will vary. Example: No, since the average hides that she did very well on her last three tests.**

25 On the last spelling test, the class average for 24 students was 78.

   a. If someone who was absent takes the spelling test and gets a score of 80, will the class average go up or down? **up**

   b. By how much will the class average change? (Hint: Find the total number of points scored by the 24 students who first took the test.) **0.08 points**

   c. By how much would it have changed the average if the absent student had a score of 100? **0.88 points**

Unit 4   Lesson 88 • **317**

Unit 4 Lesson 88 **317**

ENRICHMENT p. 88

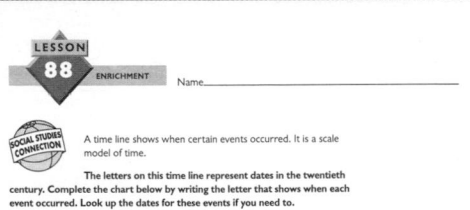

LESSON 88 ENRICHMENT   Name_____

SOCIAL STUDIES CONNECTION

A time line shows when certain events occurred. It is a scale model of time.

The letters on this time line represent dates in the twentieth century. Complete the chart below by writing the letter that shows when each event occurred. Look up the dates for these events if you need to.

1900   A B   C   D E F   G   H   2000
          1950

The year for each event is included for your information.

Event	Letter
The United States enters World War II. (1941)	D
John Glenn becomes the first American to orbit the Earth in space. (1962)	G
Robert Goddard launches the first liquid-fuel rocket. (1926)	C
Marie Curie becomes the first person to win two Nobel Prizes. (1911)	B
World War II ends. (1945)	E
The first U.S. space station, *Skylab*, goes into orbit. (1973)	H
The Wright brothers make the first successful airplane flight. (1903)	A
The transistor is invented. (1946)	F

Look up and fill in the dates for the events listed in the chart below. Then make a time line for these dates. Choose a scale carefully, because the events span more than **4500 years.** See answers below.

Event	Date
Elizabeth I becomes queen of England.	1558
Samuel Morse invents the telegraph.	1837
Abraham Lincoln gives the Gettysburg Address.	1863
George Washington becomes the first president of the United States.	1789
The Great Pyramid is built in Egypt. approx. 2800 B.C.	2600 B.C.
Leonardo da Vinci paints the *Mona Lisa*.	1503
Bill Clinton becomes the 42nd president of the United States.	1993

Choose other events and mark them on your time line.

88 • Math Explorations and Applications Level 6

ASSESSMENT p. 35

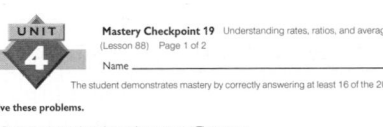

UNIT 4   **Mastery Checkpoint 19** Understanding rates, ratios, and averages
(Lesson 88)   Page 1 of 2

Name_____

The student demonstrates mastery by correctly answering at least 16 of the 20 problems.

Solve these problems.

On Friday seven people took a mathematics test. Their scores were 95, 98, 90, 89, 100, 85, and 80.

1 What was the average score? — 91

2 How many people had an above-average score? — 3

3 How many people had a below-average score? — 4

4 How many people had exactly the average score? — 0

Dr. Monroe drove about 400 kilometers in six hours and used 37 liters of gasoline.

5 About what was her average speed? — 66.7 km/h

6 About how many kilometers did Dr. Monroe drive for each liter of gasoline? — 10.8

7 If she continued at that average speed, how far could she have gone in nine hours? — about 600 km

8 About how many liters of gasoline would she have used to drive 750 kilometers if she were using gasoline at the same rate? — 69.4

There are five people in the Funamura family. The Funamura family drinks 6 gallons of milk per week.

9 How many gallons a day do they drink? — about 0.86

10 If each person drinks about the same amount of milk, how many gallons a week on the average does each person drink? — about 1.2

11 Apples at the grocery store are $1.50 for a 3-kg bag or 59¢ per kilogram loose. Which is less expensive? — 3-kg bag (50¢/kg)

12 A 226-gram bag of potato chips costs $1.29. A 150-gram bag of the same brand of potato chips costs $0.89. Which is the better buy? — 226-g bag

Math Explorations and Applications Level 6 • **35**

In Closing Choose one of the problems on pages 316–317. Ask students to explain what the problem asks and what they need to do, step-by-step, to solve it.

ALTERNATIVE ASSESSMENT

Performance Assessment Ask students to formulate a real-life problem involving rates and one involving finding an average. Have them write out the problems and provide answers to each.

Mastery Checkpoint 19

At this time most students should demonstrate mastery of finding the mean of a set of data and solving problems involving ratios and rates by correctly answering at least 80% of the problems on pages 316–317 or on Assessment Blackline Masters pages 35–36 in a reasonable amount of time. Results of this assessment may be recorded on the Mastery Checkpoint Chart.

Assessment Criteria

Did the student . . .

✓ demonstrate understanding of the concept of arithmetic average, or mean, by correctly answering at least 80% of the problems on page 314?

✓ demonstrate and express understanding of ratio and rate?

✓ correctly answer at least 80% of the problems on pages 316–317?

REAL-WORLD CONNECTION

Homework Ask students to gather numerical data about ten items of interest to them, such as sports scores and statistics, CD sales or prices, and so on. Challenge them to find the mean of their set of data. Ask them to think of ways that rates are involved in their own lives and to share these relationships or descriptions with classmates.

Mean, Median, and Mode

LESSON PLANNER

Objectives

▶ to present methods of finding the mean, median, and mode of a set of data

▶ to demonstrate how to compare characteristics and uses of these three measures of central tendency

▶ to provide some realistic applications of averages

Context of the Lesson
This lesson is the third of six lessons on ratios, rates, averages, and proportions.

 MANIPULATIVES

Program Resources

Reteaching Master

Practice Master 89

Enrichment Master 89

For extra practice:
  CD-ROM* Lesson 89

❶ Warm-Up

 Problem of the Day Present the following problem: Jed got the following grades on his math tests: 70, 88, 63, 57, 88, and 52. Jed wants to use one measure of average to present his scores in the best light. His teacher uses another to present them as accurately as possible. Which measure does each use, and why? (Jed would use mode; his test average becomes 88; the teacher would use mean, which is 69.7, or median, which is 66.5; either is more representative of his scores.)

Problem-Solving Strategies Ask students who have solved the Problem of the Day to share how they solved it and any strategies they used.

MENTAL MATH Have students brainstorm a list of averages they commonly see or hear, or use themselves. If your students are already familiar with different measures of central tendency, ask them to tell whether they think each is a mean, a median, or a mode, and why they think so.

Mean, Median, and Mode

In the previous lesson we defined the average as the number you get when you add together a bunch of numbers and divide by the number of numbers. So the average of 3, 4, and 5 would be (3 + 4 + 5) divided by 3, which is 4. This is usually called the **mean.**

Two other numbers that are sometimes called averages are the **median** and the **mode.**

The **median** of a set of numbers is the middle number when the numbers are put in order from least to greatest.

For example, in the set 3, 3, 4, 6, 6, 7, 8, 8, 9, 10, and 17, the number 7 is the median because it is in the middle (there are five numbers on either side of it) when the numbers are put in order.

Notice that the mean of the numbers is $7\frac{4}{11}$, a number fairly close to the median. Often the mean and median are equal or close to being equal.

If there is an even number of numbers, the median is the mean of the two middle numbers.

For example, in the set 4, 4, 5, 7, 7, and 8, the two numbers in the middle are 5 and 7. The median is $\frac{5+7}{2} = \frac{12}{2} = 6$.

Median

The **mode** is the number that appears most often in a set of numbers. If more than one number ties for "the most often," all of them are modes. So, in the last set of data above, 4 and 7 are both modes.

COOPERATIVE LEARNING You may wish to present a problem using information students generate that they then analyze using each of the measures of average. For example, they can find the average class shoe size, pencil length, arm-span, or smile width.

*available separately

Find the mean, median, and mode of each of the following sets of numbers.

1 1, 2, 2, 3, 3, 4, 5, 5, 5, 5, 5, 6, 7, 7, 8, 8, 9

2 6, 7, 7, 8, 8, 9, 10, 10, 10, 10, 10, 11, 12, 12, 13, 13, 14

3 2, 4, 4, 6, 6, 8, 10, 10, 10, 10, 10, 12, 14, 14, 16, 16, 18

	mean	median	mode
1	5	5	5
2	10	10	10
3	10	10	10

4 Compare the sets of numbers in problems 1, 2, and 3. Is there something you could do to the numbers in problem 1 to get those in problem 2? In problem 3? What? **To get the numbers in problem 2, add 5 to the numbers in problem 1. To get the numbers in problem 3, multiply the numbers in problem 1 by 2.**

5 What is the relationship of the mean, the median, and the mode in problem 2 to the corresponding averages in problem 1? How do those averages in problem 3 compare with the ones in problem 1? **The mean, median, and mode in problem 2 are 5 more than the corresponding averages in problem 1. The mean, median, and mode in problem 3 are twice as great as the ones in problem 1.** Find the mean, median, and mode of the following sets of numbers.

6 201, 202, 202, 203, 203, 204, 205, 205, 205, 205, 205, 206, 207, 207, 208, 208, 209 **mean = 205; median = 205; mode = 205**

7 100, 200, 200, 300, 300, 400, 500, 500, 500, 500, 500, 600, 700, 700, 800, 800, 900 **mean = 500; median = 500; mode = 500**

8 103, 104, 104, 105, 105, 106, 107, 107, 107, 107, 107, 108, 109, 109, 110, 110, 111 **mean = 107; median = 107; mode = 107**

9 10, 10, 10, 10, 14, 15, 15, 19, 50 **mean = 17; median = 14; mode = 10**

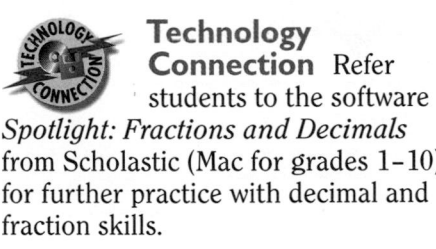

Solve this problem. **Union members used the mode, the owner used the mean, and the mediator used the median. Answers will vary. Using problem 9 as a hint, the set of wages would be: $10,000; $10,000; $10,000; $10,000; $14,000; $15,000; $15,000; $19,000; and $50,000. The owner's salary is $50,000.**

10 A small business was having a labor dispute. The union members claimed that the average wage was $10,000. The owner claimed that the average wage was $17,000. A mediator was hired who examined the records and said the average was really $14,000. How could all three be correct? Write a set of wages for which all three of these numbers could be called the average. Which salary do you think is the owner's? (Hint: review your results for problem 9.)

Unit 4 Lesson 89 • 319

❷ Teach

Using the Student Pages Provide a set of data similar to the middle set on page 318. Ask students to tell you what the average of the set is. Expect that most will calculate the mean, because that is the number most commonly called the average and the one they have had experience calculating in the previous lesson. Remind students that median and mode are also measures of average and discuss how to determine each for a set of data. You may wish to point out that median is a particularly useful measure to use when you wish to exclude extreme scores, and that mode is often the measure referred to when the term "typical" is used; for example, in statements such as "Pizzas typically have six slices."

As students work on the problems on page 319, encourage them to stop and discuss their answers to problems 4 and 5 before continuing. Students can see that the numbers in problem 2 are each 5 greater than the corresponding numbers in problem 1 and that the mean, median, and mode are also 5 greater. In problem 3, all numbers and measures are twice the corresponding numbers in problem 1.

Technology Connection Refer students to the software *Spotlight: Fractions and Decimals* from Scholastic (Mac for grades 1–10) for further practice with decimal and fraction skills.

◆ LESSON 89 Mean, Median, and Mode

Teach

Using the Student Pages Have students do the problems on pages 320 and 321 independently. As needed, discuss procedures for adding integers, as students will need to do so for problems 14 and 15 on page 320. As a class, you may wish to discuss answers to problem 20 on page 321. Invite students to create and discuss problems similar to it.

◆ LESSON 89   Mean, Median, and Mode

Solve these problems.

11 Ashley, Heather, and Charlene were having a long jump contest. They decided that each person would get to jump five times, and the person with the greatest average for the five jumps would win. After they finished, they each examined the results, and each one declared herself the winner. The lengths of each of their jumps in centimeters are reported below. Explain what happened, and why each claimed she was the winner. *

Long Jump Distances					
	Jump 1	Jump 2	Jump 3	Jump 4	Jump 5
Ashley	173	173	180	181	183
Heather	164	174	174	179	184
Charlene	162	162	175	209	212

12 The high temperatures (in degrees Fahrenheit) for Tucson, Arizona for each day of one week were

> Monday, 98; Tuesday, 104; Wednesday, 110; Thursday, 112; Friday, 114; Saturday, 113; and Sunday, 109.

What was the average high temperature in Tucson for that week? **about 109°F**

13 The low temperatures in Madison, Wisconsin for one week were

> Monday, 7; Tuesday, 4; Wednesday, 2; Thursday, 0; Friday, 6; Saturday, 8; Sunday, 12.

What was the average low temperature in Madison for that week? **about 6°F**

14 One week in Madison the low temperatures were all negative. They were

> Monday, –7; Tuesday, –8; Wednesday, –12; Thursday, –14; Friday, –15; Saturday, –18; and Sunday, –20.

What was the average low temperature in Madison that week? **about –13°F**

15 One week in Minneapolis some low temperatures were negative and some were positive. They were

> Monday, 2; Tuesday, 3; Wednesday, 0; Thursday, –4; Friday, –3; Saturday, –1; and Sunday, 3.

What was the average low temperature in Minneapolis that week? **0°F**

* Each person won using a different kind of average. Ashley had the greatest median, Heather had the greatest mode, and Charlene had the greatest mean.

320 • Fractions and Mixed Numbers

Physical Education Connection Ask students to brainstorm and discuss several averages used in sports that are very useful in understanding performance in that sport. Have them debate whether the mode or the mean is the more useful measure in each case. Challenge students who enjoy baseball to figure out how earned-run average is calculated (divide earned runs allowed by number of innings pitched, multiply by 9).

RETEACHING p. 29

LESSON 89 RETEACHING Name_____

To find the median of a set of numbers, first make sure that all of the numbers are listed in order from least to greatest. The middle number will be the **median**.

Example 1:

Find the median for the following set of numbers.

2, 8, 6, 10, 12, 4, 8, 10, 8, 10

List the numbers from least to greatest.

2, 4, 6, 8, 8, 10, 10, 10, 12

Find the middle number(s). If there are two middle numbers, the median is their average.

2, 4, 6, 8, |8, 8,| 10, 10, 10, 12

median = $\frac{8+8}{2} = 8$

The **mode** is the number (or numbers) that is used most often. If no number is used more often than the other numbers, there is no mode.

Example 2:

Find the mode from Example 1. The numbers 8 and 10 are each used three times. The modes of the set of numbers are 8 and 10.

Find the median and mode for each set of numbers.

1 5, 8, 9, 12, 4, 6, 8, 5, 7, 12 _7.5; 5, 8, and 12_

2 8, 8, 10, 15, 12, 16, 9, 18, 20, 10, 16 _12; 8, 10, and 16_

3 18, 26, 14, 30, 22, 24, 16, 12, 30, 32 _23; 30_

4 118, 124, 120, 139, 147, 115, 118, 135 _122; 118_

5 134, 165, 142, 156, 127, 98, 126, 131 _132.5; no mode_

6 2.6, 3.5, 1.4, 9.6, 5.7, 4.3, 4.7 _4.3; no mode_

7 1500, 2746, 3419, 1896, 3419, 4647 _3082.5; 3419_

8 3.5, 12.6, 5.6, 15.6, 47.2, 1.6, 5.9 _5.9; no mode_

9 1400, 2745, 1497, 2531, 1874, 2796, 1457 _1874; no mode_

Math Explorations and Applications Level 6 • **29**

16 Dirk sells pennants and pins at local weekend football games. His profit has been an average of $12 per game for the past four games. There will be a total of 16 weekends during the football season. If he continues to average $12 per game, how much money will he make all together? **$192**

17 Ms. Evander drove 17 miles on Monday, 23 miles on Tuesday, 0 miles on Wednesday, 53 miles on Thursday, 53 miles on Friday, 87 miles on Saturday, and 0 miles on Sunday. What was her average miles driven per day?

about 33 miles per day

18 Mr. Mahaffey drives an average of 273 miles per week. Assuming he does that all year, how many miles will he drive in a year? **14,196**

19 Ms. Gerber filled her car with gas on Monday morning. She then drove 56 miles on Monday, 43 miles on Tuesday, 76 miles on Wednesday, 68 miles on Thursday, and 58 miles on Friday. Then she filled the tank with 16.2 gallons of gas. What was the average number of miles she drove on a gallon of gas during that week? **18.6**

20 Mr. Lewis announced that the average number of children in a family in the country of Fractonia is 2.3. Do you think this is a mean, a median, or a mode? Why? **It must be a mean. The mode must be a whole number since each item of data must be a whole number. The median must be either a whole number or a number with only a five to the right of the decimal point.**

21 Deanna ran a lawn-mowing business one summer. For the first four weeks her earnings were $10, $30, $50, and $50.

a. What were her average earnings per week? **$35**

b. Do you think she will have the same average after the next four weeks? **Answers may vary. Possible answer: no, her average will probably be higher now that her business is more established.**

Unit 4   Lesson 89 • **321**

PRACTICE p. 89

Name_____

Find the mean, the median, and the mode for each set of data. If necessary, round your answers to the nearest tenth.

1 2, 6, 8, 10, 10, 10, 10   8; 9; 10

2 15, 15, 16, 16, 16, 17, 18, 20, 20   17; 16; 16

3 2, 6, 8, 10, 12, 14   8.7; 9; no mode

4 15, 15, 16, 17, 17, 19, 19, 20, 20   17.6; 17; 15, 17, 19, and 20

5 100, 115, 120, 120, 125, 130, 130, 130, 130   122.2; 125; 130

6 65, 75, 78, 80, 83, 86, 87, 88, 94, 95   83.1; 84.5; no mode

7 14,000; 14,000; 14,000; 16,000; 18,000; 21,000   16,166.7; 15,000; 14,000

8 2.9, 3.7, 4.8, 5.1, 6.7   4.64; 4.8; no mode

9 4, 4, 5, 6, 6, 7, 7, 8, 8, 8, 8, 9, 9, 9, 10, 10   7.375; 8; 8

10 15, 15, 15, 16, 16, 17, 18, 19, 20, 20   17.1; 16.5; 15

11 700, 700, 800, 800, 800, 900, 900, 900, 900   822.2; 800; 900

12 1200, 1500, 1700, 1800, 2300, 2400   1816.7; 1750; no mode

13 120, 130, 156, 289, 413, 479, 576   309; 289; no mode

14 40, 50, 60, 70, 70, 70, 80, 90, 90, 90   71; 70; 70 and 90

15 2.4, 5.2, 7.6, 7.6, 8.1, 8.3, 8.7, 9.6   7.1875; 7.85; 7.6

Math Explorations and Applications Level 6 • 89

ENRICHMENT p. 89

Name_____

Find the batting average of each player on your favorite baseball team for each game of a given year's season. Use The Cruncher: *Baseball Statistics* project to find the following statistics.

1 What is the batting average for each player?
Answers will vary.

2 What is the average number of runs scored by the team as a whole?
_____

3 What is each team's batting average?
_____
_____

4 What are the pitching statistics for the pitchers?
_____

Math Explorations and Applications Level 6 • 89

---

3 Wrap-Up

In Closing In summary, ask students to tell how to find the mean, median, and mode of a set of data. Ask them to explain what happens to each measure when the same number is added to each number in a set of data.

Performance Assessment Ask students to find the mean, median, and mode of the following set of numbers: 2, 2, 3, 4, 5, 6, 9, 11. [5.25, 4.5, 2]

Assessment Criteria

Did the student . . .

✓ correctly compute means, medians, and modes?

✓ correctly answer 8 of the 11 problems on pages 320–321?

✓ understand what happens to the mean of a set of data when a constant is added to or multiplied by each member of the set?

Homework Using figures for seven days, have students figure out the average amount of time they spend on homework each day and also the average amount of time they spend watching television each day. Students should save this data for use at the end of Lesson 91.

Meeting Individual Needs

Be sure that students rewrite all numbers in a set in order from least to greatest to more easily find the median of the set. Using this approach also will help students identify the mode more easily.

LESSON 90

Student Edition pages 322–323

Choosing an Appropriate Average

LESSON PLANNER

Objective

▶ to involve students in a discussion of which concept of average is most useful in a given situation

Context of the Lesson This is the fourth of six lessons on finding and using ratios, rates, averages, and proportions.

 MANIPULATIVES   **Program Resources**

Practice Master 90

Enrichment Master 90

For extra practice:
CD-ROM* Lesson 90
Cumulative Review, page 572

---

① Warm-Up

 Problem of the Day Present the following problem to the class: For the past six weeks, Norma scored 85 on each of her science tests. What conclusion can you draw about the measures of mean, median, and mode for Norma's scores? (They are all the same.)

Problem-Solving Strategies Ask students who have solved the Problem of the Day to share how they solved it and any strategies they used.

 Have students find these quotients mentally.

a. $350 \div 7 = (50)$ b. $4200 \div 6 = (700)$

c. $30,000 \div 50 = (600)$ d. $24,000 \div 8 = (3000)$

e. $480 \div 12 = (40)$ f. $6000 \div 15 = (400)$

② Teach

Using the Student Pages Have students think about the problems on pages 322 and 323 individually and do any necessary calculations. Then have them discuss in small groups or as a whole class their reasons for choosing the particular average they chose. For problem 2, all three measures are the same. The reasons students give are more important than the specific answer.

322 Fractions and Mixed Numbers

Choosing an Appropriate Average

Whether the mean, the median, or the mode is the best average to use depends on the situation and the information you are describing.

For each of the following situations, decide whether the mean, median, or mode is appropriate and explain why. Calculate the appropriate average in each case if the necessary information is given in the problem. **Accept all reasonably defended answers**

❶ What is the average number of days in a month?   **31 is the median and the mode.**

❷ What is the average number of days in a week?   **mean, median, or mode (all are the same); 7**

❸ What is the average number of minutes you are in school each day?   **The mode is most appropriate since it excludes weekends.**

❹ What is the average number of students in each sixth-grade class at your school? **mean, median, or mode would work**

❺ What is the average age of everyone in your classroom, including your teacher?

❻ What is the average height of students in your class? **mean**

❼ What is the average salary of the governors of the 50 states? **mean (possibly mode or median)**

❽ What is the average number of people who have voted in your town in the last five elections? **mean**

❾ **none (you would either want the average age of the students or the age of the teacher)**

322 • Fractions and Mixed Numbers

Why teach it this way?

It is important for students to appreciate that different real-life situations often can be described better using one form of average than another. This lesson introduces this concept. As averages arise in math and other contexts throughout the year, discuss with students which average is most appropriate.

Social Studies Connection Invite students to make a graph or chart of the salaries of the governors of each state and the states' populations. Discuss whether the figures appear to be related.

RETEACHING

No reteaching is necessary at this time, other than to review the distinction among the three measures. You may want to assign Enrichment Master 90 to all students.

---

*available separately

For each situation tell whether the mean, median, or mode is appropriate and explain why. **Accept all reasonably defended answers.**

9 I own a small business and wish to find out how much I spend on salaries each month, so I want to know the average salary that is paid to my 20 employees. **mean, since it can be used to find the total cost of salaries**

10 I am considering accepting a job in a small company, so I ask what the average salary is for their employees. **probably the mode, the salary most people get; possibly the median**

11 What is my average grade on mathematics tests taken so far this term? **mean**

12 I get paid once a month. I want to calculate my average pay per week, after taxes. **The mean would be the only one easy to find.**

13 I am trying to convince my parents to give me a greater allowance than the $7 a week I receive now. I find out the allowances my friends receive. Two of them get $6 a week, one gets $7, one gets $10, and one gets $20.

   a. What kind of average should I use to show that I should receive a greater allowance? **mean**

   b. What kind of average might my parents use to justify my current allowance? **mode or median**

14 I am conducting a telephone survey for the school newspaper on the average number of hours of sleep students report they get each night. **probably mode would be best, since extremes won't affect it much**

FANTASTIC FACT

The United States is the country with the greatest number of telephones, about 143,325,000. The country with the greatest ratio of telephones to population is Sweden, with an average of 68.43 telephones for every 100 people. The United States ranks fifth, with 56.12 telephones for every 100 people.

Use the Cumulative Review on page 572 after this lesson.

Unit 4   Lesson 90 • **323**

For problem 9, the total cannot be found by using the median or the mode. Guide students to understand why this is so, and why the total cost of salaries can be found by multiplying the mean salary by the number of employees.

❸ Wrap-Up 🕐 5 MINUTES

In Closing Ask students to summarize their views about which kinds of situations appear to require which kind of measure of average.

Performance Assessment Ask students to suppose that you are opening a shoe store and you are interviewing a shoe store owner to find out as much as you can about the business. Also explain to them that you wish to find out averages to know how many of which styles and sizes to stock, and how much you expect to spend on rent, utilities, and employee salaries. Ask students to explain which measures of average the store owner should use to give you the best information. Have them explain their reasoning.

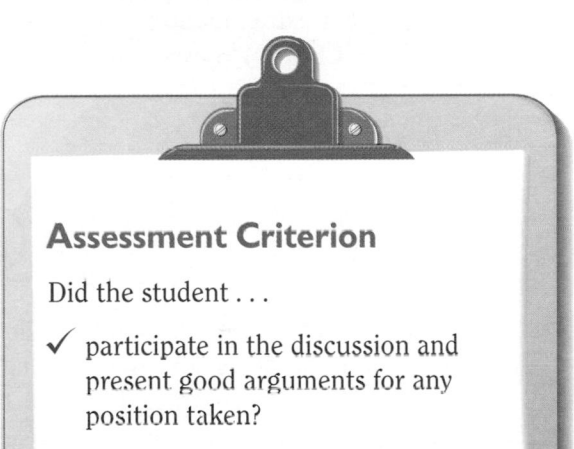

Assessment Criterion

Did the student . . .

✓ participate in the discussion and present good arguments for any position taken?

Homework Ask students to discuss their answer to problem 13 with family members. Ask them to try to come up with family situations involving averages that can be best described mathematically using the measures of mean and median.

GIFTED & TALENTED **Meeting Individual Needs**
   Challenge students to create a set of five numbers for which the mean is 50 and the median and mode are 45. (sample answer: 65, 60, 45, 45, 35)

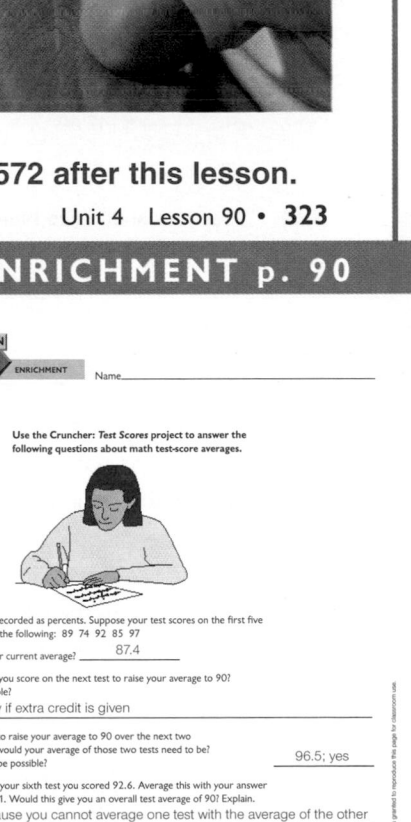

Unit 4   Lesson 90   **323**

Solving Proportions

LESSON PLANNER

Objectives

▶ to provide problems that can be solved using proportions

▶ to present several methods for solving problems involving proportions and provide practice in doing so

Context of the Lesson This is the fifth of six lessons on ratios, rates, averages, and proportions.

 **MANIPULATIVES**

almanac or encyclopedia

Program Resources

Reteaching Master

Practice Master 91

Enrichment Master 91

The Cruncher*

For extra practice:
CD-ROM* Lesson 91

---

 ① Warm-Up 🕐 5 MINUTES

 Problem of the Day Present the following problem to the students: Five numbers have a mean of 52.75. If 6 is subtracted from each of the numbers, what is the mean of the five new values? What is the new mode? (46.75; cannot tell)

Problem-Solving Strategies Ask students who have solved the Problem of the Day to share how they solved it and any strategies they used.

MENTAL MATH Explain to students that at Milt's Model Shop, five jars of glue sell for $12. Ask them to explain how to use mental math to figure out how many jars can be bought for $60. ($60 \div 12 = 5$, $5 \times 5 = 25$)

Solving Proportions

Jing-Mei, Alex, Sam, Abby, and Sara started a lawn mowing business during summer vacation. They put their income into a special bank account and kept a record of the number of hours they worked. At the end of the summer they decided to divide the money in proportion to the number of hours each worked. They earned a total of $1230.

The table on page 325 shows how many hours each person worked:

◆ How many hours did they work all together? **100**

To divide the money proportionally, the business partners could write equal ratios:

$$\frac{\text{hours worked}}{\text{total hours worked}} = \frac{\text{money earned}}{\text{total money earned}}$$

Two equal ratios are called a proportion. Solving a proportion means finding the missing number.

By writing and solving this proportion, each partner can compute his or her share of the money.

For instance, since Sara worked 12 out of the 100 total hours, to find Sara's share of the money, we can solve the proportion $\frac{12}{100} = \frac{n}{1230}$, where n is her share.

One way to solve for a missing term in a proportion is to find a common denominator for the two ratios. Once the denominators are the same, if the ratios are equal, the numerators must also be equal.

Example: To solve this problem we can write the fractions with a common denominator of 12,300.

◆ What should we multiply the numerator and denominator of $\frac{12}{100}$ by to get a denominator of 12,300? **123**

◆ What should we multiply the numerator and denominator of $\frac{n}{1230}$ by to get a denominator of 12,300? **10**

$\frac{12}{100} = \frac{1476}{12,300}$, and $\frac{n}{1230}$ means the same as $\frac{10 \times n}{12,300}$, so we say $\frac{1476}{12,300} = \frac{10 \times n}{12,300}$.

Since the fractions have the same denominator, they must also have the same numerator.

$1476 = 10 \times n$, so n must be $1476 \div 10$, which is 147.6. Sara has earned $147.60.

Why teach it this way?

This informal introduction to proportions connects naturally to the previous work with fractions. Although students should be encouraged to use any correct methods for solving the problems in this lesson, they should also develop a sense of usefulness of proportional reasoning.

① From the information in the chart calculate each person's share of the $1230.00 they accumulated in the bank account. Using a computer or other means, draw the chart and complete it.

Name	Hours Worked	Fraction of Money Earned	Dollars Earned
Jing-Mei	30	$\frac{30}{100}$	**$369.00**
Alex	15	$\frac{15}{100}$	**$184.50**
Sam	25	$\frac{25}{100}$	**$307.50**
Abby	18	$\frac{18}{100}$	**$221.40**
Sara	12	$\frac{12}{100}$	**$147.60**
Total	**100**	**1**	$1230.00

Solve these problems. Check that your answers make sense.

② Was this a fair way to divide the income? Why or why not? **Answers may vary. Sample response: Yes, because each person got paid according to the hours he or she worked.**

③ What other ways could they have used? **They could have divided the money in proportion to the number of lawns mowed.**

④ What other methods besides equal ratios could they have used to divide the money proportionally? **They could have changed the fractions of hours to percents or decimals; they could have multiplied 1230 by the fractions of hours**

② Teach

Using the Student Pages Begin pages 324 and 325 by asking students to try to figure out how much money Sara should get, using whatever method they wish. Discuss their answers and methods. One reasonable approach is to multiply $1230 by 0.12, because Sara did $\frac{12}{100}$ of the work. After going over students' methods, show how to set up the proportion shown and the method for solving it. Have students complete the table by whatever means they wish, but encourage them to try the proportion method in order to practice it. Students can use a blank **Cruncher*** spreadsheet to help them copy and complete the table.

Social Studies Connection Discuss with students the relevance of political surveys and what politicians can learn from polling a sample of a population. Ask them whether they have ever taken part in a survey and to describe the circumstances. Ask what difficulties may arise when trying to conduct a survey. What might prevent a survey from providing accurate information? Who other than politicians might use the information gathered in a survey?

*available separately

◆ LESSON 91 Solving Proportions

Teach

![COOPERATIVE LEARNING] **Using the Student Pages** Have students work in groups to solve the problems on page 326, to research the needed information about rivers, and to complete the table on page 327. Have **almanacs** and **encyclopedias** available. Remind students to consider the size of a standard textbook page and the size of the illustration needed in order to be legible.

Students can use a blank **Cruncher*** spreadsheet to help them copy and complete the table.

The answers given for page 327 are possible answers only. As students may discover, different sources may give slightly different information about the names and lengths of rivers.

◆ LESSON 91 Solving Proportions

You can use proportions to solve problems involving scale drawings. Map scales can be written as ratios.

The Amazon River in South America is about 3900 miles long. If a drawing uses the scale 1 inch = 300 miles, how long should the drawing of the Amazon River be?

To solve this problem we can write a proportion like this:

$$\frac{1 \text{ inch}}{300 \text{ miles}} = \frac{n}{3900 \text{ miles}}, \text{ or just } \frac{1}{300} = \frac{n}{3900}$$

◆ What is the least common multiple of 300 and 3900? **3900**

◆ By what should we multiply the numerator and denominator of $\frac{1}{300}$?

We can rewrite the proportion as $\frac{13}{3900} = \frac{n}{3900}$. Since the denominators are equal, the numerators must be equal, so $n = 13$. The drawing should be 13 inches long.

GEOGRAPHY CONNECTION

How long will a diagram of the river be if drawn to the following scales?

❶❶ The length of the drawing must be less than 11 inches (more if it's placed diagonally on the page) but more than 4 inches so that it is identifiable. A scale of 500 miles = 1 inch would be about right. That would make the drawing about 8 inches long.

❺ 10 miles = 1 inch **390 inches ($32\frac{1}{2}$ feet)**

❻ 100 miles = 10 inches **390 inches ($32\frac{1}{2}$ feet)**

❼ 100 miles = $\frac{1}{8}$ inch **$4\frac{7}{8}$ inches**

What scale should be used to draw the Amazon River with the following lengths?

❽ 6 inches **650 miles = 1 inch**

❾ 12 inches **325 miles = 1 inch**

❿ 15 inches **260 miles = 1 inch**

❶❶ If you were drawing a map of the Amazon River to include in a geography textbook, what scale would you use? The page size is $8\frac{1}{2}$ inches by 11 inches. Explain your answer.

VENEZUELA
COLOMBIA
Atlantic Ocean
PERU Amazon River
BRAZIL
BOLIVIA
Pacific Ocean
ARGENTINA

326 • Fractions and Mixed Numbers

ART CONNECTION

Art Connection Tell students that if you mix blue paint with red paint in the ratio of 1 liter to 3 liters, you will get purple paint. Ask them to tell how many liters of blue and red paint are needed to make 8 liters of purple. (6 L red, 2 L blue)

RETEACHING p. 30

LESSON **91** RETEACHING Name_____

A landscaping job pays $1500. Each person will be paid according to the number of hours worked, as shown in the table below. How much should each person be paid?

One way to find how much each person earns is to write proportions. Find the total number of hours worked.

5 + 18 + 12 + 4 + 16 + 5 = 50 hours

Find the fractional part of the total hours each person worked. Bob: $\frac{5}{50}$

Now write a proportion.

$\frac{5}{50} = \frac{n}{1500}$ To get a common denominator of 1500, find $\frac{5}{50} \times \frac{30}{30}$.

$\frac{150}{1500} = \frac{n}{1500}$ Since the denominators are the same, the numerators must be the same.

Since n = 150, Bob earned $150.

Complete the table below.

Name	Hours Worked	Fraction of Total Hours Worked	Amount Earned
Bob	5	$\frac{1}{10}$	$150
Carmen	8	$\frac{4}{25}$	$240
Doug	12	$\frac{6}{25}$	$360
Emily	4	$\frac{2}{25}$	$120
Francesca	16	$\frac{8}{25}$	$480
Gordon	5	$\frac{1}{10}$	$150
Total	50	1	$1500

30 • Math Explorations and Applications Level 6

---

*available separately

Do research to find the five longest rivers in the world in addition to the Amazon. Using a computer or other means, draw a chart like this one, and complete the information in the chart for each river. Data may vary depending on the source used.

Longest Rivers of the World

River	Approximate Length (miles)	Country of Source	Country of Outflow	Scale to Fit in a Standard Geography Textbook
Amazon	3900	Peru	Brazil	500 miles = 1 inch
Nile	4200	Burundi	Egypt	600 miles = 1 inch
Chang Jiang	3700	China	China	500 miles = 1 inch
Ob-Irtish	3400	China	Russia	500 miles = 1 inch
Huang He	3000	Tibet	China	400 miles = 1 inch
Congo	3000	Zaire	Zaire	400 miles = 1 inch

Scales are good examples only.

The world's highest waterfall is Angel Falls on the Carrao River in Venezuela. It has a drop of 3212 feet.

Unit 4   Lesson 91 • **327**

❸ Wrap-Up

In Closing Ask students to summarize the methods presented for solving a proportion. Have them include in their Math Journals a statement about real-life uses of ratios and proportions.

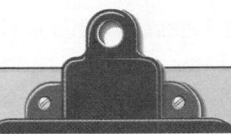

Performance Assessment Explain to students that a certain map uses the scale 1 inch = 40 miles. Ask them to explain a way to figure how far apart, in miles, two towns are that are 2.5 inches apart on the map. (Multiply 2.5 × 40 = 100 miles.)

Assessment Criteria

Did the student . . .

✓ correctly solve the problems involved in completing the tables?

✓ demonstrate ability to solve proportions correctly?

Homework Ask students to recall the data they gathered for lesson 89 about homework time and TV-watching time. Have them use that information to write a ratio comparing the two, and then to write and solve a proportion to figure out how much time they spend doing homework for every hour they spend watching TV.

PRACTICE p. 91

LESSON 91 PRACTICE   Name_____

A group of friends purchased some raffle tickets. They accidentally mixed up all of the tickets, so they agreed that if any ticket won the $1000 prize, they would all split the money, based on the original number of tickets purchased. Suppose one of the tickets wins.

Figure out how much of the $1000 each friend would win.

	Number of Tickets Bought	Money Won
Becky	5	❶ $100
Tomas	8	❷ $160
Andre	10	❸ $200
Julia	15	❹ $300
Marcia	12	❺ $240

A highway is 1240 miles long. How long will a diagram of the highway be if drawn to the following scales?

❻ 10 miles = 1 inch ____124 inches____

❼ 100 miles = 1 inch ____12.4 inches____

❽ 50 miles = 1 inch ____24.8 inches____

❾ 200 miles = 1 inch ____6.2 inches____

❿ 20 miles = 1 inch ____62 inches____

Math Explorations and Applications Level 6 • 91

ENRICHMENT p. 91

LESSON 91 ENRICHMENT   Name_____

The Golden Ratio is a proportion that is thought to be particularly pleasing. In line segment AC below, $\frac{AB}{AC}$ equals $\frac{BC}{AB}$ equals 0.618, the Golden Ratio. A Golden Rectangle has sides that fit this ratio.

The Golden Rectangle is often found in nature. The chambered nautilus is a mollusk whose shell has this shape. Often paintings and architecture contain Golden Rectangles.

Try to find examples of the Golden Rectangle in the objects around you, in art reproductions, and in pictures of plants and animals. Measure the length and width to the nearest millimeter. Use a calculator to find the ratio.

Object	Width	Length	Ratio

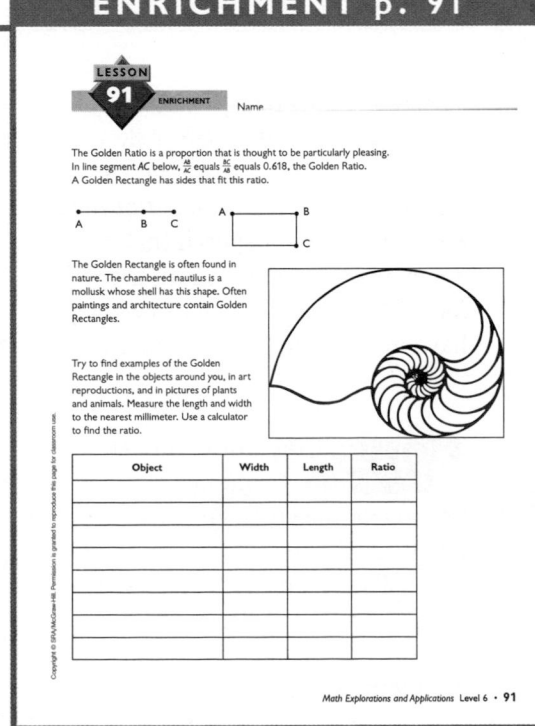

Math Explorations and Applications Level 6 • 91

LESSON 92
Similar Figures

LESSON PLANNER

Objectives

▶ to demonstrate how ratios and proportions can be used to determine the length of something that cannot be measured directly

▶ to present the relationship between similar figures and proportions

Context of the Lesson This is the last of six lessons on ratios, rates, averages, and proportions. Similar figures were discussed in Level 5 and will be covered again in Unit 6.

 MANIPULATIVES
geoboards
(optional)

Program Resources
Practice Master 92
Enrichment Master 92
For extra practice:
CD-ROM* Lesson 92

1 Warm-Up

 **Problem of the Day** Present the following problem: If 6 FLURBS equal 3 NERTS, and 4 PLUDS equal 5 FLURBS, how many NERTS are equal to 1 PLUD? ($\frac{5}{8}$ NERTS = 1 PLUD)

Problem-Solving Strategies Ask students who have solved the Problem of the Day to share how they solved it and any strategies they used.

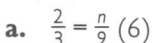 Have students solve for *n* mentally.

a. $\frac{2}{3} = \frac{n}{9}$ (6) b. $\frac{3}{5} = \frac{12}{n}$ (20)

c. $\frac{n}{6} = \frac{20}{24}$ (5) d. $\frac{15}{n} = \frac{3}{1}$ (5)

2 Teach

 **Using the Student Pages** Discuss the problem at the top of page 328. Ask students to try to figure out how tall the flagpole is from the given information. Ask them to explain their methods.

LESSON 92
Similar Figures

Grant wants to know how tall the flag pole is. He can't climb the pole to measure it, so he decides to use the shadow of the pole to help him. He puts a small pole in the ground as vertically (or straight up) as he can. He measures the small pole from the ground to the top. It is 2 meters tall. He measures the shadow of the small pole. It is 3 meters long. Then he measures the shadow of the flag pole. It is 27 meters long. From this information he thinks he can figure out how tall the pole is.

He will use the fact that the corresponding sides of the two triangles are in proportion. He can solve the equation $\frac{2}{3} = \frac{x}{27}$. x equals 18 meters.

Answer these questions.

❶ Can you see how he will do that? What is the height of the flag pole?

In general, if two figures are similar, the corresponding sides are in proportion.

❷ The triangles shown below are similar with corresponding sides *AB* measuring 10 cm and *DE* measuring 20 cm. The measures of *AC* and *CB* are 8 cm and 13 cm. Find the lengths of *DF* and *FE*. **length of *DF* = 16cm; length of *FE* = 26 cm**

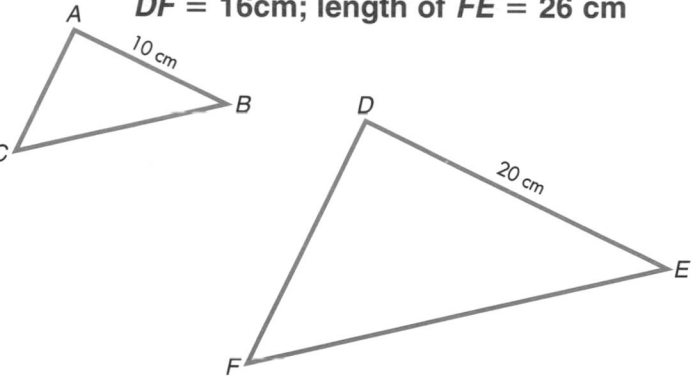

 **Language Arts Connection** Ask students to define and compare the terms *similar figure* and *simile* (a figure of speech that compares two things, using the word *like*). Have students discuss what they have in common. (both are used to indicate likeness)

COOPERATIVE LEARNING Invite cooperative groups to investigate similarity. For example, have one student draw a figure on graph paper. The others in the group draw figures similar but not identical to it on the same sheet and explain why his or her figure is similar to the others.

RETEACHING

MANIPULATIVES You may wish to have students work with **geoboards** to explore the concept of similar figures. One student can use a rubber band to make a triangle, rectangle, or other figure on the geoboard and another can make a figure that is similar to it. Students can measure to check that the corresponding sides are in the same ratio and that the corresponding angles are congruent. If geoboards are unavailable, students can use dot paper and rulers.

*available separately

Solve these problems.

3 The three figures shown below are similar. The lengths of the sides of *ABCDE* are given in the figure as are the lengths of *GH* and *LM*. What are the lengths of the other four sides of *GHIJK* and *LMNOP*?

HI = 50; IJ = 37.5; JK = 45; KG = 40; MN = 8; NO = 6; OP = 7.2; PL = 6.4

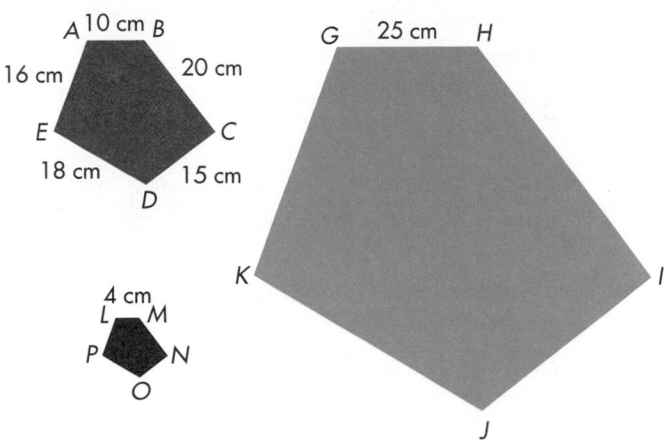

4 Alexa wants to find out how tall a certain spruce tree is. She measures the shadow of the tree. It is 60 feet. She knows that she is 5 feet tall. She measures her shadow, and it is 12 feet long. How tall is the spruce tree? **25 feet**

PRACTICE p. 92

ENRICHMENT p. 92

Encourage different ones. If no student suggests it, point out that the flagpole and its shadow and the small pole and its shadow are similar figures, and then demonstrate how to set up the proportion $\frac{2}{3} = \frac{h}{27}$, where *h* represents the height of the flagpole. Work out the proportion to show that the height of the taller pole is 18 meters. Explain that for any two similar figures, corresponding lengths are in proportion. You may wish to give examples using models of boats and airplanes, and so on. You can show that within each model the parts are in the same orientation and their sizes are in the same proportion as they are in the real object. You can point out, for instance, that in a model of a train engine, the length and width are in the same proportion as the length and width of the actual engine. Have students solve the remaining problems on pages 328 and 329 independently.

3 Wrap-Up ⏱ 5 MINUTES

In Closing To summarize the lesson, have students state what they think is the main idea to be learned from this lesson. Students can write this in their Math Journals.

Informal Assessment Observe students as they work on the problems on these pages. You may wish to ask students to explain their reasoning as they are solving a particular problem.

Assessment Criteria

Did the student . . .

✓ participate in the discussion of how to decide how tall the flagpole is?

✓ complete the problems on the two pages?

✓ make reasonable comments about the main point of the lesson?

Homework Have students apply the indirect measuring method introduced in the lesson to figure out the height of a tall pole, such as a lamppost, flagpole, or telephone pole around the school or in their neighborhood. Students can work with a partner from class or with a family member.

LESSON 93
Student Edition pages 330–331
Unit 4 Review

Using the Student Pages Use this Unit Review as a preliminary unit test to indicate areas in which an individual student is having difficulty or in which the entire class may need help. If students do well on the Unit Review, you may wish to skip directly to the next unit. If not, you may want to spend a day or so helping students overcome their individual difficulties before they take the Unit Test.

Next to each instruction line is a list of the lessons in the unit covered in that set of problems. Students can refer to the specific lesson for additional instruction if they need help. You can also use this information to make additional assignments based on the previous lesson concepts.

Problems 1–8 If students miss more than one of these fraction problems, try to identify the nature of the difficulty. Use **craft sticks** or other math manipulatives if necessary. Be sure that students understand for problems 5–8 that multiplying $\frac{1}{3} \times 24$ is the same as taking $\frac{1}{3}$ of 24.

Problems 9–16 Give extra help to those students who miss more than one of these fraction of fractions problems. Remind them that the essential point is that numerators should be multiplied and denominators should be multiplied. Do not count unreduced answers wrong, but suggest that students should reduce fractions for simplicity in the future.

Problems 17–21 If students miss more than one of these problems involving decimal equivalents of fractions, try to identify the reason. Suggest further work on memorization of the equivalents through playing the "Equivalence 2" Game Mat. Also suggest the "Up to 1" game on page 245 and the "Up to 2" game on page 282. Remind those students whose problem is with short division that the decimal point in the quotient should line up with the point in the dividend.

LESSON 93
Unit 4 Review

Lesson 65 Solve.

❶ $\frac{1}{2}$ of 30 **15**   ❷ $\frac{1}{4}$ of 24 **6**   ❸ $\frac{1}{6}$ of 18 **3**   ❹ $\frac{1}{5}$ of 20 **4**

Lesson 65 Multiply.

❺ $\frac{1}{3} \times 24$ **8**   ❻ $\frac{1}{6} \times 66$ **11**   ❼ $\frac{1}{7} \times 21$ **3**   ❽ $\frac{1}{4} \times 40$ **10**

Lesson 66 Solve these problems.

❾ $\frac{1}{2}$ of $\frac{1}{4}$ $\frac{1}{8}$ ❿ $\frac{3}{4}$ of $\frac{4}{15}$ $\frac{1}{5}$ ⓫ $\frac{2}{3}$ of $\frac{6}{7}$ $\frac{4}{7}$ ⓬ $\frac{3}{5}$ of $\frac{4}{5}$ $\frac{12}{25}$

Lessons 66 and 67 Multiply.

⓭ $\frac{1}{4} \times \frac{2}{9}$ $\frac{1}{18}$ ⓮ $\frac{1}{3} \times \frac{7}{11}$ $\frac{7}{33}$ ⓯ $\frac{1}{6} \times \frac{4}{5}$ $\frac{2}{15}$ ⓰ $\frac{2}{3} \times \frac{5}{7}$ $\frac{10}{21}$

Lesson 67 For each fraction write the decimal equivalent or an approximation rounded to the nearest thousandth.

⓱ $\frac{3}{8}$ **0.375** ⓲ $\frac{3}{4}$ **0.75** ⓳ $\frac{4}{3}$ **1.333** ⓴ $1\frac{1}{9}$ **1.111** ㉑ $2\frac{1}{5}$ **2.2**

Lessons 72 and 73 Add or subtract.

㉒ $\frac{4}{7} + \frac{2}{7}$ $\frac{6}{7}$ ㉓ $\frac{4}{7} - \frac{2}{7}$ $\frac{2}{7}$ ㉔ $\frac{2}{3} - \frac{1}{6}$ $\frac{3}{6}$ (or $\frac{1}{2}$)   ㉕ $\frac{2}{3} + \frac{1}{6}$ $\frac{5}{6}$

㉖ $\frac{3}{8} - \frac{1}{4}$ $\frac{1}{8}$ ㉗ $\frac{3}{8} + \frac{3}{4}$ $\frac{9}{8}$ (or $1\frac{1}{8}$)   ㉘ $\frac{4}{5} - \frac{1}{2}$ $\frac{3}{10}$ ㉙ $\frac{4}{5} + \frac{1}{2}$ $\frac{13}{10}$ (or $1\frac{3}{10}$)

Lessons 79 and 80 Add or subtract. Check your answers to be sure they make sense.

㉚ $3\frac{1}{2} - 1\frac{1}{3}$ $2\frac{1}{6}$ ㉛ $3\frac{1}{2} + \frac{1}{3}$ $3\frac{5}{6}$ ㉜ $4\frac{1}{4} + 1\frac{1}{3}$ $5\frac{11}{12}$ ㉝ $4\frac{1}{4} - 1\frac{2}{3}$ $2\frac{7}{12}$

㉞ $3\frac{1}{8} + \frac{5}{8}$ $3\frac{6}{8}$ (or $3\frac{3}{4}$)   ㉟ $3\frac{1}{8} - \frac{5}{8}$ $2\frac{4}{8}$ (or $2\frac{1}{2}$)   ㊱ $2\frac{3}{5} + 2\frac{1}{10}$ $4\frac{7}{10}$ ㊲ $2\frac{3}{5} - 2\frac{1}{10}$ $\frac{5}{10}$ (or $\frac{1}{2}$)

Lessons 83 and 85 Divide.

㊳ $\frac{3}{4} \div \frac{1}{3}$ $\frac{9}{4}$ (or $2\frac{1}{4}$)   ㊴ $\frac{2}{9} \div \frac{3}{5}$ $\frac{10}{27}$ ㊵ $2\frac{1}{4} \div \frac{2}{3}$ $\frac{27}{8}$ (or $3\frac{3}{8}$)   ㊶ $\frac{3}{4} \div \frac{1}{2}$ $\frac{3}{2}$ (or $1\frac{1}{2}$)

㊷ $3\frac{1}{2} \div \frac{2}{3}$ $\frac{21}{4}$ (or $5\frac{1}{4}$)   ㊸ $\frac{4}{5} \div \frac{1}{5}$ **4**   ㊹ $1\frac{3}{4} \div \frac{7}{8}$ **2**   ㊺ $5\frac{1}{3} \div 8$ $\frac{16}{24}$ (or $\frac{2}{3}$)

330 • Fractions and Mixed Numbers

RETEACHING

Students who have difficulty with this Unit Review should have further opportunity to review and to practice the skills before they proceed on with the next unit. For each set of problems there are specific suggestions for reteaching. These suggestions can be found in the margins.

Solve these problems.

46 It was 2:45 when Eva told her friend to meet her in $2\frac{1}{2}$ hours. At what time were they supposed to meet? **5:15**

47 If you roll a 0–5 cube, what is the probability of getting a 1, 2, or 3? $\frac{3}{6}$ **(or** $\frac{1}{2}$**)**

Lessons 65,
75, 76, 79,
80, 88 and 89

48 The fuel gauge in Mr. Grigori's car shows that the gasoline tank is $\frac{3}{4}$ full. The tank can hold 48 liters of gasoline. About how many liters of gasoline are in the tank? **36**

49 If you roll a 5–10 cube, what is the probability of getting a 9 or 10? $\frac{2}{6}$ **(or** $\frac{1}{3}$**)**

50 Which costs less, a $69.95 pair of in-line skates marked "$\frac{1}{3}$ off" or "$\frac{1}{3}$ the regular price"? $\frac{1}{3}$ **the regular price**

51 Mrs. Lau is planning to drive to Westfield by going through Newton. The trip to Newton takes about $1\frac{1}{4}$ hours. The trip from Newton to Westfield takes about $6\frac{1}{2}$ hours. About how long will it take Mrs. Lau to get to Westfield? $7\frac{3}{4}$ **h**

52 About $\frac{3}{4}$ of the students in Aaron's class ate lunch in the cafeteria. About what fraction of the class didn't eat lunch in the cafeteria? $\frac{1}{4}$

53 The railroad fare from West Town to South Town is $3.20. The railroad says that its fares are about $0.08 per kilometer traveled. About how far is it from West Town to South Town on the railroad? **40 km**

54 The Better Sports Store sold nine bicycles last weekend. The prices of the bicycles sold were $85, $100, $120, $120, $120, $130, $135, $140, and $220. Find the mean, median, and mode of the prices. **mean $130, median $120, mode $120**

55 Mr. Keith filled his car's gas tank, drove 180 miles, and then filled his gas tank with 7.4 gallons of gas. About how many miles per gallon did his car get? **about 24.3**

 Problems 22–29 Students who miss more than one of these problems involving adding and subtracting fractions may benefit from playing the "Circo 11" game (page 265) and the "Make 1" game (page 289).

Problems 30–37 Reteach those students who miss more than one of these mixed-number problems. Give these students extra practice with converting mixed numbers to improper fractions. You may also encourage them to add or subtract the fractional parts and whole number parts separately when possible.

Problems 38–45 Reteach as necessary, using simpler numbers and objects or pictures of geometric figures to show the correct procedure for solving problems involving division by fractions.

 **Problems 46–55** If students miss more than two of these word problems, try to determine why in an individual interview. Have the students read and act out a problem, using pictures, **play money*,** the students' imaginations, or anything else that helps to make the problem clearer.

 **Portfolio Assessment** If you have not already assigned the Portfolio Assessment task provided on Assessment Blackline Masters page 89, it can be used at this time to evaluate students' ability to use ratios to solve problems.

 **Performance Assessment** The Performance Assessment Task 2 provided on Assessment Blackline Masters pages 74–75 can be used at this time to evaluate students' proficiency with probability, mixed numbers, averages, and proportions. You may want to administer this assessment with individual students or in small groups.

Unit Project If you have not already assigned the "Fair Advertising" project on pages 338 and 339, you may wish to do so at this time. This project is a good opportunity for students to practice analyzing advertising for fairness.

PRACTICE p. 93

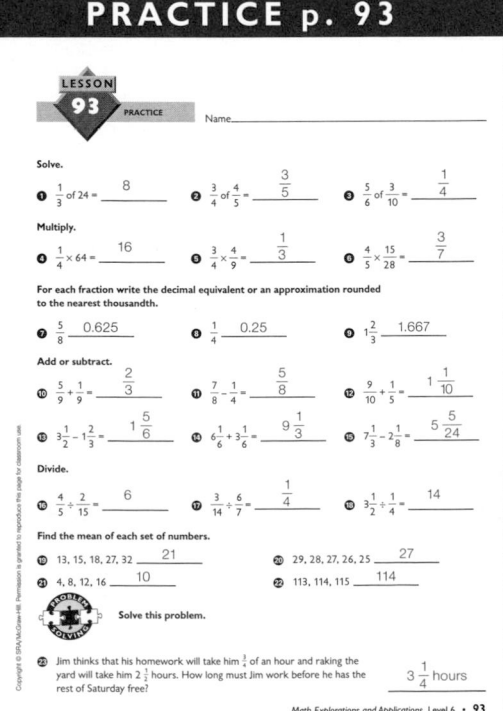

ENRICHMENT p. 93

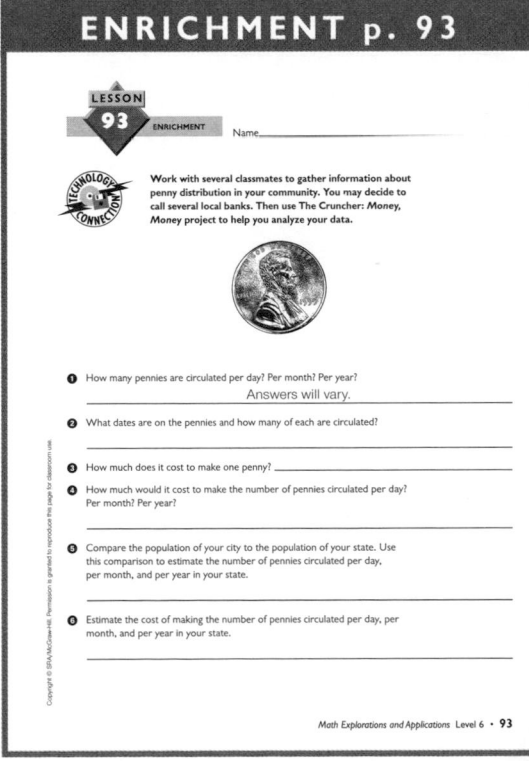

LESSON 94 Unit 4 Practice

Student Edition pages 332–335

Unit 4 Practice

Using the Student Pages The purpose of these pages is to provide additional practice for those students who demonstrated a need for it on the Unit Review. You may wish to assign only the specific exercises in this Unit Practice in which students need further reinforcement. Each instruction line gives the lessons in the unit it covers so that you or students can refer to the specific lesson for additional review and instruction.

 Students who do not require additional practice on specific concepts may enjoy playing the "Inverso" game on page 335, which involves approximating multiplicative inverses. You may also wish to have them play any other games you have played so far, such as the "Make 1" game on page 289, which provides extensive practice in adding and subtracting fractions mentally. You may challenge students to play a variation of this game in which the goal is 2 instead of 1. These students may also help by playing appropriate games with students who need remedial practice or by actually teaching certain procedures to other students.

 You may want to use the Cumulative Review on page 573 after this lesson.

Lesson 65 Solve.

1 $\frac{1}{3}$ of 12 **4** **2** $\frac{2}{3}$ of 12 **8** **3** $\frac{1}{4}$ of 12 **3** **4** $\frac{3}{4}$ of 12 **9**

5 $\frac{1}{7}$ of 28 **4** **6** $\frac{1}{8}$ of 72 **9** **7** $\frac{3}{8}$ of 72 **27** **8** $\frac{2}{8}$ of 72 **18**

9 $\frac{1}{4}$ of 72 **18** **10** $\frac{1}{5}$ of 60 **12** **11** $\frac{3}{4}$ of 60 **45** **12** $\frac{4}{4}$ of 60 **60**

13 $\frac{1}{2}$ of 60 **30** **14** $\frac{2}{2}$ of 60 **60** **15** $\frac{1}{9}$ of 72 **8** **16** $\frac{3}{4}$ of 100 **75**

17 $\frac{1}{5}$ of 100 **20** **18** $\frac{3}{5}$ of 100 **60** **19** $\frac{1}{10}$ of 100 **10** **20** $\frac{3}{10}$ of 100 **30**

Lesson 65 Multiply.

21 $\frac{3}{7} \times 28$ **12** **22** $\frac{6}{7} \times 28$ **24** **23** $\frac{1}{5} \times 35$ **7** **24** $\frac{2}{5} \times 35$ **14**

25 $\frac{4}{5} \times 35$ **28** **26** $\frac{3}{5} \times 60$ **36** **27** $\frac{1}{3} \times 60$ **20** **28** $\frac{2}{3} \times 60$ **40**

29 $\frac{1}{4} \times 60$ **15** **30** $\frac{2}{4} \times 60$ **30** **31** $\frac{2}{9} \times 72$ **16** **32** $\frac{5}{9} \times 72$ **40**

33 $\frac{8}{9} \times 72$ **64** **34** $\frac{9}{9} \times 72$ **72** **35** $\frac{1}{4} \times 100$ **25** **36** $\frac{7}{10} \times 100$ **70**

37 $\frac{9}{10} \times 100$ **90** **38** $\frac{1}{2} \times 100$ **50** **39** $\frac{2}{2} \times 100$ **100** **40** $\frac{10}{10} \times 100$ **100**

Lesson 65 Solve.

41 $\frac{1}{2}$ of 10 **5** **42** $\frac{1}{4}$ of 12 **3** **43** $\frac{3}{4}$ of 16 **12** **44** $\frac{1}{3}$ of 30 **10**

45 $\frac{2}{3}$ of 30 **20** **46** $\frac{3}{5}$ of 50 **30** **47** $\frac{7}{10}$ of 100 **70** **48** $\frac{1}{8}$ of 80 **10**

49 $\frac{3}{8}$ of 24 **9** **50** $\frac{1}{7}$ of 14 **2** **51** $\frac{1}{6}$ of 36 **6** **52** $\frac{1}{9}$ of 72 **8**

53 $\frac{2}{9}$ of 72 **16** **54** $\frac{3}{9}$ of 72 **24** **55** $\frac{4}{9}$ of 72 **32** **56** $\frac{2}{3}$ of 45 **30**

Lessons 66 and 70 Multiply.

57 $\frac{3}{7} \times \frac{1}{3}$ $\frac{1}{7}$ **58** $\frac{1}{3} \times \frac{2}{5}$ $\frac{2}{15}$ **59** $\frac{1}{2} \times \frac{3}{4}$ $\frac{3}{8}$ **60** $\frac{1}{3} \times \frac{2}{9}$ $\frac{2}{27}$

61 $\frac{1}{6} \times \frac{1}{3}$ $\frac{1}{18}$ **62** $\frac{1}{7} \times \frac{1}{2}$ $\frac{1}{14}$ **63** $\frac{2}{7} \times \frac{1}{2}$ $\frac{1}{7}$ **64** $\frac{3}{5} \times \frac{1}{4}$ $\frac{3}{20}$

65 $\frac{4}{5} \times \frac{1}{4}$ $\frac{1}{5}$ **66** $\frac{5}{9} \times \frac{3}{10}$ $\frac{1}{6}$ **67** $\frac{2}{3} \times \frac{5}{7}$ $\frac{10}{21}$ **68** $\frac{1}{2} \times \frac{3}{8}$ $\frac{3}{16}$

332 • Fractions and Mixed Numbers

Lesson 67

Write the decimal equivalent or an approximation to the nearest thousandth.

69 $\frac{1}{5}$ **0.2** **70** $\frac{2}{5}$ **0.4** **71** $\frac{4}{5}$ **0.8** **72** $\frac{1}{2}$ **0.5** **73** $\frac{1}{4}$ **0.25**

74 $\frac{1}{3}$ **0.333** **75** $\frac{3}{6}$ **0.5** **76** $\frac{4}{6}$ **0.667** **77** $\frac{2}{3}$ **0.667** **78** $\frac{5}{6}$ **0.833**

79 $\frac{3}{8}$ **0.375** **80** $\frac{4}{8}$ **0.5** **81** $\frac{5}{8}$ **0.625** **82** $\frac{7}{8}$ **0.875** **83** $\frac{7}{9}$ **0.778**

84 $\frac{1}{9}$ **0.111** **85** $\frac{2}{9}$ **0.222** **86** $\frac{3}{9}$ **0.333** **87** $\frac{4}{9}$ **0.444** **88** $\frac{5}{9}$ **0.556**

Lessons 72, 73, 79, and 80

Add or subtract.

89 $\frac{3}{5} + \frac{1}{5}$ **$\frac{4}{5}$** **90** $\frac{3}{5} - \frac{1}{5}$ **$\frac{2}{5}$** **91** $\frac{5}{7} + \frac{3}{7}$ **$\frac{8}{7}$ (or $1\frac{1}{7}$)** **92** $\frac{5}{7} - \frac{3}{7}$ **$\frac{2}{7}$**

93 $\frac{4}{9} + \frac{7}{9}$ **$\frac{11}{9}$ (or $1\frac{2}{9}$)** **94** $\frac{11}{12} - \frac{5}{12}$ **$\frac{6}{12}$ (or $\frac{1}{2}$)** **95** $\frac{1}{4} + \frac{1}{3}$ **$\frac{7}{12}$** **96** $1\frac{1}{4} + 2\frac{1}{3}$ **$3\frac{7}{12}$**

97 $\frac{3}{5} - \frac{1}{2}$ **$\frac{1}{10}$** **98** $3\frac{3}{5} - 2\frac{1}{2}$ **$1\frac{1}{10}$** **99** $2\frac{2}{3} + 1\frac{1}{6}$ **$3\frac{5}{6}$** **100** $1\frac{1}{4} + 2\frac{3}{8}$ **$3\frac{5}{8}$**

101 $3\frac{3}{4} - 1\frac{2}{3}$ **$2\frac{1}{12}$** **102** $10\frac{1}{2} + 5\frac{3}{4}$ **$16\frac{1}{4}$** **103** $11\frac{2}{5} - 9\frac{5}{6}$ **$1\frac{17}{30}$** **104** $6\frac{1}{4} - 3\frac{7}{8}$ **$2\frac{3}{8}$**

Lessons 66, 69, 79, 80, 83, and 85

Multiply or divide. Give answers in the form of proper fractions or mixed numbers. Reduce if possible.

105 $\frac{1}{6} \times \frac{1}{5}$ **$\frac{1}{30}$** **106** $\frac{1}{3} \times \frac{1}{2}$ **$\frac{1}{6}$** **107** $\frac{1}{6} \div \frac{1}{2}$ **$\frac{1}{3}$** **108** $\frac{3}{4} \times \frac{2}{3}$ **$\frac{1}{2}$**

109 $\frac{2}{3} \times \frac{3}{4}$ **$\frac{1}{2}$** **110** $\frac{5}{6} \div \frac{1}{6}$ **5** **111** $1\frac{5}{6} \div \frac{1}{6}$ **11** **112** $1\frac{1}{2} \div \frac{1}{2}$ **3**

113 $1\frac{1}{2} \div \frac{2}{3}$ **$2\frac{1}{4}$** **114** $2\frac{3}{4} \times \frac{4}{5}$ **$2\frac{1}{5}$** **115** $1\frac{1}{3} \times 1\frac{1}{3}$ **$1\frac{7}{9}$** **116** $2\frac{7}{8} \div 1\frac{1}{4}$ **$2\frac{3}{10}$**

117 $\frac{3}{7} \div 2\frac{1}{3}$ **$\frac{9}{49}$** **118** $2\frac{1}{2} \times 2\frac{1}{2}$ **$6\frac{1}{4}$** **119** $3\frac{1}{3} \div 3\frac{1}{3}$ **1** **120** $2\frac{1}{4} \div 3$ **$\frac{3}{4}$**

Unit 4 Practice • **333**

Technology Connection You may wish to refer students to the Internet site *Brain Teasers,* provided by the Eisenhower National Clearinghouse for Mathematics and Science Education (http://www.hmco.com/school/math/brain/). Each Thursday, a new brain teaser is posted to challenge students' problem solving skills.

◆ **LESSON 94   Unit 4 Practice**

◆ **LESSON 94   Unit 4 Practice**

Lessons 65,
75, 76, 79, 80,
88 and 89

Solve these problems.

121 Bob's Bargain Store is having a sale in which every item in the store is $\frac{1}{3}$ off the regular price. What is the sale price of each of these items?

   a. Radio—regular price $18 **$12.00**

   b. Coat—regular price $66 **$44.00**

   c. Baseball cap—regular price $9.99 **$6.66**

122 Nina's club has a rule that at least $\frac{2}{3}$ of the members must be present for a vote. Of the 24 members, 20 of them were present.

   a. Is that enough for a vote? **yes**

   b. What is the fewest number of members that can be there for a vote? **16**

123 Brian's scores on his last ten spelling tests were 90, 90, 90, 95, 90, 80, 90, 90, 100, and 90.

                               mean 90.5, median 90,

   a. Find the mean, median, and mode of his scores. **mode 90**

   b. What type of average best reflects Brian's performance in spelling? **median or mode**

124 Ms. Sloan is driving from Arkville to Zooport, a distance of 260 kilometers. When she starts, the odometer in her car shows 35,640.4 kilometers.

   a. About what will the odometer show when Ms. Sloan is about halfway there? **35770.4 km**

   b. About what will the odometer show when she returns to Arkville (she takes a direct route each way)? **36160.4 km**

   c. When Ms. Sloan left Arkville, the fuel gauge showed that her gasoline tank was $\frac{3}{4}$ full. When she arrived at Zooport, the tank was $\frac{1}{4}$ full. Does she have enough gasoline to get back to Arkville? **no**

125 If you roll a 5–10 cube, what is the probability of rolling a

   a. 7? $\frac{1}{6}$ **b.** 5? $\frac{1}{6}$

   c. 7 or a 5? $\frac{2}{6}$ **(or $\frac{1}{3}$)**   **d.** one-digit number? $\frac{5}{6}$

   e. two-digit number? $\frac{1}{6}$ **f.** number greater than 6? $\frac{4}{6}$ **(or $\frac{2}{3}$)**

   g. number less than 7? $\frac{2}{6}$ **(or $\frac{1}{3}$)**   **h.** 7 or less? $\frac{3}{6}$ **(or $\frac{1}{2}$)**

334 · Fractions and Mixed Numbers

RETEACHING

Students who have difficulty with this Unit Practice should have further opportunity to review and to practice the skills before they proceed on with the next unit. Beside each set of problems is a reference to the lesson or lessons from which the problems were taken. You may want to review the individual lessons with students who are having difficulty with them.

Inverso Game

COOPERATIVE LEARNING

Players:	One or more
Materials:	One calculator for each player
Object:	To get as close to the goal of 1 as you can
Math Focus:	Using a calculator and approximating the reciprocal of numbers

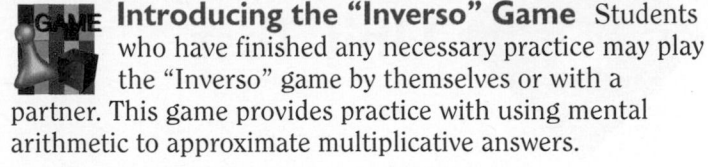

Introducing the "Inverso" Game Students who have finished any necessary practice may play the "Inverso" game by themselves or with a partner. This game provides practice with using mental arithmetic to approximate multiplicative answers.

RULES

1. Enter any multidigit number on the calculator.
2. Push ✕.
3. Enter a decimal number less than 1 (you are trying to get a product close to 1).
4. Push ═. How close to 1 did you get?

SAMPLE GAME

Renata entered 56,234 by pushing 5 6 2 3 4 . Then she pushed ✕.

She thought, "What number times 56,234 will be about 1?"

She entered 0.00002 by pushing . 0 0 0 0 2 .

Then she pushed ═, and the display showed 1.12468 .

"That's not bad for a first try," she said.

OTHER WAYS TO PLAY THIS GAME

1. Start over. Enter 0.00002 ✕ 56,234. After pushing ═, push ✕, enter another number (trying to get even closer to 1), and push ═. Keep doing this to see if you can get 1 exactly or get very close.

2. Play "Inverso" with a partner. You enter a number, and then your partner tries to get as close to 1 as possible with one multiplication. Then reverse roles. Whoever gets closer to 1 wins that round.

3. Choose other goals instead of 1.

e the Cumulative Review on p. 573 after this lesson.

Unit 4 Practice • **335**

PRACTICE p. 94

LESSON 94 PRACTICE   Name_____

Solve.

1. $\frac{1}{4}$ of 16 = __4__   2. $\frac{5}{8}$ of 72 = __45__   3. $\frac{7}{10}$ of 200 = __140__

4. $\frac{2}{3}$ of 84 = __56__   5. $\frac{3}{4}$ of 24 = __18__   6. $\frac{5}{6}$ of 42 = __35__

Multiply.

7. $\frac{4}{7} \times 35 =$ __20__   8. $\frac{2}{5} \times 25 =$ __10__   9. $\frac{3}{4} \times \frac{8}{9} =$ __$\frac{2}{3}$__

Write the decimal equivalent or an approximation to the nearest thousandth.

10. $\frac{4}{5}$ __0.8__   11. $\frac{2}{9}$ __0.222__   12. $\frac{3}{16}$ __0.188__   13. $\frac{4}{11}$ __0.364__

Add or subtract.

14. $\frac{2}{9} + \frac{4}{9} =$ __$\frac{2}{3}$__   15. $\frac{3}{4} - \frac{1}{3} =$ __$\frac{5}{12}$__   16. $2\frac{1}{6} + 3\frac{1}{4} =$ __$5\frac{5}{12}$__

17. $5\frac{1}{3} - 2\frac{5}{8} =$ __$2\frac{17}{24}$__   18. $4\frac{1}{6} + 5\frac{2}{3} =$ __$9\frac{5}{6}$__   19. $6\frac{7}{8} - 4\frac{1}{2} =$ __$2\frac{3}{8}$__

Multiply or divide.

20. $\frac{3}{8} \times \frac{9}{10} =$ __$\frac{5}{12}$__   21. $1\frac{2}{3} \times 3\frac{3}{4} =$ __$4\frac{7}{12}$__   22. $5\frac{3}{4} \div 1\frac{1}{2} =$ __$3\frac{5}{6}$__

Find the mean of each set of numbers.

23. 5, 10, 15, 20, 25 __15__   24. 23, 23, 24, 25, 26 __24.2__

25. 40, 42, 44, 46, 48, 50, 52 __46__   26. 10, 10, 20, 30, 30, 40, 50 __27.14__

94 • *Math Explorations and Applications Level 6*

ENRICHMENT p. 94

LESSON 94 ENRICHMENT   Name_____

The operation and equal signs are missing in each of the sentences below. Draw a +, −, ×, ÷, or an = in each box to make a true sentence. Each sentence will need one = sign, and it may be in any box.

Answers will vary. Possible answers are given.

1. $\frac{3}{5}$ ☐ $\frac{1}{2}$ ☐ $\frac{1}{3}$ ☐ $\frac{23}{30}$

2. $\frac{3}{4}$ ☐ $\frac{1}{3}$ ☐ $\frac{1}{4}$ ☐ $\frac{1}{2}$

3. $\frac{4}{7}$ ☐ 2 ☐ $\frac{1}{3}$ ☐ $\frac{6}{7}$

4. 3 ☐ $\frac{4}{5}$ ☐ $\frac{1}{5}$ ☐ $\frac{1}{5}$

5. $\frac{1}{6}$ ☐ $\frac{1}{2}$ ☐ $\frac{1}{3}$ ☐ $\frac{2}{3}$

6. $\frac{1}{2}$ ☐ $\frac{3}{6}$ ☐ $2\frac{1}{2}$ ☐ $\frac{2}{5}$

7. $2\frac{2}{3}$ ☐ $1\frac{1}{6}$ ☐ $\frac{2}{3}$ ☐ 1

8. 2 ☐ $3\frac{5}{6}$ ☐ $1\frac{1}{2}$ ☐ $1\frac{1}{6}$

9. $2\frac{3}{4}$ ☐ $1\frac{1}{4}$ ☐ $1\frac{1}{2}$ ☐ $\frac{7}{10}$

10. $4\frac{3}{4}$ ☐ $\frac{2}{5}$ ☐ $\frac{1}{3}$ ☐ $2\frac{1}{20}$

94 • *Math Explorations and Applications Level 6*

Unit 4 Practice **335**

Using the Student Pages The Unit Test on Student Edition pages 336 and 337 provides an opportunity to formally evaluate your students' proficiency with concepts developed in this unit. It is similar in content and format to the Unit Review. Students who did well on the Unit Review may not need to take this test. Students who did not do well on the Unit Review should be provided with additional practice opportunities, such as the Unit Practice pages, before taking the Unit Test. As an alternative, you may wish to have these students take the Unit Test on Assessment Blackline Masters pages 37–39 or the Unit Test in standardized format, provided on Assessment Blackline Masters pages 114–121.

Solve.

1 $\frac{1}{2}$ of 24 **12** **2** $\frac{1}{4}$ of 20 **5** **3** $\frac{1}{6}$ of 24 **4** **4** $\frac{1}{3}$ of 12 **4**

Multiply.

5 $\frac{1}{9} \times 27$ **3** **6** $\frac{1}{3} \times 18$ **6** **7** $\frac{1}{4} \times 12$ **3** **8** $\frac{1}{5} \times 25$ **5**

Solve.

9 $\frac{1}{3}$ of $\frac{3}{7}$ $\frac{1}{7}$ **10** $\frac{1}{6}$ of $\frac{5}{6}$ $\frac{5}{36}$ **11** $\frac{1}{7}$ of $\frac{3}{4}$ $\frac{3}{28}$ **12** $\frac{2}{3}$ of $\frac{2}{3}$ $\frac{4}{9}$

Multiply.

13 $\frac{1}{4} \times \frac{2}{7}$ $\frac{1}{14}$ **14** $\frac{1}{3} \times \frac{2}{3}$ $\frac{2}{9}$ **15** $\frac{1}{5} \times \frac{3}{4}$ $\frac{3}{20}$ **16** $\frac{3}{5} \times \frac{1}{3}$ $\frac{3}{15}$ (or $\frac{1}{5}$)

For each fraction write the decimal equivalent or an approximation rounded to the nearest thousandth.

17 $\frac{1}{7}$ **18** $\frac{5}{8}$ **19** $1\frac{1}{4}$ **20** $\frac{5}{3}$ **21** $2\frac{4}{9}$

0.143 0.625 1.25 1.667 2.444

Add or subtract.

22 $\frac{3}{5} + \frac{1}{5}$ $\frac{4}{5}$ **23** $\frac{3}{5} - \frac{1}{5}$ $\frac{2}{5}$ **24** $\frac{3}{4} - \frac{3}{8}$ $\frac{3}{8}$ **25** $\frac{3}{4} + \frac{3}{8}$ $\frac{9}{8}$ (or $1\frac{1}{8}$)

26 $\frac{3}{6}$ $(\frac{1}{2})$

27 $\frac{9}{6}$ $(1\frac{1}{2})$

28 $\frac{17}{10}$ $(1\frac{7}{10})$

32 $1\frac{3}{6}$ $(1\frac{1}{2})$

34 $3\frac{5}{10}$ $(3\frac{1}{2})$

40 $\frac{40}{3}$ $(13\frac{1}{3})$

26 $\frac{5}{6} - \frac{1}{3}$ **27** $\frac{5}{6} + \frac{2}{3}$ **28** $\frac{9}{10} + \frac{4}{5}$ **29** $\frac{9}{10} - \frac{4}{5}$ $\frac{1}{10}$

Add or subtract. Check your answers to be sure they make sense.

30 $2\frac{1}{4} - 1\frac{1}{8}$ $1\frac{1}{8}$ **31** $2\frac{1}{4} + 1\frac{1}{8}$ $3\frac{3}{8}$ **32** $3\frac{1}{3} - 1\frac{5}{6}$ **33** $4\frac{1}{3} + 1\frac{5}{6}$ $6\frac{1}{6}$

34 $3\frac{1}{5} + \frac{3}{10}$ **35** $3\frac{1}{5} - \frac{3}{10}$ $2\frac{9}{10}$ **36** $2\frac{3}{4} + 4\frac{1}{3}$ **37** $5\frac{1}{2} - 2\frac{5}{8}$ $2\frac{7}{8}$

$7\frac{1}{12}$

Divide.

38 $\frac{2}{3} \div \frac{5}{6}$ $\frac{4}{5}$ **39** $\frac{1}{3} \div \frac{2}{3}$ $\frac{1}{2}$ **40** $2\frac{2}{9} \div \frac{1}{6}$ **41** $4\frac{1}{2} \div \frac{3}{4}$ **6**

42 $3\frac{3}{8} \div 2\frac{1}{4}$ **43** $3 \div \frac{4}{7}$ **44** $\frac{1}{35} \div 1\frac{5}{7}$ **45** $1\frac{1}{5} \div 1\frac{1}{2}$

$\frac{3}{2}$ (or $1\frac{1}{2}$) $\frac{21}{4}$ (or $5\frac{1}{4}$) $\frac{12}{15}$ (or $\frac{4}{5}$)

Solve these problems.

46 The fuel gauge in Mrs. Miller's car shows that the gasoline tank is $\frac{1}{4}$ full. The tank can hold 72 liters of gasoline. About how many liters of gasoline are in the tank? **18 L**

47 It was 1:30 when Elia told his friend to meet him in $3\frac{1}{4}$ hours. At what time were they supposed to meet? **4:45**

48 If you roll a 0–5 cube, what is the probability of getting a 2 or a 3? $\frac{2}{6}$ **(or $\frac{1}{3}$)**

49 If you roll a 5–10 cube, what is the probability of getting a 9? $\frac{1}{6}$

50 The railroad fare from Northfield to Eastland is $5.40. The railroad says its fares are about $0.09 per kilometer traveled. About how far is it from Northfield to Eastland on the railroad? **60 km**

51 Which costs less, a $25.00 basketball marked "$\frac{2}{3}$ off" or "$\frac{2}{3}$ the regular price"? $\frac{2}{3}$ **off**

52 Mr. Waneta is planning to drive from Blueville to Greenfield by going through Endtown. The trip to Endtown takes about $11\frac{1}{4}$ hours. The trip from Endtown to Greenfield takes about $2\frac{1}{2}$ hours. About how long will it take Mr. Waneta to get to Greenfield? **$13\frac{3}{4}$ h**

53 About $\frac{7}{8}$ of the students in Bill's class walk to school. About what fraction of the class doesn't walk to school? $\frac{1}{8}$

54 The high temperatures in Tepidtown last week were 18°C, 15°C, 17°C, 18°C, 17°C, 16°C, and 18°C. Find the mean, median, and mode of these temperatures. **mean 17, median 17, mode 18**

55 In four hours of fishing Wyn caught six fish. How many fish did she average per hour? **$1\frac{1}{2}$ fish per hour**

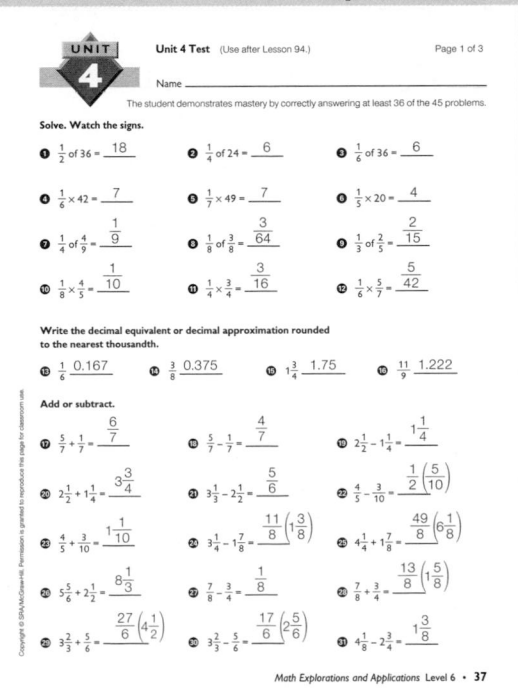

ASSESSMENT p. 37

PRESENTING THE PROJECT

Project Objective

▶ to analyze advertisements and learn to identify those that are fair and those that are misleading

Have students work in cooperative groups to discuss the advertisements on pages 338 and 339, as well as those found in local newspapers. You may wish to have students write reports on what is fair or unfair about them, or you can ask students to rewrite those advertisements that are not fair in order to make them fair. Although it is true that some advertisements are misleading, it is important not to leave students with the idea that many merchants are dishonest. In fact, the opposite is true; most merchants are honest, and the vast majority of advertisements are fair and not misleading.

Following are some of the misleading points in the advertisements on the student pages:

SuperDuper Potato Chips Nobody keeps potato chips for five years. Is 50 cents the same as only 50 cents?

Super Cola Saving 40 cents on a $1.29 item is a big savings, but here you must spend $50 to get the savings, and you can do it only on Saturdays. Perhaps other stores that charge more for the soda will have greater savings on the other items you must buy.

Videocassettes Are the cassettes really free, or do they cost $9.95?

Shoe Store You don't know how many shoes are half price. Apparently not very many, because running shoes and ladies' shoes have only very small markdowns.

FAIR ADVERTISING

Work in groups to study and discuss these advertisements. Write what is fair about them. Write what is unfair about them.

Why teach it at this time?

Although this project can be done at any time and at many grade levels, we suggest doing it after the students have completed units on percents and fractions with money applications, features of many advertisements.

FREE
VIDEO CASSETTE

Just send $9.95 to pay for shipping and handling to:

J. R. RESOURCE COMPANY
Post Office Box 843
Anytown, USA 50023
Be sure to include your name and address.

Mark's Shoe Store
1/2 Price SALE

All shoes are on SALE
Some are as much as **1/2 OFF** regular price.

All running shoes are $1.00 off regular price.
All ladies' shoes are $1.50 off regular price.

OPEN DAILY   9 a.m. to 7 p.m.
          CLOSED SUNDAY

Find advertisements in the newspaper. Work in cooperative groups
to decide which are fair and which are not fair.

Make three scrap albums: one for the fair advertisements, one
for those that are not fair, and one for those of which you are
not sure.

Unit 4 Wrap-Up • **339**

What Is a Math Project? If this is the first time you
have used math projects in your classroom, you may want to
refer to pages 98–99 in this Teacher's Guide for more
detailed information about effectively implementing and
assessing projects.

Homework Collecting advertisements and classifying
them as fair or unfair is an appropriate homework
assignment.

Wrapping Up the Project Consider maintaining the
scrapbooks mentioned at the bottom of page 339 for the
remainder of the semester, and have students continue to
bring in advertisements as they are found. Consider having
students write to advertisers who have particularly unfair or
misleading advertisements, asking for more information
about the product being advertised, and pointing out the
apparent unfairness.

Assessing the Project Make note of those students who
raise questions about advertisements and those who are also
swayed by ensuing discussion. These are signs that the
students are able to think critically. Those students who
don't raise questions and those who are unable to be swayed
by discussion need more exposure to this sort of project and
should be placed in cooperative groups with more able
students for the next projects.

COOPERATIVE LEARNING **Math CrossSections** SRA's *Math
CrossSections* is a set of eight units that
provide real-world math projects related to famous places in
the United States. These open-ended projects focus on
problem solving and reinforce reading, research, and study
skills. The eight units are:

The White House (Washington, D.C.)
747 DFW (Texas)
California's Giant Sequoias (California)
Pencil Making (Tennessee)
Barging Through the Locks (Michigan)
Atlanta's Olympic Stadium (Georgia)
Madison Square Garden (New York)
The Denver Mint (Colorado)

Use projects from *Barging Through the Locks* to give students
further opportunity to work with fractions and ratios.

UNIT 5

Algebra Readiness

UNDERSTANDING VARIABLES

OVERVIEW

This unit begins with work on collecting and organizing data. Students review how to graph ordered pairs and how to produce a set of ordered pairs for a function rule. Students graph linear functions. They learn to interpolate and extrapolate ordered pairs from a graph. Students investigate other topics related to graphing functions such as using negative numbers, using inverse functions, finding a function rule for a given set of ordered pairs, and graphing nonlinear functions. Students also review geometric concepts about congruency, transformations, symmetry, perimeter, and circumference.

Integrated Topics in This Unit Include:

♦ **choosing among different types of graphs**

♦ **graphing ordered pairs**

♦ **producing ordered pairs for a function rule**

♦ **developing ideas of translation, rotation, and reflection**

♦ **graphing linear functions**

♦ **interpolating and extrapolating from a graph**

♦ **making and interpreting line graphs**

♦ **using negative numbers to graph functions**

♦ **graphing composite functions**

♦ **using inverse functions to find unknowns**

♦ **reviewing standard function notation**

♦ **finding terms of sequences**

♦ **graphing perimeter and circumference functions**

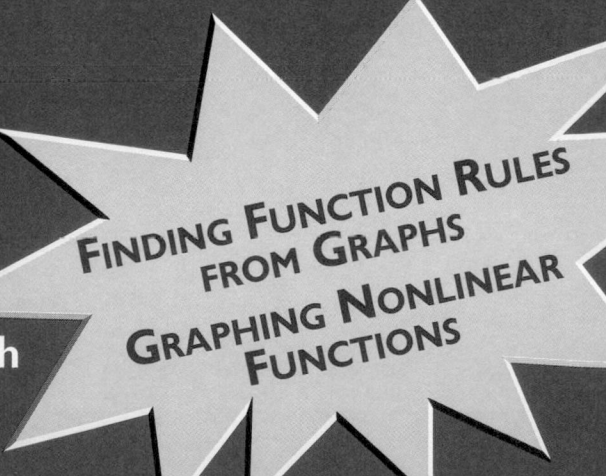

FINDING FUNCTION RULES FROM GRAPHS

GRAPHING NONLINEAR FUNCTIONS

> *It is essential that in grades 5-8, students explore algebraic concepts in an informal way to build a foundation for the subsequent formal study of algebra. Such informal explorations should emphasize physical models, data, graphs, and other mathematical representations rather than facility with formal algebraic manipulation.*
>
> —NCTM Curriculum and Evaluation Standards for School Mathematics

GAMES

Motivating Mixed Practice

Games provide **basic math skills** practice in cooperative groups. Playing the games also develops **mathematical reasoning.**

Hockey Game Mat	Lesson 98	page 352
Get the Point	Lesson 105	page 375
Find the Function Rule	Lesson 109	page 387

THINKING STORY

Integrated Problem Solving

Thinking Stories provide opportunities for students to work in **cooperative groups** and develop **logical reasoning** while they integrate **reading skills** with mathematics.

Diet for a Small Terrier

Part 1	Lesson 105	pages 376–377
Part 2	Lesson 108	pages 384–385
Part 3	Lesson 115	pages 408–409

Story Summary In "Diet for a Small Terrier" Mr. Breezy's training school for dogs is presented with the challenge of helping a terrier lose weight. As the story progresses, students will read graphs and calculate nutritional values to determine what diet to assign the dog. In addition, they will compare the terrier's rate of weight loss to that of the dog's owner, deciding at what rate the dog should be expected to lose weight in order to have a diet as successful as a person's.

PROJECT

Making Connections

The Unit Project makes real-world connections. Students work in **cooperative groups** to problem solve and to communicate their findings.

The project presented in the Unit Wrap-Up asks students to attempt to determine, without counting, the number of books in the school library, as well as other statistics. The project will also involve conducting interviews with library staff to gather actual information to compare with the students' estimates. Students can work on this project in their free time throughout the unit.

UNIT 5
ALGEBRA READINESS
LESSON PLANS

LESSON	PACING	PRIMARY OBJECTIVES	FEATURE	RESOURCES	NCTM STANDARD
95 Creating a Graph **342–345**	2 days	to collect and interpret experimental data		Reteaching Master Practice Master 95 Enrichment Master 95	2, 4, 10
96 Interpreting a Graph **346–347**	1 day	to show an example of how a graph can be used to show trends		Reteaching Strategy Practice Master 96 Enrichment Master 96	2, 4, 10
97 Misleading Graphs ... **348–349**	1 day	to encourage students to look at graphs with some care before jumping to conclusions		Reteaching Strategy Practice Master 97 Enrichment Master 97	2, 3, 4, 10
98 Organizing Data **350–353**	1 day	✓ to assess students' ability to organize data	ACT IT OUT ▨ Game	Reteaching Strategy Practice Master 98 Enrichment Master 98 Assessment Masters	2, 3, 4, 10
99 Ordering Pairs and Function Rules **354–355**	1 day	✓ to review how to produce a set of ordered pairs of numbers for a function rule	▨	Reteaching Master Practice Master 99 Enrichment Master 99 Assessment Masters	2, 4, 5, 8, 9
100 Translation, Rotation, Reflection, and Symmetry **356–361**	1 day	to develop the ideas of translation, rotation, and reflection		Reteaching Strategy Practice Master 100 Enrichment Master 100	4, 12
101 Graphing Fractions **362–363**	1 day	to review how to determine whether an ordered pair satisfies a given function rule		Reteaching Master Practice Master 101 Enrichment Master 101	2, 4, 6, 8, 9
102 Graphing Data **364–367**	1 day	to demonstrate how a graph can be used to interpolate and to extrapolate		Reteaching Strategy Practice Master 102 Enrichment Master 102	3, 4, 10
103 Making and Interpreting Line Graphs **368–369**	1 day	to practice making and interpreting graphs that involve negative numbers		Reteaching Strategy Practice Master 103 Enrichment Master 103	1, 4, 5, 10
104 Graphing Functions: Negative Values **370–373**	1 day	to demonstrate that graphs of some function rules are straight lines		Reteaching Master Practice Master 104 Enrichment Master 104	1, 2, 3, 4, 5, 6, 8, 9
105 Practice with Graphing **374–377**	1 day	to practice locating points with positive and negative coordinates on a two-dimensional coordinate system	Thinking Story Game	Reteaching Strategy Practice Master 105 Enrichment Master 105	1, 2, 3, 4, 8
106 Graphing Composite Functions **378–379**	1 day	to show how to find ordered pairs for composite function rules		Reteaching Strategy Practice Master 106 Enrichment Master 106	3, 4, 8, 9
107 Inverse Functions **380–381**	1 day	to review how to use inverse functions		Reteaching Master Practice Master 107 Enrichment Master 107	3, 4, 6, 8, 9
108 Keeping Sharp **382–385**	1 day	to provide practice interpreting data presented in a table	Thinking Story	Reteaching Strategy Practice Master 108 Enrichment Master 108	1, 2, 3, 4, 5, 7, 10
109 Determining Rules for Ordered Pairs **386–387**	1 day	to demonstrate how to determine a linear function rule given two or more ordered pairs that satisfy the rule	Game	Reteaching Strategy Practice Master 109 Enrichment Master 109	2, 4, 8, 9

340c Algebra Readiness

LESSON	PACING	PRIMARY OBJECTIVES	FEATURE	RESOURCES	NCTM STANDARD
110 **Interpreting Data**.... 388–389	1 day	to provide an opportunity to interpret, discuss, and make inferences from data		Reteaching Strategy Practice Master 110 Enrichment Master 110	3, 7, 10
111 **Using Formulas**...... 390–393	1 day	to practice evaluating functions for values of the independent variable		Reteaching Master Practice Master 111 Enrichment Master 111	2, 4, 8, 9
Mid-Unit Review..... 394–397			✓	Assessment Masters	
112 **Standard Notation for Functions** 398–399	1 day	to review the standard algebraic notation for writing function rules		Reteaching Master Practice Master 112 Enrichment Master 112	2, 8, 9
113 **Finding Terms of Sequences**........... 400–401	1 day	✓ to evaluate students' ability to understand and use function notation	✓	Reteaching Strategy Practice Master 113 Enrichment Master 113 Assessment Master	3, 7, 8, 9
114 **Graphing Linear Functions** 402–405	2 days	to practice graphing a linear function by plotting two appropriate points		Reteaching Master Practice Master 114 Enrichment Master 114	2, 4, 8, 9, 12
115 **Order of Operations**.......... 406–409	1 day	to demonstrate the need for a convention for the order of operations	Thinking Story	Reteaching Strategy Practice Master 115 Enrichment Master 115	1, 2, 3, 4, 5, 7
116 **Graphing Nonlinear Functions**............ 410–411	1 day	to practice working with examples of nonlinear functions and their graph		Reteaching Strategy Practice Master 116 Enrichment Master 116	2, 4, 8, 9, 12, 13
117 **More Nonlinear Functions**............. 412–413	1 day	to introduce the standard notation for nonlinear function rules		Reteaching Master Practice Master 117 Enrichment Master 117	2, 3, 4, 8, 9
118 **Graphing a Perimeter Function**............. 414–415	1 day	to demonstrate how to use a graph to determine the function rule the line represents		Reteaching Strategy Practice Master 118 Enrichment Master 118	1, 2, 3, 4, 8, 9, 12, 13
119 **Determining the Function Rule** 416–419	1 day	to demonstrate finding the rule for a linear function from its graph		Reteaching Master Practice Master 119 Enrichment Master 119	1, 2, 3, 4, 8, 9
120 **Finding Circumference**....... 420–423	2 days	to practice using approximations of π to calculate a circle's circumference		Reteaching Master Practice Master 120 Enrichment Master 120	1, 2, 3, 4, 7, 12, 13
121 **Average Monthly Temperature**........ 424–425	1 day	to provide practice in interpreting data in a table		Reteaching Strategy Practice Master 121 Enrichment Master 121	1, 2, 3, 4, 10
122 **Unit 5 Review** 426–427		to review algebra readiness		Practice Master 122 Enrichment Master 122	
123 **Unit 5 Practice**....... 428–431		to practice algebra readiness		Practice Master 123 Enrichment Master 123	
Unit 5 Test 432–433		to review algebra readiness	✓	Assessment Masters	
Unit 5 Wrap-Up..... 434–435			Project		

UNIT CONNECTIONS

INTERVENTION STRATEGIES

In this Teacher's Guide there will be specific strategies suggested for students with individual needs—ESL, Gifted and Talented, Special Needs, Learning Styles, and At Risk. These strategies will be given at the point of use. Here are the icons to look for and the types of strategies that will accompany them:

English as a Second Language

These strategies, designed for students who do not fluently speak the English language, will suggest meaningful ways to present the lesson concepts and vocabulary.

Gifted and Talented

Strategies to enrich and extend the lesson will offer further challenges to students who have easily mastered the concepts already presented.

Special Needs

Students who are physically challenged or who have learning disabilities may require alternative ways to complete activities, record answers, use manipulatives, and so on. The strategies labeled with this icon will offer appropriate methods of teaching lesson concepts to these students.

Learning Styles

Each student has his or her individual approach to learning. The strategies labeled with this icon suggest ways to present lesson concepts so that various learning modalities—such as tactile/kinesthetic, visual, and auditory—can be addressed.

At Risk

These strategies highlight the relevancy of the skills presented, making the connection between school and real life. They are directed toward students who appear to be at risk of dropping out of school before graduation.

TECHNOLOGY CONNECTIONS

The following materials, designed to reinforce and extend lesson concepts, will be referred to throughout this Teacher's Guide. It might be helpful to order the software and laser disc or to check them out of the school media center or local community library. If the school does not provide Internet access, consider visiting a local library, college, or business specializing in Internet services. Some students may be able to access the Internet at home.

 *Look for this* **Technology Connection** *icon.*

- Current U.S. Weather, http://www/mit/edu:8001/usa.html (Internet)

- *Mighty Math Cosmic Geometry,* from Edmark, Mac, IBM, for grades 6–8 (software)

- *Core Concepts in Math: Problem Solving Series: Problem Solving with Tables, Graphs, and Statistics,* from BFA/Systems Impact, for grades 5–9 (laser disc)

- *GraphPower,* from Ventura Educational Systems, Mac, for grades K–8 (software)

- *The Tabletop, Senior Edition,* from TERC, Mac, IBM, for grades 4–12 (software)

- *Hands on Math 3,* from Ventura, Mac, for grades K–8 (software)

- *Eagle Eye Mystery,* from Electronic Arts, IBM, Mac, for grades 2–8 (software)

- *Classroom Grade Level Math Programs,* from Jostens Home Learning, Mac, IBM, for grades K–8 (software)

CROSS-CURRICULAR CONNECTIONS

This Teacher's Guide offers specific suggestions on ways to connect the math concepts presented in this unit with other subjects students are studying. Students can connect math concepts with topics they already know about, and can find examples of math in other subjects and in real-world situations. These strategies will be given at the point of use.

Look for these icons:

 Geography

 Health

 Social Studies

 Music

 Science

 Math

 Art

 Physical Education

 Language Arts

 Careers

LITERATURE CONNECTIONS

These books will be presented throughout the Teacher's Guide at the point where they could be used to introduce, reinforce, or extend specific lesson concepts. You may want to locate these books in your school or your local community library.

 *Look for this* **Literature Connection** *icon.*

♦ *Charts and Graphs* by Caroline Arnold, F. Watts, 1984

♦ *Charlie and the Great Glass Elevator* by Roald Dahl, Windrush, 1987

♦ *A Grain of Rice* by Helena Claire Pittman, Hastings House, 1986

♦ *What's Cooking, Jenny Archer?* by Ellen Conford, Little, Brown Co., 1989

♦ "Presidential Puzzle" in *Math Mini-Mysteries* by Sandra Markle, Maxwell Macmillan International, 1993

♦ *Anno's Magic Seeds* by Mitsumasa Anno, Philomel, 1994

♦ *Math Wiz* by Betsy Duffey, Viking, 1990

♦ *Melisande* by Edith Nesbit, Harcourt Brace Jovanovich, 1989

♦ *Is a Blue Whale the Biggest Thing There Is?* by Robert E. Wells, A. Whitman, 1993

♦ *All in a Day* by Mitsumasa Anno, Philomel Books, 1986

♦ *And Then There Was One: The Mysteries of Extinction* by Margery Facklam, Sierra Club Books, 1990

♦ *Origami in the Classroom* by Chiyo Araki, C. E. Tuttle, 1968

♦ *The Librarian Who Measured the Earth* by Kathryn Lasky, Little, Brown & Co., 1994

ASSESSMENT OPPORTUNITIES AT-A-GLANCE

LESSON	PORTFOLIO	PERFORMANCE	FORMAL	SELF	INFORMAL	CUMULATIVE REVIEW	MULTIPLE-CHOICE	MASTERY CHECKPOINTS	ANALYZING ANSWERS
95					✓				
96					✓				
97		✓							
98			✓					✓	
99			✓			✓		✓	✓
100					✓				
101	✓								
102					✓				
103		✓				✓			
104	✓								✓
105					✓				
106		✓							
107					✓				
108				✓		✓			
109		✓							
110					✓				
111		✓							
Mid-Unit Review	✓	✓	✓						
112		✓							✓
113			✓	✓		✓		✓	
114	✓								
115				✓					
116	✓								
117		✓							
118					✓	✓			
119		✓							
120					✓				
121	✓								
122	✓	✓	✓						
123						✓			
Unit Test			✓				✓		

ASSESSMENT OPTIONS

PORTFOLIO ASSESSMENT

Throughout this Teacher's Guide are suggested activities in which students draw pictures, make graphs, write about mathematics, and so on. Keep students' work to assess growth of understanding as the year progresses.

Lessons 101, 104, Mid-Unit Review, 114, 116, 121, and 122

PERFORMANCE ASSESSMENT

Performance assessment items focus on evaluating how students think and work as they solve problems. Opportunities for performance assessment can be found throughout the unit. Rubrics and guides for grading can be found in the Assessment Blackline Masters.

Lessons 97, 103, 106, 109, 111, Mid-Unit Review, 112, 117, 119, and 122

FORMAL ASSESSMENT

A Mid-Unit Review, Unit Review, and Unit Test help assess students' understanding of concepts, skills, and problem solving. The *Math Explorations and Applications* CD-ROM Test Generator can create additional unit tests at three ability levels. Also, Mastery Checkpoints are provided periodically throughout the unit.

Lessons 98, 99, Mid-Unit Review, 113, 122, and Unit Test

SELF ASSESSMENT

Throughout the program students are given the opportunity to check their own math skills.

Lessons 108, 113, and 115

INFORMAL ASSESSMENT

A variety of assessment suggestions are provided, including interviews, oral questions or presentation, debates, and so on. Also, each lesson includes Assessment Criteria, a list of questions about each student's progress, understanding, and participation.

Lessons 95, 96, 100, 102, 105, 107, 110, 118, and 120

CUMULATIVE REVIEW

Cumulative Reviews, covering material presented thus far in the year, are provided in the unit for use as either assessment or practice.

Lessons 99, 103, 108, 113, 118, and 123

MULTIPLE-CHOICE TEST (STANDARDIZED FORMAT)

Each unit provides a unit test in standardized format, presenting students with an opportunity to practice taking a test in this format.

MASTERY CHECKPOINT

Mastery Checkpoints are provided throughout the unit to assess student proficiency in specific skills. Checkpoints reference appropriate Assessment Blackline Masters and other assessment options. Results of these evaluations can be recorded on the Mastery Checkpoint Chart.

Lessons 98, 99, and 113

ANALYZING ANSWERS

Analyzing answers items suggest possible sources of student error and offer teaching strategies for addressing difficulties.

Lessons 99, 104, and 112

Look for these icons:

> **"***In order to develop mathematical power in all students, assessment needs to support the continued mathematics learning of each student.***"**
>
> —*NCTM Assessment Standards*

 **MASTERY CHECKPOINTS**

WHAT TO EXPECT FROM STUDENTS AS THEY COMPLETE THIS UNIT

⑳ ORGANIZING DATA—LESSON 98

By this time most students should understand how to organize data in such a way as to derive useful information from the data. Ask students to describe the advantages of making an organized list of data and of graphing the data. You may also wish to assign Assessment Blackline Masters pages 40–41 to determine mastery. Results of this assessment may be recorded on the Mastery Checkpoint Chart.

㉑ ORDERED PAIRS AND FUNCTION RULES—LESSON 99

By this time most students should be able to produce a set of ordered pairs of numbers for a function rule. Observe students as they work on page 355 or on Assessment Blackline Masters pages 42–43. Results of this assessment may be recorded on the Mastery Checkpoint Chart.

㉒ DETERMINING FUNCTION RULES (STANDARD NOTATION)—LESSON 113

Most students should be able to determine function rules from a set of ordered pairs, express the rules in standard notation, and correctly complete a table of ordered pairs derived from a function. You might assess this by observing students as they play the "Find the Function Rule" game or by using Assessment Blackline Master page 47. Results of this assessment may be recorded on the Mastery Checkpoint Chart.

PROGRAM RESOURCES

THESE ADDITIONAL COMPONENTS OF *MATH EXPLORATIONS AND APPLICATIONS* CAN BE PURCHASED SEPARATELY FROM **SRA/McGRAW-HILL.**

LESSON	BASIC MANIPULATIVE KIT	GAME MAT PACKAGE	TEACHER MANIPULATIVE KIT	INTERMEDIATE MANIPULATIVE KIT	INTERMEDIATE OVERHEAD MANIPULATIVE KIT	*THE CRUNCHER* SOFTWARE	*MATH EXPLORATIONS AND APPLICATIONS* CD-ROM
95						project	Lesson 95
96							Lesson 96
97							Lesson 97
98		Hockey Game				spreadsheet	Lesson 98
99							Lesson 99
100				mirrors rulers			Lesson 100
101				rulers			Lesson 101
102			scale			spreadsheet	Lesson 102
103						spreadsheet	Lesson 103
104						spreadsheet	Lesson 104
105							Lesson 105
106						spreadsheet	Lesson 106
107	Number Cubes						Lesson 107
108						project	Lesson 108
109							Lesson 109
110							Lesson 110
111							Lesson 111
112							Lesson 112
113							Lesson 113
114	Number Cubes						Lesson 114
115							Lesson 115
116							Lesson 116
117							Lesson 117
118				rulers			Lesson 118
119	Number Cubes						Lesson 119
120				tape measure rulers		project	Lesson 120
121						spreadsheet	Lesson 121
122							Lesson 122
123							Lesson 123

Algebra Readiness

INTRODUCING THE UNIT

Using the Student Pages Begin your discussion of the opening unit photo by asking students, "How can you tell by looking at a graph whether a population is increasing or decreasing?" Then read aloud the paragraph on the student page that highlights working in government as a career. This helps make the connection between school and work and encourages students to explore how math is used in the real world.

ACTIVITY Make clear that the government makes decisions about needs for housing, job training, health care, and many other aspects of life based on analyzing information. Ask students to find out the name of a government agency with offices in your community. Have them write a sentence telling what kind of information that agency uses and how it helps the community.

FYI Explain to students that governments have depended on analyzing numbers for thousands of years. Early rulers needed to know things such as how much food their people would need and how much food they were producing in order to ward off famine. Other resources were similarly tracked, creating the need for a body of individuals, called bureaucrats, who could both obtain and manage information about the country or empire. Explain that this need for intelligent and educated people was a prime impetus behind the rise of organized education. In third-century China the job of bureaucrat was one of the most highly sought professions in the empire. During this period, known as the Han dynasty, thousands of applicants from all over China would vie for a position as a bureaucrat. To win a spot, they would have to pass a grueling test in which death was the punishment for cheating. The Han empire was so vast that more than 30,000 government workers were required to run its various departments. This same system, with minor variations, was in place across the world in ancient times and is still used today as modern government workers gather and analyze information that tells the executive and legislative branches how they are doing.

UNIT 5

Algebra Readiness

UNDERSTANDING VARIABLES

- graphs—double bar, multiple line, and circle
- graphing ordered pairs and function rules
- graphing negative numbers
- graphing linear and nonlinear functions

SCHOOL TO WORK CONNECTION

Government workers use math . . .

Government workers use graphs all the time. Part of their job is to gather information about the national population. This information includes the number of people per household, how many are employed, how many are looking for work, how many are homeless, and so on. Information is sorted, graphed, and analyzed.

340

Thinklab™ 2

SRA's *Thinklab™ 2* provides a series of creative and logical problem-solving opportunities for individual students. The problems are designed to appeal to different cognitive abilities.

▶ Use Problems 101–110 with this unit to reinforce object manipulation (ways and means of dealing with specific data).

▶ Use Problems 111–120 with this unit to reinforce creative insight (extrapolation from, and beyond, given data).

▶ Use Problems 121–125 with this unit to integrate object manipulation, creative insight, logical analysis, quantitative thinking, and brainstorming and to incorporate social interaction.

▶ Use Problems 126–135 with this unit to reinforce logical analysis (absorbing multiple data, testing hypotheses, and planning a set of operations).

Stress to students that the kind of statistics that government workers use are everywhere in the media. Point out how often unemployment statistics appear on television and in newspapers. Explain that decisions about how to spend money and how to run the economy are driven by these numbers. Any worker in this area, whether in the Department of Health and Human Services or the Department of Defense, needs to know the value and uses of numbers.

Home Connections You may want to send Home Connections Blackline Masters pages 54–55 home to introduce this unit.

Unit Project This would be a good time to assign the "Library Research" project on pages 434 and 435. Students can begin working on the project in cooperative groups in their free time as you work through the unit. This project is a good opportunity for students to apply the concept of collecting and analyzing complicated data to real-world problem solving.

Cooperate 3

Cooperate 3, published by SRA, provides a series of creative and logical problem-solving opportunities for cooperative groups. The problems are designed to provide practice in problem solving, communication, reasoning, and making connections. *Cooperate 3* presents the following cognitive strategies—perceiving spatial relations, ordering and sequencing, logical deduction, establishing and testing hypotheses, sequential exploration, identifying starting points, attending to detail, organizing information, and screening irrelevant information. Each Problem Card emphasizes a principal strategy as well as reinforcing other strategies.

▶ Use Problem Cards 21–24 with this unit to emphasize establishing and testing hypotheses.

▶ Use Problem Card 25 with this unit to emphasize screening irrelevant information.

LESSON 95
Creating a Graph

Student Edition pages 342–345

LESSON PLANNER

Objectives

▶ to teach students to collect and interpret experimental data

▶ to provide experience in reporting data by choosing among different kinds of graphs

Context of the Lesson This is the first of 24 lessons about creating and interpreting graphs.

 **MANIPULATIVES**   **Program Resources**

none   Reteaching Master

Practice Master 95

Enrichment Master 95

The Cruncher*: *Go for Fun Survey*

For extra practice:
CD-ROM* Lesson 95

Note: This lesson may take more than one day.

---

① Warm-Up ⏱ 5 MINUTES

Problem of the Day Present the following problem to the class: In the map below, regions that share a border need to be different colors. What is the least number of colors needed to color the map? (3)

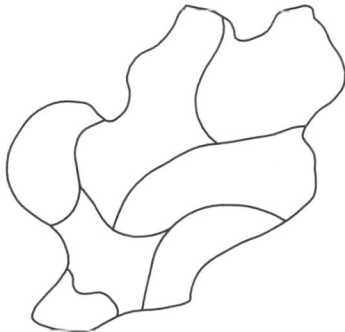

Problem-Solving Strategies Ask students who have solved the Problem of the Day to share how they solved it and any strategies they used.

LESSON 95
Creating a Graph

Ethan was doing seed germination experiments. This table shows the data he recorded for one of his experiments.

Day	Percent Germination
1	0
2	4
3	24
4	40
5	10
6	2
7	0
8	0

✱ **Accept all reasonably defended answers. In this case the bar graph gives more useful data because it shows how the percentage of seeds that germinated from day to day. The circle graph shows the same results, but it is difficult to see how germination changed from day to day.**

To show the results of his work, Ethan decided to make a graph.

◆ Which of these graphs better shows the results of Ethan's experiment? Explain your answer. ✱

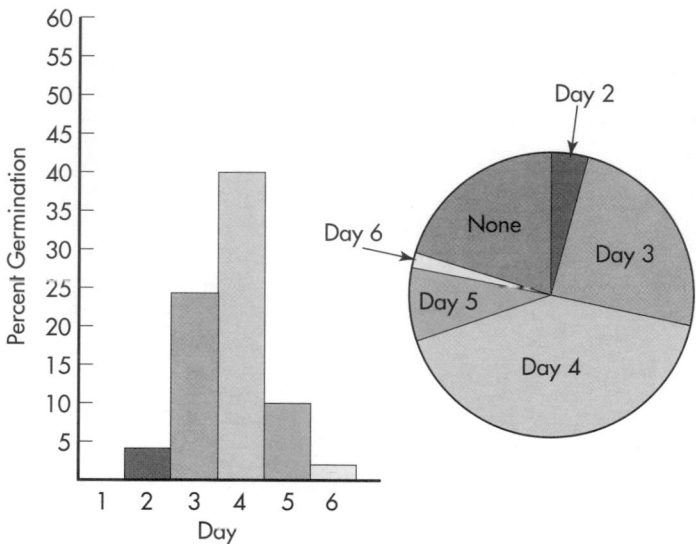

342 • Algebra Readiness

Why teach it this way?

It is important for students to understand that sometimes one kind of graph is more useful than another for showing data. It can be a very productive experience for students to get a firsthand appreciation of the importance of gathering valid and meaningful data and to understand the issues and difficulties involved in doing so.

A group of students decided to study the Scrumptious Ice Cream Parlor to see which of the five flavors of ice cream the store offered sold the best. The students spent all day in the store and recorded their results in the chart.

Flavor	Percent of Ice Cream Sold
Vanilla	50
Chocolate	30
Strawberry	13
Raspberry	5
Pistachio	2

To show their results, the students decided to make a graph.

◆ Which of these graphs better shows the results of the survey? Explain your answer. **Accept all reasonably defended answers. In this case the circle graph better shows the data. Here time is not a factor; we are only interested in how much of each flavor was sold.**

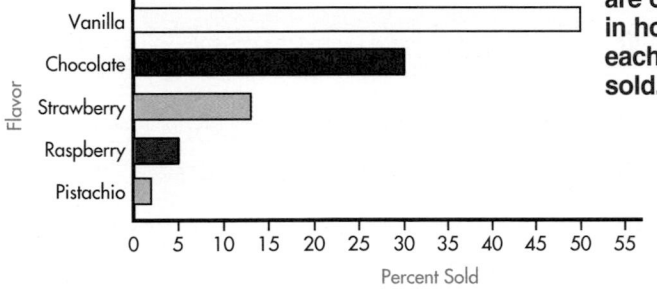

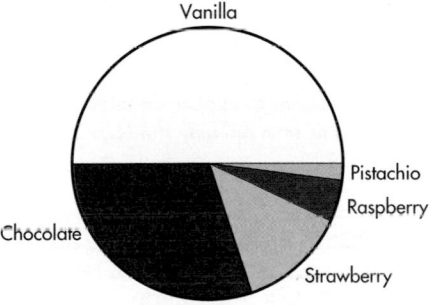

Unit 5   Lesson 95 • **343**

MENTAL MATH Have students find the following percents mentally.

a. 50% of 50 (25)		**b.** 25% of 400 (100)	
c. 66⅔% of 60 (40)		**d.** 40% of 60 (24)	
e. 150% of 30 (45)		**f.** 20% of 150 (30)	
g. 3% of 400 (12)		**h.** 200% of 45 (90)	

❷ Teach

Using the Student Pages Before students work on page 342, help them understand the meaning of germination by explaining it as the end of dormancy and the beginning of growth of a seed. Point out that it is usually recognizable by the visible emergence of the young sprout from the seed.

Guide students to see that the bar graph provides more useful data because it shows how the percentage of seeds that germinated changed from day to day. Point out that although the circle graph shows the same results, it is difficult to see from the graph how germination progressed from day to day.

Help students to understand how the circle graph is most effective for showing the data about the ice cream on page 343. Guide them to see that a circle graph compares parts to a whole and to one another visually. In this case it shows us how much of each flavor was sold out of the total amount sold.

◆ LESSON 95 Creating a Graph

Teach

COOPERATIVE LEARNING **Using the Student Pages** Have students work cooperatively in groups to figure out how to gather, combine, display, and analyze data, and then present their findings. Students can use the questions on page 344 as guidelines. Groups should attempt to get a reasonable representative sample from each grade. If it suits your class, you may wish to talk informally about the idea of random sampling.

Answers to problems 1–11 will vary. Accept any well-reasoned answers. For problem 8, students should recognize that a line graph would not be appropriate.

Students can use **The Cruncher***: *Go for Fun Survey* spreadsheet to organize and display their data.

◆ LESSON 95 Creating a Graph

How much time do students in your school watch television each week? Take a survey.

Before beginning the survey, think about the following questions. Be prepared to explain your choices. ✶

1 About how many students are in your school?

2 About how many students must you ask to be reasonably certain that your data is meaningful?

3 About how many students must be asked from each grade?

4 Should you do a separate survey for each grade?

5 Should you ask questions orally, or should you prepare a written survey?

6 What results do you expect to find?

7 Conduct a survey keeping in mind the decisions you made in the above problems. Copy and complete the chart on page 345.

8 Decide which kind of graph is most meaningful for your data.

9 Graph your results. Consider using graphing software.

10 Are you surprised at the results of your survey? Why or why not?

11 Do you think the results would be similar if you asked how much time students spent reading? Why or why not?

The first U.S. President to appear on television was Franklin Roosevelt, who was seen opening the New York World's Fair on April 30, 1939.

✶ **These questions are a guide to discussion. There are no right or wrong answers. However, students should realize that they need a representative sample of the school population or of each grade's population.**

344 • Algebra Readiness

Social Studies Connection You may wish to invite someone who has had professional experience conducting surveys and interpreting survey results, such as a staff member of an elected official, a person who works for an information-gathering organization, or a person who works in advertising or marketing, to address the class on this subject.

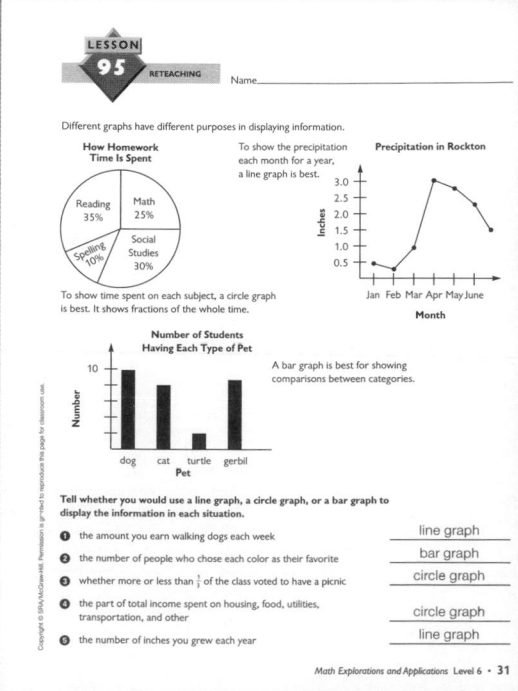

*available separately

Use a computer or other means to draw and complete a chart from the information you collected.

Hours each week watching television	Number of students	Percentage of students
between 0 and 4		
between 4 and 8		
between 8 and 12		
between 12 and 16		
between 16 and 20		
between 20 and 24		
between 24 and 28		
more than 28		

One way to find the percentage of students in each category is to express the number of students out of the total number as a fraction, and then convert the fraction to a decimal and the decimal to a percent.

For example, suppose five of the 45 sixth graders you surveyed say they watch between 12 and 16 hours of television each week.

Write the fraction $\frac{5}{45}$.

Convert the fraction to a decimal. 5 ÷ 45 is about 0.111.

To change the decimal to a percent, multiply by 100.

$0.111 \times 100 = 11.1$

So about 11.1% of the students surveyed said they watch between 12 and 16 hours of television each week.

Unit 5   Lesson 95 • **345**

---

③ Wrap-Up

In Closing To summarize the lesson, have students critique their own surveying procedures and the results they obtained. They can include their thoughts in their Math Journals. They can write how they might do the survey differently next time.

Informal Assessment Circulate and observe students as they work in their groups. Check to see that all students are actively participating in the process of planning the task, gathering data, recording data, displaying data, and analyzing data.

Assessment Criteria

Did the student . . .

✓ participate in and contribute to the discussions and activities?

✓ reflect critical thinking when analyzing the way he or she conducted the survey and displayed the results?

Homework Have students talk with family members about the way they conducted their survey, what they learned about their topic, and the process of surveying to gather information. Have them share feedback with classmates the next day.

Interpreting a Graph

LESSON PLANNER

Objectives

▶ to present an example of how a graph can be used to show trends

▶ to encourage students to think about how some events influence others

Context of the Lesson This is the second of 24 lessons about creating and interpreting graphs.

 MANIPULATIVES

Program Resources

Practice Master 96

Enrichment Master 96

For extra practice:
CD-ROM* Lesson 96

❶ Warm-Up ⏱ 5 MINUTES

 **Problem of the Day** Present the following problem to students: Maria's watch is five minutes fast but she thinks it is five minutes slow. It is a ten-minute walk to the library. If she leaves for a 5:00 reading when her watch says 4:50, how early or late will she be for the reading? (five min early)

Problem-Solving Strategies Ask students who have solved the Problem of the Day to share how they solved it and any strategies they used.

 Have students solve for *n*.

a. $2 - 5 = n \ (-3)$

b. $6 - 0 = n \ (6)$

c. $4 + n = -1 \ (-5)$

d. $0 - 4 = n \ (-4)$

e. $n - 3 = -2 \ (1)$

f. $(-7) + n = -5 \ (2)$

❷ Teach

Using the Student Pages Look at the graph on page 346 with students. Ask them to explain different aspects of the graph, such as why it begins in 1984 and not 1974, for example. Make sure students understand how to read the graph.

Interpreting a Graph

Long-playing record albums were first successfully introduced in 1948 and dominated music sales for several decades. Compact disc players were introduced in 1983.

This graph shows the sales of record albums and compact discs each year from 1984 through 1994.

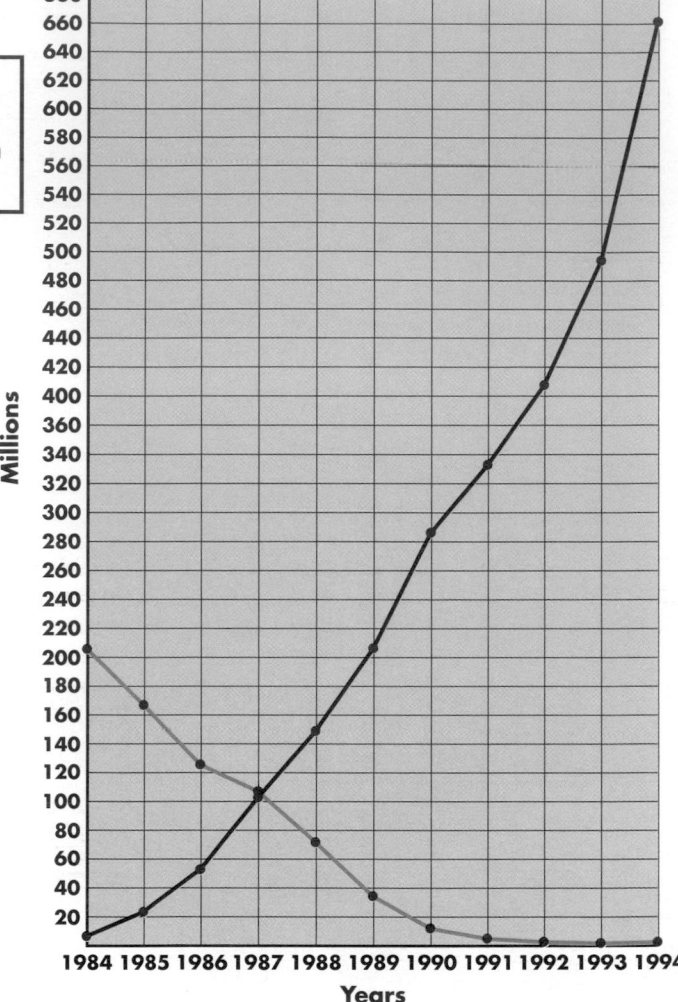

Physical Education Connection Invite students to use an almanac to find Olympic track-and-field records in the same event for women and men, and then construct a double-line graph showing both winning times, heights, or lengths over a period of several Olympics up to the present time. Have them write a description of what their graphs show about trends in track-and-field results for women and men.

Real-World Connection Ask students to talk about who might use the product information that double-line graphs can show.

RETEACHING

Help students who have difficulty reading the graph by encouraging them to trace each line separately with a finger to see the trends. To compare data from the same year, students should draw or trace a vertical line at that year.

*available separately

Answer the following questions about the graph.

1 About how many more record albums than CDs were sold in 1984?
about 200 million

2 About how many more CDs than record albums were sold in 1994?
about 660 million

3 In what year did CD sales first exceed record album sales? **1988**

4 How do you account for the shapes of the two graphs? **As technology has advanced, people have stopped buying records and started buying CDs.**

5 What would you predict about the difference in record album and **Answers may** CD sales in 2004? **vary. If the sales of CDs increases, the difference will increase. Otherwise, the difference will probably stay the same.**

6 Do you think CD sales will ever decline like record album sales did? Why or why not? **Answers may vary. If CDs are replaced by a new technology, their sales may decline like record album sales did.**

7 If a line for cassette sales was added to this graph, what do you think it **Answers may** would look like? **vary. It may look similar to the graph of record album sales. However, cassette sales probably have not declined as dramatically as record album sales.**

8 In what other ways could this data have been presented? **Answers may vary. Possible answers: double bar graph, stacked bar graph, two separate line or bar graphs.**

9 Do you think this kind of graph was the best way to present this data? **Answers will** Why or why not? **vary. Possible answers: This way was best because it clearly shows changes over time and makes it easy to compare record and CD sales.**

10 Think of two other measures that would be interesting to compare over a period of years. Collect data and display it in an appropriate graph. **Answers may vary.**

Unit 5   Lesson 96 • **347**

Assign the questions on page 347 for independent work. You may wish to assign problem 10 as a research project for students to work on over a period of several days. Then discuss the answers to questions 4–9 with the class. Guide students to notice that the total sales of record albums and CDs remained fairly constant (at about 200 million) until about 1988, when sales of CDs began to increase more quickly. Students should infer from the graph that sales of record albums declined because sales of CDs kept increasing. When discussing question 7, you may wish to point out that sales of cassettes peaked at 450.1 million in 1988 and have declined slowly since then. If students remark that music listening seems to be on a rapid rise each year, you can tell them that if cassette sales for the years 1984–1994 were included in the chart, they would see that the total sale of records, cassettes, and CDs has not continued to increase as dramatically in recent years.

③ Wrap-Up

In Closing To summarize the lesson, ask students to describe the apparent effect the sale of CDs has had on records and also to explain how the graph shows that relationship.

Informal Assessment Ask students to examine the graphs and to predict what continuing the lines would tell them about future sales of records and CDs. Ask them to explain the advantages of using a double-line graph rather than a double-bar graph for showing the trends in sales.

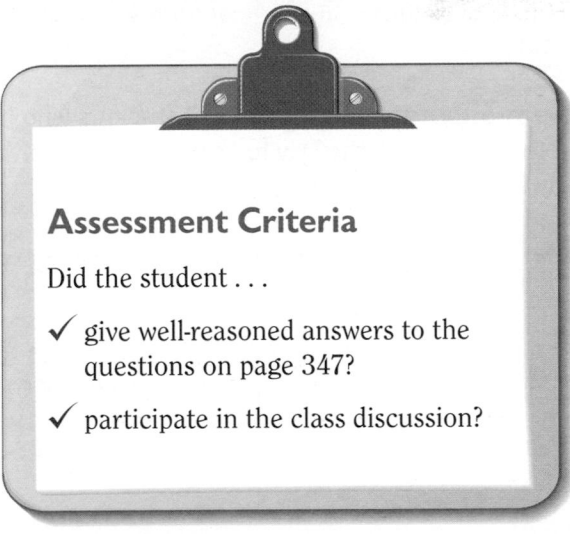

Assessment Criteria

Did the student . . .

✓ give well-reasoned answers to the questions on page 347?

✓ participate in the class discussion?

Homework Have students share with family members what they learned about the apparent relationship between record sales and CD sales. Invite them to brainstorm with their families other products and their replacements whose sales were greatly affected by an invention, decision, or advancement in technology.

PRACTICE p. 96

LESSON 96 PRACTICE   Name_____

Look at the graph below and answer the questions.

1 What is the highest dropout rate shown at Franklin High School? **60%**

2 What was the dropout rate in 1960? **45%**

3 During what two years were the dropout rates the same? **1965, 1970**

4 What seems to be the overall trend in the dropout rate? **decreasing**

5 Explain why this trend may be happening.
Answers will vary. Sample answer: Students may be realizing the importance of staying in school.

Franklin High School Dropout Rate

96 • *Math Explorations and Applications* Level 6

ENRICHMENT p. 96

LESSON 96 ENRICHMENT   Name_____

A pictograph compares quantities by using pictures. The pictograph below shows the number of tornadoes in six states in 1993.

Tornadoes in 1993

Wyoming	
Michigan	
Tennessee	
Alabama	
Delaware	
Maine	

Each ▼ represents two tornadoes.   Each ▼ represents one tornado.

How many tornadoes occurred in each state?

1 Wyoming **12**

2 Michigan **11**

3 Tennessee **10**

4 Alabama **8**

5 Delaware **5**

6 Maine **2**

7 Montana had 19 tornadoes. How would you show this on the pictograph?

▼▼▼▼▼▼▼▼▼▼

8 Gather information from your classmates on a topic of interest. Make a pictograph to show your results. See students' graphs.

96 • *Math Explorations and Applications* Level 6

LESSON 97

Misleading Graphs

LESSON PLANNER

Objectives

▶ to demonstrate how technically accurate graphs can be used to mislead the casual observer

▶ to encourage students to look at graphs with some care before drawing conclusions

Context of the Lesson This is the third of 24 lessons on creating and interpreting graphs.

MANIPULATIVES
none

Program Resources
Practice Master 97
Enrichment Master 97
For extra practice:
CD-ROM* Lesson 97

❶ Warm-Up ⏱ 5 MINUTES

Problem of the Day Present this problem to students: Latrell read the following in an advertisement: "Dentists agree—ULTIMATE TOOTHPASTE works best!" What about this claim, if anything, may be misleading? (Answers will vary. Discuss with students.)

Problem-Solving Strategies Ask students who have solved the Problem of the Day to share how they solved it and any strategies they used.

 Have students evaluate the following expressions.

a. $3 \times 4^2 = (48)$ **b.** $12 \times 10^3 = (12,000)$

c. $100 - 7^2 = (51)$ **d.** $5^3 + 10^3 = (1125)$

❷ Teach

Using the Student Pages Have students work in small groups to answer questions 1–4 on page 348. Then have the class discuss the answers. The key point to make is that the increase in profits for the first two years, although less than 1% of total profits,

---

LESSON 97

Misleading Graphs

Aaron took over his father's company in 1993. In 1995 he published the graph shown below to show how the profits had increased over the years he had been running the company.

❶ Approximately what were the profits for each of the years 1993, 1994, and 1995? **$14.00 million; $14.06 million; $14.10 million**

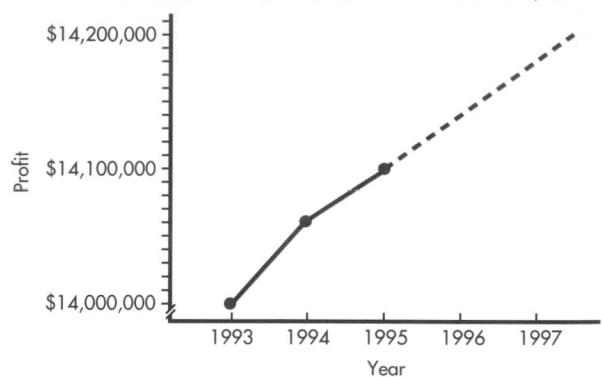

In the year 1997 Aaron published the graph shown below to show there had been very little change in the profits of the company since he took over.

❷ Approximately what were the profits for each of the years 1993 through 1997? **1993: $14 million; 1994: $14 million; 1995: $14 million; 1996: $13 million; 1997: $12 million**

❸ **the second graph, since it shows actual data, not a projection; it also uses a more relevant scale**

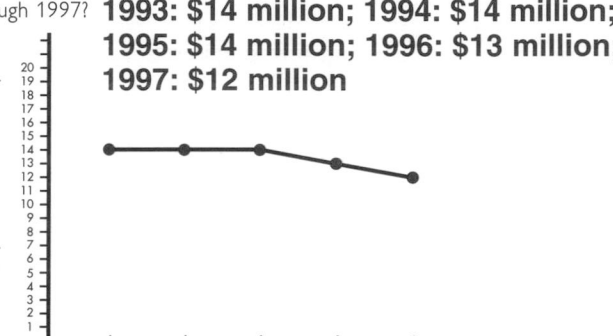

❸ Comment on the two graphs that Aaron chose to publish. Which one do you think is more honest? Why?

❹ In the first graph above, what do you think the dotted line indicates?
It indicates a projection that profits will continue to rise in the future.

Why teach it at this time?

Students are studying the value of graphs as tools to display information. While students should appreciate ways that graphs can show trends and generally give a clear picture of data, it is important for them to realize that graphs can also be used to create a particular impression, even a misleading one. Students can learn the importance of reading graphs critically to be sure they understand the information provided.

RETEACHING

Provide examples to show students that by altering the scale (by not starting at 0, for example), by changing the size of the increments (say, from 10s to 100s), and by simply placing the increments farther apart or closer together, they can make a line graph show the same information very differently. Review how changing just the height of a symbol used on a picture graph or a bar on a bar graph can change the appearance of data. Provide other examples similar to the one on page 349.

*available separately

The Serious Cereal Company hired new management in 1993. In 1997 the management published the following picture graph to show how much sales had increased.

⑤ What, approximately, was the total number of boxes sold in 1993 and 1997? **1993: 150,000; 1997: 300,000**

⑥ With just a quick look, does it seem to you that the sales had more than doubled? Why do you suppose that is? **Yes; the box on the right is twice as wide and twice as thick, as well as twice as tall, as the box on the left.**

Think about two boxes. One is twice as long in each dimension as the other.

⑦ How many of the small boxes would fit in the big one? Discuss this with your classmates. Could you fit four of the small boxes in a front layer inside the larger box? Could you also fit four boxes in a back layer? **8; yes; yes**

⑧ Picture graphs can be misleading. What do you think might be a clearer way for the Serious Cereal Company to use picture graphs without making people think that the sales had been multiplied by 8 instead of 2? **Answers may vary. Using two small boxes stacked on top of each other would have been a much clearer method of reporting the information.**

Unit 5 Lesson 97 • **349**

---

has been made to appear very significant on the graph because the profit axis of the graph starts at $14,000,000. The decline in profits from 1995 to 1997 is nearly $2 million, or close to 14%. Discuss that although neither graph is actually dishonest, both are certainly self-serving.

When discussing the graph on page 349, the key point to get across is that in a clear graph, the year 1997 would show two of the small boxes stacked rather than one box that is eight times as large as the smaller one for 1993. Although sales have doubled, the size of the second box gives the impression that sales have been even better than that.

❸ Wrap-Up

In Closing In summary, ask students to explain how graphs can mislead in the way they present data. Ask them to write a brief statement about how not to be fooled by a deceptive graph.

Performance Assessment Ask students to explain one way to design the scales of a graph in order to present data in a particular light, such as to make sales seem greater or less than they actually are.

Assessment Criteria

Did the student . . .

✓ participate constructively in the discussion about misleading graphs?

✓ write a comprehensible statement about misleading graphs?

Homework Challenge students to create their own misleading graphs. Tell them to design the graph so that an effort of theirs seems more substantial than it actually was. Possible topics for students' graphs can be test scores, chores accomplished, or performance in sports activities.

LESSON 98
Organizing Data

LESSON PLANNER

Objectives

▶ to review how organizing data on a chart and graphing the data help in using the information

▶ to review and provide practice in locating points on a graph

✓ to assess students' ability to organize data

Context of the Lesson This is the fourth of 24 lessons on functions and graphing. In reviewing and extending their work on functions, not only are students learning one of the most powerful and pervasive ideas in mathematics, but they are also getting practice in written and mental arithmetic. This lesson contains Mastery Checkpoint 20 to assess students' ability to organize data.

✋ MANIPULATIVES

graph paper
(1 cm squares)

Program Resources

"Hockey" Game Mat

Practice Master 98

Enrichment Master 98

Assessment Masters

The Cruncher*

For additional math integration:
Math Throughout the Day*

For extra practice:
CD-ROM* Lesson 98

❶ Warm-Up ⏱

Problem of the Day Present the following problem to the class: Maria's aunt did not take very much money with her to work in the city yesterday. She spent half of what she took on her bus ticket. Then she spent half of what she had left for her subway ticket. When she got off the train, she bought coffee for $1. She purchased a newspaper with half the money she had left then. When she finally got to work, she had only a quarter with her. How much money did Maria's aunt take with her to work yesterday? ($6)

Problem-Solving Strategies Ask students who have solved the Problem of the Day to share how they solved it and any strategies they used.

LESSON 98
Organizing Data

Is Business Booming?

Jeremy dropped a handful of small pieces of paper on the table.

"What are you doing?" Lydia asked.

"I want to see how my dog-walking business is doing," Jeremy said. "Each week since I started my business, I have written down on a slip of paper how much money I made that week. These are my business records."

◆ Can you tell from Jeremy's records how well his business is doing? **Although we can tell some things about Jeremy's business from his assortment of figures, drawing conclusions from that unorganized information is much more time-consuming and error-prone than doing so from more orderly records.**

Literature Connection You may wish to have students read *Charts and Graphs* by Caroline Arnold to learn more about plotting coordinate pairs.

*available separately

"All these slips of paper are confusing," said Lydia. "I think you ought to put your records in order. I'll help you if you like."

"Sure," Jeremy said. "Let's get started."

They put the slips in order, with the first week first, the second week second, and so on. Then they made a chart for all the information.

Week	Profit	Week	Profit
1	$5.00	11	35.00
2	0.00	12	45.00
3	5.00	13	25.00
4	15.00	14	45.00
5	20.00	15	45.00
6	15.00	16	40.00
7	35.00	17	30.00
8	30.00	18	45.00
9	45.00	19	40.00
10	40.00	20	50.00

"Look!" said Jeremy. "On the 20th week I hit an all-time high profit of $50.00. That's $10.00 better than the week before—a 25% increase in one week. My business is booming!"

◆ Is this chart a better way to keep records than the slips of paper Jeremy was using? **Yes, but it does not show patterns or trends clearly. A graph would be better.** Do you agree with Jeremy that his business is booming? **Why or why not? Explain your answer in your Math Journal.** **No, Jeremy is making his statement based on a very short time period.**

Unit 5 Lesson 98 • **351**

Technology Connection Refer students to the Internet site *Current U.S. Weather* (http://www.mit.edu:800/usa.html). Actual weather and temperature data can be used to create their own graphic displays. Students can click on specific locations to get details and a forecast.

MENTAL MATH Write these problems one at a time. Have students solve the problems using mental math and invite them to explain their strategies:

a.
$$\begin{array}{r} 90 \\ -29 \\ \hline (61) \end{array} \qquad \text{(add 1} \quad \begin{array}{r} 91 \\ -30 \\ \hline 61 \end{array} \text{)}$$

b. $5 \times 40 = (200)$

$50 \times 40 = (2000)$

c. $7 \times 300 = (2100)$

$2100 \div 7 = (300)$

$2100 \div 70 = (30)$

d. $6 \times 6 = (36)$

$6 \times 60 = (360)$

$6 \times 600 = (3600)$

$3600 \div 6 = (600)$

e.
$$\begin{array}{r} 623 \\ -298 \\ \hline 325 \end{array} \qquad \text{(add 2} \quad \begin{array}{r} 625 \\ -300 \\ \hline 325 \end{array} \text{)}$$

f.
$$\begin{array}{r} 752 \\ -202 \\ \hline 550 \end{array} \qquad \text{(subtract 2} \quad \begin{array}{r} 750 \\ -200 \\ \hline 550 \end{array} \text{)}$$

g.
$$\begin{array}{r} 2003 \\ +\ 498 \\ \hline 2501 \end{array} \qquad \text{(} \quad \begin{array}{r} 2000 \\ +\ 498 \\ \hline 2498 \end{array} \quad \begin{array}{r} 2498 \\ +\ 3 \\ \hline 2501 \end{array} \text{)}$$

h. $5 \times 10 = (50)$

$50 \times 10 = (500)$

$50 \times 100 = (5000)$

$5000 \div 50 = (100)$

❷ Teach

Using the Student Pages Demonstrate the "Hockey" Game Mat, which provides practice with coordinate graphing, before beginning work on pages 350–353 so that students who finish early can play. Then read with the class the story about Jeremy's business. Stop to discuss the bulleted questions.

◆ LESSON 98 Organizing Data

Teach

Using the Student Pages As you discuss page 352 with the class, make sure students recognize that the graph clearly shows Jeremy's business has leveled off after initial gains. You may wish to show this by copying the graph on the chalkboard and drawing a line that "smooths out" the variations in the points, leveling off after nine or ten weeks.

On the chalkboard or using an overhead projector, demonstrate how to plot the point (2, 5) used as the example on page 353. Invite students to plot other points on the chalkboard. As you discuss problems 1–4, emphasize that order makes a difference: the first coordinate tells how far to the right; the second coordinate tells how far up.

Students may also use a blank **Cruncher*** spreadsheet to make a bar graph of the data from Jeremy's business.

Introducing the "Hockey" Game Mat This game provides practice in coordinate graphing, as well as in probabilistic thinking and looking ahead. Complete instructions for playing are on the Game Mat. Be sure students understand how to move, in what order moves are to be made, when it is necessary to shoot, and how sides are changed. A copy of this game can also be found on page 618 of this Teacher's Guide.

◆ LESSON 98 Organizing Data

"I'm not so sure that your business is booming," Lydia told Jeremy. "It may not even be growing anymore."

"I don't understand," said Jeremy. "What's wrong with my figures?"

"Nothing," said Lydia. "But let's make a picture of the information. Maybe a graph will help us see more clearly how your business is doing."

"OK," said Jeremy. Then he and Lydia made a graph like this one.

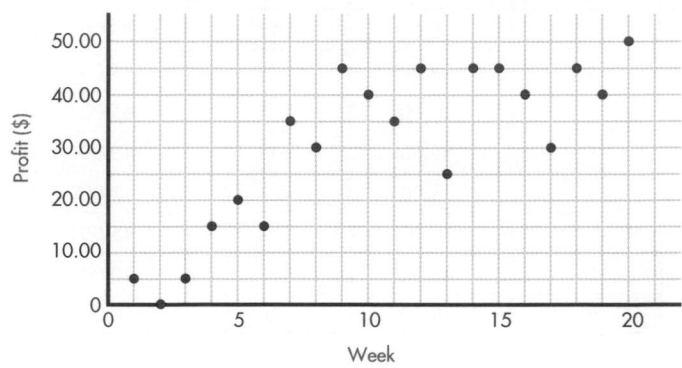

◆ Does the graph make it easier to see how Jeremy's business is doing? **yes; the graph shows that business grew during its initial 9 or 10 weeks but then leveled off.**

◆ How do you think Jeremy's business is doing? **Although Jeremy's business is not booming and not even growing, it is still good and steady. Jeremy is making a relatively constant amount of money each week.**

RETEACHING

Guide students who are having difficulty plotting points to start by placing their finger on the origin (0, 0), and then guide them to always move sideways first and then up. For (3, 8), for example, first say, "Move to the right three places." Check that they do this. Then say, "Now move up eight places." Repeat this procedure as often as needed, emphasizing the instruction "over and up." Also, be sure students understand that the whole number coordinates in each pair correspond to intersection points, not the spaces between them.

PRACTICE p. 98

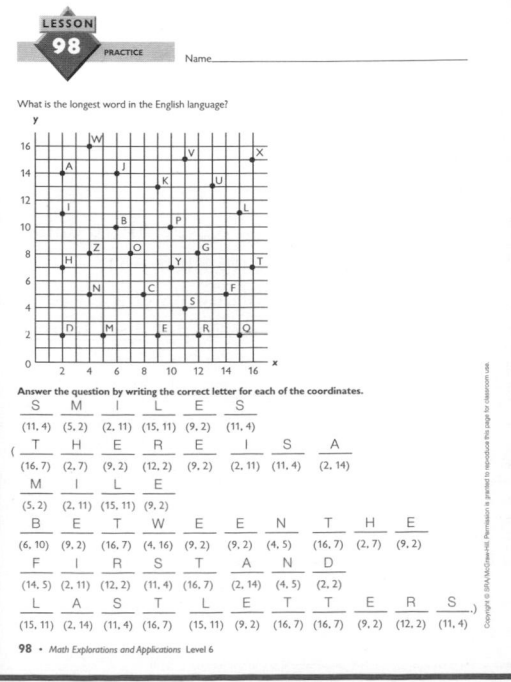

*available separately

We use graphs to help organize, understand, and interpret information.

To locate (or plot) a **point** corresponding to a pair of numbers on a graph, we start at the origin and go right as many steps as the first number shows, and then up as many steps as the second number shows.

Example Plot the point (2, 5). Start at the origin (0, 0).

Go two steps to the right.   Go five steps up.

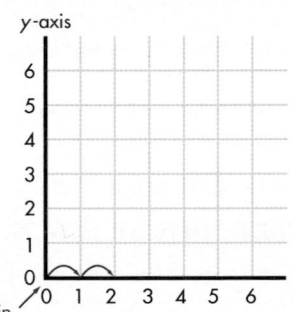 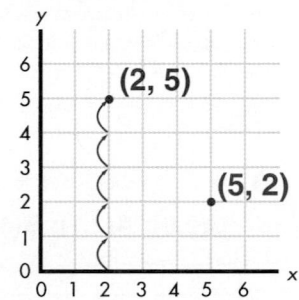

origin

❶ Suppose you had plotted (2, 5) by first going five steps up and then going two steps to the right. Would you have arrived at the same point? **yes**

❷ If you go five steps to the right and two steps up, will you arrive at the same point? **no**

❸ Are the points (2, 5) and (5, 2) the same? **no**

❹ On a sheet of graph paper draw coordinate **axes** (an x-axis and a y-axis). Plot and label the points (2, 5) and (5, 2). **See graph.**

Unit 5   Lesson 98 • **353**

---

❸ Wrap-Up

In Closing Summarize the lesson by asking students to explain why it is useful to organize information and to display it.

Mastery Checkpoint 20

By this time, most students should understand how to organize data in such a way as to derive useful information from them. Ask students to describe the advantages of making an organized list of data and of graphing the data. You may also wish to assign Assessment Blackline Masters pages 40–41 to determine mastery. Results of this assessment may be recorded on the Mastery Checkpoint Chart.

Assessment Criteria

Did the student . . .

✓ understand the disadvantages of Jeremy's original record-keeping approach?

✓ understand the ways that the organized list made the data more useful?

✓ understand how the graph shows trends in the data?

Homework Ask students to collect some numerical data about their daily activities, such as time watching TV, listening to the radio, or doing homework or chores. Have them list the data and then graph it on a coordinate grid. Ask them to write a summary describing what their graph shows about the data.

Meeting Individual Needs

Check for patterns in students' errors. You might notice that some consistently reverse coordinates or move one more or one less than the correct number. This latter difficulty may clear up if you concentrate on points like (1, 1), (0, 1), (1, 0), (2, 0), and (2, 1).

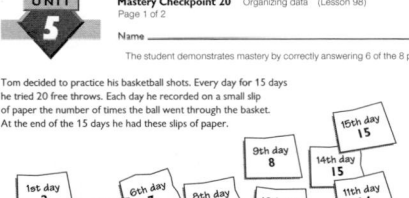

Ordered Pairs and Function Rules

LESSON PLANNER

Objectives

✓ to review how to produce a set of ordered pairs of numbers for a function rule

▶ to review how to locate points whose coordinates are not whole numbers

Context of the Lesson This is the fifth of 24 lessons on functions and graphing. This lesson contains Mastery Checkpoint 21 to assess students' understanding of ordered pairs and function rules.

 **MANIPULATIVES**
graph paper

Program Resources
Reteaching Master
Practice Master 99
Enrichment Master 99
Assessment Masters
For extra practice:
  CD-ROM* Lesson 99
  Cumulative Review, page 574

① Warm-Up ⏱ 5 MINUTES

 Problem of the Day Present the following problem: Using as many of the digits 1, 2, 4, 6, and 8 as you wish, write the least counting number that is greater than 5000 and the greatest counting number that is less than 5000. The numbers may not have repeating digits. (6124; 4862)

Problem-Solving Strategies Ask students who have solved the Problem of the Day to share how they solved it and any strategies they used.

MENTAL MATH Continue to provide multidigit arithmetic problems that can be solved mentally. Invite students to explain their strategies.

a. 4 × 10 = (40)
40 × 10 = (400)
400 × 10 = (4000)
40,000 ÷ 400 = (100)

b. 7 × 3 = (21)
70 × 30 = (2100)
700 × 300 = (210,000)
210,000 ÷ 300 = (700)

c. 799
−299
―――
(500)

d. 698
−499
―――
(199)

(continued on page 355)

354 Algebra Readiness

Ordered Pairs and Function Rules

 ALGEBRA READINESS

An **ordered pair** of numbers is a pair of numbers in which order is important. Ordered pairs can occur in many ways.

Dates, for example, are often given by listing the number of the month and then the day of the month. The two numbers are usually separated with a slash mark. So 3/25 would mean March 25. Many people do this in reverse. To them, 25/3 would mean the 25th of March.

❶ Tell what date each of these might mean.

*Dec. 11
or Nov. 12

**June 10
or Oct. 6

a. 3/20
Mar. 20
b. 15/6
June 15
c. 13/12
Dec. 13
d. 12/13
Dec. 13
e. 12/12
Dec. 12
f. 11/12
*
g. 6/10
**
h. 26/5
May 26

The pair of numbers that tells the location of a point on a graph is an ordered pair, because order is important in graphing. For example, (2, 5) and (5, 2) are ordered pairs for different points. We call the pair of numbers that tells the location of a point on a graph the **coordinates** of that point.

❷ Write the coordinates for each of these points: O, A, B, C, D, E, and F.

$$O(0,0); A(2,1); B(4,2); C(8,4); D(10,5); E(14,7); F(3,1\frac{1}{2})$$

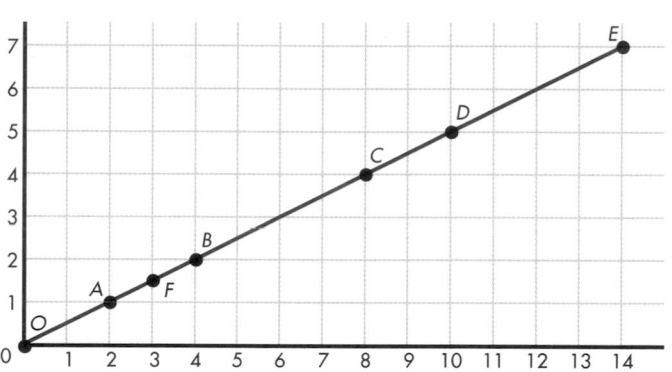

354 • Algebra Readiness

LESSON
99 RETEACHING   Name_____

To graph a function, you need ordered pairs (x, y). Use a rule that tells you how to find y when you know x.

Example: Graph x —(+5)→ y for x = 1, 2, 3, 4, and 5.

x	+5	y	ordered pair
Let x = 1.	1 + 5 = 6	6	(1, 6)
Let x = 2.	2 + 5 = 7	7	(2, 7)
Let x = 3.	3 + 5 = 8	8	(3, 8)
Let x = 4.	4 + 5 = 9	9	(4, 9)
Let x = 5.	5 + 5 = 10	10	(5, 10)

Graph the ordered pairs. (1, 6) means right 1, up 6.

Graph each rule for x = 1, 2, 3, 4, and 5.

❶ x —(+1)→ y

❷ x —(×4)→ y

32 • Math Explorations and Applications Level 6

LESSON
99 PRACTICE   Name_____

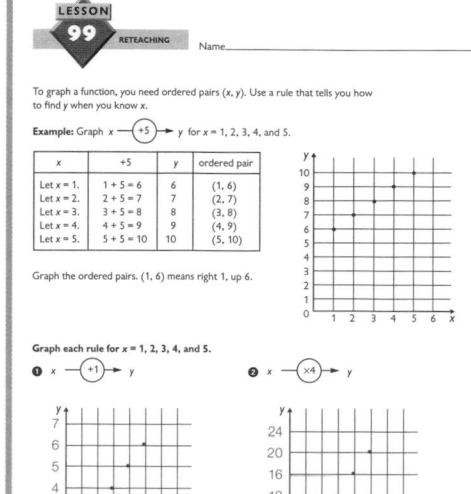

ALGEBRA READINESS

For each of the function rules, make a set of five ordered pairs of numbers. Graph each set of ordered pairs.
Pairs chosen may vary.

❶ x —(+3)→ y

❷ x —(+3)→ y

❸ x —(×3)→ y

❹ x —(−4)→ y

❺ x —(+2)→ y

❻ x —(−1)→ y

Math Explorations and Applications Level 6 • 99

*available separately

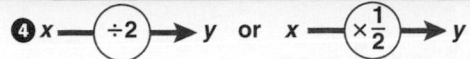

4 $x \longrightarrow \div 2 \longrightarrow y$ or $x \longrightarrow \times \frac{1}{2} \longrightarrow y$

A **function rule** can be used to generate ordered pairs. For example, the rule $x \longrightarrow \times 3 \longrightarrow y$ can be used to generate ordered pairs in this way:

A. Choose a number. For example, 2.

B. Multiply it by 3. $2 \times 3 = 6$

C. Write the ordered pair. The first number, or input, is the number chosen; the second number, or output, is three times that number: (2, 6).

3 Choose four more numbers. Use each number to make an ordered pair from the rule $x \longrightarrow \times 3 \longrightarrow y$. (Use x as the first number and y as the second.)   **For example: (0,0); (1,3); (3,9); (2.5, 7.5)**

4 Can you think of a function rule that could be used to generate the ordered pairs for the points O, A, B, C, D, E, and F on page 354?

For each of the function rules in problems 5–10, make a set of five ordered pairs of numbers. (Use the number you choose for x as the input and the corresponding value of y as the output.)
Answers shown are examples only.

5  $x \xrightarrow{\times 4} y$
(0,0), (1,4), (2,8), (4,16)

6 $x \xrightarrow{\div 2} y$
(0,0), (1,$\frac{1}{2}$), (2,1), (10,5)

7 $y \xleftarrow{-4} x$
(0,–4), (2,–2), (4,0), (9,5)

8 $x \xrightarrow{-3} y$
(0,–3), (1,–2), (3,0), (8,5)

9 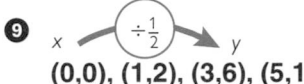 $x \xrightarrow{\div \frac{1}{2}} y$
(0,0), (1,2), (3,6), (5,10)

10 $x \xrightarrow{+3} y$
(0,3), (1,4), (2,5), (6,9)

11 Graph each set of ordered pairs that you made for problems 5–10. Compare your graph with those made by others in the class.

◆ Did you all plot the same points? **Not all the students will plot the same points, but they will all plot the same line.**

◆ In what way are your graphs similar?

Use the Cumulative Review on page 574 after this lesson.

Unit 5   Lesson 99 • **355**

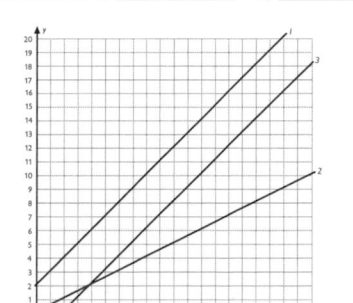

Mental Math (continued)

e. $\begin{array}{r} 623 \\ -290 \\ \hline (333) \end{array}$

❷ Teach

Using the Student Pages Discuss ordered pairs of things, beginning with names. Then use the example of stating months and days. Do problem 1 on page 354 with the class. Note that 1f and 1g are ambiguous. Next discuss coordinates as another example of ordered pairs. After students do problem 2, make sure they understand how to find the coordinates of point F. Before starting page 355 with students, write the function rule $x \longrightarrow \times 3 \longrightarrow y$

on the chalkboard and have students give ordered pairs for it. Students may more easily answer problem 4 if you list the ordered pairs in a chart. Have students use **graph paper** to do problems 5–11 on their own, then discuss the problems.

❸ Wrap-Up

In Closing Ask students to explain how to locate ordered pairs on a graph and how to graph a set of ordered pairs.

ANALYZING ANSWERS Students often have difficulty deciding on the values to use for the x-coordinate. Suggest they use any number; if the calculation becomes difficult, they can try another number. Ask them why some numbers are more complicated to work with than others for a given function rule.

Mastery Checkpoint 21

By this time most students should be able to produce a set of ordered pairs of numbers for a function rule. Observe students as they work on page 355 or on Assessment Blackline Masters pages 42–43.

Assessment Criteria

Did the student . . .

✓ correctly make a set of ordered pairs for each function rule?

✓ express understanding of the relationships among some of the function rules?

Homework Assign Practice Master 99 to provide further work with function rules.

Unit 5   Lesson 99 **355**

Translation, Rotation, Reflection, and Symmetry

LESSON PLANNER

Objectives

▶ to review the concept of congruence

▶ to develop the ideas of translation, rotation, and reflection as they relate to congruence

Context of the Lesson This lesson is a pause in the sequence on creating and interpreting graphs.

 MANIPULATIVES

rulers* or straightedges

tracing paper

mirrors* (optional)

Program Resources

Practice Master 100

Enrichment Master 100

For extra practice:
CD-ROM* Lesson 100

① Warm-Up ⏱ 5 MINUTES

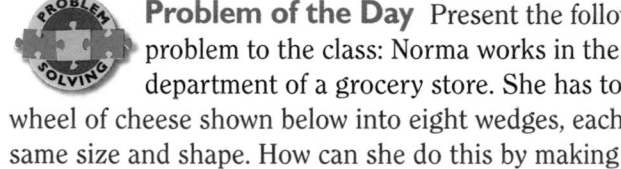

Problem of the Day Present the following problem to the class: Norma works in the cheese department of a grocery store. She has to cut the wheel of cheese shown below into eight wedges, each the same size and shape. How can she do this by making only three cuts? (Slice the circular face into fourths with two cuts, then make one cut across the cheese, halfway up, parallel to the cutting board.)

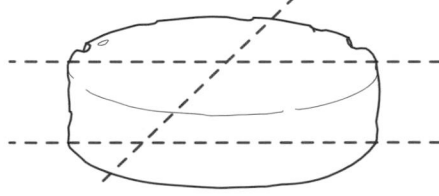

Problem-Solving Strategies Ask students who have solved the Problem of the Day to share how they solved it and any strategies they used.

Translation, Rotation, Reflection, and Symmetry

Two figures are **congruent** if we can fit one exactly on top of the other, or if we can imagine doing so. We can show that two figures are congruent by describing what we would have to do to fit them on top of each other.

One method of moving a figure to see if it fits on top of another is called **translation.** In a translation we simply move one figure in a straight line until it fits exactly on the other one.

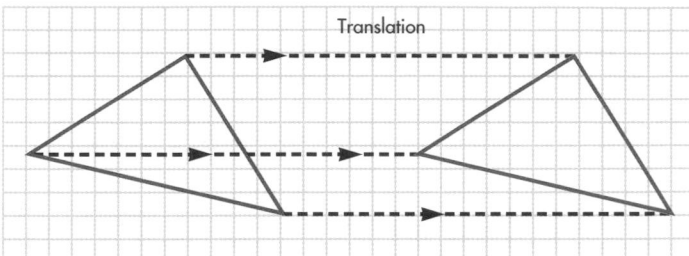

Another method of moving a figure to see if it fits on top of another is to turn the figure in a circle around a point. In the **rotation** shown here, what is the point around which the figure is being rotated? **P**

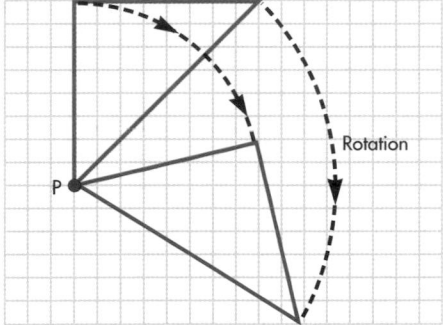

356 • Algebra Readiness

Why teach it at this time?

This lesson provides practice with close observation of figures on a grid. Translations, rotations, and reflections were covered in the Level 4 and Level 5 programs. This lesson provides an opportunity to relate those concepts to the coordinate grid.

*available separately

Sometimes figures look exactly alike, but one is a mirror image of the other. In this case we would have to flip one of the images over to make them fit. You can imagine cutting a triangle out of a sheet of paper and flipping it in order to make it fit on another. We can also show that two images would fit on each other by using a mirror and showing that one looks just like the other when it is reflected in a mirror. In the figure below the two triangles are mirror images of each other.

◆   Where would you put the mirror to show this?   **See figure.**

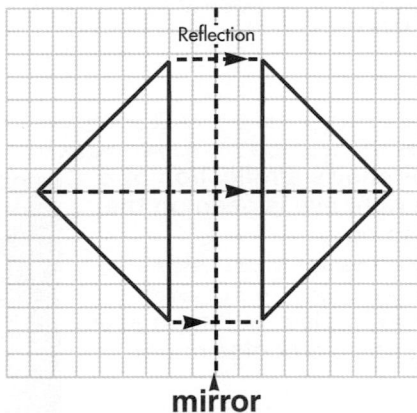

mirror

We say that a figure has a **line of symmetry** if there is a line that could be drawn so the figure looks the same on one side as on the other. Or we could place a mirror on the line and the figure looks the same with the mirror as without it.

Unit 5   Lesson 100   •   **357**

Why teach it this way?

Providing opportunities for students to manipulate the figures to explore the different movements allows students to gain a more concrete understanding of the differences among the three transformations. In particular, the difference between a translation (only a slide) and a reflection is shown.

MENTAL MATH Ask students to tell what comes next and why. Accept any well-reasoned answers.

a.   1, 2, 2, 3, 3, 3, 4, 4, 4, (4—each numeral appears that number of times)

b.   1, 3, 6, 10, 15, (21—1 + 2 + 3 + 4 + 5 + 6)

c.   2, 6, 18, 54, (162—multiply by 3)

d.   A, D, G, J, (M—skip two letters)

e.   100, 85, 65, 40, (10—subtract 15, 20, 25, and 30)

❷ Teach

Using the Student Pages Have students trace the first triangle on page 356 onto their tracing paper. Next they can slide the tracing in a straight line, without turning the tracing paper, until the tracing is directly over the triangle to the right. Ask them if it fits. Because the answer is "Yes," we say the triangles are congruent. Tell students that sliding the paper is called *translation*. Have students place the same tracing over the top triangle in the rotation figure. Because it fits, the two triangles are also congruent. Then, have them turn their triangle, keeping point *P* in the same spot. It fits the bottom triangle, so these two are congruent as well. Point out that this motion (turn) of the paper is called a *rotation*.

Have students place the traced triangle over the left triangle on page 357. It should fit. Now have them pick up their tracing paper and "flip" it so the side that was on top is now on the bottom. There is a fit, so these two triangles are congruent. Tell students that the flipping motion of the paper is called a *reflection* and that the line through which the reflection seems to have taken place is called a *line of symmetry*, as is the line through the center of the face on page 357.

◆ LESSON 100 Translation, Rotation, Reflection, and Symmetry

Teach

Using the Student Pages Have students answer the questions on pages 358 and 359. Students can work in small groups to brainstorm answers to questions 5–8. Be sure that students explain their reasoning to each other.

LEARNING STYLES **Meeting Individual Needs**

Students who are weak kinesthetic or visual learners may have some difficulty with this lesson. Be alert to this, and if possible, pair them with students who have an easier time comprehending movements of figures, predicting results, and spotting symmetry.

Mathematics is not a solitary activity. It should be done and learned with others. Games, activities, projects, proofs, problem-formulation activities, and so on are all activities that should be carried on in groups. Where possible, those groups should involve children of different abilities, different interests, and different backgrounds; and each member of the group should be expected to make substantial contributions and derive substantial satisfaction.

—Stephen S. Willoughby, *Mathematics Education for a Changing World*

◆ LESSON 100 Translation, Rotation, Reflection, and Symmetry

Answer these questions.

1 Which of the motions described in the previous two pages reminds you of a sled ride? **translation**

2 Which of the motions reminds you of a merry-go-round ride? **rotation**

3 Which reminds you of folding a sheet of paper to make a paper airplane? **reflection**

4 When you see a photograph of yourself, do you look different from the way you look in the mirror? Why do you suppose that is? **Yes, since the mirror shows a reflection of a face. The right eye is seen on the left, and so on**

5 Think about the world around you. Describe five actions that might reasonably remind somebody of a translation. **examples: putting a sheet on a bed, using a cookie cutter**

6 Describe five actions or activities that might reasonably remind somebody of a rotation. **examples: twisting a bottle lid, spinning a globe**

7 Describe five objects or actions that might reasonably remind somebody of a reflection. **examples: turning the pages of a book, looking into a still pond**

8 List five objects in your classroom that have lines of symmetry. **examples: desks, chalkboard, floor tiles, blank pieces of paper, and unused pieces of chalk**

For each of the following figures, tell how many lines of symmetry the figure has.

⑨ A
1

⑩ C
1

⑪ H
2

⑫ L
0

⑬ M
1

⑭ S
0

⑮ X
4

⑯ Y
1

⑰ Z
0

⑱ ○
an infinite number

⑲ □
4

⑳ ⬡
8

Unit 5   Lesson 100 • **359**

You may wish to make a copy of page 359 and have students draw in all lines of symmetry, or you can have them trace the figures and draw the lines of symmetry using a different color. You may want to have **tracing paper** and **rulers*** available.

For problem 14, some students may observe that the figure is symmetrical about a point in the middle, although there is no line of symmetry.

Students may find it helpful to use **mirrors*** to check whether they have drawn the lines of symmetry accurately. If the mirror is held on the line of symmetry, the half-figure and its reflection should be identical to the original figure.

GIFTED & TALENTED   Meeting Individual Needs
Draw the clock below on the chalkboard. Tell students that what they are looking at is a mirror reflection of the clock. Ask them to give the actual time. (11:20)

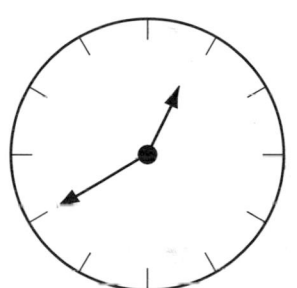

Technology Connection Refer students to the software *Mighty Math Cosmic Geometry* from Edmark (Mac, IBM, for grades 6–8) for further practice with constructions and transformations, 2-D and 3-D coordinates, length, perimeter, area, and volume.

LESSON 100 Translation, Rotation, Reflection, and Symmetry

Teach

 **Using the Student Pages** Have students work on pages 360 and 361 with a partner if they wish. They can use **tracing paper** to see what motions are needed for some of the figures although, in general, this should not be necessary. Students may notice that a translation and a rotation may always be used to place one line segment on top of a congruent line segment of a congruent figure. One figure will then either be on top of the other, or be on top of the other after a reflection over that line segment.

Answers for page 361:

Answers may vary. Samples are given below.

21. Translate *ABC* so that *B* fits on top of *Y*. Rotate *ABC* around point *B* until *A* fits on top of *X* and *C* fits on top of *Z*.

22. Translate *EFGH* so that *E* fits on top of *P*. Rotate *EFGH* around point *P* until *F* fits on top of *O*, *G* fits on top of *R*, and *H* fits on top of *S*.

23. Translate *ABCD* so that *C* fits on top of *G*. Reflect *ABCD* so that *B* fits on top of *F*, *A* fits on top of *E*, and *D* fits on top of *H*.

24. Translate *KLMN* so that *K* fits on top of *P*. Rotate *KLMN* around point *P* until *N* fits on top of *S*. Reflect *KLMN* along line *PS* so that *L* fits on top of *Q* and *M* fits on top of *R*.

25. Translate circle *P* so that point *P* fits on top of point *Q*.

26. Translate *ABCDE* so that *A* fits on top of *J*. Rotate *ABCDE* until *B* is on top of *K*, *C* is on top of *F*, *D* is on top of *G*, and *E* is on top of *H*.

LESSON 100 Translation, Rotation, Reflection, and Symmetry

It is always possible to move one figure to another congruent figure in the same plane by translations, rotations, and reflections. For example, we can move triangle *ABC* so it is on top of triangle *DEF* by translating the figure so that *A* fits on top of *D*. Then rotate the translated triangle around point *D* until *B* fits on top of *E* and *C* fits on top of *F*.

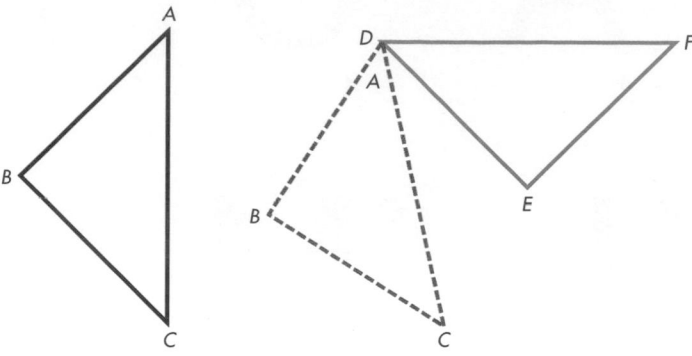

In the example below, we must first reflect trapezoid *GHIJ*. We can then move the reflected trapezoid *GHIJ* so it is on top of trapezoid *KLMN*. Reflect the figure so that *I* fits on top of *L*. Then rotate the trapezoid around point *L* until *H* is on top of *M*, *G* is on top of *N*, and *J* is on top of *K*.

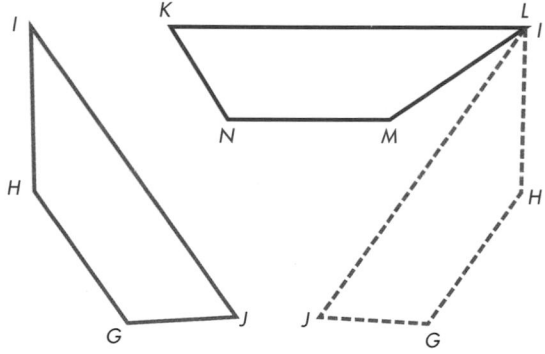

360 • Algebra Readiness

RETEACHING

 To help students better understand reflection and lines of symmetry, have them play the following game with a partner. The two students use **pattern blocks** with which they make shapes on either side of a designated line of symmetry. One student places a block on one side of the line and then the other student must place a block on the other side of that line, in the same orientation. Students take turns adding to the figure by placing blocks and matching each placement to maintain the symmetry.

Describe how you could use translations, rotations, and reflections to move one of the figures in each problem to be on top of the other.
See answers in margin.

㉑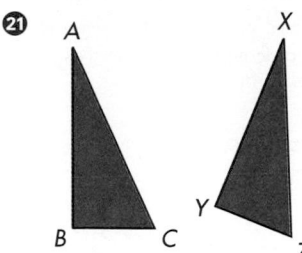

㉒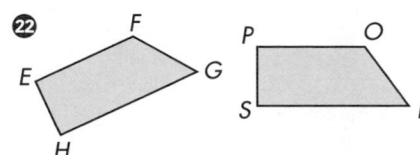

㉓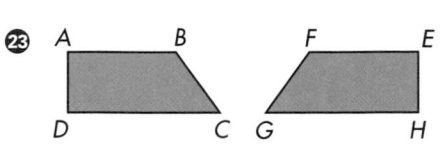

㉔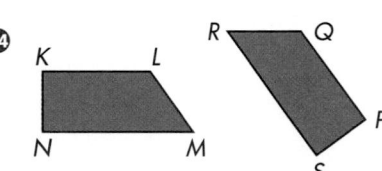

㉕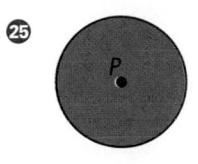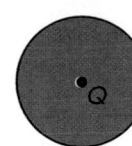

㉖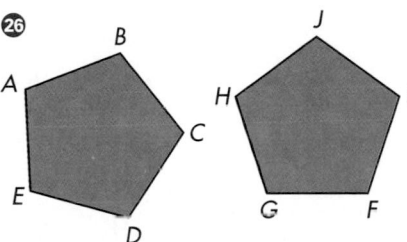

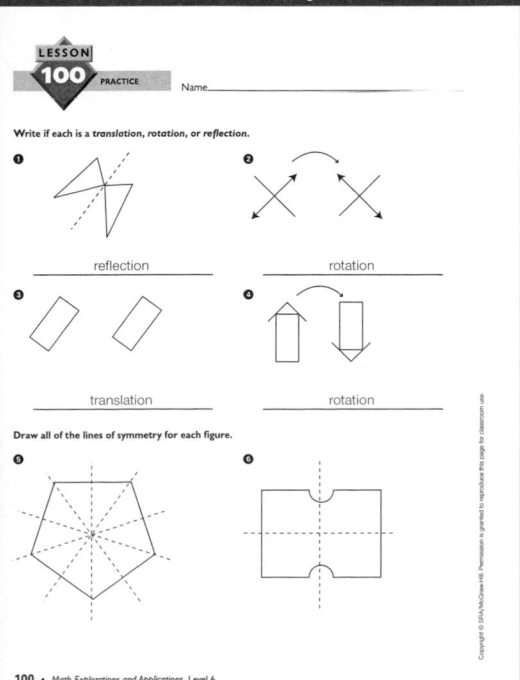

Unit 5   Lesson 100 • **361**

PRACTICE p. 100

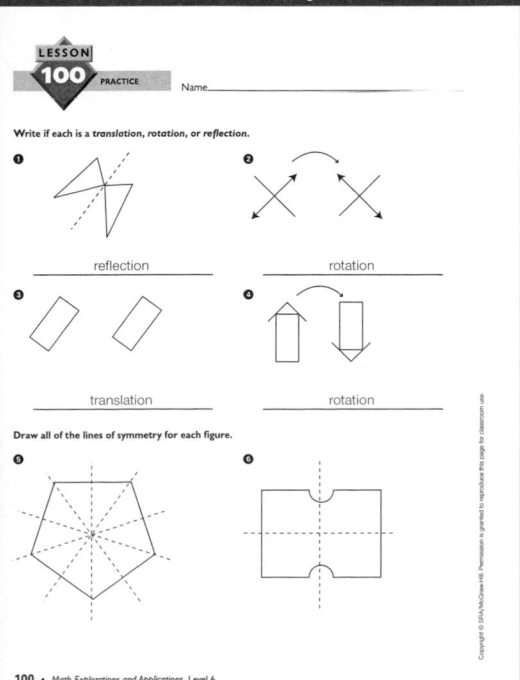

ENRICHMENT p. 100

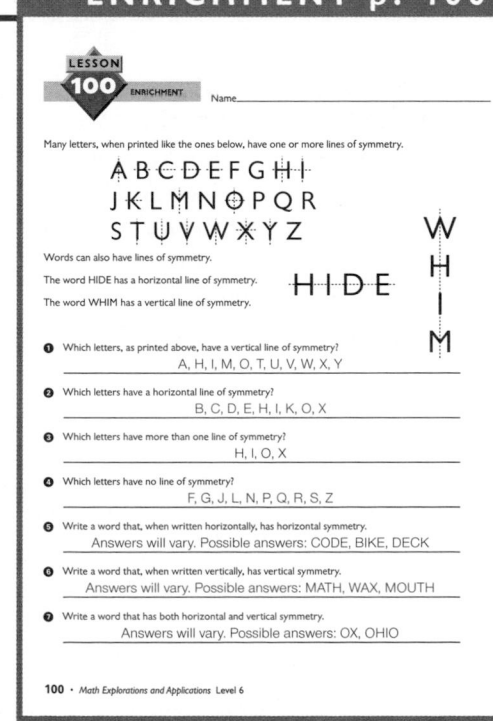

❸ Wrap-Up ⏱ 5 MINUTES

In Closing To summarize the lesson, ask students to explain how to tell whether two figures are congruent. Ask them to describe what *symmetry* means. Have them give examples of translation, rotation, and reflection.

 **Informal Assessment** Observe students as they work on the problems on these pages. Ask them to explain the difference between translation and reflection.

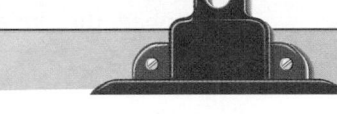

Assessment Criteria

Did the student . . .

✓ correctly complete the activities on these pages?

✓ demonstrate clear understanding of the concepts of congruence, symmetry, translation, rotation, and reflection?

 Homework Ask students to write descriptions of each kind of motion and to draw pictures to accompany the descriptions.

LESSON 101

Student Edition pages 362–363

Graphing Functions

LESSON PLANNER

Objectives

▶ to review how to graph a function by finding and graphing pairs of numbers that satisfy the function rule

▶ to demonstrate that when the ordered pairs for a simple multiplication function rule like

$x \longrightarrow \boxed{\times 3} \longrightarrow y$ are graphed, they lie along

a straight line through (0,0)

▶ to review how to determine whether an ordered pair satisfies a given function rule

Context of the Lesson This is the sixth of 24 lessons on functions and graphing.

 MANIPULATIVES

millimeter rulers* (for use with cm graph paper)

Program Resources

Reteaching Master
Practice Master 101
Enrichment Master 101

For extra practice:
CD-ROM* Lesson 101

---

1 Warm-Up 🕐 5 MINUTES

 Problem of the Day Present the following problem: Greg is a fussy eater and has a specific rule about what he will eat. Among his favorite foods are turnips, beef, chicken, corn, and gingerbread, but he will never eat tuna, lettuce, ravioli, or cake. Which will he eat, a radish or chocolate? Why? (radish; he only likes foods that end in consonants)

Problem-Solving Strategies Ask students who have solved the Problem of the Day to share how they solved it and any strategies they used.

MENTAL MATH As in previous lessons, present multidigit problems that students can solve mentally. Invite students to share their strategies.

a. 499
   −299
   (200)

b. 842
   +316
   (1158)

c. 3 × 33 = (99)
   3 × 333 = (999)
   30 × 33 = (990)
   30 × 333 = (9990)
   999 ÷ 333 = (3)

d. 7 × 2 = (14)
   7 × 20 = (140)
   70 × 20 = (1400)
   700 × 20 = (14,000)
   14,000 ÷ 20 = (700)

362 Algebra Readiness

PRACTICE

LESSON 101

Graphing Functions

 ALGEBRA READINESS

A function expresses a relationship between two numbers. We often call these numbers x and y.

If we can use the first number in an ordered pair as x in a function rule and get the second number as y, then we say the ordered pair (x, y) satisfies the function rule.

Examples: Does the ordered pair (2, 6) satisfy the function rule

$x \longrightarrow \boxed{\times 3} \longrightarrow y?$

Use the first number as x. $\quad 2 \longrightarrow \boxed{\times 3} \longrightarrow y$

Do you get the second number for y? $\quad 2 \longrightarrow \boxed{\times 3} \longrightarrow 6$

Yes. So (2, 6) satisfies the function rule $x \longrightarrow \boxed{\times 3} \longrightarrow y.$

Does the ordered pair (4, 8) satisfy the function rule

$x \longrightarrow \boxed{\times 3} \longrightarrow y?$ $\qquad 4 \longrightarrow \boxed{\times 3} \longrightarrow 12$

No, (4, 8) does not satisfy the function rule $x \longrightarrow \boxed{\times 3} \longrightarrow y.$

1 Which of these ordered pairs will satisfy the function rule $x \longrightarrow \boxed{\times 3} \longrightarrow y?$

(a.) (8, 24)　**(b.)** (1.5, 4.5)　**c.** (7, 20)　**d.** $(2\frac{1}{2}, 6\frac{1}{2})$

2 Which of these ordered pairs will satisfy the function rule $x \longrightarrow \boxed{-7} \longrightarrow y?$

a. (10, 7)　**(b.)** (20, 13)　**(c.)** (9.3, 2.3)　**d.** $(8\frac{1}{4}, 1\frac{3}{4})$

Copy each ordered pair. Replace x or y with the correct number so that the pair satisfies the rule $x \longrightarrow \boxed{\times 3} \longrightarrow y.$

3 (3, y) **9**　　**4** (1, y) **3**　　**5** (0, y) **0**　　**6** (2, y) **6**

7 (2.4, y) **7.2**　**8** (0.1, y) **0.3**　**9** (0.6, y) **1.8**　**10** (3.5, y) **10.5**

11 (1.4, y) **4.2**　**12** (1.7, y) **5.1**　**13** (0.4, y) **1.2**　**14** (0.8, y) **2.4**

15 (1.1, y) **3.3**　**16** (2.7, y) **8.1**　**17** (3.2, y) **9.6**　**18** (x, 9) **3**

19 (x, 11.1) **3.7**　**20** (x, 12) **4**　**21** (x, 13.2) **4.4**　**22** (x, 15) **5**

362 • Algebra Readiness

Literature Connection You may wish to have students read *Charlie and the Great Glass Elevator* by Roald Dahl. Have them graph the comparison of ages of their extended family with those of the ages they would be after taking Wonka-Vite or Vita-Wonk.

RETEACHING p. 33

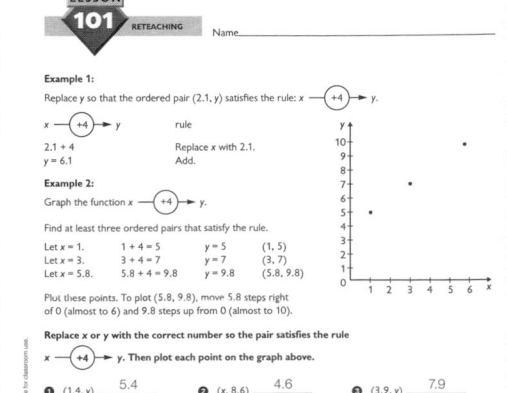

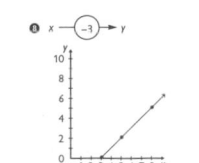

*available separately

We often graph functions to help us see and understand some of their characteristics.

To graph the function that has the rule

x —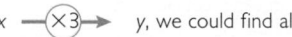— y, we could find all

ordered pairs that satisfy this rule and then graph them. Of course, we can't find all the ordered pairs. But we should be able to decide where they would be by plotting a few of them and thinking about the pattern.

On a sheet of graph paper, draw coordinate axes like the ones shown here. Graph the 20 ordered pairs you found for

x —×3→ y when you did

problems 3–22 on page 362. We have plotted (2.4, 7.2) for you to show you how to plot ordered pairs with decimals.

To plot (2.4, 7.2), start at the origin, move 2.4 steps to the right and 7.2 steps up. (Estimate the tenths as best you can. Use a millimeter ruler if it helps.)

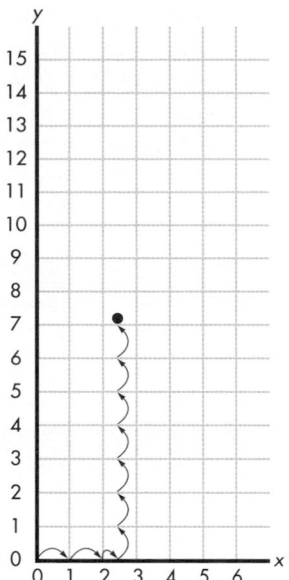

◆ How can you estimate 2.4 steps? **It's a little less than 2.5 steps.**

◆ Do you notice anything interesting about the points you graphed? **They are all on a straight line.**

◆ If you graphed the point (107, 321), do you think it would be on the same **line** as the other points? **yes**

◆ Can you think of a point that satisfies the rule x —×3→ y that wouldn't be on the line? **no**

◆ How many points of a line do you need to know to decide where the line goes? **2**

Graph these functions. **Be sure to check students' graphs carefully.**

㉓ x —÷2→ y ㉔ x —−3→ y

㉕ x —×2→ y ㉖ x —+7→ y

Unit 5   Lesson 101 • **363**

❷ Teach

Using the Student Pages Review the examples on page 362 with the class, then have students work individually on problems 1 and 2. Explain that you are going to make a graph of the function rule x —×3→ y by finding and plotting 20 ordered pairs that satisfy the rule. Do a few problems with the class, including one in which x must be determined (problems 18–22). Discuss how to use a **millimeter ruler*** or estimation to locate a point such as 4.1. Have students work individually to find and graph the 20 ordered pairs. Then go over the discussion questions on page 363. Point out that all the points appear to be on a line that passes through the origin (0, 0). The line is "going up" three times as fast as it is "going to the right." Any point that satisfies the function rule will have a y-value that is three times as great as its x-value. So, any point satisfying the rule will be on the line. For any rule involving only multiplication or only division, the line will go through the point (0, 0), so you need only one other point to determine the line. Have students work on problems 23–26.

❸ Wrap-Up

In Closing To summarize, ask students to explain what it means if an ordered pair *satisfies* the function rule.

Portfolio Assessment Have students choose a function, graph it on centimeter grid paper, and write an explanation of their work to include in their Math Portfolios.

Assessment Criteria

Did the student . . .

✓ correctly find the missing coordinate in an ordered pair so that the pair satisfies a given function rule?

✓ recognize that the ordered pairs for each rule lie on a straight line?

Homework Challenge students to express their age, in years, as a function of the age of another family member and to draw a graph of that function rule.

PRACTICE p. 101

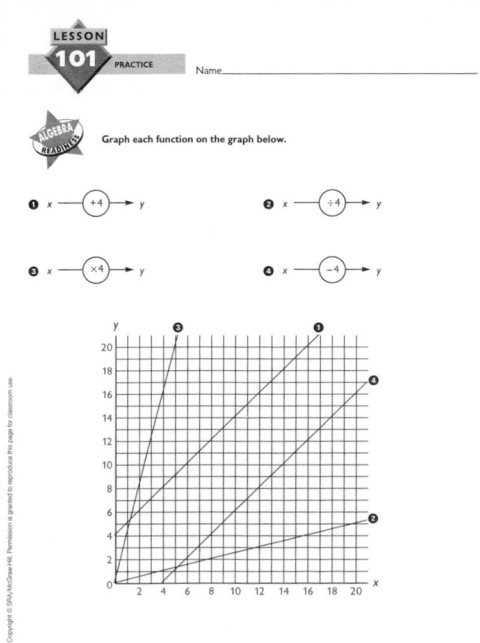

ENRICHMENT p. 101

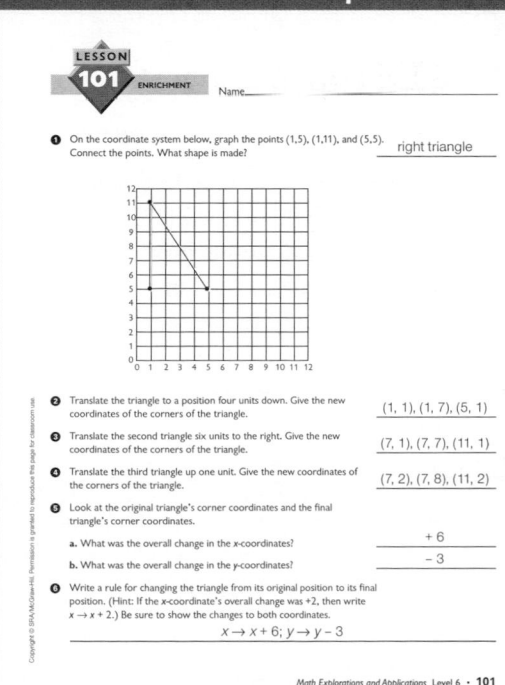

Graphing Data

LESSON PLANNER

Objectives

▶ to demonstrate how a graph can be used to interpolate (infer information between plotted points)

▶ to demonstrate how a graph can be used to extrapolate (infer information beyond the range of the farthest plotted point)

Context of the Lesson This is the seventh of 24 lessons on functions and graphing.

MANIPULATIVES
graph paper
scale (optional)

Program Resources
Practice Master 102
Enrichment Master 102
The Cruncher*

For extra practice:
CD-ROM* Lesson 102

❶ Warm-Up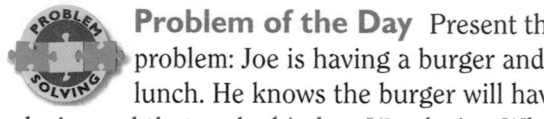

Problem of the Day Present the following problem: Joe is having a burger and chips for lunch. He knows the burger will have 600 calories and that each chip has 18 calories. What is the maximum number of chips Joe can eat and still keep his calorie intake under 1000 calories? (22)

Problem-Solving Strategies Ask students who have solved the Problem of the Day to share how they solved it and any strategies they used.

 Draw this chart on the chalkboard and present the following information: Here are the results of a four-day free-throw tournament. Each person shot ten free throws, and this chart shows how many each made. Then ask the questions that follow on page 365.

Open Court Free-Throw Tournament

	Day 1	Day 2	Day 3	Day 4
Smith	6	5	9	5
Johnson	8	3	3	7
Marzetta	4	5	9	6
Yang	7	7	7	6

Graphing Data

Often it is difficult to tell whether information that is collected or presented in no particular order fits into any pattern. As we saw in Lesson 98, it is usually helpful to organize data in order to draw conclusions.

Captain Sanchez of Allaway Airlines likes to keep records of how much weight was on board his airplane and how many passengers he had for each trip. The passengers and their luggage and all other freight are weighed before each flight. He calls this the "carried weight." After 12 flights Captain Sanchez had these records:

Flight Number	1	2	3	4	5	6
Number of Passengers	9	22	4	11	15	17
Carried Weight (pounds)	1569	3826	739	1936	2631	2994

Flight Number	7	8	9	10	11	12
Number of Passengers	11	5	14	2	9	24
Carried Weight (pounds)	1923	917	2468	385	1597	4198

On the 13th flight somebody forgot to weigh the passengers, luggage, and other freight. Captain Sanchez knew there were 20 passengers. He wanted to know the approximate weight of passengers, luggage, and freight.

◆ How could he estimate the weight? **Something may be done to the data to see if there is a pattern, such as graphing the data or**
Captain Sanchez knew that his plane should not have more than 5500 **putting the**
pounds in carried weight. **data in order from the least number of passengers to the greatest.**

◆ How could he estimate how many passengers could be carried without going above the 5500-pound limit? **See answer above.**

Why teach it this way?

In this lesson students make inferences about data shown in tables and graphs. Identifying trends in data and making estimates based on the interpolations and extrapolations are key real-life skills with many useful applications in several different disciplines. Real-life data frequently will not lie along a straight line.

*available separately

Find the *y*-coordinate of the point for which the *x*-coordinate is 20. A reasonable estimate is 3500 lb. Find the *x*-coordinate of the point for which the *y*-coodinate is 5500. About 31 or 32 is a reasonable estimate.

Solve these problems.

1 Draw a graph of the information from Captain Sanchez's records. Use a full sheet of graph paper. Draw and label your axes as shown here. The point for the first flight (9, 1569) is already plotted.

◆ How can you use your graph to help answer the questions on page 364?

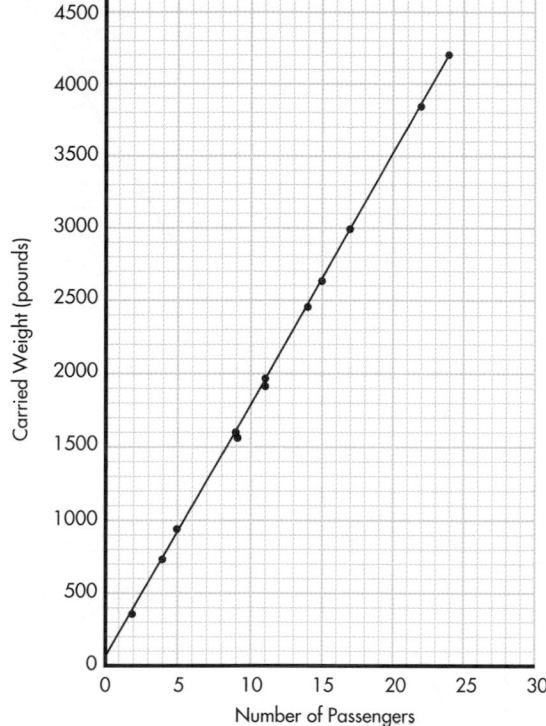

2 Use your graph to estimate the carried weight if the number of passengers is

a. 20	**b.** 30	**c.** 7	**d.** 0
3500 lb	**5100–5200 lb**	**1200 lb**	**20–40 lb**

3 Use your graph to estimate the number of passengers on board if the carried weight is

a. 4400 lb	**b.** 1775 lb	**c.** 26 lb
26	**10**	**0**
d. 220 lb	**e.** 2300 lb	**f.** 3000 lb
1	**13**	**17**

Unit 5   Lesson 102 • **365**

Literature Connection You may wish to have students read *A Grain of Rice* by Helena Claire Pittman. Have them use a graph to show the increasing amounts of rice a farmer's son receives.

Mental Math (continued)

a. Who had the highest score on each day? (Day 1, Johnson; Day 2, Yang; Day 3, Smith and Marzetta tied; Day 4, Johnson.)

b. Who had the highest total? (Yang)

c. What were their average scores? (Smith, 6.25; Johnson 5.25; Marzetta, 6; and Yang, 6.75)

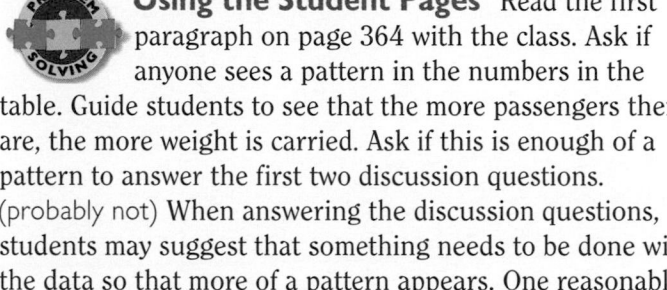

Using the Student Pages Read the first paragraph on page 364 with the class. Ask if anyone sees a pattern in the numbers in the table. Guide students to see that the more passengers there are, the more weight is carried. Ask if this is enough of a pattern to answer the first two discussion questions. (probably not) When answering the discussion questions, students may suggest that something needs to be done with the data so that more of a pattern appears. One reasonable idea is to arrange the data in order from the least number of passengers to the greatest number. This change would show that each passenger increases the carried weight by about 176 pounds. Another reasonable plan is to graph the data and look for a pattern.

Have students use **graph paper** to graph the data, referring them to the graph shown on student page 365. Guide students to plan their axes so that they can plot points as high as 5500 and as far to the right as 32. Ask whether all the points on completed student graphs are on the same line; ask why not. (No, because there are 2 different weights for 9 passengers and 2 different weights for 11 passengers.) Point out, however, that the points almost fall along a line. Have students draw a line on their graphs that is very close to all the points. Call attention to the fact that the line does not go through the origin presumably because there is freight as well as passengers and their luggage.

Students can also use a blank **Cruncher*** spreadsheet to create a chart and graph of this data.

Have students work individually or in pairs to solve problems 2 and 3. You may wish to help students get started by doing problem 2a with the class. Explain how to locate the *y*-coordinate of the point for which the *x*-coordinate is 20 by going to 20 on the horizontal axis then straight up to the drawn line. Accept all reasonable estimates for these problems.

---

*available separately

◆ LESSON 102 Graphing Data

Teach

Using the Student Pages
Have students work individually on problems 4–10 on page 367, giving help as needed. The graph on page 366 and problems 4–6 on page 367 are analogous to those on pages 364–365. Discuss problems 7–10 after students have had a chance to work on them.

◆ LESSON 102 Graphing Data

Captain Fligh of Wing-It Airlines kept records just like the ones Captain Sanchez kept. When Captain Fligh graphed the data for her first ten flights, her graph looked like this:

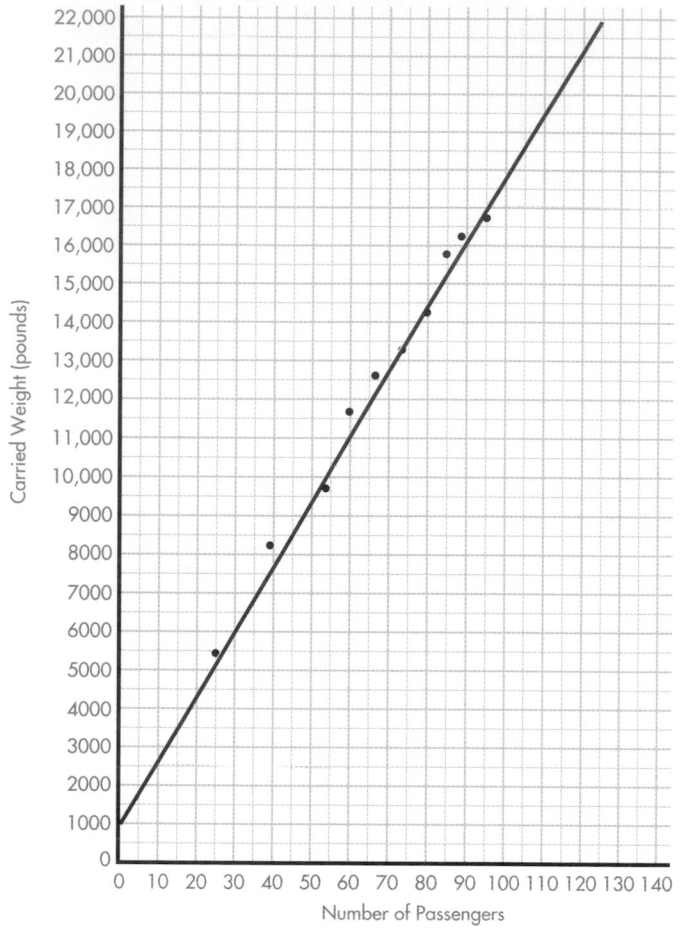

Technology Connection You may want to refer students to the laser disc *Core Concepts in Math: Problem-Solving Series: Problem Solving with Tables, Graphs, and Statistics* from BFA/Systems Impact (for grades 5–9), which is designed to teach strategies to solve common problems in data interpretation and organization. The laser disc applies real-world problems in its lessons on tables, graphs, introductory statistics, and data collection.

RETEACHING

Ask students who have difficulty interpolating or extrapolating to gather in small groups to make and analyze a simpler graph. For instance, you can collect about ten identical or nearly identical objects. Have students weigh and record the weights of a few of these items. Have them graph the results and draw a straight line as close to the points as they can. Then work with the students, checking by measurement, and asking such questions as, "How much would four of these items weigh? Ten of the items? One item?"

9 The average weight (with luggage) for a passenger is about 174 lb. Assuming that the average weight of a passenger is 140 lb, the average weight of luggage per passenger is 34 lb.

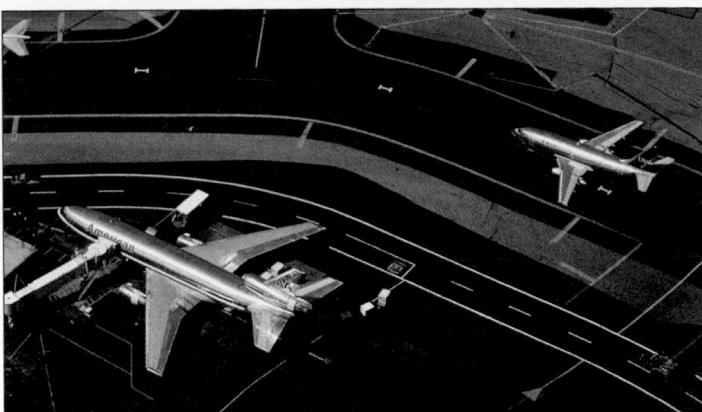

Solve these problems.

4 Captain Fligh's airplane can have no more than 22,000 pounds in carried weight. About how many passengers can be carried without going over the limit? **about 122**

5 About how much carried weight would there be if the number of passengers were

a. 50?	**b.** 100?	**c.** 0?	**d.** 45?
9500 lb	**18,000 lb**	**1200 lb**	**8800 lb**

6 About how many passengers would there be if the carried weight were

a. 15,500 lb?	**b.** 11,000 lb?	**c.** 2000 lb?	**d.** 1000 lb?
85	**58**	**5**	**0**

7 On the average, about how much does a passenger and his or her luggage on Captain Fligh's flights weigh? **Answers will vary but should be around 167 lb.**

8 Suppose an average passenger weighs about 140 pounds. On the average, about how much luggage does a passenger take on board one of Captain Fligh's flights? **Answers will vary, but if the average weight (with luggage) per passenger is 167 lb, the average weight of luggage per passenger is 27 lb.**

9 On the average, about how much luggage does a passenger take on board one of Captain Sanchez's flights? **See answer above.**

10 Why do you think there is a difference? **Answers will vary. Perhaps there is something special about Captain Sanchez's flights or the passengers that travel on Captain Fligh's flights.**

Unit 5 Lesson 102 • **367**

---

❸ Wrap-Up

In Closing Summarize the lesson by asking students why someone might be interested in knowing the kinds of information shown on their graphs.

 **Informal Assessment** Observe students as they make their graphs and interpolate and extrapolate from the data the graphs present. Select a few questions from the pages and ask students to explain how they arrived at their answers.

Assessment Criteria

Did the student . . .

✓ make the graphs correctly and draw lines according to the points plotted?

✓ give reasonable estimates for numbers of passengers and weights?

✓ demonstrate understanding of how to interpolate and extrapolate data from the information on the graph?

Homework Ask students to select, organize, graph, and make inferences about real data they find in local newspapers or magazines.

PRACTICE p. 102

LESSON 102 PRACTICE   Name_____

Number of Customers in Party	1	2	8	3	6	12	5	15	18	25
Total Restaurant Check	$6	$15	$65	$21	$47	$85	$36	$110	$130	$176

1 Draw a graph of the information about the restaurant checks.

(graph: Cost (in dollars) vs. Number of Customers)

Use your graph to estimate the total check if the number of customers in the party is as follows.

2 4 about $28   **3** 10 about $75   **4** 16 about $116

Use your graph to estimate the number of customers in a party if the total restaurant check is as follows.

5 $53 7   **6** $71 9   **7** $145 20

102 • *Math Explorations and Applications Level 6*

ENRICHMENT p. 102

LESSON 102 ENRICHMENT   Name_____

What snack does the picture on the right show?

Answer the graphing problem questions to solve the riddle.

Chuck of Chuck's Cheddar Cheese factory kept a record of the number of employees and the amount of cheese they produced each month. After eight months, he had these records.

Month	1	2	3	4	5	6	7	8
Number of Employees	6	17	12	3	9	15	10	8
Pounds of Cheese	900	2465	1860	429	1368	2100	1380	1176

(graph: Cheese Produced (in pounds) vs. Number of Employees)

1 Draw a graph of the information from Chuck's records.

Complete the following problems using the graph. Write the letter for each problem on the blank with the answer for that problem.

Use your graph to estimate the number of pounds of cheese produced in a month for each number of employees given.

2 5 600 E   **4** 20 2600 N

3 14 2000 S   **5** 19 2500 A

Use your graph to estimate the number of employees needed to produce the number of pounds of cheese given.

6 100 1 C   **8** 1500 11 R

7 500 4 Q   **9** 1000 7 K

C	H	E	E	S	E	A	N	D	Q	U	A	C	K	E	R	S
1	600	600	2000	600	2500	2600		4	2500	1	7	600	11	2000

102 • *Math Explorations and Applications Level 6*

Unit 5 Lesson 102 **367**

LESSON 103

Making and Interpreting Line Graphs

LESSON 103

Making and Interpreting Line Graphs

Ms. Cruz's sixth grade class kept a record of the outdoor temperature at 10:00 A.M. each day for a month. The first three days the temperatures were 3°C, 5°C, and 4°C. The class made a table to keep track of the temperatures.

Day	1	2	3	4	5	6	7	8	9	10	11	12	13	14
Temperature (°C)	3°	5°	4°											

Day	15	16	17	18	19	20	21	22	23	24	25	26	27	28
Temperature (°C)														

On the fourth day the thermometer looked like this one.

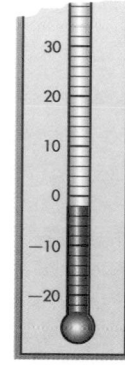

°Celsius

◆ What temperature should the class write for the fourth day? **−2°**

◆ What month do you think it was when the class kept these records? Why? **February, since there are only 28 days in the table.**

368 • Algebra Readiness

LESSON 103

Making and Interpreting Line Graphs

Student Edition pages 368–369

LESSON PLANNER

Objectives

▶ to review graphing negative numbers

▶ to provide practice in making and interpreting graphs that involve negative numbers used in realistic situations

Context of the Lesson This is the eighth of 24 lessons on functions and graphing. Using and interpreting negative numbers was taught in the fifth-grade program, particularly in the context of temperatures and money owed. Graphing in four quadrants was also taught in the fifth-grade program.

 MANIPULATIVES

graph paper

newspaper (optional)

Program Resources

Practice Master 103

Enrichment Master 103

The Cruncher*

For extra practice:
CD-ROM* Lesson 103
Cumulative Review, page 575

1 Warm-Up ⏱ 5 MINUTES

 **Problem of the Day** Present the following problem to students: What day is three days after tomorrow if four days after yesterday is Tuesday? (Wednesday)

Problem-Solving Strategies Ask students who have solved the Problem of the Day to share how they solved it and any strategies they used.

 MENTAL MATH In each of the following problems, have students show thumbs up if you have enough money and thumbs down if you do not.

a. I have $30.00. Can I buy a shirt for $27.00 plus 4% sales tax? (thumbs up)

b. I have $100.00. Can I buy a small television set for $92.00 plus 10% sales tax? (thumbs down)

c. I have $50.00. Can I buy a skirt for $19.95 and a blouse for $25.00 plus 5% sales tax? (thumbs up)

(continued on page 369)

Social Studies Connection Challenge students to use the financial pages of the newspaper to track the closing price of one stock or fund for a week. Demonstrate how to find this information, as needed. Have students plot the information on a graph. (They can plot the actual prices or the daily increase or decrease.) Ask them to write a summary of what their graph shows.

RETEACHING

Other than the continuation of any extra help begun in previous lessons, reteaching is not recommended at this time.

*available separately

Day	1	2	3	4	5	6	7	8	9	10	11	12	13	14
Temperature (°C)	3°	5°	4°	−2°	−4°	0°	1°	6°	9°	10°	7°	1°	0°	0°

Day	15	16	17	18	19	20	21	22	23	24	25	26	27	28
Temperature (°C)	1°	−3°	−6°	−8°	−4°	−1°	3°	2°	1°			−1°	2°	4°

No temperature was recorded for the 24th and 25th. Those days were on a weekend, and the students who were supposed to record the temperature forgot to do it.

Use a computer or other means to create a graph of the temperatures in the chart. Draw and label the axes like this:

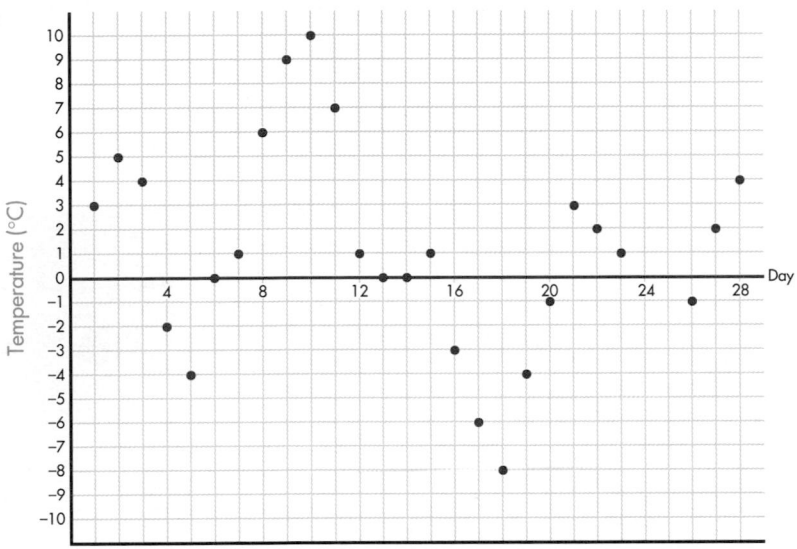

◆ How will you plot the point (4, −2)? **Start at (0,0); move right 4 spaces and down 2 spaces.**

◆ About what do you think the temperatures were on the 24th and 25th? **Answers will vary. The temperatures were probably somewhere between 2°C and −2°C.**

Use the Cumulative Review on page 575 after this lesson.

Unit 5 Lesson 103 • **369**

PRACTICE p. 103

LESSON **103** PRACTICE Name_____

Day	1	2	3	4	5	6	7	8	9	10	11	12	13	14	15
Temperature (°F)	15	18	21	17	14	16	10	8	11	9	7	5	12	10	9

Day	16	17	18	19	20	21	22	23	24	25	26	27	28	29	30
Temperature (°F)	4	3	0	−1	5	4	3	−4	−3	0	−6	−9	−4	0	−3

Make a graph from the temperatures in the chart.

Math Explorations and Applications Level 6 • 103

ENRICHMENT p. 103

LESSON **103** ENRICHMENT Name_____

By observing the direction of a line graph, you can tell what is happening to the data. A line graph can be decreasing, constant, or increasing. An example of each is shown below.

a. Increasing b. Constant c. Decreasing

In an increasing graph, as the x-coordinate increases, the y-coordinate increases.

In a constant graph, as the x-coordinate increases, the y-coordinate remains the same.

In a decreasing graph, as the x-coordinate increases, the y-coordinate decreases.

Match each data set with an appropriate graph above: a, b, or c.

❶ x-axis: distance a plane has traveled down the runway on takeoff
y-axis: speed of the plane
_____ a

❷ x-axis: number of computer modems purchased
y-axis: total cost
_____ a

❸ x-axis: number of minutes a candle is burning
y-axis: height of the candle
_____ c

❹ x-axis: the past ten years
y-axis: height of a 35-year-old adult
_____ b

❺ x-axis: number of pictures taken on a roll of film
y-axis: number of pictures left on a roll of film
_____ c

❻ x-axis: hours a car is in a parking lot
y-axis: gallons of gas in the tank
_____ b

❼ x-axis: minutes a pan of water has been boiling
y-axis: amount of water in the pan
_____ c

❽ x-axis: days of the year
y-axis: your age from the day after your birthday until the day before your next birthday
_____ a

Math Explorations and Applications Level 6 • 103

Mental Math (continued)

d. I have $90.00. Can I buy four theater tickets at $22.00 each plus 4% tax? (thumbs down)

e. I have $100.00. Can I buy four car tires at $20.00 each plus 4% tax? (thumbs up)

❷ Teach

Using the Student Pages Discuss page 368 with the class. In the second discussion question, although Ms. Cruz's class may have stopped after 28 days for some other reason, class records were probably for February. The temperatures are consistent with winter in a northern city. Before students start to graph the data, discuss how the coordinate axes shown were planned. Note that there must be space for 28 days (each space may stand for two days if necessary) and horizontal lines from −8° to 10°.

Plot several points on page 369 with the class, including (4, −2); then let students work alone to plot the remaining points using **graph paper**. Students can also use a blank **Cruncher*** spreadsheet to graph this data. Discuss what the graph might look like between points. Guide students to see that they cannot always interpolate between plotted points with certainty.

❸ Wrap-Up

In Closing Ask students to define *negative numbers*.

 **Performance Assessment** Have students list reasonable daily low temperatures for a midwinter week in a cold climate. Remind them to include negative numbers. Have students plot the temperatures on a set of axes.

Assessment Criteria

Did the student . . .

✓ express understanding of the difference between positive and negative numbers?

✓ show ability to plot both positive and negative numbers on a set of coordinate axes?

✓ show ability to interpolate from information shown in such a graph?

Homework Have students plot on a graph the actual daily high temperatures in your area for one week.

*available separately

Unit 5 Lesson 103 **369**

LESSON 104

Graphing Functions: Negative Values

LESSON 104 Student Edition pages 370–373

Graphing Functions: Negative Values

You have learned that with a function rule, you can choose values for *x* and find values for *y*, and then graph the ordered pairs. In this lesson you'll learn about graphing functions that involve negative numbers.

Do you remember the graph of the function with the rule $x \rightarrow \boxed{\times 3} \rightarrow y$? It looked like a straight line. To graph that function, you used only 0 and positive numbers (numbers greater than 0) for *x* and *y*. What happens if you also use negative numbers (numbers less than 0) for *x* and *y*?

❶ Use a computer or other means to create a table, and complete the table so that each ordered pair satisfies the rule $x \rightarrow \boxed{\times 3} \rightarrow y$.

x	5	1	0	−2	−1	−5	−3	−4	−1.5	−2.5
y	15	■	■	■	■	■	■	■	■	■

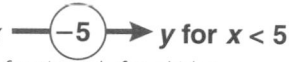
3 0 −6 −3 −15 −9 −12 −4.5 −7.5

Hint for multiplying 3 × (−2): Think of −2 as losing $2. If you lose $2 each day for three days, what will your financial condition be? Then what is 3 × (−2)?

❷ Graph the ten ordered pairs you found in problem 1. Draw the axes. Draw your *x*-axis so it goes from −5 to 5 and your *y*-axis so it goes from −15 to 15. Are all the points on one straight line? **yes**

❸ Find a function rule for which some positive values for *x* result in negative values for *y*.

Answers will vary.
Possible answer: $x \rightarrow \boxed{-5} \rightarrow y$ for *x* < 5

❹ Find a function rule for which some negative values of *x* result in positive values for *y*.

Answers will vary.
Possible answer: $x \rightarrow \boxed{+4} \rightarrow y$ for *x* > −4

370 • Algebra Readiness

LESSON PLANNER

Objectives

▶ to demonstrate that graphs of functions with rules like $x \rightarrow \boxed{\times 2} \rightarrow y$ and $x \rightarrow \boxed{-4} \rightarrow y$ are straight lines even when negative coordinates are involved

▶ to provide practice in arithmetic with negative numbers

▶ to review graphing negative numbers

▶ to provide practice in making and interpreting graphs that involve negative numbers used in realistic situations

▶ to provide practice in analyzing data and solving problems, some of which call for open-ended discussion

Context of the Lesson This is the ninth of 24 lessons on functions and graphing.

👆 MANIPULATIVES   Program Resources

graph paper
straightedges

Reteaching Master
Practice Master 104
Enrichment Master 104
The Cruncher*

For extra practice:
CD-ROM* Lesson 104

---

❶ Warm-Up ⏱ 5 MINUTES

Problem of the Day Present the following problem: If Eric leaves his house at 7 P.M. he will arrive at the ballgame in time. His watch is five minutes fast, but Eric thinks it is ten minutes slow. If he leaves when he thinks it is 7 P.M., how early or late will he be, or will he be on time? (15 min early)

Problem-Solving Strategies Ask students who have solved the Problem of the Day to share how they solved it and any strategies they used.

Why teach it this way?

In this lesson arithmetic with negative numbers is limited to what was taught in the fifth-grade program, which is arithmetic that has physical meaning. For example, problems like −3 × (−4) and −3 ÷ (−4) are not included because students are not likely to think of them in terms of a practical problem.

Use a computer or other means to draw the tables below, and complete each table so that each ordered pair satisfies the given rule. Then graph each set of ordered pairs.

Check students' graphs carefully.

x —(×2)→ y

5

x	0	4	−3	1.4	−2.5	0.7
y	■	■	■	■	■	■

0   8   −6   2.8   −5.0   1.4

x —(−4)→ y

6

x	10	5	4	2	0	−2
y	■	■	■	■	■	■

6   1   0   −2   −4   −6

x —(+2)→ y

7

x	0	5	−5	−2.5	−0.5	−1
y	■	■	■	■	■	■

2   7   −3   −0.5   1.5   1

8 Look at your graphs for problems 2, 5, 6, and 7.

a. Do the points in each graph fall on a straight line?   **yes**

b. In each case, do you think that other points that satisfy the rule would fall on the line you graphed?   **yes**

c. In every case, do you think that the coordinates of every point on the line satisfy the function rule?   **yes**

9 If you were sure a graph would be a straight line, how many points would you need to plot to draw the line?   **2**

Unit 5   Lesson 104 • **371**

Literature Connection You may wish to have students read *What's Cooking, Jenny Archer?* by Ellen Conford. Ask them to graph the profits and losses at Jenny's lunch-making service.

MENTAL MATH Challenge students to answer the following questions by using the chart. Copy the chart onto the chalkboard. The chart shows money raised for the Student Council by selling small bags of popcorn. Present the following problem. You may want to ask for estimates before students do any computations.

	M	T	W	Th	F
Kelly	$5	$6	$15	$36	$4
Eileen	$7	$8	$16	$17	$19
Kim	$16	$11	$21	$17	$15
TOTAL	$28	$25	$52	$70	$38

Who had the greatest average? (Kim)

What was it? ($16 per day)

Whose was the lowest average? (Kelly's)

What was it? ($13.20 per day)

Who had the most sales? (Kim)

What was her total? ($80)

❷ Teach

Using the Student Pages Discuss enough of page 370 to get students started so they can work on problems 1–7 independently. You may want to choose one integral negative *x*-value and one non-integer negative *x*-value from problem 1 to discuss. As students work on these problems, give help as needed. Be sure all students are drawing coordinate axes for each graph that are large enough to accommodate all the points to be graphed. Then, with the class, discuss answers to problems 8 and 9. For problem 9, point out that if someone knows the graph is a straight line, one needs only two points to determine the line. Explain to students that it makes good sense to try a third point to check whether the graph is indeed a straight line and to catch any error that may have been made in the calculations or in plotting the first two points.

Students may use a blank **Cruncher*** spreadsheet to create tables and graphs for problems on pages 370–371, or have **graph paper** and **straightedges** available for students.

*available separately

Unit 5 Lesson 104 **371**

◆ LESSON 104 Graphing Functions: Negative Values

Teach

COOPERATIVE LEARNING **Using the Student Pages** Discuss the chart on page 372 with the class. Have students work in small groups on questions on page 373 and then report their conclusions to the class. Discuss the last four questions with the class.

Students can use a blank **Cruncher*** spreadsheet to graph the cash flow of the restaurant.

Graph of Mrs. Brooks's data:

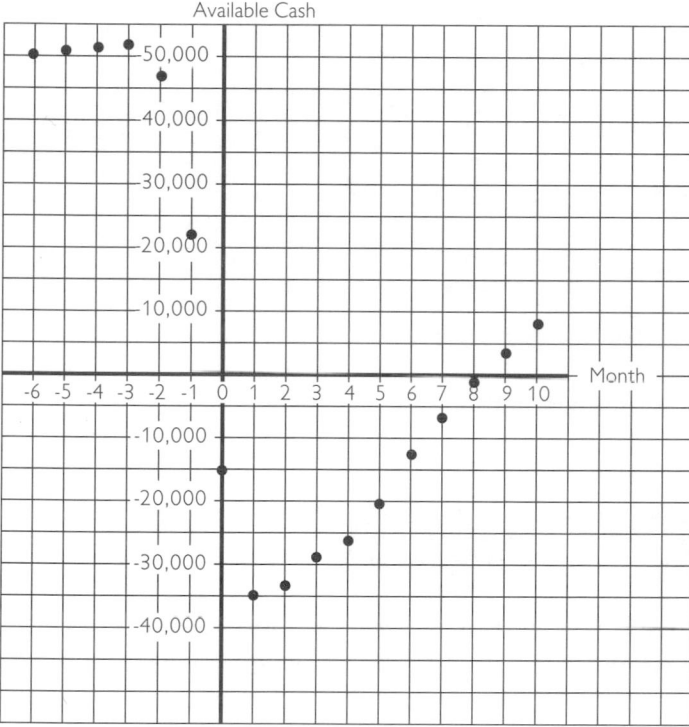

◆ LESSON 104 Graphing Functions: Negative Values

Mrs. Brooks decided to open a restaurant. She started a corporation six months before the restaurant opened and deposited $50,000 in the corporation's bank account. She kept records of the amount of cash the corporation had for $1\frac{1}{2}$ years. In her records she called the month the restaurant opened "0 month" and gave earlier months negative numbers. Study her records and then answer the questions on the next page.

Mrs. Brooks's Restaurant, Inc.

Month	Available Cash ($)
−6	50,000
−5	50,200
−4	50,400
−3	50,600
−2	45,700
−1	21,300
0	−15,000
+1	−35,000
+2	−33,700
+3	−29,100
+4	−25,600
+5	−20,100
+6	−12,500
+7	−6,700
+8	−1,500
+9	+4,100
+10	+8,800

The chart above shows the available cash at the beginning of each month in Mrs. Brooks's corporation. (All figures are rounded to the nearest hundred dollars.)

372 • Algebra Readiness

 **Meeting Individual Needs**

As you may have done previously, guide kinesthetic learners who need help plotting the ordered pairs on the coordinate grid by having them put a finger at the origin and asking questions about the direction and number of spaces to move. Also do some problems in which a point is given on the grid and the student must write its coordinates. For these, have students start at the origin and move their fingers first sideways, then up or down to the given point. Ask guiding questions such as, "How far did you have to move sideways? Did you move right or left? Why? How far did you move up or down? Why?"

Technology Connection Refer students to the software *GraphPower* from Ventura Educational Systems (Mac, for grades K–8) for practice in selecting appropriate formats. Graph forms available include: pictograph, vertical/horizontal bar graph, line graph, circle graph, and box-and-whisker graph.

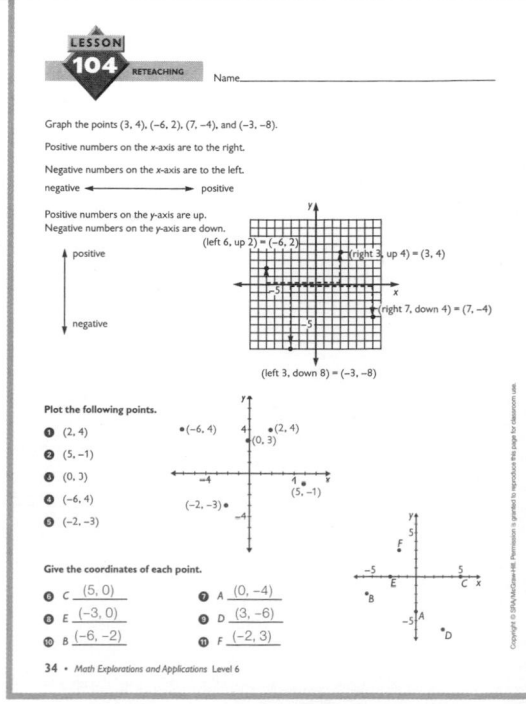

*available separately

Use the chart to answer these questions.

10 At the beginning of which month did the restaurant have the least cash? **+1**

11 In which month did the available cash drop the most? Why do you think this might have happened? **The month from −1 to 0; A great deal of food and supplies had to be bought at this time.**

12 In which month did the available cash increase the most? **the month from +5 to +6**

13 What does it mean for a business to have a negative amount of available cash? **The business owes more money than it has.**

14 How could the business have earned money before the restaurant opened? **The initial deposit could have earned interest, or Mrs. Brooks could have added to the amount.**

15 Mrs. Brooks wanted to take $1000 per month profit from her corporation. **She could take out up to $3000 a month, but she may want to**
a. Could she do so without endangering her business? **build a cash cushion**
b. Could she take $2000 per month? **before taking profits.**

16 What is the greatest amount Mrs. Brooks could take out in profit each month? **around $3000–$4000**

17 Do you think the restaurant will be a successful business? Why? **Yes, since for a $50,000 initial investment, it is making somewhat more than $4000 a month, or about $50,000 a year.**
Graph the data. Then use the graph to answer the next question. **See margin.**

18 If profit is not removed and the pattern continues, how much available cash do you think there is likely to be on the first of the 19th month? on the first of the 24th month? Why? **$50,000; $76,000; If the pattern continues we can make predictions based on that pattern. By graphing the data it is easier to predict a trend.**

Unit 5   Lesson 104 • **373**

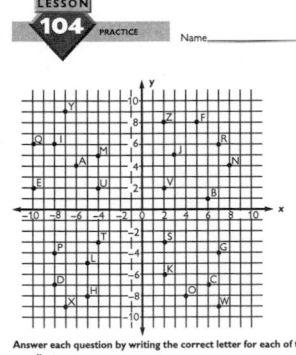

❸ Wrap-Up
5 MINUTES

In Closing Summarize the lesson by asking students to explain the advantages of a business person keeping a chart like the one that Mrs. Brooks kept.

When discussing students' answers to the last four questions about Mrs. Brooks's restaurant, remind students that the trend shown by the data can be seen by some as not being clearly established and that, therefore, decisions and predictions based on the data cannot be made with any assurance. Student responses about how successful the restaurant appears to be now, and will be in the future, will vary. Accept any answers students can justify.

Portfolio Assessment Have students put in their Math Portfolios a description of the advantages and limitations of the kind of record keeping Mrs. Brooks did. Have them include their graphs of the data in her table.

Assessment Criteria

Did the student . . .

✓ correctly determine and graph the ordered pairs, including those that contain coordinates with negative values, that satisfy the function rule
$x \longrightarrow \boxed{\times 3} \longrightarrow y$?

✓ express understanding of the information presented in the table about Mrs. Brooks's restaurant?

✓ express understanding of both the benefits and the limitations of using tables to interpret data and to make predictions?

Homework Assign Practice Master 104 for further practice with graphing functions.

LESSON 105

Student Edition pages 374–377

Practice with Graphing

LESSON PLANNER

Objectives   TEKS 7, 11A
TAAS 2, 11

▶ to provide practice in locating points with positive and negative coordinates on a two-dimensional coordinate system

▶ to help students develop the broad ability to use mathematical common sense

Context of the Lesson   This lesson, the tenth of 24 lessons on functions and graphing, contains the first part of "Diet for a Small Terrier," a three-part Thinking Story.

 **MANIPULATIVES**

crayons or markers (four colors)

graph paper

overhead projector (optional)

Program Resources

Practice Master 105

Enrichment Master 105

For career connections:
  Careers and Math*

For extra practice:
  CD-ROM* Lesson 105

1 Warm-Up 🕐 5 MINUTES

Problem of the Day   Present the following problem to the class: What fraction of the figure is shaded? ($\frac{1}{64} + \frac{4}{64} + \frac{16}{64} = \frac{21}{64}$)

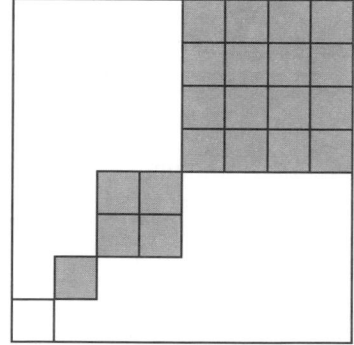

Problem-Solving Strategies   Ask students who have solved the Problem of the Day to share how they solved it and any strategies they used.

MIXED **PRACTICE**

LESSON 105

GAME

Practice with Graphing

 **COOPERATIVE LEARNING**

Get the Point Game

Players:	Two
Materials:	Graph paper, crayons or markers (four colors), a black pen or pencil
Object:	To find the coordinates of the secret point
Math Focus:	Locating and plotting coordinates on a graph, intuitive geometry, and mathematical reasoning

RULES

1. Decide what size "playing field" will be used. Each player makes a playing field by drawing coordinate axes on a sheet of graph paper.

2. The first player chooses a secret point with integer coordinates and draws two straight lines through the point, cutting in half each square through which they pass. (See the Sample Game.) This separates the playing field into four parts. The first player then colors each of the four parts a different color.

3. Without seeing what the first player has done, the second player guesses a point by calling out its coordinates. Then the first player tells the color of that point. A point on one of the two dividing lines is described as black.

4. The second player keeps guessing points until he or she gets the secret point.

5. Players switch roles.

374 · Algebra Readiness

 **Art Connection**   Invite students to create a design. They can figure out different coordinate pairs to connect in order to make pictures or different shapes on graph paper. Students can color in their designs, or they can exchange lists of coordinate pairs with partners who have to connect the points to complete the "coordinate art."

374 Algebra Readiness

*available separately

SAMPLE GAME

Lynn and Keith decided on a playing field that goes from −5 to 5 on each axis. Lynn was the first player. She chose (3, −2) as the secret point, drew two lines, and colored the sections as shown.

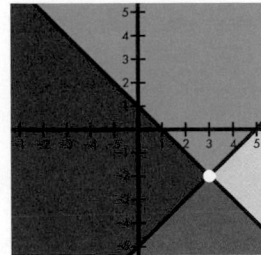

Keith made a playing field just like Lynn's but without the lines and colors. On his field Keith kept a record of each move.

1. Keith said, "(0, 0)." Lynn said, "Red." Keith circled the point (0, 0) in red.

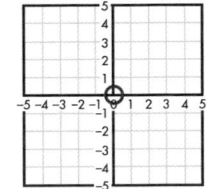

2. Keith said, "(1, 1)." Lynn said, "Green." Keith circled the point (1, 1) in green. He knew there was a line between (0, 0) and (1, 1).

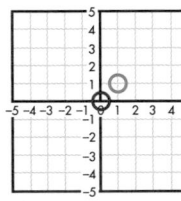

3. Keith said, "(4, −2)." Lynn said, "Yellow." Keith circled that point in yellow. Now Keith knows that the line lies between (1, 1) and (4, −2).

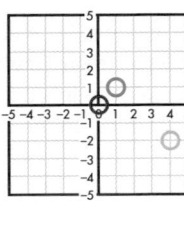

4. Keith said, "(2, 0)." Lynn said, "Green." Keith circled that point in green. Now Keith knows that the line is between (2, 0) and (4, −2).

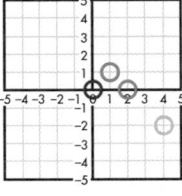

5. Keith said, "(4, −1)." Lynn said, "Black." Keith circled that point in black. Now Keith knows where the line is. He draws it to find the point where the two lines intersect.

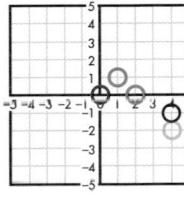

6. Keith said, "(3, −2)." Lynn said, "That's the point I chose. You got it in six moves."

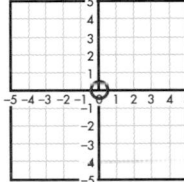

Unit 5   Lesson 105 • **375**

Literature Connection Have students read "Presidential Puzzle" in *Math Mini–Mysteries* by Sandra Markle. Ask them to complete the activity to find the facial features of Mount Rushmore indicated by the graph overlay.

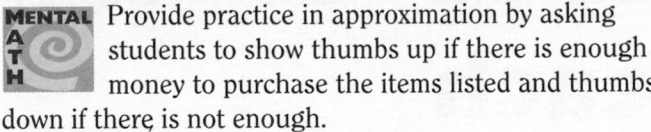

Provide practice in approximation by asking students to show thumbs up if there is enough money to purchase the items listed and thumbs down if there is not enough.

a. I have $30.00. I have a 15% discount coupon on a $35.00 lamp. (thumbs up)

b. I have $75.00. My car needs a tune-up for $35.00, a battery for $25.00, and wiper blades for $10.50, and there is 5% tax. (thumbs up)

c. I have $25.00. I want two new books at $12.50 each plus 5% tax. (thumbs down)

d. I have $88.00. Can I buy a stereo for $95.00 with 15% off? (thumbs up)

e. I have $500.00. Is that enough for two round-trip tickets to Salt Lake City at $228.00 for each person plus 6% tax? (thumbs up)

f. My gas tank holds 20 gallons, and it is half full. Gas is $1.50 a gallon. Can I fill it up for $20.00? (thumbs up)

❷ Teach

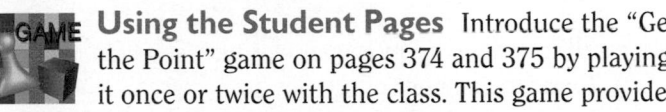

Using the Student Pages Introduce the "Get the Point" game on pages 374 and 375 by playing it once or twice with the class. This game provides practice in coordinate graphing and deductive reasoning. Choose a point, draw the lines, and color (using four colors of **crayons** or **markers**) the regions on a sheet of **graph paper** so that none of the students can see. Draw another grid on the chalkboard or on an **overhead projector**. Then have students try to guess the point by naming one point at a time so that you can show on the grid what is known after each guess. Be sure students understand the game. Then have them play it in pairs or in small groups, taking turns acting as the referee. A copy of this game can also be found on page 32 of the Home Connections Blackline Masters.

◆ **LESSON 105** Practice with Graphing

Teach

 **Using the Thinking Story** In this first part of "Diet for a Small Terrier," the focus is on determining which of the various figures obtained from published data is most appropriate to a particular situation. The problem Marcus faces is to figure out how much to feed a dog of a specific weight, given different information from different sources.

Answers to Thinking Story Questions:

1. For Tiny's desired weight of 5 kilograms: according to the graph 500 calories per day; according to the rule for active dogs, 550 calories per day; and according to the rule for inactive dogs, 400 calories per day.

2. If Portia sees that Tiny gets plenty of exercise, 550 calories (the amount for an active dog) should be right.

3. The graph is for an "average," or moderately active, dog. The other figures are for very active and very inactive dogs. An average dog will probably have a medium level of activity and so will need a number of calories between the extremes.

4. About 90 calories (accept any answer between 80 and 100). To get the number of calories per kilogram, students can read from the graph—for example, how many calories per day a 10-kilogram dog needs (about 900)—and then divide by the weight. The answer varies somewhat with the weight of the dog, as is shown by the curvature of the graph. Small dogs need more calories per kilogram; larger dogs need fewer.

Though the rules Marcus found in the book on dog care do not take this into account, they can be remembered easily, while the graph is harder to remember. You might wish to discuss the conflict between convenience and accuracy that often comes up when presenting data. It could be helpful to ask students how data for active and inactive dogs could be included on the graph (by having three different lines on the same graph).

Marcus tells his father that he is in trouble—he's got three different answers to his problem, and he doesn't know which is most appropriate. Have students predict in their Math Journals what Marcus's father will tell him.

◆ **LESSON 105** Practice with Graphing

THINKING STORY

Diet for a Small Terrier

Part 1

The telephone rang at Breezy's training school for dogs. "Mr. Breezy," said the caller. "I have a toy terrier named Tiny. I'd like to send him to you."

"Sorry," said Mr. Breezy. "We have a hard enough time training real dogs. I don't think we could train a toy."

"Tiny is a very real dog—toy terrier is his breed," said the caller. "Besides, I don't want you to teach Tiny anything. Tiny used to be a trim little dog who weighed 5 kilograms. Now he has grown lazy and fat. I'd like to send him to you for exercise and diet. I want him to get back his youthful figure."

"Dog reducing isn't exactly my line," said Mr. Breezy. "But I'll give it a try. Bring Tiny over."

When Tiny came, the first thing Mr. Breezy did was weigh him. Tiny weighed almost exactly 7 kilograms "It shouldn't be too hard to get a dog to lose 2 kilograms," said Mr. Breezy. "Portia, your job will be to see that Tiny gets plenty of exercise every day. Marcus, your job will be to see that Tiny gets just the right amount to eat each day."

"How much is that?" Marcus asked.

376 • Algebra Readiness

Health Connection
Ask students to find out what their own calorie intake should be. Challenge them to create a line graph showing information about calorie intake, such as any correlation between calorie intake and age or calorie intake and weight.

RETEACHING

As needed, use a grid on the chalkboard or overhead projector to review with students how to locate points in all four quadrants of the coordinate grid. Provide practice doing so, with one student naming a point and another finding and labeling it. Then assign pairs to play "Get the Point," using a smaller playing field before progressing to a larger one.

"You'll have to look that up in a book," said Mr. Breezy. "Since we want Tiny to weigh 5 kilograms, we should feed him the right number of calories for a 5-kilogram dog."

Marcus checked two different books on dog care. From the first book he learned that very active dogs need about 110 calories a day for each kilogram of weight. Inactive dogs—dogs that lie around most of the time—need only about 80 calories a day for each kilogram. In the second book Marcus found the graph shown on this page. It told how many calories a day an average dog needs, depending on how much it weighs.

Recommended Number of Calories per Day

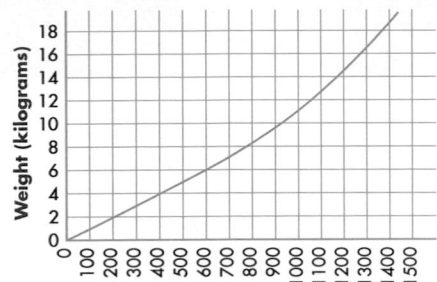

Recommended Number of Calories per Day

"I'm in trouble, Dad," Marcus said. "I have three different answers to how many calories a day Tiny should eat."

. . . to be continued

Work in groups. Discuss your answers and how you figured them out. Then compare your answers with those of other groups. Answers are in margin.

❶ What are the three answers that Marcus got?

❷ Which do you think is the best answer? Why?

❸ How could you explain the fact that the graph gives an answer that is between the other two answers?

❹ According to the graph, about how many calories a day should a dog eat for each kilogram of its weight? Is it the same for dogs of all sizes?

Unit 5   Lesson 105 • **377**

❸ Wrap-Up

In Closing Summarize the lesson by asking students to explain, as if to a student who has never read a line graph, how to interpret the graph on page 377. Then have them summarize the information on the graph.

Informal Assessment Circulate through the room as students play the "Get the Point" game. Make sure that they are playing correctly and that guessers are making good use of the information they are given.

Assessment Criteria

Did the student . . .

✓ demonstrate that he or she knows how to play the game?

✓ demonstrate understanding of how to locate points with positive and negative coordinates on a coordinate grid?

✓ participate meaningfully in the Thinking Story discussion?

Homework Have students discuss with a family member the problem Marcus faces in the Thinking Story. Ask them to share with classmates any unusual or perceptive views gathered at home.

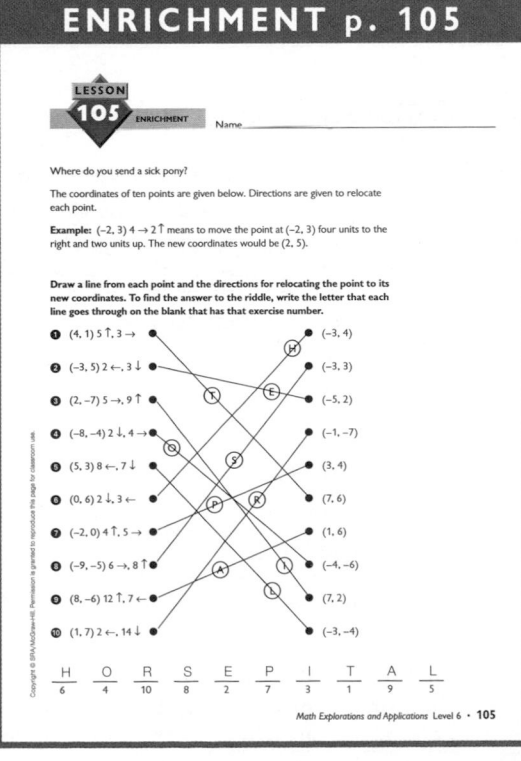

Graphing Composite Functions

LESSON PLANNER

Objectives

▶ to demonstrate how to find ordered pairs for composite function rules (for example, given the rule

$x \longrightarrow (×3) \longrightarrow n \longrightarrow (+4) \longrightarrow y$, if x is 3, what is y?)

▶ to show that graphs of composite linear functions are straight lines

▶ to provide more practice in graphing

Context of the Lesson This is the 11th of 24 lessons on functions and graphing.

 **MANIPULATIVES**
graph paper

Program Resources
Practice Master 106
Enrichment Master 106
The Cruncher*
For extra practice:
CD-ROM* Lesson 106

 **1 Warp-Up**

Problem of the Day Present the following problem: James has twice as much money as Frank, but $2 less than Valerie. All together, they have $27. How much money does each have? (James, $10; Frank, $5; Valerie, $12)

Problem-Solving Strategies Ask students who have solved the Problem of the Day to share how they solved it and any strategies they used.

MENTAL MATH Have students solve for y in the function

$x \longrightarrow (×2) \longrightarrow n \longrightarrow (+2) \longrightarrow y$ if:

a. x is 3 (8) **b.** x is 2 (6)

c. x is 9 (20) **d.** x is 4 (10)

SPECIAL NEEDS **Meeting Individual Needs**
You may need to provide additional practice and teaching for students who still struggle with operations involving negative numbers or plotting points on a coordinate grid.

378 Algebra Readiness

Graphing Composite Functions

 **ALGEBRA READINESS**

Sometimes a function can involve more than one operation. In this lesson you'll learn about using rules with more than one step.

We call a function a **composite function** if two (or more) rules are put together to make its rule.

Example: $x \longrightarrow (×2) \longrightarrow n \longrightarrow (+5) \longrightarrow y$

This composite rule says to first multiply the number x by 2 and then add 5 to the result to get y.

Suppose you start with 3. $3 \longrightarrow (×2) \longrightarrow n \longrightarrow (+5) \longrightarrow y$

$3 × 2$ is 6. So n is 6. $3 \longrightarrow (×2) \longrightarrow 6 \longrightarrow (+5) \longrightarrow y$

$6 + 5 = 11$. So y is 11. $3 \longrightarrow (×2) \longrightarrow 6 \longrightarrow (+5) \longrightarrow 11$

If 3 is the first number, then 11 is the last number. The ordered pair (3, 11) satisfies the rule.

Use a computer or other means to draw the tables below, and complete the tables so that each ordered pair satisfies the given rule.

$x \longrightarrow (×2) \longrightarrow n \longrightarrow (−5) \longrightarrow y$ $x \longrightarrow (×\frac{1}{2}) \longrightarrow n \longrightarrow (+3) \longrightarrow y$

1

x	3	2	0	−2	−3	−5
y	11	■	■	■	■	■

9 5 1 −1 −5

2

x	0	2	5	−2	−4	−5
y	■	■	■	■	■	■

3 4 $5\frac{1}{2}$ 2 1 $\frac{1}{2}$

Graph each set of ordered pairs in problems 1 and 2.

◆ What do you think is true of the graph of each of these functions? **They are both straight lines.**

378 · Algebra Readiness

Why teach it at this time?

Later in this unit students will learn how to find the equation for a composite linear function using a set of ordered pairs or a graph of the function. This lesson introduces them to a procedure for evaluating and graphing composite functions and to the idea that the numbers in a function have specific meanings.

 **LITERATURE CONNECTION**

Literature Connection Have students read *Anno's Magic Seed*s by Mitsumasa Anno. Ask them to graph the number of seeds planted each year after Jack's discovery.

RETEACHING

Extensive reteaching suggestions are given in the next lesson. You may wish to postpone reteaching until then. The Enrichment Master for this lesson could be assigned at this time.

---

*available separately

❻ The steepness will be the same, but the first function crosses the y-axis at 1 and the second crosses at 3.

Answer the following. **Be sure to check students' graphs carefully.**

❸ On one sheet of graph paper, graph each of the following function rules. After the first two or three, you should be able to guess where the next graph will be.

a. $x \xrightarrow{\times 2} n \xrightarrow{+1} y$ **b.** $x \xrightarrow{\times 2} n \xrightarrow{+3} y$

c. $x \xrightarrow{\times 2} n \xrightarrow{+5} y$ **d.** $x \xrightarrow{\times 2} n \xrightarrow{+7} y$

e. $x \xrightarrow{\times 2} n \xrightarrow{-1} y$ **f.** $x \xrightarrow{\times 2} n \xrightarrow{-3} y$

❹ On one sheet of graph paper, graph each of the following function rules. After the first two or three, you should be able to guess where the next graph will be.

a. $x \xrightarrow{\times \frac{1}{4}} n \xrightarrow{+3} y$ **b.** $x \xrightarrow{\times \frac{1}{2}} n \xrightarrow{+3} y$

c. $x \xrightarrow{\times 1} n \xrightarrow{+3} y$ **d.** $x \xrightarrow{\times 2} n \xrightarrow{+3} y$

e. $x \xrightarrow{\times 4} n \xrightarrow{+3} y$ **f.** $x \xrightarrow{\times 5} n \xrightarrow{+3} y$

❺ Explain what the graph of the function rule $x \xrightarrow{\times 2} n \xrightarrow{+2} y$ will look like compared to the graphs in problem 3.

a line between the graphs of problems 3a and 3b.

❻ Explain the difference between the graphs of the function rules

$x \xrightarrow{\times 3} n \xrightarrow{+1} y$ and $x \xrightarrow{\times 3} n \xrightarrow{+3} y$.

❼ Explain what the graph of the function rule $x \xrightarrow{\times 3} n \xrightarrow{+3} y$ will look like compared to the graphs in problem 4.

a line between the graphs of problems 4d and 4e.

❽ Explain the difference between the graphs of the function rules

$x \xrightarrow{\times 1} n \xrightarrow{+5} y$ and $x \xrightarrow{\times 2} n \xrightarrow{+5} y$.

The first function will be less steep than the second function.

Unit 5 Lesson 106 • **379**

PRACTICE p. 106

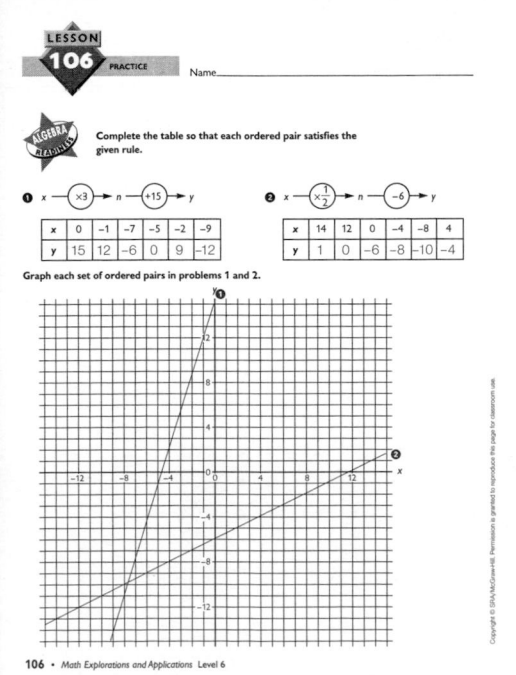

ENRICHMENT p. 106

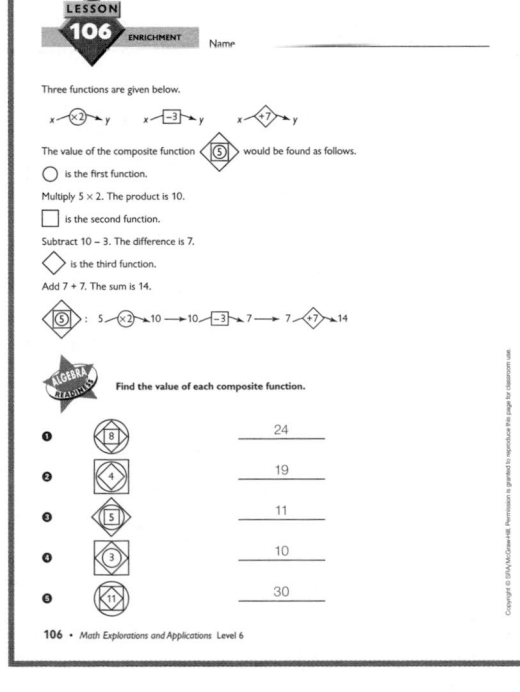

---

❷ Teach

Using the Student Pages Discuss the top of page 378. On the chalkboard, write a rule such as

$x \xrightarrow{\times 3} n \xrightarrow{+2} y$. Ask

students to tell what the rule says to do. (Multiply by 3, then add 2.) Then ask, "If x is 2, what is y?" (8) Repeat the problem with other values for x. Then repeat it with the composite function on page 378. Point out that solutions for the variables x and y are expressed as an ordered pair, and that one ordered pair for the function on the chalkboard is (2, 8).

Have students work independently on the rest of pages 378 and 379. Students can use a blank **Cruncher*** spreadsheet or **graph paper** to create tables and to graph the function rules. Tell students that if all the points on their graph do not fall on a straight line, they should check the arithmetic for those points and then check the position of the points. Note that all the composite functions have straight-line graphs. Students should recognize that the first number in each function affects the graph's steepness and the second number determines where the graph will cross the y-axis.

❸ Wrap-Up ⏱ 5 MINUTES

In Closing Summarize the lesson by asking students to tell what all the graphs on these pages have in common.

Performance Assessment Observe students as they work on completing the tables and graphing the functions. Look to see that they are following the rules accurately and that their graphs are straight lines.

Assessment Criteria

Did the student . . .

✓ demonstrate an understanding of the concept of composite functions?

✓ draw correct straight-line graphs for each function?

✓ reach correct conclusions about the effects of changing one number in a function?

Homework Assign Practice Master 106 for further practice with graphing composite functions.

Unit 5 Lesson 106 **379**

Inverse Functions

LESSON PLANNER

Objectives

▶ to review how to use inverse functions to find an *x*-value for a given *y*-value and a given function rule

▶ to provide practice in graphing linear functions

Context of the Lesson This is the 12th of 24 lessons on functions and graphing.

🖐 **MANIPULATIVES** **Program Resources**

graph paper

Number Cubes (0–5 and 5–10)

Reteaching Master

Practice Master 107

Enrichment Master 107

For extra practice:
    CD-ROM* Lesson 107

❶ Warm-Up ⏱ 5 MINUTES

Problem of the Day Present the following problem to the class: Fred entered a spelling contest. After the first round, half the spellers who entered had been eliminated. After the second round, two-thirds of the remaining spellers had been eliminated. In the third round, five more spellers were out. Fred was the spelling champion! How many spellers entered the contest? (36)

Problem-Solving Strategies Ask students who have solved the Problem of the Day to share how they solved it and any strategies they used.

MENTAL MATH Have students play variations of the "Roll a Problem" game, using the rules on pages 46 and 63. Roll the cubes and play along with the class, writing your problem on the board. Ask students to use approximation, if possible, to decide whether their score is greater than yours. Use these forms.

Copies of these games (both multiplication and division) can be found on pages 11 and 12 in the Home Connections Blackline Masters.

Inverse Functions

You have learned how to find a value for *y* given a function rule and a value for *x*. In this lesson you'll review how to use **inverse operations** to find *x* when a value for *y* is given.

Suppose you have a function rule and you know a value for *y*. How can you find the corresponding value for *x*?

Example:

For this function rule, if *y* is 29, what is *x*?

First find *n* by using the inverse operation of −9.

Use +9.

29 + 9 = 38

So *n* is 38.

Find *x* by using the inverse operation of ×4.

Use ÷ 4.

38 ÷ 4 = 9.5

So *x* is 9.5.

Let's check. If we use 9.5 for *x*, do we get 29 for *y*?

9.5 × 4 = 38, and 38 − 9 = 29. That checks.

❶ Use a computer or other means to create the table below, and complete the table for the function rule *x* ⟶ ×4 ⟶ *n* ⟶ −9 ⟶ *y*. Remember, when *x* is given, work the usual way. When *y* is given, work backward—undo each step in reverse order.

x	9.5	0.5	4	5	3	3	$2\frac{1}{2}$	$2\frac{3}{4}$	$2\frac{1}{4}$	$2\frac{13}{16}$
y	29	−7	7	11	3	3	1	2	0	$2\frac{1}{4}$

RETEACHING p. 35

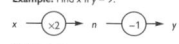

⭐ **SPECIAL NEEDS** **Meeting Individual Needs**

Students who have difficulty finding *y*-values because they lose track of what *n* is may have more success if they include an extra column or row when they copy a table. In this middle row they can write the values for *n* as they compute them. This strategy might simplify the procedure. Encourage these students to omit this middle row as soon as they think they are comfortable without it.

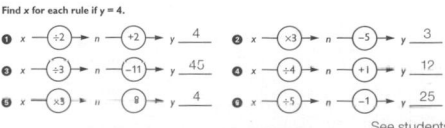

Use a computer or other means to draw the tables below, and complete each table for the given function rule. Then graph the functions.

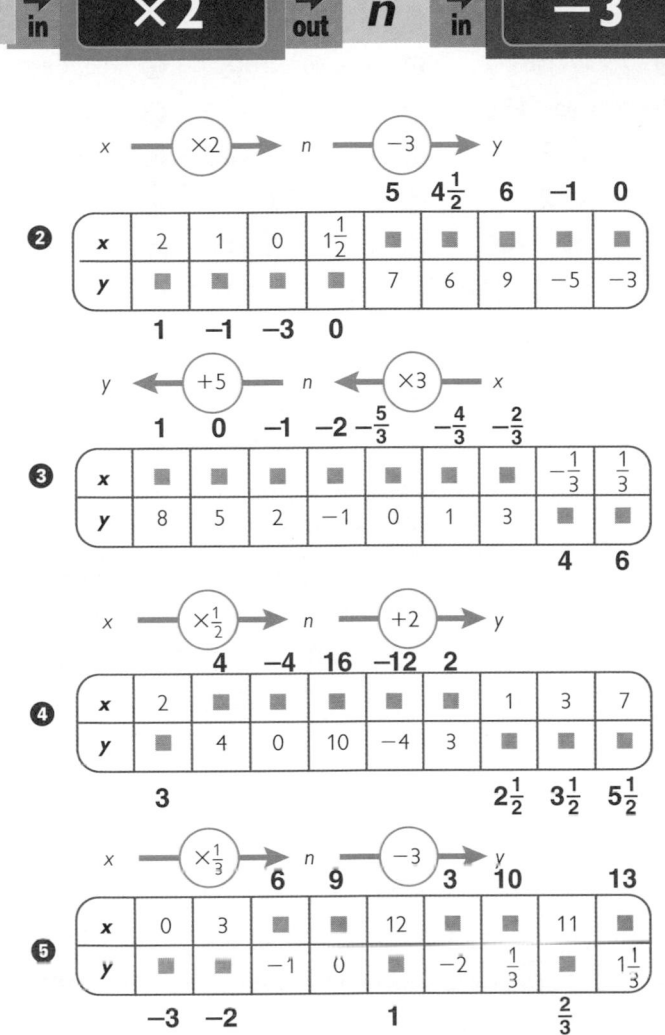

x →in ×2 →out n →in −3 →out y

2 x —(×2)→ n —(−3)→ y

				5	4½	6	−1	0
x	2	1	0	1½	■	■	■	■	■
y	■	■	■	■	7	6	9	−5	−3

1 −1 −3 0

3 y ←(+5)— n ←(×3)— x

1 0 −1 −2 −5/3 −4/3 −2/3

							−1/3	1/3
x	■	■	■	■	■	■	■	■	■
y	8	5	2	−1	0	1	3	■	■

4 6

4 x —(×½)→ n —(+2)→ y

4 −4 16 −12 2

							1	3	7
x	2	■	■	■	■	■	1	3	7
y	■	4	0	10	−4	3	■	■	■

3 2½ 3½ 5½

5 x —(×⅓)→ n —(−3)→ y

6 9 3 10 13

							11	
x	0	3	■	■	12	■	■	11	■
y	■	■	−1	0	■	−2	1/3	■	1⅓

−3 −2 1 2/3

Unit 5 Lesson 107 • **381**

---

❷ Teach

Using the Student Pages Emphasize that we can get from any y-value to an x-value by undoing the actions of a function rule in reverse order. Practice this with the rule on page 380 until all students understand. Then have them do the rest of problem 1 by completing the table. Note that in problem 1 the ordered pair (3, 3) is repeated in the table. This gives students the chance to work both ways, to find x when given y and to find y when given x.

A gift-wrapping analogy may help students work with inverse operations. Go over the steps for wrapping a gift. To unwrap the gift, we undo the steps in reverse order, just as with function rules.

Have students do problems 2–5 on page 381 individually. Have **graph paper** available. The graphs provide a self-checking device: if a point is not on the same straight line as the other points of that function, there is presumably an error.

❸ Wrap-Up

In Closing To summarize the lesson, ask students to give an example of an inverse function.

Informal Assessment Circulate through the room, observing students as they work on the tables on page 381. Ask students to explain what they do to complete them and to describe how they are making their graphs of the functions.

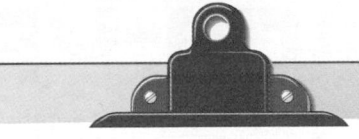

Assessment Criteria

Did the student . . .

✓ demonstrate understanding of how to undo operations to solve inverse functions?

✓ complete the function tables correctly by solving for either x or y?

✓ correctly graph the functions?

Homework Have students make up inverse tables for classmates to complete and then graph at home.

Unit 5 Lesson 107 **381**

LESSON 108 Keeping Sharp

Student Edition pages 382–385

Keeping Sharp

Think. Work quickly. Watch the signs.

❶ 30 + 40 **70**	❷ 40 − 30 **10**	❸ 400 + 300 **700**
❹ 400 − 300 **100**	❺ 3 + 4 **7**	❻ 4 − 3 **1**
❼ 3 × 4 **12**	❽ 30 × 40 **1200**	❾ 300 × 400 **120,000**
❿ 7 × 8 **56**	⓫ 70 × 80 **5600**	⓬ 700 × 800 **560,000**
⓭ 70 + 80 **150**	⓮ 7 + 8 **15**	⓯ 700 + 800 **1500**
⓰ 8 − 7 **1**	⓱ 800 − 700 **100**	⓲ 8 + 6 **14**
⓳ 8 − 6 **2**	⓴ 8 × 6 **48**	㉑ 80 − 60 **20**
㉒ 80 + 60 **140**	㉓ 80 × 60 **4800**	㉔ 800 × 600 **480,000**
㉕ 800 − 600 **200**	㉖ 800 + 600 **1400**	㉗ 9 × 7 **63**
㉘ 900 × 700 **630,000**	㉙ 900 + 700 **1600**	㉚ 90 + 70 **160**
㉛ 17 − 8 **9**	㉜ 170 − 80 **90**	㉝ 1700 − 800 **900**
㉞ 7 + 5 **12**	㉟ 70 + 50 **120**	㊱ 500 + 700 **1200**

Solve each chain calculation from left to right, unless you see a faster (and correct) way to get the answer. For example, to do $7 \times 3 + 5 \times 6$, multiply 7×3 (to get 21), add 5 (to get 26), and multiply by 6 (to get 156). But to do $11 \times 9 \times 7 \times 5 \times 3 \times 1 \times 0$, you should see that the answer must be 0.

㊲ $3 + 4 \times 7 - 9 \div 8 + 5 \times 7$ **70**

㊳ $9 \times 8 \times 7 \times 6 \times 5 \times 4 \times 3 \times 2 \times 1 \times 0$ **0**

㊴ $10 + 9 + 8 + 7 + 6 + 5 + 4 + 3 + 2 + 1$ **55**

㊵ $10 + 10 + 10 + 10 + 10 + 5$ **55**

㊶ $10 + 9 + 1 + 8 + 2 + 7 + 3 + 6 + 4 + 5$ **55**

㊷ What is the sum of the whole numbers from 1 through 10? **55**

㊸ $20 + 20 + 20 + 20 + 20 + 20 + 20 + 20 + 20 + 10$ **190**

㊹ What is the sum of the whole numbers from 1 through 19? **190**

LESSON PLANNER

Objectives

▶ to review arithmetic facts and to encourage students to use shortcuts when making calculations

▶ to provide practice interpreting data presented in a table and using an appropriate graph to display that data

▶ to help students develop the broad ability to use mathematical common sense

Context of the Lesson This lesson, the 13th of 24 lessons covering topics in functions and graphing, also reviews arithmetic and chain calculations. This lesson also contains part 2 of "Diet for a Small Terrier," a three-part Thinking Story.

 MANIPULATIVES
none

Program Resources

Practice Master 108

Enrichment Master 108

The Cruncher*: *Go for Fun Survey*

For career connections:
Careers and Math*

For extra practice:
CD-ROM* Lesson 108
Cumulative Review, page 576

---

❶ Warm-Up ⏱ 5 MINUTES

 **Problem of the Day** Present the following problem to the class: Shawanda bought six limes and three melons at the store. The limes and the melons were priced by the piece. The cashier told her that the total price, without tax, was $3.28. Shawanda instantly knew that the cashier had made an error. How did she know this? (328 is not a multiple of 3.)

Problem-Solving Strategies Ask students who have solved the Problem of the Day to share how they solved it and any strategies they used.

 **MENTAL MATH** Present the following pairs of fractions. Ask students to give a fraction that is greater than one and less than the other. Invite several responses, as there is an unlimited number of answers for each.

(continued on page 383)

Why teach it this way?

Presenting data first in table form and then asking students to select and construct a graph to display that data allows them to see why some graphs are more appropriate than others for showing certain kinds of information.

COOPERATIVE LEARNING You may wish to have students work in groups to compile and graph data about water use. Group members can estimate the gallons together, but each student should make a different graph for purposes of comparison. Then groups can present their graphs and findings.

*available separately

SCIENCE CONNECTION

Solve these problems.

The average American uses 240 gallons of fresh water each day. Here's how the water is used.

45 Using a computer or other means, make and complete a chart like the following.

Use of Water	Approximate Percent of Use	Number of Gallons Used
Drinking and cooking	4	
Washing dishes	6	
Washing clothes	13	
Bathing	18	
Flushing toilet	22	
Outside the home (washing automobiles, watering lawns and flowers, and so on)	37	
Total	100	240

46 How average are you? Using a computer or other means, make a table like the one shown and estimate how much water you use for each item.

Many people believe that water needs to be conserved. That's especially true in parts of the country such as the dry regions in the southwest.

47 What are some ways you can conserve water? Discuss your answer. **Examples: take shorter showers, turn off the faucet in between uses, and so on**

48 It's not easy to measure how much water we use, but perhaps you can think of ways to measure some uses. Discuss ways you might do this.
Answers will vary.

49 If everyone in your class could conserve 2 gallons of water a day, how many gallons would be conserved in one year? **Answer should be 730 gallons × number of students in the class.**

50 Suppose everyone in the country could conserve 2 gallons a day. How many gallons could be conserved in one year? (The U.S. population as of the 1990 census was about 249,000,000.) **181,770,000,000 gallons**

51 Prepare a report to show how typical Americans can conserve 2 gallons of water every day. Show your data in chart or graph form.
Answers will vary.

Unit 5   Lesson 108 • **383**

Mental Math (continued)

a. $\frac{1}{3}$ and $\frac{1}{2}$ ($\frac{5}{12}$, $\frac{4}{9}$, $\frac{3}{8}$ are possible)

b. $\frac{1}{4}$ and $\frac{2}{5}$ ($\frac{3}{10}$, $\frac{11}{40}$, $\frac{7}{20}$ are possible)

c. $\frac{1}{2}$ and $\frac{3}{4}$ ($\frac{5}{8}$, $\frac{2}{3}$, $\frac{7}{12}$ are possible)

d. $\frac{2}{5}$ and $\frac{5}{8}$ ($\frac{1}{2}$, $\frac{9}{20}$, $\frac{3}{5}$ are possible)

e. $\frac{2}{3}$ and $\frac{7}{8}$ ($\frac{3}{4}$, $\frac{5}{6}$, $\frac{17}{24}$ are possible)

❷ Teach

SCIENCE CONNECTION

Using the Student Pages Time students' work on page 382. To do so, write the number of elapsed minutes on the chalkboard and have students write the number they see when they finish. Anyone who finishes in less than five minutes with fewer than three or four wrong answers is doing well. When all students have finished, ask whether any have seen a quick way to do problems 40, 42, and 44, and discuss their answers. (Find pairs that make sums of 10 in problems 40 and 42; make pairs with sums of 20 in problem 44)

Discuss how the data about fresh-water use in the table on page 383 may have been obtained, and have students copy and complete the table. Next ask them to create a table with their estimations of how much water they, or their whole family, use. As needed, show students the approximate size of a gallon. Point out that the graph of the table needs to be comparative, so a line graph, which shows changes over time, is not the best choice. When students have completed their graphs, display a bar graph, circle graph, and picture graph that they have made to show the data. Ask them to tell which kind of graph works best and why.

Students can use **The Cruncher***: *Go for Fun Survey* project to create a table and a pie chart with the information on page 383.

REAL-WORLD CONNECTION

Real-World Connection Invite students to compile data on something else they use on a daily basis, such as electricity or natural gas, to chart and then graph. Have them present their graphs to the class.

◆ **LESSON 108** **Keeping Sharp**

Teach

Using the Thinking Story Part 2 of "Diet for a Small Terrier" focuses on the type and quantity of food Tiny needs and how Marcus can use nutrition information from a box or can of dog food to meet those needs. You may wish to invite students who are dog or cat owners to tell what they know about canned and dry food and about information that appears on labels on both kinds of food.

Answers to Thinking Story Questions:

1. 345 calories for the dry dog food; 129 calories for the canned.

2. Tiny should get 159 grams of dry dog food or 426 grams of canned food in order to obtain 550 calories.

3. Canned dog food is about two-thirds water, which accounts for a lot of weight but no calories. Students cannot be expected to know this fact, of course, but they should be able to figure out that the moistness of canned dog food makes it heavier than dry dog food, so it would have less food value for its weight.

4. The canned dog food: It has a much greater protein-to-carbohydrate ratio than the dry. It has one half as much protein as carbohydrates, whereas the dry dog food has about one third as much protein as carbohydrates.

TEKS 11A   TAAS 11

Ask students to consider the dog food package labels shown in the story and then write in their Math Journals about the kind of information they would like to see on the packaging of foods that people eat. Have them explain how they would use this information.

◆ **LESSON 108** **Keeping Sharp**

THINKING STORY

Diet for a Small Terrier

Part 2

You may want to refer to the first part of this Thinking Story on pages 376–377.

Marcus figured out that the overweight toy terrier, Tiny, should have a diet of 550 calories a day. Then he had to figure out how much dog food that was. In a book on dog care Marcus read that each gram of protein or carbohydrate gives about 4 calories. Each gram of fat gives about 9 calories. Then he studied the labels on two kinds of dog food. Here is what he found:

> **Dry Dog Food**
> Each 100 Grams Contains
> Protein 20 grams
> Carbohydrate 55 grams
> Fat 5 grams

> Canned Dog Food
> Each 100 Grams Contains
> Protein 10 grams
> Carbohydrate 20 grams
> Fat 1 gram

. . . to be continued

Literature Connection Have students read *Math Wiz* by Betsy Duffey to learn how one boy thinks of daily occurrences in mathematical terms.

RETEACHING

For students who have difficulty mentally multiplying multiples of 10 with reasonable speed, review this method: For example, to multiply 30 × 800, think, "3 × 800 is 2400; since 30 is 10 times as great as 3, then 30 × 800 is 10 times as great as 2400, or 24,000."

Work in groups. Discuss your answers and how you figured them out. Then compare your answers with those of other groups.   **Answers are in margin.**

① How many calories are there in 100 grams of the dry dog food? How many in 100 grams of the canned dog food?

② If Tiny is fed only dry dog food, how many grams of it should he get each day? How many grams should he get if he is fed only canned dog food?

③ How could you explain the fact that dry dog food contains so many more calories per 100 grams than canned dog food?

④ If you wanted a dog to get a greater ratio of protein to carbohydrate, which dog food would you feed it, the dry or the canned?

Use the Cumulative Review on page 576 after this lesson.

Unit 5   Lesson 108 • **385**

PRACTICE p. 108

Solve. Work quickly. Watch the signs.

① 50 + 60 =	110	② 40 + 80 =	120
③ 400 − 100 =	300	④ 80 − 30 =	50
⑤ 8 − 3 =	5	⑥ 800 + 300 =	1100
⑦ 800 × 300 =	240,000	⑧ 5 + 6 =	11
⑨ 9 + 6 =	15	⑩ 80 + 60 =	140
⑪ 8 × 6 =	48	⑫ 8 − 6 =	2
⑬ 800 × 600 =	480,000	⑭ 50 × 90 =	4500
⑮ 90 − 50 =	40	⑯ 90 + 50 =	140
⑰ 9 − 5 =	4	⑱ 900 × 500 =	450,000
⑲ 7 × 3 =	21	⑳ 70 × 30 =	2100
㉑ 700 + 300 =	1000	㉒ 7000 − 3000 =	4000
㉓ 30 × 70 =	21,000	㉔ 700 × 3 =	2100
㉕ 110 × 8 =	880	㉖ 1100 + 800 =	1900
㉗ 1100 − 800 =	300	㉘ 80 × 1100 =	88,000

Do each chain calculation from left to right.

㉙ 4 × 5 − 6 ÷ 2 + 6 × 8 =	104
㉚ 5 − 1 × 8 ÷ 4 − 6 × 0 =	0
㉛ 10 + 20 + 30 + 40 + 50 + 60 =	210
㉜ 7 × 8 ÷ 4 × 3 − 10 ÷ 6 =	38
㉝ 32 ÷ 16 + 7 × 8 − 9 × 4 =	252
㉞ 17 − 9 × 6 ÷ 3 + 4 × 8 =	160
㉟ 13 + 12 + 11 + 10 + 9 + 8 + 7 =	70

108 • *Math Explorations and Applications* Level 6

ENRICHMENT p. 108

Chain calculations are done from left to right.

$$6 × 8 ÷ 3 + 2 = 18$$
$$48 ÷ 3 + 2$$
$$16 + 2$$
$$18$$

In the following chain calculations, the operations linking the numbers are missing. Fill in each square with +, −, ×, or ÷ to get the given result. More than one arrangement of signs may be possible. You may use the signs as many times as necessary in each exercise.   Answers will vary. Possible answers are given.

① 10 ×2 5 + 3 = 7	② 8 + 4 ÷ 2 − 1 = 5
③ 5 − 1 + 6 ÷ 2 × 1 = 5	④ 9 + 3 − 4 − 1 = 7
⑤ 7 − 2 + 3 × 1 + 2 = 4	⑥ 6 − 2 × 3 − 4 = 8
⑦ 8 ÷ 2 × 3 + 1 = 12	⑧ 7 + 5 × 4 − 3 ÷ 2 = 3
⑨ 6 − 4 × 3 + 1 = 7	⑩ 5 × 4 ÷ 2 ÷ 3 ÷ 5 = 6
⑪ 9 + 3 × 2 + 1 + 5 = 5	⑫ 9 × 2 ÷ 3 − 5 × 4 = 4

Challenge: Find a second way to fill in the operations for each exercise to get the same result.

① 10 ÷ 2 + 5 − 3 = 7	② 8 ÷ 4 × 2 + 1 = 5
③ 5 − 1 + 6 ÷ 2 − 1 = 5	④ 9 + 3 + 4 × 1 = 7
⑤ 7 + 2 − 3 × 1 + 2 = 4	⑥ 6 + 2 × 3 − 4 = 8
⑦ 8 × 2 − 3 − 1 = 12	⑧ 7 + 5 − 4 − 3 − 2 = 3
⑨ 6 − 4 × 3 + 1 = 7	⑩ 5 − 4 + 2 ÷ 3 ÷ 5 = 6
⑪ 9 × 3 − 2 × 1 − 5 = 5	⑫ 9 − 2 × 3 − 5 + 4 = 4

108 • *Math Explorations and Applications* Level 6

---

③ **Wrap-Up**  5 MINUTES

In Closing   To summarize the lesson, have students explain why the graph they chose effectively represents the data from the table about water use.

Have students keep a record of their completion times and numbers of correct responses for the problems on page 382. Emphasize that their goal should be to improve their performance. They can use this record to compare their progress later in the year on similar pages such as page 401 in Lesson 113.

Assessment Criteria

Did the student . . .

✓ finish page 382 in less than five minutes and get fewer than four incorrect answers?

✓ choose an appropriate graph to display the data in the table about water use?

✓ participate in the discussion of the Thinking Story?

Homework   Have students examine cans and boxes of five different foods to discover the kinds of information shown (and not shown) on the labels. Students can bring in packaging for purposes of analysis and comparison.

Determining Rules from Ordered Pairs

LESSON
109

Determining Rules from Ordered Pairs

ALGEBRA READINESS

x	0	1	2	3	4	5	6	7	8	9	10
y	5	8	11	14	17	20	23	26	29		

Kwan made up the ordered pairs in this table by using a function rule. Using this table, can you find the function rule?

◆ How much does y increase each time x increases by 1? **y increases by 3**

◆ What is x multiplied by to get n? **3**

◆ For each value of x, how much greater is y than n? **5**

◆ What is the function rule? $x \longrightarrow \boxed{\times 3} \longrightarrow n \longrightarrow \boxed{+5} \longrightarrow y$

◆ What values of y do you think should correspond to 9 and 10? **32 and 35**

1 What rule could have produced the ordered pairs in this table?

x	0	1	2	3	4	5	6
y	1	3	5	7	9		

2 What values of y do you think should correspond to 5 and 6? **11 and 13**

3 Look at the table below. What rule could have produced these ordered pairs? $x \longrightarrow \boxed{\times 2} \longrightarrow n \longrightarrow \boxed{-1} \longrightarrow y$

4 What values of y do you think should correspond to 9, 11, and 13?

x	1	3	5	7	9	11	13
y	1	5	9	13	**17**	**21**	**25**

1 $x \longrightarrow \boxed{\times 2} \longrightarrow n \longrightarrow \boxed{+1} \longrightarrow y$

386 · Algebra Readiness

LESSON PLANNER

Objective

▶ to demonstrate how to determine a linear function rule given two or more ordered pairs that satisfy the rule

Context of the Lesson
This is the 14th of 24 lessons on functions and graphing.

 MANIPULATIVES
rulers
tape measures*

Program Resources
Practice Master 109
Enrichment Master 109
For extra practice:
CD-ROM* Lesson 109

❶ Warm-Up ⏱ 5 MINUTES

PROBLEM SOLVING

Problem of the Day Present the following problem to the class: Leslie entered a whistling contest. After the first round, half the contestants had been eliminated. After the next round, half the remaining whistlers were gone. After the third round, $\frac{3}{4}$ of those still in the contest were eliminated. The fourth round eliminated three more whistlers. Leslie was crowned whistling champion at that point. How many whistlers entered the contest? (64)

Problem-Solving Strategies Ask students who have solved the Problem of the Day to share how they solved it and any strategies they used.

MENTAL MATH / MANIPULATIVES
Present several common classroom objects. Start with polygons and add circles to the group. You may wish to draw some on the chalkboard as well. Ask students to estimate the perimeter of an object. Then have a student check the estimates by measuring before you present the next object. Have **tape measures*** and **rulers** available.

❷ Teach

Using the Student Pages You may wish to introduce the "Find the Function Rule" game, which provides practice in deducing function rules, before beginning work on page 386. As students finish, they can play the game with partners or in small groups.

386 Algebra Readiness

Science Connection Ask students to peruse their science texts or even to talk with their science teacher to come up with some real-life function rules, such as those for converting between metric and traditional measurements. Invite students to enter data for the variables to explore applications of those rules.

Literature Connection Have students read *Melisande* by Edith Nesbit. Ask them to determine function rules for the growth of Melisande's hair.

RETEACHING

Aside from continuing any extra help begun in previous lessons, extra teaching and practice is not essential at this time. You may want to assign Enrichment Master 109 at this time.

*available separately

Find the Function Rule Game

C⬡OPERATIVE LEARNING

Players:	Two or more
Materials:	One calculator
Object:	To find the function rule put into the calculator
Math Focus:	Using a calculator, mental arithmetic (addition and multiplication), finding simple function rules, and mathematical reasoning

RULES

1. The lead player chooses an addition or multiplication rule (for example, ×8) and makes the calculator a function machine that uses that rule. To do this for ×8, for example, the lead player pushes 8, ×, 8, = and then pushes 0, =. The display should show ⬚0. (Some calculators work differently.)

2. The second player puts a number into the calculator and sees what comes out. (For example, to put in the number 5, he or she would push 5, =.)

3. The second player tries to figure out the function rule. If the player doesn't get it, he or she tries again. The player puts in another number, sees what comes out, and tries again to figure out the rule.

4. After the second player has found the rule, the lead shifts.

SAMPLE GAME

Luis was the first player. He decided to enter the function rule ×4.

Dory took the calculator. She decided to see what came out when she put in 1. The display read ⬚4. Dory thought: "1 —(?)→ 4." Dory said that the function rule was +3.

Luis said no, so Dory tried again. She put in 10. The display read ⬚40.

Dory figured out that the function rule was ×4. That was correct. It was Dory's turn to be lead player.

Unit 5 Lesson 109 • **387**

Work on the discussion questions on page 386 with the class. Point out that *y* increases by 3 each time *x* increases by 1, suggesting that *x* is being multiplied by 3. Therefore, the rule could be $x \longrightarrow \boxed{\times 3} \longrightarrow n \longrightarrow \boxed{?} \longrightarrow y$, where the *?* is an addition or subtraction rule. Once this is determined, students can decide what the *?* is by choosing any of the ordered pairs. Doing so establishes the rule as

$x \longrightarrow \boxed{\times 3} \longrightarrow n \longrightarrow \boxed{+5} \longrightarrow y.$ Have students do problems 1–4 on their own, giving help as needed.

GAME **Introducing the "Find the Function Rule" Game** Demonstrate the "Find the Function Rule" game by playing several rounds with the class. This game provides practice in finding simple function rules, as well as in mental arithmetic and mathematical reasoning. Play long enough so that all students are familiar with the rules. Then have them play in pairs or in small groups.

❸ Wrap-Up ⏱ 5 MINUTES

In Closing Summarize the lesson by asking students to describe the strategies they used in the "Find the Function Rule" game.

Performance Assessment Present a table with the following ordered pairs: (0, 2), (1, 5), (2, 8) and (3, 11). Ask students to write the function rule for the ordered pairs in the table and to give the *y*-values for *x*-values of 4, 6, and 8.

$(x \longrightarrow \boxed{\times 3} \longrightarrow n \longrightarrow \boxed{+2} \longrightarrow y ; 14, 20, 26)$

PRACTICE p. 109

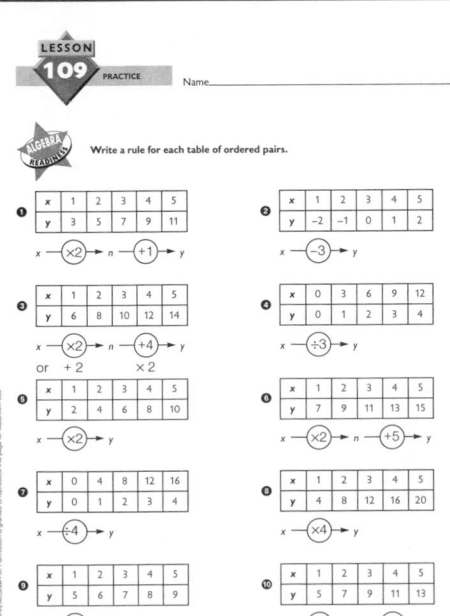

ENRICHMENT p. 109

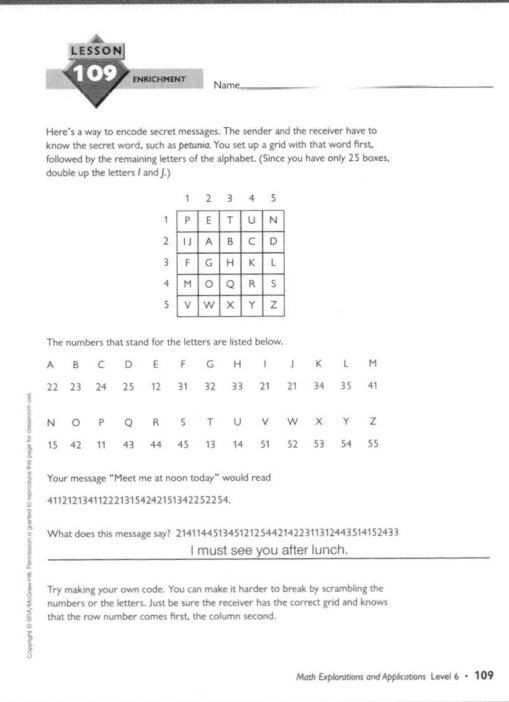

Assessment Criteria

Did the student . . .

✓ demonstrate understanding of how to determine a function rule by examining a table of ordered pairs?

✓ demonstrate ability to use a function rule to complete a table of ordered pairs?

Homework Have students play "Find the Function Rule" with a family member for further practice with determining function rules. A copy of this game can also be found on page 33 of the Home Connections Blackline Masters.

Interpreting Data

LESSON PLANNER

Objectives

▶ to provide an opportunity to interpret, discuss, and make inferences from data

▶ to provide practice in approximation

Context of the Lesson This lesson is another pause in the 24-lesson sequence on functions and graphing. Students will study and interpret a table that provides information about public library systems.

 MANIPULATIVES

Program Resources

Practice Master 110

Enrichment Master 110

For extra practice:
CD-ROM* Lesson 110

① Warp-Up ⏱ 5 MINUTES

 Problem of the Day Present the following problem to students: In its brief life of five days, a big bug ate 160 small bugs. Each day it ate ten more bugs than it did on the previous day. How many bugs did it eat on the first day of its life? (12)

Problem-Solving Strategies Ask students who have solved the Problem of the Day to share how they solved it and any strategies they used.

MENTAL MATH Have students solve these problems. Invite them to explain their strategies.

a.	693 −199 (494)	(add 1	694 −200 494)
b.	4200 ÷ 6 = (700)	c.	80 × 50 = (4000)
d.	90 × 70 = (6300)	e.	4800 ÷ 60 = (80)
f.	341 × 100 = (34,100)	g.	2700 ÷ 30 = (90)
h.	2100 ÷ 3 = (700)	i.	80 × 70 = (5600)
j.	10 × 100 = (1000)	k.	450 ÷ 9 = (50)
l.	9300 −3999 (5301)	(add 1	9301 −4000 5301)
m.	864 +309 (1173)	864 + 300 = 1164 1164 + 9 = 1173	

Interpreting Data

SELECTED LIBRARY SYSTEMS IN THE UNITED STATES

Library Name and Location	Population Served	Number of Branches	Total Number of Books	Annual Circulation	Acquisition Expenditures
Atlanta-Fulton (GA)	714,418	31	1,950,552	2,104,745	$2,446,408
Buffalo & Erie County (NY)	968,584	52	4,000,000	8,500,000	$2,700,000
Chicago (IL)	2,783,726	82	11,463,011	7,156,442	$9,100,000
Detroit (MI)	1,027,954	25	1,680,000	1,267,000	$2,375,000
Miami-Dade (FL)	1,627,866	31	3,300,000	8,000,000	$5,000,000
Free Library of Philadelphia (PA)	1,585,577	53	5,129,439	6,178,951	$5,488,460
St. Louis County (MO)	842,936	17	2,013,472	9,456,114	$3,095,022
San Francisco (CA)	726,700	26	2,008,619	3,363,144	$1,015,855
Tucson-Pima (AZ)	734,247	18	1,138,300	5,200,000	$1,836,730

This chart gives information about selected library systems in the United States.

First study the chart. Then use the information in the chart to answer and discuss the questions below. Use a calculator. Try to support your answers. **Answers will vary. Possible answers are given.**

❶ Which city library is most likely to have a specific book? **Buffalo, since it has the greatest number of books per person.**

❷ Do you think that, on the average, the people in some cities read more than people in other cities? Which city do you think has a population that reads a lot? **yes; Buffalo, since it has the greatest number of books per person**

❸ Which library system do you think is the most efficient? Why? **San Francisco, since it has the lowest operating cost per book circulated**

❹ If you know the population of a city, can you accurately predict how many branches or how many books its library will have? Why or why not? **No, because some cities have greater populations than others but fewer branches and/or fewer books.**

❺ Now use the information in the chart to make up questions. Discuss them with a friend.

ESL **Meeting Individual Needs**

Have ESL students work with native English-speaking students who can help them understand the distinctions among the terms at the top of the columns. For example, without guidance, students might find confusing the distinction between "total number of books" and "annual circulation."

RETEACHING

Students who have difficulty making inferences from the information in the table on page 388 should be assured that each of the questions can have more than one answer and that as long as they can justify their responses, they should feel comfortable. For students having difficulty with page 389, check to see if the trouble is with rounding, applying upper and lower bounds, or moving decimal points. Refer to the Reteaching Masters for Lessons 21 and 36.

*available separately

In each problem two of the answers are obviously wrong and one is correct. Choose the correct answer without using pencil and paper and without using a calculator.

6 4.2 × 7   **(a.)** 29.4   **b.** 36.4   **c.** 22.4

7 6 × 10.5   **a.** 605   **b.** 6.105   **(c.)** 63

8 3.1 × 3.1   **(a.)** 9.61   **b.** 21.1   **c.** 8.91

9 7.5 × 2.2   **a.** 26.25   **(b.)** 16.5   **c.** 12.75

10 1.05 × 25   **(a.)** 26.25   **b.** 23.25   **c.** 265.6

11 32 × 2.15   **a.** 59.3   **(b.)** 68.8   **c.** 164.45

12 1.2 × 1.2   **a.** 0.42   **(b.)** 1.44   **c.** 12.2

13 1.02 × 1.05   **(a.)** 1.071   **b.** 0.152   **c.** 0.701

14 9.8 × 22   **a.** 232.6   **(b.)** 215.6   **c.** 228.9

15 0.19 × 15   **a.** 0.915   **b.** 19.5   **(c.)** 2.85

16 0.05 × 3.5   **a.** 3.505   **b.** 4.05   **(c.)** 0.175

17 0.13 × 0.21   **(a.)** 0.0273   **b.** 2.073   **c.** 0.273

In each problem decide which answer is correct or is the closest approximation.

18 412 ÷ 16   **a.** 4.16   **(b.)** 25.75   **c.** 101.35

19 108 ÷ 25   **(a.)** 4.32   **b.** 3.85   **c.** 10.85

20 5700 ÷ 12   **(a.)** 475   **b.** 4750   **c.** 47.5

21 72.5 ÷ 0.75   **a.** 67.25   **(b.)** 96.67   **c.** 62.75

22 316 ÷ 36.1   **(a.)** 8.75   **b.** 10.15   **c.** 31.6

23 1050 ÷ 2.62   **a.** 800.76   **b.** 100.76   **(c.)** 400.76

24 1.82 ÷ 1.4   **a.** 2.3   **b.** 0.97   **(c.)** 1.3

25 0.073 ÷ 0.071   **a.** 0.97   **b.** 10.83   **(c.)** 1.03

26 882 ÷ 0.63   **a.** 600   **(b.)** 1400   **c.** 2200

Solve these problems.

27 The Wooden Soldier toy store had a sale on giant balloons—200 for $10.00. Ian thought, "Then one balloon will cost 50¢." Was he right?   **no**

28 The Wildlife Club is planning a trip for 20 people to the zoo. Admission costs $4.50. Will admission for the group cost less than $100? **yes**

Unit 5   Lesson 110 • **389**

PRACTICE p. 110

ENRICHMENT p. 110

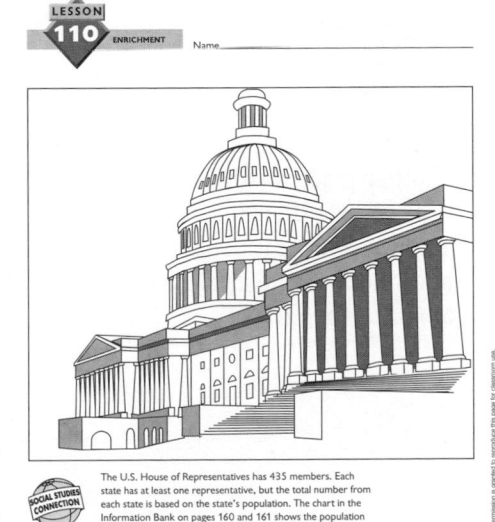

② Teach

Using the Student Pages Go over the table on page 388. As needed, explain what each of the columns means. Demonstrate how to make inferences and draw conclusions from the data. For example, ask students to make some rough comparisons of the Atlanta and Buffalo library systems regarding number of branches per person, number of books, and so on. Ask them to tell which population they think reads more. Continue with similar questions.

COOPERATIVE LEARNING Next discuss problem 1 with students. Then have them form small groups to talk about the other problems and to make up their own questions. Have each group present its reactions and its questions to the class for a discussion.

Have students complete the problems on page 389 on their own.

③ Wrap-Up

In Closing To summarize the lesson, ask students to explain how they would determine the average number of books a person in their city or town reads.

ALTERNATIVE ASSESSMENT **Informal Assessment** Visit with groups as they discuss the questions. Listen to students' reasoning to informally determine how well they are able to make inferences from the data in the table.

Assessment Criteria

Did the student . . .

✓ make reasonable inferences supported by references to data in the table?

✓ correctly answer 19 of the 23 problems on page 389?

Homework Have students make up problems similar to those on page 389, including answer choices, and exchange problems with a classmate.

Unit 5   Lesson 110   **389**

LESSON 111 — Using Formulas

Student Edition pages 390–393

Using Formulas

LESSON 111 — Using Formulas

ALGEBRA READINESS

Function rules are useful for many real-life applications. A formula is a function rule in which the letters stand for specific measurements. You can use any letters in a formula, but usually we use the first letter of the word describing the measurement for which the letter stands.

Some people use the formula $C° \xrightarrow{\times 2} n \xrightarrow{+30} F°$

to approximate a Celsius temperature given a Fahrenheit temperature.

◆ What does C° stand for? **Celsius temperature**

◆ What does F° stand for? **Fahrenheit temperature**

◆ Why don't we use d to stand for degrees Celsius?
because d could also stand for degrees Fahrenheit

Solve these problems.

❶ Use a computer or other means to make a table like the one below, and use the above formula to complete it.

C°	−10	0	10	20	30	40	50	60	70	80
F°	10	30	**50**	**70**	**90**	**110**	**130**	**150**	**170**	**190**

❷ The correct formula for getting exact values of Celsius temperature given a Fahrenheit temperature is $C° \xrightarrow{\times \frac{9}{5}} n \xrightarrow{+32} F°$.
Write and complete a table like the one for problem 1. **See margin.**

❸ Look at the tables for problems 1 and 2.
   a. For what values of F and C are the numbers fairly close? **0, 10, 20**
   b. For which values are they quite different? **70, 80**

Sometimes it is useful to convert from a Fahrenheit temperature to a Celsius temperature. Look at the function rule for converting from Celsius to Fahrenheit, and think about its inverse.

❹ Write a formula for converting from Fahrenheit temperature to Celsius temperature. $F° \xrightarrow{-32} n \xrightarrow{\times \frac{5}{9}} C°$

❺ Use the formula to complete the following table. Round your answers to the nearest degree.

F°	−10	0	10	20	30	40	50	60	70	80
C°	−23	−18	−12	−7	−1	4	10	16	21	27

390 · Algebra Readiness

LESSON PLANNER

Objectives

▶ to provide practice evaluating functions for values of the independent variable

▶ to demonstrate some useful examples of functions

Context of the Lesson This is the 15th of 24 lessons on functions and graphing.

MANIPULATIVES   **Program Resources**
none   Reteaching Master
                   Practice Master 111
                   Enrichment Master 111
                   For extra practice:
                       CD-ROM* Lesson 111

---

❶ Warm-Up

5 MINUTES

Problem of the Day Present the following problem to the class: In two years Manny will be three times as old as he was six years ago. How old is he now? (10)

Problem-Solving Strategies Ask students who have solved the Problem of the Day to share how they solved it and any strategies they used.

MENTAL MATH Have students solve the following equations mentally.

a. $x + 5 = 12$ ($x = 7$)   b. $2 \times x + 1 = 9$ ($x = 4$)

c. $y \times 3 = 24$ ($y = 8$)   d. $n - 15 = 5$ ($n = 20$)

GIFTED & TALENTED **Meeting Individual Needs**
Present the following problem to more advanced students: Andy is driving from his house to Luisa's. If he drives at an average speed of 25 miles per hour, he will be one hour late. If he drives at an average speed of 50 miles per hour, he will be one hour early. How far is Luisa's house from Andy's house? (100 miles) You may wish to suggest that students use a trial-and-error approach to this problem.

REAL-WORLD CONNECTION

Real-World Connection Have students estimate the distance they travel to school or to another place to which they regularly walk or ride their bicycles and the amount of time it usually takes them, and calculate the approximate speed at which they travel.

6 You can tell how far a car or bicycle or other moving object has gone using the formula $t \xrightarrow{\times r} d$ where d is the distance the bicycle has gone, r is the average rate the bicycle went, and t is the time it was going. So, for example, if you ride at an average speed of 10 miles per hour for three hours, you will go 10 × 3 or 30 miles. Copy and complete the following chart for a rate of 10 miles per hour.

time traveled in hours	0	1	2	3	4	10	2.5
distance in miles	0	**10**	**20**	**30**	**40**	**100**	25

7 Mary rides her bicycle at an average rate of 15 miles per hour. Copy and complete the chart showing how far she will go for each of the given times.

time traveled in hours	1	3	5	10	20	100
distance in miles	15	45	75	150	300	1500

8 Do you think Mary could ride at an average speed of 15 miles per hour for 100 hours without stopping? If not, what could the figures in the table mean? **No, she would get tired; the figures in the table show how far Mary could ride if she didn't get tired.**

9 Ms. Smith is driving on an interstate highway at an average speed of 50 miles per hour. Make a chart showing how far she will travel for each hour from 0 through 10 hours. **See chart in margin.**

10 The **perimeter**, or distance, around a rectangle is the sum of all four of its sides. So if the sides of a rectangle are 3 in., 7 in., 3 in., and 7 in., then the perimeter is 20 in.

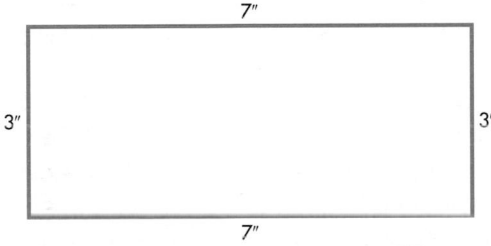

Write a formula for finding the perimeter of a rectangle if one side is 3 inches and another is w inches. 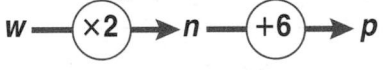 $w \xrightarrow{\times 2} n \xrightarrow{+6} p$

Unit 5   Lesson 111 • **391**

 **Technology Connection** Refer students to the software *The Table Top, Senior Edition* from TERC (Mac, IBM, for grades 4–12) for practice with recording and organizing data, graphing, comparing data, and analyzing trends. Data can be viewed in box plots, histograms, Venn diagrams, scatter plots, and cross tabulations.

 **② Teach**

Using the Student Pages Review with students the difference between degrees Celsius and degrees Fahrenheit. Talk about what would typically be hot, moderate, and cold temperatures in each scale. Have students use the formula presented to approximate today's temperature in degrees Celsius. Then have students work independently or in pairs to complete the tables and problems on pages 390–393.

Discuss students' answers to problem 3. Point out that for normal outdoor temperatures the approximation formula works pretty well. For 50 degrees Fahrenheit it is precisely correct.

Answer to problem 2:

C°	F°
−10	14
0	32
10	50
20	68
30	86
40	104
50	122
60	140
70	158
80	176

Answer to problem 9:

Time (hours)	Distance (miles)
0	0
1	50
2	100
3	150
4	200
5	250
6	300
7	350
8	400
9	450
10	500

◆ LESSON 111 Using Formulas

Teach

Using the Student Pages When discussing student answers to problem 15 on page 392, point out that many telephone companies use what is known as a "step function," and that any fractional values will be different from their answers in problem 11. They should recognize that the "real-life" cost for a call of 2.5 minutes would be $0.30, not $0.25, because callers have to pay for the entire minute, no matter how much of it they spend on the phone. Ask students what a 3.5-minute phone call would cost in real life at $0.10 a minute. ($0.40)

Students may need help with problem 17 on page 393. The function for this situation requires two intermediate steps when written in arrow notation. Encourage students to first express the function in words. For example, they could say "Take the number of hours and subtract 1. Then multiply by $1.50. Finally, add $2.00."

> *There are four important steps that children should follow to learn mathematics and to be willing and able to use it effectively to solve problems of all kinds: (1) derive the mathematics from their own reality, (2) discover and use the power of abstract thought, (3) practice, and (4) apply the mathematics to something that is of interest to them.*
>
> –Stephen S. Willoughby,
> *Mathematics Education for a Changing World*

◆ LESSON 111 Using Formulas

Solve these problems.

11 The cost of a telephone call made on a weekend with a particular long distance company is 10 cents a minute. This can be shown using the formula $t \xrightarrow{\times 10} c$, where t stands for the number of minutes talked and c stands for the cost in cents. Copy and complete the following chart:

time talked in minutes	0	1	2	3	4	10	2.5
cost in cents	0	**10**	**20**	**30**	**40**	**100**	25

12 Do you see any connection between your chart for problem 11 and your chart for problem 6? **They are the same.**

13 On weekdays the same telephone company charges 15 cents a minute. Write a formula for calculating the cost of a telephone call on weekdays. Then copy and complete the table below.

$$t \xrightarrow{\times 15} c$$

time talked in minutes	1	3	5	10	20	100
cost in cents	**15**	**45**	**75**	**150**	**300**	**1500**

In the real world, telephone companies usually have a charge for a minute or any part of a minute. So if the company says they charge 10 cents a minute, they usually mean that as soon as you start talking, you will be charged 10 cents, and as soon as the call goes beyond one minute the charge goes up to 20 cents (but for exactly one minute the charge would still be 10 cents).

14 Would that fact change any of the numbers you have put in your charts for problem 11 or 13?
Yes, in problem 11 the 2.5 minute call would cost 30¢.

15 If the telephone company in problems 11–13 uses this method,

  a. how much would you be charged for a weekend call that lasts 4 minutes, 15 seconds? **50¢**

  b. how much would you be charged for a weekday call that lasts 9 minutes, 53 seconds? **$1.50**

392 • Algebra Readiness

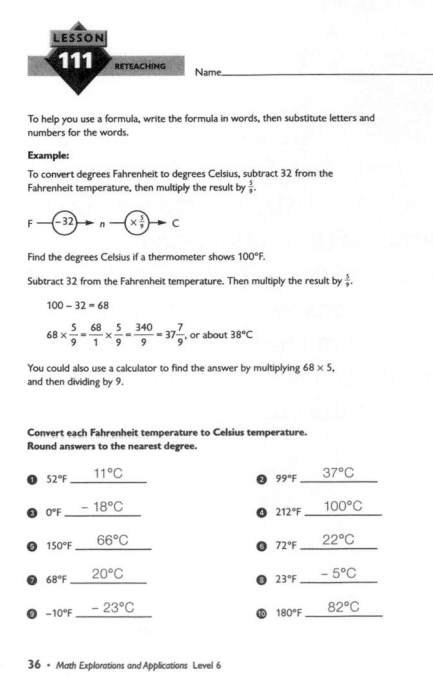

RETEACHING p. 36

LESSON 111 RETEACHING Name_____

To help you use a formula, write the formula in words, then substitute letters and numbers for the words.

Example:

To convert degrees Fahrenheit to degrees Celsius, subtract 32 from the Fahrenheit temperature, then multiply the result by $\frac{5}{9}$.

$$F \xrightarrow{-32} n \xrightarrow{\times \frac{5}{9}} C$$

Find the degrees Celsius if a thermometer shows 100°F.

Subtract 32 from the Fahrenheit temperature. Then multiply the result by $\frac{5}{9}$.

$$100 - 32 = 68$$

$$68 \times \frac{5}{9} = \frac{68}{1} \times \frac{5}{9} = \frac{340}{9} = 37\frac{7}{9}, \text{ or about } 38°C$$

You could also use a calculator to find the answer by multiplying 68×5, and then dividing by 9.

Convert each Fahrenheit temperature to Celsius temperature. Round answers to the nearest degree.

1 52°F ___11°C___	**2** 99°F ___37°C___
3 0°F ___–18°C___	**4** 212°F ___100°C___
5 150°F ___66°C___	**6** 72°F ___22°C___
7 68°F ___20°C___	**8** 23°F ___–5°C___
9 –10°F ___–23°C___	**10** 180°F ___82°C___

36 • *Math Explorations and Applications Level 6*

⑰ h ──(−1)──→ n ──(×1.5)──→ m ──(+2)──→ c

Solve these problems.

⑯ A parking garage charges $2.00 for the first hour a car is parked and $1.50 for each additional hour or part of an hour.

a. How much will the garage charge for a car parked for two hours? **$3.50**

b. How much will the garage charge for a car parked for four hours? **$6.50**

⑰ Write a formula to find the charge for a car parked for h hours if h is a whole number.

⑱ Use the formula to complete the following chart.

hours parked	1	3	5	8	10	14	24
charge	$2.00	$5.00	$8.00	$12.50	$15.50	$21.50	$36.50

⑲ Use the chart to help you answer these questions.

a. How much will the garage charge for a car parked $2\frac{1}{2}$ hours? **$5.00**

b. How much will the garage charge for a car parked 8 hours, 45 minutes? **$14.00**

c. How much more would it cost to park a car for 2 hours, 10 minutes than to park a car for 45 minutes? **$3.00**

⑳ A taxi company charges 30¢ for every $\frac{1}{5}$ mile.

a. How much will it cost to go 1 mile? **$1.50**

b. How much will it cost to go 7 miles? **$10.50**

c. How much will it cost to go $7\frac{2}{5}$ miles? **$11.10**

㉑ Write a formula to find the charge for m miles if m is a whole number.

㉒ Use the formula to complete the following chart.

miles traveled	2	3	5	8	10
cost	$3.00	$4.50	$7.50	$12.00	$15.00

㉑ m ──(×5)──→ n ──(×0.3)──→ c or m ──(×1.5)──→ c where c is the cost in dollars

---

③ **Wrap-Up** ⏱ 5 MINUTES

In Closing To summarize the lesson, ask students to tell how accurate the approximation formula is for converting temperatures and how easy it is to use compared with the true formula.

 **Performance Assessment** Ask students to find the cost of a 5-minute telephone call that costs 12¢ a minute and to write a formula to find the cost of other calls at that rate.

Assessment Criteria

Did the student . . .

✓ correctly complete all the tables?

✓ understand how to express a function rule in arrow notations?

✓ understand the difference between a continuous function and a step function?

Homework Have students use the exact and approximate temperature conversion formulas to express today's high and low temperatures in degrees Celsius and degrees Fahrenheit.

PRACTICE p. 111

LESSON 111 PRACTICE   Name_____

Find the Fahrenheit temperature for each Celsius temperature given. Round answers to the nearest degree.

❶ 0°C __32°F__   ❷ 42°C __108°F__   ❸ 57°C __135°F__

❹ 8°C __46°F__   ❺ 32°C __90°F__   ❻ 65°C __149°F__

Find the Celsius temperature for each Fahrenheit temperature given. Round answers to the nearest degree.

❼ 25°F __−4°C__   ❽ 44°F __7°C__   ❾ 68°F __20°C__

❿ 82°F __28°C__   ⓫ 95°F __35°C__   ⓬ 110°F __43°C__

Find how far a person will have driven at 45 miles per hour for each time given.

⓭ 2 hours __90 miles__   ⓮ 3 hours __135 miles__   ⓯ 4 hours __180 miles__

⓰ 45 minutes __33.75 miles__   ⓱ $1\frac{1}{2}$ hours __67.5 miles__   ⓲ $2\frac{3}{4}$ hours __123.75 miles__

Find the perimeter of each rectangle whose length and width are as follows.

⓳ length 8 cm, width 5 cm _____26 cm_____

⓴ length 18 in., width 12 in. _____60 in._____

㉑ length 9 feet, width $4\frac{1}{2}$ feet _____27 ft_____

㉒ length 27 mm, width 32 mm _____118 mm_____

㉓ length 18 yards, width 14 yards _____64 yd_____

㉔ length 97 m, width 83 m _____360 m_____

ENRICHMENT p. 111

LESSON 111 ENRICHMENT   Name_____

GAME
Players: Two
Materials: Cards (below), two 0-5 and two 5-10 cubes
Object: To be the first player to total 100 points

Rules

1. Copy and cut out the expression cards below. Turn over and mix up the cards. Put them face down in two piles.

2. For each round, both players turn over the top card in a pile.

3. Taking turns, one player chooses and rolls two cubes.

4. The other player decides which is the y value and which is the x value.

5. Each player evaluates the expression on his or her card, using the cube values. Record each player's expression value.

6. Draw a new expression card and play another round. Add each player's new expression value to the previous total.

7. The winner is the first player to total at least 100 points. Game results will vary.

4x − 3	6y − 4	2x + 4y	3x − 2
5y − 4	3x + 2y	3x − 7	5x − 3y
6x − 3y	2y − 1	2x + 3y	3x − 2y

Mid-Unit Review

The Mid-Unit Review pinpoints troublesome skill areas for students, allowing plenty of time for additional practice and reteaching before the unit ends. If students did not do well on the Mid-Unit Review and have completed additional practice, you may want to use the Mid-Unit Review provided on Assessment Blackline Masters pages 44–46.

Using the Student Pages Have students complete problems 1–40 on pages 394–397 on their own. You may wish to read through the graphs and charts for problems 1–7 and 30–33 with the students. You might treat this review as a formal assessment of students' skills and have students complete this review as a timed test. See suggestions for administering timed tests on page 49.

Mid-Unit Review

Solve these problems.

The owner of Fred's Frozen Yogurt Factory surveyed his customers and then made the following table to show which of his five flavors sells the best.

Flavor Sold	Percent of Frozen Yogurt Sold
Vanilla Supreme	40
Chocolate Surprise	30
Strawberry Sundae	18
Just Peachy	7
Going Coconuts	5

❶ To display these results, Fred decided to make a graph. Which kind of graph—bar graph or line graph—best shows the results of the survey? Why?

Miguel took over the Tasty Tortilla company in 1995. In 1997 he made the graph shown below to show how his profits have been increasing since he began running the company.

❷ Approximately what were the profits for each of the years 1995, 1996, and 1997?

$12 million; $13 million; $14 million

In the year 1999 Miguel made the graph shown below.

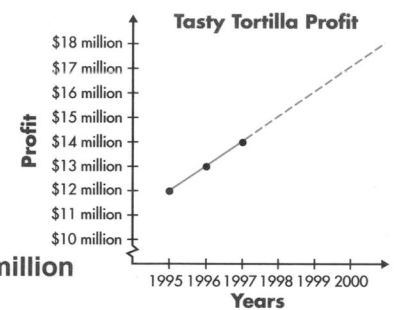

❸ Approximately what were the profits for each of the years 1995 through 1999?

1995: $12 million; 1996: $13 million; 1997: $14 million; 1998: $14 million; 1999: $14 million

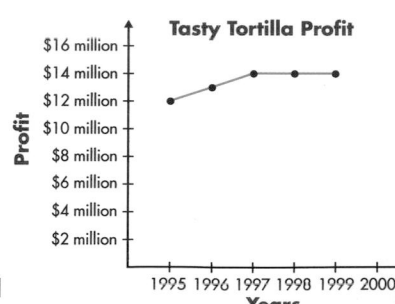

❶ a bar graph, because it compares information. Line graphs show trends or how the data change over time. Accept all reasonably defended answers.

---

7 Anna's business is doing well, but it is not booming. Her profits have remained constant since week 9.

Solve these problems.

4 Miguel is planning to publish one of these graphs to show investors. Which one do you think is more honest? Why? **the second graph, since it shows actual profits, not projections**

5 What do you think the dotted line in the first of Miguel's graphs indicates? **what profits would be if they continued to rise as they did from 1995 to 1997**

The chart below shows the weekly profits Anna made in her small dog-walking business.

Week	Profit	Week	Profit
1	$12.00	9	$25.00
2	$10.00	10	$24.00
3	$10.00	11	$25.00
4	$12.00	12	$28.00
5	$15.00	13	$25.00
6	$18.00	14	$24.00
7	$16.00	15	$20.00
8	$20.00	16	$25.00

6 Make a graph based on the data in Anna's table. **See margin.**

7 Anna says her business is booming. Do you agree? Why or why not?
See above.

On a sheet of graph paper draw coordinate axes so that each axis is at least 12 units long.

8 Plot and label the point (3, 7). **Check student's work.**

9 Plot and label the point (7, 3).

For each of the function rules in problems 10–12, make a set of five ordered pairs of numbers. (Use the number you choose for x as the input and the corresponding value of y as the output.) **Answers will vary. Examples are given.**

10 $x \longrightarrow \boxed{\times 3} \longrightarrow y$
(0, 0), (1, 3), (4, 12)

11 $x \longrightarrow \boxed{+4} \longrightarrow y$
(0, 4), (1, 5), (6, 10)

12 $x \longrightarrow \boxed{-\frac{1}{2}} \longrightarrow y$
$(0, -\frac{1}{2}), (1, \frac{1}{2}), (4\frac{1}{2}, 4)$

Unit 5 Mid-Unit Review • **395**

Answer to problem 6:

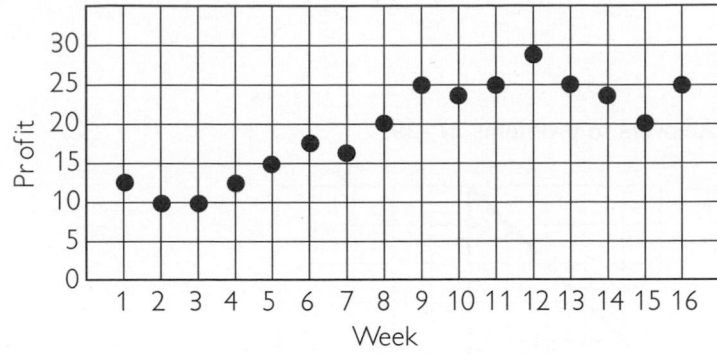

◆ UNIT 5 Mid-Unit Review

Answers to problems 27–29:

27.
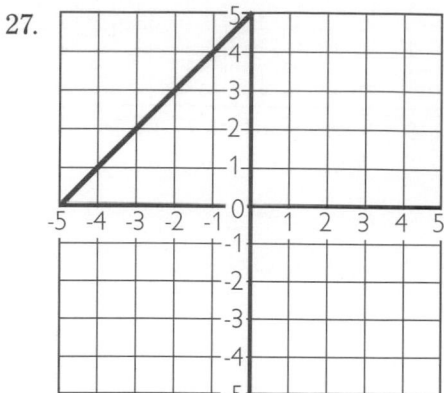

28.
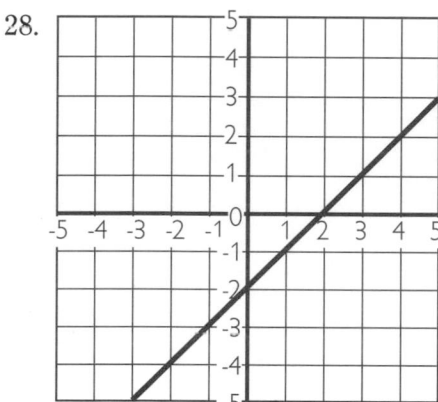

29.
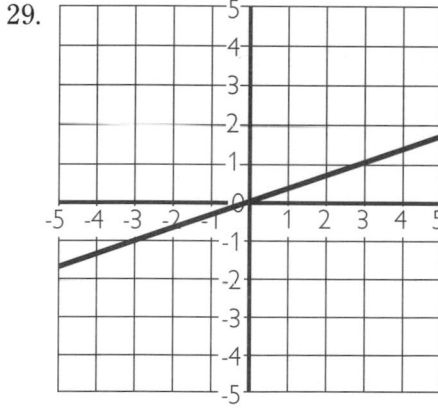

◆ UNIT 5 Mid-Unit Review

For each of the following, tell whether it is most like a rotation, a reflection, or a translation.

13 turning a page in a book **reflection**

14 a hockey puck moving over the ice **translation**

15 twisting the lid on a jar **rotation**

For each of the following figures, tell how many lines of symmetry the figure has.

16   **17**   **18**

2   0   1

Copy each ordered pair. Replace x or y with the correct number so that the pair satisfies the rule $x \xrightarrow{\times 4} y$.

19 (2, y) **8** **20** (0.4, y) **1.6** **21** (2.5, y) **10.0** **22** (1.6, y) **6.4**

23 (x, 20) **5** **24** (x, 2.4) **0.6** **25** (2.2, y) **8.8** **26** (x, 12) **3**

Graph these functions. **See graphs in margin.**

27 $x \xrightarrow{+5} y$ **28** $x \xrightarrow{-2} y$ **29** $x \xrightarrow{\div 3} y$

30 Ed rides his bicycle at an average rate of 16 miles an hour. Copy and complete the chart showing how far he will go for each of the given times.

time traveled in hours	0	1	2.5	4	10
distance in miles	■	■	■	■	■

0   16   40   64   160

31 What rule could have produced the ordered pairs in this table?

x	0	1	2	3	4
y	−1	2	5	8	11

$x \xrightarrow{\times 3} n \xrightarrow{-1} y$

Aaron is exercising to keep fit. He has kept the following record of the number of push-ups he does each day.

Use the table below to answer the following questions.

Day	1	2	3	4	5	6	7	8	9	10	11
Push-ups	11	13	15	17	20	■	■	30	34	37	42

32 Describe the progress Aaron has made. How many push-ups would you predict Aaron might do on the 15th day? **about 55 or 60**

33 About how many push-ups do you think Aaron might have done on days 6 and 7? **about 23 or 24; about 26 or 27**

Copy and complete each table so that each ordered pair satisfies the given rule. Then graph each set of ordered pairs. See graphs in margin.

34

x	0	2	4	2.5	−2
y	**0**	**6**	**12**	**7.5**	**−6**

35 x ──(+4)──> y

x	−1	4	1.5	−2.5	−4
y	**3**	**8**	**5.5**	**1.5**	**0**

36 x ──(×2)──> n ──(+4)──> y

x	0	2	3	−1	−3
y	**4**	**8**	**10**	**2**	**−2**

37 x ──(+3)──> n ──(×2)──> y

x	0	2	4	5	−2
y	**6**	**10**	**14**	**16**	**2**

In each problem two of the three answers are obviously wrong and one is correct. Choose the correct answer using mental arithmetic.

38 1.4×5
a. 0.7
b. **7**
c. 70

39 0.4×30
a. 0.012
b. 0.12
c. **12**

40 3.2×6.5
a. 0.208
b. **20.8**
c. 208

ASSESSMENT p. 44

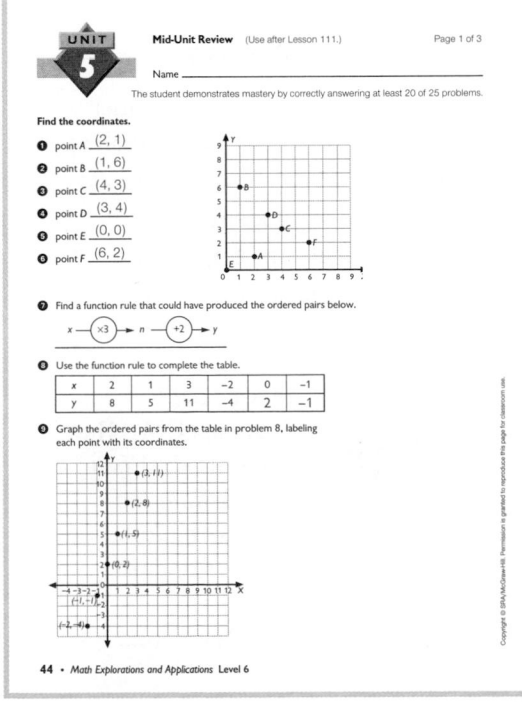

Answers to problems 34–37:

34.
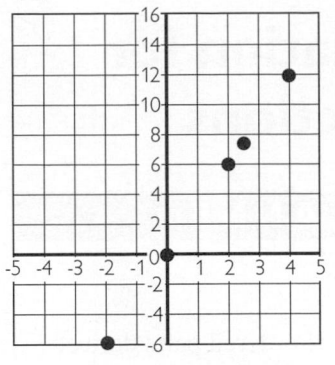

35.
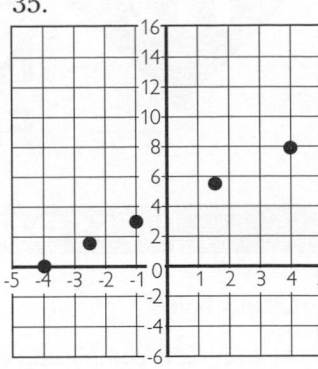

36.
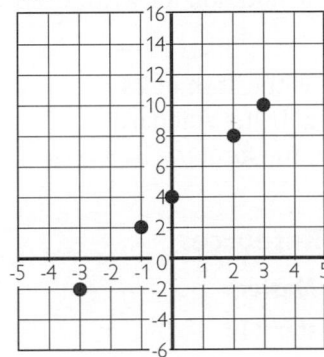

37.
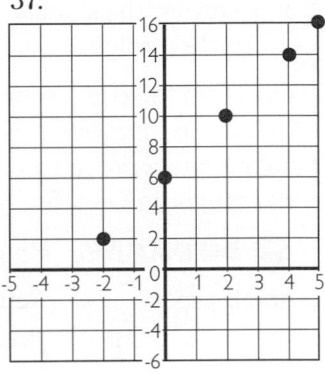

Home Connections You may want to send Home Connections Blackline Masters pages 56–57 home, which provide additional activities families can complete together. These activities apply the skills being presented in this unit.

Portfolio Assessment The Portfolio Assessment task provided on Assessment Blackline Masters page 90 can be used at this time to evaluate students' ability to solve problems involving negative numbers and functions.

Performance Assessment The Performance Assessment Task 1 provided on Assessment Blackline Masters pages 76–77 can be used at this time to evaluate students' proficiency with functions and graphing. You may want to administer this assessment with individual students or in small groups.

Unit Project This would be a good time to assign the "Library Research" project on pages 434 and 435. Students can begin working on the project in cooperative groups in their free time as you work through the unit. This project is a good opportunity for students to apply the concept of collecting and analyzing complicated data to real-world problem solving.

LESSON 112 — Standard Notation for Functions

Student Edition pages 398–399

Standard Notation for Functions

LESSON PLANNER

Objectives

▶ to review completing a table of ordered pairs derived from a function

▶ to review the standard algebraic notation for writing function rules

Context of the Lesson This is the 16th of 24 lessons on functions and graphing. Using standard notation to write function rules in the form $y = 3x + 5$ was taught in Level 5.

✋ MANIPULATIVES   **Program Resources**

graph paper

Reteaching Master

Practice Master 112

Enrichment Master 112

For extra practice:
CD-ROM* Lesson 112

---

① Warp-Up  5 MINUTES

Problem of the Day Present the following problem to students: Lupe paid $36 for two dozen tulips and one dozen roses. Roses cost twice as much as tulips. What do one tulip and one rose cost? (tulip: $0.75; rose: $1.50)

Problem-Solving Strategies Ask students who have solved the Problem of the Day to share how they solved it and any strategies they used.

 Have students solve these problems mentally. Invite them to explain their strategies.

a. $560 \div 70 = (8)$

b. $420 \div 6 = (70)$

c. $6300 \div 9 = (700)$

d. $90 \times 40 = (3600)$

e. $100 \times 0 = (0)$

f. $360 \div 40 = (9)$

g. $2100 \div 3 = (700)$

h. $5600 \div 80 = (70)$

i. $2700 \div 30 = (90)$

j. $28 \times 100 = (2800)$

k. $\begin{array}{r} 486 \\ +503 \\ \hline (989) \end{array}$

l. $\begin{array}{r} 864 \\ -309 \\ \hline (555) \end{array}$

Standard Notation for Functions

You have learned one way to write a function rule. In this lesson you'll learn about another form—one that is more commonly used in algebra.

Function rules are usually written in a form shorter than the form we have been using.

For $x \to (\times 2) \to n \to (+5) \to y$, we could say, "Multiply x by 2 and add 5."

This could be written: $2 \times x + 5 = y$. Since the $\times$ sign and the x could easily be confused, it is customary to leave out the $\times$ sign if one number is represented by a letter. When we want to tell someone to multiply x by 2 and then add 5 to get y, we write:

$$2x + 5 = y$$

We read this as "two x plus 5 equals y."

If we want to tell someone to divide x by 4 to get y, we could write it in two ways:

$$x \div 4 = y \qquad \text{or} \qquad \frac{x}{4} = y$$

We would read these as "x divided by 4 equals y" and "x over 4 equals y."

Write each of these rules in the short form.

① $x \to (\times 4) \to n \to (+5) \to y$
$$4x + 5 = y$$

② $x \to (\div 3) \to n \to (-1) \to y$
$$\frac{x}{3} - 1 = y$$

③ $x \to (\div 7) \to n \to (-8) \to y$
$$\frac{x}{7} - 8 = y$$

④ $x \to (\times 1) \to n \to (+5) \to y$
$$x + 5 = y$$

⑤ $x \to (\times \frac{1}{2}) \to n \to (+7) \to y$
$$\frac{1}{2}x + 7 = y$$

⑥ $x \to (+5) \to y$
$$x + 5 = y$$

⑦ $x \to (\times \frac{2}{3}) \to n \to (-\frac{1}{2}) \to y$
$$\frac{2}{3}x - \frac{1}{2} = y$$

⑧ $x \to (\times 4) \to n \to (+0) \to y$
$$4x = y$$

⑨ $x \to (\div 2) \to n \to (+6) \to y$
$$\frac{x}{2} + 6 = y$$

⑩ $x \to (\times \frac{1}{5}) \to n \to (-3) \to y$
$$\frac{x}{5} - 3 = y$$

398 • Algebra Readiness

Why teach it this way?

Standard algebraic notation is easier to write than the arrow notation used up to this point and is more widely used and understood. Students should understand that they may still use arrow notation if it helps them to solve a problem.

 **Literature Connection** Have students read *Is a Blue Whale the Biggest Thing There Is?* by Robert E. Wells. Ask them to use standard notation to express the size comparisons given in the book.

RETEACHING p. 37

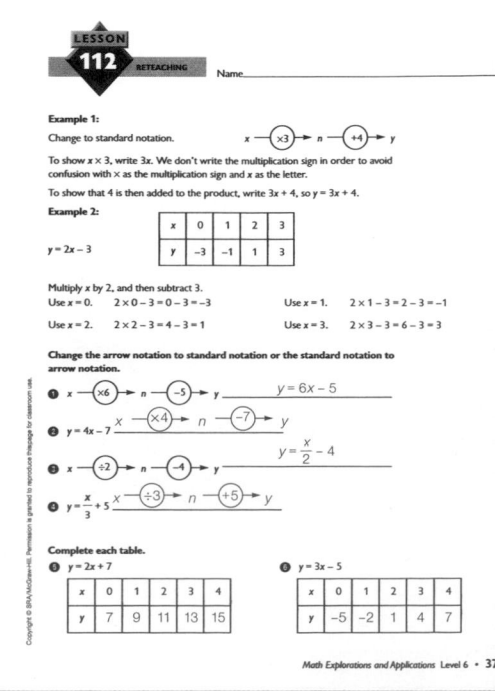

*available separately

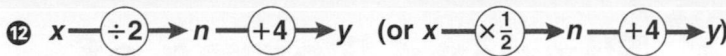

12 x —$\div 2$→ n —$+4$→ y (or x —$\times\frac{1}{2}$→ n —$+4$→ y)

Write each rule in the longer form, using arrows.

11 $3x - 5 = y$ **12** $\frac{1}{2}x + 4 = y$ **13** $x - 8 = y$

11 x —$\times 3$→ n —-5→ y **13** x —-8→ y

14 $\frac{x}{2} = y$ **15** $y = 5x$ **16** $y = 5x + 3$

15 x —$\times 5$→ y **16** x —$\times 5$→ n —$+3$→ y

17 $y = \frac{2}{3}x - 8$ **18** $y = \frac{x}{4} - 7$ **19** $y = x + 1$

17 x —$\times\frac{2}{3}$→ n —-8→ y **18** x —$\div 4$→ n —-7→ y

You may use the long form whenever you find it more convenient.

19 x —$+1$→ y

Use spreadsheet software or other means to complete each table and graph the function. You may use or think about the longer form for function rules, if that helps. **Check students' graphs.**

20 $y = 3x + 5$

x	0	1	2	3	−1	−2	−3
y	5	8	11	14	2	−1	−4

21 $y = \frac{1}{2}x + 5$

x	0	2	4	−2	−4	1	−1
y	5	6	7	4	3	$5\frac{1}{2}$	$4\frac{1}{2}$

22 $y = 2x - 7$

x	1	0	3	6	9	−3	−6	$-\frac{9}{2}$
y	−5	−7	−1	3	5	0	1	

22 $y = 2x - 7$

x	1							
y		−7	−1	3	5	0	1	

Below: −5 and then 0, 3, 6, 9, −3, −6, $-\frac{9}{2}$

23 $y = \frac{2}{3}x + 3$

x	0	3	6	9	1	−1	0
y	3	5	7	9	1	−1	0

14 x —$\div 2$→ y (or x —$\times\frac{1}{2}$→ y)

PRACTICE p. 112

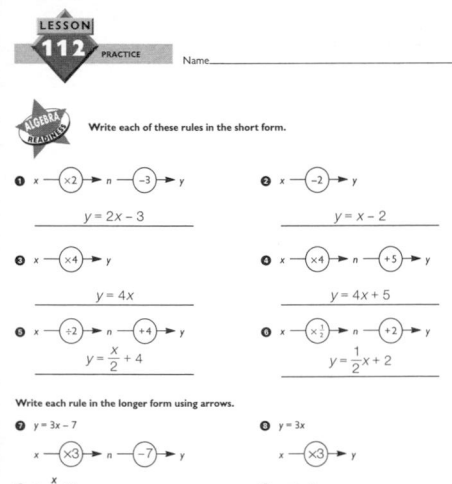

LESSON **112** PRACTICE Name_____

Write each of these rules in the short form.

1 x —$\times 2$→ n —-3→ y
$y = 2x - 3$

2 x —-2→ y
$y = x - 2$

3 x —$\times 4$→ y
$y = 4x$

4 x —$\times 4$→ n —$+5$→ y
$y = 4x + 5$

5 x —$\div 2$→ n —$+4$→ y
$y = \frac{x}{2} + 4$

6 x —$\times\frac{1}{2}$→ n —$+2$→ y
$y = \frac{1}{2}x + 2$

Write each rule in the longer form using arrows.

7 $y = 3x - 7$
x —$\times 3$→ n —-7→ y

8 $y = 3x$
x —$\times 3$→ y

9 $y = \frac{x}{2} + 1$
x —$\div 2$→ n —$+1$→ y

10 $y = x - 1$
x —-1→ y

11 $y = 2x + 6$
x —$\times 2$→ n —$+6$→ y

12 $y = \frac{1}{3}x + 4$
x —$\times\frac{1}{3}$→ n —$+4$→ y

112 • Math Explorations and Applications Level 6

ENRICHMENT p. 112

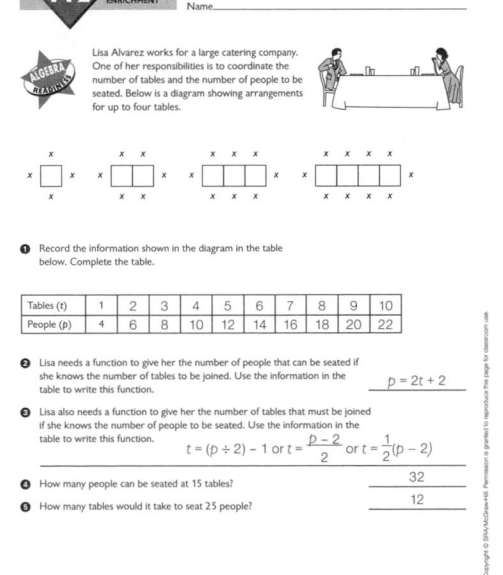

LESSON **112** ENRICHMENT Name_____

Lisa Alvarez works for a large catering company. One of her responsibilities is to coordinate the number of tables and the number of people to be seated. Below is a diagram showing arrangements for up to four tables.

1 Record the information shown in the diagram in the table below. Complete the table.

Tables (t)	1	2	3	4	5	6	7	8	9	10
People (p)	4	6	8	10	12	14	16	18	20	22

2 Lisa needs a function to give her the number of people that can be seated if she knows the number of tables to be joined. Use the information in the table to write this function. $p = 2t + 2$

3 Lisa also needs a function to give her the number of tables that must be joined if she knows the number of people to be seated. Use the information in the table to write this function. $t = (p \div 2) - 1$ or $t = \frac{p-2}{2}$ or $t = \frac{1}{2}(p - 2)$

4 How many people can be seated at 15 tables? 32

5 How many tables would it take to seat 25 people? 12

112 • Math Explorations and Applications Level 6

---

2 Teach

Using the Student Pages With the class, go over the example and a few of the first 19 problems. Include at least one in which the y appears to the left of the equals sign. Point out that $y = x + 1$ and $x + 1 = y$ are two ways to write the same function rule. Have students do the remaining problems on their own. Have **graph paper** available. Then, discuss the answers. For problems 4 and 6, explain that because multiplying by 1 does not change a number, $1x$ may be written as x, but accept the answer $1x + 5$. Remind them that graphs serve as a check for 20–23. Points that do not fall along the same straight line should be checked for errors in calculation or in plotting.

3 Wrap-Up

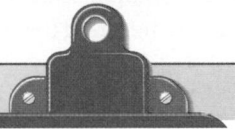

In Closing Summarize the lesson by asking students to read equations such as the following: $3x + 8 = 14$.

Watch for confusion when the multiplication sign is omitted. Remind students to reinstate the sign when a number substitutes for the variable. For example, to evaluate $y = 8x$ when x is 3, some students say that y is 83. Remind them to think $y = 8 \times 3$. Students may also have difficulty with the order of operations. Remind them to use parentheses to show which calculation to do first. For example, if they substitute 4 for x in the equation $y = 3x + 5$, they can write: $y = (3 \times 4) + 5$.

Performance Assessment Write the long, arrow form of a function on the chalkboard. Ask students to rewrite it using standard algebraic notation.

Assessment Criteria

Did the student . . .

✓ demonstrate ability to translate between function rules in arrow notation and algebraic notation?

✓ correctly complete the tables for the function rules expressed in algebraic notation and graph the functions?

Homework Have students play any game previously introduced in the unit with a family member.

Finding Terms of Sequences

LESSON PLANNER

Objectives

▶ to provide practice identifying missing terms in a sequence

▶ to review arithmetic facts and to encourage students to see that using mental arithmetic makes some calculations easier

✓ to evaluate students' ability to understand and use function notation

Context of the Lesson This is the 17th of 24 lessons on functions and graphing. It contains a Mastery Checkpoint on the use of function notation.

 MANIPULATIVES

Program Resources

Practice Master 113

Enrichment Master 113

Assessment Master

For extra practice:
CD-ROM* Lesson 113
Cumulative Review, page 577

① Warm-Up  5 MINUTES

 Problem of the Day Present the following problem to the class: In its seven-day life, a large fly ate 210 smaller flies. Each day it ate six more flies than it did the day before. How many flies did it eat on the very first day of its life? (12)

Problem-Solving Strategies Ask students who have solved the Problem of the Day to share how they solved it and any strategies they used.

MENTAL MATH Have students respond to the following using mental math.

a. $3 \times 21 = (63)$

b. $50 \times 14 = (700)$

c. $5 \times 32 = (160)$

d. $25 \times 12 = (300)$

e. $7 \times 21 = (147)$

f. $5 \times 36 = (180)$

Finding Terms of Sequences

In each of the following sequences, there is a pattern that allows you to predict the next number or numbers by following that pattern. You may see several patterns that would give different results for missing numbers.

 ALGEBRA READINESS

For each sequence, write the missing numbers according to your pattern. Tell what your pattern is.

Example: 1, 7, 3, 9, ___, ___, ___.
Answer: 5, 11, 7.
Pattern: Add 6, then subtract 4, alternately.

① 20, 25, 30, **35**, **40**, **45**, **50**   Add 5.

② 1, 2, 4, 8, **16**, **32**, **64**, **128**   Multiply by 2.

③ 64, 32, 16, **8**, **4**, **2**, 1, $\frac{1}{2}$.   Divide by 2.

④ 0, 4, 2, 6, 4, 8, **6**, **10**, **8**, **12**   Add 4, then subtract 2, alternately.

⑤ 0, 0, 2, 6, 8, 24, **26**, **78**, **80**.   Multiply by 3, then add 2, alternately.

⑥ 100, 95, 90, **85**, **80**, **75**, **70**   Subtract 5.

⑦ 100, **90**, 80, **70**, 60, **50**, **40**   Possible answer: Subtract 10.

⑧ 0, **0**, 5, 20, 25, **100**, 105, **420**, 425.   Multiply by 4, then add 5, alternately.

⑨ 1, 4, 9, 16, **25**, **36**, **49**, **64**.   Possible answer: Take the position in the sequence, and multiply it by itself.

For each set of ordered pairs, give a function rule in the short form.

⑩

x	0	1	2	3	−1	−2
y	3	7	11	15	−1	−5

$y = 4x + 3$

⑪

x	0	2	4	6	8	10
y	1	2	3	4	5	6

$y = \frac{1}{2}x + 1$ (or $y = \frac{x}{2} + 1$)

RETEACHING

No reteaching on identifying patterns is necessary at this time. You may want to assign Enrichment Master 113 at this time.

PRACTICE p. 113

For each sequence write the missing numbers. Tell what the pattern is.

❶ 1, 3, 6, 8, 11, 13, 16, 18, 21, __23__, __26__, __28__
Add 2, add 3.

❷ 1, 3, 9, 27, 81, __243__, __729__, __2187__
Multiply by 3.

❸ 0, 20, 40, 60, __80__, 100, __120__, __140__, 160
multiples of 20

❹ 65,536; 16,384; 4096; __1024__; 256; __64__, __16__
Divide by 4.

❺ 3, 4, 8, 9, 18, 19, 38, __39__, __78__, __79__
Add 1, multiply by 2.

❻ 1, 1, 2, 3, 5, 8, 13, __21__, __34__, __55__
After the first two numbers, add the previous two numbers to get the next number.

❼ 146, 143, 140, 137, __134__, __131__, __128__
Subtract 3.

❽ 1, 7, 5, 11, 9, 15, 13, __19__, __17__, __23__
Add 6, subtract 2.

❾ 0, 15, 30, 45, 60, __75__, __90__, __105__
Add 15 or multiples of 15.

Math Explorations and Applications Level 6 • 113

---

*available separately

Think. Work quickly. Watch the signs.

⑫ 40 + 50 **90** ⑬ 50 − 40 **10** ⑭ 500 − 400 **100**
⑮ 500 + 400 **900** ⑯ 5 + 4 **9** ⑰ 5 − 4 **1**
⑱ 5 × 4 **20** ⑲ 500 × 400 **200,000** ⑳ 50 × 40 **2000**
㉑ 7 × 6 **42** ㉒ 70 × 60 **4200** ㉓ 700 × 600 **420,000**
㉔ 7 + 6 **13** ㉕ 600 + 700 **1300** ㉖ 700 − 600 **100**
㉗ 7 − 6 **1** ㉘ 70 + 60 **130** ㉙ 8 + 4 **12**
㉚ 8 − 4 **4** ㉛ 8 × 4 **32** ㉜ 15 − 8 **7**
㉝ 150 − 80 **70** ㉞ 1500 − 800 **700** ㉟ 80 × 70 **5600**
㊱ 70 × 70 **4900** ㊲ 600 × 900 **540,000** ㊳ 9 × 6 **54**
㊴ 90 + 60 **150** ㊵ 90 − 60 **30** ㊶ 90 × 60 **5400**

Do each chain calculation from left to right, unless you see a faster way. For example, to do 7 × 3 + 5 × 6, multiply 7 × 3 (to get 21), add 5 (to get 26), and multiply by 6 (to get 156).

㊷ 5 × 8 ÷ 2 + 7 − 2 **25**
㊸ 10 × 3 × 2 × 1 + 10 **70**
㊹ 30 ÷ 5 × 6 − 6 + 7 **37**
㊺ 50 + 50 + 50 + 50 + 50 **250**
㊻ 8 + 1 + 2 + 3 + 5 + 7 **26**
㊼ 4 × 9 × 2 × 5 **360**
㊽ 7 × 8 − 6 ÷ 10 + 4 × 4 ÷ 6 **6**
㊾ 5 × 9 + 3 ÷ 8 + 1 × 5 + 5 ÷ 5 − 5 − 5 **−2**
㊿ 10 × 9 × 8 × 7 × 6 × 5 × 4 × 3 × 2 × 1 × 0 **0**
(51) 12 × 9 × 6 × 3 × 0 **0**
(52) 9 + 8 + 7 + 6 + 5 + 4 + 3 + 2 + 1 **45**
(53) 10 + 10 + 10 + 10 + 5 **45**
(54) 9 + 1 + 8 + 2 + 7 + 3 + 6 + 4 + 5 **45**
(55) 20 + 20 + 20 + 20 + 20 + 20 + 20 + 20 + 20 + 20 + 10 **210**
(56) What is the sum of the whole numbers from 1 through 20? **210**

Use the Cumulative Review on page 577 after this lesson.

ENRICHMENT p. 113

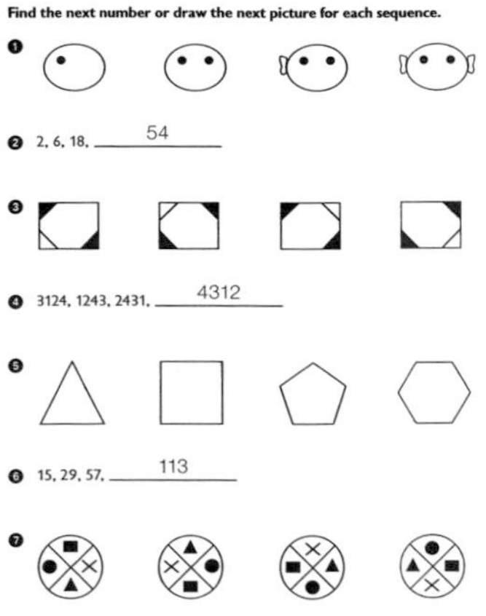

LESSON 113 ENRICHMENT Name__________

A sequence can be a set of numbers or pictures that follows a pattern. For example, in the sequence 1, 2, 3, ___, the next number would be 4.

Find the next number or draw the next picture for each sequence. Answers will vary. Possible answers are given.

❶

❷ 2, 6, 18, 54

❸

❹ 3124, 1243, 2431, 4312

❺

❻ 15, 29, 57, 113

❼

Math Explorations and Applications Level 6 • **113**

ASSESSMENT p. 47

UNIT 5 **Mastery Checkpoint 22** Using function rules (standard notation) (Lesson 113)

Name __________

The student demonstrates mastery by correctly answering at least 5 of the 6 problems.

For each set of ordered pairs, give a function rule in the short form. (That is, in the form y = *Ax* + *B*, where *A* and *B* are numbers.)

❶

x	0	1	2	3	−1
y	1	4	7	10	−2

$y = 3x + 1$

❷

x	0	3	6	9	12
y	2	3	4	5	6

$y = \frac{1}{3}x + 2 \left(y = \frac{x}{3} + 2\right)$

❸

x	2	3	0	−1	1
y	6	8	2	0	4

$y = 2x + 2$

❹

x	0	5	10	15	20
y	−1	1	3	5	7

$y = \frac{2}{5}x - 1$

❺

x	2	1	0	3	−1
y	5	1	−3	9	−7

$y = 4x - 3$

❻

x	−7	2	0	−3	1
y	0	9	7	4	8

$y = x + 7$

Math Explorations and Applications Level 6 • **47**

❷ Teach

ALGEBRA READINESS

Using the Student Pages Go over the example at the top of page 400 with the class. Then assign the sequences for students to work on independently. Emphasize that students may notice several patterns or that they may describe them in more than one way.

You may wish to time students as they work on page 401 and compare the times to those students had for page 382. Afterwards, discuss with students how pairing addends—for example, making sums of 10s in problems 52 and 54—can speed up their work and improve accuracy.

❸ Wrap-Up

5 MINUTES

In Closing To summarize the lesson, ask students to explain how to look for a pattern to find missing terms in a sequence.

SELF ASSESSMENT

Have students compare their performance and time on the problems on page 401 with their efforts on previous skill-review pages.

Mastery Checkpoint 22

Most students should be able to determine function rules from a set of ordered pairs, express the rules in standard notation, and correctly complete a table of ordered pairs derived from a function. You might assess this by observing students as they play the "Find the Function Rule" game or by using Assessment Blackline Masters page 47. Assessment results may be recorded in the Mastery Checkpoint Chart.

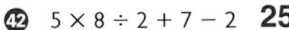

Assessment Criteria

Did the student . . .

✓ demonstrate understanding of how to find missing terms in a sequence?

✓ correctly answer at least 85% of the problems on page 401?

✓ find and use shortcuts to speed up calculations?

Homework Have students work with family members to develop a numerical or alphabetical secret code. They can write a sentence in code and challenge classmates to decipher it.

Graphing Linear Functions

LESSON PLANNER

Objectives

▶ to provide practice in graphing a linear function by plotting two appropriate points

▶ to provide practice in writing function rules and in graphing perimeter functions for rectangles of given proportions

▶ to provide practice in using functions to clarify a realistic situation

Context of the Lesson This is the 18th of 24 lessons on functions and graphing.

 MANIPULATIVES

graph paper

set of coordinate axes on an overhead projector or on the chalkboard

Program Resources

Number Cubes (0–5 and 5–10)

Reteaching Master

Practice Master 114

Enrichment Master 114

For extra practice: CD-ROM* Lesson 114

Note: This lesson may take more than one day.

① Warm-Up

 Problem of the Day Present the following problem to the class: Serena's bedroom is in the shape of a rectangle. It is 3.5 yards wide and has a perimeter of 15.5 yards. Her ceiling is 3.0 yards high. She wants to place a wall unit along one of the longer walls. What is the greatest possible length of this piece of furniture? (4.25 yards)

Problem-Solving Strategies Ask students who have solved the Problem of the Day to share how they solved it and any strategies they used.

MENTAL MATH Have students play a few rounds of the "Roll a Problem" game, as described in the *Mental Math* section of Lesson 107. Select variations according to the needs of the class. A copy of this game can also be found on pages 11 and 12 of the Home Connections Blackline Masters.

Graphing Linear Functions

 **ALGEBRA READINESS**

You have learned how to satisfy a function rule by finding one coordinate given the other. In this lesson you'll practice graphing certain functions, and you'll discover what their graphs will look like.

To graph a function correctly, you must know where every point of the graph is. But often there is enough regularity so that a few points will determine where the others are.

Example: Graph the function $y = \frac{1}{2}x - 4$.

Choose some value of x.	Let's say 10.
Find the corresponding value of y.	$y = \frac{1}{2} \times 10 - 4 = 1$
Graph that point.	Graph (10, 1).
Choose another value of x.	Let's say 0.
Find the corresponding value of y.	$y = \frac{1}{2} \times 0 - 4 = (-4)$
Graph that point.	Graph (0, −4).

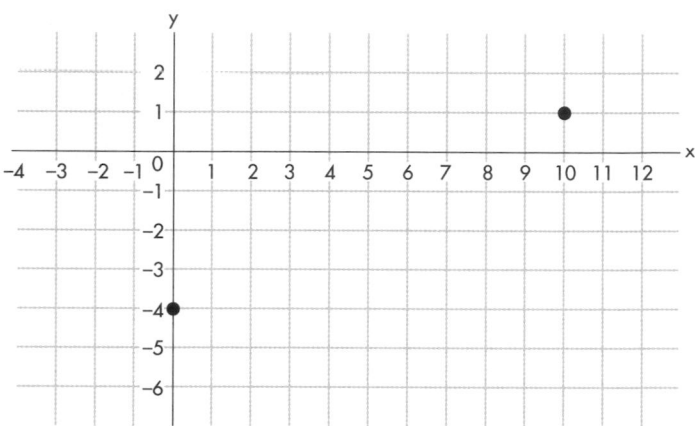

We have seen that functions with rules of the form $y = Ax + B$ have graphs that are straight lines.

◆ How many straight lines can you draw through one point? **an infinite number**

◆ How many straight lines can you draw through two points? **1**

 **Literature Connection** Have students read *All in a Day* by Mitsumasa Anno. You can use the book as a guide to time differences around the world.

*available separately

Draw a line through (10, 1) and (0, –4). You can draw just one straight line through the two points you plotted for the function $y = \frac{1}{2}x - 4$.

If a function has the form $y = Ax + B$, you can draw the line if you know just two points.

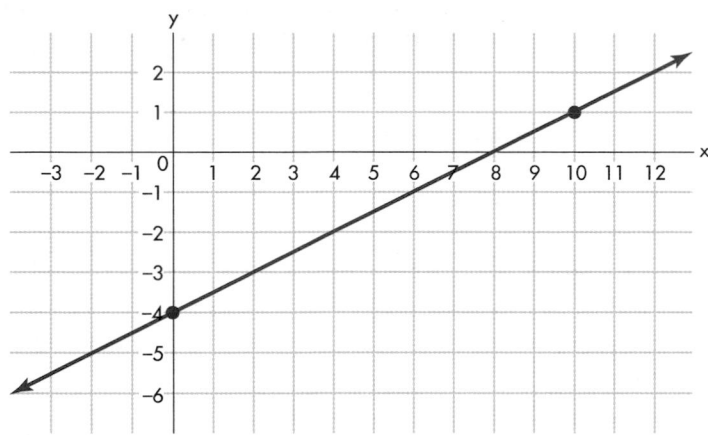

Let's check to see that it makes sense to say that this line is a graph of the function $y = \frac{1}{2}x - 4$.

◆ Choose any other value of x (besides 0 and 10). Find the corresponding value of y for the rule $y = \frac{1}{2}x - 4$. Are the numbers in the ordered pair the coordinates of a point on the line? **yes**

◆ Choose any point on the line. Do the coordinates of that point satisfy the rule $y = \frac{1}{2}x - 4$? **yes**

For each function rule, graph the function. (Choose any values you wish for x and find the corresponding values for y.) See graphs in margin.

❶ $y = \frac{1}{2}x + 2$ ❷ $y - 3x + 1$ ❸ $y = 4x - 6$

❹ $y = 2x - 7$ ❺ $y = \frac{2}{3}x - 2$ ❻ $y = \frac{3}{4}x + 5$

❼ Were you able to graph each function using only two points? **yes**

❽ When would it make sense to use more than two points when graphing a function? **when you want to check your work, or when you're not sure the graph will be a straight line**

Unit 5   Lesson 114 • **403**

 **Technology Connection** Refer students to the software *Hands on Math 3* from Ventura (Mac, for grades K-8), which provides practice with graphing activities, hundreds charts, a number balance, dominoes, line design, and fraction bars.

❷ Teach

Using the Student Pages Go over the example and questions on pages 402 and 403 with students. Begin by writing a function rule on the chalkboard; it can be the one on page 402 or another like it. Ask students to explain how you might graph the function. Try to elicit from them that they can pick any numbers they wish for *x* and then find the corresponding values for *y*. Also be sure to elicit the idea that the graph will be a straight line. Point out to students that all ordered pairs that fit the function rule will be points that lie on that line, but if they choose some values for *x* (for the example on page 402, less than −4 or greater than 12), the points may lie outside the edges of the paper. Have students work on problems 1-8 using **graph paper**.

Answers to problems 1–6:

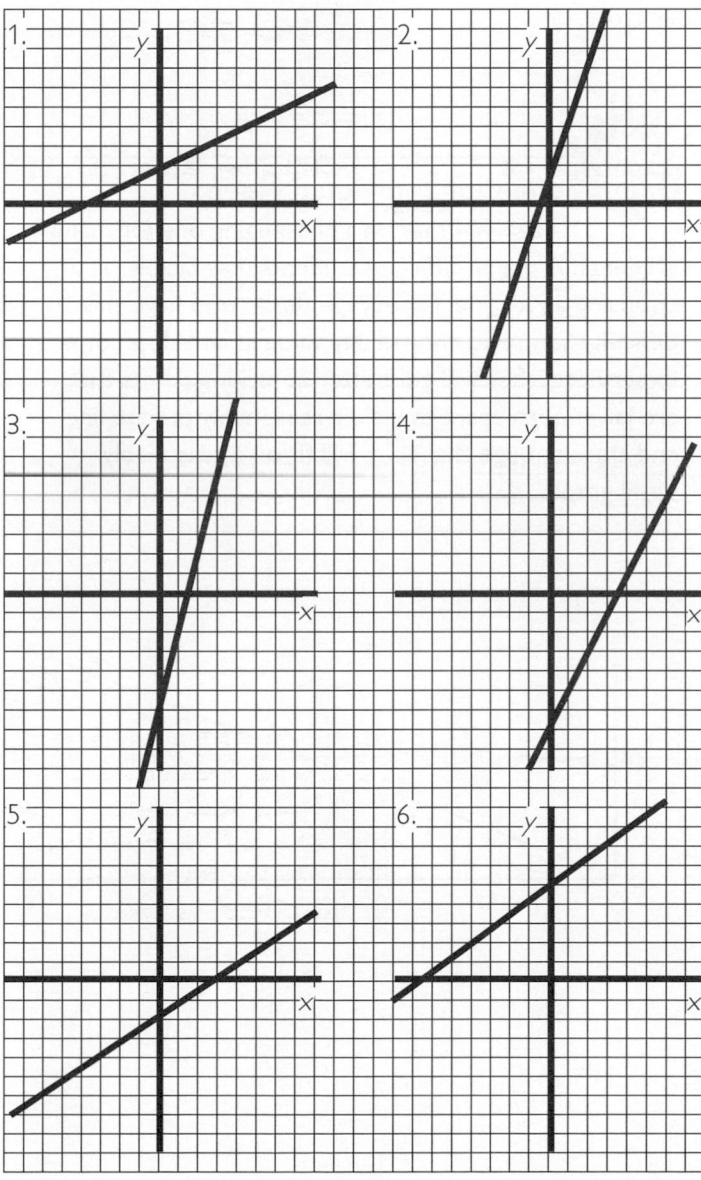

◆ **LESSON 114 Graphing Linear Functions**

Teach

Using the Student Pages Work with the class on the example on page 404 and give students as much help as necessary to get them started on problem 10. After they have worked individually or in small groups on that problem, discuss it and the questions that arise. At this point you may wish to discuss with students why it would not make sense to choose a negative value for *x*. Then assign the remaining problems on this page and on page 405.

You may wish to have students work in pairs on Rita's newspaper sales problems. Ask students what they can say about the point on their graphs at which the profit lines cross.

SPECIAL NEEDS
Meeting Individual Needs
Page 404 may be a challenging one for many students. A major difficulty students may face is choosing an *x*-value. Encourage those who have this difficulty simply to choose any value at all. After some experience, they will get better at picking points that are far enough apart to yield a reasonably precise line and close enough that they will fit on a reasonably sized graph.

Answer to problem 19:

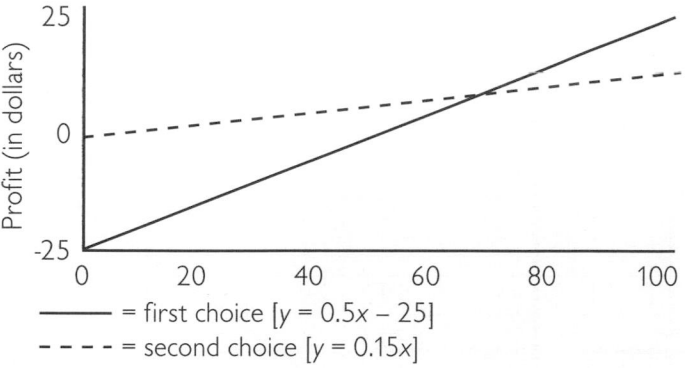

—— = first choice [*y* = 0.5*x* − 25]
- - - - = second choice [*y* = 0.15*x*]

◆ **LESSON 114 Graphing Linear Functions**

Some rules for functions are given in words rather than in symbols and numbers.

Example: Let *x* be the length of a side of an **equilateral triangle** and let *y* be the perimeter of the triangle. Try to write a function rule in the form *y* = *Ax* + *B* for this function. Graph the function.

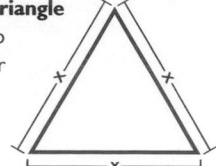

Remember, equilateral means all sides have the same length.

Draw a picture if it helps.

The length of each side of the triangle is *x*. Then the perimeter, *y*, is *x* + *x* + *x*, or 3 times *x*.

We can write this as *y* = 3*x*. We graph it by choosing some values for *x* and finding the corresponding values for *y*.

Examples:

x	1	3	4	7	8
y	3	9	12	21	24

9 Choose at least three more values of *x* and find the corresponding values of *y*. Do these points fall on the graph of *y* = 3*x*? **yes**

10 Here is another function rule in words. Let *x* be the length of the short side of a rectangle and 3*x* be the length of the long side. Let *y* be the perimeter of the rectangle. Write the rule in the form *y* = *Ax* + *B*. Then graph the function. **y = 8x**

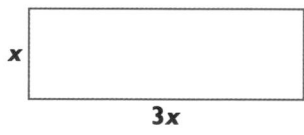

11 Choose at least three more values of *x* and find the corresponding values of *y*. Do these points fall on the graph you made for problem 10? **yes**

12 For the example and for problem 10, choose a point on the graph that has coordinates that have not been calculated yet. Do the coordinates of the point satisfy the function rule? **yes**

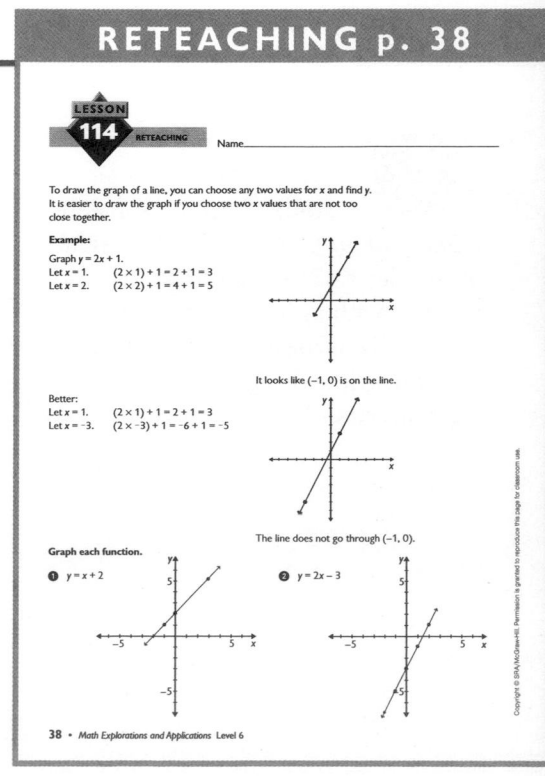

Function rules and graphs can be used to solve many kinds of problems. Here is one example of a situation that can be made clearer using functions.

Rita sells newspapers. She can usually sell 70 or 80 papers in a day. She sells the papers for 50¢ each. The newspaper company has offered her two different ways of getting paid.

The first choice is that they will give her as many papers as she wants, and she gets to keep 15¢ for each paper she sells. She would return the unsold papers to the company.

The second choice is that she will buy 100 papers from the company at the beginning of the day for $25. She gets to keep all the money people pay her for the papers and need not return any unsold papers. If she loses money, we would say that is a negative profit for the day, so she would have a profit of negative $25 (or –$25) if she sold no papers.

Solve the following problems.

⓭ Suppose Rita takes the first choice. Express her profit using a function rule in which x is the number of papers she sells and y is her profit. **$0.15x = y$**

⓮ Suppose Rita takes the second choice. Express her profit using a function rule. **$0.5x - 25 = y$**

⓯ If Rita sold 20 papers in a day, which choice would be better for her? What would her profit be with each choice? **the first choice; $3, −$15**

⓰ How many papers must she sell to break even (have a "profit" of $0) with the second choice? **50**

⓱ What would her profit be using the first choice if she sold 50 papers? **$7.50**

⓲ If she sold 80 papers, what would her profit be with each choice? Which is better? **first choice: $12; second choice: $15; the second choice is better**

⓳ Draw a double line graph showing her profit for different numbers of papers sold for each choice. About how many papers must she sell in order to do better with the second choice than with the first?

See graph in margin; 72

⓴ Given Rita's choice, what would you do? Why? **Answers will vary.**

Unit 5   Lesson 114 • **405**

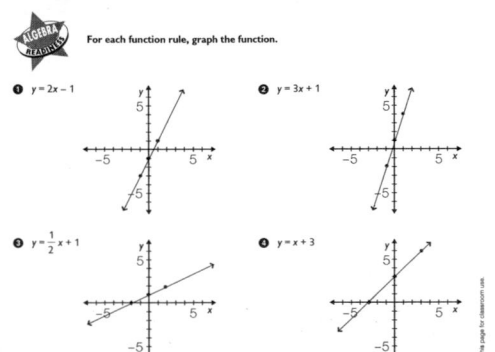

③ Wrap-Up  5 MINUTES

In Closing To summarize the lesson, ask students to tell what kind of graph the function $y = Ax + B$ will have.

ALTERNATIVE ASSESSMENT **Portfolio Assessment** Have students explain what they would do to graph the function $y = 3x - 3$.

Assessment Criteria

Did the student . . .

✓ demonstrate understanding of what the graph of a linear function looks like?

✓ show ability to recognize a linear function?

✓ demonstrate understanding of how to graph a linear function?

✓ demonstrate understanding of how to use graphs of linear functions to solve certain kinds of problems?

Homework Tell students that you predict that the price of one $1 magazine will go up $0.25 a year for several years, and that the price of another $1 magazine will go up 20% a year for the foreseeable future. Ask them to use a graph to figure out when the second magazine will cost more than the first.

Order of Operations

LESSON PLANNER

Objectives

▶ to demonstrate the need for a convention for the order of operations of addition and multiplication

▶ to review arithmetic facts and basic operations with whole numbers, decimals, and fractions

▶ to help students develop the broad ability to use mathematical common sense

Context of the Lesson This lesson provides a pause in the lesson sequence on functions and graphing, and provides practice in computational skills with whole numbers, decimals, fractions, and the use of and need for parentheses. This lesson also contains Part 3 of "Diet for a Small Terrier," a three-part Thinking Story.

 MANIPULATIVES

calculators that use different rules for the order of operations*

Program Resources

Practice Master 115

Enrichment Master 115

For career connections:
Careers and Math*

For extra practice:
CD-ROM* Lesson 115

1 Warm-Up  5 MINUTES

 Problem of the Day Ask students to choose a simple everyday activity that can be broken down into many parts that need to be done in a particular order, such as making toast, making scrambled eggs, brushing teeth, making a bed, or typing a letter. Have students list all the steps involved in doing the activity from start to finish, in the correct order. Students should hold on to these lists for analysis later in the lesson.

Problem-Solving Strategies Ask students who have solved the Problem of the Day to share how they solved it and any strategies they used.

MENTAL MATH Have students use the data to decide who had the highest average and who is the best bowler:

(continued on page 407)

Order of Operations

Bill and Jordan each have a calculator. On his calculator Bill did the following problem: $3 + 5 \times 7 =$. The answer the calculator showed was 38. Jordan tried the same problem on her calculator. The answer the calculator showed was 56. They decided one of the calculators must be making a mistake.

◆ Which one do you think was making a mistake? Why? **neither; They each did the operations in a different order.**

◆ Solve the problem on your calculator. What answer do you get?

◆ Does anyone in your class get a different answer? **Students should get either 56 or 38.**

Many people solve problems like $3 + 5 \times 7$ from left to right and do the computations as they get to them. In this case, $3 + 5 = 8$ and $8 \times 7 = 56$. Others follow a rule that says that when there are multiplications and additions in the same problem, we should always do the multiplications first, and then the additions. They would first say $5 \times 7 = 35$, and then, $3 + 35 = 38$. Still a third rule might be to do additions first and then multiplications. With this method the answer would be 56.

For each of the following problems, find the answer using each of the three rules: (1) left to right; (2) multiplications first; (3) additions first.

❶ $7 + 3 \times 10$
100; 37; 100

❷ $3 \times 10 + 7$
37; 37; 51

❸ $4 + 8 \times 5$
60; 44; 60

❹ $8 \times 5 + 4$
44; 44; 72

❺ $73 + 27 \times 10$
1000; 343; 1000

❻ $10 \times 27 + 73$
343; 343; 1000

❼ $10 \times 7 + 3$
73; 73; 100

❽ $5 \times 8 + 4$
44; 44; 60

❾ $73 \times 10 + 27$
757; 757; 2701

❿ $5 + 5 \times 5$
50; 30; 50

⓫ $5 \times 5 + 5$
30; 30; 50

⓬ $10 + 10 \times 10$
200; 110; 200

If you know the situation that led to an arithmetic problem, you can find the answer. Otherwise, you will need some rule to follow. Sometimes we can eliminate confusion by using **parentheses** (always do the computations inside parentheses first). Sometimes we wish to use a different rule, but it is important that people reading our work use the same rule.

The two most common rules are to work from left to right and to do the multiplications (and divisions) before the additions (and subtractions).

Consider the short way of writing a function rule such as $7 + 3x = y$. If x is 2, what is y? Can you see why people who study algebra using this notation often use the convention of multiplication first, then addition? **13; In algebra, you solve the part of the equation with the variable in it first.**

Why teach it this way?

There is a need for conventions in mathematics, as well as in other aspects of life. However, though logic can show the need for a convention, it may not tell which convention is best. You might wish to point this out to students when discussing the order of operations convention.

*available separately

Solve for *n*. Work from the inner parentheses to the outer parentheses.

⑬ $(3 + 4) \times 5 = n$ **35**
⑭ $3 + (4 \times 5) = n$ **23**
⑮ $(7 + 6) \times (3 + 4) = n$ **91**
⑯ $12 - (6 + 4) = n$ **2**
⑰ $(12 - 6) + 4 = n$ **10**
⑱ $(24 \div 3) + 5 = n$ **13**
⑲ $24 \div (3 + 5) = n$ **3**
⑳ $30 - (6 \times 2) = n$ **18**
㉑ $(30 - 6) \times 2 = n$ **48**
㉒ $34 - ((8 \times 2) + 3) = n$ **15**
㉓ $(34 - 8) \times (2 + 3) = n$ **130**
㉔ $((34 - 8) \times 2) + 3 = n$ **55**
㉕ $4 + ((16 \div 4) \times 5) = n$ **24**
㉖ $(4 + (16 \div 4)) \times 5 = n$ **40**
㉗ $((4 + 16) \div 4) \times 5 = n$ **25**

Solve for *n*. Use shortcuts when you can.

㉘ $100 \times 100 = n$ **10,000**
㉙ $99 \times 101 = n$ **9999**
㉚ $3.1 \times 2.9 = n$ **8.99**
㉛ $2.9 \times 3.1 = n$ **8.99**
㉜ $100.1 \times 59.9 = n$ **5995.99**
㉝ $6 \times 5 = n$ **30**
㉞ $60 \times 5 = n$ **300**
㉟ $61 \times 5 = n$ **305**
㊱ $61 \times 50 = n$ **3050**
㊲ $610 \times 50 = n$ **30,500**
㊳ $75 \times 2 = n$ **150**
㊴ $75 \times 3 = n$ **225**
㊵ $75 \times 4 = n$ **300**
㊶ $75 \times 5 = n$ **375**
㊷ $75 \times 6 = n$ **450**

Watch the signs. If the answer is an improper fraction, you can leave it or change it to a mixed number.

㊸ $\frac{1}{2} + \frac{1}{2} = n$ **1**
㊹ $\frac{1}{2} - \frac{1}{2} = n$ **0**
㊺ $\frac{2}{2} - \frac{1}{2} = n$ $\mathbf{\frac{1}{2}}$
㊻ $\frac{3}{2} - \frac{1}{2} = n$ **1**
㊼ $\frac{3}{2} - \frac{1}{4} = n$ $\mathbf{\frac{5}{4}}$ **(or $\mathbf{1\frac{1}{4}}$)**
㊽ $\frac{3}{2} - \frac{1}{8} = n$ $\mathbf{\frac{11}{8}}$ **(or $\mathbf{1\frac{3}{8}}$)**
㊾ $\frac{1}{2} \times \frac{1}{2} = n$ $\mathbf{\frac{1}{4}}$
㊿ $\frac{1}{4} \div \frac{1}{2} = n$ $\mathbf{\frac{1}{2}}$
(51) $\frac{3}{8} + \frac{1}{4} = n$ $\mathbf{\frac{5}{8}}$
(52) $\frac{7}{8} + \frac{1}{4} = n$ $\mathbf{\frac{9}{8}}$ **(or $\mathbf{1\frac{1}{8}}$)**
(53) $1\frac{1}{4} + 1\frac{1}{4} = n$ $\mathbf{\frac{10}{4}}$ **(or $\mathbf{2\frac{1}{2}}$)**
(54) $1\frac{2}{3} + \frac{1}{3} = n$ **2**
(55) $1\frac{2}{3} + \frac{2}{3} = n$ $\mathbf{\frac{7}{3}}$ **(or $\mathbf{2\frac{1}{3}}$)**
(56) $1\frac{2}{3} + \frac{3}{3} = n$ $\mathbf{\frac{8}{3}}$ **(or $\mathbf{2\frac{2}{3}}$)**
(57) $1\frac{2}{3} - \frac{3}{3} = n$ $\mathbf{\frac{2}{3}}$
(58) $\frac{3}{4} + \frac{2}{8} = n$ **1**
(59) $7 \times \frac{2}{4} = n$ $\mathbf{\frac{7}{2}}$ **(or $\mathbf{3\frac{1}{2}}$)**
(60) $7 \div \frac{2}{4} = n$ **14**
(61) $\frac{1}{7} \div \frac{2}{4} = n$ $\mathbf{\frac{2}{7}}$
(62) $\frac{2}{7} \div \frac{2}{4} = n$ $\mathbf{\frac{4}{7}}$
(63) $\frac{3}{7} \div \frac{2}{4} = n$ $\mathbf{\frac{6}{7}}$
(64) $\frac{2}{3} \times 2 = n$ $\mathbf{\frac{4}{3}}$ **(or $\mathbf{1\frac{1}{3}}$)**
(65) $\frac{2}{3} \times 3 = n$ **2**
(66) $\frac{2}{3} \times \frac{1}{2} = n$ $\mathbf{\frac{1}{3}}$
(67) $\frac{2}{3} \times 2\frac{1}{2} = n$ $\mathbf{\frac{5}{3}}$ **(or $\mathbf{1\frac{2}{3}}$)**
(68) $\frac{2}{3} \times 3\frac{1}{2} = n$ $\mathbf{\frac{7}{3}}$ **(or $\mathbf{2\frac{1}{3}}$)**
(69) $2\frac{1}{2} - \frac{3}{8} = n$ $\mathbf{2\frac{1}{8}}$
(70) $2\frac{1}{2} - \frac{5}{8} = n$ $\mathbf{1\frac{7}{8}}$
(71) $2\frac{1}{2} - \frac{7}{8} = n$ $\mathbf{1\frac{5}{8}}$
(72) $2\frac{1}{2} - 1\frac{1}{8} = n$ $\mathbf{1\frac{3}{8}}$

Real-World Connection Have students form groups and show each other the lists they made for the Problem of the Day. Invite group members to carefully review the lists to make sure all parts of the activity described are included and are presented in the correct order. Students may be surprised to find that making completely accurate lists is not so easy.

Mental Math (continued)

Bowling Scores

Mary	Fred	Judy
135	125	145
117	120	119
180	145	178

(Mary clearly had a higher average than Fred. Judy's score was higher than Mary's in two out of three games, and was only two points lower than Mary's in the third game. Answers for the best bowler may vary from "Judy" to "can't tell," because three games give insufficient information.)

❷ Teach

Using the Student Pages For page 406, ask students to determine the answer to 3 + 5 x 7 without using their calculators. Unless they have been informed that the algebraic order of operations is correct, most are likely to say "56." Then assign the exercises.

Before students work on page 407, discuss the last paragraph on page 406, pointing out that students, when using technology such as a **calculator***, need to be sure they know which order of operations it is applying. Go over one or two problems on page 407 involving parentheses. Be sure students understand how to evaluate expressions with more than one set of parentheses. Have students complete page 407 independently. Ask them to record their scores for problems 28–72.

*available separately

◆ LESSON 115 Order of Operations

Teach

Using the Thinking Story In this last segment of "Diet for a Small Terrier," the focus is on proportional reasoning—comparing the weight loss of a small dog with that of a grown person. Ask students to think about the owner's complaint and Marcus's response.

Answers to Thinking Story Questions:

1. No. The key idea here is that weight loss is proportional to body weight and not a fixed amount. One way for students to appreciate this is to imagine how very different Tiny would be if he lost 5 kg, whereas if the owner lost 5 kg she would not look very different at all.

2. Tiny lost 0.1 kg the first week. At that rate it will take 20 weeks for him to lose 2 kg and get down to 5 kg.

3. 20 weeks

4. There are various ways to justify this statement, but all amount to saying that the proportion of weight lost by Tiny is the same as that lost by the owner. One way it can be expressed is to say that Tiny weighed $\frac{1}{10}$ as much as the owner and lost $\frac{1}{10}$ as much in a week. Another way is for students to show that the owner lost $\frac{1}{70}$ of her weight the first week, and so did Tiny (100 grams ÷ 7000 grams = $\frac{1}{70}$).

MATH JOURNAL Ask students to write a different ending to the story in their Math Journals, one in which Marcus explains to the dog owner why Tiny's progress has been better than she thinks it has been.

◆ LESSON 115 Order of Operations

Diet for a Small Terrier

Part 3

You may want to refer to the earlier parts of this Thinking Story on pages 376–377 and 384–385.

After a week of exercise and dieting, Tiny was much livelier. But he was still a fat little terrier. When the owner came to visit, Marcus and Mr. Breezy put Tiny on the scale. He weighed 6.9 kilograms. "Why, Tiny has lost hardly any weight at all!" the owner said angrily. "He weighed 7 kilograms when I brought him to you, and he weighs about the same now. When I went on a diet last year I lost a kilogram a week. I thought you could do that well with a dog. I thought in just two weeks he'd be down to 5 kilograms. He'll never get there at this rate."

"I'm sorry we failed," said Mr. Breezy. "You can take Tiny back. I won't charge you for the week."

"Excuse me," said Marcus, "but I have a question. How much did you weigh when you started your diet?"

"About 70 kilograms, if you must know," said the owner.

"And how long did it take you to get down to 50 kilograms?"

Literature Connection Have students read *And Then There Was One: The Mysteries of Extinction* by Margery Fackham. Ask them to create arithmetic problems for each other to solve, using the statistics about animals and plants presented in the book.

RETEACHING

No reteaching on order of operations is necessary at this time.

"Well, I never actually got there," she said. "I quit dieting after ten weeks, when I was down to 60 kilograms."

"Then I think we may be doing as well with Tiny's diet as you did with yours," Marcus said.

. . . the end

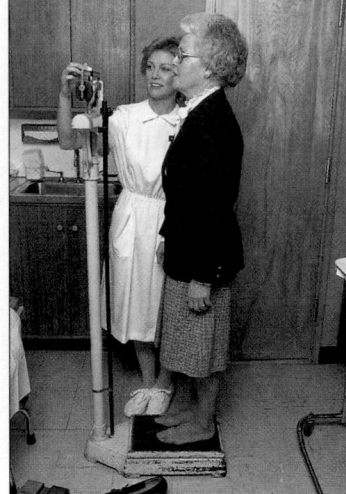

Work in groups. Discuss your answers and how you figured them out. Then compare your answers with those of other groups. Answers are in margin.

1 Is it reasonable to expect a small dog to lose as much weight in a week of dieting as a large person? Why or why not?

2 How much weight did Tiny lose in the first week? If he keeps losing that much every week, how long will it take him to get down to a weight of 5 kilograms?

3 How long would it have taken the owner to get down to a weight of 50 kilograms at the rate she was losing weight?

4 Try to show with numbers why you could say that Tiny's diet is going as well as his owner's diet did.

Unit 5   Lesson 115 • **409**

---

③ Wrap-Up ⏱ 5 MINUTES

 **In Closing** To summarize what the lesson has to say about order of operations, ask students to suggest everyday conventions (such as driving on the right side of the road) and talk about why we follow each one. Then have students compare conventions in mathematics with those from society. Ask them to write a statement for their Math Journals in which they discuss the need for a convention regarding the order of operations.

 Have students compare their scores on questions 28–72 with scores on previous reviews of operations with whole numbers, decimals, and fractions.

Assessment Criteria

Did the student . . .

✓ participate constructively in the discussion about conventions?

✓ demonstrate an understanding of the idea of different orders of operations?

✓ correctly answer at least 48 of the 60 problems on page 407?

✓ contribute to the Thinking Story discussion?

✓ understand the point about proportional thinking that Marcus made in the Thinking Story?

Homework Invite students to investigate more about pet weight-loss issues by asking a veterinarian, pet store owner, or pet owner how pets can lose (or gain) weight. Have them report back to the class on their findings.

PRACTICE p. 115

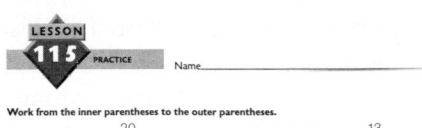

LESSON 115 PRACTICE   Name_____

Work from the inner parentheses to the outer parentheses.

1. (7 + 3) × 2 = __20__
2. 7 + (3 × 2) = __13__
3. (12 ÷ 4) + 2 = __5__
4. 12 ÷ (4 + 2) = __2__
5. ((6 + 9) ÷ 3) –2 = __3__
6. (6 + (9 ÷ 3)) –2 = __7__
7. 6 + ((9 ÷ 3) –2) = __7__
8. (13 –4) × (2 + 7) = __81__
9. (13 –((4 × 2)) + 7 = __12__
10. 13 – ((4 × 2) + 7) = __−2__

Solve. Use shortcuts when you can.

11. 8 × 6 = __48__
12. 80 × 6 = __480__
13. 81 × 6 = __486__
14. 8.1 × 6 = __48.6__
15. 8.1 × 0.6 = __4.86__
16. 81 × 60 = __4860__
17. 30 × 6 = __180__
18. 30 × 7 = __210__
19. 30 × 8 = __240__
20. 30 × 9 = __270__

Solve. Watch the signs. If the answer is an improper fraction, you can leave it or change it to a mixed number.

21. $\frac{1}{3} + \frac{1}{3}$ = $\frac{2}{3}$
22. $\frac{2}{3} - \frac{1}{2}$ = $\frac{1}{6}$
23. $\frac{1}{3} - \frac{1}{3}$ = $\frac{0}{8}$
24. $\frac{2}{3} + \frac{1}{9}$ = $\frac{1}{9}$
25. $\frac{9}{9} - \frac{1}{9}$ = $\frac{8}{9}$
26. $\frac{1}{3} + \frac{1}{2}$ = $\frac{1}{3}$
27. $\frac{12}{11} - \frac{1}{11}$ = 1
28. $1\frac{1}{3} + 1\frac{1}{3}$ = $2\frac{2}{3}$
29. $\frac{2}{3} + \frac{1}{6}$ = $\frac{1}{2}$
30. $1\frac{7}{8} + \frac{1}{8}$ = 2

Math Explorations and Applications Level 6 • 115

ENRICHMENT p. 115

LESSON 115 ENRICHMENT   Name_____

The order in which you do operations is important. By changing the order, you may get a different result.

In these number sentences you have been given the numbers but no operation signs. Place an operation sign in each square to make the number sentence true.

Note: You may need to add one or more sets of parentheses.

1. (8 ☐+☐ 4) ☐÷☐ 2 ☐−☐ 6 = 0

2. (8 ☐−☐ 4) ☐×☐ (2 ☐+☐ 6) = 32

3. (8 ☐÷☐ 4 ☐−☐ 2) ☐×☐ 6 = 0

4. 8 ☐×☐ (4 ☐+☐ 2) ☐÷☐ 6 = 8

In these number sentences you have been given the operation signs and parentheses, but no numbers. Place the numbers 2, 4, 6, and 8, one in each ☐, to make the number sentences true.

5. ☐8☐ × ☐4☐ – (☐6☐ + ☐2☐) = 24

6. $\frac{☐6☐ ☐2☐}{☐4☐}$ + ☐8☐ = 9

7. ☐6☐ × (☐8☐ – ☐2☐) + ☐4☐ = 40

8. $\frac{☐8☐}{☐6☐ ☐2☐}$ + ☐4☐ = 6

Math Explorations and Applications Level 6 • 115

Graphing Nonlinear Functions

Graphing Nonlinear Functions

LESSON PLANNER

Objective

▶ to provide practice in working with examples of nonlinear functions and their graphs

Context of the Lesson This is the 19th of 24 lessons on functions and graphing.

 MANIPULATIVES

Program Resources

Practice Master 116

Enrichment Master 116

For extra practice:
CD-ROM* Lesson 116

---

① Warm-Up

Problem of the Day Present the following problem: The graph shows the amount of water that was in the bathtub while Henry bathed.

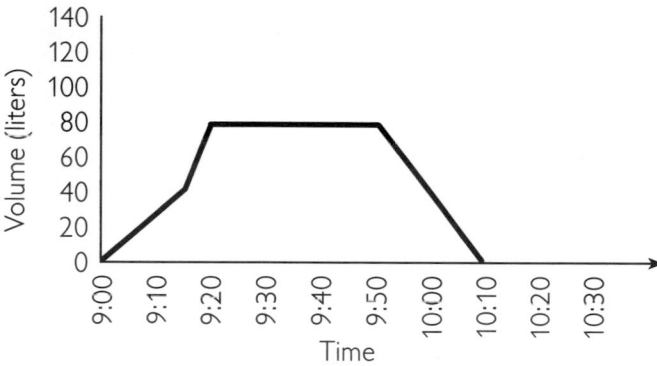

What happened at 9:15, at 9:20, and at 9:50? (At 9:15, Henry increased the flow of water; at 9:20, he turned off the faucet; and at 9:50, he began letting water out of the tub.)

Problem-Solving Strategies Ask students who have solved the Problem of the Day to share how they solved it and any strategies they used.

 **MENTAL MATH** Provide practice with fractions by writing these problems on the chalkboard. Ask students to show thumbs up if the answer is greater than 2, thumbs down if it is less than 2, and stand if it equals 2.

a. $\frac{7}{8} + \frac{2}{8}$ (thumbs down)   **b.** $\frac{1}{3} + \frac{1}{6}$ (thumbs down)

c. $\frac{1}{5} \times 15$ (thumbs up)   **d.** $8 \times \frac{1}{4}$ (stand)

(continued on page 411)

 **ALGEBRA READINESS**

Not all functions are in the form $y = Ax + B$. In this lesson you'll learn about other functions and the lines they form when their ordered pairs are graphed.

Here is a function rule in words. Let x be the length of the side of a square in centimeters. Let y be the area of the square in square centimeters.

Solve.

❶ Use a computer or other means to draw and complete this table of ordered pairs for the function rule.

x	1	2	3	4	5	6	0.5	1.5	2.5	0.1
y	1	4	■	■	■	■	■	■	■	■

9   16   25   36   0.25 2.25 6.25 0.01

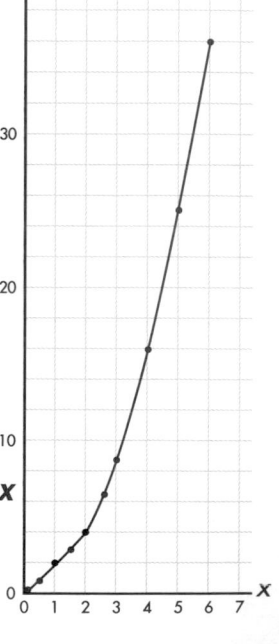

❷ Copy and complete the graph of the function rule. (That is, graph the ordered pairs from problem 1.)

◆ Do the points you graphed fall on a straight line? **no**

◆ Is it possible for x to be less than 0? Explain.
no; a square cannot have a negative side length
We call this kind of function nonlinear.

◆ What does nonlinear mean? **not a line**

❸ On your graph, connect the points with a smooth curved line.
See graph at right.

❹ Try to write a function rule in the short form, using x and y.

$$y = x \times x \quad \text{or} \quad y = x^2 \quad \text{or} \quad y = xx$$

❺ Would it be possible to draw a graph of this data based on only two ordered pairs? **no**

Why **teach it at this time?**

Although students were exposed to nonlinear functions, such as growth curves, in earlier grades and earlier lessons (e.g. Lessons 96 and 105), this is the first time they will have an algebraic rule for a nonlinear function. The work with exponents in Unit 2 prepared students for the next lesson, which will show in more detail how to use exponents to write function rules of this type.

RETEACHING

Extra teaching is not suggested at this time, aside from giving help with calculating ordered pairs and locating points.

Think about the function that has this rule: x is the length (in centimeters) of the short side of a rectangle, 3x is the length (in centimeters) of the long side, and y is the area (in square centimeters) of the rectangle.

Here are three rectangles that meet these conditions.

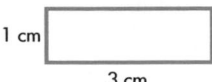
1 cm
3 cm

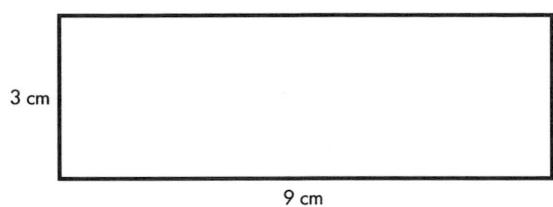
3 cm
9 cm

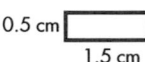
0.5 cm
1.5 cm

Solve.

6 Draw a few more rectangles that meet the conditions. **Accept any rectangle in which the length is three times as long as the width.**

7 Use a computer or other means to make and complete a table of ordered pairs for the function. **Be sure that for each ordered pair the length is three times the width.**

8 Graph the ordered pairs. Connect them with a smooth curve. **Check students' graphs carefully.**

9 Is your graph of this function a straight line? **no**

10 Is it possible for x to be less than 0? **no**

11 Try to write a function rule in the short form, using x and y.

$$y = 3x \times x \quad \text{or} \quad y = 3x^2 \quad \text{or} \quad y = 3xx$$

Unit 5   Lesson 116 • **411**

Mental Math (continued)

e. $\frac{5}{6} + \frac{1}{3}$ (thumbs down)   **f.** $10 \times \frac{7}{10}$ (thumbs up)

g. $\frac{3}{4} \div \frac{1}{3}$ (thumbs up)   **h.** $\frac{1}{2} \div \frac{1}{5}$ (thumbs up)

❷ Teach

Using the Student Pages Go over the function rule at the top of page 410. Then ask students to do problems 1–3 on their own. Check that students have drawn their graphs correctly. Then discuss the rest of the questions with the class. It is essential for students to realize that functions with or without an algebraic rule can have graphs that are not straight lines. It is not necessary for them to draw a precise, smooth curve. Accept function rules written in any of the forms shown for the answer to problem 4. Use of exponents is explained in more detail in Lesson 117. Go over the material at the top of page 411 with students, providing help as needed.

❸ Wrap-Up

In Closing Ask students to give a function rule for the area of a square with sides W and an area of Y. (Y = W × W; Y = WW; Y = W²)

Portfolio Assessment Ask students to record some real life functions that might not have a straight line graph (for example, speed of a car or train).

PRACTICE p. 116

LESSON 116 PRACTICE   Name_____

For each function rule complete the table of ordered pairs, and then graph the function rule.

1 Let x be the length of one side of a rectangle in centimeters. Let 2x be the length of the longer side in centimeters. Let y be the area in square centimeters.

x	1	2	3	4	5
y	2	8	18	32	50

2 Let x be the length of one side of a rectangle in centimeters. Let y be the length of the other side in centimeters. The area is always 512 square centimeters.

x	1	2	4	8	16	32
y	512	256	128	64	32	16

116 • Math Explorations and Applications Level 6

ENRICHMENT p. 116

LESSON 116 ENRICHMENT   Name_____

In the years 1958–1995 the postal rates for the first ounce of first-class mail went from $0.04 to $0.32. The changes are shown in the table below. Graph the rates according to their year of change.

Year	'58	'63	'68	'71	'74	'75	'78	'81	'81	'85	'88	'91	'95
Rate	$0.04	$0.05	$0.06	$0.08	$0.10	$0.13	$0.15	$0.18	$0.20	$0.22	$0.25	$0.29	$0.32

First-Class Postal Rates 1958–1995

1 Is your graph linear? **no**

2 What explanation might you give for the shape of the graph? Answers will vary.

3 What might you predict that the postal rate for the first ounce of first-class mail would be in the year 2005? Answers will vary.

4 Are there any groups of three or more years whose points lie along a straight line? If so, list them. 1958–1963–1968 and 1968–1971–1974

116 • Math Explorations and Applications Level 6

Assessment Criteria

Did the student . . .

✓ correctly complete the table of ordered pairs for the function rule and draw the graph correctly?

✓ demonstrate understanding of how to write function rules using algebraic notation?

Homework Have students choose a game introduced in this unit to play with a family member. Alternately, invite students to create a problem like the Problem of the Day for family members to solve, and to share with classmates during the next math class.

Unit 5 Lesson 116 **411**

More Nonlinear Functions

LESSON PLANNER

Objectives

▶ to introduce the standard notation for function rules such as $y = x^2$, $y = 3x^2$, and $y = 3x^2 - 5x + 8$

▶ to provide more practice in graphing nonlinear functions

Context of the Lesson This is the 20th of 24 lessons on functions and graphing.

 MANIPULATIVES   **Program Resources**

Reteaching Master

Practice Master 117

Enrichment Master 117

For extra practice:
CD-ROM* Lesson 117

 ## ① **Warm-Up** ⏱ 5 MINUTES

 **Problem of the Day** Present the following problem: Two high-speed trains are speeding toward the same station from opposite directions. One is traveling at a speed of 3 mi/min. The other is moving at a speed of 2 mi/min. They are 1000 miles apart. How far apart will they be 2 minutes before they reach the station? (10 miles)

Problem-Solving Strategies Ask students who have solved the Problem of the Day to share how they solved it and any strategies they used.

MENTAL MATH Have students answer the following decimal and fraction problems. Ask them to respond using thumbs up if the answer is more than 2 and thumbs down if it is less than 2.

a. 0.9×0.4 (thumbs down)

b. 8×0.36 (thumbs up)

c. $0.98 - 0.35$ (thumbs down)

d. 7×0.3 (thumbs up)

e. $\frac{3}{4} + \frac{7}{16}$ (thumbs down)

f. $0.32 + 0.59$ (thumbs down)

g. $\frac{9}{10} - \frac{2}{5}$ (thumbs down)

h. $1\frac{2}{10} + 1.2$ (thumbs up)

More Nonlinear Functions

 *ALGEBRA READINESS*

You've learned that functions of the form $y = Ax + B$ have graphs that are straight lines, while some other functions do not. In this lesson you'll graph more nonlinear functions.

Solve.

① Use a computer or other means to make and complete this table of ordered pairs for the function rule $y = xx$.

				3	4			0.04	0.16	0.36	0.64			
x	0	1	2	■	■	5	0.1	0.2	0.3	0.4	0.5	0.6	0.7	0.8	0.9
y	■	■	4	9	16	25	■	■	■	■	■	■	■	■	■
	0	1						0.01	0.09		0.25		0.49		0.81

A function rule such as $y = xx$ is more commonly written with exponents: $y = x^2$. (Remember, 3×3 can be written as 3^2, 5×5 as 5^2, and so on. So xx can be written as x^2.) We read $y = x^2$ as "y equals x squared."

To write $3xx$ with exponents, we write $3x^2$. The term $3x^2$ means to multiply 3 times x times x (the 3 is used as a factor only once). We read $y = 3x^2$ as "y equals three x squared."

③ **The graphs are identical except for the scale on the y-axis.**

② Graph the function that has the rule $y = x^2$. You may copy and complete the graph that has been started here.

③ What is the relationship between this graph and the graph you drew for problem 2 on page 410?

④ What would the graph of $y = x^2 + 2$ look like? **It would have the same shape as $y = x^2$ but be shifted up 2 units.**

⑤ What would the graph of $y = x^2 - 3$ look like? **It would be the same shape as $y = x^2$ but be shifted down 3 units.**

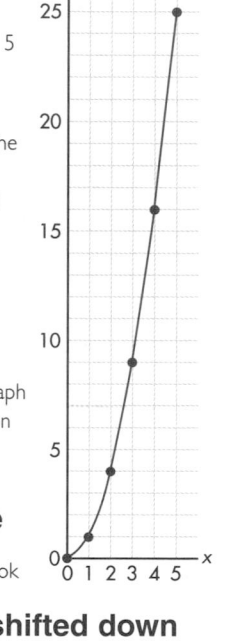

 **SPECIAL NEEDS**

Meeting Individual Needs

If students have difficulty with the order of operation when finding y-values for a function like $y = 3x^2$ or $y = 2x^2 + 5x + 5$, consider having them write out the steps. For example, for $y = 2x^2 + 5x + 5$:

1. Multiply the value of x by itself and multiply that product by 2.

2. Multiply 5 times x.

3. Record 5.

4. Add the results of steps 1–3.

RETEACHING p. 39

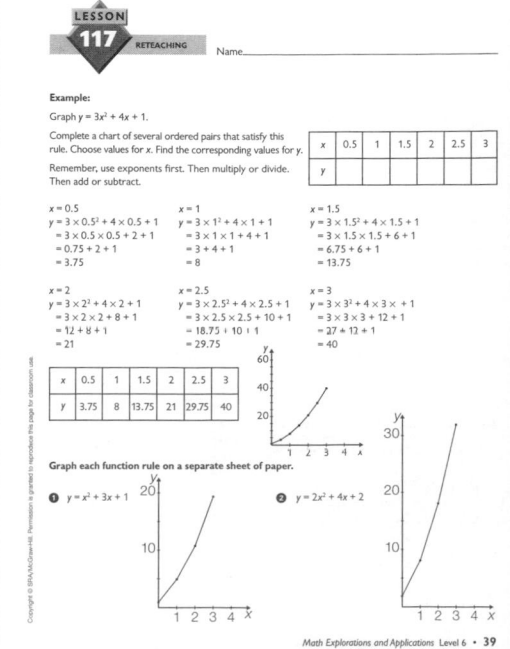

*available separately

Look at this function rule: $y = 2x^2 + 5x + 5$.

If x is 3, what is y?

Here is how we can find out.

$y = 2x^2 + 5x + 5$

$y = (2 \times 3^2) + (5 \times 3) + 5$

$y = (2 \times 9) + (5 \times 3) + 5$

$y = 18 + 15 + 5$

$y = 38$

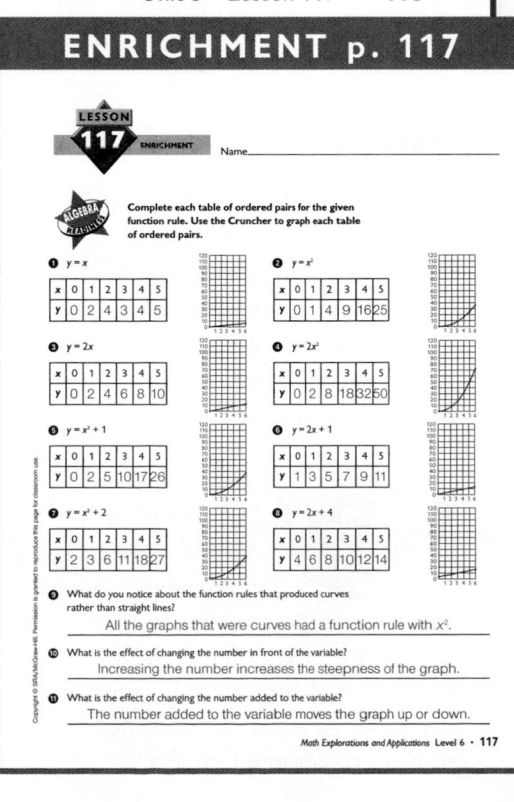

(3, 38)

To avoid confusion when solving problems like this one, we agree that we will do all the multiplication and division first, then the addition and subtraction.

Solve.

6 Use a computer or other means to make and complete this table of ordered pairs for the function rule $y = 2x^2 + 5x + 5$.

x	0	1	2	3	0.5	1.5	2.5
y	■	■	■	■	■	■	■

5 12 23 38 8 17 30

7 Use the ordered pairs you found in problem 6 to graph $y = 2x^2 + 5x + 5$. You may copy and complete the graph that has been started here.

8 Why do we need to know what order of operations to use in finding ordered pairs for this function? **Otherwise, we could get different answers, and we want the function to have only one output for each input.** **9** Use a computer or other means to make and complete this table of ordered pairs for the function rule $y = 3x^2 - 2x + 4$.

x	0	1	2	3	0.5	1.5	2.5
y	4	5	12	25			

3.75 8.75 17.75

10 Use the ordered pairs you found in problem 9 to graph the function $y = 3x^2 - 2x + 4$. **Check students' graphs carefully.**

Unit 5 Lesson 117 • **413**

PRACTICE p. 117

LESSON 117 PRACTICE Name_____

Complete each table of ordered pairs for the given function rule.

1 $y = \frac{x^2}{4} + 4$

x	0	1	2	3	4	5	6	7
y	4	4.25	5	6.25	8	10.25	13	16.25

2 $y = \frac{x^2}{5} + x + 1$

x	0	0.5	1	1.5	2	2.5	3	3.5	4	4.5	5
y	1	1.55	2.2	2.95	3.8	4.75	5.8	6.95	8.2	9.55	11

3 Use the ordered pairs you found in problem 1 to graph the function $y = \frac{x^2}{4} + 4$.

4 Use the ordered pairs you found in problem 2 to graph the function $y = \frac{x^2}{5} + x + 1$.

Math Explorations and Applications Level 6 • 117

ENRICHMENT p. 117

LESSON 117 ENRICHMENT Name_____

Complete each table of ordered pairs for the given function rule. Use the Cruncher to graph each table of ordered pairs.

1 $y = x$

x	0	1	2	3	4	5
y	0	2	4	3	4	5

2 $y = x^2$

x	0	1	2	3	4	5
y	0	1	4	9	16	25

3 $y = 2x$

x	0	1	2	3	4	5
y	0	2	4	6	8	10

4 $y = 2x^2$

x	0	1	2	3	4	5
y	0	2	8	18	32	50

5 $y = x^2 + 1$

x	0	1	2	3	4	5
y	0	2	5	10	17	26

6 $y = 2x + 1$

x	0	1	2	3	4	5
y	1	3	5	7	9	11

7 $y = x^2 + 2$

x	0	1	2	3	4	5
y	2	3	6	11	18	27

8 $y = 2x + 4$

x	0	1	2	3	4	5
y	4	6	8	10	12	14

9 What do you notice about the function rules that produced curves rather than straight lines?
All the graphs that were curves had a function rule with x^2.

10 What is the effect of changing the number in front of the variable?
Increasing the number increases the steepness of the graph.

11 What is the effect of changing the number added to the variable?
The number added to the variable moves the graph up or down.

Math Explorations and Applications Level 6 • 117

---

❷ Teach

Using the Student Pages Discuss the material below the table of ordered pairs on page 412. Then have students work independently on problems 1–5. Note that finding the x-values for $y = 9$ and $y = 16$ in problem 1 involves finding a square root. Students can do this by trial and error.

Go over the example on page 413 with the class. Then have students work individually on problems 6–10.

❸ Wrap-Up

In Closing To summarize the lesson, ask students to tell in what order they perform operations to find the output of $y = 3x^2 + 5x + 5$.

Performance Assessment Have students complete a table of ordered pairs for the function $y = 3x^2 - 5x + 8$ and then use the ordered pairs to graph the function.

Assessment Criteria

Did the student . . .

✓ correctly use the operations to complete the tables of ordered pairs for the functions presented?

✓ correctly graph each function?

Homework Assign Practice Master 117 for further practice with nonlinear functions.

LOOKING AHEAD In the next lesson each student will need a millimeter ruler.

LESSON 118

Graphing a Perimeter Function

LESSON 118 Graphing a Perimeter Function

LESSON PLANNER

Objective

▶ to demonstrate how to use a graph to determine the function rule the line represents

Context of the Lesson This is the 21st of 24 lessons on functions and graphing.

 **MANIPULATIVES**

graph paper
rulers*

Program Resources

Practice Master 118
Enrichment Master 118

For extra practice:
CD-ROM* Lesson 118
Cumulative Review, page 578

1 Warm-Up

 **Problem of the Day** Present the following problem: Inez has a rectangular swimming pool that is 40 feet long and 22 feet wide. It is 3 feet deep in some parts and as deep as 10 feet in others. There is a strip of cement, 2 feet wide, around the edge of the pool. Inez wants to put in a fence to enclose this border. The fence will have two 3-foot openings. How much fencing does she need? (134 ft)

Problem-Solving Strategies Ask students who have solved the Problem of the Day to share how they solved it and any strategies they used.

 Have students estimate the areas, in suitable units of measure, of rectangular classroom objects and surfaces. Compare estimates. Ask volunteers to use **rulers*** to measure each item to check estimates before the class moves on to the next item.

Graphing a Perimeter Function

In this lesson you will learn whether there is a relationship between the length of a side and the perimeter of a square.

Side (x)	■	■	■	■	■	■	■	■	■	■	■	■	■	■
Perimeter (y)	■	■	■	■	■	■	■	■	■	■	■	■	■	■

Use a computer or other means to make a table like the one shown. In your table, record the results of the following measurements.

❶ Measure the length of a side of each of the nine squares below. Then measure or calculate the perimeter of each square. **See squares for answers.**

❷ On a sheet of paper, draw at least six more squares of different sizes. Measure a side and either measure or calculate the perimeter of each square you draw. **Answers will vary.**

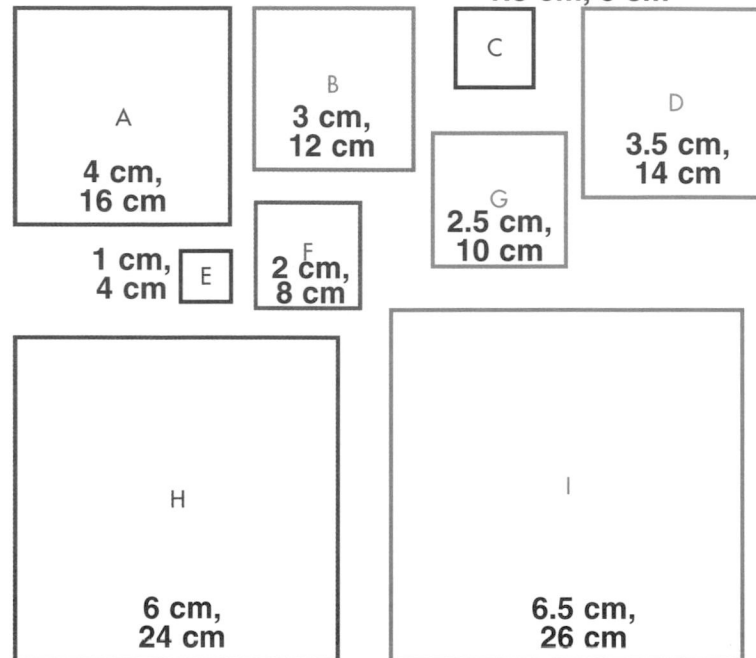

1.5 cm, 6 cm

C

B
3 cm,
12 cm

A

D
3.5 cm,
14 cm

4 cm,
16 cm

G
2.5 cm,
10 cm

1 cm,
4 cm E

F
2 cm,
8 cm

H

I

6 cm,
24 cm

6.5 cm,
26 cm

Why **teach it this way?**

Note that the function rule $p = 4x$ could have been figured out without measuring and graphing. The measuring and graphing approach is useful in cases in which, the rule is not as obvious, as in the activity in Lesson 120 on determining the value of π.

 **Literature Connection** Have students read *Origami in the Classroom* by Chiyo Araki. Prepare different-sized squares for origami projects. Ask students to determine side length or perimeter as requested and then to try some of the origami projects.

RETEACHING

Aside from giving extra help with measuring and graphing during the activities, extra teaching and practice is not suggested at this time.

---

*available separately

Graph the 15 ordered pairs from your table. Then answer these questions.

3 Do all the points fall on about the same straight line? **yes**

4 Does your graph look like the one to the right? **yes**

5 Can you tell from this graph what you multiply a side of a square by to find its perimeter? **yes (4)**

Here is a closer look at part of the graph.

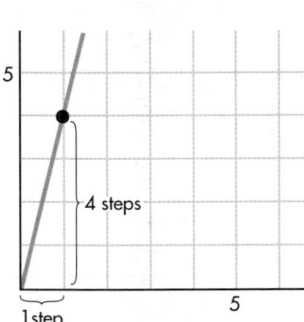

1 step
4 steps

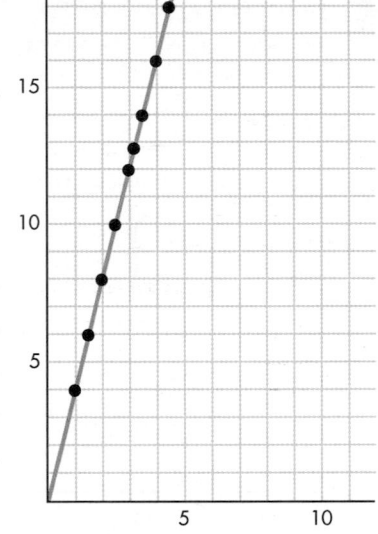

Draw a square that is 10 centimeters on a side. Measure or calculate its perimeter.

◆ Is the perimeter 40 centimeters? **yes**

◆ Is that 4 × 10? **yes**

The formula for finding the perimeter of a square can be written as:

$$y = 4x$$

with y as the perimeter and x as the length of a side. The formula is sometimes written this way:

$$p = 4s$$

with p as the perimeter and s as the length of a side.

Use the Cumulative Review on page 578 after this lesson.

Unit 5 Lesson 118 • **415**

---

2 Teach

Using the Student Pages Have students work individually on pages 414–415. Have **graph paper** available. Those who finish early and successfully can help classmates who are struggling. When everyone has finished, discuss both pages with the class. For problems 1 and 2 the perimeters should be about four times the length of a side in all cases. Nine of the answers will be those on the student page, and the other six will vary. In discussing problem 5 on page 415, point out that because the graph is a straight line, students can write a function rule in the form $y = Ax + B$. The line goes up four steps for every step to the right, so they can write $y = 4x + B$. Point out, furthermore, that because the line goes through the origin, B must be 0, because otherwise the point $(0, 0)$ would not satisfy the rule. So they can write $y = 4x$ for this function.

3 Wrap-Up 5 MINUTES

In Closing To summarize the lesson, ask students to explain what the formula $p = 4s$ means.

Informal Assessment Circulate through the room and observe students as they measure, record, and graph the ordered pairs from their tables. Ask them to explain what their graphs show about the relationship between the length of a side of a square and the perimeter of that square.

Assessment Criteria

Did the student . . .

✓ make accurate measurements of the lengths of the sides of the squares?

✓ correctly record and graph the ordered pairs?

✓ express understanding of how the graph shows the function $p = 4s$ and how this function can be used to find the perimeter of a square or the length of a side of a square?

Homework Have students choose two items at home that they think are square and check whether they might be square by measuring the sides. Make sure they record their figures.

Unit 5 Lesson 118 **415**

Determining the Function Rule

LESSON PLANNER

Objective

▶ to demonstrate and provide practice with finding the rule for a linear function from its graph

Context of the Lesson
This is the 22nd of 24 lessons on functions and graphing.

 MANIPULATIVES

Program Resources

Number Cubes (0–5 and 5–10)

Reteaching Master

Practice Master 119

Enrichment Master 119

For extra practice:
CD-ROM* Lesson 119

❶ Warm-Up ⏱ 5 MINUTES

 **Problem of the Day** Present the following problem to the class: The area of the rectangular rug in Maureen's room is 33 square feet. The rug is $2\frac{3}{4}$ ft wide. What is the perimeter of the rug? ($29\frac{1}{2}$ ft)

Problem-Solving Strategies Ask students who have solved the Problem of the Day to share how they solved it and any strategies they used.

MENTAL MATH Have students play a few rounds of "Cubo," a game they first played in Lesson 6. First, have them play a round or two in which they try to get 21 or close to it. Then challenge them to use a roll of four Number Cubes to get, in turn, each of the numbers from 0 to 10. The entire class should use the same roll. A copy of this game can also be found on page 9 of the Home Connections Blackline Masters.

Determining the Function Rule

 ALGEBRA READINESS

In previous lessons you made graphs from function rules. In this lesson you'll figure out a function rule given a graph of that rule.

If you have a straight-line graph, you can figure out a rule for the function.

The number of steps up for each step to the right tells you what to multiply x by.

The place where the line crosses the y-axis tells you what to add (or subtract).

Example: Figure out a function rule for this graph.

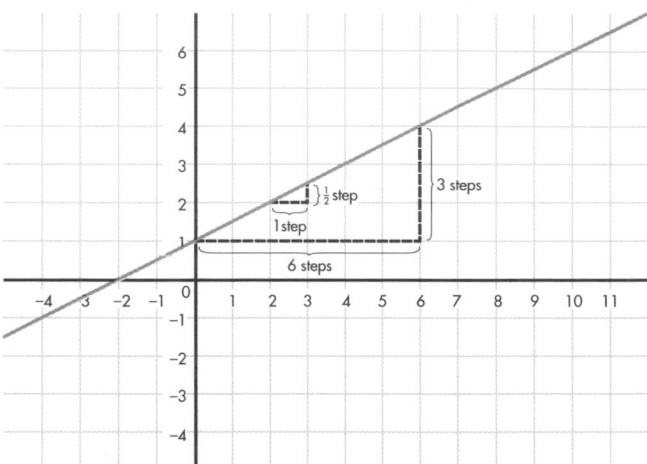

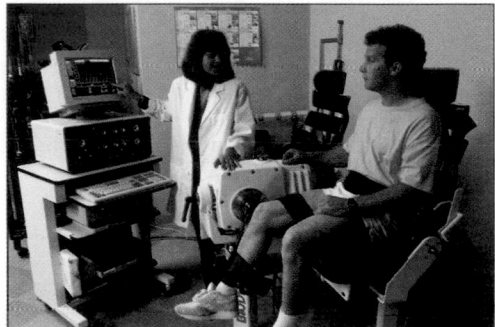

416 • Algebra Readiness

Why teach it this way?

The usual term for the coefficient A in an equation such as $y = Ax + b$ is the slope. However, introducing the term slope at this time is not recommended because it is unlikely that students will remember it until they study algebra.

*available separately

Here is a way to figure out a function rule for the graph.

First, figure out the number of steps up for each step to the right. Here are two ways to do this.

a. Choose a point on the line.
Go to the right one step.
How far up did the line go?

For example, (2, 2).

$\frac{1}{2}$ step

b. Choose a point on the line.
Go to the right any number of steps.
How far up did the line go?

Divide to find out how many steps up for each step to the right.

For example, (0, 1).
Try 6 steps.

3 steps

$3 \div 6 = \frac{1}{2}$

The line goes up a half step for every step to the right. So the number x is multiplied by $\frac{1}{2}$. The function rule is $y = \frac{1}{2}x +$ "something." Remember that the "something" can be either positive or negative.

Second, find the point where the line crosses the y-axis. This is the point (0, 1). Because it is on the line, (0, 1) must satisfy the function rule. Since the graph is a straight line, we know that the rule is in the form $y = Ax + B$.

When $x = 0$, then $y = A \times 0 + B$, so $y = B$.

In this case, since $y = 1$ when $x = 0$, B must be 1.

You can do either of these steps first. B is always the value of y when $x = 0$. Another way to say this is that B is the y-coordinate of the point where the line crosses the y-axis.

So, the function rule for this graph must be $y = \frac{1}{2}x + 1$.

You can use these steps to find the function rule for any graph that is a straight line.

Unit 5   Lesson 119 • **417**

② Teach

Using the Student Pages Begin the discussion by asking students to tell what form a function rule must have if the graph of the function is a straight line. ($y = Ax + B$). Then explain that to determine the rule for a given straight-line graph, the values of A and B need to be determined. In other words, students need to figure out what number x is multiplied by, and what number is added or subtracted.

Next, go over the examples on pages 416–417. To demonstrate that A relates to how steep the line is, you might have volunteers graph the following functions on the chalkboard:

$y = \frac{1}{2}x$ $y = x$

$y = 2x$ $y = 3x$

Then, to demonstrate that B relates to the point at which the graph crosses the y-axis, have other volunteers graph these functions on the board:

$y = x + 1$ $y = x + 4$

$y = x + 0$ (or $y = x$) $y = x - 3$

Have students discuss the similarities and differences among the graphs in each set. Point out that in the first set all graphs pass through the origin (0, 0), but that each has a different value for A and therefore a different amount of steepness. They should see that all the graphs in the second set have the same amount of steepness, but have different values for B, and therefore cross the y-axis at different points.

◆ LESSON 119 Determining the Function Rule

Teach

Using the Student Pages Have students complete the problems on pages 418–419 on their own. Provide help as needed.

◆ LESSON 119 Determining the Function Rule

For each graph, determine a function rule.

1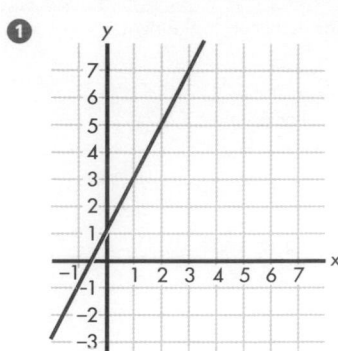

$$y = 2x + 1$$

2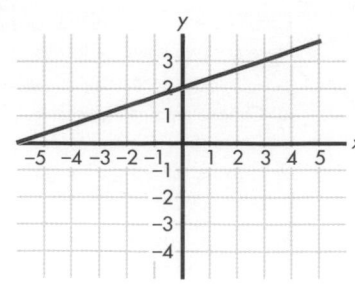

$$y = \frac{1}{3}x + 2$$

3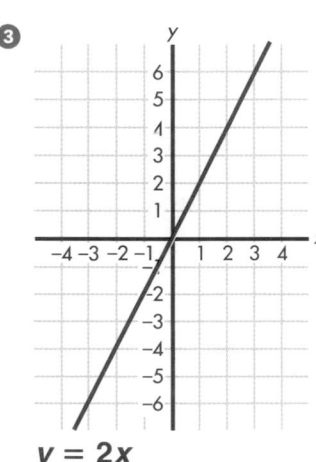

$$y = 2x$$

4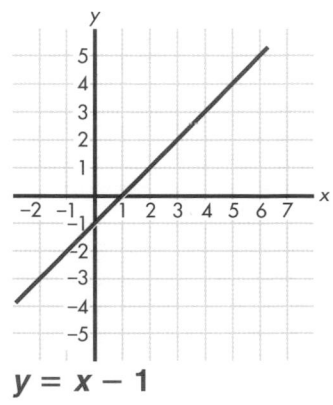

$$y = x - 1$$

Hints: Write 1x as x.
To get from 0 to −1, subtract 1.

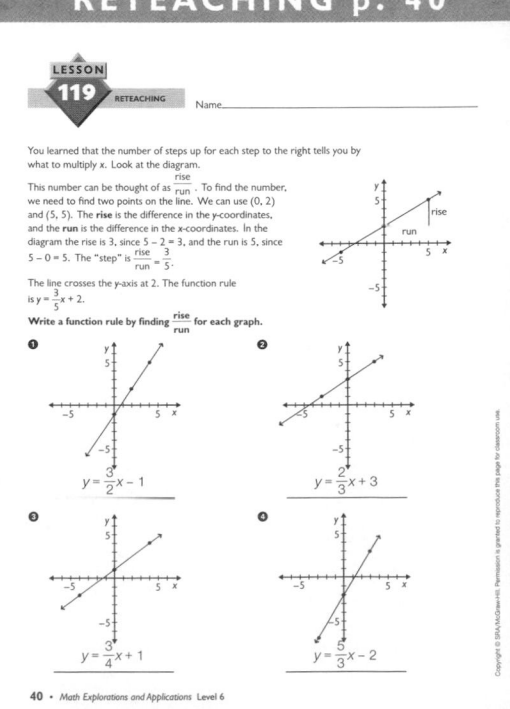

RETEACHING p. 40

LESSON 119 RETEACHING Name

You learned that the number of steps up for each step to the right tells you by what to multiply x. Look at the diagram.

This number can be thought of as $\frac{rise}{run}$. To find the number, we need to find two points on the line. We can use (0, 2) and (5, 5). The **rise** is the difference in the y-coordinates, and the **run** is the difference in the x-coordinates. In the diagram the rise is 3, since 5 − 2 = 3, and the run is 5, since 5 − 0 = 5. The "step" is $\frac{rise}{run} = \frac{3}{5}$.

The line crosses the y-axis at 2. The function rule is $y = \frac{3}{5}x + 2$.

Write a function rule by finding $\frac{rise}{run}$ for each graph.

1 $y = \frac{3}{2}x - 1$

2 $y = \frac{2}{3}x + 3$

3 $y = \frac{3}{4}x + 1$

4 $y = \frac{5}{3}x - 2$

40 • Math Explorations and Applications Level 6

Meeting Individual Needs

To help students predict how steep the graph of a given function rule will be, give rules like $y = 2x$, $y = 3x$, $y = 5x$, $y = 5x + 3$, and $y = 2x + 5$. As you do, focus students on the coefficient of x and the steepness of each graph.

To help students predict where a graph for a given function rule will cross the y-axis, have them find what y is when $x = 0$. After several examples, students can see that for a function rule of the form $y = Ax + B$, when x is 0, y is B. They can see that B is the y-coordinate of the point where the line crosses the y-axis.

Solve for the variable. Use shortcuts when you can.

5 $n = 3 \times 20$ **60**   **6** $4 \div \frac{1}{2} = w$ **8**   **7** $6.1 \times 3.0 = n$ **18.3**

8 $w - 3.5 = 13.5$ **17.0**   **9** $\frac{1}{2} \times \frac{3}{4} = n$ **$\frac{3}{8}$**   **10** $16 \times 1000 = p$ **16,000**

11 $n \times 20 = 400$ **20**   **12** $165.2 - 5.2 = n$ **160.0**   **13** $25 \times 25 = t$ **625**

14 $x + 625 = 630.5$ **5.5**   **15** $50 \times 50 = n$ **2500**   **16** $50 \times 51 = n$ **2550**

17 $1000 \div t = 25$ **40**   **18** $c \div 25 = 4000$ **100,000**   **19** $n \times 6 = 36$ **6**

20 $15 \div n = 5$ **3**   **21** $\frac{13}{13} \times \frac{57}{57} = n$ **1**   **22** $30 \times w = 930$ **31**

1698.2 **23** $16.982 \times 100 = t$ **24** $450 + 550 = n$ **1000**   **25** $5 + n = 7.45$ **2.45**

26 $\frac{16}{49} \times 1 = n$ **$\frac{16}{49}$**   **27** $y \div 12 = 4$ **48**   **28** $3\frac{1}{2} \times 4 = n$ **14**

29 $3\frac{1}{2} \times 40 = d$ **140**   **30** $75 + \frac{35}{35} = n$ **76**   **31** $169 \div 13 = t$ **13**

32 $\frac{19}{23} \times 0 = n$ **0**   **33** $y \times 12 = 144$ **12**   **34** $196 \div 14 = n$ **14**

Solve. Use shortcuts when you can.

35
$$\begin{array}{r} 750 \\ 750 \\ 750 \\ + 750 \\ \hline 3000 \end{array}$$

36
$$\begin{array}{r} 10,000 \\ -\ 9,950 \\ \hline 50 \end{array}$$

37 $24\overline{)288}$ **12**

38 $12\overline{)288}$ **24**

39 $65\overline{)1235}$ **19**

40
$$\begin{array}{r} 16\frac{4}{5} \\ + 13\frac{3}{15} \\ \hline 30 \end{array}$$

41 $19\overline{)1235}$ **65**

42 $1.9\overline{)123.5}$ **65**

Solve these problems.

43 Leah can swim 100 meters in 105 seconds. Can she swim 1000 meters in 17.5 minutes (1050 seconds)? **probably not because she will get tired**

44 Today Leah swam 100 meters in $1\frac{2}{3}$ minutes. Was that a faster pace than 100 meters in 105 seconds? **yes**

Unit 5   Lesson 119 • **419**

PRACTICE p. 119

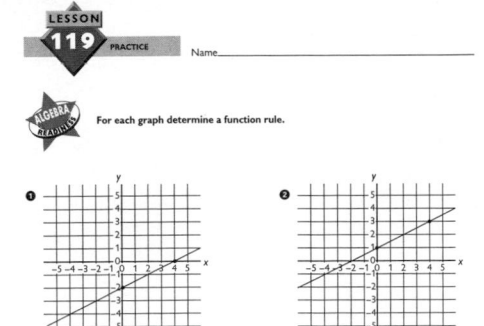

Math Explorations and Applications Level 6 • **119**

ENRICHMENT p. 119

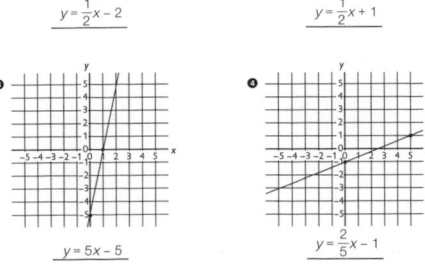

Solve this puzzle. Use one square for any decimal points in your answers.

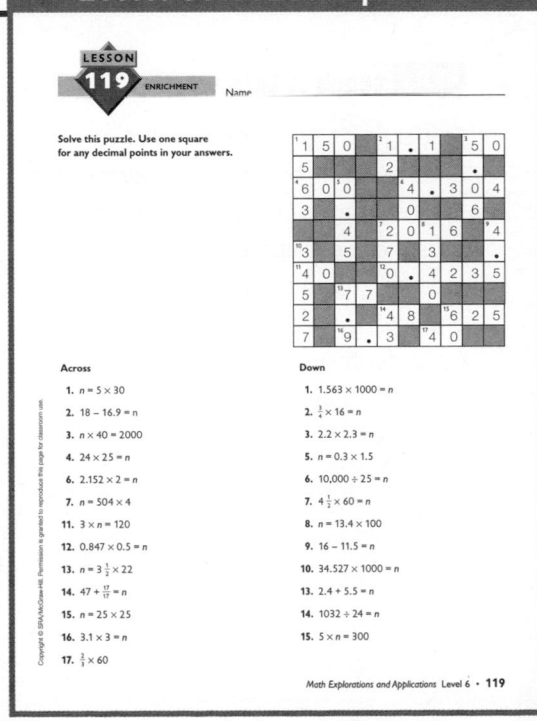

Across

1. $n = 5 \times 30$
2. $18 - 16.9 = n$
3. $n \times 40 = 2000$
4. $24 \times 25 = n$
6. $2.152 \times 2 = n$
7. $n = 504 \times 4$
11. $3 \times n = 120$
12. $0.847 \times 0.5 = n$
13. $n = 3\frac{1}{2} \times 22$
14. $47 + \frac{17}{17} = n$
15. $n = 25 \times 25$
16. $3.1 \times 3 = n$
17. $\frac{4}{5} \times 60$

Down

1. $1.563 \times 1000 = n$
2. $\frac{3}{4} \times 16 = n$
3. $2.2 \times 2.3 = n$
5. $n = 0.3 \times 1.5$
6. $10,000 \div 25 = n$
7. $4\frac{1}{2} \times 60 = n$
8. $n = 13.4 \times 100$
9. $16 - 11.5 = n$
10. $34.527 \times 1000 = n$
13. $2.4 + 5.5 = n$
14. $1032 \div 4 = n$
15. $5 \times n = 300$

Math Explorations and Applications Level 6 • **119**

---

3 Wrap-Up

In Closing To summarize the lesson, ask students to explain how to determine the function rule from a line graph.

Performance Assessment Have students work in pairs. Ask one to draw the graph of a function on the chalkboard. Ask the other student to figure out the function rule for it. Then have students change roles.

Assessment Criteria

Did the student . . .

✓ understand how to tell where a given function crosses the y-axis?

✓ understand how to tell the number of steps up for each step to the right in a given function?

✓ correctly answer at least 30 of the 40 problems on page 419?

Homework Ask students to draw, on the same set of axes, the parallel graphs of three functions that cross the y-axis at different points. Students should write each function above its graph.

LOOKING AHEAD You will need metric tape measures and different-sized circular objects for Lesson 120. You may wish to ask students to bring the objects to class.

LESSON 120
Finding Circumference

LESSON PLANNER

Objectives

▶ to have students approximate the value of π, the ratio of the circumference of a circle to the diameter of the circle, by graphing a set of measurements

▶ to provide practice in using approximations of π to calculate the circumference of a circle

▶ to provide practice for comparing, in terms of convenience and precision, the use of 3.14 and $3\frac{1}{7}$ as approximations of π

▶ to provide practice in multiplying whole numbers and decimals and in multiplying whole numbers and mixed numbers

Context of the Lesson
This is the 23rd of 24 lessons on functions and graphing. In this lesson students will first approximate by measuring and graphing, and then use and compare two commonly used approximations for π, 3.14 and $3\frac{1}{7}$.

👆 MANIPULATIVES

centimeter rulers and tape measures*

compasses

string

circular objects, various

calculator*

graph paper

Program Resources

Number Cubes (0–5 and 5–10)

Reteaching Master

Practice Master 120

Enrichment Master 120

The Cruncher*: *How Did They Ever Figure Out Pi?*

For extra practice:
CD-ROM* Lesson 120

Note: This lesson may take more than one day.

---

① Warm-Up ⏱ 5 MINUTES

Problem of the Day Present the following problem to students: Draw a clock face with the numbers clearly visible. Then draw a line segment dividing your clock in half so that the sum of the numbers on one half circle equals the sum of the numbers on the other half. (Line should be drawn from between the 9 and 10 across to between the 3 and 4.)

Problem-Solving Strategies Ask students who have solved the Problem of the Day to share how they solved it and any strategies they used.

Finding Circumference

In this lesson you'll investigate to discover whether there is a relationship between the **diameter** (the greatest distance across) and the **circumference** (the distance around) of a circle.

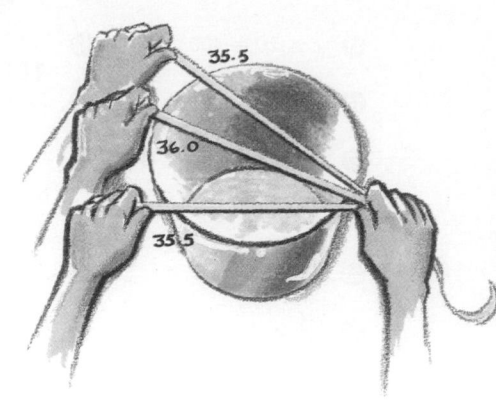

◆ Use a tape measure to measure the diameter and the circumference of at least five different circles or circular objects.

◆ Measure the diameter by holding one end of your tape measure (or ruler) at a point on the circle. Move the other end until the distance is the greatest. If you use a tape measure (or a string), be sure to pull it tight. In this picture, 36 centimeters is a good approximation of the diameter of the circle.

◆ Measure the circumference by wrapping a tape measure or string around the object. Measure as close to the edge as you can, particularly if the object has two bases of different sizes.

Why teach it this way?

Students can gain a deeper understanding of geometric relationships by doing hands-on investigations of those relationships. In this case, measuring to discover the relationship between the diameter and circumference of a circle will help students to better understand the meaning of π.

❶ **They should be. If not, students should repeat their measurements on those circles that are off the line.**

Write your measurements in a table like this one.

Circle	Diameter (cm) (x)	Circumference (cm) (y)
top of wastebasket	▪	▪
large jar	▪	▪
water glass	▪	▪
tire	▪	▪

Answers will depend on size of items measured.

Graph the ordered pairs from your table. Then answer these questions.

❶ Are all the points you graphed approximately on a straight line?

❷ About how many steps up does your graph go for each ten steps to the right? About how many steps up does it go for each step to the right? **Answers to the first part should be between 30 and 33. Answers to the second part should be between 3.1 and 3.2.**

❸ Write a formula relating the circumference and the diameter of a circle. **Students who are using 3.1, for example, as the multiplier (coefficient), might write: $y = 3.1x$ or $c = 3.1d$ or even**

$$d \longrightarrow \boxed{\times 3.1} \longrightarrow c$$

❹ The **radius** of a circle is the distance from the center to a point on the circle. What is the relationship between the radius and the diameter of a circle? **The diameter is twice the radius (or the radius is half the diameter).**

❺ Rewrite your formula from problem 3 to use the radius instead of the diameter. **Answers will vary. The multiplier should be twice what it was in problem 3.**

❻ Use your formula from problem 3 to predict the circumference of a circle that is 50 centimeters in diameter. **Answers will vary but generally will be between 150 and 165 centimeters.**

❼ If a circle is 50 centimeters in diameter, what is its radius? **25 cm**

❽ Draw a circle 50 centimeters in diameter and measure its circumference. How close was your prediction? **The circumference should be between 155 and 160 cm. Predictions should be very close.**

Unit 5   Lesson 120   •   **421**

Literature Connection Have students read *The Librarian Who Measured the Earth* by Kathryn Lasky. Ask students to explain how Eratosthenes determined the circumference of the earth.

MENTAL MATH Continue playing "Cubo," as in the previous lesson.

❷ Teach

MANIPULATIVES **Using the Student Pages** As needed, review with students the terms *diameter* and *circumference*. Discuss and demonstrate the method for measuring diameter, as illustrated on page 420. Explain that if students can locate the center of the circle, they can measure the diameter along any segment through the center with endpoints on the circle. You will need to provide various **circular objects** for students to measure. **String, compasses, rulers,** and **tape measures*** will be useful for this activity.

COOPERATIVE LEARNING Have students work in small groups for the activity on page 421. Members should check one another's measurements. Students can use **The Cruncher*:** *How Did They Ever Figure Out Pi?* spreadsheets to record their measurements. Have **graph paper** available.

Note: π, the ratio of circumference to diameter, is an irrational number with a decimal expansion that neither terminates nor repeats. Approximations of π have been made to thousands of places. To the nearest ten-millionth, π is 3.1415927. For most practical purposes, an approximation of $3\frac{1}{7}$ or 3.14 is sufficient.

*available separately

◆ LESSON 120 Finding Circumference

Teach

Using the Student Pages Briefly discuss the information in the first paragraph. Explain that the true value of π is between 3.141 and 3.142 and that $3\frac{1}{7}$ is a close approximation. Have students do problems 9–16 on page 422 on their own. Students can use **The Cruncher*:** *How Did They Ever Figure Out Pi?* to help them calculate their answers. When they have completed the problems, discuss the answers.

From the results, students should realize that π is close to both $3\frac{1}{7}$ and 3.14, and that $3\frac{1}{7}$ is just slightly closer to π. They could also determine that $3\frac{1}{7}$ is closer by looking at 3.14 and the decimal approximation of $3\frac{1}{7}$ (3.1428571) and comparing these to the decimal approximation of π (3.1415927). The differences between the results obtained using the various approximations can be considered small, especially in light of the much less precise measurements with which students are used to working. Have **calculators*** available for problem 13.

Have students solve the problems on page 423 on their own.

![SPECIAL NEEDS] **Meeting Individual Needs**
For students who have difficulty multiplying decimals and whole numbers, see the suggestions in Lesson 30. For students having trouble converting between improper fractions and mixed numbers, see the suggestions in Lesson 78.

◆ LESSON 120 Finding Circumference

The Greek letter π (pronounced "pi") is used to indicate the ratio of the circumference of a circle to its diameter.

$C = \pi d$ is the formula for finding the circumference (C) of a circle when the diameter (d) is known. To find the circumference, multiply d by π.

π is a definite fixed number between 3.141 and 3.142. The fraction $3\frac{1}{7}$ is a good approximation. The circumference (C) and diameter (d) of different circles vary, but π stays the same.

Answer the following questions.

9 In problems 2 and 3 on page 421, was your estimate of π about 3.14? An answer of 3 or more, but less than 3.3, would be considered close.

10 Use 3.14 for π to find the approximate circumference of a circle with a diameter of

a. 10 centimeters	b. 20 meters	c. 25 centimeters
31.4 cm	**62.8 m**	**78.5 cm**
d. 7 meters	e. 21 centimeters	f. 30 centimeters
21.98 m	**65.94 cm**	**94.2 cm**

11 Use $3\frac{1}{7}$ (or $\frac{22}{7}$) for π to find the approximate circumference of a circle with a diameter of

a. 10 centimeters   b. 20 meters   c. 25 centimeters
$31\frac{3}{7}$ cm (31.43 cm)   **$62\frac{6}{7}$ m (62.86 m)**   **$78\frac{4}{7}$ cm (78.57 cm)**
d. 7 meters   e. 21 centimeters   f. 30 centimeters
22 m   **66 cm**   **$94\frac{2}{7}$ cm (94.29 cm)**

12 In finding a circumference, when is it easier to use 3.14 for π and when is it easier to use $3\frac{1}{7}$?

13 To seven places, the best approximation of π is 3.1415927. Use this number and a calculator to find the approximate circumference of each circle in problem 10. **a. 31.415927 cm; b. 62.831854 m; c. 78.539817 cm; d. 21.991148 m; e. 65.973446 cm; f. 94.24778 cm**

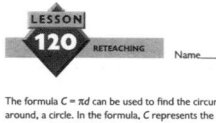

14 Which approximations were closer to those in problem 13, those you found in problem 10 (using 3.14 for π) or those you found in problem 11 (using $3\frac{1}{7}$)? (Change your answers in problem 11 to decimals so you can compare them with your answers in problem 13.) **The approximations from problem 11, since $3\frac{1}{7}$ is just slightly closer to π than is 3.14.**

15 Is there a great difference in your answers for problems 10, 11, and 13? **no**

16 Write a formula for finding the circumference of a circle when the radius is known. **$c = 2\pi r$**

12 In general, it is easier to use $3\frac{1}{7}$ (or $\frac{22}{7}$) when the diameter is a multiple of 7. Otherwise, it is usually easier to use 3.14, especially if the diameter is a power of 10.

422 • Algebra Readiness

9 If the students' estimates are far from the values suggested, have them go back to check their measurements or arithmetic.

Technology Connection You may want to refer students to *Eagle Eye Mystery* from Electronic Arts (IBM, Mac for grades 2–8) to provide practice in collecting and organizing data, deductive reasoning, and reading skills.

RETEACHING p. 41

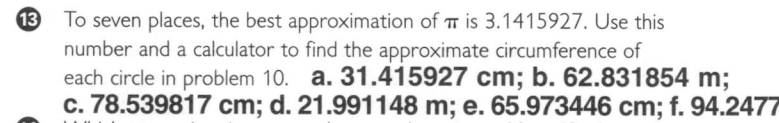

LESSON 120 RETEACHING Name_____

The formula $C = \pi d$ can be used to find the circumference, or distance around, a circle. In the formula, C represents the length of the circumference, d represents the length of the diameter, and π represent the ratio of the circumference to the diameter.

The number π cannot be written out completely, but two common approximations are used in problems. As an improper fraction, π is represented by $\frac{22}{7}$. As a decimal, π is represented by 3.14.

Example 1:
Use $\frac{22}{7}$ for π to find the approximate circumference of a circle with a diameter of 14 centimeters.
$C = \pi d$
$C = \frac{22}{7} \times 14 = 44$ centimeters

Example 2:
Use 3.14 for π to find the approximate circumference of a circle with a diameter of 12 meters.
$C = \pi d$
$C = 3.14 \times 12 = 37.68$ meters

Use $\frac{22}{7}$ for π to find the approximate circumference of a circle with a diameter of

1 10 centimeters. $31\frac{3}{7}$ centimeters   **2** 20 meters. $62\frac{6}{7}$ meters
3 25 centimeters. $78\frac{4}{7}$ centimeters   **4** 7 meters. 22 meters

Use 3.14 for π to find the approximate circumference of a circle with a diameter of

5 10 centimeters. 31.4 centimeters   **6** 20 meters. 62.8 meters
7 25 centimeters. 78.5 centimeters   **8** 7 meters. 21.98 meters

Math Explorations and Applications Level 6 • **41**

***available separately**

Solve these problems. Try to do them in your head. Use shortcuts when you can.

⑰ 9 × 8 **72**   ⑱ 9 + 8 **17**   ⑲ 9 − 8 **1**

⑳ 90 × 800 **72,000** ㉑ 6 × 7 **42**   ㉒ 7 × 60 **420**

㉓ 420 ÷ 60 **7**   ㉔ 4200 ÷ 60 **70**   ㉕ 8 × 7 **56**

㉖ 80 × 7000 **560,000** ㉗ 80 − 70 **10**   ㉘ 6 × 3 **18**

㉙ 6 ÷ 3 **2**   ㉚ 6 + 3 **9**   ㉛ 6 − 3 **3**

㉜ 60 + 3 **63**   ㉝ 63 ÷ 7 **9**   ㉞ 630 ÷ 90 **7**

㉟ 63 − 7 **56**   ㊱ 7 × 70 **490**   ㊲ 70 ÷ 7 **10**

㊳ 7 + 70 **77**   ㊴ 70 − 7 **63**   ㊵ 490 ÷ 7 **70**

㊶ 49 − 7 **42**   ㊷ 9 × 9 **81**   ㊸ 9 + 9 **18**

㊹ 18 ÷ 9 **2**   ㊺ 810 ÷ 90 **9**   ㊻ 180 − 9 **171**

Multiply or divide. Watch the signs.

㊼ 8.76 × 10 **87.6**   ㊽ 87.6 × 100 **8760**   ㊾ 87.6 ÷ 10 **8.76**

㊿ 0.876 × 1000 **876**   51 793.6 ÷ 100 **7.936** 52 79.36 × 10 **793.6**

53 0.7936 × 100 **79.36** 54 79.36 ÷ 10 **7.936** 55 8.457 × 10 **84.57**

56 8.457 × 1000 **8457**   57 8.457 ÷ 100 **0.08457** 58 845.7 ÷ 1000 **0.8457**

59 1234 × 10 **12,340**   60 1234 ÷ 1000 **1.234**   61 12.34 × 100 **1234**

62 1.234 × 100 **123.4**   63 0.5796 × 1000 **579.6** 64 57.96 ÷ 10 **5.796**

65 579.6 ÷ 10,000 **0.05796** 66 5.796 × 100 **579.6** 67 0.5796 × 10 **5.796**

Solve these problems.

68 If hot dog buns come in packages of ten, how many packages are needed to get 75 buns? **8**

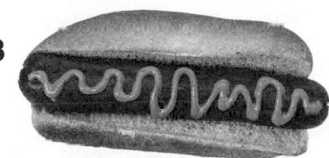

69 One hot dog costs 75¢. How much will 100 hot dogs cost? **$75.00**

Unit 5 Lesson 120 • **423**

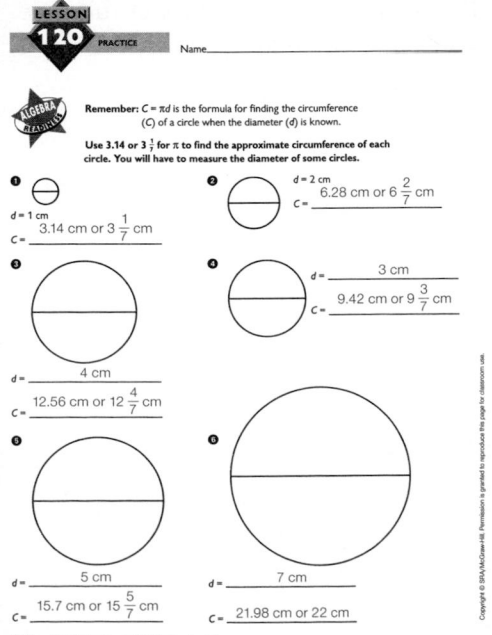

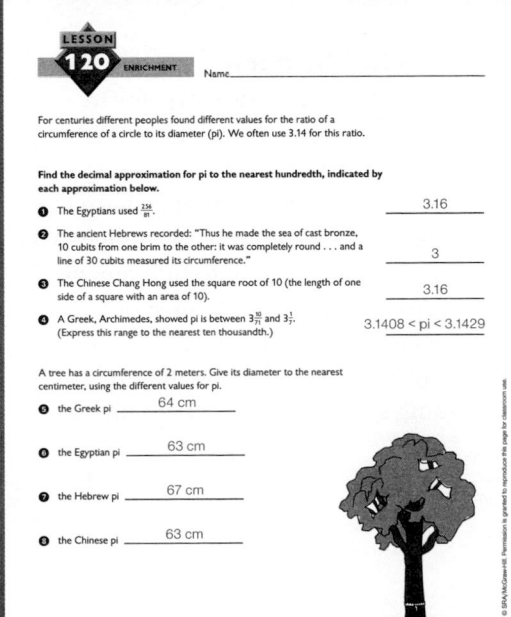

③ Wrap-Up

In Closing Summarize the lesson by asking students to define *circumference, radius,* and *diameter.*

Informal Assessment Circulate through the room and observe students as they make their circles and measurements and complete their graphs. Note which students are having difficulty and provide help as needed.

Assessment Criteria

Did the student . . .

✓ make measurements to discover a reasonable approximation for π?

✓ express understanding of the meaning of π?

✓ correctly use approximations for π to solve the problems on page 422?

✓ correctly answer at least 80% of the problems on page 423?

Homework Have students use measuring tools and their understanding of π to find the circumference of several circular objects in their homes. Alternately, students can measure each circumference and then use that information to find each diameter.

LESSON 121

Average Monthly Temperature

Student Edition pages 424–425

LESSON PLANNER

Objectives

▶ to provide practice in interpreting data in a table

▶ to provide practice in making inferences from data in a table

Context of the Lesson This is the last of 24 lessons on functions and graphing. It provides an informal introduction to periodic functions.

MANIPULATIVES
graph paper

Program Resources
Practice Master 121
Enrichment Master 121
The Cruncher*
For extra practice:
CD-ROM* Lesson 121

① Warm-Up

Problem of the Day Present the following problem to the class: Using the numbers 5–13, make a 3 × 3 square in which the sum of the numbers in each row, column, and diagonal is the same. (One possible answer is top row—12, 5, 10; middle row—7, 9, 11; bottom row—8, 13, 6.)

Problem-Solving Strategies Ask students who have solved the Problem of the Day to share how they solved it and any strategies they used.

MENTAL MATH Write sets of four or five whole numbers on the chalkboard. Ask students to mentally find or approximate the mean of each set.

② Teach

Using the Student Pages Discuss the information in the table. Ask students to suggest which measure of average was used to come up with the data. Ask them to tell which measures of average they think are most useful and least useful for describing average monthly temperatures. You may wish to review the meaning of the term *range* with students.

LESSON 121

Average Monthly Temperature

GEOGRAPHY CONNECTION

As you have seen throughout this unit, charts and graphs can help you analyze data and find patterns. Here is another example.

The following chart gives the average monthly temperatures (in degrees Celsius) in six cities.

	J	F	M	A	M	J	J	A	S	O	N	D
New York	0	1	5	11	17	22	25	24	20	14	8	2
Chicago	−4	−3	3	10	16	22	24	23	19	13	4	−2
Phoenix	11	14	14	19	27	31	34	34	29	23	16	13
San Francisco	9	11	12	13	14	17	14	17	18	16	13	10
Miami	19	20	22	24	26	27	27	28	28	26	22	20
Perth	24	25	23	20	16	15	15	16	17	18	20	22

Study the chart. Then discuss answers to these questions.

❺ The temperatures are coolest in June & July and warmest in January & February. Cities in the southern hemisphere have their seasons opposite to ours.

① Which city has the greatest range in average monthly temperatures? **Chicago**

② In which city do you think people need to spend the most money on clothing? **Chicago**

③ Which city would be likely to have the highest heating costs? **Chicago**

④ Which city has the warmest climate? Which has the coolest climate? **Miami; Chicago**

⑤ Perth is in Australia. Do you notice any difference between the temperature patterns in Perth and the patterns in the U.S. cities? Why is there a difference?

COOPERATIVE LEARNING Work in groups to make up other questions from the chart. Discuss them with your group.

Science Connection Invite students to suggest cities in this country that might have a great range in temperatures and those that might have a more narrow range. Ask them to do research to find out what factors influence the range of temperatures in a region. This activity may be expanded to temperature ranges of cities in other countries.

RETEACHING

Reteaching is not necessary at this time. You may want to assign Practice Master 121 at this time.

*available separately

For each city in the chart on page 424, make a graph of the normal monthly temperatures. Repeat the data for two months at each end of the year, so that your graphs look like this:

City: _____

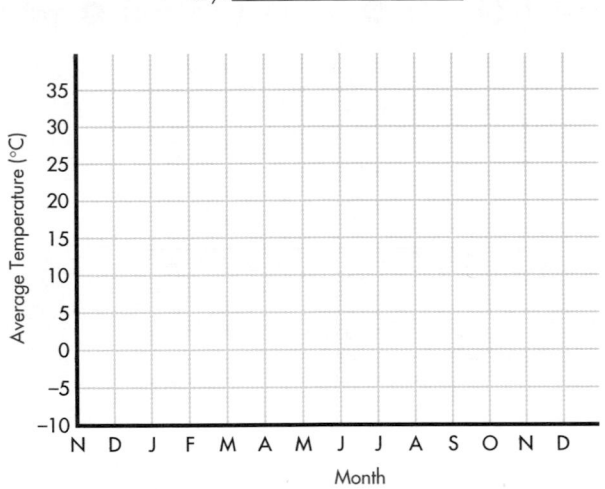

Look at the data and the graphs.

6 Try to explain why the temperatures change as they do. **Answers will vary, but they should focus on the seasonal changes in temperature.**

7 Try to explain the differences among the graphs for different cities. **Answers will vary. Some differences can be explained by differences in latitude; others by proximity of the city to a large body of water.**

8 Is there any number in the chart that looks as if it might have been a mistake? **The July figure for San Francisco looks (and indeed is) incorrect because it breaks the smooth curve that is followed for other cities and for San Francisco elsewhere on its graph.**

Functions that repeat themselves in a certain period are called *periodic functions*. The average monthly temperatures you graphed are periodic functions. Can you think of other periodic functions?

The hottest inhabited city on Earth is Djibouti, in the country of Djibouti in northeastern Africa, with an average temperature of 30°C (86°F).

Unit 5   Lesson 121 • **425**

Have students work on pages 424 and 425 independently. Students can use a **Cruncher*** spreadsheet or **graph paper** to help them graph the data. Go over their responses to the questions. Then have students form groups to discuss questions they have formulated using the data in the table. Invite groups to share some of the more interesting questions with the class.

When answering problems 6–8 on page 425, students may suggest examples of periodic functions that may be stated informally and might relate to tidal changes, seasonal changes, changes in body temperatures, or angular changes, such as hand position on a clock face.

❸ Wrap-Up

In Closing To summarize the lesson, ask students to tell the kinds of information about data a graph might show that might not be as apparent in a table.

Portfolio Assessment Have students write a summary of what the table and graph tell them about life in these cities. Ask them to explain how they made some of the inferences they did, and invite them to place their writings in their Math Portfolios.

Assessment Criteria

Did the student . . .

✓ make reasonable inferences from the data in the table?

✓ correctly graph the data from the table?

Homework Have students use an almanac or other source to compile the same data for these same cities. Ask them to compare their findings with what appears in the table in the textbook, and to describe any differences in the two sets of data.

PRACTICE p. 121

The following table gives average monthly precipitation (in inches) in five cities.

	J	F	M	A	M	J	J	A	S	O	N	D
New York	3.4	3.3	4.1	4.2	4.4	3.7	4.4	4.0	3.9	3.6	4.5	3.9
Chicago	1.5	1.4	2.7	3.6	3.3	3.8	3.7	4.2	3.8	2.4	2.9	2.5
Phoenix	0.7	0.7	0.9	0.2	0.1	0.1	0.8	1.0	0.9	0.7	0.7	1.0
San Francisco	4.4	3.2	3.1	1.4	0.2	0.1	0	0.1	0.2	1.2	2.9	3.1
Miami	2.0	2.1	2.4	2.9	6.2	9.3	5.7	7.6	7.6	5.6	2.7	1.8

1 Which city has the greatest range in average monthly precipitation?   Miami

2 Which city has the wettest climate?   Miami

3 Which city has the driest climate?   Phoenix

4 Which city probably has to limit watering lawns due to water shortages?   Phoenix

5 In which city would a cactus probably grow outdoors?   Phoenix

6 In which city would it be least likely to rain in the summer?   San Francisco

7 Which city gets the most precipitation in spring?   New York

Math Explorations and Applications Level 6 • 121

ENRICHMENT p. 121

On the clock shown below, addition can be shown by moving in a clockwise direction. Since moving 13 units around the clock from 0 would place you at 1, we say 0 + 13 = 1. (Note that 12 has been replaced with 0.)

1 Use the clock above to find the end positions for each move.

Start	0	0	0	0	4	4	4	4	8	8	8	8
Add	4	8	12	16	4	8	12	16	4	8	12	16
End	4	8	0	4	8	0	4	8	0	4	8	0

2 Graph the results of adding each number along the *x*-axis to 0.

3 How would you describe the clock-arithmetic function?   periodic function

Math Explorations and Applications Level 6 • 121

---

*available separately

Unit 5 Lesson 121 **425**

LESSON 122 Unit 5 Review

Using the Student Pages

Use this Unit Review as a preliminary unit test to indicate areas in which an individual student is having difficulty or in which the entire class may need help. If students do well on the Unit Review, you may wish to skip directly to the next unit. If not, you may spend a day or so helping students overcome their individual difficulties before they take the Unit Test.

Next to each instruction line is a list of the lessons in the unit covered in that set of problems. Students can refer to the specific lesson for additional instruction if they need help. You can also use this information to make additional assignments based on the previous lesson concepts.

Problems 1–6

Students who miss more than one of these problems about naming coordinates should be assessed individually. Try to correct any consistent error, such as reversing the coordinates or choosing numbers that are one unit off, by using an appropriate strategy from Lesson 98 or Lesson 104.

Problem 7

Students who have difficulty with this graph should be checked individually and given appropriate help as needed.

Answer to problem 7:

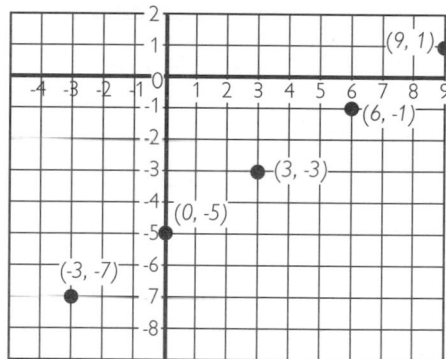

Problems 8–10

Give extra help to those students who miss any of these problems involving graphing functions. If the difficulty is with choosing *x*-values, explain that usually 0 is a good first choice, and that other "simple" numbers such as 1, 5, and 10 are good as well. If the trouble is with finding *y*-values, show how to compute the functions. If standard notation is causing difficulty, reteach the convention.

Answers to problems 8–10:

8.   9.   10.

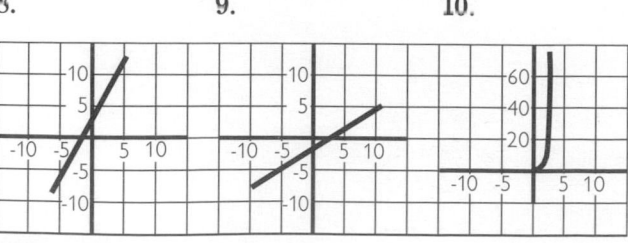

LESSON 122 Unit 5 Review

Lessons 98, 101, and 104

What are the coordinates of

1. point A? **(4, 1)**   2. point B? **(2, 3)**   3. point C? **(−1, 2)**

4. point D? **(0, −4)**   5. point E? **(−5, −4)**   6. point F? **(4, −3)**

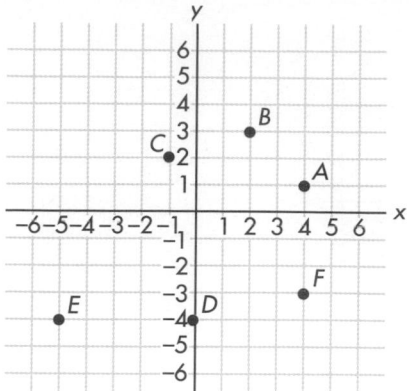

Lessons 99, 101, and 104

On your paper, graph the ordered pairs shown in the table. Label each point with its coordinates, for example (−3, −7).

7.

x	−3	0	3	6	9
y	−7	−5	−3	−1	1

Lessons 101, 106, 112, 114, 116, and 117

Graph each of these functions.

8. $y = 2x + 1$

9. $y = \frac{1}{2}x - 2$

10. $y = 2x^2$ (Graph this for values of x that are 0 or greater.)

Lesson 113

Find the next three terms of each sequence.

11. 0, 6, 12, 18, ___, ___, ___   **24, 30, 36**

12. 729, 243, 81, 27, ___, ___, ___   **9, 3, 1**

13. 2, 5, 11, 23, ___, ___, ___   **47, 95, 191**

10 **If four or five points are plotted correctly—(0, 0), (1, 2), (2, 8) and (3, 18)—that should be considered correct, even without a curved line through them.**

RETEACHING

Students who have difficulty with this Unit Review should have further opportunity to review and to practice the skills before they proceed on with the next unit. For each set of problems there are specific suggestions for reteaching. These suggestions can be found in the margins.

Lesson 109 Each of these tables of ordered pairs was made from a function rule of the form $y = Ax + B$ (A and B are numbers). In each case give the function rule.

14

x	0	5
y	−5	5

$y = 2x − 5$

15

x	0	1
y	1	4

$y = 3x + 1$

Lesson 120 Use 3.14 or $3\frac{1}{7}$ for π to find the approximate circumference of a circle with a diameter of

16 7 centimeters
22 cm
(21.98 cm)

17 10 centimeters
31.4 cm
($31\frac{3}{7}$ cm)

18 20 centimeters
62.8 cm
($62\frac{6}{7}$ cm)

Lesson 119 Give a function rule for each of these graphs.

19
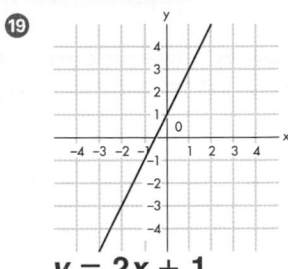

$y = 2x + 1$

20

$y = \frac{1}{2}x − 1$

Lesson 100 For each pair of figures, tell whether a rotation, a reflection, or a translation could be used to fit one on top of the other.

21
translation

22

rotation or reflection

23
reflection

24

translation

Lessons 95 and 96 Solve this problem.

25 Jeffrey is making a graph showing the amount of the time he spends on math, spelling, English, science, and social studies homework for one month. On which graph would it be easier to see the fraction of time he spent on each subject—a line graph or a circle graph? **circle graph**

Unit 5 Review • **427**

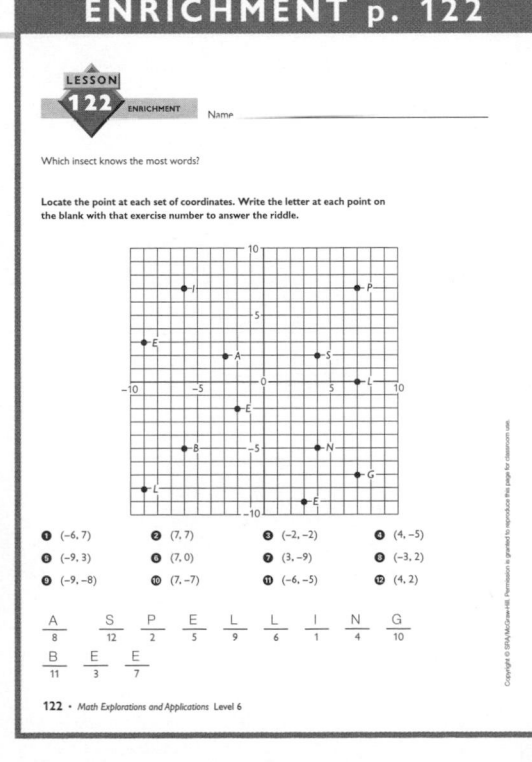

PRACTICE p. 122

ENRICHMENT p. 122

Problems 11–13 Help students who are having difficulty continuing the sequences to find a pattern in the first four terms in each problem. Encourage them to begin by checking for common differences or quotients.

Problems 14–15 Focus on these rules with students who miss more than one of these problems involving finding function rules:

1. Choose any two ordered pairs. Divide the difference in *y*-values by the difference in *x*-values. The answer will be the coefficient of the *x*-value.

2. Use either ordered pair to get the number to be added or subtracted. For example, in problem 14 you could use $y = 2x + B$. Use (5, 5): $5 = 2 \times 5 + B$ or $5 = 10 + B$. What can you add to or subtract from 10 to get 5? (Subtract 5.) So the rule is $y = 2x − 5$.

3. Check to see that your rule is correct by making sure the other given ordered pair satisfies the rule.

Invite students who need additional practice to play the "Find the Function Rule" game (page 387).

Problems 16–18 Explain the circumference formula further to students who miss more than one of these circumference problems.

Problems 19 and 20 Give extra practice in the Unit Practice to students who miss either of these problems.

Problems 21–24 Encourage students who have difficulty with these problems to trace one of the figures in each pair and observe how the paper must be moved to coincide with the other figure.

Problem 25 For students who have difficulty choosing the appropriate graph, provide sample line and circle graphs for them to interpret.

Portfolio Assessment If you have not already assigned the Portfolio Assessment task provided on Assessment Blackline Masters page 90, it can be used at this time to evaluate students' ability to solve problems involving negative numbers and functions.

Performance Assessment The Performance Assessment Task 2 provided on Assessment Blackline Masters pages 78–79 can be used at this time to evaluate students' proficiency with functions and graphing. You may want to administer this assessment with individual students or in small groups.

Unit Project If you have not already assigned the "Library Research" project on pages 434 and 435, you may wish to do so at this time. This project is a good opportunity for students to apply the concept of collecting and analyzing complicated data to real-world problem solving.

Using the Student Pages The purpose of these pages is to provide additional practice for those students who demonstrated a need for it on the Unit Review. You may wish to assign only the specific exercises in this Unit Practice in which students need further reinforcement. Each instruction line gives the lessons in the unit it covers so that you or students can refer to the specific lesson for additional review and instruction.

Students who do not require additional practice on specific concepts may enjoy playing any of the games you have played so far, such as the "Get the Point" game on page 374, which requires skills in plotting points and using deductive reasoning. These students may also help by practicing flashcard drills and playing appropriate games with students who need remedial practice or by actually teaching certain procedures to other students.

Social Studies Connection If students question the answer to problem 2, ask them when the United States were established, and have them check to find the first United States president who was born after that date.

You may want to use the Cumulative Review on page 579 after this lesson.

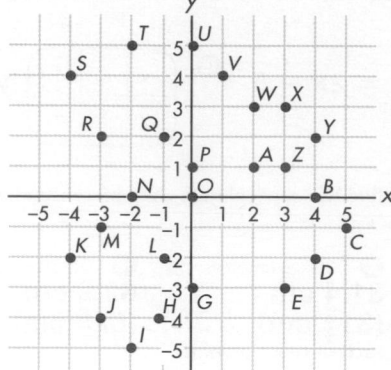 

Lessons 99, 101, and 104

On your paper answer these questions by writing the correct letter for each of the coordinates on the graph above.

1 Who was the first United States president to die in office? **William Henry Harrison**

(2, 3), (−2, −5), (−1, −2), (−1, −2), (−2, −5), (2, 1), (−3, −1)
(−1, −4), (3, −3), (−2, 0), (−3, 2), (4, 2)
(−1, −4), (2, 1), (−3, 2), (−3, 2), (−2, −5), (−4, 4), (0, 0), (−2, 0)

2 Who was the first United States president to be born in the United States? **Martin Van Buren**

(−3, −1), (2, 1), (−3, 2), (−2, 5), (−2, −5), (−2, 0)

(1, 4), (2, 1), (−2, 0)   (4, 0), (0, 5), (−3, 2), (3, −3), (−2, 0)

3 Who was the first vice president to become president? **John Adams**

(−3, −4), (0, 0), (−1, −4), (−2, 0)

(2, 1), (4, −2), (2, 1), (−3, −1), (−4, 4)

4 Who was the only president to serve two terms that did not follow each other? **Grover Cleveland**

(0, −3), (−3, 2), (0, 0), (1, 4), (3, −3), (−3, 2)

(5, −1), (−1, −2), (3, −3), (1, 4), (3, −3), (−1, −2), (2, 1), (−2, 0), (4, −2)

Use this code to make up messages, questions, or riddles. Give them to a friend to decode.

If students have difficulty with problem 10, point out that they have worked with problems in which $B = 0$ for lines with the function rule $y = Ax + B$ and that it is possible to have a function rule for which $A = 0$. Such a function rule, $y = B$, is called a *constant function*. The same y-value always comes out, no matter what x-value we put in.

You may be interested in knowing possible rules for the sets of ordered pairs that do not yield straight lines: (5) $y = 2^x$, (11) $y = x^2$, and (12) $y = \frac{x^2}{2}$.

Lessons 99, 101, 104, 109, and 119   Graph each set of ordered pairs. Decide whether each set of ordered pairs could have come from a function rule of the form $y = Ax + B$. (Are all the points on one straight line?) If the set could have come from a function rule of the form $y = Ax + B$, tell what the rule is.

⑤

x	0	1	2	3	4
y	1	2	4	8	16

no

⑥

x	0	1	2	3	4
y	−5	−2	1	4	7

yes; $y = 3x - 5$

⑦

x	0	1	2	3	4
y	0	2	4	6	8

yes; $y = 2x$

⑧

x	0	2	6	−4	3
y	−2	−1	1	−4	$-\frac{1}{2}$

yes; $y = \frac{1}{2}x - 2$

⑨

x	0	1	2	3	4
y	1	3	5	7	9

yes; $y = 2x + 1$

⑩

x	0	2	5	1.3	7
y	7	7	7	7	7

yes; $y = 7$

⑪

x	0	1	2	3	4
y	0	1	4	9	16

no

⑫

x	0	2	4	3	1
y	0	2	8	4.5	0.5

no

⑬

x	0	1	2	3	4
y	0	$\frac{1}{2}$	1	$1\frac{1}{2}$	2

yes; $y = \frac{1}{2}x$

⑭

x	0	3	−1.2	4	2.6
y	0	3	−1.2	4	2.6

yes; $y = x$

Lesson 113   Give the next three terms of each sequence.

⑮   0, 1, 3, 6, 10, ___, ___, ___   **15, 21, 28**

⑯   4, 8, 12, 16, ___, ___, ___   **20, 24, 28**

⑰   3, 6, 12, 24, ___, ___, ___   **48, 96, 192**

Unit 5 Practice • **429**

Technology Connection   Refer students to the software *Classroom Grade Level Math Programs* from Jostens Home Learning (Mac, IBM, for grades K–8) for practice with topics including interpreting data (line, bar, and circle graphs; photographs; and consumer math).

◆ LESSON 123 Unit 5 Practice

Answers to problems 18–25:

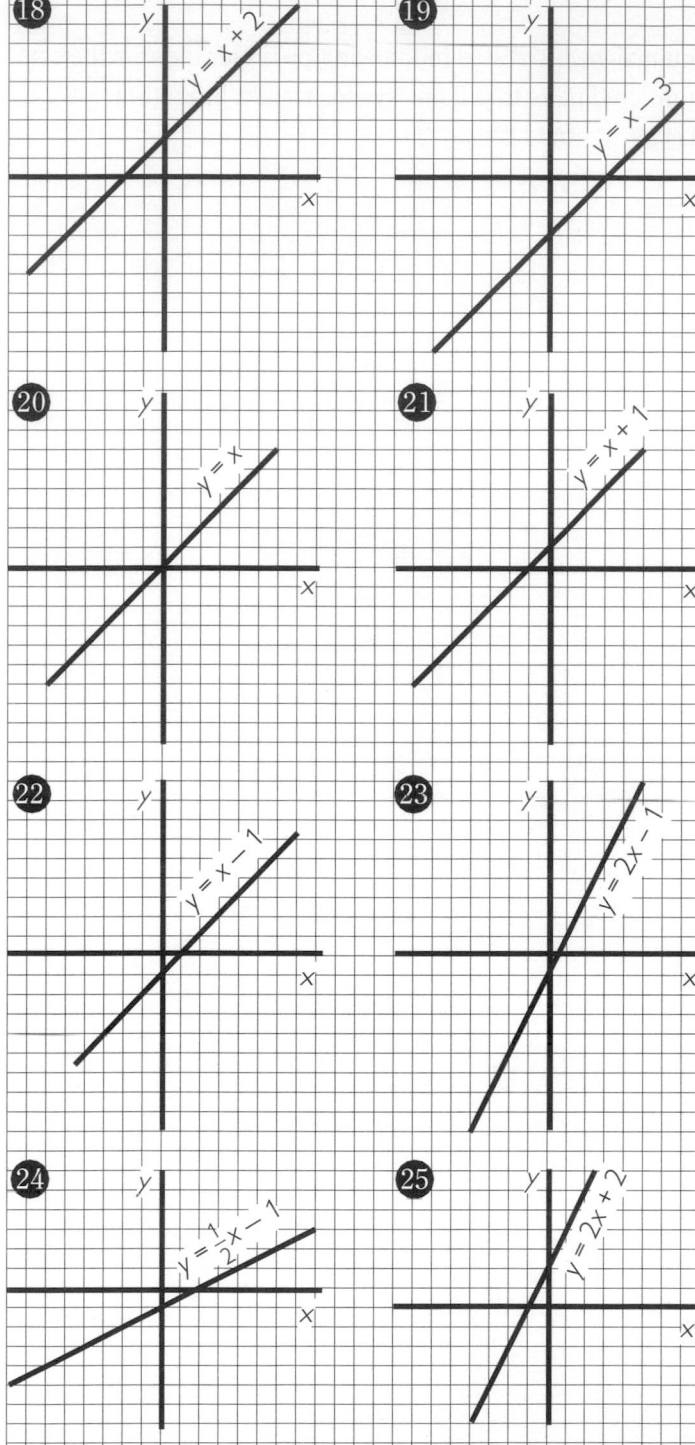

◆ LESSON 123 Unit 5 Practice

Lessons 101, 106, 112, and 114

Graph each of these functions. **Graphs are in margin.**

18 $y = x + 2$ **19** $y = x - 3$ **20** $y = x$

21 $y = x + 1$ **22** $y = x - 1$ **23** $y = 2x - 1$

24 $y = \frac{1}{2}x - 1$ **25** $y = 2x + 2$ **26** $y = 2x - 3$

27 $y = \frac{1}{2}x + 2$ **28** $y = \frac{1}{3}x - 2$ **29** $y = \frac{1}{3}x + 3$

Lessons 116 and 117

Graph each of these functions. (Use only values of x that are 0 or greater.) **See graphs in margin.**

30 $y = x^2$ **31** $y = \frac{1}{2}x^2 + 4x$ **32** $y = 2x^2 - 4x + 1$

Lesson 120

Use 3.14 or $3\frac{1}{7}$ for π to find the approximate circumference of a circle with a diameter of

33 7 cm	**34** 3.5 cm	**35** 14 cm	**36** 100 cm	**37** 10 cm
21.98 cm	**10.99 cm**	**43.96 cm**	**314 cm**	**31.4 cm**
or 22 cm	**or 11 cm**	**or 44 cm**	**or $314\frac{2}{7}$ cm**	**or $31\frac{3}{7}$ cm**

38 20 cm	**39** 1 cm	**40** 5 cm	**41** 6 cm	**42** 2 cm
62.8 cm	**3.14 cm**	**15.7 cm**	**18.84 cm**	**6.28 cm**
or $62\frac{6}{7}$ cm	**or $3\frac{1}{7}$ cm**	**or $15\frac{5}{7}$ cm**	**or $18\frac{6}{7}$ cm**	**or $6\frac{2}{7}$ cm**

43 0.5 cm	**44** 0.1 cm	**45** 9.1 cm	**46** 4 cm	**47** 23 cm
1.57 cm	**0.314 cm**	**28.574 cm**	**12.56 cm**	**72.22 cm**
or $1\frac{4}{7}$ cm	**or $\frac{11}{35}$ cm**	**or $28\frac{6}{10}$ cm**	**or $12\frac{4}{7}$ cm**	**or $72\frac{2}{7}$ cm**

Lesson 120

Use 3.14 or $3\frac{1}{7}$ for π to find the approximate diameter of a circle with a circumference of

48 314 cm	**49** 62.8 cm	**50** 22 cm	**51** 44 cm	**52** 50 cm
100 cm	**20 cm**	**7 cm**	**14 cm**	**15.92 cm**
				or $15\frac{10}{11}$ cm

Lesson 100

For each pair of figures, tell whether a rotation, a reflection, or a translation could be used to move one figure on top of the other.

53    **54**

reflection   **rotation**

RETEACHING

Students who have difficulty with this Unit Practice should have further opportunity to review and to practice the skills before they proceed on with the next unit. Beside each set of problems is a reference to the lesson or lessons from which the problems were taken. You may want to review the individual lessons with students who are having difficulty with them.

Lesson 119   Give a function rule for each of these graphs.

Answers to problems 26–32:

55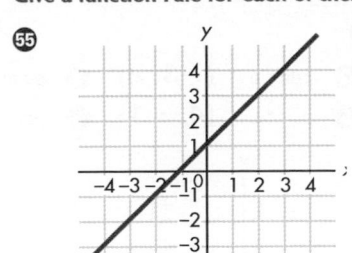

$$y = x + 1$$

56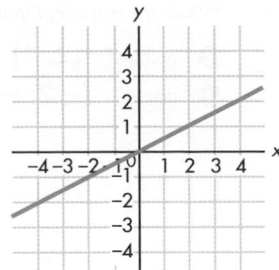

$$y = \tfrac{1}{2}x$$

57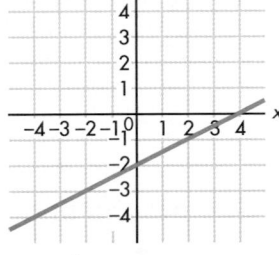

$$y = \tfrac{1}{2}x - 2$$

58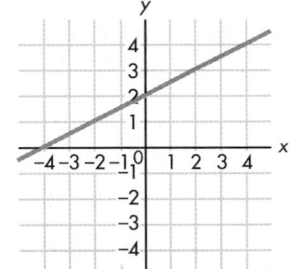

$$y = \tfrac{1}{2}x + 2$$

59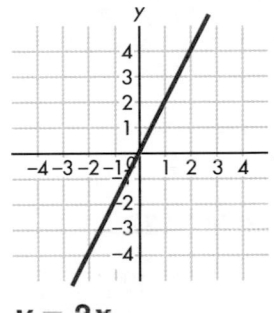

$$y = 2x$$

60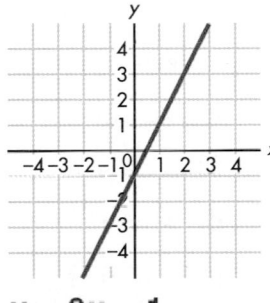

$$y = 2x - 1$$

Use the Cumulative Review on page 579 after this lesson.

Unit 5   Lesson 123 • **431**

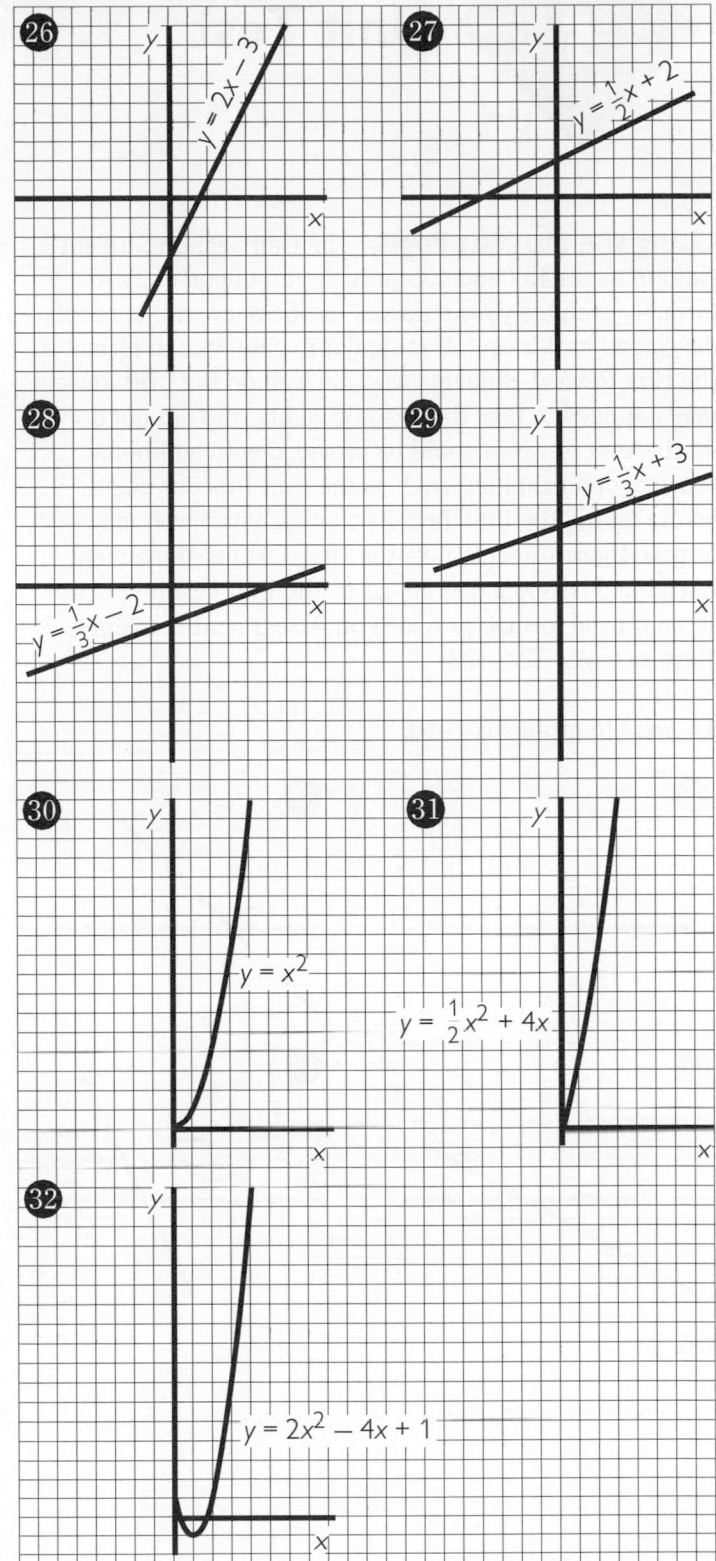

26   $y = 2x - 3$

27   $y = \tfrac{1}{2}x + 2$

28   $y = \tfrac{1}{3}x - 2$

29   $y = \tfrac{1}{3}x + 3$

30   $y = x^2$

31   $y = \tfrac{1}{2}x^2 + 4x$

32   $y = 2x^2 - 4x + 1$

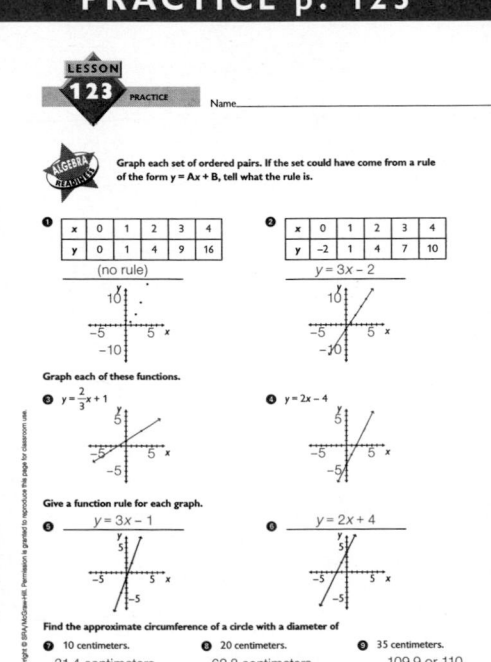

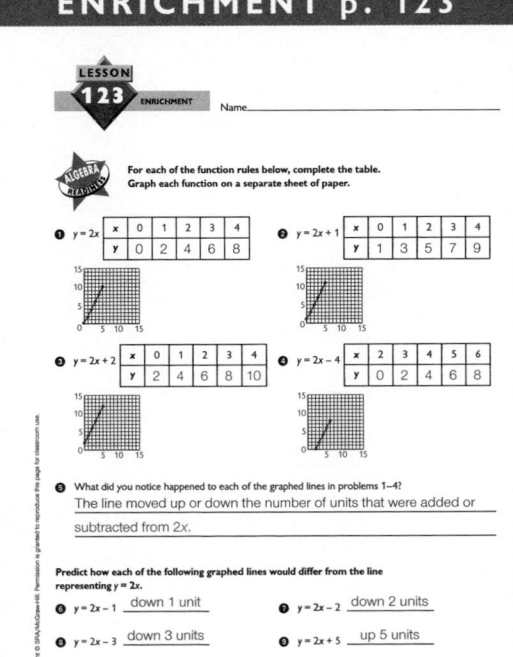

Unit 5 Practice   **431**

Using the Student Pages The Unit Test on Student Edition pages 432 and 433 provides an opportunity to formally evaluate your students' proficiency with concepts developed in this unit. It is similar in content and format to the Unit Review. Students who did well on the Unit Review may not need to take this test. Students who did not do well on the Unit Review should be provided with additional practice opportunities, such as the Unit Practice pages, before taking the Unit Test. As an alternative, you may wish to have these students take the Unit Test on Assessment Blackline Masters pages 48–51 or the Unit Test in standardized format, provided on Assessment Blackline Masters pages 122–128.

Answers to problems 7–10:

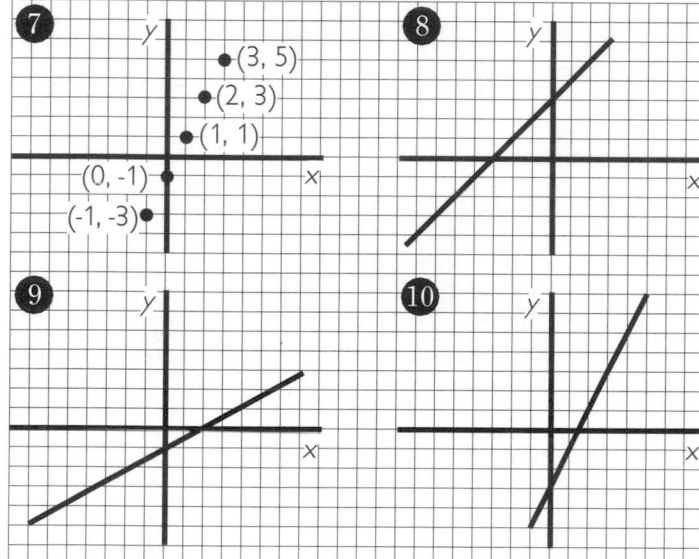

What are the coordinates of

① point A? **(2, 1)** ② point B? **(−3, 2)** ③ point C? **(0, −3)**

④ point D? **(−2, −1)** ⑤ point E? **(4, −1)** ⑥ point F? **(−3, −2)**

⑦ On your paper, graph the ordered pairs shown in the table. Label each point with its coordinates. For example, (−1, −3). **See graph in margin.**

x	−1	0	1	2	3
y	−3	−1	1	3	5

Graph each of these functions. **See graphs in margin.**

⑧ $y = x + 3$ ⑨ $y = \frac{1}{2}x - 1$ ⑩ $y = 2x - 3$

Solve this problem.

⑪ A business is keeping track of its monthly sales for one year. It wants to show how sales have been growing. On which graph would it be easier to see the growth in sales—a line graph or a circle graph? **line graph**

Give the next three terms of each sequence.

⑫ $\frac{1}{4}, \frac{1}{2}, 1, 2,$ ___, ___, ___ **4, 8, 16**

⑬ 3, 5, 9, 17, ___, ___, ___ **33, 65, 129**

⑭ 7, 14, 21, 28, ___, ___, ___ **35, 42, 49**

Each of these tables of ordered pairs was made from a function rule of the form $y = Ax + B$. In each case, give the function rule.

15

x	−1	0
y	2	4

$y = 2x + 4$

16

x	0	2
y	0	1

$y = \frac{1}{2}x$

Use 3.14 or $3\frac{1}{7}$ to find the approximate circumference of a circle with a diameter of

17 14 centimeters
44 cm
(43.96 cm)

18 1 centimeter
3.14 cm
($3\frac{1}{7}$ cm)

19 30 centimeters
94.2 cm
($94\frac{2}{7}$ cm)

Give a function rule for each graph.

20 $y = 2x - 2$

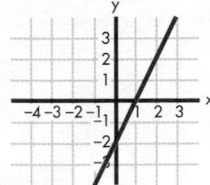

21 $y = \frac{1}{2}x + 2$

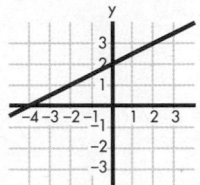

For each pair of figures, tell whether a rotation, a reflection, or a translation could be used to move one figure on top of the other.

22

reflection

23

translation

24

rotation

25

reflection or rotation

Unit 5 Test • **433**

ASSESSMENT p. 48

UNIT 5

Unit 5 Test (Use after Lesson 123.)   Page 1 of 4

Name _____

The student demonstrates mastery by correctly answering at least 24 of the 30 problems.

Write the coordinates of the following points:

1. point A _(1, 4)_
2. point B _(−3, 2)_
3. point C _(−2, −5)_
4. point D _(0, −3)_
5. point E _(3, −2)_

6. Graph the ordered pairs shown in the table. Label each point with its coordinates, for example, (−3, −7).

x	4	−2	−4	5	−1
y	−2	0	−1	4	3

Graph each of these functions.

7. $y = x - 4$
8. $y = \frac{1}{2}x + 3$
9. $y = x^2 + 2$

48 • Math Explorations and Applications Level 6

Student Edition pages 434–435

Wrap-Up

PRESENTING THE PROJECT

Project Objectives

▶ to gain experience collecting and analyzing complex data

Begin by discussing how students might find the answers. Discussion should focus on the notion that although all answers can be estimated, not all can be checked without asking somebody who knows (for example, the annual budget).

Consider having students work in cooperative groups for a period of several days and estimate the answers. Then allow discussion in which students give the reasons for their estimates. Follow this with an opportunity for each group to make new estimates based upon their interpretation of the discussion. Next, obtain whatever precise data are available from school or library authorities, or ask the librarian to visit your class to give more precise answers to these questions. Next, allow students to work in the same cooperative groups and compare the library with other libraries (see page 388). Each group can then write a report showing why their chosen library operates more efficiently or less efficiently than other libraries.

Students can use a blank **Cruncher*** spreadsheet to display their data.

Library Research

Collect information about your school library or your public library. Use the information you collect to complete the chart on page 435.

First estimate each answer, and record your estimates. Then think about how to find more precise answers. If you want to interview anyone, be sure to plan in advance what questions you will ask. You may want to make an appointment to be sure that the person you need to talk with will be available.

If you need to look up information in books or other records, think about where those resources might be found.

Why teach it at this time?

Although this project can be done at any time, it is likely that a few students will connect their analyses of library data with the use of functions. For example, some students might want to make a chart and graph showing the number of books in different libraries with the amount of money spent each year. Do the two sets of data correlate in some way? If one library's data does not correlate, does it mean that library operates differently than most libraries? Is that library more efficient or less efficient?

*available separately

	FIRST ESTIMATE	ACTUAL OR SECOND ESTIMATE
Number of books in the library		
Annual circulation		
Number of people served by the library		
Annual budget		
Busiest day		
Least busy day		
Number of new books purchased in the past year		
Number of books discarded in the past year		

What are some other questions that will provide useful information?

Discuss the answers to these questions. **Answers will vary. See model problem on 388.**

◆ About how much money is spent each year for each person served by the library?

◆ About how much money is spent each year for each book that is circulated?

Using the information you collect, compare your library with some of the library systems listed on page 388. Then make suggestions for making your library more effective.

Unit 5 Wrap-Up • **435**

What Is a Math Project? If this is the first time you have used math projects in your classroom, you may want to refer to pages 98–99 in this Teacher's Guide for more detailed information about effectively implementing and assessing projects.

Homework Have students prepare a report comparing the local public library with the school library.

Wrapping Up the Project Using all of the collected data, conduct a discussion on which library of those studied is the most efficient. Discussion should focus on how you measure efficiency. Is it the number of books circulated per dollar spent? Is it the number of books per number of people served?

Assessing the Project Note those students who show an ability to ask questions and extract answers from the collected data, as opposed to those students who merely answer questions that are given to them. The first group shows evidence of higher order thinking, and the latter group would benefit from more activities of this sort.

COOPERATIVE LEARNING **Minds on Math** SRA's *Minds on Math* is a series of units covering problem solving, data collection, number sense, measurement, money, and geometry and spatial relations. Each unit provides a series of open-ended projects for individuals or small groups. These projects develop problem-solving and critical-thinking skills, utilize real-world materials, emphasize language, and integrate cross-curricular connections. Use projects from *Representing Data* to help students learn to make inferences and predictions based on data.

UNIT 6

Geometry

PLANE AND SOLID FIGURES

OVERVIEW

In this unit students find the area of several different shapes and the volume of a rectangular prism. The students review metric measures and estimate length, weight, temperature, and volume. Students measure angles and investigate angles in polygons and angles formed in diagrams with parallel lines.

Integrated Topics in This Unit Include:

♦ finding the area of a rectangle

♦ finding the surface area and volume of a rectangular prism

♦ discussing the effects of error on measurements

♦ finding areas of triangles, parallelograms, and trapezoids

♦ classifying triangles and quadrilaterals

♦ determining length when area is given

♦ finding square roots

♦ estimating and measuring length, weight, temperature, and volume

♦ converting measures in the metric and the customary systems

♦ classifying and measuring angles

♦ finding sums of angles in polygons

♦ identifying congruent and similar figures

♦ making circle graphs

♦ exploring the Pythagorean theorem

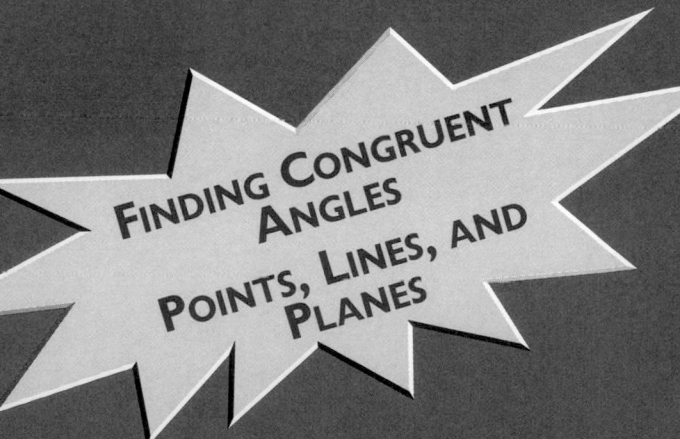

FINDING CONGRUENT ANGLES
POINTS, LINES, AND PLANES

> *"A teacher's questioning techniques and language in directing students' thinking are critical to the students' development of an understanding of geometric relationships. Students should be challenged to analyze their thought processes and explanations."*
>
> —*NCTM Curriculum and Evaluation Standards for School Mathematics*

GAMES

Motivating Mixed Practice

Games provide **basic math skills** practice in cooperative groups. Playing the games also develops **mathematical reasoning.**

Three Questions   Lesson 134   page 473

THINKING STORY

Integrated Problem Solving

Thinking Stories provide opportunities for students to work in **cooperative groups** and develop **logical reasoning** while they integrate reading skills with mathematics.

On the Move

Part 1	Lesson 125	pages 442–443
Part 2	Lesson 134	pages 474–475
Part 3	Lesson 142	pages 500–501

Story Summary In "On the Move" a family attempts to calculate the cost of moving from one apartment to another. As the story progresses, students will be required to use estimating skills to decide what moving company would be cheapest: the one that charges by weight, the one that charges by the room, the one that charges by the hour, or the one that charges by cubic yard of moving-van space.

PROJECT

Making Connections

The Unit Project makes real-world connections. Students work in **cooperative groups** to solve problems and to communicate their findings.

The project presented in the Unit Wrap-Up asks students to measure how long it takes ice to melt. Students participate in an ice-melting contest and record the results. Then, using the information gathered, students should cooperatively determine the "best shape" that allows ice to last the longest. Students can work on this project during free time throughout the unit.

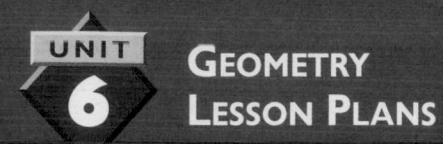

UNIT 6 GEOMETRY LESSON PLANS

LESSON	PACING	PRIMARY OBJECTIVES	FEATURE	RESOURCES	NCTM STANDARD
124 Area of a Rectangle 438–439	1 day	to review finding the area of a rectangle		Reteaching Strategy Practice Master 124 Enrichment Master 124	1, 2, 3, 4, 12, 13
125 Surface Area 440–443	1 day	to practice visualizing three-dimensional figures based on two-dimensional patterns	Thinking Story	Reteaching Master Practice Master 125 Enrichment Master 125	1, 2, 3, 4, 12, 13
126 Volume of a Rectangular Prism 444–447	2 days	to review and calculate the volume of a rectangular prism		Reteaching Master Practice Master 126 Enrichment Master 126	1, 2, 3, 4, 12, 13
127 Area and Volume 448–451	2 days	to provide a hands-on experience with perimeter, area, surface area, and volume		Reteaching Strategy Practice Master 127 Enrichment Master 127	1, 2, 3, 4, 12, 13
128 Area of a Right Triangle 452–455	1 day	to practice finding the area of a right triangle		Reteaching Strategy Practice Master 128 Enrichment Master 128	7, 12, 13
129 Parallelograms 456–459	1 day	to review the formula for finding the area of a parallelogram		Reteaching Master Practice Master 129 Enrichment Master 129	7, 12, 13
130 Area of a Triangle 460–463	1 day	to review the formula for finding the area of any triangle		Reteaching Master Practice Master 130 Enrichment Master 130	4, 7, 12, 13
131 Area of a Trapezoid 464–465	1 day	to explain how to develop a formula for finding the area of a trapezoid		Reteaching Strategy Practice Master 131 Enrichment Master 131	1, 2, 3, 4, 12, 13
132 Areas of Figures on a Grid 466–467	1 day	to practice finding areas of geometric figures		Reteaching Strategy Practice Master 132 Enrichment Master 132	4, 7, 12, 13
133 Triangles and Quadrilaterals 468–471	1 day	to present some of the known properties of triangles and quadrilaterals		Reteaching Strategy Practice Master 133 Enrichment Master 133	4, 12
134 Classifying Figures ... 472–475	1 day	to encourage the development of logical procedures for isolating one of several objects	Thinking Story Game	Reteaching Strategy Practice Master 134 Enrichment Master 134	1, 2, 3, 4, 12
135 Determining Lengths from Given Areas 476–477	1 day	to show how to use area formulas to determine different lengths from given areas		Reteaching Strategy Practice Master 135 Enrichment Master 135	9, 12, 13
136 Square Roots 478–481	1 day	to provide students with opportunity to observe patterns among square roots		Reteaching Master Practice Master 136 Enrichment Master 136	7, 8, 12, 13
137 Estimating Measures 482–483	1 day	to practice estimating and measuring		Reteaching Strategy Practice Master 137 Enrichment Master 137	4, 7, 13
Mid-Unit Review 484–487				Assessment Masters	
138 Multiplying and Dividing by Powers of 10 488–489	1 day	to review and provide practice in multiplying and dividing by powers of 10		Reteaching Strategy Practice Master 138 Enrichment Master 138	5, 7
139 The Metric System 490–493	1 day	to practice converting from one metric unit to another		Reteaching Master Practice Master 139 Enrichment Master 139	13

LESSON	PACING	PRIMARY OBJECTIVES	FEATURE	RESOURCES	NCTM STANDARD
140 **The Customary System** 494–495	1 day	to review converting units within the customary system		Reteaching Master Practice Master 140 Enrichment Master 140	13
141 **Estimating Volume** 496–497	1 day	to practice estimating relative volume		Reteaching Strategy Practice Master 141 Enrichment Master 141	3, 4, 12, 13
142 **Keeping Sharp** 498–501	1 day	to practice applications of fractions	Thinking Story	Reteaching Strategy Practice Master 142 Enrichment Master 142	1, 2, 3, 4, 7
143 **Angles and Rotation** 502–505	1 day	to review the meaning of *angle* and of terms indicating angle size		Reteaching Strategy Practice Master 143 Enrichment Master 143	12
144 **Measuring Angles**.... 506–509	1 day	to review measuring angles		Reteaching Master Practice Master 144 Enrichment Master 144	12, 13
145 **Corresponding Angles and Vertical Angles**....... 510–513	1 day	to show some of the relationships among the angles formed by a line intersecting two parallel lines		Reteaching Strategy Practice Master 145 Enrichment Master 145	12, 13
146 **Straight and Supplementary Angles** 514–517	1 day	✓ to assess students' understanding of geometric concepts	♦	Reteaching Master Practice Master 146 Enrichment Master 146 Assessment Masters	12, 13
147 **Angles of Polygons** 518–521	1 day	to show how to determine the sum of the angles of any polygon		Reteaching Master Practice Master 147 Enrichment Master 147	4, 8, 12, 13
148 **Points, Lines, and Planes**................ 522–525	1 day	to consider relationships among points, lines, and planes		Reteaching Strategy Practice Master 148 Enrichment Master 148	4, 12
149 **Congruent and Similar Figures** 526–527	1 day	to review the concepts of congruence and similarity		Reteaching Master Practice Master 149 Enrichment Master 149	12
150 **Compass Constructions**........ 528–533	2 days	to provide practice in using a compass		Reteaching Strategy Practice Master 150 Enrichment Master 150	2, 4, 12
151 **Circle Graphs** 534–537	1 day	to demonstrate how to read and construct a circle graph		Reteaching Strategy Practice Master 151 Enrichment Master 151	2, 4, 5, 10
152 **Right Triangles: Squares of Sides** 538–539	1 day	to provide an opportunity to explore the Pythagorean theorem		Reteaching Strategy Practice Master 152 Enrichment Master 152	1, 2, 3, 4, 7, 12
153 **Unit 6 Review**........ 540–541		to review geometry		Practice Master 153 Enrichment Master 153	
154 **Unit 6 Practice** 542–543		to provide practice with geometry		Practice Master 154 Enrichment Master 154	
155 **More Practice** 544–545		to provide practice with geometry		Practice Master 155 Enrichment Master 155	
156 **Practice** 546–547		to provide practice with geometry		Practice Master 156 Enrichment Master 156	
Unit 6 Test........... 548–549		to review geometry	♦	Assessment Masters	
Unit 6 Wrap-Up..... 550–551			project		

UNIT CONNECTIONS

INTERVENTION STRATEGIES

In this Teacher's Guide there will be specific strategies suggested for students with individual needs—ESL, Gifted and Talented, Special Needs, Learning Styles, and At Risk. These strategies will be given at the point of use. Here are the icons to look for and the types of strategies that will accompany them:

English as a Second Language
These strategies, designed for students who do not fluently speak the English language, will suggest meaningful ways to present the lesson concepts and vocabulary.

Gifted and Talented
Strategies to enrich and extend the lesson will offer further challenges to students who have easily mastered the concepts already presented.

Special Needs
Students who are physically challenged or who have learning disabilities may require alternative ways to complete activities, record answers, use manipulatives, and so on. The strategies labeled with this icon will offer appropriate methods of teaching lesson concepts to these students.

Learning Styles
Each student has his or her individual approach to learning. The strategies labeled with this icon suggest ways to present lesson concepts so that various learning modalities—such as tactile/kinesthetic, visual, and auditory—can be addressed.

At Risk
These strategies highlight the relevancy of the skills presented, making the connection between school and real life. They are directed toward students who appear to be at risk of dropping out of school before graduation.

TECHNOLOGY CONNECTIONS

The following materials, designed to reinforce and extend lesson concepts, will be referred to throughout this Teacher's Guide. It might be helpful to order the software, videos and laser discs or to check them out of the school media center or local community library. If the school does not provide Internet access, consider visiting a local library, college, or business that specializes in Internet access. Some students may be able to access the Internet at home.

 *Look for this* **Technology Connection** *icon.*

- *Core Concepts in Math: Mastering Informal Geometry,* from BFA/Systems Impact, Mac, IBM, for grades 5–9 (software or laser disc)
- *Mighty Math Cosmic Geometry,* from Edmark, Mac, IBM, for grades 6–8
- *Math Mystery Theatre: The Curse of the Tomb of King Tut Tut Cubit,* from EdCon/Imperial International, VHS, for grades 2–8 (video)
- *The Math Map Trip,* from Educational Activities, Mac, IBM, for grades 4–8
- *Geometry,* from Sensei, Mac, IBM, for grades 6–12
- *Galileo Lesson Plans,* http://www-hpcc.astro.washington.edu/scied/galileo.html (Internet)
- *Mathematics Curriculum and Teaching Program,* from the National Council of Mathematics, Inc., Mac, IBM, for grades K–10 (video, software, and printed material)
- *Modumath: Arithmetic, Square Roots,* from VTAE, VHS, IBM, for grades 6–12 (video, software, or laser disc)
- *Mastering Math II,* from Queue, Mac, IBM, for grades 5–12 (software)
- *Geometry,* http://www/geom.umn.edu/apps/gallery.html (Internet)
- *Cosmic Golf,* from Milliken, Mac, for grades 4–8
- *Classroom Grade Level Math Programs,* from Jostens Home Learning, Mac, IBM, for grades K–8
- *Math Workshop,* from Broderbund, Mac, IBM, for grades K–8
- *Geometry Inventory,* from Logal, Mac, for grades 6–12
- *GraphPower,* from Ventura Educational Systems, Mac, for grades K–8
- *Home Grade Level Math Programs,* from Josten Home Learning, Mac, IBM, for grade 6

CROSS-CURRICULAR CONNECTIONS

This Teacher's Guide offers specific suggestions on ways to connect the math concept presented in this unit with other subjects students are studying. Students can connect math concepts with topics they already know about, and they can find examples of math in other subjects and in real-world situations. These strategies will be given at the point of use.

Look for these icons:

 Geography

 Health

 Social Studies

 Music

 Science

 Math

 Art

 Physical Education

 Language Arts

 Careers

LITERATURE CONNECTIONS

These books will be presented throughout the Teacher's Guide at the point where they could be used to introduce, reinforce, or extend specific lesson concepts. You may want to locate these books in your school or your local community library.

 *Look for this* **Literature Connection** *icon.*

♦ *Woodworking for Kids* by Kevin McGuire, Sterling, 1993

♦ *Area and Volume* by Marion Smoothey, Marshall Cavendish, 1993

♦ *Triangles and Pyramids* by Sally Morgan, Thomson Learning, 1995

♦ "Create Your Own Rainbirds" in *Math Wizardry for Kids* by Margaret Kenda and Phyllis S. Williams, Barron's Educational Series, 1995

♦ *Area* by Jane Jonas Srivastava, Crowell, 1974

♦ *Amazing Buildings* by Philip Wilkinson, Dorling Kindersley, 1993

♦ *Pablo Picasso* by Ernest Raboff, Doubleday, 1968

♦ *Origami* by Irmgard Kneissler, Childrens Press, 1992

♦ *Sea Squares* by Joy Hulme, Hyperion Books for Children, 1991

♦ *Measuring Up* by Sandra Markle, Atheneum Books for Young Readers, 1995

♦ *MicroAliens: Dazzling Journeys with an Electron Microscope* by Howard Tomb, Farrar, Straus & Giroux, 1993

♦ *The Liter Is* by Jerolyn Ann Nentl, Crestwood House, 1976

♦ *Brain Teasers and Mind-Benders* by Ann Axworthy, Sterling, 1979

♦ *Erin McEwan, Your Days Are Numbered* by Alan Ritchie, Knopf, 1990

♦ *Mathematics* by Irving Adler, Doubleday, 1990

♦ *Math for Every Kid* by Janice VanCleave, Wiley, 1991

♦ *Quadrilaterals* by Marion Smoothey, Marshall Cavendish, 1993

♦ *The Greedy Triangle* by Marilyn Burns, Scholastic, 1994

♦ *Math Fun with Trick Lines and Shapes* by Rose Wyler and Mary Etling, J. Messner, 1992

♦ *Circles* by Martha Smoothey, Marshall Cavendish, 1993

♦ *How to Get Fabulously Rich* by Thomas Rockwell, Franklin Watts, 1990

ASSESSMENT OPPORTUNITIES AT-A-GLANCE

LESSON	PORTFOLIO	PERFORMANCE	FORMAL	SELF	INFORMAL	CUMULATIVE REVIEW	MULTIPLE-CHOICE	MASTERY CHECKPOINTS	ANALYZING ANSWERS
124		✓							
125					✓				
126		✓				✓			
127		✓							
128		✓							
129		✓				✓			
130					✓				
131		✓							
132					✓				
133		✓							
134					✓	✓			
135	✓								
136	✓								
137					✓				
Mid-Unit Review	✓	✓	✓						
138		✓							
139		✓				✓			
140	✓								
141	✓								
142		✓							
143		✓							
144					✓	✓			
145					✓				
146			✓					✓	
147		✓							
148					✓	✓			
149		✓							
150		✓							
151					✓	✓			
152		✓							
153	✓	✓	✓						
154									
155									
156					✓				
Unit Test			✓				✓		

✔ ASSESSMENT OPTIONS

PORTFOLIO ASSESSMENT

Throughout this Teacher's Guide are suggested activities in which students draw pictures, make graphs, write about mathematics, and so on. Keep students' work to assess growth of understanding as the year progresses.

Lessons 135, 136, Mid-Unit Review, 140, 141, and 153

PERFORMANCE ASSESSMENT

Performance assessment items focus on evaluating how students think and work as they solve problems. Opportunities for performance assessment can be found throughout the unit. Rubrics and guides for grading can be found in the front of the Assessment Blackline Masters.

Lessons 124, 126, 127, 128, 129, 131, 133, Mid-Unit Review, 138, 139, 142, 143, 147, 149, 150, 152, and 153

FORMAL ASSESSMENT

A Mid-Unit Review, Unit Review, and Unit Test help assess students' understanding of concepts, skills, and problem solving. The *Math Explorations and Applications* CD-ROM Test Generator can create additional unit tests at three ability levels. Also, Mastery Checkpoints are provided periodically throughout the program.

Mid-Unit Review, Lessons 146, 153, and Unit Test

INFORMAL ASSESSMENT

A variety of assessment suggestions is provided, including interviews, oral questions or presentations, debates, and so on. Also, each lesson includes Assessment Criteria, a list of questions about each student's progress, understanding, and participation.

Lessons 125, 130, 132, 134, 137, 144, 145, 148, and 151

CUMULATIVE REVIEW

Cumulative Reviews, covering material presented thus far in the year, are provided in the unit for use as either assessment or practice.

Lessons 126, 129, 134, 139, 144, 148, 151, and 156

MULTIPLE-CHOICE TEST (STANDARDIZED FORMAT)

Each unit provides a unit test in standardized format, presenting students with an opportunity to practice taking a test in this format.

MASTERY CHECKPOINT

Mastery Checkpoints are provided throughout the program to assess student proficiency in specific skills. Checkpoints reference appropriate Assessment Blackline Masters and other assessment options. Results of these evaluations can be recorded on the Mastery Checkpoint Chart.

Lesson 146

Look for these icons:

> *" Grades based on demonstrated depth of mathematical knowledge communicate more about students' developing mathematical understanding than grades based on a student's relative position in the class or on percentage points. "*
>
> —*NCTM Assessment Standards*

MASTERY CHECKPOINTS

WHAT TO EXPECT FROM STUDENTS AS THEY COMPLETE THIS UNIT

23 UNDERSTANDING GEOMETRY— LESSON 146

By this time, most students should show an understanding of basic geometric concepts (names of figures, finding areas, and so on) and be able to use a protractor with ease. You can assess these skills by observing students as they work on and discuss pages 514–516 or by assigning Assessment Blackline Masters pages 54–55. Results of this assessment may be recorded on the Mastery Checkpoint Chart.

UNIT 6

PROGRAM RESOURCES

THESE ADDITIONAL COMPONENTS OF *MATH EXPLORATIONS AND APPLICATIONS* CAN BE PURCHASED SEPARATELY FROM **SRA/MCGRAW-HILL.**

LESSON	BASIC MANIPULATIVE KIT	GAME MAT PACKAGE	TEACHER MANIPULATIVE KIT	INTERMEDIATE MANIPULATIVE KIT	INTERMEDIATE OVERHEAD MANIPULATIVE KIT	THE CRUNCHER SOFTWARE	MATH EXPLORATIONS AND APPLICATIONS CD-ROM
124							Lesson 124
125			scale	geometric volume set			Lesson 125
126	Number Cubes			base-10 materials interlocking cubes rulers	base-10 blocks	spreadsheet	Lesson 126
127				tape measure rulers			Lesson 127
128							Lesson 128
129							Lesson 129
130							Lesson 130
131							Lesson 131
132							Lesson 132
133				protractors rulers			Lesson 133
134							Lesson 134
135							Lesson 135
136							Lesson 136
137	Number Cubes		scale beakers	thermometers, tape measures, rulers	thermometer		Lesson 137
138							Lesson 138
139							Lesson 139
140							Lesson 140
141			beakers	funnels			Lesson 141
142				fraction tower cubes	fraction tiles		Lesson 142
143							Lesson 143
144				protractors			Lesson 144
145				protractors			Lesson 145
146				protractors			Lesson 146
147				protractors		spreadsheet	Lesson 147
148							Lesson 148
149							Lesson 149
150				protractors rulers			Lesson 150
151				protractors		projects	Lesson 151
152							Lesson 152
153	Number Cubes			protractors			Lesson 153
154							Lesson 154
155							Lesson 155
156				protractors		project	Lesson 156

INTRODUCING THE UNIT

Using the Student Pages Begin your discussion of the opening unit photo by asking students, "How would you use geometry to design a house?" Then read aloud the paragraph on the student page that highlights a career as an architect. This helps make the connection between school and work and encourages students to explore how math is used in the real world.

ACTIVITY Ask students to use a ruler, compass, and protractor to make a blueprint of your classroom.

FYI Point out that people have been building things since before the beginning of recorded history. The first structures were probably for shelter—crude huts built from wood and animal bones and skin. In time, people put up more permanent buildings. The pyramids, built over 5000 years ago by the ancient Egyptians, were constructed with astounding precision. As massive as these piles of stone were, the angles of each side had to be exact, or the final effect of decades of labor by thousands of people would look lopsided. No one knows for certain just how these huge monuments were created. What is known is that however they were made, the builders knew about math, especially geometry. This knowledge was not lost but continued to form the basis for the architectural feats of later generations. Whether it was the stout castles and soaring cathedrals of Medieval Europe or the astounding 3000-mile-long wall of imperial China, builders counted on math to make their ideas a reality.

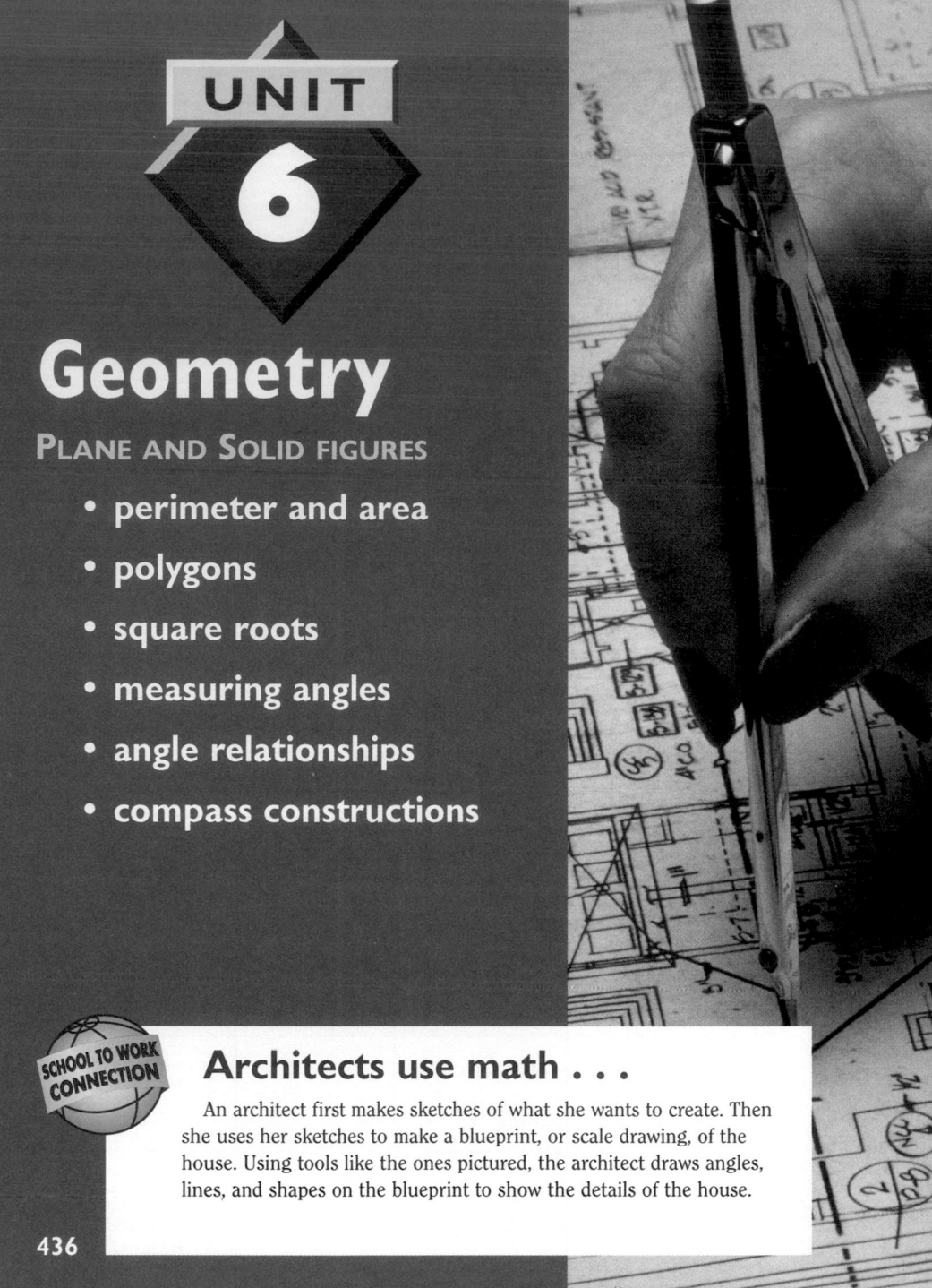

UNIT 6
Geometry
PLANE AND SOLID FIGURES

- **perimeter and area**
- **polygons**
- **square roots**
- **measuring angles**
- **angle relationships**
- **compass constructions**

SCHOOL TO WORK CONNECTION

Architects use math . . .

An architect first makes sketches of what she wants to create. Then she uses her sketches to make a blueprint, or scale drawing, of the house. Using tools like the ones pictured, the architect draws angles, lines, and shapes on the blueprint to show the details of the house.

436

Thinklab™ 2

SRA's *Thinklab™ 2* provides a series of creative and logical problem-solving opportunities for individual students. The problems are designed to appeal to different cognitive abilities.

▶ Use Problems 136–145 with this unit to reinforce quantitative thinking (interpreting and synthesizing data).

▶ Use Problems 146–160 with this unit to reinforce brainstorming (generating ideas and evaluating solutions).

Make clear to students that architects today are just as dependent on numbers and math. Math is important to architects and engineers because it is through mathematical equations that they learn how strong each part of a building must be in order to stand. Even large office buildings must be able to resist such natural forces as wind and earthquakes. Modern builders have the added help of computers when it comes to finding out if their plans will work. When the design is done, a simulation on a computer can test their work without any risk. It is still important for an architect to follow the actual building of his or her idea, and for most of them at least some time is spent at the work site, making sure the final product matches the plan, or blueprint, they created in an office.

Home Connections You may want to send Home Connections Blackline Masters pages 58–59 home to introduce this unit.

Unit Project This would be a good time to assign the "Melting Ice Cubes" project on pages 550 and 551. Students can begin working on the project in cooperative groups in their free time as you work through the unit. This project is a good opportunity for students to apply the concept of setting up an experiment and analyzing results using surface area in real-world problem solving.

437

 *Cooperate 3*

Cooperate 3, published by SRA, provides a series of creative and logical problem-solving opportunities for cooperative groups. The problems are designed to provide practice in problem solving, communication, reasoning, and making connections. *Cooperate 3* presents the following cognitive strategies—perceiving spatial relations, ordering and sequencing, logical deduction, establishing and testing hypotheses, sequential exploration, identifying starting points, attending to detail, organizing information, and screening irrelevant information. Each Problem Card emphasizes a principal strategy as well as reinforcing other strategies.

▶ Use Problem Card 26 with this unit to emphasize screening irrelevant information.

▶ Use Problem Card 27–28 with this unit to emphasize perceiving spatial relations.

▶ Use Problem Cards 29–30 with this unit to emphasize logical deduction.

LESSON PLANNER

Objectives

▶ to review and provide practice in finding the area of a rectangle

▶ to provide practice with multiplication

▶ to demonstrate that when one of two factors is between 0 and 1, the product is less than the other factor

Context of the Lesson This is the first of four lessons on surface area and volume.

 MANIPULATIVES

tiles (optional)

Program Resources

Practice Master 124

Enrichment Master 124

For extra practice:
CD-ROM* Lesson 124

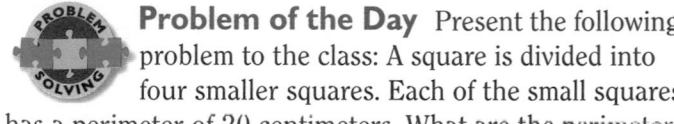

① Warp-Up ⏱ 5 MINUTES

 Problem of the Day Present the following problem to the class: A square is divided into four smaller squares. Each of the small squares has a perimeter of 20 centimeters. What are the perimeter and area of the large square? (perimeter = 40 centimeters; area = 100 square centimeters)

Problem-Solving Strategies Ask students who have solved the Problem of the Day to share how they solved it and any strategies they used.

MENTAL MATH Have students solve the following problems mentally:

a.	360 ÷ 6 = (60)	**b.**	3500 ÷ 7 = (500)
c.	320 ÷ 40 = (8)	**d.**	46 − 18 = (28)
e.	5606 ÷ 8 = (700 R6)	**f.**	737 − 198 = (539)
g.	5 × 7 = (35)	**h.**	50 × 7 = (350)
i.	2400 ÷ 8 = (300)	**j.**	72 × 40 = (2880)
k.	50 × 90 = (4500)	**l.**	400 × 6 = (2400)
m.	23 + 46 = (69)	**n.**	50 × 70 = (3500)
o.	500 × 700 = (350,000)	**p.**	5^2 = (25)

Luke has a tabletop that was made with small colored tiles that are 1 centimeter on a side.

The tabletop is 70 centimeters long and 50 centimeters wide. How many tiles does Luke need to make another tabletop just like the one he has? **3500**

 1 cm

◆ How do you find the area of a rectangle?

The formula that is most often used to find the area of a rectangle is this:

$$A = bh$$

In this formula b stands for the measure of the base, h stands for the measure of the height in the same units, and A stands for the area in square units.

Remember: We omit the × sign in written formulas to avoid confusion with the letter x. So bh means $b × h$.

Example: Find the area of a rectangle with a base of 20 centimeters and a height of 9 centimeters.

$A = bh$
$A = 20$ cm × 9 cm
$A = 180$ cm^2

Find the area of the rectangles with these bases and heights. Be sure to include the correct unit in your answers.

❶ base = 10 cm
height = 25 cm **250 cm²**

❷ base = 12 cm
height = 25 cm **300 cm²**

❸ base = 100 cm
height = 100 cm **10,000 cm²**

❹ base = 99 cm
height = 101 cm **9999 cm²**

❺ base = 98 cm
height = 102 cm **9996 cm²**

❻ base = 97 cm
height = 103 cm **9991 cm²**

❼ base = 96 cm
height = 104 cm **9984 cm²**

❽ base = 95 cm
height = 105 cm **9975 cm²**

❾ base = 195 cm
height = 205 cm **39,975 cm²**

❿ base = 295 cm
height = 305 cm **89,975 cm²**

Solve.

⓫ How many square tiles 1 centimeter on a side would be needed to cover a square tabletop 1 decimeter on a side? (10 cm = 1 dm) **100**

⓬ How many square tiles 1 centimeter on a side would be needed to cover a square tabletop 1 meter on a side? (100 cm = 1 m) **10,000**

Why teach it at this time?

This review of finding the area of a rectangle provides a basis for work in later lessons on surface area and the area of triangles, parallelograms, and trapezoids.

RETEACHING

For students having difficulty with area, do some problems in which the area is found by counting squares, perhaps using sets of **tiles**.

*available separately

Here are some symbols you should know:

cm^2 means "square centimeters"

dm^2 means "square decimeters"

m^2 means "square meters"

㉓ Assuming both factors are positive: 1) if both factors are greater than 1, the product will be greater than either factor; 2) if one factor is less than 1, the product will be less than the other factor; 3) if both factors are less than 1, the product will be less than either factor; 4) if 0 is a factor, the product is 0.

◆ The symbol for millimeters is *mm*. What do you think the symbol is for square millimeters? For square kilometers? **mm²; km²**

Find the area of each rectangle. Be sure to include the correct unit in your answers.

⑬ base = 12 cm, height = 14 cm
168 cm²

⑭ base = 1.2 cm, height = 1.4 cm
1.68 cm²

⑮ base = 0.12 cm, height = 0.14 cm
0.0168 cm²

⑯ base = 7 cm, height = 4 cm
28 cm²

⑰ base = 7 cm, height = 0.4 cm
2.8 cm²

⑱ base = 0.7 cm, height = 0.4 cm
0.28 cm²

⑲ base = 1.5 cm, height = 3 cm
4.5 cm²

⑳ base = 1.5 cm, height = 0.3 cm
0.45 cm²

㉑ base = 4 cm, height = 5 cm
20 cm²

㉒ base = 4 cm, height = 0.5 cm
2.0 cm²

㉓ Look at problems 13–22 and their answers.

   a. If you multiply two factors together, is the product always greater than either factor?

   b. When is it greater?

   c. When is it not greater?

SOCIAL STUDIES CONNECTION

㉔ The Up-Rise Company wants to build a large office building on a lot that it owns in Boomville. According to a Boomville law, you cannot put up an office building unless the lot is at least $\frac{1}{2}$ square kilometer. The dimensions of the rectangular lot are 0.82 kilometer and 0.55 kilometer.

   a. Is the lot big enough? **no**

   b. How far would you have to walk to go all the way around the lot? **2.74 km**

㉕ The High-Town Company owns a rectangular lot in Boomville that is 1.5 kilometers by 0.6 kilometer. How many smaller lots of at least 0.5 square kilometer can be made from this lot? **1**

㉖ Research to find out building codes in your community. **Answers will vary.**

Unit 6   Lesson 124 • **439**

② Teach

Using the Student Pages Briefly discuss the material at the top of page 438. Review the convention of leaving out the × sign when using letters to stand for numbers: $A = bh$ means $A = b \times h$.

Have students solve the problems on pages 438–439 on their own. When they finish, discuss problem 24. Some students may notice the following pattern for problems 3–10: $(x - y) \times (x + y) = x^2 - y^2$. For example, $95 \times 105 = (100 - 5) \times (100 + 5) = 100^2 - 5^2 = 10,000 - 25 = 9975$.

The answers shown are those most students will give. However, you may wish to make the point that if answers were rounded, they might better indicate the precision warranted by the given measurements. For example, the answer to problem 15 could be reported as 0.017 or 0.02.

③ Wrap-Up ⏱ 5 MINUTES

In Closing To summarize the lesson, invite students to give an example to support each of the cases described in the answer to question 23.

ALTERNATIVE ASSESSMENT

Performance Assessment Have students first estimate, then find, the area of a rectangular slip of paper 10.2 cm by 14.7 cm. (149.94 cm²)

Assessment Criteria

Did the student . . .

✓ correctly answer at least 75% of the problems on pages 438–439?

✓ express understanding of what can be known about the product when one or both factors are greater or less than 1, and when one factor is 0?

Homework Have students first estimate, then find, the area in square centimeters of a few rectangular objects around their homes.

Student Edition pages 440–443

Surface Area

LESSON PLANNER

Objectives

▶ to introduce the concept of surface area through problems involving heat lost through the sides and walls of a building

▶ to provide practice in finding the area of rectangles

▶ to provide practice in visualizing three-dimensional figures based on two-dimensional patterns

▶ to help students develop the broad ability to use mathematical common sense

Context of the Lesson
This lesson, the second of four lessons on surface area and volume, contains the first installment of "On the Move," a three-part Thinking Story.

 MANIPULATIVES

centimeter
graph paper

geometric set*
(optional)

scale*

Program Resources

Reteaching Master

Practice Master 125

Enrichment Master 125

For career connections:
    Careers and Math*

For extra practice:
    CD-ROM* Lesson 125

① Warm-Up ⏱ 5 MINUTES

 **Problem of the Day** Present the following problem to the class: This is a picture of the Big Box box factory, as seen from a higher floor in a building across the street. Imagine that you are flying directly above the factory. Draw a picture of what you would see.

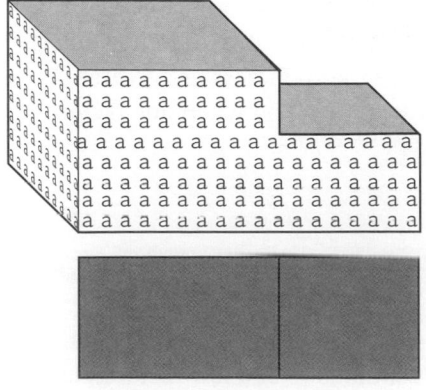

Surface Area

Buildings lose heat through their walls and windows. The heat lost from a building is greater if the surface area of the building is greater. So to find the expected heat loss, you must find the surface area of the building. The **surface area** of a three-dimensional (3-D) figure is the sum of the areas of all its faces.

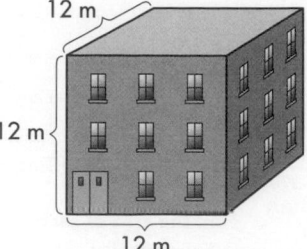

The illustration above shows the Big Block Company.

① What is the area of the front of the Big Block Company's building? **144 m²**

② What is the area of the back of the building? **144 m²**

③ What is the area of each side? **144 m²**

④ What is the area of the roof? **144 m²**

⑤ If no heat is lost through the ground, there are five faces (front, back, two sides, top) through which heat can be lost. What is the total area of these five faces? **720 m²**

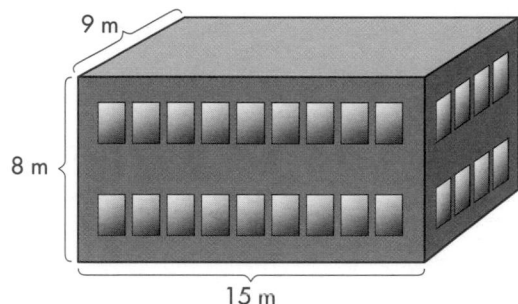

⑥ What is the total area of the top and four sides of the building above? **519 m²**

⑦ What is the total area of the top and four sides of a building that is 20 meters long, 12 meters wide, and 14 meters tall? (Draw a picture if it helps.) **1136 m²**

⑧ What is the total area of the top and four sides of a building that is 25 meters long, 10 meters wide, and 8 meters tall? **810 m²**

440 • Geometry

 **Literature Connection** Have students approximate the surface area of one of the completed projects in Kevin McGuire's *Woodworking for Kids*.

*available separately

Solve these problems.

9 If you could fold this figure along the dotted lines and glue the edges together, what solid figure would the pattern make? **a cube**

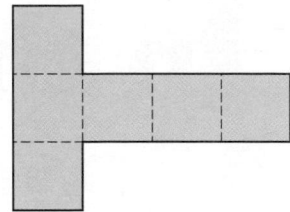

There are other patterns that would also make a cube if folded. Some people call such two-dimensional patterns for three-dimensional figures **nets**. For each of the following nets, decide whether you could fold it to make a cube. You may wish to make a pattern to see if it works.

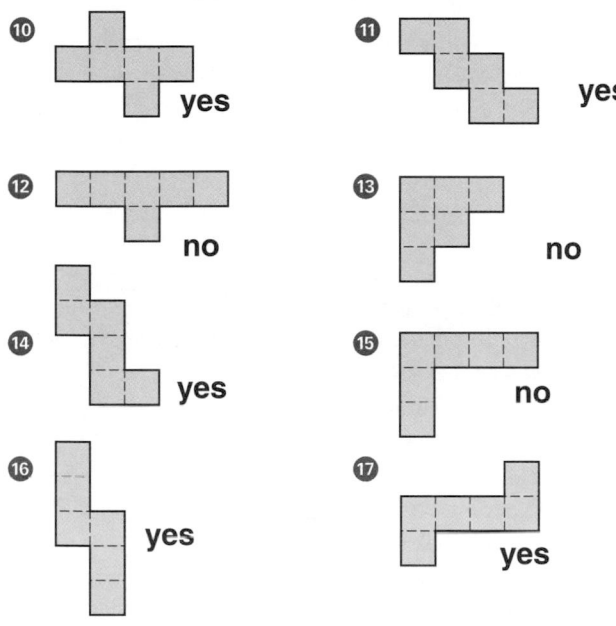

10 **yes**

11 **yes**

12 **no**

13 **no**

14 **yes**

15 **no**

16 **yes**

17 **yes**

18 For each of the patterns that can be made into a cube, find the total surface area of the cube be if the side of each square is:

a. 1 cm   **b.** 2 cm   **c.** 3 cm   **d.** 4 cm
6 cm²   **24 cm²**   **54 cm²**   **96 cm²**

Unit 6   Lesson 125 • **441**

 **Technology Connection** Refer students to the laser disc or software *Core Concepts in Math: Mastering Informal Geometry* from BFA/Systems Impact (Mac, IBM, for grades 5–9) for practice with perimeter and circumference, volume, line and angle relationships, similarity, graphing figures on a coordinate system, and drawing side views and cross-sections.

*available separately

Problem-Solving Strategies Ask students who have solved the Problem of the Day to share how they solved it and any strategies they used.

 Review the procedure for finding the area of a rectangle. Then present three nonrectangular objects and, using pieces of **centimeter graph paper** as a reference, ask students to show thumbs up if they think the area is more than a given number of square centimeters or thumbs down if it is less. For example, "Is a nickel more than 6 square centimeters?" (thumbs down: this can be verified by placing it on the graph paper); "Is it more than 3 square centimeters?" (thumbs up: this is harder to estimate) Other possible objects include an irregular shape drawn on the chalkboard or a clock face. Discuss different strategies for determining the area of the object.

② Teach

 **Using the Student Pages** Discuss heat loss and exposed surface area of a building and the relationship between them. Explain that the front, back, and two sides of a building are often referred to as the four sides of a building. Then have students do problems 1–8 on page 440 on their own. Suggest that they draw pictures for the buildings described in problems 7 and 8. For page 441, have **centimeter graph paper** available. Students can use it to solve the problems or to confirm their answers by cutting out and folding the nets shown to try to make the shapes. You may wish to work the first one or two problems with the class. Work with students in need of more instruction and demonstrate the folds that make the figures. Or, have students work together so that students who are good visual learners are paired with those who are not.

 For students having difficulty with surface area, use three-dimensional objects such as those in the **geometric volume set*** to show, for example, that the front and back of a rectangular solid are the same size and shape and have the same area, as do the top and bottom and the two sides.

◆ LESSON 125 Surface Area

Teach

Using the Thinking Story Part 1 of "On the Move" focuses on comparing the fees of three moving companies that determine their prices in three different ways. First, have students talk about what they know about moving costs and about ways moving companies charge for their services. Point out that when companies charge by the hour, they usually include absolutely all the time they spend on the job, from picking up the truck and getting it to your home, to returning to their final destination at the end of the day.

Answers to Thinking Story Questions:

1. Scratchit Brothers. Since the apartment has five rooms (six counting the bathroom), Aickenback will charge at least $800. Even if Scratchit Brothers spent ten hours to do the move, their bill would be only $600.

2. Aickenback's charges are probably based on rooms of average size. Because the rooms in Portia and Ferdie's apartment are small, it would be uneconomical for them to pay for moving by the room. However, someone who had very large rooms with a lot of furniture might find that Aickenback was cheaper. Aickenback's room charge would still be $160, but Scratchit Brothers would charge more because moving all the furniture would take longer. Scratchit Brothers' prices might also be higher if they were moving the furniture over long distances, since they would charge for travel time.

3. No, they can estimate by weighing one item and then multiplying the weight by the number of items they have. For example, if they had six similar chairs, they could weigh one chair and then multiply by 6. They can weigh one box of books and estimate how many boxes there would be.

4. The emphasis of this problem is on developing a logical procedure for arriving at an estimate. If possible, provide a suitable weighing device or **scale*** so students can weigh different books. The problem involves applying the concepts of average and rate. Different approaches might include: Weighing a variety of books, calculating an average weight and thickness, and then calculating how many of these average books would fit on a 24 in. shelf and how much these books would weigh; or weighing and measuring the height of a representative stack of books, and from this calculating an average rate of pounds per inch of thickness and multiplying this by the total length of the shelves. If there is no weighing device available, provide this information to students: A stack of hardcover books weighs 11 lb and is 8 in. high; a stack of ten paperback books weighs 4.5 lb and is 6 in. high. Based on these figures, the estimated total weight of the books in the bookcase is about 219 lb.

◆ LESSON 125 Surface Area

THINKING STORY

On the Move

Part 1

Ferdie and Portia were going to move again. The apartment building where they lived was being torn down. Their mother had found another apartment on the other side of town. It was just like the one they were leaving. It had three small bedrooms, a tiny kitchen, and a living room in which three people were a crowd.

"Moving can cost a lot of money," their mother said. "Portia, would you call some movers? Find out which one will give us the best deal."

After a few phone calls Portia reported: "This is confusing. First I called Scratchit Brothers. They said they would charge us $60 an hour for the crew and the truck."

"Oh, dear," said their mother. "Last time it took the movers almost all day to move us. I think we have even more things now."

"Well," said Portia, "Aickenback Movers will move us for $160 per room. Rockyway Movers charges by weight—10¢ a pound. That sounds cheapest to me, but I'm not sure."

"We'll have to weigh everything in the house to figure it out," said Ferdie. He got out the bathroom scale and started piling dishes and cups on it. "After I weigh all the dishes, you can weigh all the books," he told Portia.

. . . to be continued

CULTURAL DIVERSITY Some students may be completely unfamiliar with the way moving companies work and with their different pricing methods. So, when you assign the Thinking Story, you may need to spend some time talking about the moving process, inviting students whose families have moved to tell the class what it was like.

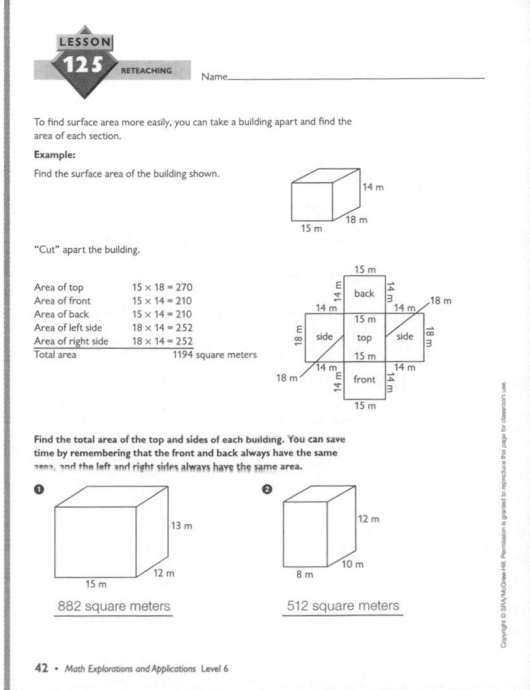

RETEACHING p. 42

LESSON 125 RETEACHING   Name_____

To find surface area more easily, you can take a building apart and find the area of each section.

Example:
Find the surface area of the building shown.

"Cut" apart the building.

Area of top   15 × 18 = 270
Area of front   15 × 14 = 210
Area of back   15 × 14 = 210
Area of left side 18 × 14 = 252
Area of right side 18 × 14 = 252
Total area   1194 square meters

Find the total area of the top and sides of each building. You can save time by remembering that the front and back always have the same area, and the left and right sides always have the same area.

❶ 882 square meters

❷ 512 square meters

42 • Math Explorations and Applications Level 6

*available separately

Work in groups. Discuss your answers and how you figured them out. Then compare your answers with those of other groups. Answers are in margin.

❶ Which mover is likely to charge less, Scratchit Brothers or Aickenback? How do you know?

❷ How do you know there will be such a large difference in what Scratchit Brothers and Aickenback would charge for this move? Can you think of a case in which the difference might be the other way around?

❸ Do Portia and Ferdie have to weigh every single thing in the apartment to estimate what Rockyway Movers would charge? What is an easier way to estimate the weight?

❹ In the apartment are two bookcases. Each bookcase has four shelves, and each shelf is 24 inches long. Three shelves are full of paperback books. The others are full of hardcover books. Estimate the total weight of books. Be prepared to defend your estimate. If possible, use a scale or a balance and weigh some real books to help you make a good estimate.

Unit 6   Lesson 125 • **443**

Have students think of any hidden costs in the moving process and record them in their Math Journals. Also ask them to tell which mover they would choose and what other issues they would take into consideration when making their decision.

❸ Wrap-Up

In Closing To summarize the lesson, ask students to explain how to compare the prices charged by different moving companies.

Informal Assessment Circulate through the room and observe students as they work on the surface-area problems and on the Thinking Story questions.

Assessment Criteria

Did the student . . .

✓ understand the concept of surface area of a rectangular prism?

✓ find all the nets that form cubes in the problems on page 441?

✓ participate in finding answers to the Thinking Story problems?

Homework Have students estimate the surface area of the outside of their homes. Students who live in large homes or apartment buildings can confine their efforts to the surface area of one floor of the building.

PRACTICE p. 125

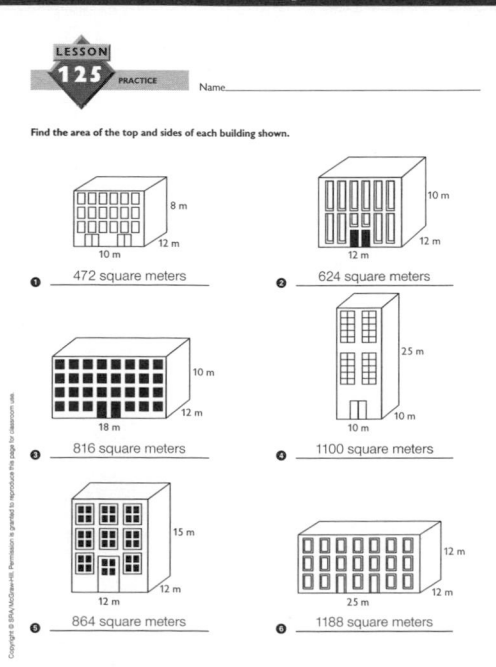

LESSON 125 PRACTICE Name _____

Find the area of the top and sides of each building shown.

❶ 472 square meters
❷ 624 square meters
❸ 816 square meters
❹ 1100 square meters
❺ 864 square meters
❻ 1188 square meters

Math Explorations and Applications Level 6 • 125

ENRICHMENT p. 125

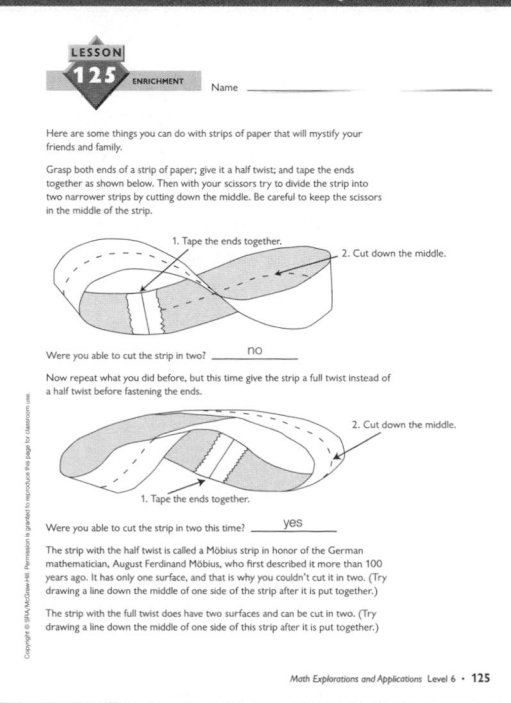

LESSON 125 ENRICHMENT Name _____

Here are some things you can do with strips of paper that will mystify your friends and family.

Grasp both ends of a strip of paper; give it a half twist; and tape the ends together as shown below. Then with your scissors try to divide the strip into two narrower strips by cutting down the middle. Be careful to keep the scissors in the middle of the strip.

1. Tape the ends together.   2. Cut down the middle.

Were you able to cut the strip in two? no

Now repeat what you did before, but this time give the strip a full twist instead of a half twist before fastening the ends.

2. Cut down the middle.
1. Tape the ends together.

Were you able to cut the strip in two this time? yes

The strip with the half twist is called a Möbius strip in honor of the German mathematician, August Ferdinand Möbius, who first described it more than 100 years ago. It has only one surface, and that is why you couldn't cut it in two. (Try drawing a line down the middle of one side of the strip after it is put together.)

The strip with the full twist does have two surfaces and can be cut in two. (Try drawing a line down the middle of one side of this strip after it is put together.)

Math Explorations and Applications Level 6 • 125

Volume of a Rectangular Prism

LESSON PLANNER

Objectives

▶ to review and provide practice in calculating the volume of a rectangular prism

▶ to provide practice in relating shape, volume, and exposed surface area

Context of the Lesson This is the third of four lessons on surface area and volume.

 MANIPULATIVES

blocks or cubes*

calculators*

measuring materials*

Program Resources

Reteaching Master

Practice Master 126

Enrichment Master 126

The Cruncher*

For extra practice:
CD-ROM* Lesson 126
Cumulative Review, page 580

Note: This lesson may take more than one day.

❶ Warn-Up ⏱ 5 MINUTES

 **Problem of the Day** Present the following problem to the students: Ed's land has an area of half a square kilometer. Ted's land is a square $\frac{1}{2}$ kilometer on each side. Whose land is larger and by how much? (Ed's, by 0.25 km²)

Problem-Solving Strategies Ask students who have solved the Problem of the Day to share how they solved it and any strategies they used.

  Have students estimate and then use **measuring materials*** to check the area of a few irregularly shaped figures. They should measure each area before estimating the next.

Volume of a Rectangular Prism

In this lesson you'll learn a formula for finding the amount of space that a figure such as the one below contains.

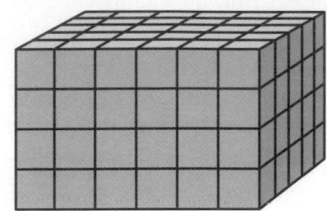

Solve the following problems.

❶ Each small block shown above is 1 centimeter on a side. That is, each block is 1 cubic centimeter. How many cubic centimeters are in the entire stack above? **120 cm³**

❷ Is there a simple multiplication you can do to show how many cubic centimeters are in the bottom layer of blocks? What is it? **yes; 5 × 6**

❸ How many cubic centimeters are in the bottom layer? **30 cm³**

❹ Does each layer have the same number of cubic centimeters in it? **yes**

❺ How many layers are there? **4**

❻ What simple multiplication can you do to show how many cubic centimeters are in the entire stack? **6 × 5 × 4**

The number of cubic centimeters in the stack is its **volume** in cubic centimeters.

 The volume of a box-shaped object (in cubic units) is equal to the product of the length, width, and height of the object (measured in the same units). This can be written in a shorter way with this formula:

$$V = lwh$$

Remember: *lwh* means $l × w × h$, or length × width × height.

❼ When determining volume, does it make a difference which measure we call the width and which we call the length? **no**

 **Technology Connection** You may want to refer students to *Mighty Mac Cosmic Geometry* from Edmark (Mac, IBM for grades 6–8) to provide practice with length; perimeter and area; surface area and volume; attributes of shapes and solids; and 2-D and 3-D coordinates.

To find the volume of a **rectangular prism** (a box-shaped object), multiply the length by the width by the height.

$$V = lwh$$

Find the volume of boxes with the following dimensions. In each case, be sure to include the correct unit in your answer.

8 length = 4 cm, width = 5 cm, height = 6 cm **120 cm³**

9 length = 10 cm, width = 20 cm, height = 2 cm **400 cm³**

10 length = 4 cm, width = 2 cm, height = 1 cm **8 cm³**

11 length = 2 dm, width = 2 dm, height = 2 dm **8 dm³**

12 length = 1 dm, width = 1 dm, height = 1 dm **1 dm³**

13 length = 10 cm, width = 10 cm, height = 10 cm **1000 cm³**

14 There are 10 centimeters in 1 decimeter. How many cubic centimeters are in 1 cubic decimeter? (Hint: Look at problems 12 and 13.) **1000**

Now find the volume of these boxes.

15 length = 1 m, width = 1 m, height = 1 m **1 m³**

16 length = 10 dm, width = 10 dm, height = 10 dm **1000 dm³**

17 There are 10 decimeters in 1 meter. How many cubic decimeters are in 1 cubic meter? **1000**

18 How many cubic centimeters are in 1 cubic meter? (There are 100 centimeters in 1 meter.) **1,000,000**

Here are some symbols you should know:

cm³ means "cubic centimeters"

dm³ means "cubic decimeters"

m³ means "cubic meters"

Unit 6 Lesson 126 • **445**

GIFTED & TALENTED **Meeting Individual Needs**
Present the following problem to students: Tom and Ray are neighbors and each has a rabbit. Each bought 48 feet of fencing, in 1-foot segments, with which to make a cage for his pet. Both of them want to use all of the fencing they bought. Ray wants to make a rectangular cage that encloses the largest possible area. Tom wants his rabbit's cage to be as small in area as possible, but at least 2 feet wide. What is the difference in the areas of the cages Tom and Ray will build? (144 − 44, or 100 square feet)

LEARNING STYLES **MANIPULATIVES** **Meeting Individual Needs**
Kinesthetic learners may experience more success by working with a concrete model of a rectangular prism. Use **blocks*** to help students figure out or count the number of cubes in each layer, the number of layers, and so on. Use the model to help students determine surface area, and also to emphasize the difference between area, measured in squares, and volume, measured in cubes.

❷ Teach

Using the Student Pages Discuss page 444 with the entire class. Introduce the term *rectangular prism* at this point. Use a concrete model of a cube built by smaller **cubes*** to demonstrate using multiplication to find its volume. When you discuss problem 2 with the class, point out that since the bottom layer is 6 cubes long by 5 cubes wide, it contains 6 × 5, or 30, cubes. The volume of the layer is 30 cubic centimeters. When discussing problem 6, explain that to find the volume of the whole stack of cubes, students must multiply the volume of a layer by the number of layers.

Have students do problems 8–16 on page 445. Then discuss problems 14, 17, and 18 with the class, keeping in mind that some people find it difficult to understand that if there are 10 centimeters in 1 decimeter, there will be 1000 cubic centimeters in 1 cubic decimeter. To help explain this fact, you can draw a picture or make a model.

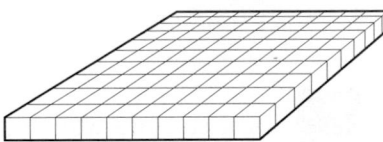

Start with the bottom layer, showing that there would be 100 cubic centimeters in a layer of a cubic decimeter. Then point out that since there are 10 layers and 100 cubic centimeters in each, there must be 1000 cubic centimeters in 1 cubic decimeter.

Students can use a blank **Cruncher*** spreadsheet to help solve the problems on pages 445–446.

◆ LESSON 126 Volume of a Rectangular Prism

Teach

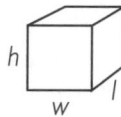

Using the Student Pages Discuss *heat loss* and *exposed surface area* so that students understand these terms and see the relationship between them. Then have students do problems 19–30. Afterward, go over all the problems.

You may wish to work out a formula for exposed surface area with students before they begin the page. Draw a cube that represents a building and label it this way:

Then show that there are two sides of area *hw*, two sides of area *hl*, and one (the top) of area *wl*, so the formula for exposed area is *A* (exposed) = 2*hl* + 2*hw* + *wl*.

Help students to see that when *total* surface area of a rectangular prism is considered (including the floor), a cube gives the least surface area for any given volume. But for a building in which the floor is not an exposed surface, a shorter but longer and wider building gives less exposed surface area for a given volume than would a cube.

Answer to problem 29:

The storage house in problem 26 and the one in problem 27 could each be defended as the most economical in terms of volume for a given surface area. The house in problem 27 has the least surface area, but it has 6 m³ less volume than the one in problem 26 (which has only 1 m³ more of exposed surface area).

 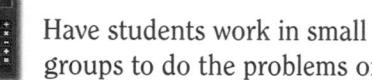 Have students work in small groups to do the problems on page 447, using a **calculator*** if they wish. Guide them to read the hint, which should help them get started. If students are having difficulty with problem 31, you may wish to point out that the length and width of the shed would have to be the same, since the rectangle with a given area and the smallest perimeter is a square.

Answer to problem 33 (page 447):

If you let *x* be the number of meters in the length (and in the width) and *h* be the number of meters in the height, the surface area is *xx* + 4*hx*, or *x*² + 4*hx*.

The volume (8000) is *hx*², so if you let *x* be 18 for example, *h* is 8000 divided by 324, or about 24.7. The surface area (without the floor) is 18² + (4 × 24.7 × 18), or about 2102.4. A smaller surface area can be found by substituting different values for *x*.

◆ LESSON 126 Volume of a Rectangular Prism

The Brick-Box Building Company wants to build a storage house that has at least 1000 cubic meters of space. To reduce heat loss and building costs, the total exposed area (four walls and the roof) should be as small as possible.

Calculate the volume and the exposed area for each of these sets of dimensions.

19 height (*h*) = 10 m, length (*l*) = 20 m, width (*w*) = 5 m   **1000 m³; 600 m²**

20 *h* = 20 m, *l* = 10 m, *w* = 5 m   **1000 m³; 650 m²**

21 *h* = 40 m, *l* = 5 m, *w* = 5 m   **1000 m³; 825 m²**

22 *h* = 10 m, *l* = 10 m, *w* = 10 m   **1000 m³; 500 m²**

23 *h* = 5 m, *l* = 20 m, *w* = 10 m   **1000 m³; 500 m²**

24 *h* = 5 m, *l* = 25 m, *w* = 8 m   **1000 m³; 530 m²**

25 *h* = 5 m, *l* = 15 m, *w* = 14 m   **1050 m³; 500 m²**

26 *h* = 6 m, *l* = 13 m, *w* = 13 m   **1014 m³; 481 m²**

27 *h* = 7 m, *l* = 12 m, *w* = 12 m   **1008 m³; 480 m²**

28 *h* = 7 m, *l* = 16 m, *w* = 9 m   **1008 m³; 494 m²**

29 Look at your results for problems 19–28. Which storage house would you build? Why?

Use a calculator to help you with these problems.

30 Can you give the dimensions of a building that has a volume of at least 1000 cubic meters and an exposed area less than 480 square meters?

30 a. no possible answer; **b.** possible answers: 6 m × 12.91 m × 12.91 m or 7 m × 11.96 m × 11.96 m; **c.** probably not. There is none for whole numbers.

a. Can you find an answer using a whole number of meters for each dimension?

b. Can you give dimensions that are not whole numbers of meters? What would the dimensions be?

c. Compare your answers with those of your classmates. Did everyone find the same answer?

Why teach it this way?

Although students have not learned formal procedures for solving word problems such as those on pages 446 and 447, even trial-and-error solutions will help to develop number sense and reinforce geometric concepts.

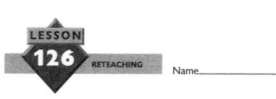

LESSON **126** RETEACHING   Name

To find volume, multiply the three dimensions of a box-shaped figure (rectangular prism). To find the surface area, find the area of each of the six faces and add the areas together.

Example:

Find the volume and surface area of the rectangular prism whose length is 15 centimeters, width is 12 centimeters, and height is 8 centimeters.

volume = 15 × 12 × 8 = 1440 cm³

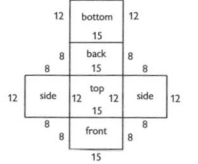

Surface area = 15 × 12   top
+ 15 × 8   front
+ 8 × 12   left side
+ 15 × 12   bottom
+ 8 × 12   right side
+ 15 × 8   back
= 180 + 120 + 96 + 180 + 96 + 120
= 792 cm²

We could also find 2 × (top + front + side).
= 2 × (180 + 120 + 96)
= 2 × 396
792 cm²

Find the volume and surface area of each rectangular prism.

1 *l* = 8 cm, *w* = 12 cm, *h* = 9 cm   864 cm³; 552 cm²

2 *l* = 16 cm, *w* = 9 cm, *h* = 21 cm   3024 cm³; 1338 cm²

3 *l* = 5 m, *w* = 4 m, *h* = 3 m   60 m³; 94 m²

4 *l* = 16 dm, *w* = 15 dm, *h* = 14 dm   3360 dm³; 1348 dm²

Math Explorations and Applications Level 6 • **43**

Work in small groups of three or four to answer these problems. You may use a calculator. Give your answers to the nearest tenth of a meter. Answers are approximate.

31 A builder would like to build a storage facility with a volume of 8000 cubic meters and the least possible total surface area. What should be the length, width, and height of the building? Try different possible values and compare your answer with those of other groups.
l = 20m, w = 20m, h = 20m

32 The builder wants to change the plans so that the volume of the building is 15,625 cubic meters. What length, width, and height would give the least possible total surface area? **l = 25m, w = 25m, h = 25m**

33 Another builder would like to build a storage facility with a volume of 8000 cubic meters and the least possible area for the walls and ceiling (there will be no floor). What should be the length, width, and height of the building?
See margin.

34 This builder wants to increase the volume of the planned building to 12,000 cubic meters. What length, width, and height would give the least possible area for the walls and ceiling? **l = 28.8m, w = 28.8m, h = 14.4m**

Hint: Try different lengths, widths, and heights that give the volume you need, then find the surface area.

For problem 31, for example, if we choose 100 for length and 80 for width, then since volume = length × width × height, the height will be 8000 ÷ (80 × 100) = 8000 ÷ 8000, which is 1. The surface area would be 2 × [(100 × 800) + (100 × 1) + (80 × 1)] = 16,360 m².

If we choose 23 for length and 13 for width, then the height will be 8000 ÷ (23 × 13) = 26.76. The surface area would be about 2524.72 m².

Try to find dimensions that give a still smaller surface area.

In your Math Journal write about the strategies your group used for solving these problems.

Use the Cumulative Review on page 580 after this lesson.

Unit 6 Lesson 126 • **447**

Some values of x and the corresponding surface areas are as follows:

x =	19	20	21	22	23
surface area =	2045	2000	1965	1920	1909

x =	25	25.1	25.2	25.3	26
surface area =	1905	1904.91	1904.88	1904.91	1907

Judging from this table, it seems reasonable that 25.2 meters (m) is a good size for the length and width, and the height should be about 12.6 m. Students may not approach the problem this formally but should arrive at this result.

③ Wrap-Up

In Closing To summarize the lesson, ask students to express a formula for finding the surface area of a cube.

Performance Assessment Ask students to find the volume and exposed surface area of a cube-shaped box that is 8 centimeters on a side. The box is sitting on a table. (V = 512 cm³; 320 cm²)

Assessment Criteria

Did the student . . .

✓ express understanding of the concepts and distinction between volume and exposed surface area?

✓ correctly answer at least 75% of the problems on pages 445–446?

✓ work with group members to find reasonable solutions to the problems on page 447?

Homework Have students choose an object at home that has the shape of a rectangular prism. Ask them first to estimate, then to find its volume and its exposed surface area. Make sure they write down their notes and figures.

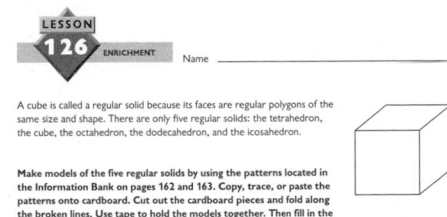

LESSON 127

Area and Volume

Student Edition pages 448–451

Area and Volume

LESSON PLANNER

Objectives

▶ to provide hands-on experience with perimeter, area, surface area, and volume

▶ to introduce the idea that when measures are added or multiplied, errors associated with them are also added or multiplied and therefore may be much greater than expected

Context of the Lesson This lesson is the fourth of four lessons about measuring perimeter, area, and volume of rectangles and rectangular prisms.

 **MANIPULATIVES**

calculators*

several tools (for measuring length in the same unit)

Program Resources

Practice Master 127

Enrichment Master 127

For extra practice: CD-ROM* Lesson 127

Note: This lesson may take more than one day.

① Warm-Up ⏱ 5 MINUTES

Problem of the Day Students may enjoy solving the following problem: How can seven coins be arranged in five lines of three coins each?

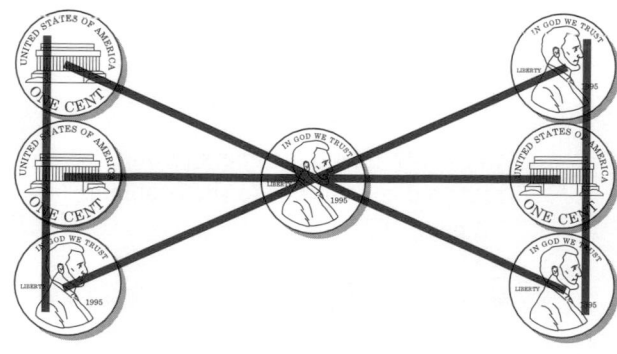

Problem-Solving Strategies Ask students who have solved the Problem of the Day to share how they solved it and any strategies they used.

You can apply what you know about perimeter, area, and volume to calculate these measurements for your classroom.

COOPERATIVE LEARNING

Work in groups of three or four. Find the perimeter and area of the floor of your classroom. (Use centimeters and square centimeters or inches and square inches—the class should decide on one unit of measure before you begin.)

① Draw a rough map of the room.

② Measure the length of each wall and label your map with these dimensions.

③ Calculate the perimeter and area using a calculator.

⑤ Guesses for differences in area are likely to be in the 10– to 100– or 100– to 1000– square centimeter range.

ALGEBRA READINESS

④ By how much do you think your perimeter measure might differ from those of other groups? less than 10 units? between 10 and 100 units? between 100 and 1000 units? between 1000 and 10,000 units? more than 10,000 units? **Guesses for differences in perimeter are likely to be in the range of 10 to 15 cm (or 5 to 10 inches).**

⑤ By how much do you think your area measure might differ from those of other groups?

Calculate the perimeter and area using the given measurements.

⑥ length = 45 cm, width = 20 cm, perimeter = ■, area = ■
130 cm; 900 cm²

⑦ length = 110 cm, width = 90 cm, perimeter = ■, area = ■
400 cm; 9900 cm²

⑧ length = 200 cm, width = 150 cm, perimeter = ■, area = ■
700 cm; 30,000 cm²

⑨ length = 1400 cm, width = 700 cm, perimeter = ■, area = ■
4200 cm; 980,000 cm²

⑩ length = 2000 cm, width = 2000 cm, perimeter = ■, area = ■
8000 cm; 4,000,000 cm²

⑪ length = 275 cm, width = 75 cm, perimeter = ■, area = ■
700 cm; 20,625 cm²

⑫ length = 51 cm, width = 49 cm, perimeter = ■, area = ■
200 cm; 2499 cm²

⑬ length = 1350 cm, width = 150 cm, perimeter = ■, area = ■
3000 cm; 202,500 cm²

Calculate the volume using the given measurements.

⑭ length = 200 cm, width = 150 cm, height = 200 cm, volume = ■
6,000,000 cm³

⑮ length = 150 cm, width = 150 cm, height = 200 cm, volume = ■
4,500,000 cm³

⑯ length = 300 cm, width = 200 cm, height = 150 cm, volume = ■
9,000,000 cm³

⑰ length = 300 cm, width = 195 cm, height = 155 cm, volume = ■
9,067,500 cm³

⑱ length = 300 cm, width = 205 cm, height = 145 cm, volume = ■
8,917,500 cm³

448 • Geometry

Why teach it this way?

The main purpose of this lesson is for students to experience firsthand the results of adding and multiplying measurements containing errors. Therefore, encourage students to use creative approaches to taking the measurements.

*available separately

Use a calculator to help solve these problems.

19 Work in small groups of three or four. Measure or estimate the height of your classroom. Using the measurements you found for problem 2 on page 448 and your figure for the height of the room, calculate the volume of the room. **Measurements will vary.**

20 Calculate the surface area of the room (the sum of the areas of the floor, ceiling, and all of the walls, including doors, windows, and so on). **Measurements will vary.**

Discuss these questions with the members of your group.

21 By how much do you think your volume figure might differ from those of other groups? **The variation in volume figures is likely to be very great, especially if centimeters or inches are used.**

22 By how much do you think your surface area figure might differ from those of other groups? **Surface area variations are likely to be in the 60– to 600– or 600– to 6000–square centimeter range.**

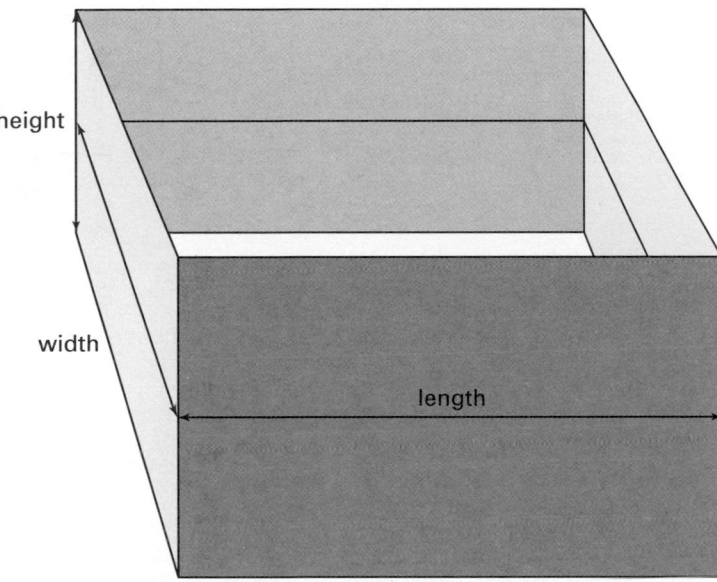

Unit 6   Lesson 127   •   **449**

 Before students form groups for the measuring activity, ask for estimates of the length, width, and ceiling height of the classroom. Ask students to explain any strategies used to make the estimates. If students are having difficulty, suggest the strategy of using a benchmark—a length students can visualize—to make their estimates. Suggest that student heights and heights of basketball hoops (10 ft) make reasonable benchmarks. Have students record their estimates for future reference.

❷ Teach

 **Using the Student Pages** Divide the class into small groups. **Measuring tools** such as rulers, yardsticks, and so on should be available. Have each group prepare a rough map of the classroom floor. Instruct students to label their maps with actual dimensions as they make them.

 After students complete the measurements, have them solve the problems on pages 448–449. When all groups have finished, discuss their answers to problems 4–5 and 21–22. Use **calculators*** to solve problems 19–20.

 Encourage students to use their combined creativity to come up with solutions for measuring seemingly unmeasurable lengths, such as the height of the ceiling. For example, one way to measure the ceiling height is to measure the length of a long stick first, then use the stick as a measuring device. Also encourage students to find ways for all group members to participate when there are more students than measuring devices. One way is for students to measure the length of their feet and then walk the distance to measure, and compare their results with those of other group members.

*available separately

◆ LESSON 127 Area and Volume

Teach

Using the Student Pages Have each group finish page 450. Then have students continue working individually with calculators on the problems on page 451. When all groups have finished page 450, have them report their calculated volumes and surface areas while a student records these findings on the chalkboard. Have the class determine the greatest differences for both surface area and volume.

If students measure using centimeters, they may discover that their **calculators*** cannot handle the greater numbers. Guide students to convert to meters. As needed, point out that because a cubic meter is 100 cm on a side, to convert the resulting cubic meters to cubic centimeters, students should multiply by 100 × 100 × 100, or 1,000,000.

Students should recognize during the discussion that when errors are multiplied (as in calculating area and volume), the total error tends to be greater than most people realize.

◆ LESSON 127 Area and Volume

In one class the map of the room looked like this:

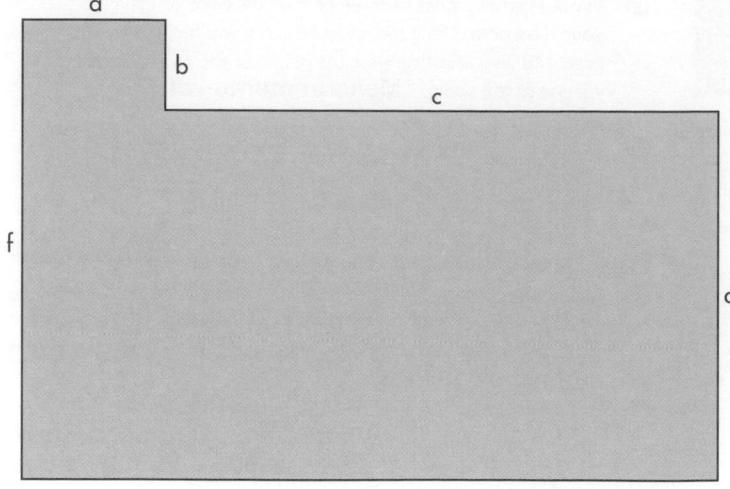

Ashley's group made the following measurements:

$a = 183$ cm	$b = 122$ cm	$c = 731$ cm **P = 3048 cm**
$d = 488$ cm	$e = 914$ cm	$f = 610$ cm **A = 468,358 cm²**

Maria's group measured:

$a = 180$ cm	$b = 122$ cm	$c = 731$ cm **P = 3036 cm**
$d = 485$ cm	$e = 911$ cm	$f = 607$ cm **A = 463,795 cm²**

Peter's group measured:

$a = 184$ cm	$b = 122$ cm	$c = 731$ cm **P = 3054 cm**
$d = 490$ cm	$e = 915$ cm	$f = 612$ cm **A = 470,798 cm²**

Solve.

23 Calculate the perimeter and area of the room using each group's measurements and compare them. **See above.**

24 Compare the perimeter, area, and volume calculated by your group with those of other groups in your class. Write one or two sentences about what you think is interesting. **Groups may compare by finding differences, ratios, or percent differences. However, accept any suggestion that is reasonable.**

450 • Geometry

Technology Connection Refer students to the video *Math Mystery Theatre: The Curse of King Tut Tut Tut Cubit* from EdCon/Imperial International (VHS, for grades 2–8) for practice with geometry, perimeter, area, and volume.

RETEACHING

Watch for students who have difficulty taking measurements or using calculators. Have them work closely with capable team members who can give pointers. Otherwise, no extra teaching is suggested at this time.

*available separately

Solve.

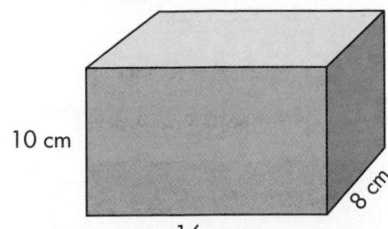

10 cm
16 cm
8 cm

25 Calculate the volume of a box 16 cm long, 8 cm wide, and 10 cm tall. **1280 cm³**

26 If each of the measures in problem 25 may be as much as 0.5 cm too low or too high, what are the greatest and least possible volumes for the box?
greatest = 1472.625 cm³; least = 1104.375 cm³

27 Find the surface area of the box in problem 25. **surface area = 736 cm²**

28 Find the greatest and least possible surface areas for the box if each measure may be up to 0.5 centimeter too low or too high. **greatest = 805.5 cm²; least = 669.5 cm²**

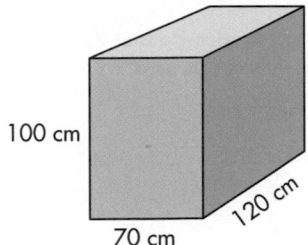

100 cm
70 cm
120 cm

29 Calculate the volume of a box that is 70 cm long, 120 cm wide, and 100 cm tall. **840,000 cm³**

30 If each of the measures in problem 29 may be as much as 1 cm too low or too high, what are the greatest and least possible volumes for the box?
greatest = 867,691 cm³; least = 812,889 cm³

31 Find the surface area of the box in problem 29.
surface area = 54,800 cm²

32 Find the greatest and the least possible surface areas for the box if each measure may be up to 1 cm too low or too high.
greatest = 55,966 cm²; least = 53,646 cm²

PRACTICE p. 127

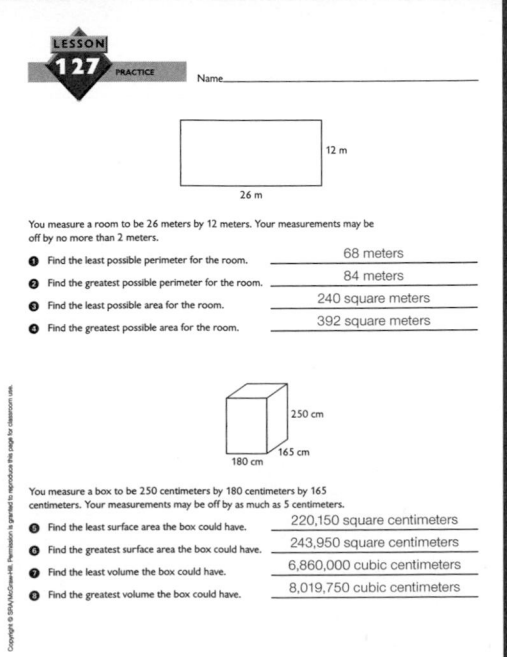

ENRICHMENT p. 127

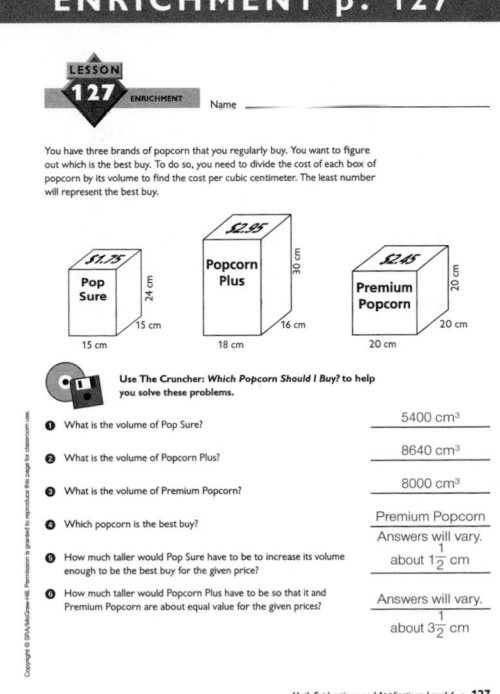

---

③ Wrap-Up

In Closing To summarize the lesson, ask students to distinguish among perimeter, area, and volume. Ask them to explain how small differences in measurements can lead to large differences in final results.

Performance Assessment Draw a box on the chalkboard and give the dimensions for its length, width, and height. Ask students to find its volume and surface area.

Assessment Criteria

Did the student . . .

✓ demonstrate understanding of how to find perimeter, surface area, and volume?

✓ correctly articulate the differences among the groups' resulting measurements as well as those for the problems on page 451?

✓ label answers with the correct unit of measurement?

Homework Have students estimate, then find the volume and surface area of a room in their home. Invite them to enlist the help of a family member.

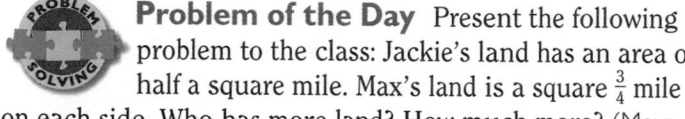

LESSON 128

Student Edition pages 452–455

Area of a Right Triangle

LESSON PLANNER

Objectives

▶ to review the formula for finding the area of a right triangle and to provide practice in finding it

▶ to provide practice in adding, subtracting, multiplying, and dividing whole numbers

Context of the Lesson This is the first of nine lessons on plane figures.

✋ **MANIPULATIVES** — **Program Resources**

measuring materials*

tracing paper or waxed paper

Practice Master 128

Enrichment Master 128

For extra practice:
CD-ROM* Lesson 128

① Warm-Up ⏱ 5 MINUTES

 Problem of the Day Present the following problem to the class: Jackie's land has an area of half a square mile. Max's land is a square $\frac{3}{4}$ mile on each side. Who has more land? How much more? (Max; $\frac{1}{16}$ square mile more)

Problem-Solving Strategies Ask students who have solved the Problem of the Day to share how they solved it and any strategies they used.

 Have students do an estimating-measures exercise that focuses on area and volume measurements. Present objects and ask students to estimate the area or volume in a given unit. Present several objects to be measured with one unit before moving on to another unit. Use **measuring materials** to check the estimates for each object before presenting the next object.

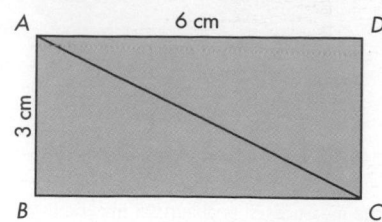

Area of a Right Triangle

Areas of right triangles are related to areas of rectangles.

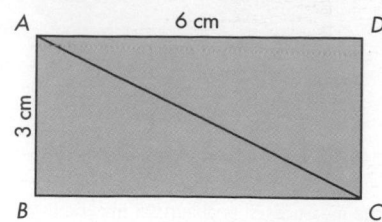

◆ What is the area of rectangle *ABCD* in square centimeters? **18 cm²**

◆ The area of triangle *ABC* is what fraction of the area of *ABCD*? $\frac{1}{2}$

◆ What is the area of triangle *ABC*? **9 cm²**

Remember: A right angle is an angle that has a measure of 90°, like the corner of this page.

Angles *A*, *B*, *C*, and *D* are right angles.

A **right triangle** is a triangle that has a right angle.

Triangles *ABC* and *CDA* are both right triangles.

◆ Can we think of every right triangle as having half the area of a rectangle that shares two of the triangle's sides? **yes**

You can determine the area of a right triangle by taking one half the area of the corresponding rectangle.

Example: What is the area of triangle *EFG*?

Since *F* is a right angle, you can draw a rectangle with *EF* and *FG* as its height and base. The area of the rectangle is 3 × 4, or 12, square centimeters. So the area of triangle *EFG* is one half of 12, or 6, square centimeters.

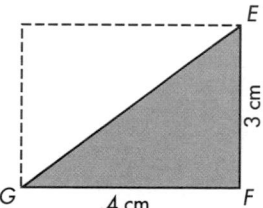

452 · Geometry

 **Literature Connection** Have students read *Triangles and Pyramids* by Sally Morgan, and use the photographs to identify right triangles and their uses, estimating the area of each.

---

*available separately

The area of a right triangle is one half the length of the base times the height.

$$A = \frac{1}{2}bh$$

(The base and height are measured on lines that meet in a right angle.)

∠C is a right angle.

Area of △ABC

$$= \frac{1}{2} bh$$

$$= \frac{1}{2} (10 \times 7.5)$$

$$= 37.5 \text{ cm}^2$$

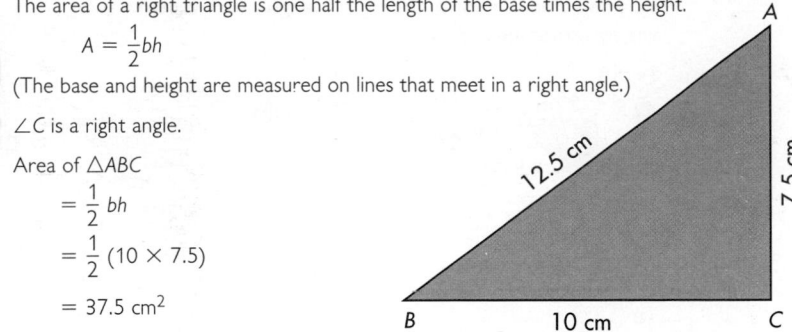

Remember, the symbol ∠ stands for angle, the symbol △ stands for triangle, and cm² stands for square centimeters.

For each of these right triangles, name the right angle, the base, and the height. Base and height are interchangeable.

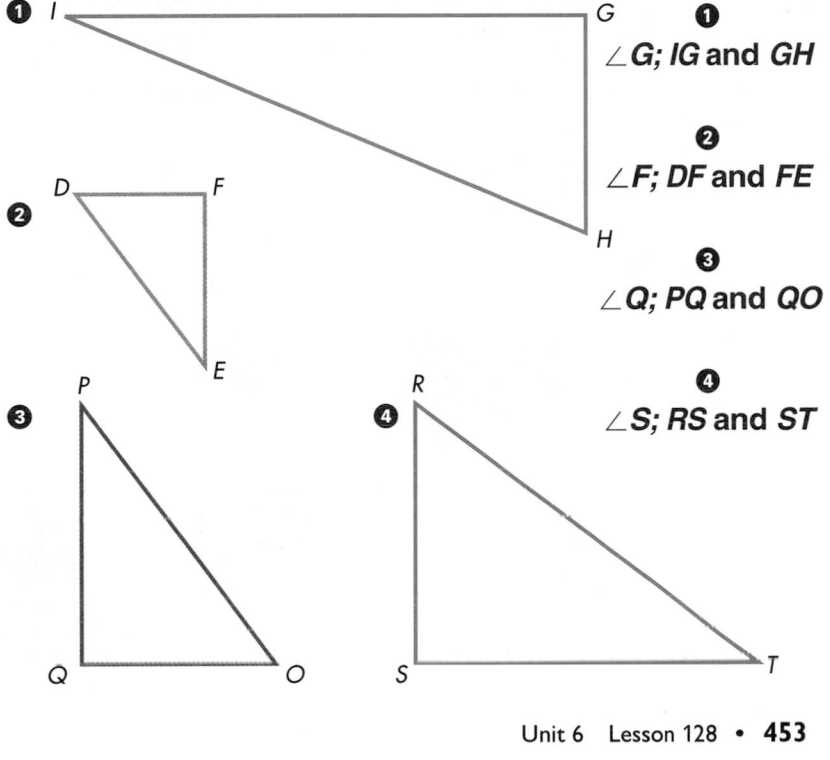

❶ ∠**G**; **IG** and **GH**

❷ ∠**F**; **DF** and **FE**

❸ ∠**Q**; **PQ** and **QO**

❹ ∠**S**; **RS** and **ST**

Unit 6   Lesson 128 • **453**

❷ Teach

Using the Student Pages Discuss with the class page 452, which describes a derivation of the formula for the area of a right triangle. If students do not see that triangles *ABC* and *CDA* are congruent, have them trace one figure onto **tracing paper** or **waxed paper** and fit it over the other. When discussing this page, ask students to tell how to check that an angle really is a right angle. Possible answers include: (1) compare it with the corner of a sheet of paper, (2) measure it with a protractor, and (3) construct a right angle by folding paper or with a ruler and a compass.

Go over the example at the top of page 453 and then have students complete problems 1–4 on their own.

Be sure students recognize that the order of the points does not matter when naming a line segment, and that the base and height of a right triangle are interchangeable.

Technology Connection Refer students to the software *The Math Map Trip* from Educational Activities (Mac, IBM, for grades 4–8) for practice with area, perimeter, averages, basic geometry, preparing charts and graphs, and much more.

◆ **LESSON 128   Area of a Right Triangle**

Teach

Using the Student Pages Assign the area problems on page 454 and the computation problems on page 455 for independent work. You may wish to review with students ways to multiply by $\frac{1}{2}$. Guide them to use the method that is easiest for them—take half of the product of the height and the base, or take $\frac{1}{2}$ of *either* the height or the base and then multiply. Remind students to give their answers to the area problems in square centimeters. If students ask why the dimensions of some of the hypotenuses are given, you can explain that this is additional information presented to be sure that they know to distinguish the hypotenuse from the base and height, and that they know what information to disregard as superfluous.

◆ **LESSON 128   Area of a Right Triangle**

Find the area of each of the right triangles shown below using the measurements given.

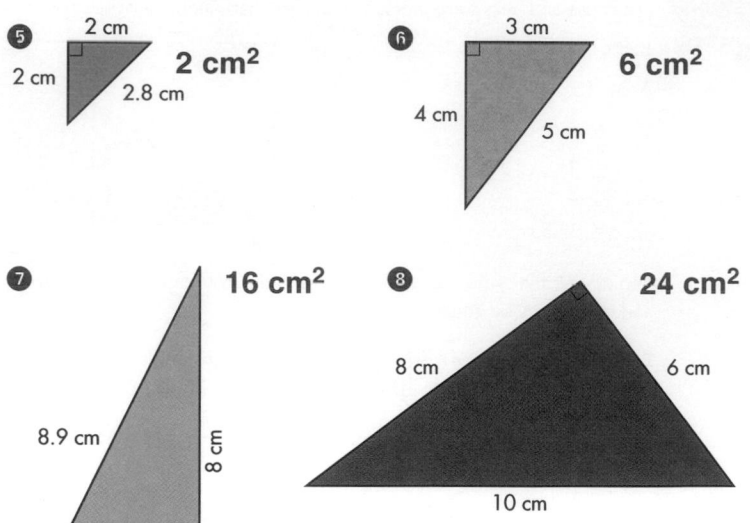

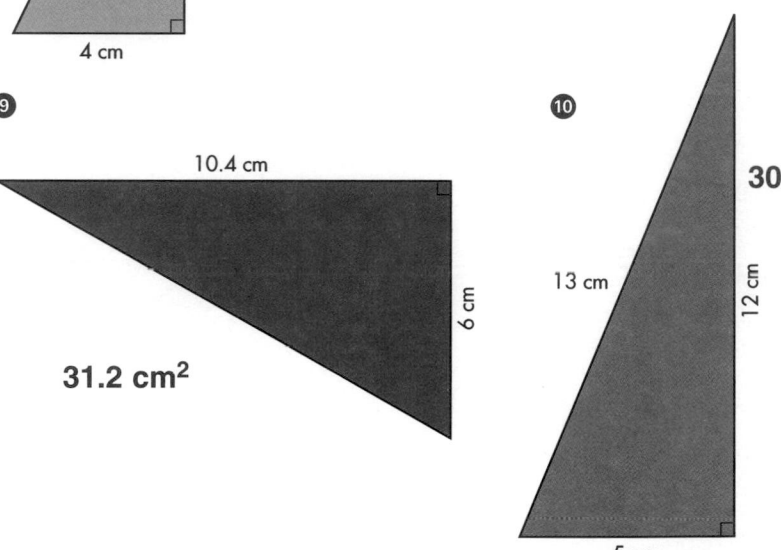

454 · Geometry

Real-World Connection Have students interview an architect or engineer, or do research in the school library, to find out about the key role that triangles play in the construction of skyscrapers and other large structures. Invite students to share their findings with classmates.

Add or subtract. Watch the signs.

⑪	⑫	⑬	⑭
738	831	1979	13,875
− 265	+ 694	− 1492	+ 8,238
473	**1525**	**487**	**22,113**

Multiply. Use shortcuts when you can.

⑮	⑯	⑰	⑱
50	49	70	71
× 50	× 51	× 70	× 69
2500	**2499**	**4900**	**4899**

Divide. Round decimal quotients to the nearest tenth when necessary.

⑲ $\overset{45}{7\overline{)315}}$ ⑳ $\overset{205.6}{9\overline{)1850}}$ ㉑ $\overset{22.7}{21\overline{)476}}$ ㉒ $\overset{11.3}{54\overline{)612}}$

㉓ $\overset{78.1}{8\overline{)625}}$ ㉔ $\overset{21.8}{38\overline{)829}}$ ㉕ $\overset{30}{25\overline{)750}}$ ㉖ $\overset{11.4}{82\overline{)933}}$

㉗ $\overset{16}{40\overline{)640}}$ ㉘ $\overset{4}{45\overline{)180}}$ ㉙ $\overset{9.1}{11\overline{)100}}$ ㉚ $\overset{31.4}{63\overline{)1979}}$

Solve.

㉛ $\frac{1}{3}$ of 15 **5** ㉜ $\frac{1}{6}$ of 24 **4** ㉝ $\frac{3}{4}$ of 8 **6** ㉞ $\frac{1}{5}$ of 20 **4**

㉟ $\frac{2}{3}$ of 15 **10** ㊱ $\frac{1}{4}$ of 8 **2** ㊲ $\frac{1}{7}$ of 21 **3** ㊳ $\frac{2}{5}$ of 20 **8**

In each problem two of the answers are clearly wrong and one is correct. Choose the correct answer.

㊴	12.3 × 2.1	**ⓐ 25.83**	**b.** 258.3	**c.** 2583
㊵	2.5 × 7.5	**a.** 0.1875	**b.** 1.875	**ⓒ 18.75**
㊶	5.6 × 23.1	**a.** 12.936	**ⓑ 129.36**	**c.** 1293.6
㊷	0.54 × 1.13	**a.** 0.06102	**ⓑ 0.6102**	**c.** 6.102
㊸	8.3 × 6.47	**ⓐ 53.701**	**b.** 537.01	**c.** 5370.1
㊹	936 × 0.28	**a.** 26.208	**ⓑ 262.08**	**c.** 2620.8
㊺	49.7 × 5.6	**a.** 27.832	**ⓑ 278.32**	**c.** 2783.2

PRACTICE p. 128

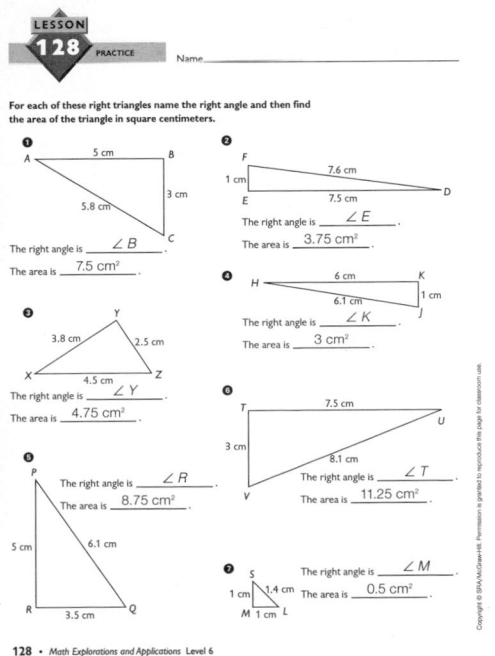

LESSON 128 PRACTICE　Name _____

For each of these right triangles name the right angle and then find the area of the triangle in square centimeters.

ENRICHMENT p. 128

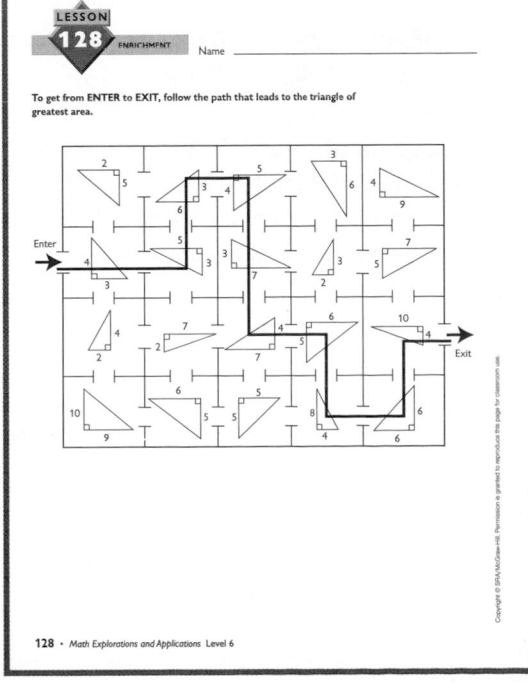

LESSON 128 ENRICHMENT　Name _____

To get from ENTER to EXIT, follow the path that leads to the triangle of greatest area.

③ Wrap-Up 🕐 5 MINUTES

In Closing To summarize the lesson, ask students to write an explanation of the derivation of the formula for area of a right triangle.

Performance Assessment Ask students to find the area of a right triangle with a base of 14 centimeters and a height of 11 centimeters. (77 sq cm)

Assessment Criteria

Did the student . . .

✓ demonstrate understanding of the derivation of the formula for area of a right triangle?

✓ successfully complete the triangle problems on pages 453 and 454?

✓ correctly solve at least 27 of the 35 problems on page 455?

Homework Have students lean a broom, book, measuring stick, or similar straight object against a wall at home. Then have them use a ruler or tape measure to find out the height (distance up the wall) and base (distance from the wall, along the floor, to the end of the object), and figure out the area of the right triangle that is created.

SPECIAL NEEDS **Meeting Individual Needs**

As needed, review with students how to identify the hypotenuse and legs of a right triangle. Point out that the longest side of the right triangle, the side opposite the right angle, is the hypotenuse, and that the other two sides are the legs, either of which can be the base or height of the triangle. Use a model of a right triangle. Point to each kind of side and demonstrate, by standing the triangle first on one leg and then on the other, that either leg can be used as the base.

LESSON 129 Parallelograms

Student Edition pages 456–459

LESSON PLANNER

Objectives

▶ to review the formula for finding the area of a parallelogram and to provide practice in using it

▶ to review the concept of parallel lines and the terms *quadrilateral* and *parallelogram*

Context of the Lesson This is the second of nine lessons on plane figures.

MANIPULATIVES

tangram pieces (optional)

Program Resources

Reteaching Master

Practice Master 129

Enrichment Master 129

For extra practice:
   CD-ROM* Lesson 129
   Cumulative Review, page 581

① Warm-Up

 **Problem of the Day** Present the following problem to the students: You have a square sheet of paper that is 10 feet on a side. If you were to cut it in half, parallel to a side, there would be two pieces. If you stacked the two pieces and cut them in half parallel to the shorter sides, there would be four square pieces. If you were to continue stacking and cutting in the same manner for a total of ten cuts, how long would the length of a side of one of the resulting squares be? (0.3125 ft or $\frac{5}{16}$ of a foot)

Problem-Solving Strategies Ask students who have solved the Problem of the Day to share how they solved it and any strategies they used.

MENTAL MATH Introduce a new type of mental drill in which you describe the amount of gasoline available, the distance to be traveled, and the approximate rate of gasoline consumption, and have students indicate the answer "Yes, there's enough gas" by showing thumbs up or "No, there's not enough gas" by showing thumbs down. If it is a borderline case, they stand up. For example, put a chart such as the one provided here on the chalkboard and fill in the first three columns in the first row. After seeing the set of numbers, students should respond with the answer for the fourth column. Then write the next row of numbers.

(continued on page 457)

LESSON 129 Parallelograms

Lines are **parallel** if they go in the same direction and are the same distance apart at all points. Two parallel lines are in the same plane and never meet. These two lines are parallel.

Of course, we can draw only a small part of a line since a line goes on forever in both directions.

Although these lines do not meet on this page, they are not parallel because we know they will meet to the right when extended.

① Examples: opposite edges of a chalkboard, parallel lines on tile floors, opposite edges of a wall

② Examples: railroad tracks, opposite edges of a building, stripes on a suit or uniform

① Look around your classroom. Find some examples of parallel lines (really, parts of parallel lines).

② Think of examples of parallel lines that are not in your classroom.

A **quadrilateral** is a figure that has four sides (*quadri-* means "four," and *lateral* means "of the side" or "sided"). Figure *ABCD* is a quadrilateral.

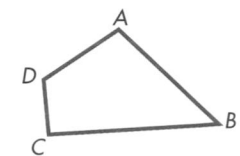

If both pairs of opposite sides of a quadrilateral are parallel, the figure is a **parallelogram**. Figure *JKLM* is a parallelogram.

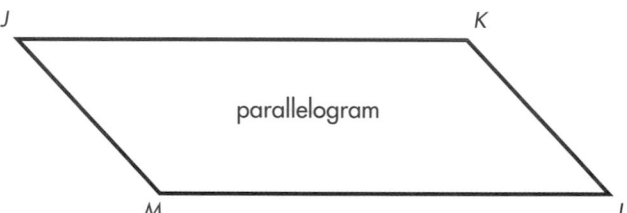

parallelogram

456 · Geometry

 **Art Connection** Provide sets of **tangram pieces**. Ask students to use all seven of them to make each of the following: a square, a rectangle, a parallelogram, and a trapezoid.

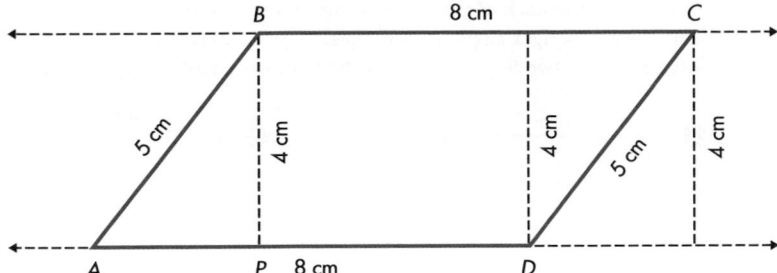

In parallelogram *ABCD*, *AB* is 5 centimeters, *BC* is 8 centimeters, *CD* is 5 centimeters, and *DA* is 8 centimeters long. The shortest distance between lines *AD* and *BC* is 4 centimeters.

◆ Can you figure out what the area of parallelogram *ABCD* is? (Hint: See if you can make it equal to the area of some rectangle.) **yes, 32 cm²**

◆ What is the area of parallelogram *EFGH*? Explain how you got your answer. **30 cm²; draw a rectangle with base of 10 and height of 3**

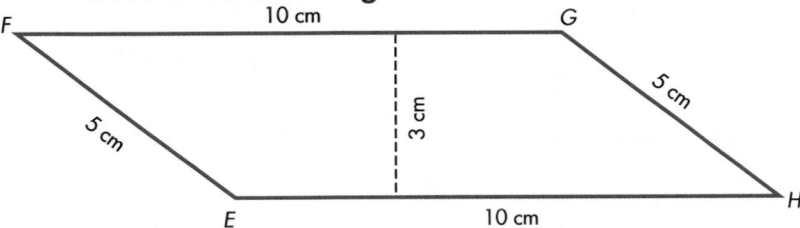

The area of a parallelogram is equal to the length of the base times the height.

A = bh

Remember, the height is measured on a line segment that is **perpendicular** to the base. Perpendicular lines intersect at right angles. So in parallelogram *EFGH*, if you choose *EH* as the base, the height is 3 centimeters (not 5 centimeters).

◆ Could we have chosen a different side as the base? **Yes, any side would work if the height were chosen properly.**

Unit 6 Lesson 129 • **457**

Mental Math (continued)

Kilometers to Be Traveled	Number of Liters in Tank	Average Number of Kilometers per Liter	Is There Enough Gasoline?
200	40	6	yes (thumbs up)
300	40	6	no (thumbs down)
320	40	7	no (thumbs down)
400	50	8	borderline (stand up)
450	50	10	yes (thumbs up)

❷ Teach

Using the Student Pages When discussing page 456 with students, emphasize that each line shown is actually only a model of part of a straight line, pointing out that a line is an idealized notion: It has no thickness, and it goes on forever. Explain that lines in a plane can either meet or not, and if the lines never meet they are called parallel lines. Ask students to give some real-life examples of parallel lines, starting with those they see in the classroom.

Discuss the material on page 457 with the class. Point out that when a parallelogram is cut on a perpendicular to form a rectangle, the perpendicular becomes the side of the new rectangle. Then emphasize that the lengths of the sloping sides of a parallelogram can be ignored in finding area; only the height and base are significant. You may wish to review key characteristics of all parallelograms with students, such as: opposite sides are both parallel and congruent, opposite angles are congruent, and a rectangle is a special form of parallelogram that has only right angles.

Technology Connection Refer students to the software *Geometry* from Sensei (Apple, Mac, IBM, for grades 6–12) for practice with points, lines and planes, parallel lines, parallelograms, similarity, right triangles, circles, areas of polygons, and coordinate geometry.

◆ LESSON 129 Parallelograms

Teach

Using the Student Pages Have students do the ten problems on page 458 on their own. Although these problems are straightforward, some students might have difficulty because of confusion between height and length of sides. Emphasize that the height is a perpendicular line segment connecting two opposite sides, which are the bases. Except when the parallelogram has all right angles, the height is not one of the sides of the figure.

Assign the problems on page 459 for independent work reviewing perimeter and circumference. Guide students to use $\frac{22}{7}$ as the approximation for π when either the diameter or the radius is a multiple of 7, as in problems 13 and 18.

GIFTED & TALENTED **Meeting Individual Needs**
Challenge students to figure out what kind of figure is formed when they connect the midpoints of all four sides of any quadrilateral. (a parallelogram)

◆ LESSON 129 Parallelograms

Find the area of each of these parallelograms in square centimeters. A right angle (for example, ⌐ or Γ) drawn at the intersection of two lines means that the lines are perpendicular.

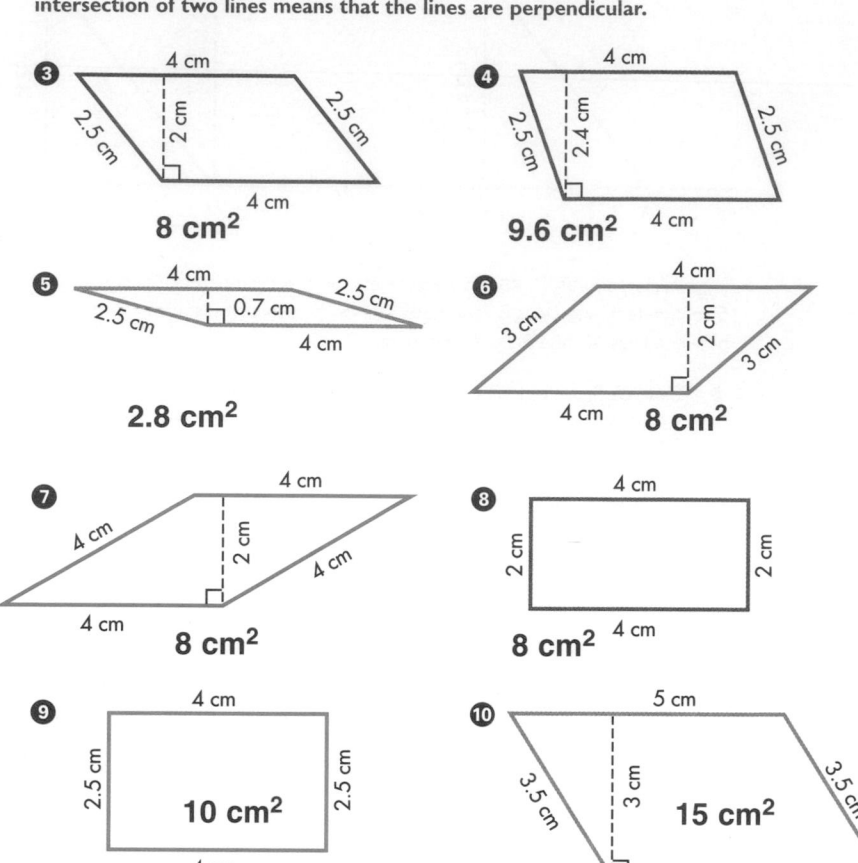

458 · Geometry

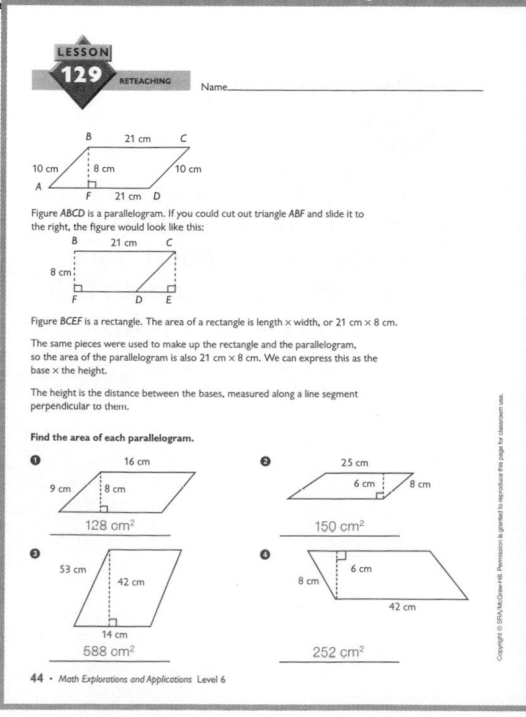

RETEACHING p. 44

Find the perimeter or circumference of each of the following figures, using the measurements given (lines that look parallel are parallel; use either 3.14 or $\frac{22}{7}$ as your value for π).

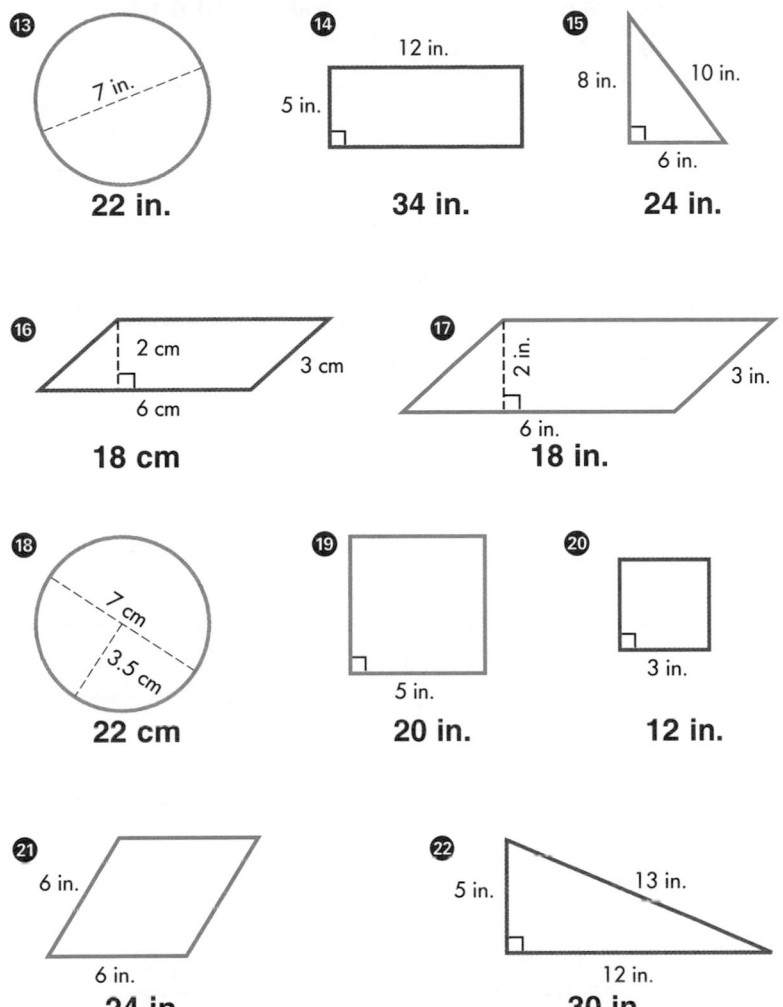

13 7 in.
22 in.

14 12 in. 5 in.
34 in.

15 8 in. 10 in. 6 in.
24 in.

16 2 cm 3 cm 6 cm
18 cm

17 2 in. 3 in. 6 in.
18 in.

18 7 cm 3.5 cm
22 cm

19 5 in.
20 in.

20 3 in.
12 in.

21 6 in. 6 in.
24 in.

22 5 in. 13 in. 12 in.
30 in.

Use the Cumulative Review on page 581 after this lesson.

❸ Wrap-Up 🕐 5 MINUTES

In Closing To summarize the lesson, ask students to identify parallel lines and parallelograms in the classroom.

ALTERNATIVE ASSESSMENT **Performance Assessment** Ask students to explain which has the greater area and by how much: a right triangle with $b = 8$ meters and $h = 12$ meters or a parallelogram with $b = 9$ meters and $h = 6$ meters? (The parallelogram's area is 6 m^2 greater.)

Assessment Criteria

Did the student . . .

✓ demonstrate understanding of the concept of parallel lines?

✓ have success using the formula to find the areas of parallelograms?

Homework Have students identify several parallelograms at home. Then have them measure the key dimensions of each and find the areas.

SPECIAL NEEDS **MANIPULATIVES** **Meeting Individual Needs**
For students who use a side of the parallelogram instead of its height when finding area, work with a drawing or a model (for example, a cardboard box with the top and bottom removed). You can show that if a parallelogram were "pushed down," the lengths of the sides would be the same but the area would decrease to 0.

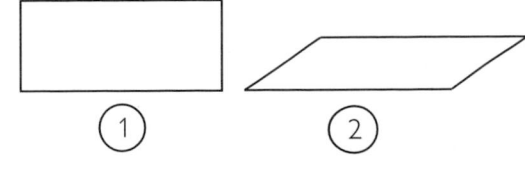

① ②

PRACTICE p. 129

LESSON 129 PRACTICE Name_____

Find the area of each of these parallelograms in square centimeters.

① 18 cm 12 cm 10 cm 12 cm 18 cm
180 cm²

② 42 cm 26 cm 20 cm 26 cm 42 cm
840 cm²

③ 24 cm 5 cm 4 cm 5 cm 24 cm
96 cm²

④ 8.5 cm 8 cm 6.2 cm 8 cm 8.5 cm
52.7 cm²

⑤ 30 cm 80 cm 70° cm 80 cm 30 cm
2100 cm²

⑥ 15 cm 20 cm 25 cm 25 cm 15 cm
300 cm²

⑦ 47 cm 29 cm
1363 cm²

⑧ 14 cm 38 cm
532 cm²

Math Explorations and Applications Level 6 • 129

ENRICHMENT p. 129

LESSON 129 ENRICHMENT Name_____

To do this project you will need some cardboard and eight brads (fasteners) to attach pieces of cardboard. Make a trapezoid and parallelogram like those shown below. Cut the sides out of cardboard and attach the corners with brads.

5 in. 4 in. 5 in. 9.5 in.   6 in. 5 in. 4 in. 4 in. 6 in.

❶ Shift the corners of the trapezoid. Does it remain a trapezoid? (Remember, a trapezoid has two sides that are parallel.) **not necessarily**

❷ Shift the corners of the parallelogram. Does it remain a parallelogram? (Remember, a parallelogram has both pairs of opposite sides parallel.) **yes**

❸ If the angles in a trapezoid change, would it still be a trapezoid always, sometimes, or never? **sometimes**

❹ If the angles in a parallelogram change, would it still be a parallelogram always, sometimes, or never? **always**

❺ Position your shapes over grid paper. Does shifting the corners change the area of the shapes? **yes**

❻ Shift the corners of the parallelogram to make a shape with the greatest possible area. How could you describe this shape? **It's a rectangle.**

Math Explorations and Applications Level 6 • 129

LESSON 130
Area of a Triangle

Student Edition pages 460–463

LESSON PLANNER

Objectives

▶ to review the formula for finding the area of any triangle and to provide practice in using it

▶ to provide experience in finding the area of figures made up of smaller figures for which area formulas are known

Context of the Lesson This is the third of nine lessons on plane figures.

 MANIPULATIVES

Program Resources

Reteaching Master

Practice Master 130

Enrichment Master 130

For extra practice:
CD-ROM* Lesson 130

---

① Warm-Up  5 MINUTES

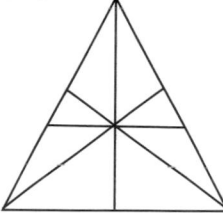 **Problem of the Day** Present the following problem: How many triangles are in the figure below? (23)

Problem-Solving Strategies Ask students who have solved the Problem of the Day to share how they solved it and any strategies they used.

 MENTAL MATH Continue the "Will I have enough gasoline?" set of exercises from the previous lesson.

(continued on page 461)

LESSON 130
Area of a Triangle

In this lesson you will review how to use the relationship between parallelograms and triangles that have the same base and height to come up with a formula for finding the area of triangles.

◆ What is the area of parallelogram *ABCD*? **18 cm²**

◆ Is △*DBC* the same shape and size as △*BDA*? (Imagine cutting out the parallelogram and then cutting along *DB* to make two separate triangles. Would you be able to fit △*DBC* exactly on △*BDA*?) **yes; yes**

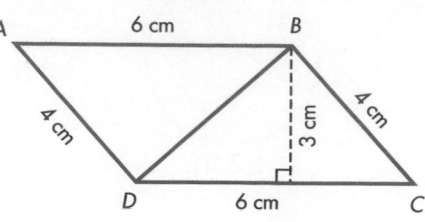

◆ What fraction of the area of *ABCD* is the area of △*DBC*? $\frac{1}{2}$

◆ What is the area of △*DBC*? **9 cm²**

◆ Suppose you cut parallelogram *ABCD* from *A* to *C*. What fraction of the area of *ABCD* is the area of △*ADC*? $\frac{1}{2}$

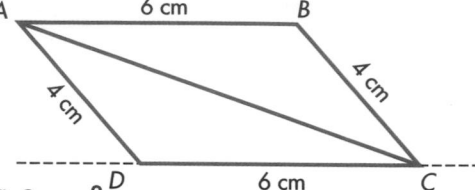

◆ What is the area of △*ADC*? **9 cm²**

◆ Is there more than one way to draw a parallelogram that shares two sides with a triangle? **yes**

◆ Do all of the parallelograms that share two sides with a triangle have the same area? **yes**

 **ALGEBRA READINESS**

The area of a parallelogram is equal to the length of the base times the height.

$$A = bh$$

The area of a triangle is equal to one half the length of the base times the height.

$$A = \frac{1}{2}\,bh$$

The height of a parallelogram is measured on a line perpendicular to a base. The height of a triangle is measured on a line perpendicular to a base. In both cases we must choose a side to be the base.

460 · Geometry

 **Literature Connection** Have students read "Create Your Own Rainbirds" in *Math Wizardry for Kids* by Margaret Kenda and Phyllis S. Williams. Have them create rainbirds and then determine the area of the triangles they created.

*available separately

Find the area of each of the following figures using the measurements given. Sides that look parallel are parallel.

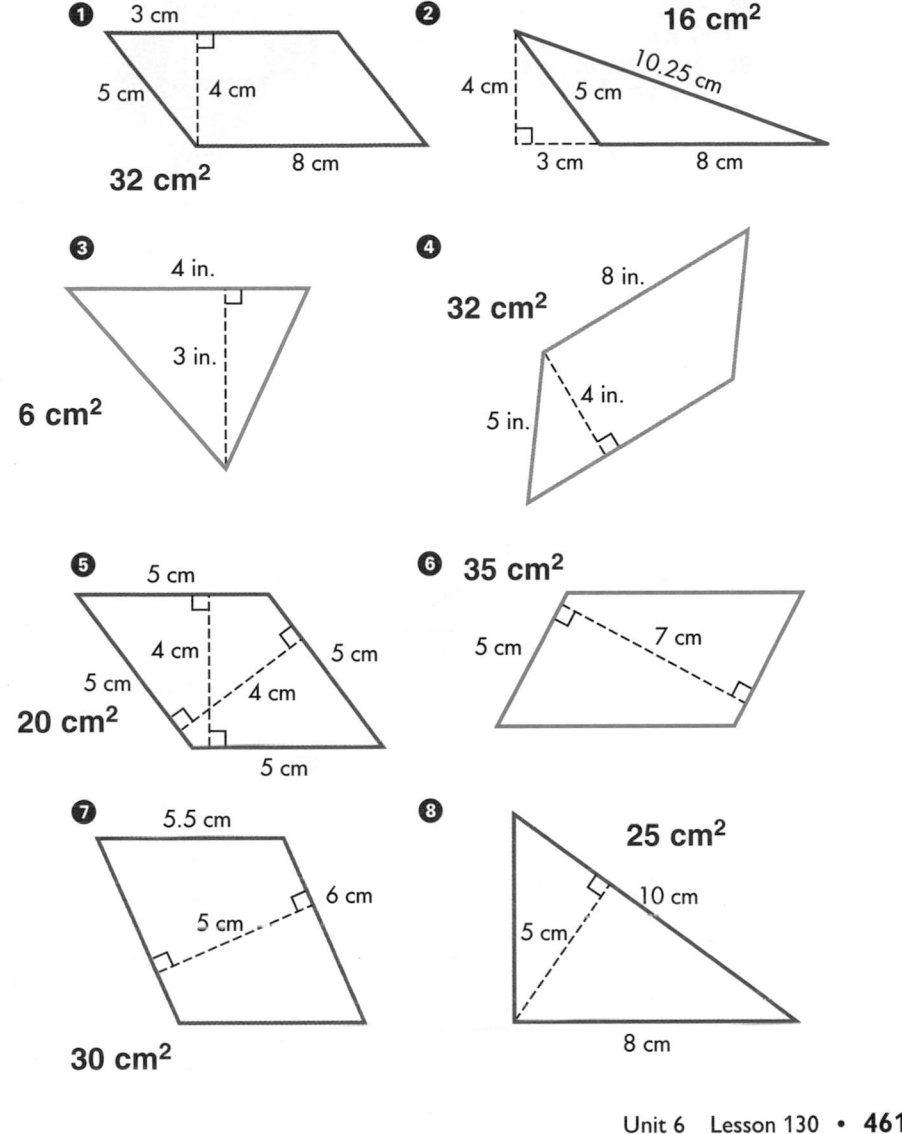

1 3 cm / 5 cm / 4 cm / 8 cm
32 cm²

2 16 cm² / 10.25 cm / 4 cm / 5 cm / 3 cm / 8 cm

3 4 in. / 3 in.
6 cm²

4 8 in. / 4 in. / 5 in.
32 cm²

5 5 cm / 4 cm / 5 cm / 5 cm / 4 cm / 5 cm
20 cm²

6 35 cm² / 5 cm / 7 cm

7 5.5 cm / 5 cm / 6 cm
30 cm²

8 25 cm² / 10 cm / 5 cm / 8 cm

Technology Connection You may want to encourage students to explore the Internet site *Galileo Lesson Plans* for grades 3–6 (http://www-hpcc.astro.washington.edu/scied/galileo.html), a combination of math and science encouraging students to locate geometric shapes.

Mental Math (continued)

Km	L	Average km/L	Thumbs...
250	40	7	(up)
300	40	7	(down)
400	50	10	(up)
550	50	10	(down)
600	60	10	(stand)

② Teach

Using the Student Pages Discuss page 460 with the class. Point out that although the formula is the same as that for a right triangle, the derivation is different. Moreover, in triangles without right angles, it is important to distinguish between a side and the height.

Draw an obtuse triangle *ABC* on the chalkboard. Encourage students to discuss how they would use the procedure shown in their book to find the area of the triangle.

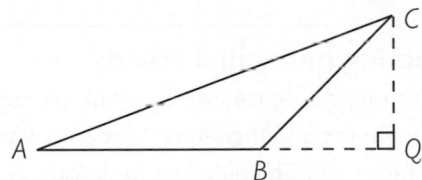

Presumably, they would complete parallelogram *ABCD* and show that *CQ* is its height and *AB* is its base.

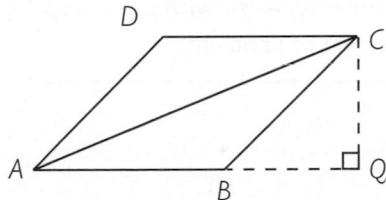

Assign the area problems on page 461 for independent work. Emphasize that the height must be measured on a line perpendicular to the base. (The base may need to be extended to show this.)

◆ LESSON 130   Area of a Triangle

Teach

Using the Student Pages Together with students, work through finding the area of the figure at the top of page 462 by breaking it up into its parts. Then assign the remaining problems on pages 462 and 463 for students to solve on their own, providing help as needed. Point out that some figures can be partitioned in more ways than one. Here is an example of one way to partition problems 14, 16, and 18.

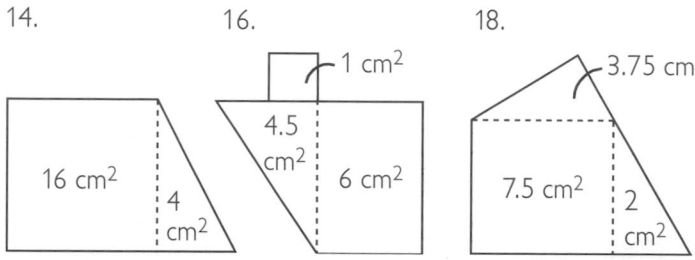

14.   16.   18.

Invite students who finish early to use graph paper to create a few irregular figures of their own, perhaps some that are more intricate than those on these pages. They should label all necessary dimensions and maybe some that are not needed. Then have students exchange papers and find the areas.

Meeting Individual Needs

Partitioning a figure into appropriate regions requires thoroughness and ingenuity. Students who find this process difficult can be guided to look for obvious rectangles, parallelograms, and triangles for which they can easily determine the base and height. Remind students that any side of a triangle can be used as a base. Encourage them to work with partners who have a facility with this kind of problem.

◆ LESSON 130   Area of a Triangle

Sometimes we can find the area of a complicated figure by breaking it up into smaller parts. For example, in this figure you can see a square (red), a triangle (green), and a parallelogram (blue).

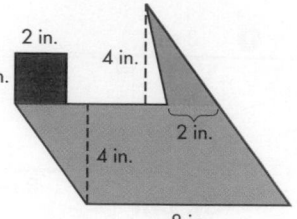

9 What is the area of the red square? **4 in.²**

10 What is the area of the green triangle? **4 in.²**

11 What is the area of the blue parallelogram? **32 in.²**

12 What is the area of the entire figure? **40 in.²**

Determine the area of each of these figures. For some of these you will need to divide the figure into triangles, parallelograms, and rectangles, and then find the sum of these areas.

13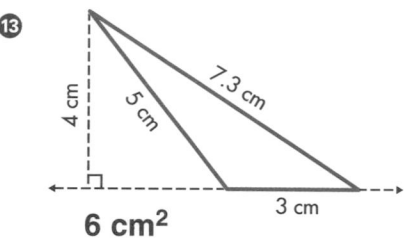

6 cm²

14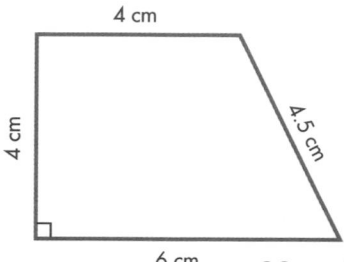

20 cm²

15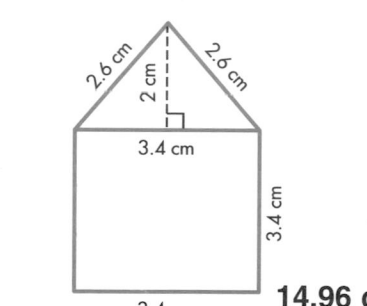

14.96 cm²

16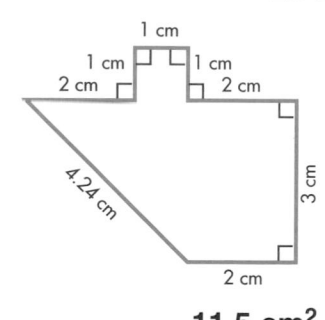

11.5 cm²

Real-World Connection Ask students to think about workers who might need to find the areas of irregular figures to do their jobs. Have them create an annotated list.

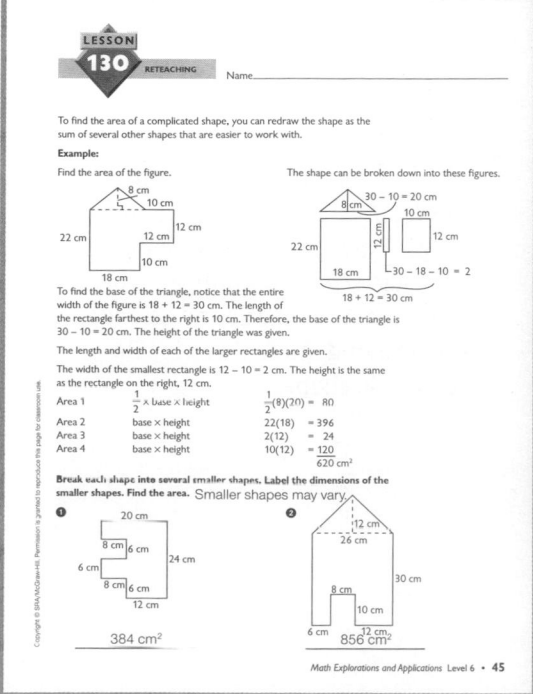

Determine the area of each of these figures by dividing the figures into triangles, parallelograms, and rectangles, and then find the sum of these areas. (If you draw lines to divide a figure, first copy the figure onto a sheet of paper. Or you can simply imagine the lines.)

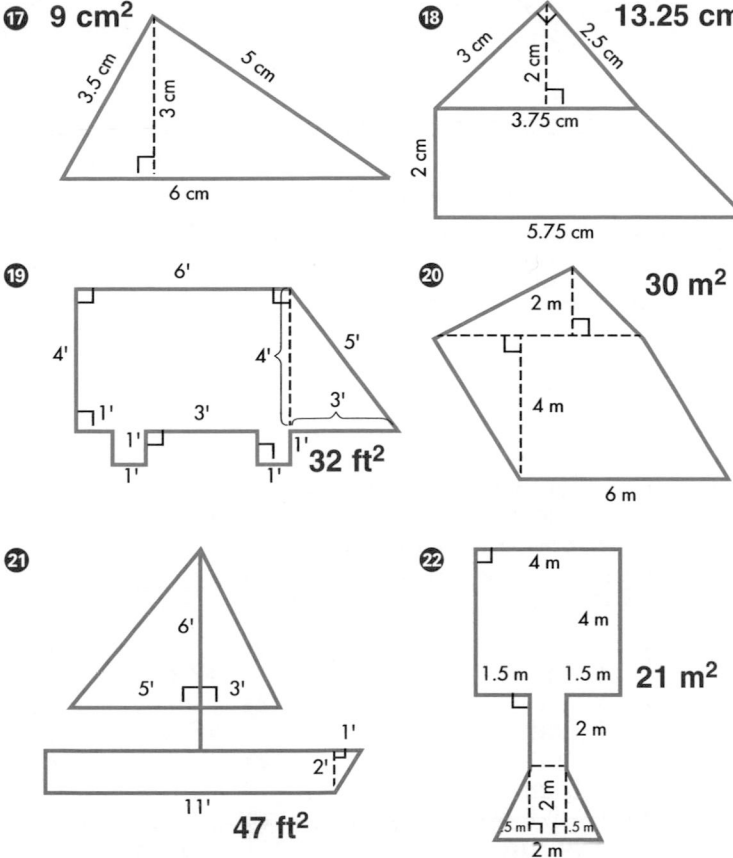

⓱ 9 cm²

⓲ 13.25 cm²

⓳

⓴ 30 m²

32 ft²

㉑

㉒ 21 m²

47 ft²

㉓ Draw two interesting pictures using only triangles, squares, parallelograms, and rectangles. Measure the needed lengths, and figure out the area of your picture.
Check students' work.

Unit 6   Lesson 130 • **463**

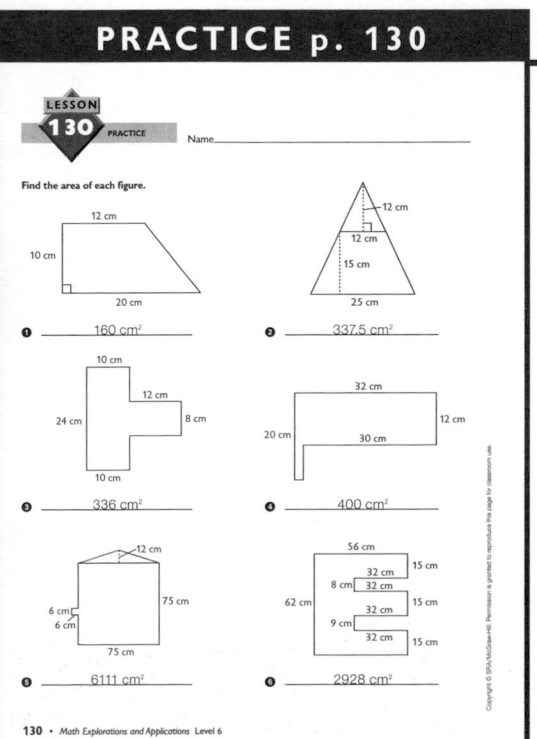
❸ Wrap-Up

5 MINUTES

In Closing To summarize the lesson, ask students to explain how to find the area of an irregular figure made up of polygons.

Informal Assessment Circulate about the room and observe students as they break down the figures into smaller polygons and find those areas. Check to see that students are applying what they have learned about identifying the bases and heights of triangles and parallelograms and about using formulas to find the areas of these polygons.

Assessment Criteria

Did the student . . .

✓ demonstrate understanding of the derivation of the formula for area of a triangle?

✓ successfully find the areas of triangles and parallelograms?

✓ successfully find the areas of irregular figures by breaking down the figures into parallelograms and triangles?

Homework Ask students to find the area of an irregular floor region at home by breaking it down into smaller parts, measuring the key dimensions of each, and then applying the area formulas. Have students draw a sketch to show their work to include in their Math Portfolios.

Area of a Trapezoid

LESSON PLANNER

Objective

▶ to explain how to develop and to provide practice in using a formula for finding the area of a trapezoid

Context of the Lesson This is the fourth of nine lessons on plane figures.

MANIPULATIVES
grid paper
measuring materials*

Program Resources
Practice Master 131
Enrichment Master 131
For extra practice:
CD-ROM* Lesson 131

① Warn-Up ⏱ 5 MINUTES

 Problem of the Day Present the following problem: Suppose there are ten pennies in a row, heads up. You want to make a rectangular border around them consisting of pennies, tails up. How many pennies will you need for this border? How many would you need if the ten pennies were arranged in two rows of five? (26 pennies; 18 pennies)

Problem-Solving Strategies Ask students who have solved the Problem of the Day to share how they solved it and any strategies they used.

 Point to a bookcase, box, or doorway in your classroom. Ask students to estimate its height, length, and width, either in meters or centimeters, or inches or feet. Invite a volunteer to use **measuring materials*** to check the estimates.

② Teach

 Using the Student Pages Review the discussion questions on page 464 with the class, having each student check the conclusions by measuring. Then have students complete problems 1–11 on their own. When they have finished, have students discuss their answers with classmates. For the figure on page 464, make sure students understand that the length m is halfway between the lengths b and B, as it is the average of the two. When discussing problem 11, students can conclude that there is a rectangle with base m, with a height that is the

464 Geometry

Area of a Trapezoid

A **trapezoid** is a quadrilateral with exactly one pair of parallel sides.

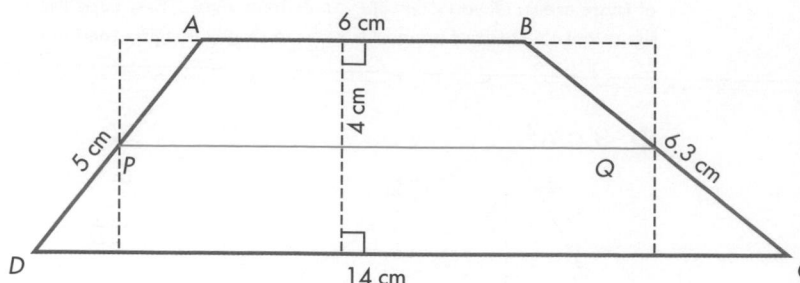

Figure ABCD is a trapezoid. Line AB is parallel to line CD.

◆ What do you think is the length of segment PQ? Why did you make that estimate? Measure to see how close your estimate is. **Answers will vary but should be close to 10 cm.**

◆ The bases of a trapezoid are the two parallel sides. If the two bases of a trapezoid measure 4 centimeters and 8 centimeters, what is the length of the "middle" segment corresponding to PQ in the figure above? **6 cm**

For problems 1–8, B is the length of the longer base of a trapezoid and b is the length of the shorter base. The length of the "middle" segment is m, halfway between the bases and on a line parallel to them. In each case tell what m is.

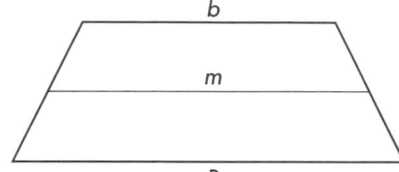

❶ $B = 10$ cm, $b = 6$ cm, $m = ?$
8 cm

❷ $B = 20$ cm, $b = 14$ cm, $m = ?$
17 cm

❸ $B = 25$ cm, $b = 15$ cm, $m = ?$
20 cm

❹ $B = 19$ cm, $b = 17$ cm, $m = ?$
18 cm

❺ $B = 5$ cm, $b = 4$ cm, $m = ?$
4.5 cm

❻ $B = 17$ cm, $b = 14$ cm, $m = ?$
15.5 cm

❼ $B = 173$ cm, $b = 115$ cm, $m = ?$
144 cm

❽ $B = 2.6$ cm, $b = 1.4$ cm, $m = ?$
2.0 cm

❾ $B = 16$ cm, $b = 14.2$ cm, $m = ?$
15.1 cm

❿ $B = 92$ cm, $b = 87$ cm, $m = ?$
89.5 cm

⓫ Try to find the area of trapezoid ABCD at the top of the page. (Hint: The broken lines may help.) **40 cm²**

464 · Geometry

Why teach it this way?

Try to impress upon students the value and technique of relating the properties of an unfamiliar figure to those of a familiar figure. Guide students to appreciate that it is this skill, not the application of the specific area formula, that is most important in this lesson.

RETEACHING

You may wish to have students draw, cut out, and manipulate the figures of the rectangle and the trapezoid to show that the areas are indeed equal.

*available separately

A way to find the area of a trapezoid is to multiply the height by the average of the bases.

The formula for this is the following:

$$A = h\left(\frac{b + B}{2}\right) \text{ or } \frac{h}{2}(b + B)$$

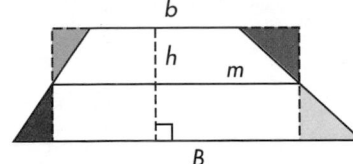

In the figure above, the green triangle is the same size as the red triangle. If you cut off the red triangle and put it where the green triangle is, the areas will match. This is also true for the blue and yellow triangles. So the area of the trapezoid is the same as the area of the rectangle with m as base and h as height: $A = hm$. But m is the average of b and B, so

$$m = \frac{b + B}{2} \text{ and } A = h\left(\frac{b + B}{2}\right)$$

Find the area of each trapezoid.

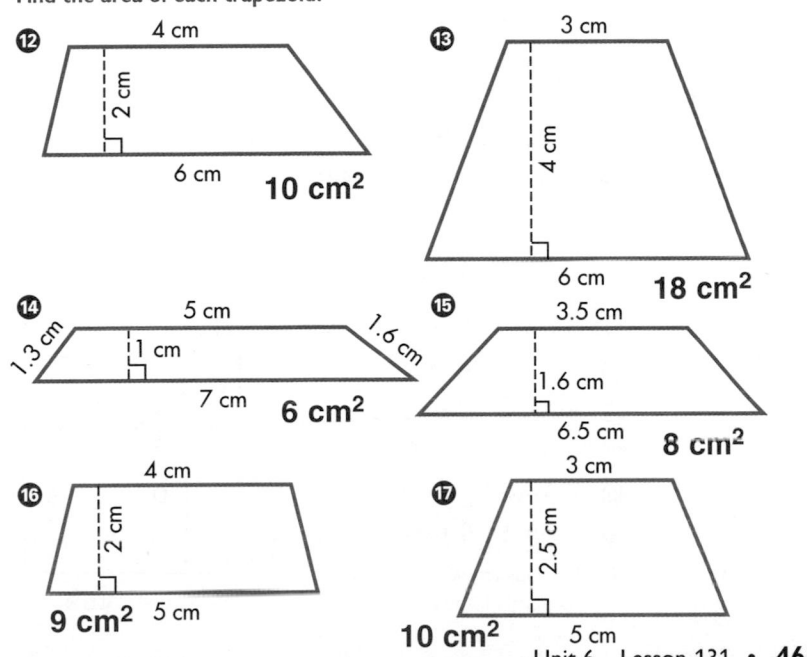

⑫ 4 cm, 2 cm, 6 cm **10 cm²**

⑬ 3 cm, 4 cm, 6 cm **18 cm²**

⑭ 5 cm, 1.3 cm, 1 cm, 7 cm, 1.6 cm **6 cm²**

⑮ 3.5 cm, 1.6 cm, 6.5 cm **8 cm²**

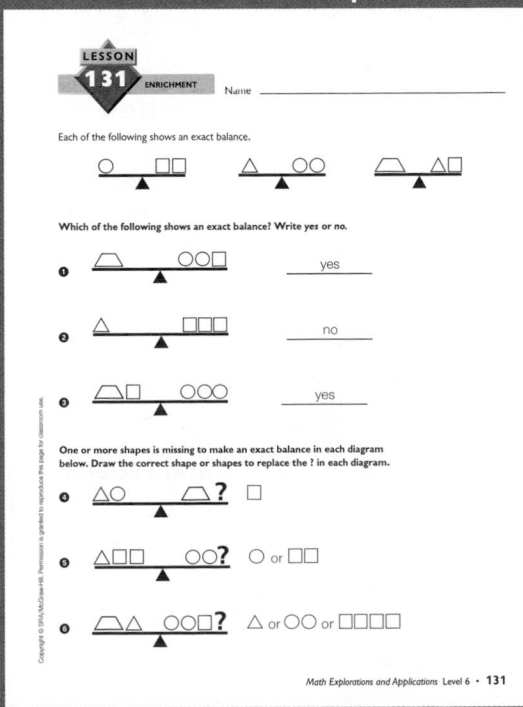

⑯ 4 cm, 2 cm, 5 cm **9 cm²**

⑰ 3 cm, 2.5 cm, 5 cm **10 cm²**

Unit 6 Lesson 131 • **465**

---

same as the trapezoid. They can conclude that the area of the trapezoid is mh or the average of its bases multiplied by its height. Point out that when m is not given, it can be found by averaging a and B.

The information provided at the top of page 465 summarizes the discussion of problem 11 from the previous page. Do one of the six problems on this page with the class and then have students complete the remaining five on their own.

❸ Wrap-Up

5 MINUTES

In Closing To summarize the lesson, ask students to explain how to determine the length of the middle segment of a trapezoid.

ALTERNATIVE ASSESSMENT

Performance Assessment Have each student draw a trapezoid on **grid paper** and exchange the paper with a partner, who uses the area formula to find the area of the figure drawn. Partners can then compare answers, explaining how they were obtained.

Assessment Criteria

Did the student . . .

✓ demonstrate understanding of how the formula for area of a trapezoid is derived?

✓ correctly apply the formula to find the area of the trapezoids shown on page 465?

Homework Challenge students to locate an object or combination of objects at home that have the shape of a trapezoid. Have students find the areas of the objects.

GIFTED & TALENTED Meeting Individual Needs
Challenge students to come up with possible dimensions of a trapezoid for which you provide only the area.

PRACTICE p. 131

ENRICHMENT p. 131

Areas of Figures on a Grid

LESSON PLANNER

Objectives

▶ to demonstrate how the area of a figure on a grid can be calculated by counting the number of units in the base and the height of the figure

▶ to provide practice in identifying and approximating bases and heights of geometric figures

Context of the Lesson This is the fifth of nine lessons on plane figures.

 MANIPULATIVES

Program Resources

Practice Master 132

Enrichment Master 132

For extra practice:
   CD-ROM* Lesson 132

❶ Warm-Up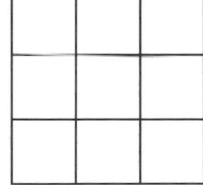

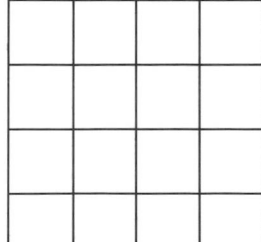 **Problem of the Day** Present the following problem to the class: How many squares of all sizes are in each of the figures below? (5 in first figure, 14 in second, 30 in third)

Problem-Solving Strategies Ask students who have solved the Problem of the Day to share how they solved it and any strategies they used.

 Present the key dimensions of several rectangles, triangles, and trapezoids. Ask students to find the area of each without using pencil and paper.

Area of Figures on a Grid

If a figure is drawn on squared paper, you can estimate the area of the figure by counting squares and parts of squares. Sometimes you can use the squares to calculate the exact area.

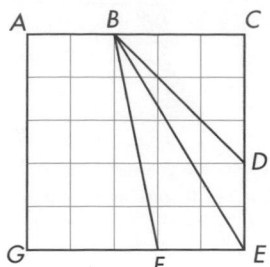

Calculate the area in square centimeters of each of these figures in the above square. Assume one square represents 1 square centimeter.

❶ square ACEG   **25 cm²**

❷ triangle BCD   **4.5 cm²**

❸ triangle BDE (Hint: Think of DE as the base of this triangle. Then the height is the perpendicular distance from B to the line EC.)   **3 cm²**

❹ triangle BEF   **5 cm²**

❺ trapezoid ABFG   **12.5 cm²**

❻ The figures in problems 2, 3, 4, and 5 cover the entire square exactly. So the sum of your answers for problems 2, 3, 4, and 5 should equal your answer for problem 1. Check to see if this is true.   **It is true.**

Calculate the area in square centimeters of each of these figures.

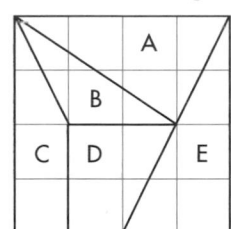

❼ triangle A   **4 cm²**

❽ triangle B   **2 cm²**

❾ trapezoid C   **3 cm²**

❿ trapezoid D   **3 cm²**

⓫ triangle E   **4 cm²**

⓬ Do your answers for problems 7 through 11 add up to the total area of the square?   **yes**

 **Literature Connection** Have students read the book *Area* by Jane Jonas Srivastava to learn different ways to measure area.

 **SPECIAL NEEDS Meeting Individual Needs**

Some students may have difficulty remembering formulas. Try to relate each formula to one the student already knows. Then give a quick drill in repeating and using the formulas.

RETEACHING

To help students who are having difficulty identifying appropriate parts of figures, review the steps. First they should try to identify a base for which the length can be determined by counting. Then explain to them that they should look next to find the height, a segment that should be measured at right angles to the base. Remind students that the base can be extended for this purpose.

*available separately

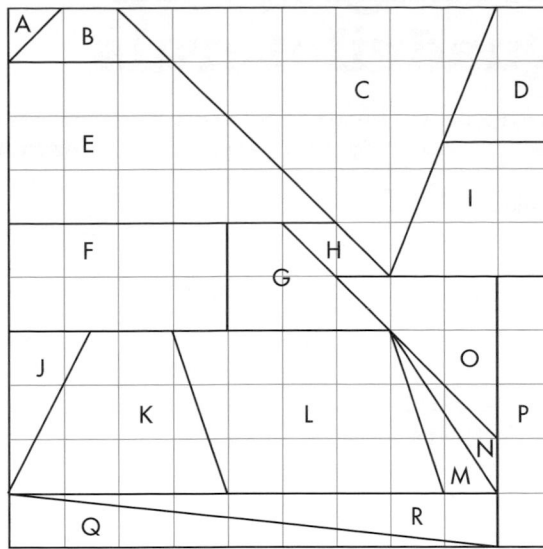

Calculate the area in square centimeters of each of these figures in the above square.

⑬ A **0.5 cm²**	**⑭** B **2 cm²**	**⑮** C **17.5 cm²**
⑯ D **3.75 cm²**	**⑰** E **13.5 cm²**	**⑱** F **8 cm²**
⑲ G **4 cm²**	**⑳** H **1 cm²**	**㉑** I **6.25 cm²**
㉒ J **2.25 cm²**	**㉓** K **8.25 cm²**	**㉔** L **12 cm²**
㉕ M **1.5 cm²**	**㉖** N **1 cm²**	**㉗** O **4.5 cm²**
㉘ P **5 cm²**	**㉙** Q **4.5 cm²**	**㉚** R **4.5 cm²**

Answer these questions.

㉛ What is the area of the entire square? **100 cm²**

㉜ What is the sum of the areas you calculated for problems 13–30? **100 cm²**

In your Math Journal record the strategies you used to find the areas of figures on the grids. How did you decide which lengths to use as bases? Were there any figures that had bases that were not whole centimeter lengths?

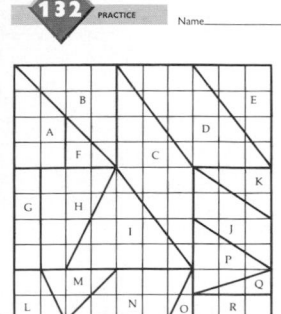

Unit 6   Lesson 132 • **467**

 **Teach**

Using the Student Pages Have students work individually on problems 1–12 on page 466. When they finish, discuss the page, focusing on the following points:

In problem 2, point out that the base can be either on the top or on the side. For problem 3, discuss that because only one side, *DE*, is along a grid line, that side should be used as the base. Guide students to see that *BC*, the perpendicular segment from the extension of *DE* to *B*, then becomes the height. In problem 4, the base *FE* is 2 units long, while the height, from *B* perpendicular to *GE*, is 5 units.

COOPERATIVE LEARNING Encourage students to work on problems 7–12 on page 466 and 13–32 on page 467 in small groups. After they complete the problems, have students check with one another to see that they agree on the areas. Invite students to explain their solution methods to one another. You may wish to remind students that bases can be extended, as needed, to determine the heights of figures.

 **Wrap-Up**

In Closing To summarize the lesson, have students explain the strategies they used to find the areas of the figures on page 467.

ALTERNATIVE ASSESSMENT **Informal Assessment** Circulate through the room as students work on finding the areas of the figures. Ask them to identify the types of figures shown, and the segments that are the bases and heights of each, to make sure they are doing the problems correctly.

Assessment Criteria

Did the student . . .

✓ correctly identify the different figures in the grid on page 467?

✓ correctly identify the bases and heights of each figure?

✓ apply the correct formulas for finding area?

Homework Have students divide a 10 × 10 grid into several regions that are triangles or identifiable quadrilaterals. Have them exchange grids with a partner, who must take the paper home and then find the area of each figure. Then partners should compare results and strategies.

Unit 6 Lesson 132   **467**

LESSON 133

Triangles and Quadrilaterals

LESSON 133

Student Edition pages 468–471

LESSON PLANNER

Objectives

▶ to present some of the known properties of triangles and quadrilaterals

▶ to teach some of the names that are used to classify triangles and quadrilaterals

Context of the Lesson This is the sixth of nine lessons on plane figures.

 MANIPULATIVES

protractors*

photos of tessellating designs (optional)

rulers*

Program Resources

Practice Master 133

Enrichment Master 133

For extra practice:
CD-ROM* Lesson 133

① Warm-Up

5 MINUTES

 **Problem of the Day** Present the following problem to students: Harry has 840 fruit trees he wants to plant in an orchard. He wants to plant the same number of trees in each row and have his orchard be as close to a square as possible. How should he plant the trees? (in a 28 × 30 rectangle)

Problem-Solving Strategies Ask students who have solved the Problem of the Day to share how they solved it and any strategies they used.

 Select a drill from among those done previously, according to the needs of your class.

Triangles and Quadrilaterals

There are names for special kinds of triangles. You already know that if one angle of a triangle is a right angle, the triangle is called a **right triangle**.

Examples:

 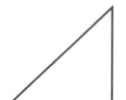 

If two sides of a triangle are the same length, the triangle is called an **isosceles triangle**.

Examples:

 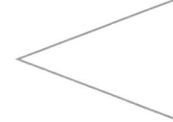 

If all three sides are the same length, it is an **equilateral triangle**.

Examples:

If no two sides are the same length, the triangle is **scalene**.

Examples:

468 • Geometry

Why teach it this way?

In exploring the questions and statements on these pages, students will use their logical reasoning skills to identify different kinds of triangles and quadrilaterals. In so doing, they can better grasp certain key geometric ideas common to many kinds of figures.

Solve these problems. **Check students' drawings.**

1 Draw a triangle that is not a right triangle or an isosceles triangle.

2 Is every equilateral triangle an isosceles triangle? **yes**

3 Draw an isosceles triangle that is not an equilateral triangle.

4 Can a triangle have two right angles? If you think so, then try to draw such a triangle. **no**

For problems 5–13, decide which triangles are scalene, isosceles, equilateral, and right triangles. Is it possible for a triangle to be more than one of these?

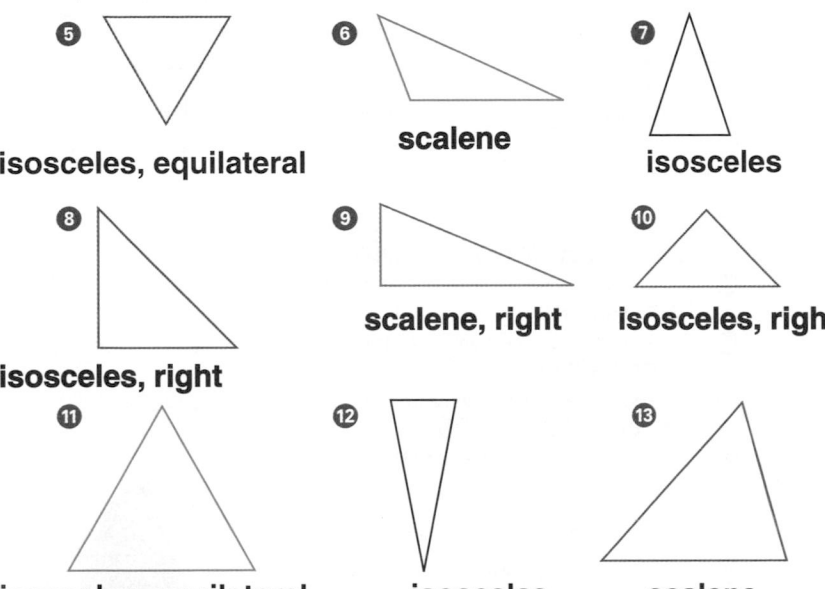

5 isosceles, equilateral

6 scalene

7 isosceles

8 isosceles, right

9 scalene, right

10 isosceles, right

11 isosceles, equilateral

12 isosceles

13 scalene

Answer the following questions.

14 If a triangle is a right triangle, could it also be an isosceles triangle? **yes**

15 If a triangle is an equilateral triangle, could it also be a right triangle? **no**

16 If a triangle is a scalene triangle, could it also be an isosceles triangle? **no**

17 If a triangle is a scalene triangle, could it also be a right triangle? **yes**

Unit 6   Lesson 133 • **469**

2 Teach

Using the Student Pages Discuss the material on page 468, comparing and contrasting the four different kinds of triangles presented. Point out that triangles can be classified by the kinds of angles they have, by the lengths of their sides, and by both their sides and angles. Guide students to see that the right triangle is a classification by angle, and the others, by sides. If students remember the meanings of *acute* and *obtuse* from previous grades, you may wish to ask them what kinds of angles are in a right triangle (one right angle, two acute angles), and what kind are in an equilateral triangle (three acute, or 60-degree, angles).

Have students try all the problems on page 469 on their own, using **rulers*** and **protractors*** as needed. They should check one another's work and discuss what they did to make sure the figures they drew for problems 1, 3, and 4 actually meet the criteria. For example, for problem 1, all three angles should be checked to see that none are right angles and all sides should be measured to see that no two are the same length. Have students debate their answers to problems 14–17.

If a student says that in problem 4 there is a point out there somewhere at which two sides perpendicular to the base will meet, commend the student for creativity but explain that it is to be assumed there is no such point.

CULTURAL DIVERSITY You may wish at this time to show students photos of Persian and other rug and tiling designs that are examples of tessellating geometric figures. Introduce and discuss the concept of tessellation. Provide additional examples for students to examine. Then ask them to figure out by exploration whether all triangles and all quadrilaterals tessellate a plane. (All triangles but only some quadrilaterals tessellate.) Invite students to create their own designs using tessellation.

◆ LESSON 133 Triangles and Quadrilaterals

Teach

Using the Student Pages Discuss with students the information about quadrilaterals at the top of page 470. Although it is not necessary at this point to formally define quadrilaterals for students, they should know that figures such as those shown below are *not* quadrilaterals and are not considered polygons.

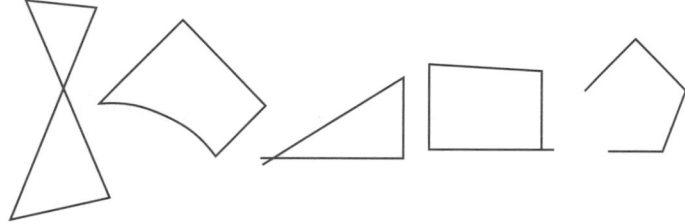

Have students work individually or in small groups on the problems on page 470. Students will find that although it is possible to draw a quadrilateral with one right angle, they will not be able to draw a trapezoid or a parallelogram with only one right angle. They can discover that if a parallelogram has one right angle, it has four right angles and is therefore a rectangle.

Have students work on page 471. Be sure all students understand the distinctions among the kinds of figures and recognize that the figure contains many larger polygons composed of smaller polygons.

◆ LESSON 133 Triangles and Quadrilaterals

We have names for special kinds of quadrilaterals. If exactly two sides of a quadrilateral are parallel, it is a **trapezoid**. If both pairs of opposite sides are parallel, the quadrilateral is a **parallelogram**.

A parallelogram in which all four angles are right angles is a **rectangle**. A rectangle with all four sides the same length is a **square**. A parallelogram with all four sides the same length is a **rhombus**.

QUADRILATERALS

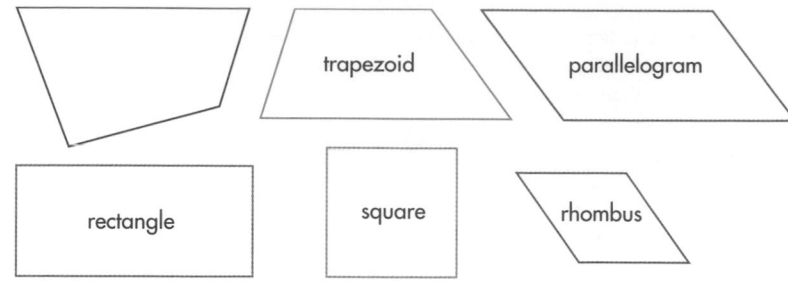

18 Try to draw a quadrilateral that has exactly one right angle.
Check students' drawings.

19 Try to draw a trapezoid that has exactly one right angle.
impossible

20 Try to draw a parallelogram that has exactly one right angle.
impossible

21 Were you able to draw the figures described in problems 18–20?
18. yes; 19. no; 20. no

22 Is every square a rectangle? **yes**

23 Is every rectangle a parallelogram? **yes**

24 Is every square a parallelogram? **yes**

25 Is every parallelogram a square? **no**

26 Is every rhombus a trapezoid? **no**

27 Is every trapezoid a rhombus? **no**

28 What figure can be described as a rhombus-rectangle?
a square

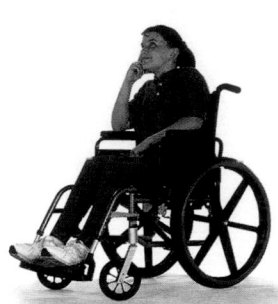

470 • Geometry

Literature Connection Have students examine the building illustrations and find particular triangles and quadrilaterals in *Amazing Buildings* by Philip Wilkinson.

You may wish to have students examine the statements about triangles and quadrilaterals within small groups so that they can discuss each statement fully and comfortably among themselves. Guide students to record key aspects of this topic and to make helpful illustrations for their Math Portfolios.

Answer the following questions. Assume that angles that look like right angles are right angles.

㉙ In the figure shown below, try to find as many squares as you can. Compare your answer with those of your classmates. Did you count large squares that had other figures inside them? **9**

㉚ How many rhombuses can you find that are not squares? **8**

㉛ How many rectangles can you find that are not squares? **104**

㉜ How many parallelograms can you find that are neither rhombuses nor rectangles? **104**

㉝ How many trapezoids can you find? **12**

㉞ How many quadrilaterals can you find that are not any of the above? **0**

㉟ How many right isosceles triangles can you find? **26**

㊱ How many other triangles can you find? **0**

㊲ Compare all your answers with those of your classmates. If there are differences, try to find out why, and decide which figures should be counted.

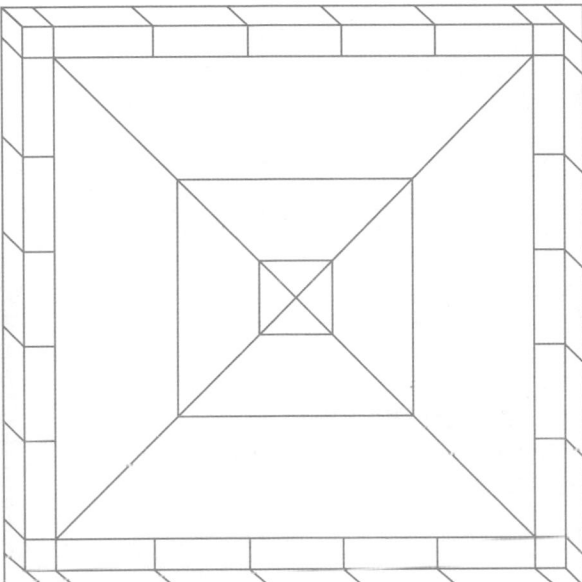

Unit 6   Lesson 133 • **471**

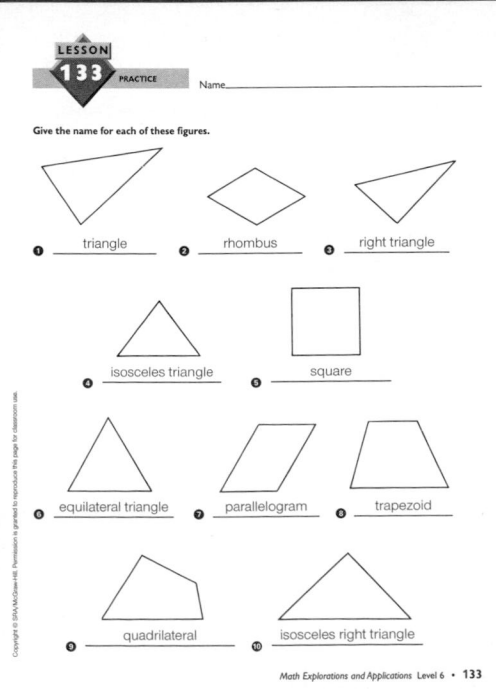
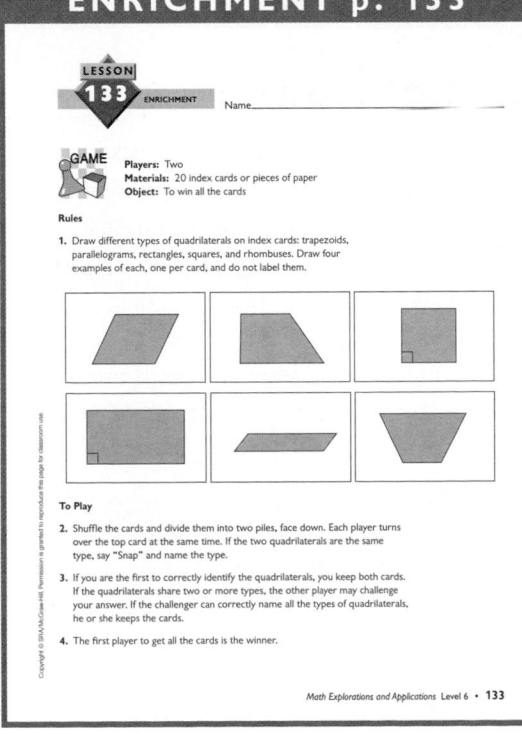

③ Wrap-Up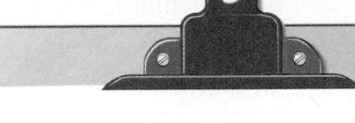

In Closing To summarize the lesson, ask students to distinguish among the different kinds of triangles and the different kinds of quadrilaterals introduced on these pages.

ALTERNATIVE ASSESSMENT **Performance Assessment** Ask students to draw on grid paper (1) a trapezoid with two right angles, (2) a right isosceles triangle, and (3) a rhombus with four right angles.

Assessment Criteria

Did the student . . .

✓ understand the distinctions among the different kinds of triangles introduced?

✓ understand the distinctions among the different kinds of quadrilaterals introduced?

Homework Have students complete Practice Master 133 for further practice with names of figures.

LOOKING AHEAD The "Three Questions" game will be introduced in the next lesson to provide practice with the names and classifications of triangles and quadrilaterals. You may wish to preteach the rules of this game to those students having difficulty with this material.

LESSON 134 Classifying Figures

LESSON 134 Classifying Figures

LESSON PLANNER

Objectives

▶ to provide practice using the previously introduced vocabulary for classifying triangles and quadrilaterals

▶ to encourage the development of logical procedures for isolating one of several objects by successively halving the number of possibilities

▶ to help students develop the broad ability to use mathematical common sense

Context of the Lesson This lesson, the seventh of nine lessons devoted to geometric figures, also contains Part 2 of "On the Move," a three-part Thinking Story.

 MANIPULATIVES

plastic or paper model of figures (optional)

Program Resources

Practice Master 134

Enrichment Master 134

For career connections:
Careers and Math*

For extra practice:
CD-ROM* Lesson 134
Cumulative Review, page 582

① Warm-Up ⏱ 5 MINUTES

 **Problem of the Day** Present the following problem to the class: How many inch cubes would it take to build a 1-foot cube, if the 1-foot cube is completely hollow on the inside? (728: two 12 × 12 sides, two 10 × 12 sides, and two 10 × 10 sides)

Problem-Solving Strategies Ask students who have solved the Problem of the Day to share how they solved it and any strategies they used.

 MENTAL MATH Have students find the area in square units of the following parallelograms, given these bases (*b*) and heights (*h*):

a. *b* = 200, *h* = 100 (20,000 sq units)

b. *b* = 12.5, *h* = 10 (125 sq units)

c. *b* = 100, *h* = 75 (7500 sq units)

d. *b* = 50.75, *h* = 100 (5075 sq units)

As you play the "Three Questions" game on page 473, you may want to find characteristics that help you sort the remaining possible figures into two approximately equal sets. The following questions may help you.

Answer these questions.

❶ Suppose that on the first question, you discover that the figure is a triangle. Considering the rules, how many different kinds of triangles are possible? **5**

❷ Can you think of a question that allows you to narrow the number of possible triangles to two or three, depending on the answer? Can you think of another question that would narrow the number of possibilities to two or three but with different triangles in the two groups? Explain.

Two possible questions: 1) Is the figure a right triangle? 2) Is the figure an isosceles triangle?

❸ Suppose that from the first answer you know that the figure is a quadrilateral. Then you ask whether the quadrilateral has two pairs of parallel sides.

❹b: 7; triangle, isosceles triangle, equilateral triangle, quadrilateral, trapezoid, parallelogram, rhombus

a. If the answer is "no," how many figures are possible? What are they? **2; quadrilateral, trapezoid**

b. If the answer is "yes," how many figures are possible? What are they? **4; parallelogram, rectangle, square, rhombus**

❹ Suppose you ask whether a figure has at least one right angle.

❺b: triangle, isosceles triangle, equilateral triangle, right triangle, isosceles right triangle, quadrilateral, trapezoid, rectangle, parallelogram

a. How many figures are possible if the answer is "yes"? What are they? **4; right triangle, isosceles right triangle, rectangle, square**

b. How many figures are possible if the answer is "no"? What are they?

❺ Suppose you ask whether the figure has four sides the same length.

a. For an answer of "yes," what are the possible figures? **square, rhombus**

b. For an answer of "no," what are the possible figures?

❻: isosceles triangle, equilateral triangle, isosceles right triangle, parallelogram, rectangle, square, rhombus; not necessarily

❻ Suppose on the first question you ask whether the figure has at least two sides of equal length. If the answer is "yes," which figures are possible? Would this help you guess the figure in three questions?

472 • Geometry

Why teach it this way?

Students must apply logical reasoning when playing the "Three Questions" game. This activity provides useful practice in classifying geometric figures as well as in basic principles of deduction. The idea of dividing a set roughly in half several times is useful in many deductive contexts.

Three Questions Game

COOPERATIVE LEARNING

Players:	Two
Materials:	Paper, pencil
Object:	After asking three questions, to identify a figure the other player has drawn
Math Focus:	Describing properties of geometric shapes and mathematical reasoning

RULES

1. The first player draws a figure and writes the name of it on a sheet of paper, making sure the second player cannot see it. The figure must be a triangle, quadrilateral, or one of the specific figures mentioned in bold on pages 468 and 470.

2. The figure may not have any extra properties not indicated by its name. For example, a quadrilateral with one right angle is not permitted.

3. The second player asks three questions, one at a time, to which the first player must answer *yes* or *no* truthfully.

4. The second player tries to name the figure the first player has drawn.

5. To win the round, the second player must correctly describe the figure as completely as possible. For example, if the figure is a rhombus and the second player says it is a parallelogram, the statement is true but not complete. So the first player would win.

SAMPLE GAME

Lena drew a trapezoid.	Harvey said:	Lena said:
	Does it have four sides?	Yes.
	Does it have two pairs of parallel sides?	No.
	Does it have one pair of parallel sides?	Yes.
	It's a trapezoid.	That's right.
Harvey won the round.		

Unit 6   Lesson 134 • **473**

Technology Connection Refer students to the software, video, and printed curriculum materials *Mathematics Curriculum and Teaching Program* from the National Council of Mathematics, Inc. (Apple, Mac, IBM, for grades K–10) for further practice with probability, estimation, geometry, problem solving, algebra, logic, number properties, and visual imagery.

② Teach

Using the Student Pages Demonstrate the "Three Questions" game, which provides practice with classifying triangles and quadrilaterals. On the chalkboard, list the names of the 11 permitted figures. Arrange the list so that the classification scheme is apparent. For example:

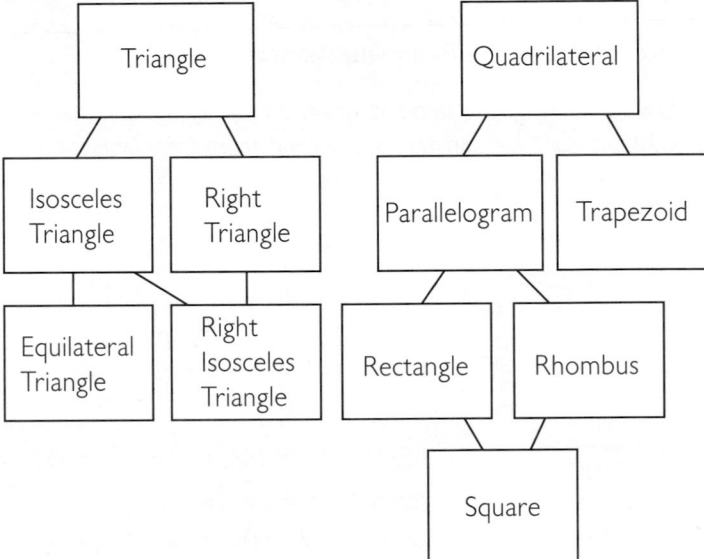

Note that each figure can also be classified in any connected category above it. Therefore, a right isosceles triangle is an isosceles triangle, a right triangle, and a triangle. Play the game several times with the class. For example, draw and label a rhombus on a piece of paper and have a volunteer ask three yes-or-no questions. After answering each question, discuss what information is known so far. Suppose that the question is "Does it have a pair of parallel sides?" From the answer "yes," the other player knows the figure is not a triangle or a general quadrilateral, so it must be some form of trapezoid or parallelogram. If the second question is "Does it have a right angle?" and the answer is "no", the questioner knows that the figure is not a rectangle or a square. If the third question is "Does it have two pairs of parallel lines?", the answer "yes" indicates that the figure must be a parallelogram or a rhombus. Now the questioner has a 50–50 chance of answering correctly. Three questions will not always be enough to reduce the possibilities to one, so the second player may have to guess at this point.

Have students form pairs or small groups to play a few rounds of the game, then answer the questions on page 472. Then go over the answers with the class. After discussing these fully, have students pair off and play more rounds of the "Three Questions" game.

◆ **LESSON 134 Classifying Figures**

Teach

Using the Thinking Story In this second part of "On the Move," the characters are trying an indirect way of figuring out the weight of a heavy couch.

Answers to Thinking Story Questions:

1. Each is carrying the same amount, 53 lbs: Students can subtract each person's normal weight from their "weight with the couch" to get the result. Because both Portia and Ferdie are holding up a back corner of the couch, its weight should be evenly distributed between them.

2. The back is heavier. Ferdie and Portia are each holding up 53 lbs, for a total of 106 lbs. Subtracting their mother's normal weight from her "weight with the couch" shows that the front part she is holding up weighs less, or 62 lbs.

3. The weight of the whole couch should be 168 lbs, the sum of the weights held by the three people. This is a good estimate as long as the couch is kept level at each weighing. If the person on the scale raises the level of the couch, the proportion of the weight that person is carrying will be reduced and the sum of the weights will be less than the actual weight of the couch.

Ask students to imagine that they have to find out the combined weight of two of their pets, neither of which can be counted on to stand still on a scale. Have them write a description of how they would weigh the two animals in their Math Journals.

◆ **LESSON 134 Classifying Figures**

On the Move

Part 2

You may want to refer to the first part of this Thinking Story on pages 442–443.

Portia, Ferdie, and their mother were still trying to figure out the weight of everything they had to move. The heaviest piece of furniture was the couch. It took all three of them to lift it, and there was no way they could get it on the scale.

"I have an idea," said Portia. "Let's lift the couch. Then while we keep it level, we'll move around and take turns standing on the scale."

"That's stupid," said Ferdie. "While one person is getting weighed, the others are holding up part of the couch that is getting weighed too."

"It's not stupid," said Portia. "Between us we'll be holding up the whole weight of the couch. If we find out how much weight each one is holding, it should add up to the weight of the couch."

They decided to try it. Portia and Ferdie each lifted a back corner of the couch. Their mother held up the front of the couch. Here is what they found out:

Literature Connection Have students read *Pablo Picasso* by Ernest Raboff to learn about an artist who used shapes in innovative ways.

RETEACHING

You may need to provide some students with the opportunity to handle **plastic models** or **paper cut-outs** of different kinds of triangles and quadrilaterals to help them better understand the properties and characteristics of these figures. Peer tutors can help these students notice the similarities and differences among the figures.

	Portia	Ferdie	Mother
Normal weight	79 lbs.	95 lbs.	134 lbs.
Weight while holding couch	132 lbs.	148 lbs.	196 lbs.

. . . to be continued

Work in groups. Discuss your answers and how you figured them out. Then compare your answers with those of other groups. Answers are in margin.

❶ According to the figures given, who is carrying more of the weight of the couch, Portia or Ferdie? How could you explain this?

❷ Which part of the couch is heavier, the front or the back? How do you know?

❸ About how much does the whole couch weigh?

Use the Cumulative Review on page 582 after this lesson.

Unit 6 Lesson 134 • **475**

PRACTICE p. 134

ENRICHMENT p. 134

---

❸ **Wrap-Up**
5 MINUTES

In Closing To summarize the lesson, ask students to explain their strategy for playing the "Three Questions" game.

 **Informal Assessment** Circulate through the room and observe as students play the game. Listen to check whether they display a knowledge of the properties of the various figures and whether they can reason logically based on the answers to their questions.

Assessment Criteria

Did the student . . .

✓ understand the ways that triangles and quadrilaterals can be classified?

✓ demonstrate an ability to think logically in response to answers to their questions?

✓ contribute to the discussion about the Thinking Story questions?

Homework For further practice classifying figures and thinking logically, have students play the "Three Questions" game with a family member. A copy of this game can also be found on page 34 of the Home Connections Blackline Masters.

ESL Meeting Individual Needs
To help students with limited English proficiency learn all the geometric vocabulary used in this lesson, you may wish to pair them with students who are fluent in English. They can act as a team for the "Three Questions" game and play other teams or individual students.

Unit 6 Lesson 134 **475**

Student Edition pages 476–477

Determining Lengths from Given Areas

LESSON PLANNER

Objective

▶ to demonstrate how to use area formulas to determine different lengths from given areas

Context of the Lesson This is the eighth of nine lessons on plane figures.

 MANIPULATIVES

Program Resources

Practice Master 135

Enrichment Master 135

For extra practice:
CD-ROM* Lesson 135

 # ① Warp-Up ⏱

 Problem of the Day Present the following problem to students: What are the dimensions of a rectangle with a length that is twice its width and a perimeter of 90 feet? What is the area of the rectangle? (*l* = 30 ft, *w* = 15 ft; *A* = 450 sq ft)

Problem-Solving Strategies Ask students who have solved the Problem of the Day to share how they solved it and any strategies they used.

MENTAL MATH Present the given areas of each of the following figures and ask students to give possible dimensions for the base and height of each figure. (Answers will vary.)

a. rectangle: 32 square feet

b. triangle: 18 square meters

c. parallelogram: 75 square centimeters

d. triangle: 20 square inches

Determining Lengths from Given Areas

 **ALGEBRA READINESS**

The area of a certain rectangle is 56 square centimeters. The base is 8 centimeters.

◆ What is the height? **7 cm**

A farmer wants to plant 40,000 square meters of land with rows of corn. He wants each row to be 800 meters long, so the cornfield should be 800 meters long.

◆ How wide should the field be? **50 m**

Answer the questions below. These formulas may help you.

Area of a parallelogram = base × height $A = bh$

Area of a triangle = $\frac{1}{2}$ (base × height) $A = \frac{1}{2}bh$

Area of a trapezoid = height (average of bases) $A = h\left(\frac{b + B}{2}\right)$

Perimeter of any figure = side + side + side, and so on.

① The area of a right triangle is 24 square centimeters. The height is 8 centimeters. What is the base? **6 cm**

② A trapezoid has bases that are 10 and 20 centimeters long. The area of the trapezoid is 60 square centimeters. What is the height of the trapezoid? **4 cm**

③ The area of a parallelogram is 48 square centimeters. The base is 6 centimeters. What is the height? **8 cm**

④ A trapezoid has a height of 8 centimeters and an area of 80 square centimeters. One base is 12 centimeters. What is the other base? **8 cm**

⑤ What is the height of an isosceles right triangle that has an area of 50 square centimeters? **10 cm**

⑥ The height of a right scalene triangle is 5 centimeters and its area is 30 square centimeters. What is the base? **12 cm**

⑦ What is the height of a trapezoid that has one base that is 14 centimeters and an area of 66 square centimeters? The other base is 8 centimeters. **6 cm**

476 · Geometry

 **Literature Connection**

Have students read *Origami* by Irmgard Kneissler. Provide the areas of different origami papers, and ask students to determine the side lengths and then to try some of the projects.

RETEACHING

As needed, review the formulas for area of triangles, parallelograms, and trapezoids. Remind students to refer to these formulas while they work. Guide students to be on the lookout for unnecessary information, such as the kind of triangle in problems 1 and 6.

---

*available separately

Solve these problems.

⑧ A rectangular garden is 20 meters long and 35 meters wide. What is its area? **700 m²**

⑨ Triangle Park is shaped like an equilateral triangle with sides that are 250 meters long. What is its perimeter? **750 m**

⑩ A parallelogram has a base of 15 centimeters. Its area is 150 square centimeters. What is its height? **10 cm**

⑪ A parallelogram has one side that is 15 centimeters. A second side is 10 centimeters. What is its area?
not enough information given

⑫ The area of a right triangle is 30 square centimeters. The base is 10 centimeters. What is the height? **6 cm**

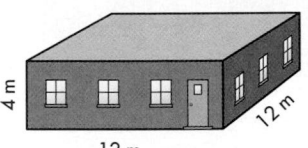

Mr. Gonzales's House

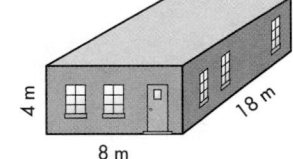

Mr. Culyer's House

⑬ What is the surface area of Mr. Gonzales's house?
336 m² (four sides and the roof)

⑭ How many square meters of living space does Mr. Gonzales's house have?
144 m²

⑮ What is the surface area of Mr. Culyer's house?
352 m² (four sides and the roof)

⑯ How many square meters of living space does Mr. Culyer's house have?
144 m²

⑰ Mr. Culyer and Mr. Gonzales like to keep the temperature in their houses the same. Both houses use the same kind of heating and cooling. Whose house will be more expensive to heat and cool? Explain your answer. *

⑱ Find the volume of each house.

a. Which has the greater volume? **Both are the same.**

b. Could you answer problem 18a without multiplying? **Yes, because the floor areas and heights are the same.**

* Accept all reasonably defended answers. One possible answer is that Mr. Culyer's home will cost more to heat and cool due to its greater surface area.

Unit 6 Lesson 135 • **477**

---

❷ Teach

Using the Student Pages Discuss the two discussion questions on page 476 with the class, inviting students to suggest solution methods. Then have students solve the remaining problems on pages 476 and 477 on their own or in pairs. Remind them to check that their answers make sense.

You may wish to encourage students who finish quickly to formulate trickier problems than the ones on these pages and then exchange them with classmates to try to solve them.

❸ Wrap-Up

In Closing To summarize the lesson, ask students what an inverse operation does.

Portfolio Assessment Ask students to include some of the problems on these pages along with their solutions to them, showing their work, in their Math Portfolios.

Assessment Criteria

Did the student . . .

✓ correctly solve at least 14 of the 18 problems on pages 476–477?

✓ check to see that his or her answers made sense?

Homework Ask students to create area or perimeter problems similar to those on these pages, but using real data based on regions in their home. They can present these to classmates, who can then try to solve them.

Meeting Individual Needs
Guide students who are visual learners to draw pictures to help them solve the problems. Then ask them how they would find the area if they had all the needed information.

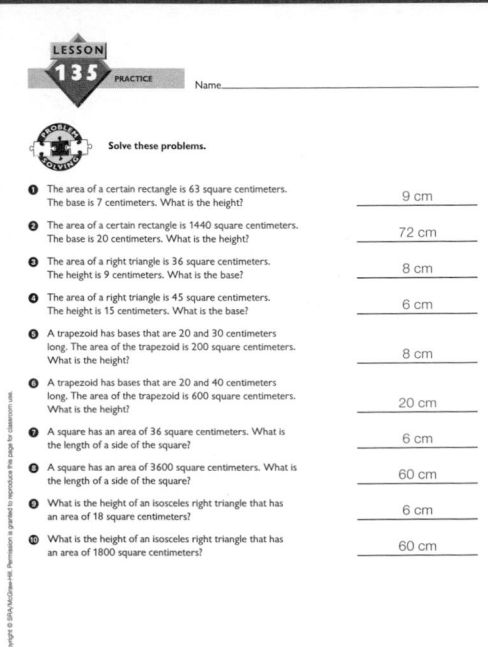
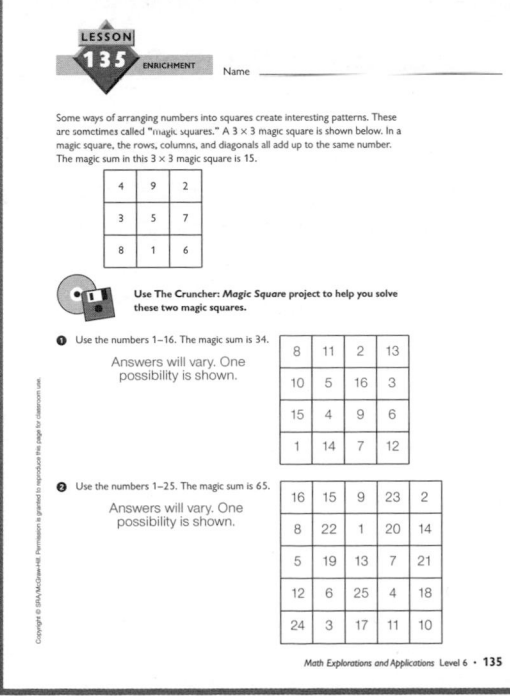

LESSON 136
Square Roots
Student Edition pages 478–481

LESSON PLANNER

Objectives

▶ to demonstrate how to find the length of the sides of a square, given the area of the square

▶ to provide students with the opportunity to observe patterns among square roots

Context of the Lesson This is the last of nine lessons on plane figures.

MANIPULATIVES
calculators*

Program Resources
Reteaching Master
Practice Master 136
Enrichment Master 136
For extra practice:
  CD-ROM* Lesson 136

① Warm-Up

Problem of the Day Present the following problem to the students: How many squares are in the figure below? (18)

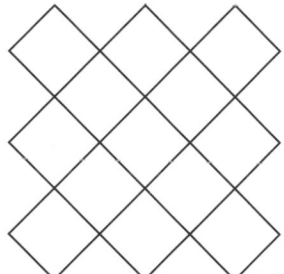

Problem-Solving Strategies Ask students who have solved the Problem of the Day to share how they solved it and any strategies they used.

 Select a mental drill from among those done previously, according to the needs of your class.

LESSON 136
Square Roots

What is the length of one side of a square that has an area of 20 cm²? You can use a calculator to help you find the answer.

The area of the square is 20 square centimeters. So if s is the length of one side, s times s must be 20. Since $4 \times 4 = 16$ and $5 \times 5 = 25$, the answer must be between 4 centimeters and 5 centimeters.

Then, since $4.5 \times 4.5 = 20.25$, the answer must be less than 4.5. But $4.4 \times 4.4 = 19.36$, so the answer must be greater than 4.4.

Notice that 20.25 is closer to 20 than 19.36 is. So the answer is probably closer to 4.5 than to 4.4. Try 4.47.

By now, you should be using a calculator. Multiply 4.47 by itself. If you continue making approximations this way, you will get to 4.472136.

If you multiply 4.472136 by itself on paper, you get 20.000000402496. If the calculator shows only the first eight digits, it will show 20 as the answer.

If you had been asked to find the length of the side to the nearest hundredth of a centimeter, you could have stopped when you realized that 4.47×4.47 (which is 19.9809) is closer to 20 than is 4.48×4.48 (which is 20.0704). So the answer to the nearest hundredth of a centimeter is probably 4.47 centimeters. To be sure, you'd multiply 4.475 by 4.475. Since the product is greater than 20, the answer to the nearest hundredth is 4.47.

478 · Geometry

Why teach it this way?

The method presented here for estimating square roots is efficient to teach, given the fact that most people seldom need to find a square root. Anyone who does need to find several square roots should probably use the square root key on a calculator.

1 Use a computer or other means to draw and complete this chart. For each area of a square, estimate the length in centimeters of a side of that square to the nearest whole centimeter, tenth of a centimeter, and hundredth of a centimeter.

Area of square (cm²)	Nearest whole number (cm)	Nearest tenth (cm)	Nearest hundredth (cm)
10	3	3.2	3.16
30	5	5.5	5.48
2	1	1.4	1.41
3	2	1.7	1.73
4	2	2.0	2.00
5	2	2.2	2.24
8	3	2.8	2.83
9	3	3.0	3.00
15	4	3.9	3.87
50	7	7.1	7.07

We call a number that can be multiplied by itself to give a second number the square root of the second number. For example, $4 \times 4 = 16$, so 4 is the square root of 16, and $5 \times 5 = 25$, so 5 is the square root of 25.

The symbol for square root is $\sqrt{}$. Your calculator may have a square root key.

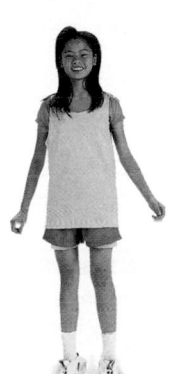

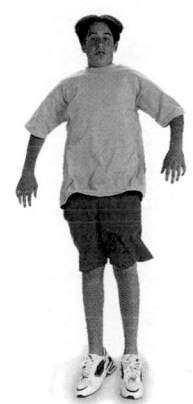

Unit 6   Lesson 136 • **479**

Technology Connection Refer students to the video, laser disc, or software *Modumath: Arithmetic, Square Roots* from VTAE (VHS, IBM, for grades 6–12) for practice using a table to find square roots of whole numbers, and methods for computing and multiplying square roots.

2 Teach

Using the Student Pages A trial-and-error method for finding square roots is provided for students. There are several other algorithms for finding square roots, and some students may discover by talking to older children or to adults that such methods exist. In contrast, the method provided here is easy to remember.

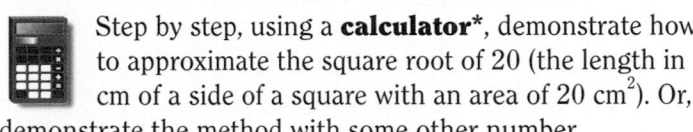

Step by step, using a **calculator***, demonstrate how to approximate the square root of 20 (the length in cm of a side of a square with an area of 20 cm²). Or, demonstrate the method with some other number.

The example gives the steps for finding the square root of 20 up to trying 4.47. The next tries might be 4.48, 4.473, 4.472, 4.4722, 4.4721, and 4.47213.

Try 4.472136×4.472136. According to the calculator, the product is 20, so you have the answer. However, as indicated in the text, the calculator drops digits that it cannot display. Thus, 4.472136 is only a close approximation but certainly close enough for all practical purposes and closer than is needed for most.

Have students copy and complete the chart on page 479 independently or in small groups. These problems can be done with or without a calculator. You may want some students to check their own answers with a calculator.

Notice that to get the answer to the nearest hundredth of a centimeter, the thousandth place digit must at least be approximated. For example, consider finding the square root of 10: $3.16 \times 3.16 = 9.9856$ and $3.17 \times 3.17 = 10.0489$. Since the difference between 10 and 9.9856 is only 0.0144 and the difference between 10 and 10.0489 is 0.0489, 3.16 is clearly closer. (In other words, the next digit—the thousandths digit—would be less than 5.) If in doubt, try 3.165 to be sure.

*available separately

◆ **LESSON 136** Square Roots

Teach

Using the Student Pages Assign pages 480 and 481 for students to work on independently or with a partner. When you go over the answers with students, ask volunteers to explain how they made their estimates for the answers to problems 12 through 16. Be sure to focus on the patterns students notice in the tables for problems 19, 21, and 23.

> *In real life, we seldom try to prove something until we have convinced ourselves that it is probably true. We don't usually convince ourselves until we have experimented with various alternatives and chosen what appears to be the most viable one. In school, too, we should encourage children to think about a particular subject, experiment, speculate, conjecture, and test before they set out to try to prove something about it.*
>
> —Stephen S. Willoughby,
> *Mathematics Education for a Changing World*

◆ **LESSON 136** Square Roots

For the following areas of a square (in square inches), try to estimate a number that would be very close to the length (in inches) of the side of the square. Do not use a calculator.

② 64 **8**   **③** 100 **10**   **④** 36 **6**   **⑤** 144 **12**   **⑥** 25 **5**

⑦ 81 **9**   **⑧** 121 **11**   **⑨** 49 **7**   **⑩** 10,000 **100** **⑪** 169 **13**

⑫ 72 **8½**   **⑬** 110 **10½**   **⑭** 42 **6½**   **⑮** 156 **12½**   **⑯** 83 **9.1**
(8.49)   **(10.49)**   **(6.48)**   **(12.49)**   **(9.11)**

In your *Math Journal* write about the strategies you used to make your estimates.

⑰ Using your calculator, find the lengths for problems 2–16 to the nearest hundredth of an inch. **See above.**

⑱ How good were your estimates? **Answers will vary.**

⑲ For each of the areas in the chart, find the corresponding length to the nearest thousandth of a centimeter.

Area of square in square centimeters	2	20	200	2000	20,000	200,000
Length of side of square in cm	▪	▪	▪	▪	▪	▪

1.414 4.472 14.142 44.721 141.421 447.214

⑳ Do you see any interesting patterns in your answers to problem 19? **See comment at left.**

㉑ For each of the areas in the chart, find the corresponding length to the nearest thousandth of a centimeter.

⑳ and ㉒ For both problems 20 and 22, each time the area is multiplied by 100, the length of the side is multiplied by 10.

Area of square in square centimeters	3	30	300	3000	30,000	300,000
Length of side of square in cm	▪	▪	▪	▪	▪	▪

1.732 5.477 17.321 54.772 173.205 547.723

㉒ Do you see any interesting patterns in your answers to problem 21? How do those relate to your answer for problem 20? Did they help you fill out the table for problem 21? **See comment at left.**

480 · Geometry

Literature Connection Have students read *Sea Squares* by Joy Hulme. You can use this book as a model for students to use to create a picture book emphasizing square roots.

RETEACHING p. 46

LESSON 136 RETEACHING   Name_____

To approximate the square root of a number, multiply numbers by themselves until you come close to the number.

Example:
Find the square root of 40 to the nearest whole number.
$6 \times 6 = 36$
$7 \times 7 = 49$
The square root of 40 is between 6 and 7. Since 40 is much closer to 36 than to 49, the square root of 40 is close to 6.

Find the length of the side of a square for each given area. Round answers to the nearest centimeter.

① 60 cm² **8 cm**   **②** 78 cm² **9 cm**

③ 52 cm² **7 cm**   **④** 35 cm² **6 cm**

⑤ 20 cm² **4 cm**   **⑥** 88 cm² **9 cm**

⑦ 30 cm² **5 cm**   **⑧** 50 cm² **7 cm**

⑨ 75 cm² **9 cm**   **⑩** 66 cm² **8 cm**

⑪ 45 cm² **7 cm**   **⑫** 115 cm² **11 cm**

⑬ 27 cm² **5 cm**   **⑭** 40 cm² **6 cm**

⑮ 97 cm² **10 cm**   **⑯** 398 cm² **20 cm**

⑰ 6 cm² **2 cm**   **⑱** 118 cm² **11 cm**

⑲ 54 cm² **7 cm**   **⑳** 32 cm² **6 cm**

46 · Math Explorations and Applications Level 6

Solve these problems.

23 For each of the areas in the chart, find the corresponding length to the nearest thousandth of a centimeter.

Area of square in square centimeters	4	40	400	4000	40,000	400,000
Length of side of square in cm	■	■	■	■	■	■

2.000 6.325 20.000 63.246 200.000 632.456

24 What was different about the answers to problem 23 compared to the answers to problems 19 and 21? **Some of the answers were whole numbers.**

25 What is the length of a side of a square that has an area of 100 square inches? **10 in.**

26 What is the length of a side of a square that has an area of 169 square centimeters? **13 cm**

27 A square field has an area of 576 square meters. What is the length of a side of that field? **24 m**

28 A farmer's field has an area of 42,436 square yards. What is the length of a side of that field? **can't tell; we don't know the shape of the field**

29 A parallelogram has a base the same length as its height. The area of the parallelogram is 225 square inches. What is its height? **15 in.**

30 A triangle has a base the same length as its height. The area of the triangle is 32 square centimeters. What is its height? **8 cm**

31 A rectangle's width is twice as great as its length. The area of the rectangle is 50 square centimeters. What is its length? **5 cm**

32 What is the perimeter of a square park with an area of 900 square feet? **120 feet**

Unit 6   Lesson 136 • **481**

PRACTICE p. 136

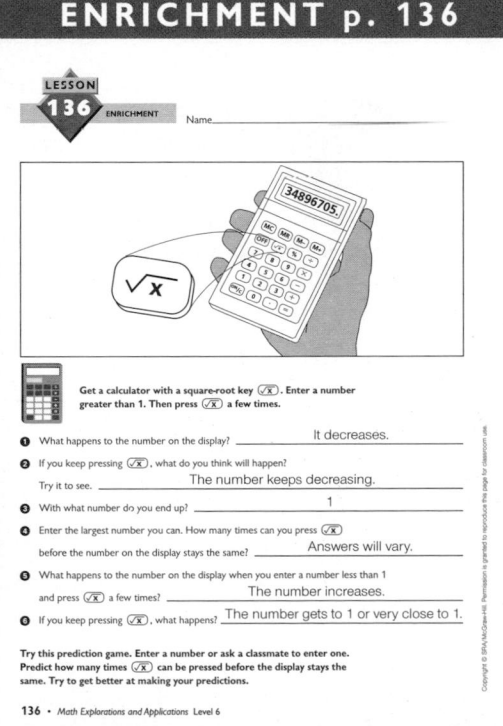

LESSON **136** PRACTICE   Name _____

Find the length of a side of a square for each given area. Round answers to the nearest hundredth.

1 2 __1.41__	**3** 3 __1.73__	**4** 4 __2__
5 5 __2.24__	**8** 8 __2.83__	**12** 12 __3.46__
7 15 __3.87__	**17** 17 __4.12__	**19** 19 __4.36__
20 20 __4.47__	**25** 25 __5__	**26** 26 __5.10__
35 35 __5.92__	**40** 40 __6.32__	**50** 50 __7.07__
60 60 __7.75__	**75** 75 __8.66__	**80** 80 __8.94__
81 81 __9__	**82** 82 __9.06__	**83** 83 __9.11__
85 85 __9.22__	**90** 90 __9.49__	**91** 91 __9.54__
92 92 __9.59__	**95** 95 __9.75__	**100** 100 __10__
200 200 __14.14__	**300** 300 __17.32__	**400** 400 __20__

Solve these problems.

A parallelogram has equal measures for base and height. Its area is 121 square inches. What is its height? __11 inches__

A triangle has the same length as its height. It has an area of 50 square inches. What is the length of its base? __10 inches__

A square field has an area of 64 square meters. What is its perimeter? __32 meters__

136 • *Math Explorations and Applications Level 6*

ENRICHMENT p. 136

LESSON **136** ENRICHMENT   Name _____

Get a calculator with a square-root key √x̄ **. Enter a number greater than 1. Then press** √x̄ **a few times.**

1 What happens to the number on the display? __It decreases.__

2 If you keep pressing √x̄ , what do you think will happen?
Try it to see. __The number keeps decreasing.__

3 With what number do you end up? __1__

4 Enter the largest number you can. How many times can you press √x̄ before the number on the display stays the same? __Answers will vary.__

5 What happens to the number on the display when you enter a number less than 1 and press √x̄ a few times? __The number increases.__

6 If you keep pressing √x̄ , what happens? __The number gets to 1 or very close to 1.__

Try this prediction game. Enter a number or ask a classmate to enter one. Predict how many times √x̄ **can be pressed before the display stays the same. Try to get better at making your predictions.**

136 • *Math Explorations and Applications Level 6*

---

③ Wrap-Up ⏱ 5 MINUTES

In Closing To summarize the lesson, ask students to explain how they would find the answer to a square root problem.

Portfolio Assessment Ask students to estimate, to the nearest half inch, the side length of a square with an area of 120 square inches.

Assessment Criteria

Did the student . . .

✓ demonstrate understanding of how to use a calculator to approximate the length of a side of a square given the area of that square?

✓ recognize the pattern in lengths of sides of squares whose areas are 100 or 10,000 times greater than one another?

Homework Have students practice finding square roots by completing this problem with a family member without using a calculator: The area of a square is 28 square centimeters. What is the length of each side?

LOOKING AHEAD For Lesson 137, in addition to common metric measure devices for measuring length, students will need metric balance scales, Celsius thermometers, and metric containers for measuring volume.

Meeting Individual Needs

For students having difficulty, focus on the steps in the procedure. For example, to find the square root of 10, choose any number and multiply it by itself. If the product is greater than 10, try again using a lesser number. If the product is less than 10, try again with a greater number.

Unit 6 Lesson 136 **481**

LESSON 137 Estimating Measures

Student Edition pages 482–483

LESSON PLANNER

Objectives

▶ to review metric measures

▶ to provide practice in estimating and measuring length, weight, temperature, and volume

Context of the Lesson This is the first of five lessons on measurement.

MANIPULATIVES

Celsius*
thermometers

metric rulers*
and meter
sticks

metric scales*

1-liter* and
other metric
measuring
containers

Program Resources

Practice Master 137

Enrichment Master 137

For extra practice:
CD-ROM* Lesson 137

① Warm-Up ⏱ 5 MINUTES

Problem of the Day Present the following problem to the class: A square has an area in square meters that is five times its perimeter in meters. What is the length of a side of the square? (20 m)

Problem-Solving Strategies Ask students who have solved the Problem of the Day to share how they solved it and any strategies they used.

MENTAL MATH Have students solve the following decimal problems mentally:

a. $100 \times 0.015 = (1.5)$ b. $1000 \times 0.1 = (100)$

c. $1 \times 0.00016 = (0.00016)$ d. $700 \times 0.001 = (0.7)$

e. $100,000 \times 0.00006 = (6)$ f. $400 \times 0.3 = (120)$

② Teach

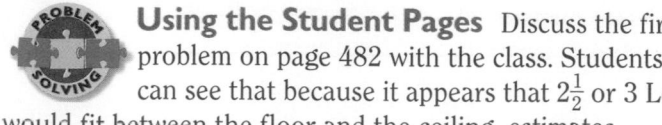

Using the Student Pages Discuss the first problem on page 482 with the class. Students can see that because it appears that $2\frac{1}{2}$ or 3 Lees would fit between the floor and the ceiling, estimates between 12 feet and 15 feet make sense.

482 Geometry

Estimating Measures

We frequently need to estimate distances, times, and other measurements. In this lesson you'll practice some everyday estimating.

① Nancy knows that Lee is about 5 feet tall. She wants to estimate the height of the gymnasium wall that Lee is standing against. About how tall do you think the wall is? **about $12\frac{1}{2}$ feet**

② Noah walks about 4 miles in an hour. He usually takes about 24 minutes to walk to school from his home. About how far do you think it is from Noah's home to school? **about 1.6 miles**

③ Tasha has noticed that she can fill four drinking glasses with a liter container of milk. She plans to have four friends over for lunch. If she and each of her friends usually drink about two glasses of milk with lunch, about how many liters of milk should Tasha have for five people? **3 or $2\frac{1}{2}$**

④ Alex knows that a pair of his father's shoes weighs about 2.2 pounds. He thinks a pair of his own shoes weighs about as much as one of his father's shoes. If this is true, about how much does a pair of Alex's shoes weigh? **about 1.1 pounds**

⑤ Janet measured the width of her desk in hand lengths. It was five hands long plus a few inches more. Janet's hand is about 5 inches long. How wide is her desk? **about 27 or 28 inches**

482 • Geometry

Literature Connection Have students do some of the puzzles and games from *Measuring Up* by Sandra Markle.

RETEACHING

Help students refine their measuring skills, as needed. For example, help them place the end of the measuring stick in the correct place each time they move it along an object, or help them sight along the surface of a liquid when measuring its volume. You may also need to help them to choose reasonable weights for the pan balances or read the calibration marks on a thermometer.

*available separately

6 Rosemary is nine years old and weighs 75 pounds. She thinks her father weighs about twice as much as she does. If this is true, about how many pounds does her father weigh? **about 150 pounds**

7 Water freezes at 0° Celsius (0°C) and boils at 100°C. A comfortable room temperature for most people is about 20°C. Normal human body temperature is 37°C. Sara wore her jacket yesterday because the weather was cool, but it was not cold enough to freeze water. About what do you think the temperature was? **between 0° and 20° C**

8 Estimate at least 20 measures yourself and then check to see what the real measures are. (Include at least two lengths, two weights, two volumes, and two temperatures.) Here are some examples of measures to estimate:

  a. length or width of the classroom

  b. a friend's height in meters and centimeters

  c. the length of this book

  d. the weight of this book

  e. the weight of your pencil

  f. the weight of a jar of paste or paint

  g. the temperature in your classroom (°C)

  h. the temperature outside today (°C)

  i. the temperature in a working refrigerator (°C)

  j. the temperature in a working freezer (°C)

  k. the volume of water in a large pitcher (in liters)

  l. the volume of a container of dish detergent

  m. the volume of water in a fish tank (in gallons)

Unit 6   Lesson 137 • **483**

 Discuss the activity in problem 8 on page 483. Suggest to students that they estimate a measurement and then check it, and then estimate and check another measurement of the same type (length, weight, and so on). Measuring to check one estimate will help improve the next estimate. Have a variety of measuring tools available—**thermometers***, **rulers***, **scales***, and so on.

COOPERATIVE LEARNING Encourage students to work in pairs or small groups to solve problem 8 at the bottom of page 483. Have partners or group members each make an estimate. Before they measure, have them compare estimates and even try to persuade each other to change estimates if necessary. Then the group can work together to measure and check the estimates.

❸ Wrap-Up

In Closing Ask students to describe the strategy they used to make better estimates as they worked through the problems.

 **Informal Assessment** Circulate through the room and observe students estimating and measuring. Invite students to convince you that their estimate is on target. Observe students as they work with others in their group. Encourage students to listen to other points of view and to express theirs in a way that will make others want to listen. Guide them to share in the measuring portion of the task so that all take part equally.

Assessment Criteria

Did the student . . .

✓ make reasonable estimates of lengths, weights, volumes, and temperatures?

✓ work cooperatively with others in his or her group?

✓ measure correctly when checking estimates?

Homework Invite students to work together with family members on an activity similar to the one at the bottom of page 483. The family can choose things to measure, make and compare estimates, and then measure together to check them.

Student Edition pages 484–487

Mid-Unit Review

The Mid-Unit Review pinpoints troublesome skill areas for students, allowing plenty of time for additional practice and reteaching before the unit ends. If students did not do well on the Mid-Unit Review and have completed additional practice, you may want to use the Mid-Unit Review provided on Assessment Blackline Masters pages 52–53.

Using the Student Pages Have students complete problems 1–50 on pages 484–487 on their own. You may wish to go through with the students the figures for problems 32–34 and the word problems 35–44. You might treat this review as a formal assessment of students' skills, and have students complete this review as a timed test. See suggestions for administering timed tests on page 49.

Mid-Unit Review

Find the area of each rectangle. Be sure to include the correct unit in your answers.

1 base = 14 cm, height = 11 cm **154 cm²**

2 base = 1.5 cm, height = 1.1 cm **1.65 cm²**

3 base = 1.4 cm, height = 12 cm **16.8 cm²**

4 base = 0.3 cm, height = 1.3 cm **0.39 cm²**

5 base = 24 cm, height = 61 cm **1464 cm²**

6 base = 0.22 cm, height = 0.5 cm **0.11 cm²**

7 What is the total area of the top and four sides of a building that is 25 meters long, 12 meters wide, and 7 meters tall? **818 m²**

Calculate the volume and the total surface area for each of these sets of dimensions.

8 $h = 20$ m, $l = 10$ m, $w = 6$ m **1200 m³; 760 m²**

9 $h = 5$ m, $l = 12$ m, $w = 8$ m **480 m³; 392 m²**

10 $h = 7$ m, $l = 11$ m, $w = 9$ m **693 m³; 478 m²**

11 $h = 12$ m, $l = 8$ m, $w = 15$ m **1440 m³; 792 m²**

12 $h = 8$ m, $l = 13$ m, $w = 10$ m **1040 m³; 628 m²**

Calculate the perimeter and area of each of these rectangles.

13 length = 25 cm, width = 30 cm
perimeter = 110 cm; area 750 cm²

14 length = 40 cm, width = 35 cm
perimeter = 150 cm; area 1400 cm²

15 length = 275 cm, width = 200 cm
perimeter = 950 cm; area 55,000 cm²

Calculate the the volume of a box with the following dimensions.

16 h = 10 cm, l = 15 cm,
w = 7 cm **1050 cm³**

17 h = 80 cm, l = 40 cm,
w = 60 cm **192,000 cm³**

Find the area of each of the right triangles shown below.

⑱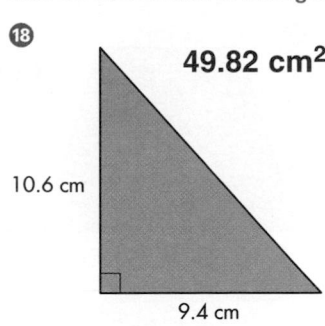

49.82 cm²

10.6 cm

9.4 cm

⑲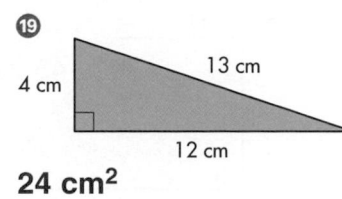

13 cm

4 cm

12 cm

24 cm²

Find the area of each of these parallelograms.

⑳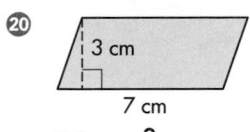

3 cm

7 cm

21 cm²

㉑

4 cm

12 cm

48 cm²

㉒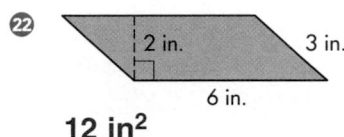

2 in.   3 in.

6 in.

12 in²

㉓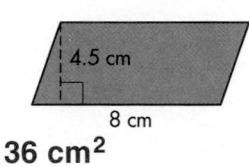

4.5 cm

8 cm

36 cm²

㉔ Determine the area of the figure. **147 in.²**

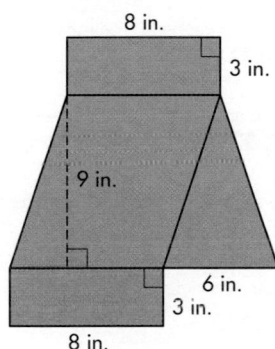

8 in.

3 in.

9 in.

6 in.

3 in.

8 in.

◆ **UNIT 6 Mid-Unit Review**

◆ **UNIT 6 Mid-Unit Review**

Find the area of each trapezoid.

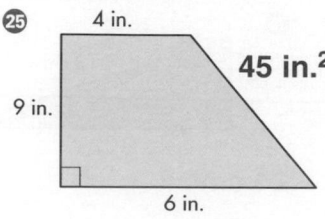

㉕ 4 in. **45 in.²** 9 in. 6 in.

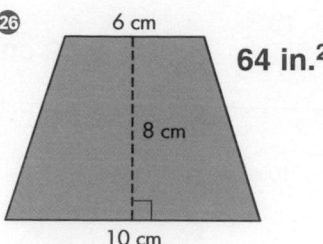

㉖ 6 cm **64 in.²** 8 cm 10 cm

Answer these questions.

㉗ Can a right triangle be isosceles? **yes**

㉘ Can a trapezoid have two sides the same length? **yes**

㉙ If a triangle is isosceles, can it also be scalene? **no**

㉚ Is every square a parallelogram? **yes**

㉛ Can a trapezoid have three right angles? **no**

A group of students measured their classroom, which had a rectangular floor. They found that the length was 810 cm and the width was 680 cm. They believe their measurements are no more than 5 cm too high or too low.

Solve.

㉜ Find the perimeter and area of the classroom floor according to the students' measurements. **2980 cm; 550,800 cm²**

㉝ Find the greatest and the least possible perimeters if the measurements are off by 5 cm. **3000 cm; 2960 cm**

㉞ Find the greatest and the least possible areas if the measurements are off by 5 cm. **558,275 cm²; 543,375 cm²**

㉟ A rectangle has an area of 48 square meters. The base is 12 meters. What is the height? **4 m**

㊱ The area of a parallelogram is 60 square centimeters. The height is 5 centimeters. What is the base? **12 cm**

486 · Geometry

Solve these problems.

37 The area of a right triangle is 42 square centimeters. The base is 14 centimeters. What is the height? **6 cm**

38 A trapezoid has bases that are 12 inches and 20 inches. The area of the trapezoid is 160 square inches. What is the height? **10 in.**

39 A garden is in the shape of an equilateral triangle. Each side is 15 meters long. What is its perimeter? **45 m**

40 What is the height of an isosceles right triangle that has an area of 32 square feet? **8 ft**

41 What is the length of a side of a square that has an area of 144 square centimeters? **12 cm**

42 A square field has an area of 1296 square meters. What is the length of a side of that field? **36 m**

43 Gregory rides his bicycle at an average speed of about 12 miles per hour. It usually takes him about 18 minutes to ride from his home to piano practice. About how far does he live from his piano teacher's house? **about 3.6 miles**

44 Anna weighs about 85 pounds. She thinks that her baby brother weighs about half as much as she does. If she is right, about how many pounds does her baby brother weigh? **about 42 or 43**

Find the area in square units of each of the figures in the rectangle below.

45 A **7.5**

46 B **12.5**

47 C **10**

48 D **5**

49 E **3**

50 F **7**

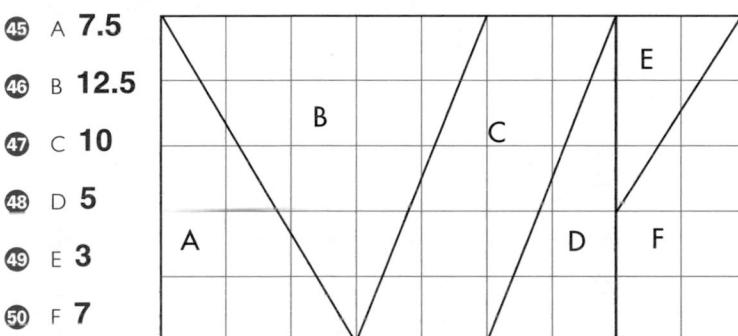

Unit 6 Mid-Unit Review • **487**

Home Connections You may want to send Home Connections Blackline Masters pages 60–61 home, which provide additional activities families can complete together. These activities apply the skills being presented in this unit.

Portfolio Assessment As students work through the second half of this unit, the Portfolio Assessment task provided on Assessment Blackline Masters page 91 can be used to evaluate students' ability to solve problems involving area, perimeter, and angle measurement.

Performance Assessment The Performance Assessment Task 1 provided on Assessment Blackline Masters pages 80–81 can be used at this time to evaluate students' proficiency with finding area and volume. You may want to administer this assessment with individual students or in small groups.

Unit Project This would be a good time to assign the "Melting Ice Cubes" project on pages 550 and 551. Students can begin working on the project in cooperative groups in their free time as you work through the unit. This project is a good opportunity for students to apply the concept of setting up an experiment and analyzing results using surface area in real-world problem solving.

ASSESSMENT p. 52

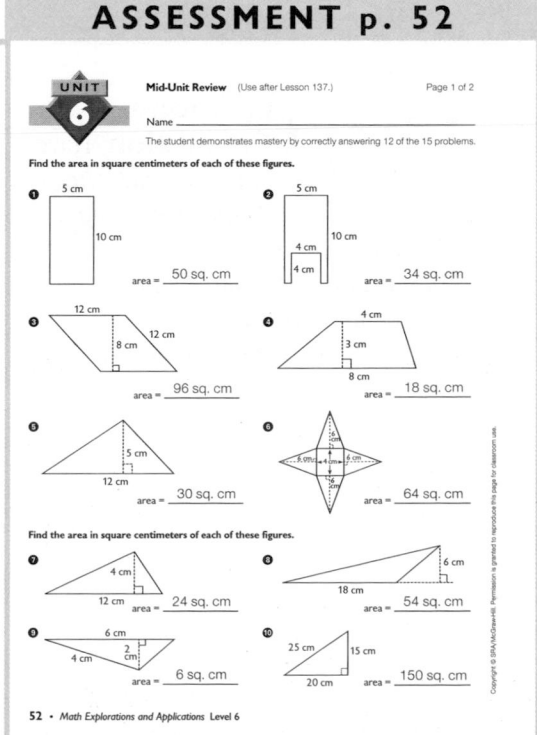

Multiplying and Dividing by Powers of 10

LESSON PLANNER

Objective

▶ to review and provide practice in multiplying and dividing by powers of 10

Context of the Lesson
This is the second of five lessons relating to measurement. This work with powers of 10 prepares students for the next lesson on converting metric units, which involves multiplying and dividing by powers of 10.

 MANIPULATIVES
none

Program Resources
Practice Master 138
Enrichment Master 138
For extra practice:
CD-ROM* Lesson 138

1 Warm-Up ⏱ 5 MINUTES

 Problem of the Day Present the following problem: To find quickly the sum of all the numbers from 1 to 10, Herman made five pairs of numbers that added to 11: 1 + 10, 2 + 9, 3 + 8, 4 + 7, and 5 + 6. Since 5 x 11 = 55, he knew that the sum of the numbers is 55. Have students use Herman's shortcut to find the sum of all numbers from 1–100. (5050; Pair off numbers to make sums of 101; there are 50; 50 x 101 = 5050)

Problem-Solving Strategies Ask students who have solved the Problem of the Day to share how they solved it and any strategies they used.

MENTAL MATH Ask students to explain how they could find each of the following products using mental math:

a. 8 x 99 = (8 x 100 = 800; 800 – 8 = 792)

b. 7 x 102 = (7 x 100 = 700; 14 + 700 = 714)

c. 6 x 47 = (6 x 50 = 300; 300 – 18 = 282)

d. 9 x 9999 = (9 x 10,000 = 90,000; 90,000 – 9 = 89,991)

Multiplying and Dividing by Powers of 10

When we convert from one metric measurement to another, we need to multiply or divide by a power of 10. Keep in shape by practicing these computing shortcuts.

Do you remember the short way for multiplying or dividing by numbers such as 10, 100, and 1000? Look at these examples:

10 × 6.54	⟶ 6.5 4	⟶ 65.4
100 × 6.54	⟶ 6.5 4	⟶ 654
1000 × 6.54	⟶ 6.5 4 0	⟶ 6540
87.5 ÷ 10	⟶ 8 7.5	⟶ 8.75
87.5 ÷ 100	⟶ 8 7.5	⟶ 0.875
87.5 ÷ 1000	⟶ 0 8 7.5	⟶ 0.0875

Multiply.

① 2.5 × 10 **25**   ② 2.5 × 100 **250**   ③ 2.5 × 1000 **2500**

④ 2.5 × 10,000 **25,000**   ⑤ 2.5 × 100,000 **250,000**   ⑥ 3.47 × 10 **34.7**

⑦ 100 × 3.47 **347**   ⑧ 3.47 × 1000 **3470**   ⑨ 10 × 0.6 **6**

⑩ 100 × 0.6 **60**   ⑪ 1000 × 97 **97,000**   ⑫ 9.7 × 1000 **9700**

⑬ 0.97 × 1000 **970**   ⑭ 0.08 × 1000 **80**   ⑮ 100 × 0.08 **8**

⑯ 9.3 × 10 **93**   ⑰ 0.93 × 1000 **930**   ⑱ 93 × 100 **9300**

Divide.

⑲ 6.2 ÷ 10 **0.62**   ⑳ 6.2 ÷ 100 **0.062**   ㉑ 6.2 ÷ 1000 **0.0062**

㉒ 6.2 ÷ 10,000 **0.00062**   ㉓ 6.25 ÷ 10,000 **0.000625**   ㉔ 34 ÷ 10 **3.4**

㉕ 34 ÷ 100 **0.34**   ㉖ 34 ÷ 1000 **0.034**   ㉗ 873 ÷ 100 **8.73**

㉘ 873 ÷ 10 **87.3**   ㉙ 69.1 ÷ 10 **6.91**   ㉚ 9.1 ÷ 100 **0.091**

㉛ 10.5 ÷ 10 **1.05**   ㉜ 0.7 ÷ 100 **0.007**   ㉝ 0.7 ÷ 10 **0.07**

 **Literature Connection** Have students read *Micro Aliens: Dazzling Journeys with an Electron Microscope* by Howard Tomb. Ask them to represent the magnification of each photo by rounding and using exponents.

RETEACHING

Some students may make the error of moving the decimal point in the wrong direction. Suggest that they check their answers by realizing that if they multiply by any number greater than 1, they will get an answer greater than the initial number. The opposite is true for division. Other students may move the decimal point the wrong number of places. Advise them to count the 0s carefully, then count the places to be moved, and then recount if necessary.

*available separately

Multiply or divide. Watch the signs.

㉞ 4.1 ÷ 100 **0.041**	㉟ 6.9 × 10 **69**	㊱ 100 × 87 **8700**
㊲ 87 ÷ 100 **0.87**	㊳ 5 ÷ 10 **0.5**	㊴ 5 ÷ 100 **0.05**
㊵ 5 × 1000 **5000**	㊶ 100 × 50 **5000**	㊷ 50 ÷ 100 **0.5**
㊸ 5 ÷ 1000 **0.005**	㊹ 5.5 ÷ 10 **0.55**	㊺ 0.2 × 100 **20**
㊻ 0.2 ÷ 10 **0.02**	㊼ 1000 × 0.08 **80**	㊽ 0.08 ÷ 10 **0.008**
㊾ 0.1 × 10 **1**	㊿ 0.1 ÷ 10 **0.01**	(51) 1.5 × 100 **150**
(52) 10,000 × 1.5 **15,000**	(53) 1.5 × 100,000 **150,000**	(54) 0.75 × 100 **75**
(55) 0.75 ÷ 10 **0.075**	(56) 75 ÷ 1000 **0.075**	(57) 75 ÷ 100,000 **0.00075**

Solve. Watch the signs.

(58) 35 + 10 **45**	(59) 35 − 10 **25**	(60) 108 ÷ 10 **10.8**
(61) 108 + 100 **208**	(62) 108 + 10 **118**	(63) 650 ÷ 100 **6.5**
(64) 650 − 100 **550**	(65) 650 × 100 **65,000**	(66) 0.7 + 10 **10.7**
(67) 0.7 × 10 **7**	(68) 3.6 + 10 **13.6**	(69) 3.6 × 10 **36**
(70) 3.6 ÷ 10 **0.36**	(71) 62.5 × 100 **6250**	(72) 62.5 + 100 **162.5**
(73) 462.5 − 100 **362.5**	(74) 0.15 × 1000 **150**	(75) 0.15 + 1000 **1000.15**
(76) 100 × 27.42 **2742**	(77) 27.42 + 10 **37.42**	(78) 115 ÷ 100 **1.15**
(79) 0.115 × 100 **11.5**	(80) 0.115 + 10 **10.115**	(81) 967.14 × 1000 **967,140**

PROBLEM SOLVING

Solve these problems.

(82) The Drama Club is selling tickets to their play for $2.50 each. They hope to sell 100 tickets. How much money would that bring in for the club? **$250**

(83) Rebecca measured a stack of 100 identical workbooks. It was 46.2 centimeters thick. How thick was each workbook? **0.462 cm**

(84) How much would a $100 pair of boots cost if sales tax is 6%? **$106**

PRACTICE p. 138

LESSON 138 PRACTICE Name________

Multiply or divide. Watch the signs.

❶ 8.5 × 10 = 85	❷ 4.3 ÷ 10 = 0.43	❸ 0.06 × 1000 = 60
❹ 2.6 ÷ 100 = 0.026	❺ 34.8 × 1000 = 34,800	❻ 47.8 ÷ 100 = 0.478
❼ 278 ÷ 10 = 27.8	❽ 56.9 ÷ 1000 = 0.0569	❾ 5.3 × 10 = 53
❿ 0.072 × 100 = 7.2	⓫ 4.27 × 100 = 427	⓬ 0.9 ÷ 10 = 0.09
⓭ 3.97 × 10 = 39.7	⓮ 74.2 ÷ 100 = 0.742	⓯ 647 × 10 = 6470
⓰ 21.4 ÷ 1000 = 0.0214	⓱ 888 × 10 = 8880	⓲ 0.43 × 100 = 43

Solve. Watch the signs.

⓳ 430 − 100 = 330	⓴ 27.9 + 100 = 127.9	㉑ 42.6 × 100 = 4260
㉒ 25.6 + 10 = 35.6	㉓ 476 ÷ 10 = 47.6	㉔ 879 ÷ 100 = 8.79
㉕ 35.9 × 100 = 3590	㉖ 52.6 + 10 = 62.6	㉗ 8.96 + 100 = 108.96
㉘ 47.6 ÷ 10 = 4.76	㉙ 79.8 − 10 = 69.8	㉚ 47.9 − 10 = 37.9
㉛ 67.6 − 10 = 57.6	㉜ 5.3 + 10 = 15.3	㉝ 912 ÷ 100 = 9.12
㉞ 4.29 ÷ 100 = 0.0429	㉟ 81 + 100 = 181	㊱ 33 × 10 = 330

138 • *Math Explorations and Applications* Level 6

ENRICHMENT p. 138

LESSON 138 ENRICHMENT Name ________

You can represent three dimensions on a piece of paper, which has only two dimensions, in a number of ways. Below is a drawing that illustrates the third dimension, depth. It uses one-point perspective. One-point perspective shows parallel lines in a drawing converge to one point. Notice that the front of the building is square. The sides follow lines that are drawn to one point, the vanishing point.

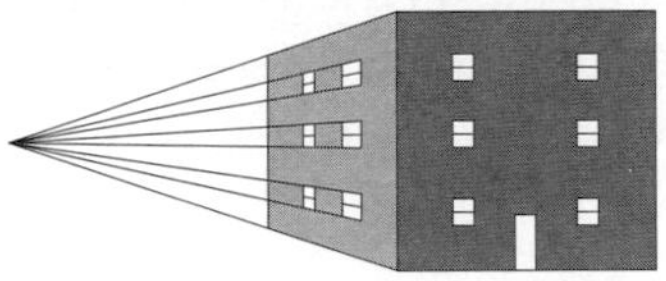

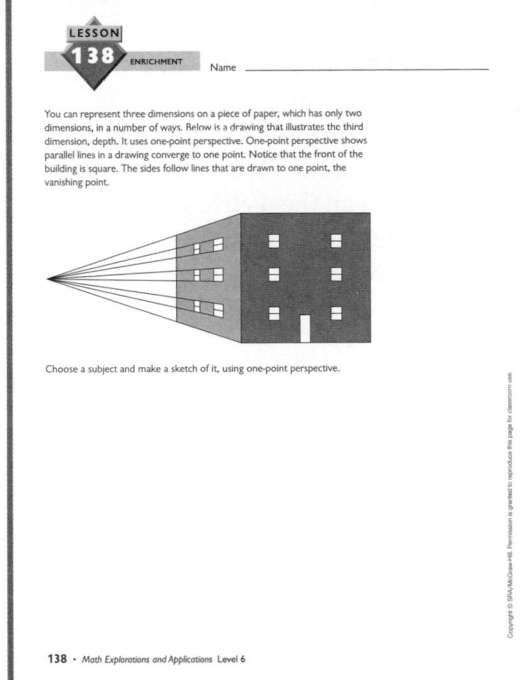

Choose a subject and make a sketch of it, using one-point perspective.

138 • *Math Explorations and Applications* Level 6

❷ Teach

Using the Student Pages After going over the examples, have students solve the problems on pages 488–489 on their own. Circulate around the room as students work and provide help as needed. If time remains, have students continue the estimating and measuring activities from Lesson 137.

❸ Wrap-Up

5 MINUTES

In Closing Ask students to give a rule for a shortcut for finding the product of a decimal number and a power of 10. Ask them to give the rule for dividing a decimal number by a power of 10.

ALTERNATIVE ASSESSMENT

Performance Assessment Ask students to give the answers to 8.4 ÷ 100 and 8.4 x 100 and to explain how they got their answers.

Assessment Criteria

Did the student . . .

✓ recall the short way for multiplying or dividing by powers of 10?

✓ correctly answer at least 80% of the problems on pages 488–489?

Homework Have students measure a stack of ten items such as coins, checkers, computer disks, and so on to determine the thickness of each item.

LOOKING AHEAD You will need to gather containers of various sizes to use in Lesson 141.

LESSON PLANNER

Objectives

▶ to review the meanings of the prefixes commonly used in the metric system

▶ to provide practice in converting from one metric unit to another

Context of the Lesson This is the third of five lessons on measurement.

 MANIPULATIVES

Program Resources

Reteaching Master

Practice Master 139

Enrichment Master 139

For extra practice:
  CD-ROM* Lesson 139
  Cumulative Review, page 583

① Warm-Up ⏱ 5 MINUTES

 **Problem of the Day** Present the following problem to students: A baseball game being played in San Francisco, on the West Coast, is being televised in Boston, on the East Coast, where Sherman is watching it. The game began at 8:05 P.M. in San Francisco and lasted for 3 hours, 15 minutes. Sherman turned off the TV as soon as the game ended. What time did Sherman turn off his TV? (2:20 A.M.)

Problem-Solving Strategies Ask students who have solved the Problem of the Day to share how they solved it and any strategies they used.

 MENTAL MATH Have students evaluate each of the following expressions.

a. $3 \times 10^3 = (3000)$

b. $6 \times 10^4 = (60,000)$

c. $2.5 \times 10^3 = (2500)$

d. $1.75 \times 10^2 = (175)$

e. $4.82 \times 10^5 = (482,000)$

f. $7.9 \times 10^4 = (79,000)$

The Metric System

In the history of the world, many systems of measurement have been used. Today almost all the world's population uses some form of the metric system.

One advantage of the metric system is that conversions from one unit to another are very easy. For example, there are 100 centimeters in a meter, so if you are 1.45 meters tall, you are 145 centimeters tall. Multiplying by powers of 10 (0.1, 1, 10, and 100, for example) is easier than multiplying by any other numbers.

The prefix in a metric unit tells you what power of 10 is involved. For example, a kilogram is 1000 grams, and a kilometer is 1000 meters.

◆ How many liters are in a kiloliter? **1000**

A centimeter is one hundredth of a meter.

◆ What fraction of a gram is a centigram? $\frac{1}{100}$

There are 1000 milliliters in 1 liter.

◆ How many millimeters are in a meter? **1000**

Some common and less common metric prefixes are listed below.

Table of Metric Prefixes

Prefix	Symbol	Power of 10	Meaning in Words
mega-	M	1,000,000 (10^6)	one million
kilo-	k	1000 (10^3)	one thousand
hecto-	h	100 (10^2)	one hundred
deka-	da	10 (10^1)	ten
—	—	1	one
deci-	d	0.1	one-tenth
centi-	c	0.01	one-hundredth
milli-	m	0.001	one-thousandth
micro-	μ	0.000001	one-millionth

 **Social Studies Connection** Invite students to conduct research in the library to find out about when the metric system began. Ask them to find out what the original standard was for the length of a meter.

*available separately

Use the table on page 490 to solve these problems.

1 How many meters are in a **kilo**meter? **1000**

2 How many grams are in a **kilo**gram? **1000**

3 How many **centi**meters are in a meter? **100**

4 How many **milli**meters are in a meter? **1000**

5 How many **milli**grams are in a gram? **1000**

6 How many **milli**liters are in a liter? **1000**

7 How many liters are in a **deka**liter? **10**

8 Which is larger, a **deka**meter or a **deci**meter? **dekameter**

9 How many **deci**meters are in a **deka**meter? **100**

10 How many **deci**liters are in a **deka**liter? **100**

11 How many **deci**grams are in a **deka**gram? **100**

12 Which is longer, a **centi**meter or a **milli**meter? **centimeter**

13 How many **milli**meters are in a **centi**meter? **10**

14 How many **milli**grams are in a **centi**gram? **10**

15 How many **milli**liters are in a **centi**liter? **10**

16 How many **centi**meters are in a **hecto**meter? **10,000**

17 How many **centi**grams are in a **hecto**gram? **10,000**

18 How many **milli**meters are in a **kilo**meter? **1,000,000 (or 10^6)**

19 How many **micro**meters are in a **mega**meter? **1,000,000,000,000 (or 10^{12})**

20 How many **micro**liters are in a **mega**liter? **1,000,000,000,000 (or 10^{12})**

Unit 6   Lesson 139 • **491**

Technology Connection Refer students to the software *Mastering Math II* from Queue (Mac, IBM, for grades 5–12) for practice with metrics. Units of measure include dry, bulk, length, liquid, weight, alternating decimal/metric, and U.S. customary conversions.

② Teach

Using the Student Pages Discuss the material and the table on page 490. Ask students to suggest other words in which those prefixes appear. Point out that *deka-* is a variation of the prefix *deca-*, and explain that the decathlon is a ten-event Olympic contest, that a decade is a ten-year period, and that our number system is a *decimal* system, based on 10 or tenths. Also explain to students that a cent is a hundredth of a dollar and that a century is 100 years. Point out that a mill (used in property tax assessment) is one thousandth of a dollar and that a millennium is 1000 years. Ask them what a kilowatt is. (a unit of power equal to 1000 watts) You may wish to have students browse through a dictionary to find more terms with these prefixes. Point out that the units of metric measurement that students already know are the most common ones: millimeter, centimeter, meter, kilometer, milligram, gram, kilogram, milliliter, and liter. Then have students refer to the table, as needed, to do the problems on page 491.

◆ LESSON 139 The Metric System

Teach

Using the Student Pages Go over the examples of converting from one unit to another on page 492, and add a few of your own choosing if you wish. For the problems on page 492, emphasize to students that the key thing to remember is that if they are converting to a *smaller* unit, there must be *more* units. For instance, point out that a distance of 2.8 meters would be very few kilometers (0.0028) but a great many millimeters (2800), because meters are smaller than kilometers but larger than millimeters. You may wish to encourage students to express their answers to the problems on this page using exponential notation. You may find it useful to discuss sensible metric measurements before assigning page 493. You may also wish to alert students that they will need to convert between two units of metric measurement in order to solve some of the problems on this page. Have students complete the problems on page 492 and the word problems on page 493 independently.

Meeting Individual Needs
Students need not memorize all the prefixes at this time; allow them to use the tables as needed. Focus any extra help on understanding which way and how many places to move the decimal point.

◆ LESSON 139 The Metric System

To convert from one unit to another, multiply or divide by the appropriate number. In the metric system this means multiplying or dividing by some power of 10 (see the table on page 490). You can do this by simply moving a decimal point (and writing in extra 0s when needed).

Example: Change 3.758 meters to centimeters.

1 meter is 100 centimeters. So 3.758 meters is 3.758 × 100 centimeters.

You can multiply 3.758 by 100 by moving the decimal point two places to the right (because there are two 0s in 100).

3.7 5 8 ———→ 375.8

So 3.758 meters = 375.8 centimeters.

Example: Change 35 grams to kilograms.

1 kilogram is 1000 grams. So 35 grams is 35 ÷ 1000 kilograms.

You can divide 35 by 1000 by moving the decimal point three places to the left (because there are three 0s in 1000).

0 3 5 ———→ 0.035

So 35 grams = 0.035 kilogram.

Convert these measurements.

21 5.68 meters to centimeters
568

22 5.68 grams to centigrams
568

23 5.68 liters to centiliters
568

24 834 meters to kilometers
0.834

25 574.2 millimeters to meters
0.5742

26 43.2 kilograms to grams
43,200

27 23 kilometers to meters
23,000

28 0.023 kilometer to meters
23

29 0.023 kilogram to grams
23

30 3 dekaliters to liters
30

31 0.12 kilogram to grams
120

32 1.2 kilograms to grams
1200

33 0.12 kilometer to meters
120

34 12 kilometers to meters
12,000

35 7.9 liters to milliliters
7900

36 79 meters to kilometers
0.079

37 416 centigrams to grams
4.16

38 135 centimeters to meters
1.35

39 753 meters to kilometers
0.753

40 753 milligrams to grams
0.753

41 753 liters to milliliters
753,000

42 14 decimeters to meters
1.4

43 2408 grams to milligrams
2,408,000

44 2408 kilometers to meters
2.408

492 · Geometry

Literature Connection Have students read the descriptions and look at the illustrations of metric measurement in *The Liter Is* by Jerolyn Ann Nentl.

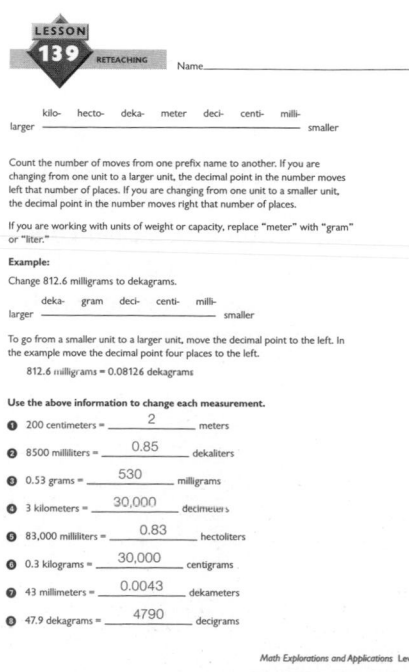

RETEACHING p. 47

Solve these problems.

45 Melissa and her friends wanted to hang a swing from a branch of a strong old oak tree in her backyard. The friends knew that the branch was 4.5 meters high. They wanted the swing to be 30 centimeters above the ground.

a. How much rope must the friends buy? **a little more than 4.2 m**

b. If they buy too little rope, will the swing be higher or lower than they had planned? **higher**

46 Sally is 148 centimeters tall. Her bookcase is 178 centimeters tall. Can Sally reach a book on the top shelf without standing on something? **yes**

47 Mr. Foster has a board that is 2.75 meters long. He cut two equal pieces off of the board. Now his board is only 2.35 meters long.

a. How many centimeters long were the pieces he cut from the board? **20 cm each**

b. Can Mr. Foster get ten more 20-centimeter pieces from the board? **yes**

c. If so, how much board will remain? **35 cm (or 0.35 m)**

48 Mackenzie and Spencer were preparing for a large picnic. They had four tables that were each 183 centimeters long. They placed the tables end to end to create one large serving table.

a. How many meters long was that table? **7.32**

b. Could those tables, placed end to end, fit in your classroom? **Answers will vary depending on the size of the classroom.**

49 One hectare is equal to 10,000 square meters.

a. If a square lot of land has an area of 1 hectare, how many meters long is it on each side? **100 m**

b. What is the perimeter of that lot? **400 m**

Use the Cumulative Review on page 583 after this lesson.

Unit 6 Lesson 139 • **493**

3 Wrap-Up

5 MINUTES

In Closing Ask students to summarize a procedure for expressing one unit of metric measurement in terms of another.

ALTERNATIVE ASSESSMENT

Performance Assessment Ask students to find the difference between 187 centimeters and 73 centimeters and to express that difference in meters. (1.14 meters)

Assessment Criteria

Did the student . . .

✓ participate in the discussion about metric prefixes?

✓ correctly answer at least 35 of the 44 problems on pages 491 and 492?

✓ successfully solve the word problems on page 493 and explain the methods he or she used to do so?

Homework Have students decide along with a family member what the best metric unit would be for measuring each of the following, and then measure each, if possible, estimating first.

a. length of an arm

b. diameter of a penny

c. length of a house key

d. length of a kitchen

e. weight of a dictionary

f. weight of a bar of soap

PRACTICE p. 139

LESSON **139** PRACTICE Name_____

Use the table to solve each problem.

Table of Metric Prefixes

Prefix	Symbol	Power of 10	Meaning in Words
mega-	M	1,000,000 (10⁶)	one million
kilo-	k	1,000 (10³)	one thousand
hecto-	h	100 (10²)	one hundred
deka-	da	10 (10¹)	ten
—	—	1	one
deci-	d	0.1	one-tenth
centi-	c	0.01	one-hundredth
milli-	m	0.001	one-thousandth
micro-	µ	0.000001	one-millionth

❶ How many liters are in a kiloliter? — 1000

❷ How many milligrams are in a gram? — 1000

❸ How many centiliters are in a liter? — 100

❹ How many milliliters are in a liter? — 1000

❺ Which is larger, a centiliter or a dekaliter? — a dekaliter

❻ Which is larger, a gram or a centigram? — a gram

❼ How many microliters are in a deciliter? — 100,000

❽ How many grams are in a dekagram? — 10

❾ How many meters are in a kilometer? — 1000

❿ Which is larger, a microliter or a milliliter? — a milliliter

⓫ How many grams are in a kilogram? — 1000

⓬ How many centimeters are in a meter? — 100

⓭ How many micrograms are in a gram? — 1,000,000

⓮ How many micrograms are in a megagram? — 1,000,000

⓯ How many liters are in a hectoliter? — 100

⓰ How many centigrams are in a hectogram? — 10,000

Math Explorations and Applications Level 6 • **139**

ENRICHMENT p. 139

LESSON **139** ENRICHMENT Name_____

Use the table to find the answers to the problems below.

Coin	Diameter	Mass
penny	1.9 cm	3 g
nickel	21 mm	0.005 kg
dime	0.017 m	2 g

❶ How many coins are there in a collection of pennies that weighs 480 grams? — 160

❷ A row of dimes laid next to one another is 340 centimeters long. How many dimes are in the row? — 200

❸ How many coins are in a collection of nickels that weighs 1.3 kilograms? — 260

❹ A collection of pennies weighs 0.32 kilogram. How much money is the collection worth? — about $1.07

❺ How much does a collection of $6.80 worth of nickels weigh (in grams)? — 680

❻ A line of pennies laid next to each other stretches for 4.294 meters. How many pennies does the line contain? — 226

❼ How much less 0.6 kilogram of nickels worth than 0.4 kilogram of dimes? — $14

❽ How much more does $7.50 in pennies weigh (in kilograms) than $7.50 in dimes? — 2.10

❾ A bag of coins weighs 0.5 kg. If it contains only dimes, how many coins does it contain? If only nickels, how many coins? — 250; 100

❿ A collection of dimes weighs 450 grams. What is the total value of the dimes? — $22.50

Math Explorations and Applications Level 6 • **139**

Student Edition pages 494–495

The Customary System

LESSON PLANNER

Objective

▶ to provide review and practice in converting units within the customary system of measurement

Context of the Lesson This is the fourth of five lessons on measurement.

 MANIPULATIVES

Program Resources

Reteaching Master

Practice Master 140

Enrichment Master 140

For extra practice:
  CD-ROM* Lesson 140

① Warn-Up

Problem of the Day Present the following problem to students: Estimate to the nearest foot and yard the distance from a classmate's chair to the classroom door. Then have a volunteer measure the actual distance. Whose estimate was closest?

Problem-Solving Strategies Ask students who have solved the Problem of the Day to share how they solved it and any strategies they used.

MENTAL MATH Have students find the following answers using mental math.

a. 50 × 12 = (600)   b. 3 × 32 = (96)

c. 16 × 10 = (160)   d. 12 × 30 = (360)

e. 40 × 600 = (24,000) f. 6000 ÷ 20 = (300)

g. 50,000 ÷ 2500 = (20) h. 4000 ÷ 50 = (80)

494 Geometry

The Customary System

The customary system is a set of measurement units commonly used in the United States. Unlike the metric system, the customary system uses many unrelated conversions. There are separate sets of conversions for capacity, length, and weight.

Answer the questions based on each set of conversions.

There are 8 fluid ounces in 1 cup.

There are 2 cups in 1 pint.

There are 2 pints in 1 quart.

There are 4 quarts in 1 gallon.

❶ How many fluid ounces are in 1 pint? **16**

❷ How many fluid ounces are in 1 quart? **32**

❸ How many fluid ounces are in 1 gallon? **128**

There are 12 inches in 1 foot.

There are 3 feet in 1 yard.

There are 1760 yards in 1 mile.

❹ How many feet are in 1 mile? **5280**

There are 16 ounces in 1 pound.

There are 2000 pounds in 1 ton.

❺ How many ounces are in 1 ton? **32,000**

There are 60 seconds in one minute.

There are 60 minutes in one hour.

There are 24 hours in one day.

There are 7 days in one week.

There are about 52 weeks in one year.

There are 10 years in one decade.

There are 10 decades in one century.

There are 10 centuries in one millennium.

494 • Geometry

 **Math Connection** Have students research the following units of measurement: fathom, league, acre, span, furlong, hand, carat, and light year. Ask students to share their findings.

 **Real-World Connection** Ask students to think of an activity they do regularly that takes about the same amount of time, such as brushing their teeth, showering, or watering plants in their home. Have them use estimation to figure out how much time they spend each year doing that activity.

LESSON 140 RETEACHING Name_____

Use fractions and labels to help you convert measurements. Write the conversions as rates so that all of the units cancel except the unit you need.

Example 1:

Change five weeks to seconds.

$$\frac{5 \text{ weeks}}{1} \times \frac{7 \text{ days}}{1 \text{ week}} \times \frac{24 \text{ hours}}{1 \text{ day}} \times \frac{60 \text{ minutes}}{1 \text{ hour}} \times \frac{60 \text{ seconds}}{1 \text{ minute}}$$

Cancel labels as you would cancel common factors when multiplying fractions.

$$\frac{5 \text{ weeks}}{1} \times \frac{7 \text{ days}}{1 \text{ week}} \times \frac{24 \text{ hours}}{1 \text{ day}} \times \frac{60 \text{ minutes}}{1 \text{ hour}} \times \frac{60 \text{ seconds}}{1 \text{ minute}}$$

$5 \times 7 \times 24 \times 60 \times 60 \text{ seconds} = 3,024,000 \text{ seconds}$

Example 2:

360 in. = ? yd

$$\frac{360 \text{ in.}}{1} \times \frac{1 \text{ ft}}{12 \text{ in.}} \times \frac{1 \text{ yd}}{3 \text{ ft}} = 360 \div (12 \times 3) = 360 \div 36 = 10 \text{ yd}$$

Use fractions and canceling to change each measurement.

❶ 3 days = ___4320___ minutes   ❷ 80,000 fluid ounces = ___625___ gallons

❸ 5 years = ___2,628,000___ minutes   ❹ 48,000 inches = ___$1333\frac{1}{3}$___ yards

❺ 16 gallons = ___256___ cups   ❻ 8 miles = ___506,880___ inches

❼ 4 days = ___345,600___ seconds   ❽ 800,000 ounces = ___25___ tons

❾ 60,000 inches = ___$1666\frac{2}{3}$___ yards   ❿ 15 gallons = ___120___ pints

48 • Math Explorations and Applications Level 6

---

494 Geometry

*available separately

15 b. years divisible by 100 but not by 400 (e.g., 1900 and 2100 are not leap years)

6 How many seconds are in one day?
86,400

7 How many minutes are in one week?
10,080

8 How many decades are in one millennium?
100

Solve these problems.

9 Suki is 63 inches tall. How many feet tall is Suki? $5\frac{1}{4}$ **or 5.25 ft**

10 A bag of grapes weighs 3 pounds. How many ounces is that? **48**

11 A recipe calls for 13 cups of apple juice. How many quarts is that? $3\frac{1}{4}$ **or 3.25**

12 Megan is planting crocuses in late fall. The directions say that the flowers will bloom in about 100 days. How many weeks is that? **14 weeks and 2 days**

13 How many seconds old are you? **Answers between 3×10^8 and 4.2×10^8 are reasonable.**

14 How much older will you be when you finish this problem? **Answers will vary.**

15 Standard years have 365 days. Leap years have 366 days.

a. How often do we have leap years? **every four years**

b. What is the exception to this rule? You may need to do research to find the answer. **See above.**

16 How many days are in one century? Keep in mind your answer to problem 15. **36,524 or 36,525**

17 How many hours will be in the twenty-first century? **876,576**

Unit 6   Lesson 140 • **495**

PRACTICE p. 140

LESSON 140 PRACTICE   Name_____

Change each measurement to the indicated unit.

1 8 feet = $2\frac{2}{3}$ yards

2 3 miles = 5280 yards

3 48 inches = 4 feet

4 1200 seconds = $\frac{1}{3}$ hours

5 3 pounds = 48 ounces

6 50 days = 7 weeks, 1 days

7 180 ounces = $11\frac{1}{4}$ pounds

8 200 ounces = 12 pounds, 8 ounces

9 2 hours = 120 minutes

10 1 mile = 63,360 inches

11 2.5 days = 60 hours

12 8 pints = 16 cups

13 5 pints = 10 cups

14 3 days = 259,200 seconds

15 16 quarts = 4 gallons

16 6000 seconds = $1\frac{2}{3}$ hours

17 3 cups = 24 fluid ounces

18 960 feet = 320 yards

19 800 fluid ounces = 6.25 gallons

20 5 yards = 180 inches

21 26 weeks = 182 days

22 4 tons = 8000 pounds

23 3 centuries = 30 decades

24 5 feet = 60 inches

140 • *Math Explorations and Applications Level 6*

ENRICHMENT p. 140

LESSON 140 ENRICHMENT   Name_____

GAME   **Players:** Two to four
Materials: 36 index cards
Object: To change the measurement of a given unit

Rules

1. On one side of 12 index cards write AMOUNT. On the other side write the following numbers, one on each card:

   1 2 4 8 12 16 20 24 32 40 48 64

2. On one side of 24 index cards, write UNIT. On the other side write the following units, one on each card. Use each unit six times.

   cups   pints   quarts   gallons

3. Shuffle the cards and place them in two piles, one with AMOUNT face up, the other with UNIT face up.

4. Players draw one card from each pile and place the cards face up.

5. Players then draw a second UNIT card and must change the measurement to the given unit.

6. If an exact change can be made using whole numbers (and is done correctly), the player scores one point.

7. Continue taking turns until all the cards have been used. The player with the most points wins.

Example:

Player 1 draws **16** and **quarts**, then draws **gallons**. She correctly changes 16 quarts to 4 gallons. She scores one point.

Player 2 draws **1** and **pints**, then draws **quarts**. 1 pint cannot be changed to a whole number of quarts. He does not score a point.

NOTE: This game can be modified to use units of weight or length.

Game answers will vary.

140 • *Math Explorations and Applications Level 6*

---

2 Teach

Using the Student Pages Have students do pages 494 and 495 independently. You may wish to discuss the fact that there are 365 days (therefore $52\frac{1}{7}$ weeks) in most years, but 366 (therefore $52\frac{2}{7}$ weeks) in leap years. When students do problem 13, in which they calculate how many seconds old they are, they should remember that leap years have extra days. You may wish to have students work in groups on this problem.

Students can keep a record in their Math Journals of their computations for finding their age in seconds. They can update this information from time to time.

3 Wrap-Up

In Closing To summarize the lesson, ask students to tell whether there are more inches or more feet in the length of the classroom, and to explain their answer.

Portfolio Assessment Have students describe the procedure for converting among units of customary measurement. Ask them to include an example of the procedure in their Math Portfolios.

Assessment Criteria

Did the student . . .

✓ correctly complete the problems on pages 494 and 495?

✓ obtain a reasonable answer to problem 13?

✓ understand that there are always more small units in a quantity than larger units?

Homework Have students and family members estimate assorted lengths, weights, and volumes around their home. They can record their estimates, and then measure to see how close each came.

LOOKING AHEAD You will need a collection of containers of assorted sizes to use in the next lesson.

Unit 6 Lesson 140   **495**

LESSON 141

Estimating Volume

Student Edition pages 496–497

LESSON PLANNER

Objectives

▶ to explore why many people have difficulty estimating the relative volumes of containers of different shapes and sizes

▶ to provide practice in estimating relative volume

Context of the Lesson This is the last of five lessons on measurement.

MANIPULATIVES

containers* in a wide variety of sizes and shapes, at least two of which are the same shape but different sizes

funnels*

water

Program Resources

Practice Master 141

Enrichment Master 141

For extra practice:
CD-ROM* Lesson 141

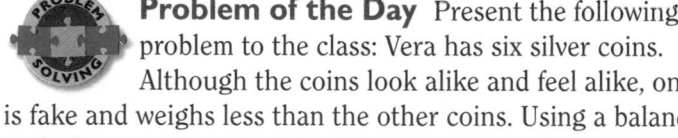

① Warm-Up

5 MINUTES

Problem of the Day Present the following problem to the class: Vera has six silver coins. Although the coins look alike and feel alike, one is fake and weighs less than the other coins. Using a balance scale, how can Vera find the fake coin using only two weighings? (One way: Put three coins on each pan and weigh them. Then weigh any two coins from the lighter pan; the fake is the lighter coin, but if the pans balance, the fake is the coin that wasn't weighed.)

Problem-Solving Strategies Ask students who have solved the Problem of the Day to share how they solved it and any strategies they used.

MENTAL MATH Have students do these problems mentally.

a. $4 \times 700 = (2800)$ b. $4 \times 70 = (280)$

c. $70 - 40 = (30)$ d. $700 - 40 = (660)$

e. $500 \times 12 = (6000)$ f. $50 \times 12 = (600)$

g. $500 - 12 = (488)$ h. $500 - 120 = (380)$

Estimating Volume

Making good estimates takes practice. The more practice you get, the more reasonable estimates you'll be able to make.

How well can you estimate relative volume? See if you get better at it as you do this activity.

Look at a group of containers of different sizes and shapes.

❶ Write down which container you think holds the least amount. Then write which one you think holds the next least amount. Keep going until you have listed all the containers in order from least to greatest volume in the table on page 497.

❷ Estimate how many times you would have to fill up the smallest container to equal the volume of the largest container. Record your estimate in the table.

❸ Use water to check your estimate for problem 2. Fill the smallest container and pour the contents into the larger container. Record how many times you did this before the large container was full. You may need to estimate a fraction of the smaller container for the last pouring. Record your result in the table.

❹ Estimate how many times you would have to fill up the smallest container to equal the volume of each of the other containers. Record your estimates in the table.

❺ Use water to check your estimates. Record your results in the table.

❻ Use these results to see if you put the containers in the right order from smallest to largest.

COOPERATIVE LEARNING You may wish to have students work collaboratively on the estimating activity. If so, make sure all participants have assigned tasks, such as collecting and labeling the containers, making and recording estimates, checking estimates by filling containers with water, summarizing results, presenting results, and cleaning up afterward.

Literature Connection Have students read *Brain Teasers and Mind-Benders* by Ann Axworthy. They can use the optical illusion activities from this book to change (perhaps) their perception of measurement.

RETEACHING

Other than guiding students through further estimating practice, no reteaching is needed.

*available separately

Use a computer or other means to draw a table like this. Make one row for each container.

Container	Estimated volume (in smallest containers)	Actual volume (in smallest containers)

How good were your estimates? Did they become more accurate as you measured more containers? How did you make your estimates? Record your answers in your Math Journal.

Discuss this question with your classmates.

Why do you think some things that we buy in the supermarket come in odd-shaped bottles?

Make a bottle display for your class or school. Collect different kinds of empty bottles and wash off their labels. Determine exactly how many ounces each contains and then label each bottle. Put the bottles in order from least to greatest capacity.

When you get a new bottle, estimate how many ounces it contains before measuring to find out. Then put the new bottle into your collection.

Unit 6   Lesson 141 • **497**

---

❷ Teach

Using the Student Pages Do the activity outlined on pages 496 and 497 with the class. Place ten or more **containers*** on your desk or on a table where everyone can see them. Label containers in some way (e.g., with letters). Rather than having each group of students check the predictions, you may want to do all of the pouring in front of the class. You may want to use a **funnel** and colored **water** for this activity.

In most groups the following patterns will emerge. Volumes of short, squat containers (as in the shape of a sphere or cube) are underestimated. Volumes of tall, thin containers are overestimated. Volumes of small containers are overestimated, whereas volumes of large containers are underestimated. Volumes of containers that are conical or smaller at the midsection than at the top or bottom are overestimated.

You may wish to raise the following points as well during the discussion. Because many people tend to make poor estimates of volume, it is advisable, whenever possible, to read labels or otherwise check volumes directly rather than trust rough impressions. Practice in estimating and checking volumes may help people make more accurate volume estimations.

❸ Wrap-Up ⏱ 5 MINUTES

In Closing To summarize the lesson, ask students how they were able to make better estimates after some practice.

Portfolio Assessment Have students write a description of their progress as volume estimators. Ask them to include any estimation strategies they have developed.

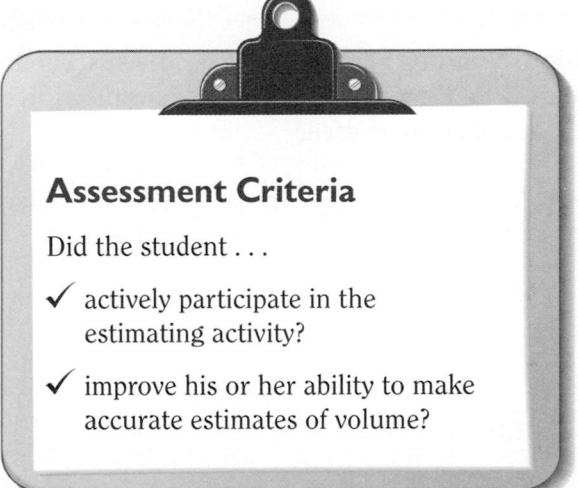

Assessment Criteria

Did the student . . .

✓ actively participate in the estimating activity?

✓ improve his or her ability to make accurate estimates of volume?

Homework Have students estimate the volumes of several containers at home with a family member.

PRACTICE p. 141

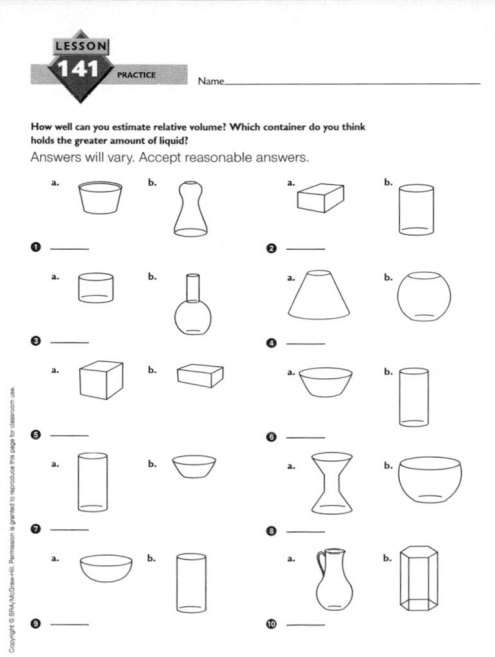

ENRICHMENT p. 141

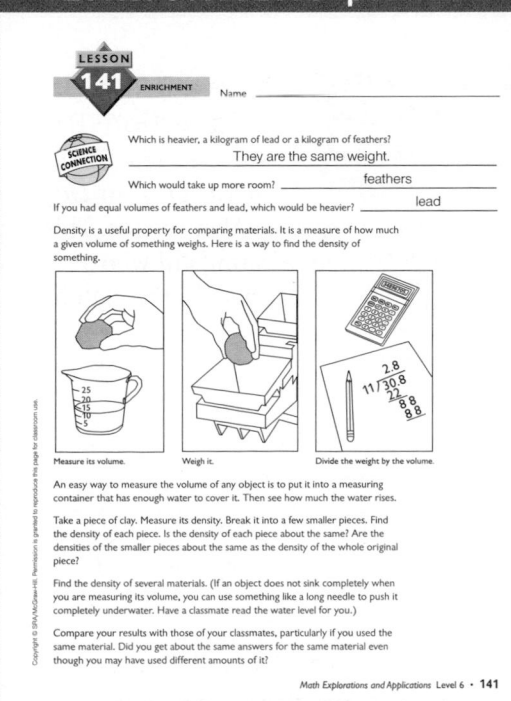

*available separately

LESSON 142
Keeping Sharp

Student Edition pages 498–501

LESSON 142
Keeping Sharp

Keep in shape by practicing these computations with fractions.

Completely reduce each fraction.

① $\frac{2}{4}$ **$\frac{1}{2}$** ② $\frac{3}{9}$ **$\frac{1}{3}$** ③ $\frac{3}{12}$ **$\frac{1}{4}$** ④ $\frac{12}{15}$ **$\frac{4}{5}$** ⑤ $\frac{4}{6}$ **$\frac{2}{3}$**

⑥ $\frac{8}{24}$ **$\frac{1}{3}$** ⑦ $\frac{6}{8}$ **$\frac{3}{4}$** ⑧ $\frac{6}{12}$ **$\frac{1}{2}$** ⑨ $\frac{3}{15}$ **$\frac{1}{5}$** ⑩ $\frac{4}{10}$ **$\frac{2}{5}$**

⑪ $\frac{6}{24}$ **$\frac{1}{4}$** ⑫ $\frac{12}{24}$ **$\frac{1}{2}$** ⑬ $\frac{10}{24}$ **$\frac{5}{12}$** ⑭ $\frac{15}{18}$ **$\frac{5}{6}$** ⑮ $\frac{12}{20}$ **$\frac{3}{5}$**

Add. Completely reduce each answer.

⑯ $\frac{1}{2}+\frac{1}{2}$ **1** ⑰ $\frac{1}{3}+\frac{1}{2}$ **$\frac{5}{6}$** ⑱ $\frac{2}{5}+\frac{1}{3}$ **$\frac{11}{15}$** ⑲ $\frac{3}{4}+\frac{1}{3}$ **$1\frac{1}{12}$**

⑳ $\frac{7}{12}+\frac{1}{3}$ **$\frac{11}{12}$** ㉑ $\frac{3}{4}+\frac{3}{4}$ **$1\frac{1}{2}$** ㉒ $\frac{2}{3}+\frac{1}{4}$ **$\frac{11}{12}$** ㉓ $\frac{1}{4}+\frac{1}{5}$ **$\frac{9}{20}$**

㉔ $\frac{2}{3}+\frac{1}{2}$ **$1\frac{1}{6}$** ㉕ $\frac{1}{6}+\frac{1}{3}$ **$\frac{1}{2}$** ㉖ $\frac{1}{4}+\frac{1}{2}$ **$\frac{3}{4}$** ㉗ $\frac{1}{5}+\frac{1}{3}$ **$\frac{8}{15}$**

Subtract. Completely reduce each answer.

㉘ $\frac{3}{4}-\frac{1}{2}$ **$\frac{1}{4}$** ㉙ $\frac{2}{3}-\frac{1}{6}$ **$\frac{1}{2}$** ㉚ $\frac{2}{5}-\frac{1}{10}$ **$\frac{3}{10}$** ㉛ $\frac{5}{6}-\frac{2}{3}$ **$\frac{1}{6}$**

㉜ $\frac{7}{8}-\frac{3}{8}$ **$\frac{1}{2}$** ㉝ $\frac{3}{4}-\frac{1}{8}$ **$\frac{5}{8}$** ㉞ $\frac{2}{3}-\frac{1}{4}$ **$\frac{5}{12}$** ㉟ $\frac{3}{5}-\frac{1}{3}$ **$\frac{4}{15}$**

㊱ $\frac{5}{8}-\frac{1}{4}$ **$\frac{3}{8}$** ㊲ $\frac{2}{3}-\frac{1}{2}$ **$\frac{1}{6}$** ㊳ $\frac{5}{9}-\frac{1}{3}$ **$\frac{2}{9}$** ㊴ $\frac{7}{10}-\frac{2}{5}$ **$\frac{3}{10}$**

Solve the following problems.

㊵ Pedro asked each of his classmates what his or her favorite sport was. Here is what Pedro's list looked like.

Favorite Sport	Number of People
basketball	8
football	4
swimming	4
baseball	3
soccer	3
tennis	2

a. What fraction of the students liked basketball best? What fraction liked tennis best? $\frac{8}{24}$ (or $\frac{1}{3}$); $\frac{2}{24}$ (or $\frac{1}{12}$)

b. If you made a fraction for each sport and added the fractions, what would the total be? **1**

LESSON PLANNER

Objectives

▶ to provide practice in reducing, adding, and subtracting fractions

▶ to provide practice with applications of fractions

▶ to help students develop the broad ability to use mathematical common sense

Context of the Lesson This lesson provides a pause in the sequence of lessons on geometry and measurement and reviews operations involving fractions. It also contains the last part of "On the Move," a three-part Thinking Story.

MANIPULATIVES
fraction models* (optional)

Program Resources
Practice Master 142

Enrichment Master 142

For career connections: Careers and Math*

For extra practice: CD-ROM* Lesson 142

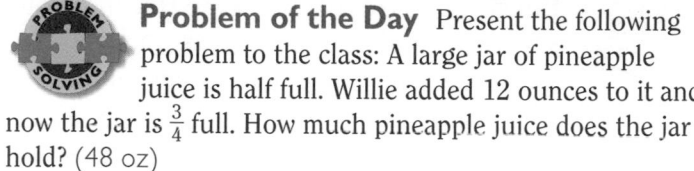

① Warp-Up
5 MINUTES

Problem of the Day Present the following problem to the class: A large jar of pineapple juice is half full. Willie added 12 ounces to it and now the jar is $\frac{3}{4}$ full. How much pineapple juice does the jar hold? (48 oz)

Problem-Solving Strategies Ask students who have solved the Problem of the Day to share how they solved it and any strategies they used.

MENTAL MATH Ask students to give the greatest common factor for each of the following pairs of numbers:

a. 4 and 8 (4)

b. 5 and 12 (1)

c. 6 and 20 (2)

d. 12 and 18 (6)

Literature Connection Have students read *Erin McEwan, Your Days Are Numbered* by Alan Ritchie. This book is about a young girl who improves her math skills through her new job.

Work in groups. Discuss your answers and how you figured them out. Then compare your answers with those of other groups.
Answers are in margin.

❶ If all your furniture were made of very light plastic foam, would Spaceway Movers be a good choice? Why or why not?

❷ Make a list of common household things that are heavy for their size.

❸ Make a list of common household things that are very light for their size.

Unit 6 Lesson 142 • **501**

❸ Wrap-Up

In Closing To summarize the lesson, ask students to name a possession of theirs that has a high density and therefore a high weight per unit volume.

Performance Assessment Ask students to express the sum and the difference of $\frac{7}{8}$ and $\frac{1}{4}$. $\left(\frac{9}{8} \text{ or } 1\frac{1}{8}, \frac{5}{8}\right)$

Assessment Criteria

Did the student . . .

✓ correctly answer at least 75% of the mixed-practice problems?

✓ demonstrate problem-solving skills when working on the word problems on page 499?

✓ contribute to the Thinking Story discussion?

✓ understand the concept of density as presented in the Thinking Story?

Homework Have students select three items from their home that they estimate to have a combined weight of five pounds. Students should weigh the items to see how close their estimate was.

Meeting Individual Needs
Challenge your more advanced students to formulate a problem for others to solve that involves finding the area of an irregular figure (such as a square with a triangle taken out of it) and uses only fractional numbers. Students can work in groups to solve each other's problems.

PRACTICE p. 142

LESSON 142 PRACTICE   Name_____

Completely reduce each fraction.

① $\frac{10}{12}$ $\frac{5}{6}$ ② $\frac{15}{18}$ $\frac{5}{6}$ ③ $\frac{45}{50}$ $\frac{9}{10}$

④ $\frac{4}{8}$ $\frac{1}{2}$ ⑤ $\frac{20}{30}$ $\frac{2}{3}$ ⑥ $\frac{96}{104}$ $\frac{12}{13}$

Add. Completely reduce your answer.

⑦ $\frac{5}{8}+\frac{3}{4}$ $1\frac{3}{8}$ ⑧ $\frac{2}{3}+\frac{1}{4}$ $\frac{11}{12}$ ⑨ $\frac{7}{8}+\frac{2}{3}$ $1\frac{13}{24}$

⑩ $\frac{5}{6}+\frac{1}{3}$ $1\frac{1}{6}$ ⑪ $\frac{7}{10}+\frac{4}{5}$ $1\frac{1}{2}$ ⑫ $\frac{5}{6}+\frac{3}{4}$ $1\frac{7}{12}$

Subtract. Completely reduce your answer.

⑬ $\frac{7}{8}-\frac{1}{3}$ $\frac{13}{24}$ ⑭ $\frac{4}{5}-\frac{1}{10}$ $\frac{7}{10}$ ⑮ $\frac{3}{4}-\frac{1}{3}$ $\frac{5}{12}$

⑯ $\frac{5}{6}-\frac{1}{2}$ $\frac{1}{3}$ ⑰ $\frac{9}{10}-\frac{1}{3}$ $\frac{17}{30}$ ⑱ $\frac{9}{10}-\frac{1}{5}$ $\frac{7}{10}$

Solve these problems.

⑲ Find the area of a painting that measures $16\frac{1}{2}$ inches by 12 inches.   198 square inches

⑳ Find the area of a field that measures $24\frac{3}{4}$ yards by 50 yards. $1237\frac{1}{2}$ square yards

142 • *Math Explorations and Applications* Level 6

ENRICHMENT p. 142

LESSON 142 ENRICHMENT   Name _____

Archimedes was a famous Greek mathematician and scientist. He lived in Syracuse and did much work for the king, Hiero.

The king once gave a goldsmith a certain amount of gold to be made into a crown. When the crown was finished, Hiero became suspicious that the goldsmith had put in some silver, which was much less expensive, in place of part of the gold. So Hiero asked Archimedes to find out if the goldsmith had cheated him.

Archimedes decided to compare the volume of the crown with the volume of the same amount of gold that Hiero had given the goldsmith. But he didn't know how to measure the volume of the crown.

Archimedes thought about this for a long while. One day as he started to take a bath, he noticed that the water overflowed as he got into the tub. He quickly reasoned that if he put the crown into a full container of water, he could measure the water that overflowed to find the volume of the crown.

He was so excited that he got out of the tub and, without bothering to dress, ran into the street, shouting, "Eureka! Eureka!" *Eureka* is a Greek word that means "I have found it."

Suppose Hiero gave the goldsmith 1000 grams of gold. Now he suspects that the crown, which does weigh 1000 grams, is half gold and half silver. Gold weighs about 19.3 grams per cubic centimeter, and silver weighs about 10.5 grams per cubic centimeter.

a. How can Archimedes find out if the crown is pure gold?
  Measure the volume of the crown and compare it to the volume of 1000 grams of gold.

b. If the crown is pure gold, what will its volume be? (Use a calculator.)
  about 51.8 cubic centimeters

c. What will the volume of the crown be if it is 500 grams of gold and 500 grams of silver? (Use a calculator.)
  about 73.5 cubic centimeters

142 • *Math Explorations and Applications* Level 6

Unit 6 Lesson 142 **501**

Angles and Rotation

LESSON PLANNER

Objective

▶ to review the meaning of *angle* as an amount of rotation, and of terms indicating angle size—*acute*, *right*, and *obtuse*

Context of the Lesson This is the first of six lessons on angles and their measurement.

MANIPULATIVES   **Program Resources**

none   Practice Master 143

Enrichment Master 143

For extra practice:
CD-ROM* Lesson 143

❶ Warm-Up

Problem of the Day Present the following problem to the class: Study Figures 1 and 2. Think about how Figure 1 was changed to form Figure 2. Then look at Figure 3. Draw how it would look if it were changed in the same way.

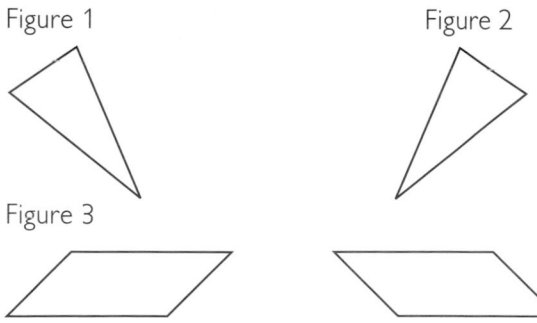

Figure 1   Figure 2

Figure 3

(The figure was reflected.)

Problem-Solving Strategies Ask students who have solved the Problem of the Day to share how they solved it and any strategies they used.

 Explain to students that each pair of angles has a combined measurement of 90. Given the first measurement, ask them to give the size of the second.

(continued on page 503)

Angles and Rotation

People find it useful to talk about directions and to measure differences between directions.

On a compass, north is the direction toward the North Pole. South is the opposite direction.

The east-west line is perpendicular to the north-south line.

Northeast is halfway between north and east. Southeast is halfway between south and east, and so on.

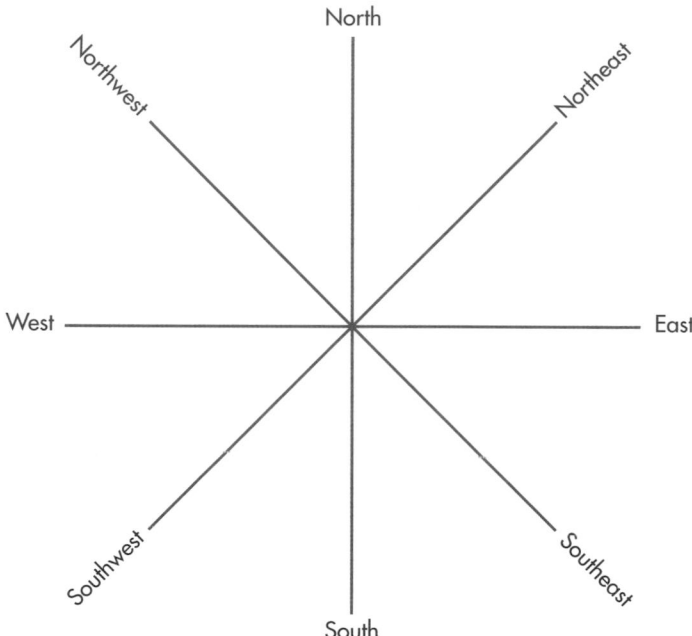

Literature Connection

Students may enjoy the section on triangles in *Mathematics* by Irving Adler.

*available separately

Suppose you are facing north and want to face west. To do that with the least possible change in your position, you would make $\frac{1}{4}$ of a complete turn. That's the least turn you could make.

What fraction of a complete turn do you need to make to go from

1 facing north to facing south? $\frac{1}{2}$

2 facing south to facing east? $\frac{1}{4}$

3 facing north to facing east? $\frac{1}{4}$

4 facing east to facing north? $\frac{1}{4}$

5 facing north to facing northwest? $\frac{1}{8}$

6 facing east to facing northwest? $\frac{3}{8}$

7 facing west to facing northeast? $\frac{3}{8}$

8 facing northwest to facing southeast? $\frac{1}{2}$

9 facing north to facing northeast? $\frac{1}{8}$

10 facing south to facing northeast? $\frac{3}{8}$

An angle that is less than $\frac{1}{4}$ of a complete turn is an **acute angle.**

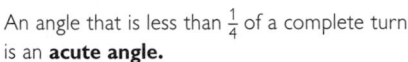

An angle that is $\frac{1}{4}$ of a turn is a **right angle.**

An angle that is between $\frac{1}{4}$ of a turn and $\frac{1}{2}$ of a turn is an **obtuse angle.**

11 What would an angle that is $\frac{1}{2}$ of a complete turn look like? **a straight line**

12 What is the least turn that would leave you facing the same direction as $\frac{3}{4}$ of a complete turn? $\frac{1}{4}$ **of a turn**

Unit 6   Lesson 143 • **503**

Technology Connection Refer students to the software *Cosmic Golf* from Milliken (Mac, for grades 4–8) for practice with angles, estimation, and distance.

Mental Math (continued)

a. 40, _____ (50)   **b.** 55, _____ (35)

c. 60, _____ (30)   **d.** 45, _____ (45)

e. 75, _____ (15)   **f.** 65, _____ (25)

g. 15, _____ (75)   **h.** 12, _____ (78)

❷ Teach

Using the Student Pages As you go over the material on pages 502 and 503, demonstrate or ask volunteers to demonstrate which direction in the classroom is north, which is south, and so on. Then have a student stand and face north and ask him or her to turn and face some other specified direction. This student should turn in whatever direction requires less turning—either clockwise or counterclockwise—so that no turn will be greater than 180 degrees. Ask the class to notice what fraction of a complete turn the student has made. Repeat this activity several times, with other volunteers, focusing on the four major directions and on right-angle turns. Ask a few students to face north at the same time. Then ask each one to turn a different amount; for example, one to turn to the west and the other to the south. Have the class determine who made the greater turn.

Do a few of the problems on page 503 with the class, and then assign the rest for students to complete independently. When they have finished, draw some angles on the chalkboard and ask students to compare their sizes. Be sure to include some obtuse angles that have shorter sides than some acute angles do. Emphasize that the size of angles is compared by comparing the amount of turning needed between the two sides, not by comparing the lengths of the sides. In fact, you can point out that the sides of angles are *rays*, which can be thought of as going on forever in the direction away from the vertex. Review the definitions of the angles at the bottom of the page.

◆ LESSON 143 Angles and Rotation

Teach

Using the Student Pages Have students work individually or in pairs to identify and classify the different angles in your classroom and on pages 504 and 505. Then discuss students' answers.

For problem 17, ask students to classify the letters according to the segments used to draw them and to disregard the angles created by the thickness of the letters. (For example, they should not consider "K" as having right angles.)

◆ LESSON 143 Angles and Rotation

Discuss these with your classmates.

13 Look around your classroom. Do you see any right angles? Describe several right angles in your classroom. **Examples: corner of a book, corner of a table, corner of the room**

14 Think about angles that are formed by things outside your classroom, such as street intersections, the sides of objects such as rugs, and so on. Describe several that are right angles. **Examples: the corner of a building, the corner of a store window, the corner of some street signs**

15 Are there any acute angles in your classroom or hallway? Describe at least five acute angles that are either inside or outside your classroom. **Examples: a partly open book, an ice-cream cone, a tent**

16 Describe at least five obtuse angles that are formed by real objects. **Examples: the corners of a stop sign, the angle between the hood and windshield of a car, a wide open door**

17 Consider the following letters:

A E F H I

K L M N T

V W X Y Z

a. List the letters that have acute angles. **A, K, M, N, V, W, X, Y, Z**

b. List the letters that have obtuse angles. **A, K, X, Y**

c. List the letters that have right angles. **E, F, H, L, T**

d. Can a letter have more than one kind of angle? **yes**

 **Language Arts Connection** Students may enjoy creating humorous definitions for the terms *acute, right,* and *obtuse* that can help them remember which is which. For example, thinking of an acute angle as "a cute little angle" may help students recall that it is the one that is smaller than a right angle. Obtuse sounds similar to "obese" and may help students remember that an obtuse is larger than a right angle.

 Help students who are having difficulty distinguishing one kind of angle from another to use the corner of a sheet of paper or piece of cardboard as a right angle. Have them line up one edge of the known right angle with one side of the unknown angle and then see if the other edge is visible (obtuse), completely hidden (acute), or exactly along the edge (right).

Tell whether each angle is acute, right, or obtuse.

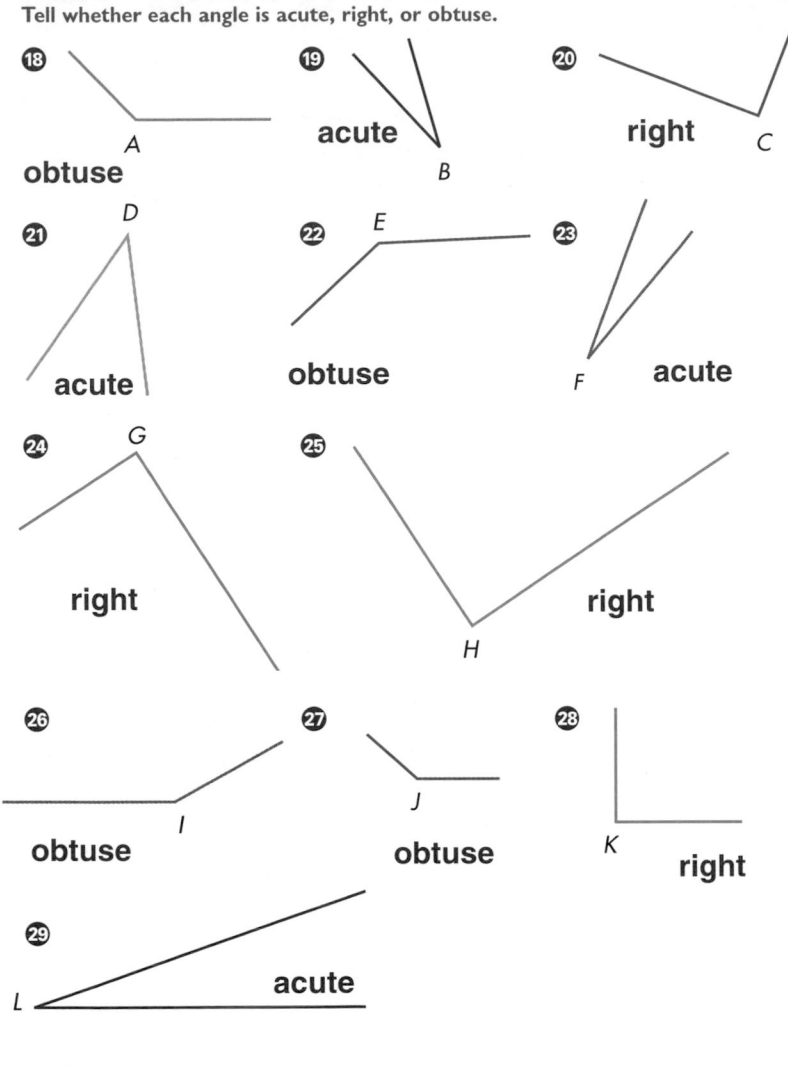

18 obtuse

19 acute

20 right

21 acute

22 obtuse

23 acute

24 right

25 right

26 obtuse

27 obtuse

28 right

29 acute

Solve.

30 Which is larger, ∠J or ∠K? Remember, when we talk about the size of an angle, we are talking about how far you must turn if you are facing along one side and you want to face along the other side. **angle J**

Unit 6 Lesson 143 • **505**

PRACTICE p. 143

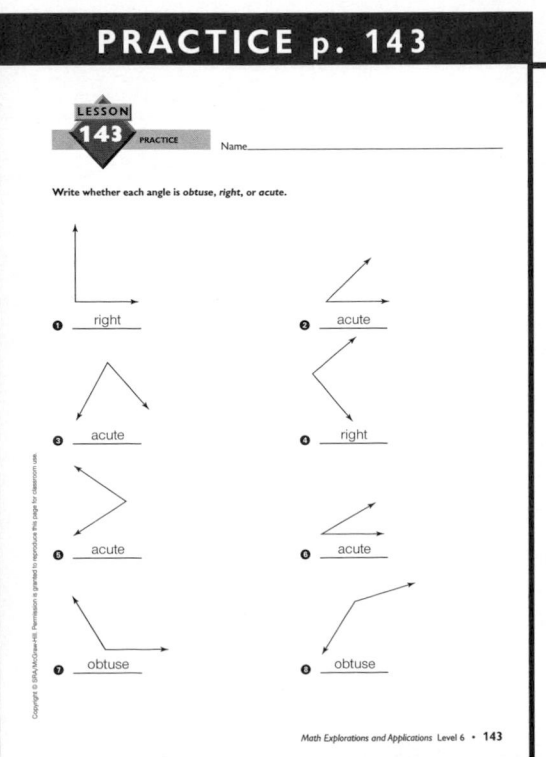

LESSON **143** PRACTICE   Name_____

Write whether each angle is obtuse, right, or acute.

1. right
2. acute
3. acute
4. right
5. acute
6. acute
7. obtuse
8. obtuse

Math Explorations and Applications Level 6 • **143**

ENRICHMENT p. 143

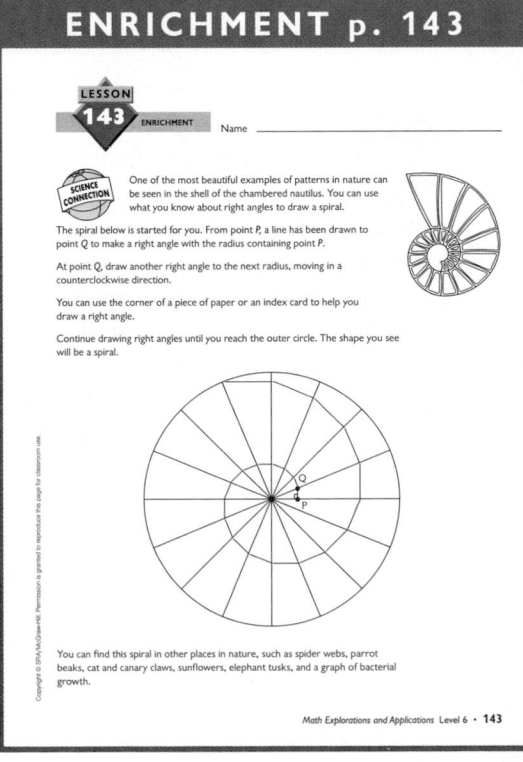

LESSON **143** ENRICHMENT   Name_____

SCIENCE CONNECTION

One of the most beautiful examples of patterns in nature can be seen in the shell of the chambered nautilus. You can use what you know about right angles to draw a spiral.

The spiral below is started for you. From point P, a line has been drawn to point Q to make a right angle with the radius containing point P.

At point Q, draw another right angle to the next radius, moving in a counterclockwise direction.

You can use the corner of a piece of paper or an index card to help you draw a right angle.

Continue drawing right angles until you reach the outer circle. The shape you see will be a spiral.

You can find this spiral in other places in nature, such as spider webs, parrot beaks, cat and canary claws, sunflowers, elephant tusks, and a graph of bacterial growth.

Math Explorations and Applications Level 6 • **143**

---

③ **Wrap-Up**

In Closing To summarize the lesson, ask students to define each of the three kinds of angles introduced in the lesson and to draw a sketch for each description.

 **Performance Assessment** Draw several examples of acute, right, and obtuse angles on the chalkboard or using an overhead projector. Present them in different orientations. Ask students to sketch each and identify it as acute, right, or obtuse.

Assessment Criteria

Did the student . . .

✓ demonstrate understanding of the concept of an angle and of how to compare sizes of angles?

✓ understand that the lengths of the sides of an angle have no bearing on the size of that angle?

✓ understand the distinctions among acute, right, and obtuse angles?

Homework Have students identify examples of acute, right, and obtuse angles in their homes. They can add this information to their Math Journals.

LOOKING AHEAD Students will need protractors for Lesson 144.

SPECIAL NEEDS **Meeting Individual Needs**
Students who confuse length of sides of angles with the size of angles may benefit from using the hands of a clock to show different angles. Ask questions such as, "What kind of angle is shown when it is 5:00?" (obtuse)

LESSON 144
Measuring Angles

Student Edition pages 506–509

LESSON PLANNER

Objectives

▶ to review measuring angles with a protractor

▶ to classify triangles by the kinds of angles each has

Context of the Lesson This is the second of six lessons on angles and their measurement.

 **MANIPULATIVES**

protractors* for each student and one for use with an overhead projector

toothpicks

Program Resources

Reteaching Master

Practice Master 144

Enrichment Master 144

For extra practice:
CD-ROM* Lesson 144
Cumulative Review, page 584

① Warb-Up ⏱ 5 MINUTES

Problem of the Day Present the following problem: Arrange six **toothpicks** in order to form six congruent triangles.

Problem-Solving Strategies Ask students who have solved the Problem of the Day to share how they solved it and any strategies they used.

 Select a mental math drill from among those done previously, according to the needs of the class.

LESSON 144
Measuring Angles

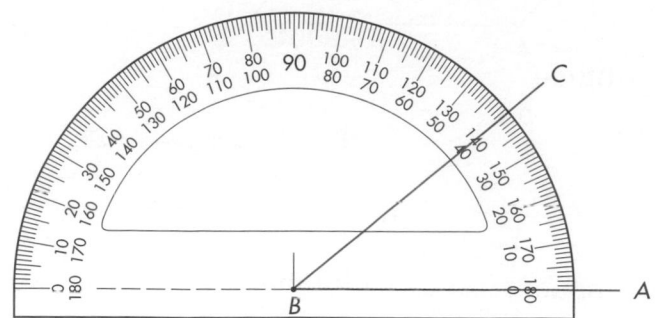

We measure angles with a *protractor*. To measure ∠ABC with the protractor shown above, follow these steps:

A. Place the protractor as shown. The small hole is over the **vertex** of the angle (point B). The broken line on the protractor lies on one side of the angle (side BA).

B. Look at the number through which the other side of the angle (BC) passes. There are two numbers, 40 and 140. If the angle is acute, use the lesser number (40). If the angle is obtuse, use the greater number (140). Since this angle is acute, we use the lesser number (40).

C. The number you found in step B is the measure of the angle in degrees. So the measure of ∠ABC is 40 degrees (40°).

Your protractor may look a little different from the one above, but the steps in using it should be almost the same. Be sure that one side of the angle is passing through 0°.

Remember, we can label an angle by its vertex (for example, ∠B). But we can also use three points to label an angle. The vertex must be the middle letter in the angle's name. The angle shown on this page could be called ∠B or ∠ABC or ∠CBA. We say its measure is 40° by writing ∠B = 40° or ∠ABC = 40° or ∠CBA = 40°.

506 · Geometry

 **Geography Connection** Explain to students that lines of latitude and longitude are measured using degrees and parts of degrees. Have them research to find out more about how latitude and longitude are measured. Have them find out the coordinates of your location. Then ask students to share their findings with the class.

*available separately

Measure each of these four angles to the nearest degree.

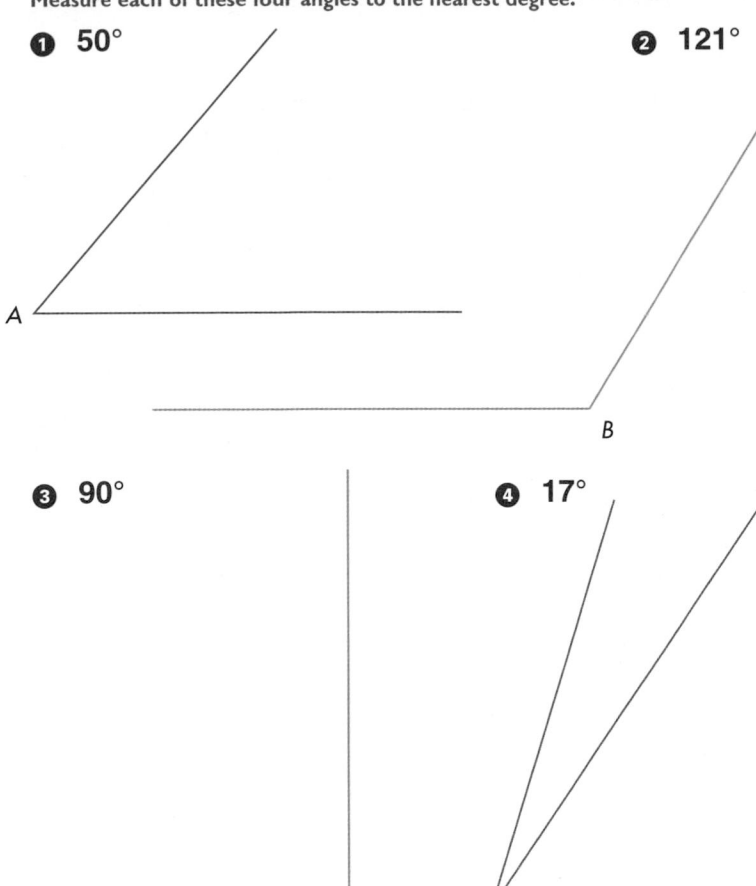

❶ 50°

❷ 121°

❸ 90°

❹ 17°

The most densely populated country on earth is **Monaco**, with a population of **31,719** and an area of **0.75 square miles.** If the United States were as densely populated as Monaco, the population would be over **140 billion.**

Unit 6   Lesson 144 • **507**

❷ Teach

Using the Student Pages Go over the steps for measuring an angle as given on page 506. Then ask students to use **protractors*** to measure the angles on page 507 on their own. Have students compare measurements with a classmate. If there is disagreement, students should discuss the differences and then watch each other as they carefully repeat the measurement. You may wish to help as needed.

> *. . . if we want students to be really good at a particular skill, or if we want them to really remember and understand a concept, we must arrange for them to practice.*
>
> –Stephen S. Willoughby,
> *Mathematics Education for a Changing World*

Technology Connection Refer students to the software *Classroom Grade Level Math Programs* from Jostens Home Learning (Mac, IBM for grades K–8) for practice with geometric figures: points, lines, angles, angle measures, polygons, and circles.

*available separately

Unit 6 Lesson 144 **507**

◆ LESSON 144 Measuring Angles

Teach

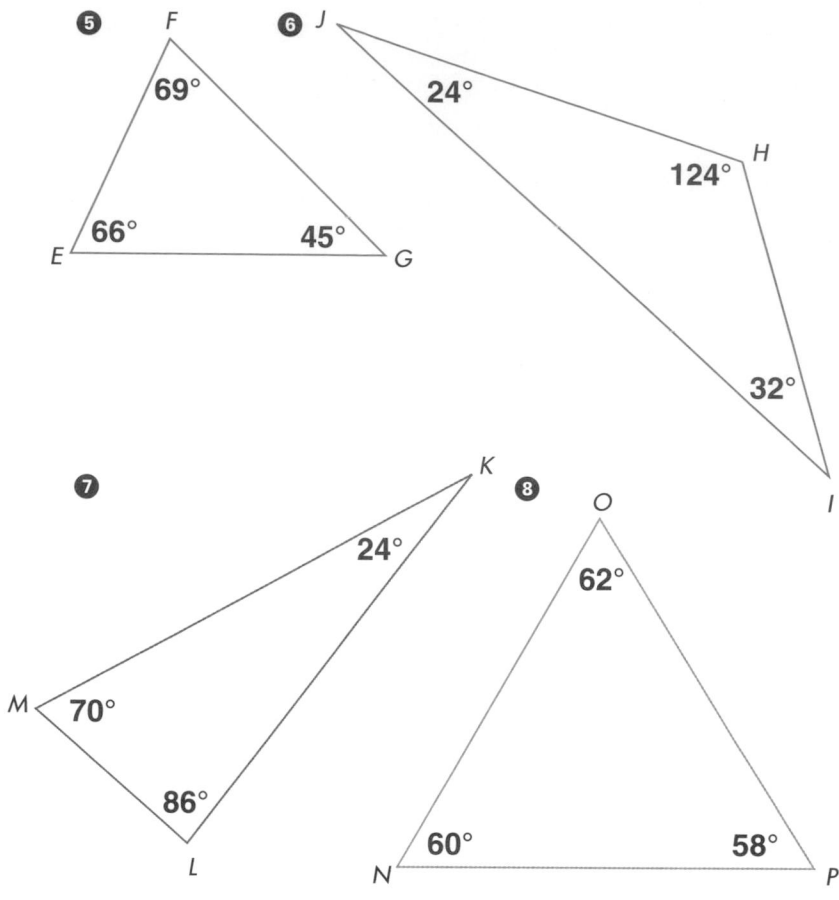

Using the Student Pages Encourage students to work together to help each other measure the angles in the triangles on page 508. They may find it helpful to trace each angle before measuring it. You may wish to challenge students to try to construct a triangle in which the sum of the angles is not 180° (and is far enough from 180° so that measurement error cannot account for the difference).

Students sometimes have difficulty using a **protractor***. Some can be assisted by peers; some will require your involvement. The following difficulties are common:

1. Students have difficulty with lining up one side of the angle with the dotted baseline on the protractor or with placing the small hole of the protractor over the vertex of the angle. Supervised practice is necessary.

2. Students are reading the incorrect number from the scale. Three remedies for this are (a) Have each student start by identifying the 0° measure as being the side of the angle on the baseline, then count by tens toward the other side of the angle; (b) Ask in advance, "Is the angle acute, right, or obtuse?" If it is acute, it must be less than 90°; if it is obtuse, it must be more than 90°; (c) Always use the same scale.

3. Students are reading the scale imprecisely. This may be part of a general difficulty with reading scales. To help, ask students to find the two multiples of 10 that are closest to the measure of the angle. For example, they might say the angle is between 120° and 130°, then count from the smaller number toward the side of the angle until they reach it.

Students can form small groups to answer the problems and classify the triangles on page 509. Ask students if it is possible for any triangle to have two obtuse angles or for a right triangle to have an obtuse angle. (no; no)

◆ LESSON 144 Measuring Angles

Measure the three angles in each triangle.

⑤ F 69° E 66° G 45°

⑥ J 24° H 124° I 32°

⑦ K 24° M 70° L 86°

⑧ O 62° N 60° P 58°

⑨ Add the measures of the three angles in △EFG. What is the sum? **180°**

⑩ What is the sum of the measure of the angles of △HIJ? of △KLM? of △NOP? **All are 180°.**

Literature Connection Have students try some of the measuring activities in the chapters about angles in *Math for Every Kid* by Janice VanCleave.

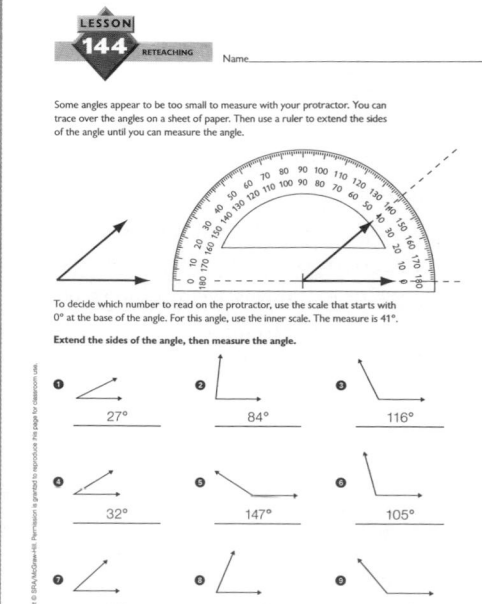

RETEACHING p. 49

LESSON 144 RETEACHING Name_____

Some angles appear to be too small to measure with your protractor. You can trace over the angles on a sheet of paper. Then use a ruler to extend the sides of the angle until you can measure the angle.

To decide which number to read on the protractor, use the scale that starts with 0° at the base of the angle. For this angle, use the inner scale. The measure is 41°.

Extend the sides of the angle, then measure the angle.

❶ 27°	❷ 84°	❸ 116°
❹ 32°	❺ 147°	❻ 105°
❼ 43°	❽ 67°	❾ 130°

Math Explorations and Applications Level 6 • 49

*available separately

⑰ no; no; a triangle must be either obtuse, right, or acute

Assume the sum of the angles of a triangle is always 180 degrees. You will see why this must be so in Lesson 146.

⑪ If one of the angles of a triangle is obtuse, what can you say about the other two angles of the triangle? **They are both acute.**

⑫ If one of the angles of a triangle is a right angle, what can you say about the other two angles? **They are both acute.**

⑬ If one of the angles of a triangle is acute, what can you say about the other two angles of the triangle? **One is acute, the other could be right, acute, or obtuse.**

Any triangle that has an obtuse angle in it is called an **obtuse triangle**. Any triangle that has a right angle in it is called a right triangle. If a triangle has no obtuse angle and no right angle (that is, it has three acute angles) it is called an **acute triangle**.

Look at the triangles below, and complete the following exercises.

⑭ Make a list of the triangles that are obtuse triangles. **D, E, H, L**

⑮ Make a list of the triangles that are right triangles. **A, C, G, K**

⑯ Make a list of the triangles that are acute triangles. **B, F, I, J**

⑰ Did any triangle appear in more than one list? Can you draw a triangle that would appear in more than one of the lists? Explain.

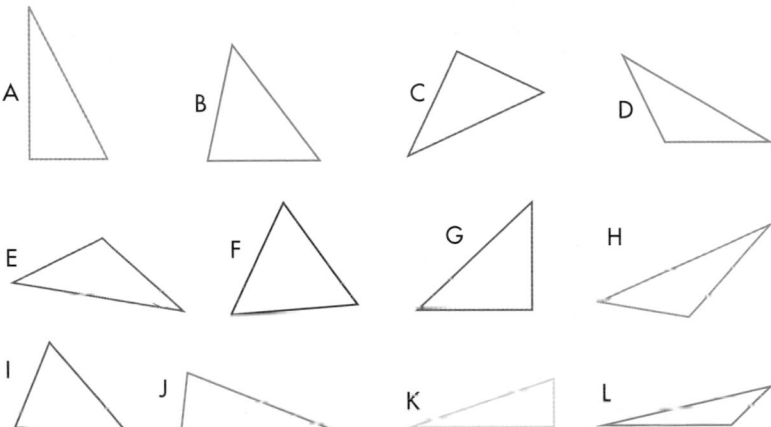

Use the Cumulative Review on page 584 after this lesson.

Unit 6 Lesson 144 • **509**

---

③ Wrap-Up ⏱ 5 MINUTES

In Closing To summarize the lesson, ask a student to demonstrate how to use a protractor.

Informal Assessment Observe students as they measure the angles with their protractors. Watch to see that they are following the correct procedure for placing the protractor on the angle and that they are reading the correct numbers on the protractor's scale.

Assessment Criteria

Did the student . . .

✓ use the protractor correctly to measure the size of the angles?

✓ understand the distinctions among right triangles, acute triangles, and obtuse triangles?

Homework Have students draw a right scalene triangle, an obtuse isosceles triangle, and a right isosceles triangle. Students can include these labeled drawings in their Math Portfolios.

LEARNING STYLES **Meeting Individual Needs**
A measuring problem students commonly experience is to let the protractor slip after it has been placed in the correct position but before they have read the scale. Guide students to work on flat, firm surfaces and to use both hands. To reduce slippage, they can firmly place at least two fingers of one hand on both the protractor and the writing surface.

PRACTICE p. 144

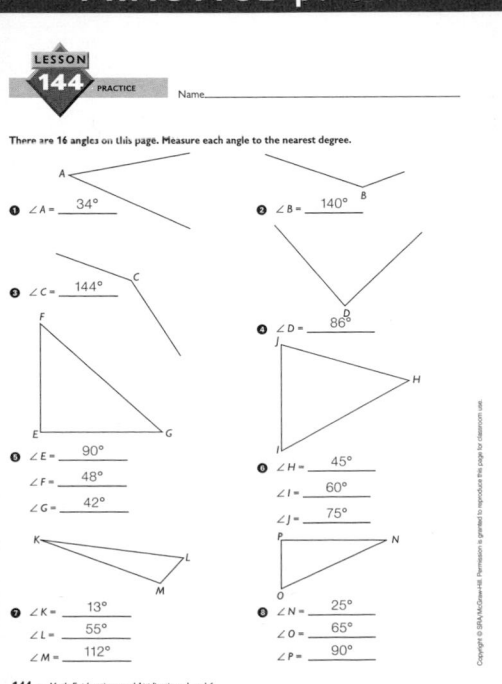

ENRICHMENT p. 144

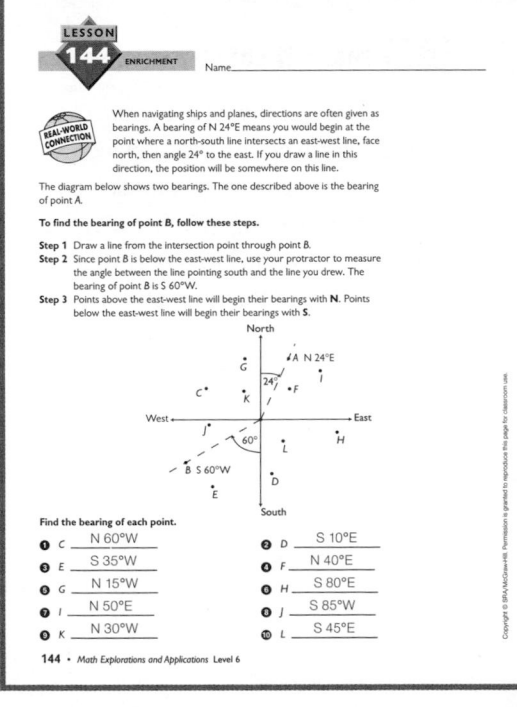

*available separately

Unit 6 Lesson 144 **509**

Corresponding Angles and Vertical Angles

EXPLORE

LESSON
145

Corresponding Angles and Vertical Angles

LESSON PLANNER

Objectives

▶ to present some relationships among the angles formed by a line intersecting two parallel lines

▶ to provide practice in measuring angles

Context of the Lesson This is the third of six lessons on angles and their measurement.

✋ MANIPULATIVES **Program Resources**

protractors* Practice Master 145

Enrichment Master 145

For extra practice:
CD-ROM* Lesson 145

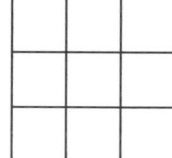

❶ Warm-Up

5 MINUTES

Problem of the Day Present the following problem to students: In this diagram, the area of each of the small squares is 9 square units. What is the perimeter of the large square? (36 units)

Problem-Solving Strategies Ask students who have solved the Problem of the Day to share how they solved it and any strategies they used.

Have students tell whether an angle having each of the numbers of degrees shown below is an acute angle, a right angle, or an obtuse angle. As you call out each number of degrees, students can answer "a," "r," or "o."

a.	25 (a)	**b.**	90 (r)
c.	45 (a)	**d.**	100 (o)
e.	95 (o)	**f.**	145 (o)
g.	115 (o)	**h.**	40 (a)
i.	70 (a)	**j.**	89 (a)

Remember: Two lines that "go in the same direction" are called parallel lines.

Because we cannot draw an entire line on a sheet of paper, we indicate a line with an arrow at each end of a line segment to show that it goes on forever in both directions.

If a line crosses two parallel lines, the angles formed in corresponding positions have the same measure. These pairs of angles are called *corresponding angles*.

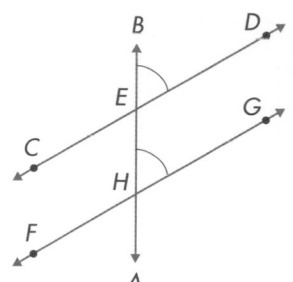

Look at angles *DEB* and *GHB*. These angles are in corresponding positions. Here ∠*DEB* has the same measure (about 58°) as ∠*GHB*. If two angles have the same measure we write = between them

$$∠DEB = ∠GHB$$

and say, "Angle *DEB* equals angle *GHB*."

◆ Can you name some other pairs of corresponding angles? **∠DEA and ∠GHA, ∠AHF and ∠AEC, ∠FHB and ∠CEB**
If two lines cross, four angles are formed. Angles that are formed in this way and are opposite to each other are called *vertical angles*. For example, ∠*AEC* and ∠*BED* are vertical angles.

◆ What other pair of vertical angles is formed by lines *AB* and *CD*? **∠DEA and ∠BEC**

◆ What do you think is true of vertical angles? **They are equal.**

∠*AED* and ∠*BEC* are vertical angles.

◆ Do they have the same measure? **yes**

◆ What can you now tell about ∠*CEH* and ∠*BHG*? **They are equal.**

◆ How can you show that ∠*BEC* and ∠*AHG* are equal? **∠BEC = ∠BHF since they are corresponding angles, and ∠BHF = ∠AHG since they are vertical angles. So, ∠BEC = ∠AHG.**

510 · Geometry

🔳 **Why** teach it this way?

Some of your students may have difficulty grasping the logic behind using vertical angles and corresponding angles to identify other angles in the diagram congruent to them. However, you should not press the issue at this time; just proceed with the lesson. Students will revisit these ideas in later grades.

*available separately

Measure each angle in each figure. Then answer the questions.

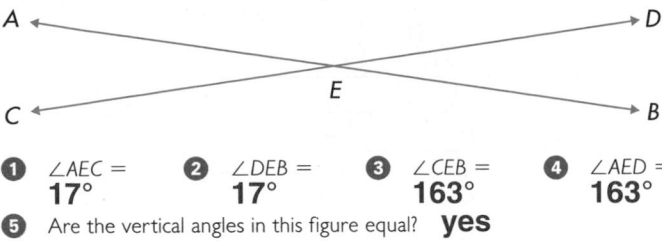

① ∠AEC =
17°
② ∠DEB =
17°
③ ∠CEB =
163°
④ ∠AED =
163°

⑤ Are the vertical angles in this figure equal? **yes**

⑥ Is the sum of the angles 360°? **yes**

⑦ What is the sum of ∠AEC and ∠CEB? **180°**

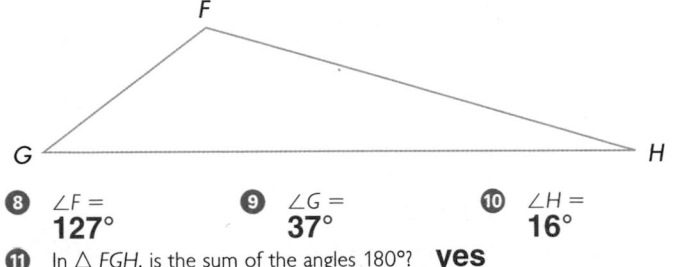

⑧ ∠F =
127°
⑨ ∠G =
37°
⑩ ∠H =
16°

⑪ In △ FGH, is the sum of the angles 180°? **yes**

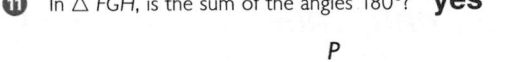

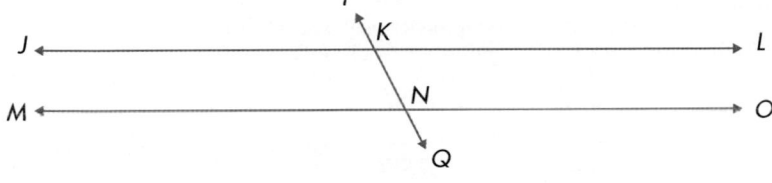

⑫ ∠PKL =
117°
⑬ ∠LKQ =
63°
⑭ ∠JKQ =
117°
⑮ ∠JKP =
63°
⑯ ∠PNO =
117°
⑰ ∠ONQ =
63°
⑱ ∠MNQ =
117°
⑲ ∠MNP =
63°

Answer these questions.

⑳ Are the vertical angles in this figure equal? **yes**

㉑ Are the corresponding angles in this figure equal? **yes**

Unit 6 Lesson 145 • **511**

② Teach

Using the Student Pages Review the term *parallel lines*. Then discuss the angles formed when a line crosses two parallel lines. Draw a figure on the chalkboard or overhead like that on page 510 and show by demonstration that corresponding angles have the same measure. Do the same for vertical angles, using a diagram that does not include parallel lines. Refer students to the diagram on page 510 and ask them to tell what the relationship between angles *CEA* and *BHG* ought to be. Guide students to see that they must be the same size since they are both the same size as ∠*BED*–angles *CEA* and *BED* are vertical angles, and angles *BED* and *BHG* are corresponding angles.

Have students use a **protractor*** to work on the problems on page 511 individually or with a partner.

◆ LESSON 145 Corresponding Angles and Vertical Angles

Teach

Using the Student Pages Assign pages 512 and 513 for independent work or have students work with partners. Make sure they understand that it will not be necessary to use protractors other than to check answers in case of a dispute. If students finish early, invite them to create their own diagrams and questions about them. Students can post these for others to use when they have free time.

Be sure students understand that the same angle may have several different names, and that they must keep this in mind when comparing their answers.

◆ **LESSON 145** Corresponding Angles and Vertical Angles

In the figure below, lines *AB*, *CD*, and *EF* are parallel to each other.

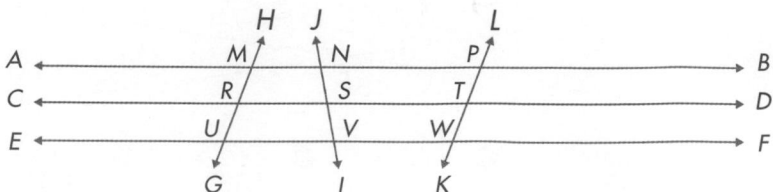

Consider ∠AMH. Answer the following questions.

㉒ What angle is the vertical angle to *AMH*? **∠BMG**

㉓ Are there several different ways to name that angle? **yes**

㉔ Are there more angles that are vertical angles for ∠*AMH*? **no**

㉕ Name an angle that is a corresponding angle of ∠*AMH*. **∠HRC or ∠HUE**

㉖ Name another angle in the figure that is a corresponding angle of ∠*AMH*.
∠HUE or ∠HRC

㉗ How could you have named these two angles differently? **∠HRC could be named ∠MRC, ∠CRM, or ∠CRH. ∠HUE could be named ∠RUE, ∠EVR, or ∠EUH.**

For each of the following angles, name its vertical angle.
Angle names will vary for problems 28–47. Examples are given.

㉘ ∠HMN	㉙ ∠JNM	㉚ ∠LPN	㉛ ∠SVU
∠AMG	**∠BNI**	**∠BPK**	**∠FVI**

㉜ ∠JNP	㉝ ∠LPB	㉞ ∠RUV	㉟ ∠SVW
∠ANI	**∠APK**	**∠EUG**	**∠EVI**

For each of the following angles, name two corresponding angles.

㊱ ∠HMN	㊲ ∠HMA	㊳ ∠AMR	㊴ ∠RMN
∠HRD, ∠HUF	**∠HRC, ∠HUE**	**∠CRG, ∠EUG**	**∠GRD, ∠GUF**
㊵ ∠FWK	㊶ ∠VWK	㊷ ∠VWT	㊸ ∠TWF
∠DTK, ∠BPK	**∠CTK, ∠APK**	**∠CTL, ∠APL**	**∠LTD, ∠LPB**
㊹ ∠NST	㊺ ∠NSR	㊻ ∠VSR	㊼ ∠VST
∠JNB, ∠JVF	**∠JNA, ∠JVE**	**∠INA, ∠IVU**	**∠IVF, ∠INB**

512 · Geometry

Literature Connection Have students read about angles and parallel lines in *Quadrilaterals* by Marion Smoothey.

In the figure below, lines *AB*, *CD*, and *EF* are parallel. Also, line *HG* is parallel to line *JI*.

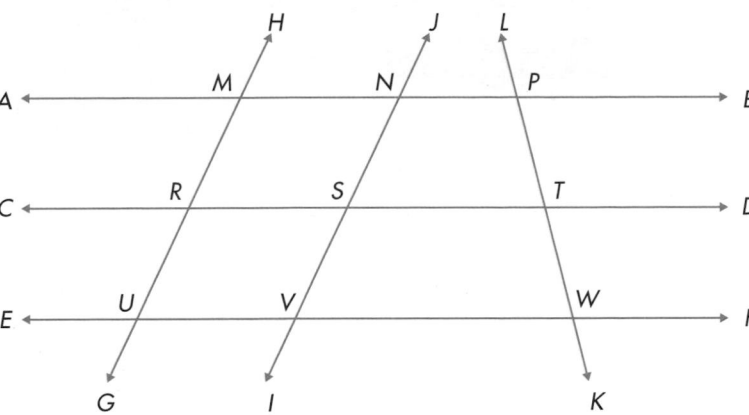

Because lines *HG* and *JI* are parallel, angles *AMH* and *MNJ* are corresponding angles. Because lines *AB* and *CD* are parallel, angles *AMH* and *CRM* are corresponding angles.

48 Since you know that corresponding angles are equal, and both *MNJ* and *CRM* are corresponding angles of ∠*AMH*, what can you say about angles *MNJ* and *CRM*? **They are equal.**

49 Using your knowledge of vertical and corresponding angles, list all the angles in the figure that are equal to ∠*AMH*. How many are there? **∠*MNJ*, ∠*RMN*, ∠*SNP*, ∠*CRM*, ∠*RSN*, ∠*URS*, ∠*VST*, ∠*EUR*, ∠*UVS*, ∠*GUV*, ∠*IVW*; 11**

50 List all the angles that are equal to ∠*HMN*. How many are there? **∠*JNP*, ∠*AMR*, ∠*MNS*, ∠*MRS*, ∠*NST*, ∠*CRU*, ∠*RSV*, ∠*RUV*, ∠*SVW*, ∠*EUG*, ∠*UVI*; 11**

51 List all the angles that are equal to ∠*LPB*. How many are there? **∠*TPN*, ∠*PTD*, ∠*STW*, ∠*TWF*, ∠*VWK*; 5**

52 List all the angles that are equal to ∠*LPN*. How many are there? **∠*BPT*, ∠*PTS*, ∠*DTW*, ∠*TWV*, ∠*FWK*; 5**

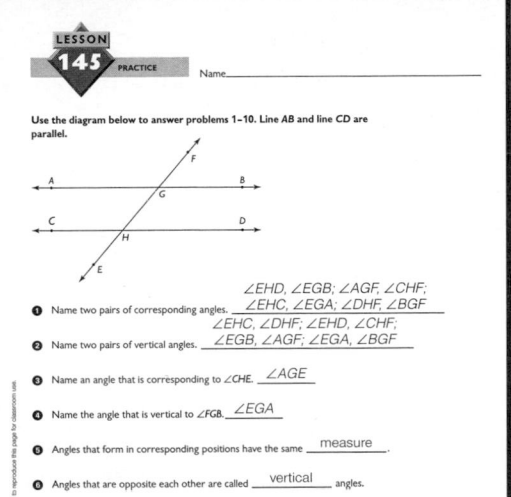

Astronauts traveling on board the space shuttle can see a sunrise every 90 minutes.

Unit 6   Lesson 145 • **513**

PRACTICE p. 145

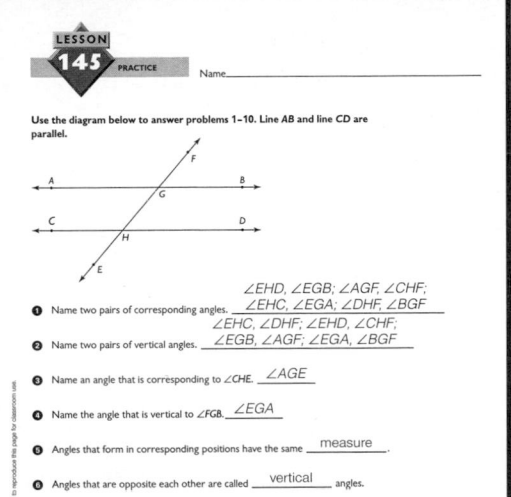

LESSON **145** PRACTICE   Name_____

Use the diagram below to answer problems 1–10. Line AB and line CD are parallel.

① Name two pairs of corresponding angles. ∠EHD, ∠EGB; ∠AGF, ∠CHF; ∠EHC, ∠EGA; ∠DHF, ∠BGF

② Name two pairs of vertical angles. ∠EHC, ∠DHF; ∠EHD, ∠CHF; ∠EGB, ∠AGF; ∠EGA, ∠BGF

③ Name an angle that is corresponding to ∠CHE. ∠AGE

④ Name the angle that is vertical to ∠FGB. ∠EGA

⑤ Angles that form in corresponding positions have the same ___measure___.

⑥ Angles that are opposite each other are called ___vertical___ angles.

⑦ Do vertical angles have the same measure? yes

⑧ What can you tell about ∠CHE and ∠FGB? They have the same measure.

⑨ What is the sum of ∠AGF and ∠AGE? 180°

⑩ What is the sum of ∠DHE, ∠EHC ∠CHF, and ∠FHD? 360°

Math Explorations and Applications Level 6 • 145

ENRICHMENT p. 145

LESSON **145** ENRICHMENT   Name_____

Roza was frosting a large flat cake that had white frosting with blue loops on top. She decided it looked plain, so she drew a knife gently through the loops, like this:

Roza found she had 11 segments of blue after making two passes with the knife. How many segments would she have after another pass, parallel to the others? After four more passes? How many bits of blue line would she have after *n* passes with the knife? 16; 36; 1 + 5*n*

Math Explorations and Applications Level 6 • 145

---

③ Wrap-Up

5 MINUTES

In Closing To summarize the lesson, ask students to define *corresponding angles* and *vertical angles* and to draw and label a diagram showing both kinds.

Informal Assessment Observe students as they work on the diagrams. Ask them to explain their reasoning for one of the problems they are working on.

Assessment Criteria

Did the student . . .

✓ demonstrate understanding of corresponding angles and vertical angles?

✓ correctly identify and name with letters the corresponding angles and vertical angles in the diagrams?

✓ demonstrate ability to use what he or she knows about corresponding and vertical angles to list other angles congruent to them and each other in the diagrams?

Homework Have students draw and label a diagram that includes a set of parallel lines and has pairs of vertical angles and corresponding angles. They can include this diagram in their Math Portfolios.

ESL **Meeting Individual Needs**
You may find it useful to familiarize students with the everyday meaning of *corresponding* so that they can better understand its meaning within the context of geometry.

Straight and Supplementary Angles

Straight and Supplementary Angles

LESSON PLANNER

Objectives

✓ to assess students' understanding of geometric concepts

▶ to introduce the concept of straight and supplementary angles

▶ to demonstrate that the sum of the angles of any triangle is 180°

Context of the Lesson This is the fourth of six lessons on angles and their measurement. This lesson contains a Mastery Checkpoint for assessing students' understanding of geometry.

 MANIPULATIVES

protractors*

Program Resources

Reteaching Master
Practice Master 146
Enrichment Master 146
Assessment Masters
For extra practice:
CD-ROM* Lesson 146

① Warm-Up ⏱

 **Problem of the Day** Present the following problem to students: A broomstick is leaning against a wall. The acute angle formed by the bottom of the stick and the floor is five times as great as the acute angle formed by the top of the stick and the wall. What is the measure of the acute angle formed by the bottom of the stick? (75 degrees)

Problem-Solving Strategies Ask students who have solved the Problem of the Day to share how they solved it and any strategies they used.

 MENTAL MATH Have students find the following percents using mental math.

a. 25% of 200 (50)   b. 75% of 60 (45)

c. 80% of 50 (40)   d. $33\frac{1}{3}$% of 90 (30)

e. 50% of 50 (25)   f. $66\frac{2}{3}$% of 90 (60)

g. $12\frac{1}{2}$% of 32 (4)   h. 60% of 60 (36)

In addition to finding corresponding angles and vertical angles, you can use other angle relationships to find measures of unlabeled angles.

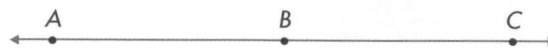

An angle whose sides go in opposite directions on a straight line is called a **straight angle.** Here ∠ABC is a straight angle.

◆ What is the measure of ∠ABC? **180°**

◆ Do you think that every straight angle has the same measure? **yes**

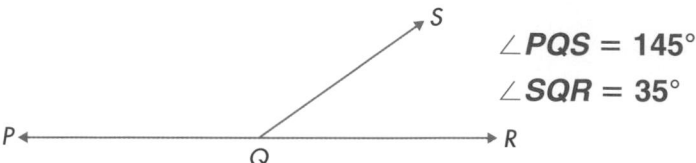

∠PQS = 145°
∠SQR = 35°

◆ Without measuring, what do you think is the sum of the measures of ∠SQR and ∠PQS? **180°**

Measure ∠SQR and ∠PQS. Then add the measures.

◆ Is the sum about 180°? **yes**

The angles ∠PQS and ∠SQR are called *supplementary angles* because their measures add up to 180°.

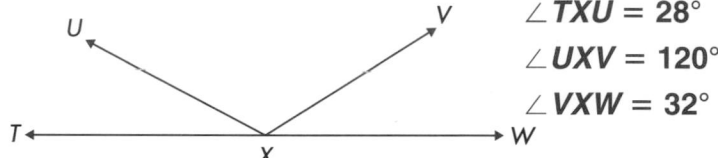

∠TXU = 28°
∠UXV = 120°
∠VXW = 32°

◆ Without measuring, what do you think is the sum of the measures of ∠TXU and ∠UXV and ∠VXW? **180°**

Measure ∠TXU, ∠UXV, and ∠VXW. Then add the measures.

◆ Is the sum about 180°? If it is not exactly 180°, why might it be off a little? **Yes, although there may be inaccuracies in measurement.**

514 • Geometry

Real-World Connection Ask students to draw a small street map of their neighborhood, in which they identify streets that show parallel lines, intersecting lines, and perpendicular lines. Their maps can show corresponding angles, supplementary angles, and straight angles. Students should identify examples of each kind of angle and line.

In the figure below, lines *AB*, *CD*, and *EF* are parallel. Also, line *HG* is parallel to line *JI*.

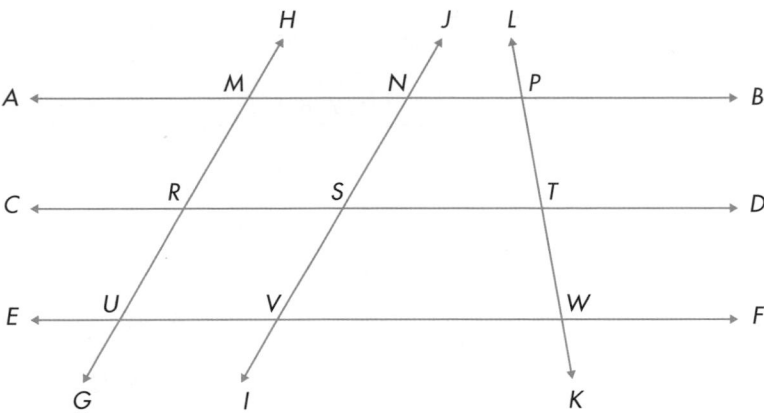

① Name a supplementary angle of ∠*HMN*. ∠**AMH**

② Name another angle that is supplementary to ∠*HMN*.
∠**RMN**

③ If the measure of ∠*HMN* is 60°, what is the measure of ∠*HMA*? **120°**

④ What is the measure of ∠*RMN*? **120°**

For the following, assume the measure of ∠*HMN* is 60° and the measure of ∠*LPB* is 100°. (We usually write these facts: ∠*HMN* = 60° and ∠*LPB* = 100°.)

Determine the measure of each of the following angles.

⑤	∠*HMA* **120°**	**⑥**	∠*VSR* **60°**	**⑦**	∠*SVE* **120°**	**⑧**	∠*IVF* **120°**
⑨	∠*AMR* **60°**	**⑩**	∠*VWK* **100°**	**⑪**	∠*PTS* **80°**	**⑫**	∠*LTD* **100°**
⑬	∠*RMN* **120°**	**⑭**	∠*FWK* **80°**	**⑮**	∠*VUG* **120°**	**⑯**	∠*JNM* **120°**
⑰	∠*RUV* **60°**	**⑱**	∠*LPN* **80°**	**⑲**	∠*VST* **120°**	**⑳**	∠*MRS* **60°**

②Teach

 **Using the Student Pages** Go over page 514 with students, allowing them time to measure using a **protractor***, as needed. Before assigning the problems on page 515, ask students some questions to gauge their understanding of supplementary angles, such as these: How many degrees are in the supplement of a right angle? (90) What kind of angle is supplementary to an obtuse angle? (acute angle) How many degrees are in the supplement of an 80-degree angle? (100) Have students work in pairs on the problems. As needed, go over how to name angles by using three capital letters, with the middle one naming the vertex of the angle. Note that no measurements are required for page 515.

 **Art Connection** Ask students to do research to find out about the style of modern painting known as Cubism. Have them write a short essay about Cubism and how Cubist painters used geometric concepts and shapes in their work. You may wish to create a bulletin board display of the reports along with examples of the work of Picasso and others. Invite students to create their own geometric art, which they can contribute to the display.

*available separately

◆ LESSON 146 Straight and Supplementary Angles

Teach

Using the Student Pages Work through one or two problems on page 516 with the class, then assign the page for independent work. Again, no measurements are necessary. You can have students form pairs or small groups to compare and discuss answers. When students discuss page 517, remind them that two angles both equal to the same angle are equal to each other. When discussing the proof that the angles of any triangle have a sum of 180°, you may wish to explain to students that this is an example of drawing upon certain mathematical ideas to prove or confirm others.

SPECIAL NEEDS

Meeting Individual Needs
Point out to students who confuse vertical angles with corresponding angles and supplementary angles that the term *vertical* comes from *vertex;* vertical angles share a common vertex. Remind students that corresponding angles are in corresponding positions in a diagram.

◆ **LESSON 146** Straight and Supplementary Angles

In the figure below, *AC* and *DG* are parallel. Answer the following questions based on the figure.

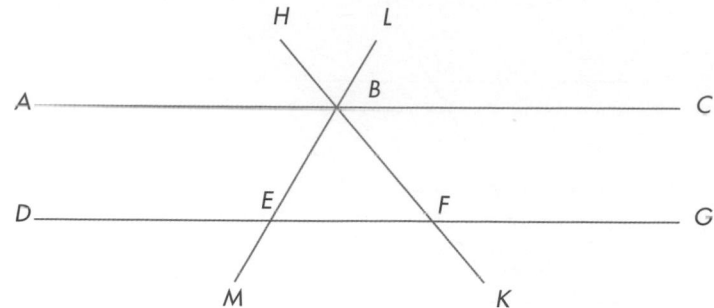

㉑ Name two angles that are supplements of ∠BEF. **∠BED and ∠MEF**

㉒ Name an angle that is a corresponding angle of ∠BEF. **∠LBC**

㉓ Assume the measure of ∠BEF is 60°. Determine the measure of each of the following angles:

a. ∠LBC **60°**   b. ∠BED **120°**   c. ∠MEF **120°**
d. ∠LBA **120°**   e. ∠ABE **60°**   f. ∠EBC **120°**

㉔ Assume the measure of ∠BFE is 50°. Name all the angles whose measure you can determine, and give the measures of those angles. **See below.**

㉕ Are there any angles in the figure that you are sure have the same measure as ∠EBF? If so, what are the angles? **yes; ∠LBH**

㉖ Find the measure of ∠HBL. **70°**

㉗ Find the sum of the measures of ∠HBA, ∠HBL, ∠LBC, ∠CBF, ∠FBE, and ∠EBA. **360°**

㉘ Find the sum of the measures of ∠DEB, ∠FEB, ∠FEM, and ∠MED. **360°**

㉙ What do you notice about your answers to problems 27 and 28? Do you think this will be true of any set of angles surrounding a point?
Both sums are 360°; yes

㉔ **∠BFG = 130°, ∠GFK = 50°, ∠KFE = 130°, ∠CBF = 50°, ∠CBH = 130°, ∠HBA = 50°, ∠ABF = 130°**

516 · Geometry

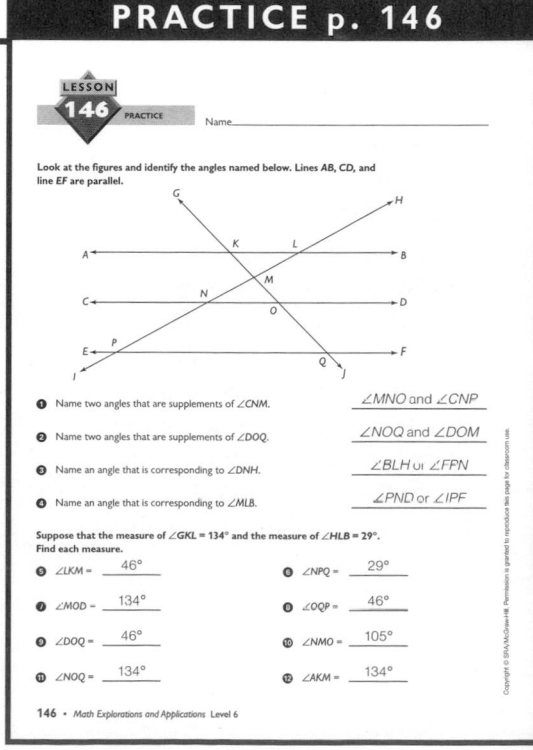

RETEACHING p. 50

PRACTICE p. 146

Look at △ABC.

Line *DE* is parallel to line *FG*.

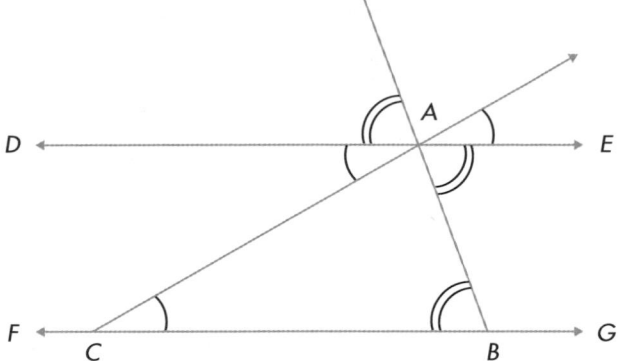

◆ If you measure ∠ACB and ∠DAC, what would you expect to find?
They are equal.

Measure the angles to check.

◆ If you measure ∠ABC and ∠BAE, what would you expect to find?
They are equal.

Measure the angles to check.

◆ What is the sum of the measures of ∠DAC, ∠CAB, and ∠BAE? **180°**

You know ∠DAC = ∠ACB and ∠BAE = ∠ABC.

◆ What do you think is the sum of the measures of ∠ACB, ∠CAB, and
∠ABC? **180°**

Since these questions would be answered the same way for any triangle,
we can consider this a proof that the sum of the angles of any triangle
is 180°.

**The Pyramids of Giza in Egypt are the only one of the Seven
Wonders of the Ancient World that still exist. The largest, sometimes
called the Great Pyramid, was built over 4000 years ago out of more
than 2,000,000 stone blocks. Each of the blocks weighs about 2.3
tons—that's about the weight of 19 baby elephants.**

Unit 6   Lesson 146 • **517**

---

❸ Wrap-Up

In Closing Ask students to define a *straight angle* and to
identify one in the classroom.

 **Mastery Checkpoint 23**

By this time, most students should demonstrate
understanding of basic geometric concepts (names of
figures, finding areas, and so on) and be able to use a
protractor with ease. You can assess these skills by
observing students as they work on and discuss pages
514–516 or by assigning Assessment Blackline Masters
pages 54–55. The results of this assessment may be
recorded on the Mastery Checkpoint Chart.

Assessment Criteria

Did the student . . .

✔ demonstrate understanding of
straight angles and supplementary
angles?

✔ show ability to understand the
deductive arguments used to find
the measures of angles by using
what they know about vertical
angles, corresponding angles,
straight angles, and supplementary
angles?

✔ understand the deductive reasoning
used to prove that the sum of the
angles in all triangles is 180°?

Homework Have students draw a straight angle, divide it
into two unequal angles, and label each. Students can put
this diagram in their Math Portfolios.

ENRICHMENT p. 146

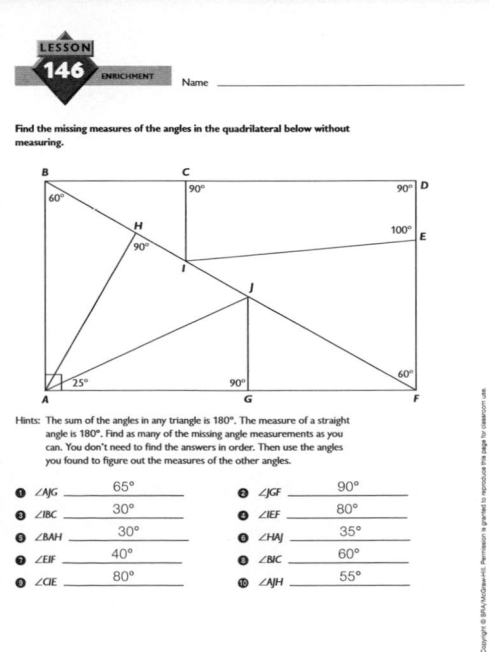

ASSESSMENT p. 54

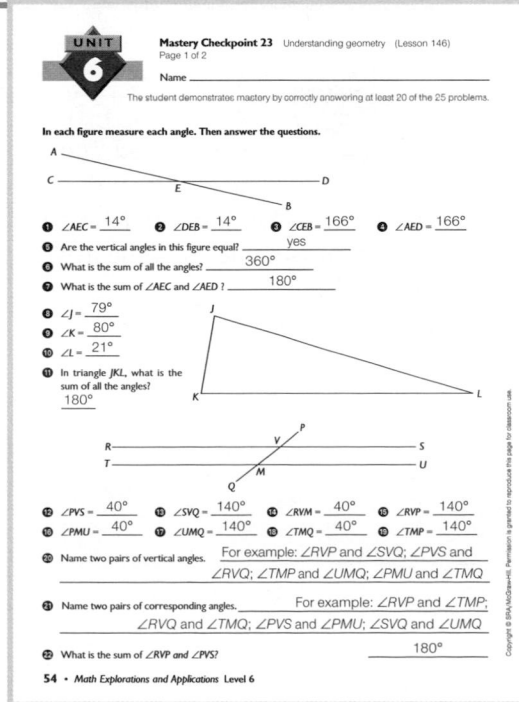

Angles of Polygons

LESSON PLANNER

Objectives

▶ to provide practice in using the knowledge that the sum of the angles of a triangle is 180°

▶ to demonstrate how to determine the sum of the angles of any polygon

▶ to introduce the concept of a regular polygon and to provide practice in drawing regular polygons

Context of the Lesson This is the fifth of six lessons on angles and their measurements.

 MANIPULATIVES

protractors*

Program Resources

Reteaching Master
Practice Master 147
Enrichment Master 147
The Cruncher*
For extra practice:
  CD-ROM* Lesson 147

① Warm-Up ⏱ 5 MINUTES

 **Problem of the Day** Present the following problem to the class: What is the least number of triangles that can be combined to form a pentagon? a hexagon? (3; 4)

Problem-Solving Strategies Ask students who have solved the Problem of the Day to share how they solved it and any strategies they used.

 MENTAL MATH Have students do the following subtractions mentally.

a. 180 – 50 = (130) b. 180 – 85 = (95)

c. 180 – 75 = (105) d. 180 – 55 = (125)

e. 540 – 180 = (360) f. 540 – 360 = (180)

g. 720 – 360 = (360) h. 720 – 540 = (180)

Angles of Polygons

For each triangle you are given the measure of two angles. Find the measure of the third angle. Then, measure the angles to check your answers.

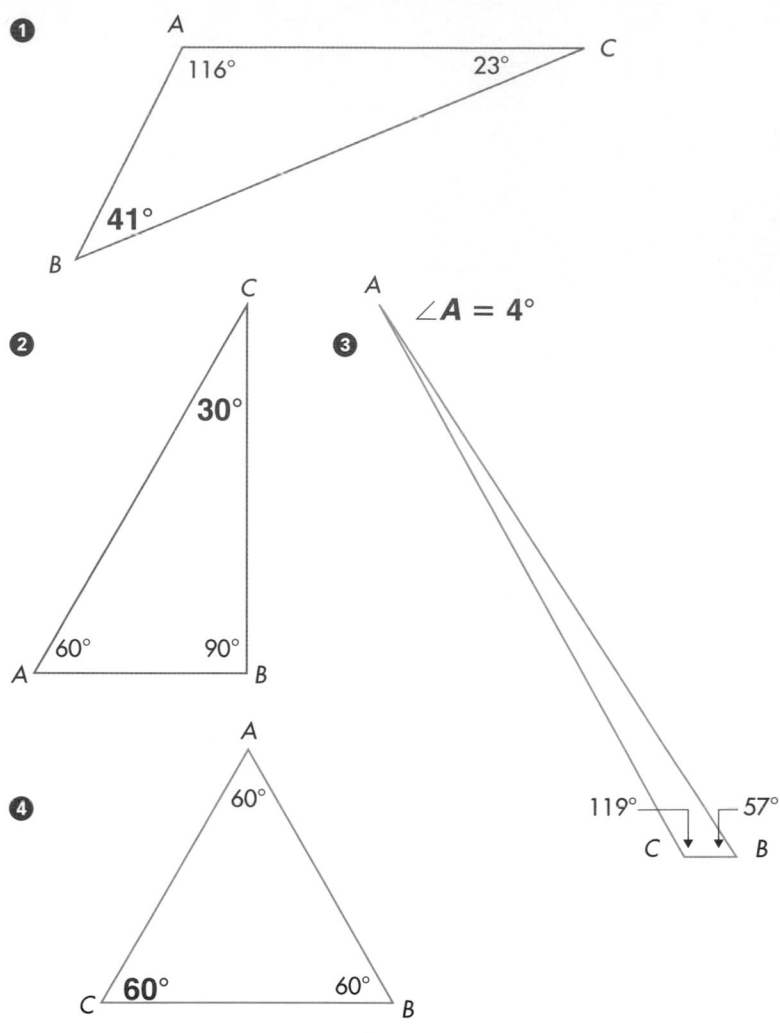

Literature Connection Have students read *The Greedy Triangle* by Marilyn Burns. Ask them to determine the angle measurements of the newly created polygons.

*available separately

◆ What do you think is the sum of
the angles of quadrilateral ABCD?
360°
Measure ∠A, ∠B, ∠C, and ∠D. Ignore
the dotted line for now. Then add the
angles to check your answer to the first
question. **98° + 64° + 77° + 121°**
Imagine you draw line BD. **= 360°**

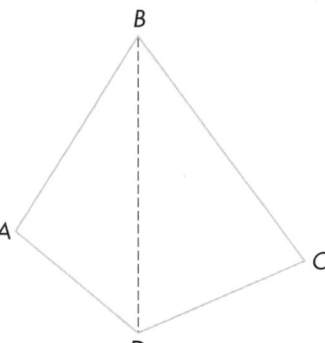

◆ What is the sum of the angles of
△ ABD? **180°**

◆ What is the sum of the angles of
△ CBD? **180°**

◆ Try to explain why the sum of the angles of quadrilateral ABCD is equal to
the sum of the angles of two triangles. **Since quadrilateral ABCD can be thought**
of as two triangles sharing a common side, the sum of its angles is the same as the sum of the
The sum of the angles of any quadrilateral is 360°. **angles in the two triangles ABD and**
BDC, or 360°.

◆ What do you think is the sum of
the measures of the angles of a
pentagon (five-sided figure)?
Explain why. (Hint: Look at how
lines GE and GJ divide the
pentagon into triangles.) **540°**

❺ What do you think is the sum of
the measures of the angles of a
hexagon (six-sided figure)? **720°**

❻ What is the sum of the measures
of the angles of a heptagon (seven-
sided figure)? **900°**

❼ What is the sum of the measures
of the angles of an **octagon** (eight-
sided figure)? **1080°**

❽ Write a function rule or formula for
finding the sum of the measures of the angles of a **polygon**, given the
number of sides. Use s for number of sides and m for the sum of the
measures of the angles. **m = (s − 2) × 180 or**

❾ Can you draw a figure for which the rule will not work? **s—②→n—×180→m**

no (except for concave
polygons such as ⋁ **)**

Unit 6   Lesson 147 • **519**

---

❷ Teach

 **Using the Student Pages** Tell the class that
you are thinking of a triangle that has one 40°
angle and one 60° angle. Ask them to give the
measure of the remaining angle. (80°) Then ask them how
they determined this. (Add 60 and 40; subtract the sum from
180.) Once students understand this technique for finding
the third angle of a triangle, have them complete page 518
on their own. Have **protractors*** available for this page.
Students can use a blank **Cruncher*** spreadsheet to explore
the relationship among the angles in a triangle.

Then have students work in pairs or in groups on the
questions on page 519, comparing and discussing their
answers. At this point you should be sure that students have
a clear idea of the kinds of figures that are polygons and the
kinds that are not. Provide examples to show that polygons
are closed figures made up of line segments only, and that
the line segments must not cross each other.

For problem 9, you may wish to note that the rule also
works for concave polygons if we allow angles to have
measures greater than 180°.

 **Technology**
Connection Refer
students to the software
Math Workshop from Broderbund
(Mac, IBM, for grades K–8) for
practice with line segments, line and
shape recognition, scale, symmetry,
basic computation, puzzle patterns,
and fractions.

◆ LESSON 147 Angles of Polygons

Teach

Using the Student Pages Have students work in pairs or in small groups on the problems on page 520, again discussing their answers as they work. Point out that each time a side is added to a polygon an additional triangle is included inside the polygon. Therefore the sum of the degrees of the angles of that polygon is increased by 180°.

For page 521, be sure students understand the distinction between sides and diagonals. Then have students work in pairs to make and complete the table. Ask them to describe the pattern they see in the relationship between the number of sides and the number of diagonals in a polygon. When discussing the handshake questions, you may wish to point out to students that each diagonal may be thought of as representing a handshake. Because each side of the polygon also represents a handshake, they must add the number of diagonals and the number of sides to find the number of handshakes.

LEARNING STYLES | **Meeting Individual Needs**
You may find it useful to have kinesthetic or social learners act out the handshaking problems and keep a record of the numbers of shakes.

◆ LESSON 147 Angles of Polygons

Andrew says, "I am thinking of a quadrilateral in which all the angles are the same size."

◆ What is the measure of each angle? (Remember, the sum of the angles of a quadrilateral is 360°.) **90°**

◆ What do we call the figure that Andrew is thinking of? **rectangle**

Solve the following problems.

⑩ In a **regular polygon** the sides are all the same size and the angles are all the same size. The sum of the angles of a pentagon is 540°. What is the measure of each angle of a regular pentagon? **108°**

⑪ Use your protractor and ruler to draw a regular pentagon. (Make each side 6 centimeters long.)

⑫ The sum of the angles of a hexagon is 720°. In a regular hexagon all six angles are the same size. What is the measure of each angle of a regular hexagon? **120°**

⑬ Use your protractor and ruler to draw a regular hexagon. (Make each side 5 centimeters long.)

⑭ Draw a regular triangle. What do we usually call this figure?
equilateral triangle

⑮ Draw a regular quadrilateral. What do we usually call this figure? **square**

⑯ Draw a regular octagon (a regular eight-sided polygon).

⑰ Use the formula you found for problem 8 on page 519 to find the sum of the measures of the angles of a 20-sided figure. **3240°**

⑱ What is the measure of each angle in a regular 20-sided figure? **162°**

⑲ What is the sum of the measures of the angles of a 100-sided figure? **17,640°**

⑳ What is the measure of each angle in a regular 100-sided figure? **176.4°**

520 · Geometry

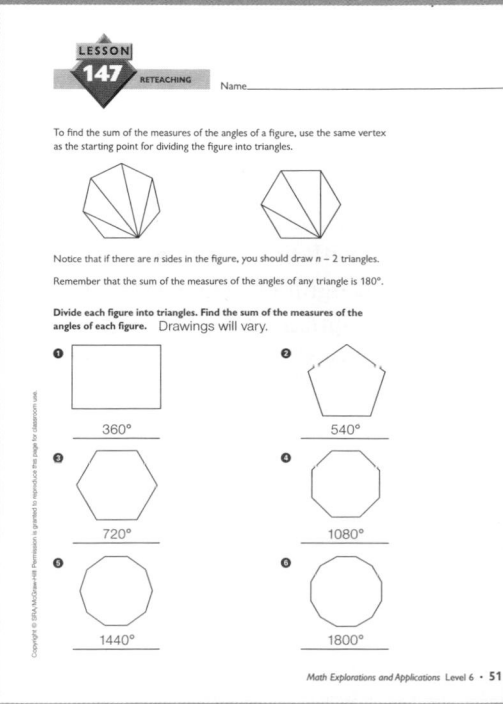

There are two kinds of line segments in this pentagon. One kind is a side. The other kind, which crosses the inside of the pentagon, is a **diagonal**.

Solve the following problems.

㉑ All possible diagonals have been drawn in this pentagon. How many diagonals are there? **5**

㉒ Draw a quadrilateral. What is the greatest number of diagonals you can draw in a quadrilateral? **2**

㉓ How many diagonals can you draw in a triangle? **0**

㉔ Use a computer or other means to draw a chart like the following, and then complete it. You might not have to draw the diagrams.

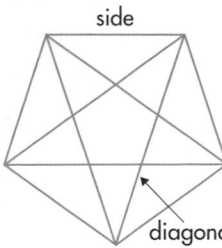

side

diagonal

Name	Number of Sides	Number of Diagonals
Triangle	3	0
Quadrilateral	4	2
Pentagon	5	5
Hexagon	6	**9**
Heptagon	7	**14**
Octagon	8	**20**
Nonagon	9	**27**
Decagon	10	**35**

㉕ If three people meet and each person shakes everybody else's hand, how many handshakes will there be? **3**

㉖ If four people meet and each person shakes everybody else's hand, how many handshakes will there be? **6**

㉗ If five people meet and each person shakes everybody else's hand, how many handshakes will there be? **10**

㉘ What is the same about the diagonal problems and the handshake problems? What is different about them? **See below.**

㉙ If ten people meet and each person shakes everybody else's hand, how many handshakes will there be? **45**

㉘ **For each handshake problem, the total number of handshakes is equal to the number of sides plus the number of diagonals in the corresponding diagonal problem.**

Unit 6   Lesson 147 • **521**

❸ Wrap-Up  5 MINUTES

In Closing To summarize the lesson, ask students to describe what a regular polygon is.

Performance Assessment Ask students to tell how many degrees are in each angle of an equilateral pentagon and explain their reasoning.

Assessment Criteria

Did the student . . .

✓ demonstrate understanding of how to determine the number of degrees in one angle of a triangle, given the measures of the other two angles?

✓ understand how to find the number of degrees in any polygon?

✓ understand the distinction between a polygon and a regular polygon?

✓ understand how to figure out the number of handshakes, given the number of people who wish to shake every other person's hand?

Homework Have students figure out how many handshakes there would be if everyone in their extended family shook hands with everyone else in the family.

Meeting Individual Needs
Challenge students with the following problem: How many games will have to be played to determine a winner in a single-elimination checker tournament that has 100 players in it? Single elimination means one loss and a player is out. (99, because there must be 99 people who lose)

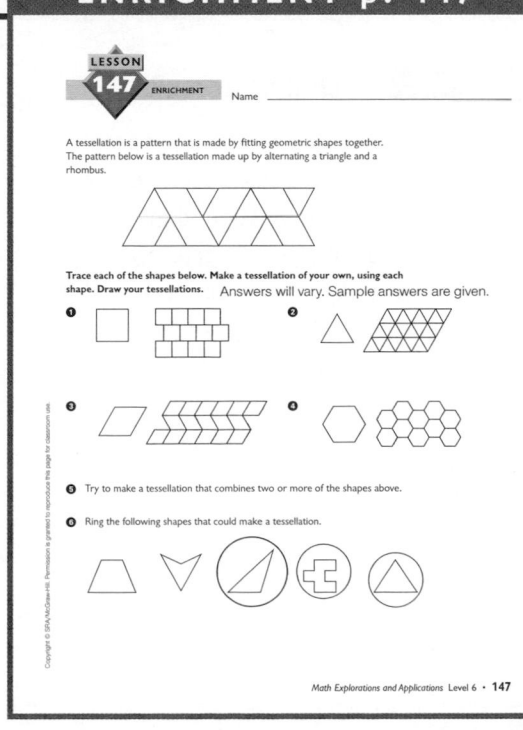

LESSON 148

Student Edition pages 522–525

Points, Lines, and Planes

Points, Lines, and Planes

Look at points *P* and *Q*.

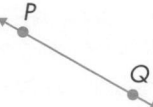

◆ How many straight lines could you draw through both *P* and *Q*? **only 1**

Mathematical lines go on forever in both directions. Any line we draw is really a **line segment** or part of a line.

Look at lines *AB* and *CD*.

◆ If these line segments were extended, would they meet? **yes**

◆ At how many points will the lines meet? **only 1**

◆ Is it possible to draw two lines that do not meet at all? **yes**

◆ How would you describe those lines?
parallel (or skew, as described below)

◆ Is it possible to choose two points so that no straight line can go through both points? **no**

◆ Can you think of two lines that do not meet but are not parallel? (Remember, the lines extend forever.)
Yes, but they are not in the same plane.

Look at the line that is made where the ceiling of your classroom meets the front wall. (This line runs across the front of the room.) Now look at the line that is made where the floor meets a side wall. (This line runs across the side of the room.)

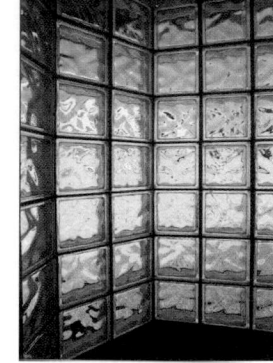

◆ Do these two lines go in the same direction? **no**

◆ Are they parallel? **no**

◆ Do the two lines meet? **no**

Lines that are not parallel and do not meet are called **skew lines**.

LESSON PLANNER

Objectives

▶ to discuss the number of points that determine a line

▶ to introduce the concept and term *skew lines*

▶ to consider relationships among points, lines, and planes

Context of the Lesson This is the sixth of six lessons on angles and their measurement.

👋 **MANIPULATIVES**
straightedges (optional)

Program Resources
Practice Master 148
Enrichment Master 148
For extra practice:
CD-ROM* Lesson 148
Cumulative Review, page 585

❶ Warm-Up ⏱ 5 MINUTES

Problem of the Day Present the following three-part problem to the class: How many line segments can you draw to connect two points? (1) To connect three points not along the same line? (3) Now find a pattern to figure out how many segments you need to connect four points, five points, and six points when, in each case, no three of them lie on the same line. (6, 10, 15)

Problem-Solving Strategies Ask students who have solved the Problem of the Day to share how they solved it and any strategies they used.

MENTAL MATH Have students use mental math to find the sum of all the whole numbers from 1 to 20. (There are ten matched pairs [1, 20; 2, 19; . . .] whose sum equals 21 in the numbers 1–20, so the sum is 10 x 21 = 210.)

Why teach it this way?

When the basic geometric concepts are presented to students using several questions for discussion, they are provided with the opportunity to debate and come to consensus on the concepts and thereby construct their own solid understanding of them.

COOPERATIVE LEARNING
Invite students to play a form of the game *Jeopardy,* using questions based on what they have learned in the last six lessons.

If you think of the shape of a flat ceiling, extended forever in all directions (forward, backward, left and right, but not up or down), you are thinking of a **plane**.

◆ Do you think the plane of your classroom ceiling and the plane of the floor meet? If not, the planes are parallel. **no**

Think of two planes that meet. (For example, think of the plane of a ceiling and the plane of a wall it meets.)

◆ Do they have more than one point in common? (Is more than one point in both planes?) **yes**

◆ How would you describe the set of all points that the two planes have in common? **a line**

Think of any line and any plane. Both go on forever.

◆ Do they meet? **Answers will vary.**

If they do meet, they are not parallel. If they do not meet, they are parallel.

◆ If the line and plane are parallel, is the line parallel to every line in the plane or just to some of them? **just some of them**

Think of a line and a plane that do meet.

◆ How many points do the line and plane have in common? **one (or else the line is on the plane)**

◆ If a line and a plane have more than one point in common, what is true of the line and plane? **The line is on the plane.**

Give examples of each of these. **Answers will vary. Examples are given.**

◆ a line and a plane that are parallel
the ceiling and the line between the floor and any of the side walls

◆ a line and a plane that meet at one point
the floor and the line between the floor and any two side walls

◆ a line and a plane that have more than one point in common
a straight line on a tile floor

Think of two points and a plane that contains both points.

◆ Can you think of another plane that contains both points? **yes**

◆ How many planes can you think of that contain both points? **an infinite number**

Unit 6 Lesson 148 • **523**

❷ Teach

Using the Student Pages Have students work on the discussion questions on pages 522 and 523 in small groups. Encourage them to discuss their answers and to come to consensus on their conclusions. Then have groups share their findings in a class discussion. When students discuss their answers to the last three discussion questions on page 522, point out that the line from the floor and the line from the ceiling are *skew lines* because they are not in the same plane.

As students work on page 523, encourage them to think in terms of real objects around them (such as walls and ceilings).

 **Art Connection** Have students draw a large angle on a sheet of paper. The angle can be acute, right, or obtuse. Have them mark off several evenly spaced points along each ray of the angle. Each ray should have the same number of points marked. Then have students number the points on one ray, in order, starting from the point closest to the vertex. Have them number the points on the other ray, this time starting with the point farthest from the vertex. Then ask students to use a **straightedge** to connect the 1s, 2s, 3s, and so on. They can use colored pencils or markers if they wish. Then display the finished art works. Invite students to examine them and compare and contrast the curves they have created. One way is to note the kinds of curves created by each kind of angle.

Unit 6 Lesson 148 **523**

◆ LESSON 148 Points, Lines, and Planes

Teach

Using the Student Pages Have students again work in groups to discuss and answer the questions on page 524. Afterward, bring the groups together for a class discussion. For problem 1 on page 524, note that unless the three points are deliberately placed on a straight line, the answer will be "no".

 Go over the information about points, lines, rays, and angles on page 525 with students. Ask them to list their examples in their Math Journals.

◆ LESSON 148 Points, Lines, and Planes

Answer these questions.

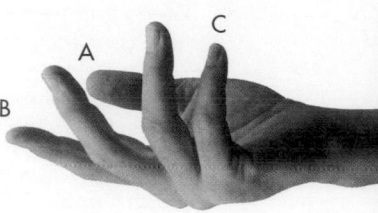

1 Think of any three points. Is there a straight line that contains all three points?
Answers may vary.
If your answer to this question is yes, then think of three points that are not on the same straight line.

Now think of a plane that goes through all three points. (For example, hold up two fingers and a thumb and imagine the tips to be points. Then place a book or piece of cardboard on the fingers and thumb to show the plane that contains those three points.)

2 Is it possible to find more than one plane through the three points? **no**

Think of three points through which there is more than one plane.

3 What is true of the three points? **They are on the same line.**

4 Can you think of three points not on the same straight line that have more than one plane through them? **no**

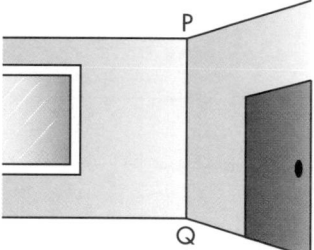

Look at the point in your classroom where the ceiling, the side wall, and the front wall meet. Let's call that point P. Now look at the point beneath that where the floor, the side wall, and the front wall meet. Let's call that point Q.

The line PQ where the two walls meet is perpendicular to the plane of the floor.

Now think of any line in the plane of the floor that goes through point Q.

5 What angle is made by line PQ and your new line? **a right angle**

6 If you measured the angle with your protractor, what would its measure be?
90°

7 Would the measure be the same for every line on the floor that goes through point Q? **yes**

 Have students read parts of *Math Fun with Trick Lines and Shapes* by Rose Wyler and Mary Etling. They can do some of the activities involving geometry.

RETEACHING

Reteaching of the material in this lesson is not necessary, as these concepts will be reinforced in future grades.

Sometimes we wish to talk about the part of a line that starts at a point and goes in only one direction. You might think of it as a half-line. Such a half-line is usually called a **ray.**

P

The mathematical objects we call points, lines, rays, and angles are ideal versions of things we see in everyday life. In mathematics we think of a point as something that has no width, depth, height, color, weight, and so on. In the real world, there isn't any such object, but there are things that are very similar to that.

We think of the mathematical points, lines, rays, and angles as models of things in the real world. We can study the mathematical objects, and they will often tell us something about how the real objects behave.

◆ Think of examples of rays in everyday life. One example is a ray of light. In your Math Journal name at least five other things from the real world that remind you of a ray.

Examples: arrows on a road sign, a piece of string, a baseball bat

◆ Think of things that remind you of a line in real life. Name five things from the real world that remind you of a line. Record these in your Math Journal.

Examples: a road, the horizon, railroad tracks

◆ Name five things in the real world that remind you of a point. Record these in your Math Journal.

Examples: cities on a map, a marble, a star

◆ On your paper draw a picture of a ray that starts at some point (label the point P) and goes in only one direction from that point. Now draw a second ray that starts at the same point P but goes in a different direction. What does the drawing look like? Sometimes an angle is defined to be two rays with the same starting point.

Use the Cumulative Review on page 585 after this lesson.

---

❸ Wrap-Up

In Closing To summarize the lesson, ask students to define *skew lines*. Ask them to explain the differences among skew lines, parallel lines, and intersecting lines.

Informal Assessment Circulate around the room and observe students as they discuss and debate the questions in groups. Check to see that all are participating actively, and that they are making an effort to come to an understanding of the concepts they are discussing. Listen to their discussions to make sure that they are using logic and examples to make their points.

Assessment Criteria

Did the student . . .

✓ participate in group discussions of the questions raised in the lesson?

✓ demonstrate understanding of the terms presented in the lesson?

✓ come up with correct examples of points, lines, skew lines, rays, and planes?

Homework Have students find and list examples of parallel, perpendicular, intersecting, and skew lines in their homes.

PRACTICE p. 148

LESSON **148** PRACTICE   Name

Label each figure as a *point*, a *line*, a *ray*, or an *angle*.

❶ ___ray___   ❷ ___point___

❸ ___angle___   ❹ ___line___

Draw or describe each of the following.

❺ two lines that have one point in common ___two intersecting lines___

❻ two rays that have one point in common ___an angle___

❼ two planes that have no points in common ___two parallel planes___

❽ two planes that have a line in common ___two intersecting planes___

148 • *Math Explorations and Applications Level 6*

ENRICHMENT p. 148

LESSON **148** ENRICHMENT   Name

GAME Imagine that these four grids are placed one on top of another. Play tic-tac-toe in three dimensions. You need four Xs or four Os in a straight line to win.

Layer 1
Layer 2
Layer 3
Layer 4

Do you see that these four Xs are in a straight line?

Layer 1   Layer 2   Layer 3   Layer 4

Rows / Columns

Before playing three-dimensional tic-tac-toe, solve the problems below to get used to picturing straight lines in space. Fill in the coordinates that will complete a straight line. The first coordinate gives the column; the second gives the row; and the third gives the layer. The first problem shows the coordinates of the Xs marked on the grids above.

(1, 4, 1)   (1, 4, 2)   (1, 4, 3)   (_1_ , _4_ , _4_)
(1, 4, 1)   (2, 4, 2)   (3, 4, 3)   (_4_ , _4_ , _4_)
(1, 4, 1)   (2, 3, 2)   (3, 2, 3)   (_4_ , _1_ , _4_)
(1, 3, 1)   (2, 3, 2)   (3, 3, 3)   (_4_ , _3_ , _4_)

Now play the game with a partner.

Layer 1   Layer 2   Layer 3   Layer 4

148 • *Math Explorations and Applications Level 6*

Congruent and Similar Figures

LESSON PLANNER

Objectives

▶ to review the concept of congruence

▶ to review the concept of similarity

Context of the Lesson This lesson provides the groundwork for the following lesson on constructing congruent figures.

 MANIPULATIVES

Program Resources

Reteaching Master

Practice Master 149

Enrichment Master 149

For extra practice:
CD-ROM* Lesson 149

❶ Warm-Up ⏱ 5 MINUTES

 **Problem of the Day** Present the following problem, drawing the figures on the chalkboard:
How has Figure 1 been rotated? (to the right)
How would Figure 2 look if it were rotated in the same way?

 Figure 1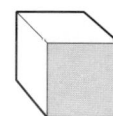

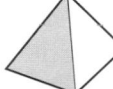 Figure 2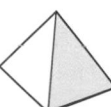

Problem-Solving Strategies Ask students who have solved the Problem of the Day to share how they solved it and any strategies they used.

 MENTAL MATH Have students tell whether the numbers in each pair of numbers are equivalent (thumbs up) or not equivalent (thumbs down).

a. $\frac{2}{3}$ and $\frac{10}{15}$ (thumbs up)

b. $\frac{1}{4}$ and 20% (thumbs down)

c. $\frac{5}{8}$ and 0.6 (thumbs down)

d. 80% and 0.8 (thumbs up)

e. 0.125 and $\frac{1}{8}$ (thumbs up)

f. 40 and 400% (thumbs down)

Congruent and Similar Figures

Look at the two figures shown here.

What do you think is true of the two figures? Get a piece of lightweight paper that you can see through. Trace one of the figures. Move your tracing so that it fits on top of the other figure. Does it fit exactly?
They fit exactly on each other.

When two figures fit exactly on each other, we say they are *congruent*.

❶ Think of some objects in everyday life that you would describe as congruent to each other. In the case of three-dimensional objects, you will not be able to put them exactly on each other, but you can think about whether they are exactly the same size and shape. Would two new automobiles of the same model from the same plant seem congruent (before any extra equipment is added)? List ten congruent pairs of objects.
yes; examples: two new pencils, two copies of the same book, two blank pieces of paper

❷ From the figures below, choose the ones that appear to be congruent. It is all right to turn the tracing paper over, so figures A and B are considered to be congruent. **C and D are congruent, and E and F are congruent.**

 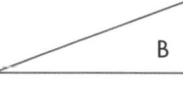 

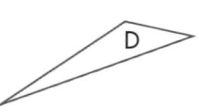  

COOPERATIVE LEARNING Have students form groups of three. One student draws an object. A second student then draws an object that is congruent, similar, or neither. The third student must decide whether what the second student drew was congruent or similar to what the first student drew. Then students change roles and repeat the activity.

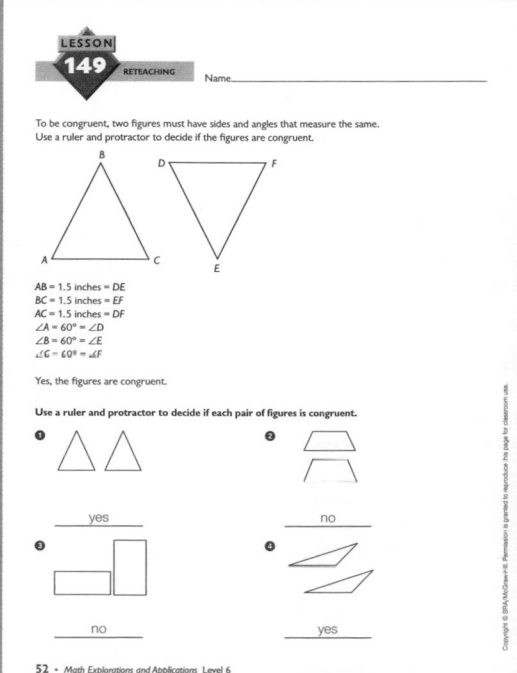
*available separately

Sometimes two figures have exactly the same shape but not the same size. An architect's scale model of a building should be exactly the same shape but be smaller than the building when it is completed. A map is supposed to be just like the cities and towns that are shown on it, with streets going at the same angles to each other and distances between objects proportional to the real distances.

The two figures shown here are similar to each other. Corresponding angles are equal and corresponding sides are proportional (the sides of the larger figure are four times the length of those on the smaller figure).

Solve.

3 Think of some objects in everyday life that you would describe as similar to each other. List ten pairs of similar objects. **Examples: a small pizza and a large pizza, a map of a city and the actual city, a large pumpkin and a small pumpkin**

4 From the figures below, choose the ones that appear to be similar to each other. **A is similar to C. B is similar to F. D is similar to G. E is similar to H.**

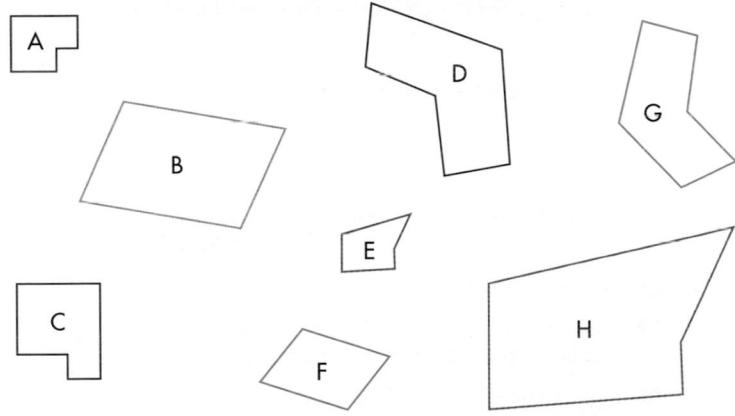

Unit 6   Lesson 149 • **527**

---

2 Teach

Using the Student Pages   Briefly discuss the fact that congruent figures are figures that are exactly alike in shape and size. Have students do page 526 independently and compare answers afterward. Note that almost any manufactured objects of a kind will be congruent.

When doing page 527, discuss that two figures are similar if they look exactly alike except for size. Point out that a good model airplane should be similar to the full-size airplane, and so on. Have students complete the two activities and then compare their answers.

3 Wrap-Up ⏱ 5 MINUTES

In Closing   To summarize the lesson, have students explain, in their own words, the meanings of *congruent* and *similar*, and the difference between them. Ask them to write a brief statement about congruence and similarity for their Math Journals.

Performance Assessment   Ask students to tell whether a baseball is similar or congruent to a basketball, or neither similar nor congruent to a basketball, and to explain their answer. (neither similar nor congruent; their shapes are slightly different)

Assessment Criteria

Did the student . . .

✓ list examples of congruent and similar objects?

✓ correctly complete the other problems?

✓ clearly and correctly explain the meaning of *similarity* and *congruence* and difference between them?

Homework   Have students look around their homes for examples of pairs of objects that are similar, congruent, or nearly similar or congruent. Students can make an organized list of these objects.

PRACTICE p. 149

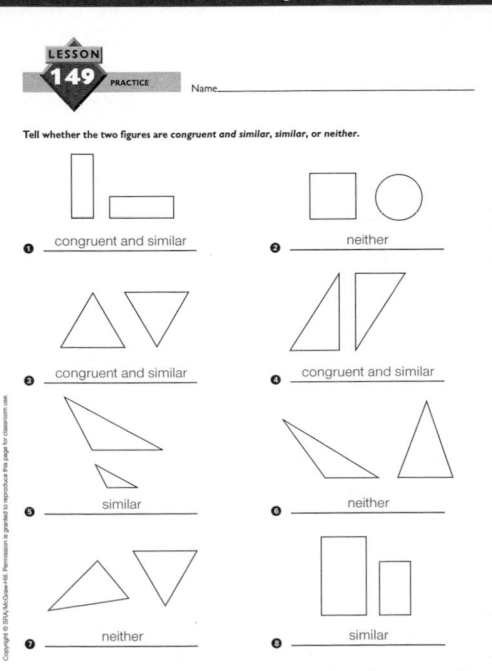

Tell whether the two figures are congruent and similar, similar, or neither.

1. congruent and similar
2. neither
3. congruent and similar
4. congruent and similar
5. similar
6. neither
7. neither
8. similar

Math Explorations and Applications Level 6 • 149

ENRICHMENT p. 149

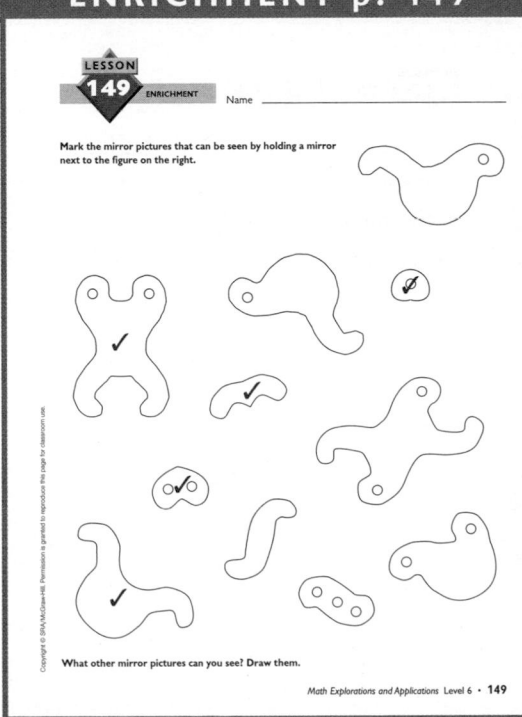

Mark the mirror pictures that can be seen by holding a mirror next to the figure on the right.

What other mirror pictures can you see? Draw them.

Math Explorations and Applications Level 6 • 149

Unit 6 Lesson 149   **527**

Compass Constructions

LESSON PLANNER

Objectives

▶ to provide practice in using a compass

▶ to review congruency properties of triangles

Context of the Lesson This is the only lesson that teaches construction of figures using a compass. If compasses are not available for all students, you may skip this lesson or do it as a demonstration for the class.

MANIPULATIVES	**Program Resources**
compasses	Practice Master 150
protractors*	Enrichment Master 150
straightedges*	For extra practice:
	CD-ROM* Lesson 150

Note: This lesson may take more than one day.

❶ Warm-Up  ⏱ 5 MINUTES

 Problem of the Day Present the following problem: Divide a circular pizza into 11 pieces with only 4 straight cuts. The pieces do not have to be the same size.

Possible answer:

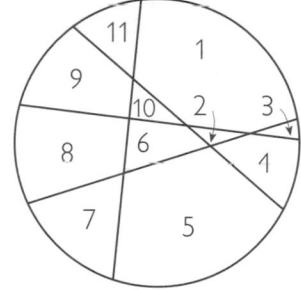

Problem-Solving Strategies Ask students who have solved the Problem of the Day to share how they solved it and any strategies they used.

MENTAL MATH Have students solve the following problems mentally:

a. 8.9 × 1000 = (8900)   **b.** 9 × 60 = (540)

c. 15 × 5 = (75)   **d.** 16.76 × 1000 = (16,760)

e. 20 × 500 = (10,000)   **f.** 25 × 5 = (125)

g. 7 ÷ 10,000 = (0.0007)   **h.** 17.6 ÷ 1 = (17.6)

Compass Constructions

A **circle** is the set of all points that are the same distance from a point called the center. Circles are hard to draw free-hand.

You can use a compass to draw a circle. If you are using a compass with a sharp point, put cardboard or something like it under your paper so that you do not make a hole in your desk.

Each point on the circle you draw with the compass is the same distance from the center. This distance is called the *radius* of the circle.

◆ How does the radius relate to the diameter?
   The radius is half the diameter.

Solve.

❶ Draw three circles that have the same center. Make one circle with a radius of 3 centimeters, one with a radius of 2 centimeters, and one with a radius of 4 centimeters. **Check students' drawings.**

❷ Do the circles meet at any point? **no**

❸ Assuming two circles do not overlap completely, what is the greatest number of points at which they could meet? **2**

❹ Can two circles meet at exactly one point? **yes**

528 · Geometry

Why teach it this way?

By making constructions in this fashion, students can get a hands-on appreciation of the meaning of *congruent segments, angles,* and *figures.*

5 Make a design like the one above. Here's how:

A. Draw a circle with about a 3-centimeter radius.

B. Draw another circle of the same size but with its center on a point of the first circle.

C. Draw a third circle (same size) with the center where the first and second circles meet.

D. Draw a fourth circle with the center where the first and third circles meet.

E. Continue in this way until you have a design like the one shown.

Unit 6   Lesson 150 • **529**

❷ Teach

Using the Student Pages Briefly discuss the material on page 528. Have students solve problems 1–4 on page 528 and problem 5 on page 529, which will familiarize them with the use of a **compass** and give them the experience needed for drawing circles proficiently. Explain to students who have difficulty keeping the point in the same place that they need to push down fairly hard on the part of the compass they are not moving.

Note: These pages should take no more than 10 or 12 minutes.

Literature Connection
Have students do some of the circle investigations in *Circles* by Martha Smoothey.

◆ LESSON 150 Compass Constructions

Teach

Using the Student Pages Instruct students to use a **straightedge*** to draw any angle on their papers and label it *ABC,* then go through steps A–E on pages 530–531 to copy the angle. When students finish, have them use a **protractor*** to measure the pair of angles to see that they are congruent. Then, have students work individually on problems 6–8.

◆ LESSON 150 Compass Constructions

Centuries ago, Greek mathematicians challenged themselves to draw angles and geometric figures using only an unmarked straightedge and a compass.

You can copy angles and lines segments with a compass and a straightedge (a ruler, for example). You could do it more easily with a straightedge and a protractor, but it is interesting to see how to do it with only a compass, just as the Greeks did.

To copy ∠ABC, you would follow these steps:

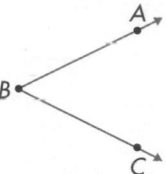

A. Draw a line segment. This will be one side of the angle you are drawing. Choose a point (let's call it Q) to be the vertex of the new angle.

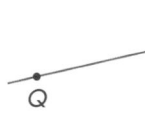 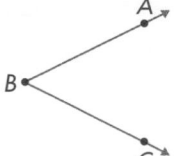

B. Using B as the center, draw part of a circle (an **arc**). Make the arc long enough so that it crosses both sides of the angle. (Let's call the two crossing points M and N.)

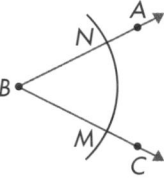

C. With the same compass setting you used in step B, draw an arc with the center at Q. (Let's call the point X where the arc crosses the line.)

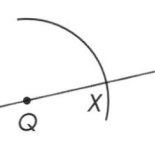 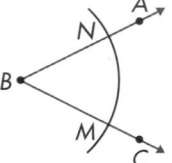

Technology Connection Refer students to the software *Geometry Inventory* from Logal (Mac, for grades 6–12) for practice with points, lines, circles, triangles, quadrilaterals, and polygons.

*available separately

D. Put the point of the compass at *M*. Set the compass so that the pencil point just touches *N*. Using this new setting, draw an arc with the center at *X*. Make sure the arc crosses the arc you drew in step C. (Let's call the point where the arcs meet *P*.)

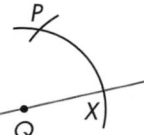 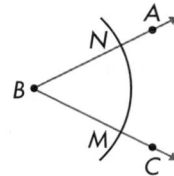

E. Draw line *QP*. Then ∠*ABC* = ∠*PQX*.

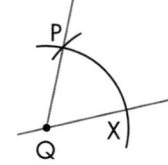 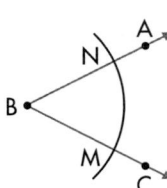

6 Draw any angle.

   a. Copy the angle with a compass and a straightedge. **Check students' work.**

   b. Measure both angles with your protractor. **Check students' work.**

   c. Do they have about the same measure? **yes**

7 Use your protractor to draw a 120° angle.

   a. Copy it with a compass and a straightedge. **Check students' work.**

   b. Measure the new angle. **Check students' work.**

   c. Is it about 120°? **yes**

8 Trace or use your protractor to draw a 90° angle.

   a. Copy the angle. **Check students' work.**

   b. Copy the angle again on each side of the angle you drew in step a.
Check students' work.

   c. Look at the figure created by the sides of the angles. What is the name of this figure? **rectangle**

Unit 6   Lesson 150 • **531**

GIFTED & TALENTED   **MANIPULATIVES**   **Meeting Individual Needs**
Challenge students to use a **compass** and **straightedge*** to construct perpendicular lines and to construct a square.

*available separately

◆ LESSON 150 Compass Constructions

Teach

Using the Student Pages Review the definition of *congruent*, and go through steps A–E with the class.

Have students complete problem 10 on page 533 and then measure and check for congruence. Have students work on problems 11 and 12 individually or in pairs, then discuss their findings as a group. If students have difficulty with problem 11, explain that they can first draw a line and copy an angle equal to one of the angles of the triangle, say, *B*. Then they can mark off a length equal to *BC*, then copy angle *C*.

If students have difficulty with problem 12, suggest that they draw a line and mark off a segment equal to *BC*. Then, using *B'* as the center, make an arc with a radius equal to *BA*. Then, with *C'* as center, make an arc with a radius equal to *CA*. Where the two arcs meet is point *A'*. Draw *A'B'* and draw *A'C'*. Triangle *A'B'C'* is congruent to triangle *ABC*.

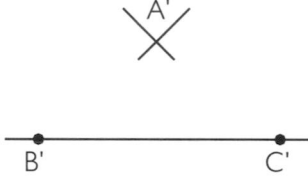

(Note that point *A'* could also be drawn below *B'C'*, and the resulting triangle would still be congruent to *ABC*.)

After working through these procedures, students can discover that the quickest and easiest way to copy a triangle is to copy three sides. Guide students to use whatever method they prefer whenever they need to copy triangles.

◆ LESSON 150 Compass Constructions

Remember, congruent figures are figures that would exactly fit on each other if you cut one out and placed it on the other.

Two triangles are congruent if their corresponding angles and corresponding sides are the same size.

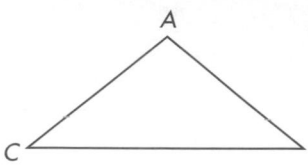

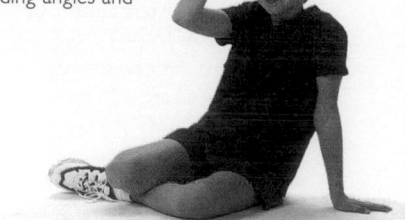

To construct a triangle congruent to triangle *ABC*, you would follow these steps:

A. Draw a line (call it *PX*).

B. Set your compass by placing its point at *C* and the pencil at *B* on the triangle. With this setting draw an arc with *P* as the center. Mark point *Q*. (*PQ* corresponds to side *CB* of triangle *ABC*.)

C. Copy ∠*C* with *P* as the vertex and *PQ* as one side. (Pages 530–531 show you how to copy an angle.) You may extend side *CA* a bit to make this easier.

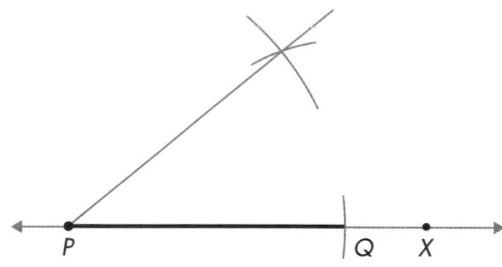

532 • Geometry

D. Mark off *PR* so that it is the same length as *AC*.

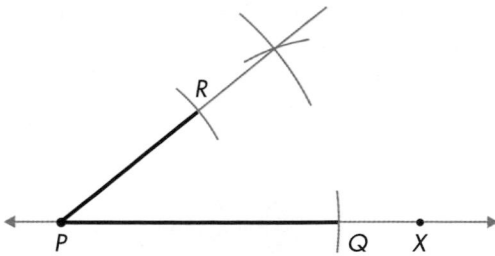

E. Draw side *RQ*.

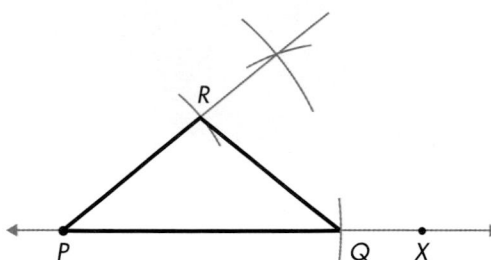

Notice that we copied only three parts of the triangle: a side, a vertex, and another side.

9 Are the other three parts the same as in the original triangle? **yes**

10 Draw any triangle. Label it *ABC*. Use a compass and a straightedge to draw a congruent triangle. **Check students' work.**

   a. To check that the triangles are congruent, measure all three sides and all three angles of each triangle.

   b. Are the corresponding parts the same size? **yes**

11 Now you know how to make a congruent triangle by copying two sides and the angle between them. Try to make a congruent triangle by copying two angles and the side between them. Measure the other parts to check. **Check students' work.**

12 Try to copy a triangle by copying three sides and no angles. (Hint: Copy one side. From each endpoint, draw an arc with a radius equal to the length of the corresponding side.) Measure the angles to check that the triangles are congruent. **Check students' work.**

---

❸ Wrap-Up

In Closing To summarize the lesson, ask students to describe how they would construct a triangle congruent to another triangle.

 **Performance Assessment** Have students use a straightedge to draw a triangle on their paper. Then ask them to make a copy of it using only a compass and a straightedge.

Assessment Criteria

Did the student . . .

✓ demonstrate understanding of the concept of congruence?

✓ correctly use a compass to construct congruent segments, angles, and triangles?

Homework Invite students to create and color a design using a compass, protractor, or other tools.

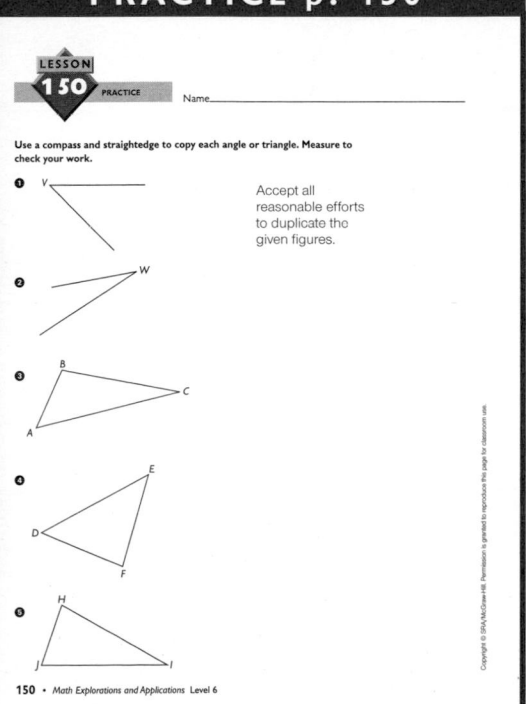

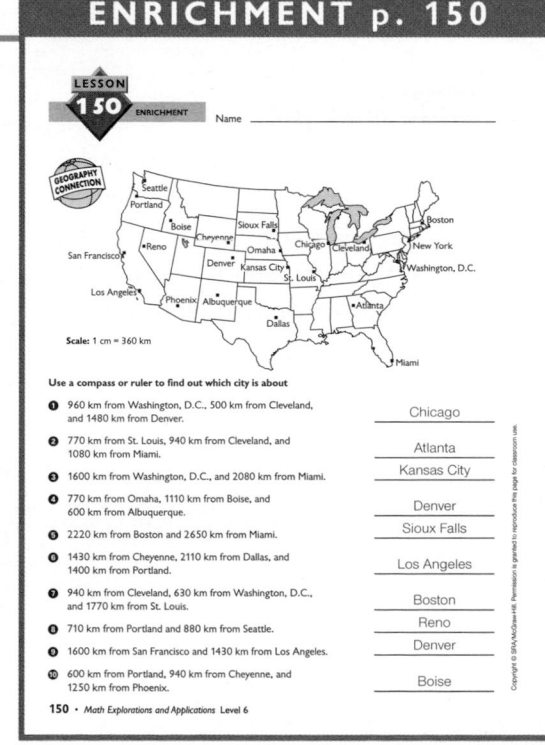

LESSON 151

Student Edition pages 534–537

Circle Graphs

Circle Graphs

Circle graphs are often used to show information. They are especially used to show what fraction or percent of the whole certain parts are. For example, this circle graph gives a picture of what fraction of our presidents belonged to each political party.

Political Parties of United States Presidents, 1787–1996

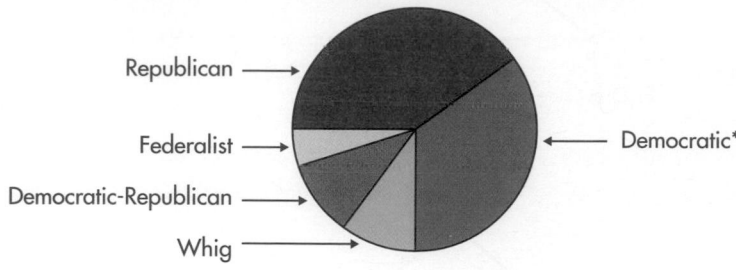

* Grover Cleveland was counted twice because his terms of office were not consecutive.

SOCIAL STUDIES CONNECTION

◆ Which of the five political parties shown has had the fewest presidents? **Federalist Party**

Two United States presidents belonged to the Federalist party.

◆ How many presidents do you think belonged to the Democratic-Republican party? **4**

◆ About how many belonged to the Democratic party? **about 15**

◆ To which two parties did the same number of presidents belong? **Whig and Democratic-Republican**

◆ About what fraction of presidents belonged to either the Democratic or the Republican party? $\frac{3}{4}$

◆ Do you know which two of our presidents were members of the Federalist party? If you do not, research to find the answer. **George Washington, John Adams**

LESSON PLANNER

Objective

▶ to demonstrate how to read and construct a circle graph

Context of the Lesson This lesson provides an opportunity for students to use their proportional reasoning in the common and useful application of circles as a way to display data.

 **MANIPULATIVES** | **Program Resources**

calculators* | Practice Master 151

compasses | Enrichment Master 151

protractors* | **The Cruncher*:** *Mystery Population*

| **The Cruncher*:** *Go for Fun Survey*

| For extra practice:
CD-ROM* Lesson 151
Cumulative Review, page 586

① Warm-Up ⏱

Problem of the Day Present the following information, drawings, and problem:

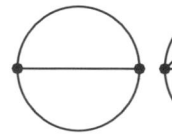  

Notice the number of regions that are formed when two, three, and four points on a circle are linked. How many regions will be formed when five points are connected? Six points? (16 regions; 31 regions)

Problem-Solving Strategies Ask students who have solved the Problem of the Day to share how they solved it and any strategies they used.

MENTAL MATH Have students give the percent equivalent for each of the following common fractions:

(continued on page 535)

Why teach it at this time?

Students have studied percents, angles, and circles. Now they can put the concepts together to make a graph that uses all these concepts to effectively present certain kinds of information.

---

*available separately

To make a circle graph, follow these steps:

A. Decide what fraction (or percent) of the circle should be used for each category. We call a fraction or part of a circle a **sector**.

B. Decide how many degrees should be in each sector of the circle. There are 360 degrees in a circle.

C. Draw a circle and locate its center. Then use a protractor to measure off each sector.

For example, here is how one of the sectors in the circle graph on page 534 might have been made. Let's take the Democratic party sector.

A. There are 42 presidents in all shown on the graph. If 15 of them belonged to the Democratic party, then we can say that $\frac{15}{42}$ were Democrats. We can also say that about 36% were Democrats. (Remember that to express a fraction as a percent, you divide the numerator by the denominator and multiply the resulting decimal by 100.)

B. The sector for the Democratic party should be 36% of 360° or about 129°.

Use a computer or other means to make and complete this chart. Consider using spreadsheet software. Then use the chart to make a circle graph like the one on page 534.

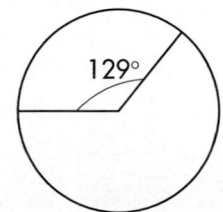

129°

Political Party	Number of Presidents Who Belonged	Fraction of Presidents Who Belonged	Percent of Presidents Who Belonged	Number of Degrees in Sector of Circle
Republican	17	■ $\frac{17}{42}$	■ 40%	■ 146
Democratic	15	$\frac{15}{42}$	36%	129
Whig	4	$\frac{4}{42}$ ■ (or $\frac{2}{21}$)	■ 9.5%	■ 34
Democratic-Republican	4	$\frac{4}{42}$ ■ (or $\frac{2}{21}$)	■ 9.5%	■ 34
Federalist	2	$\frac{2}{42}$ ■ (or $\frac{1}{21}$)	■ 5%	■ 17
Total	42	$\frac{42}{42}$ ■ (or 1)	■ 100%	■ 360°

Unit 6   Lesson 151 • **535**

Literature Connection Have students read the epilogue of *How to Get Fabulously Rich* by Thomas Rockwell, and then graph the amount of the prize each participant received.

Mental Math (continued)

a. $\frac{1}{2}$ (50%)		**b.** $\frac{3}{4}$ (75%)		**c.** $\frac{1}{3}$ ($33\frac{1}{3}$%)	
d. $\frac{2}{5}$ (40%)		**e.** $\frac{7}{8}$ ($87\frac{1}{2}$%)		**f.** $\frac{1}{8}$ ($12\frac{1}{2}$%)	
g. $\frac{1}{4}$ (25%)		**h.** $\frac{4}{5}$ (80%)		**i.** $\frac{2}{3}$ ($66\frac{2}{3}$%)	
j. $\frac{3}{10}$ (30%)		**k.** $\frac{3}{8}$ ($37\frac{1}{2}$%)		**l.** $\frac{9}{10}$ (90%)	

❷ Teach

Using the Student Pages Discuss the circle graph shown. You may want to mention that circle graphs are also called pie charts. Emphasize that this graph does not show actual numbers, in this case, the number of presidents from each party. Like many circle graphs, it shows only relative proportions. Point out that the size of each sector of the graph represents the fractional proportion of presidents from that party among the total number of presidents. Guide students to understand that if they knew the total number of presidents or the number from any one party, they could then estimate the other numbers. Have students work on the discussion questions independently or in small groups.

After discussing the steps for making the graph on page 535, go through the example of how the size of one sector is calculated. Then have students work in pairs to complete the chart and make the graph. It is not necessary for students' answers to match those shown exactly, as differences may result from rounding. Note also that the size of the circle and the placement of the sectors on the graph may differ from person to person, but that the relative sizes and central angle of each sector should not vary. Some students may need a quick review of how to use a **compass**.

You may need to demonstrate how to use a **protractor*** to make the central angles for the circle graph. It might be effective to have peer tutors show classmates a correct method.

Students may use **The Cruncher***: *Mystery Population* spreadsheet to create the graph.

*available separately

◆ LESSON 151 Circle Graphs

Teach

Using the Student Pages Have students work individually on the problems on pages 536–537. Encourage them to use **calculators*** when determining the fraction that expresses the relationship between each make of car and the total number of cars. Advise students to check their own work. For example, point out that it is good practice to add the number of degrees for all categories to be sure that the sum is 360. Remind students to label the sectors of their graphs correctly and to give their graphs a title.

Students can use **The Cruncher***: *Go for Fun Survey* to help them create the circle graph for problem 1.

◆ LESSON 151 Circle Graphs

Kamal collected data to see what color shirts students wore to school. Kamal counted 400 people the first day. He recorded his results in a table.

Use the table to solve the following problems.

Shirt Color	Number of Children
Brown or tan	80
White	100
Blue	60
Green	60
Yellow	40
Other	60
Total	**400**

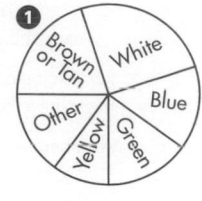

① Use a computer or other means to make a circle graph to show the information in the chart.

② If someone wore a blue and red striped shirt, did Kamal count it as both blue and red? How can you tell? **No—the total shirts recorded equals the total people counted, so each shirt was counted only once.**

③ Suppose the school has 800 students. Do you think Kamal's results would be about the same if he had counted all 800 students? Why or why not? **The results would probably be about the same because one half is a representative group.**

④ If Kamal counted 400 students the following day, would his results be the same? Why or why not? **The results would be similar but not identical because people wear different clothes each day.**

⑤ If Kamal counted students and made circle graphs each day for a week, would the graphs look very different or about the same? Explain. **The graphs would probably look about the same because the number of people was great enough that small variations wouldn't matter much.**

536 · Geometry

 **Technology Connection** Refer students to the software *GraphPower* from Ventura Educational Systems (Mac, for grades K–8) for practice in selecting appropriate formats. Graph forms available include pictograph, vertical/horizontal bar graphs, line graphs, circle graphs, and box-and-whisker graphs.

RETEACHING

Some students may have difficulty expressing fractions as percents and in taking percents of 360. Work through one or two examples, using round numbers. Invite these students to use calculators to do the division and multiplication.

AT RISK **Meeting Individual Needs**
You may wish to provide students who are at risk with data to graph that are of more interest to them (sales of music videos and CDs by category, or basketball salaries by team, for example). Invite students to make suggestions for topics and then work together to come up with reasonable estimates that they can use for their graphs.

*available separately

⑥ This chart shows the number of cars made by major manufacturers in the United States during a recent year. (The numbers are rounded to the nearest thousand.)

Manufacturer	Number of Cars
Honda®	499,000
Chrysler® Corporation	551,000
Ford Motor® Corporation	1,221,000
General Motors® Corporation	2,720,000
Toyota®	399,000
Total	**5,390,000**

⑦

⑦ Make a circle graph to show this information.

⑧ What other kinds of graphs would be appropriate for this information? **possible answers: bar graph, pictograph**

Find a graph in a newspaper or magazine. In your Math Journal explain why that type of graph was chosen to represent the data.

Use the Cumulative Review on page 586 after this lesson.

Unit 6   Lesson 151 • **537**

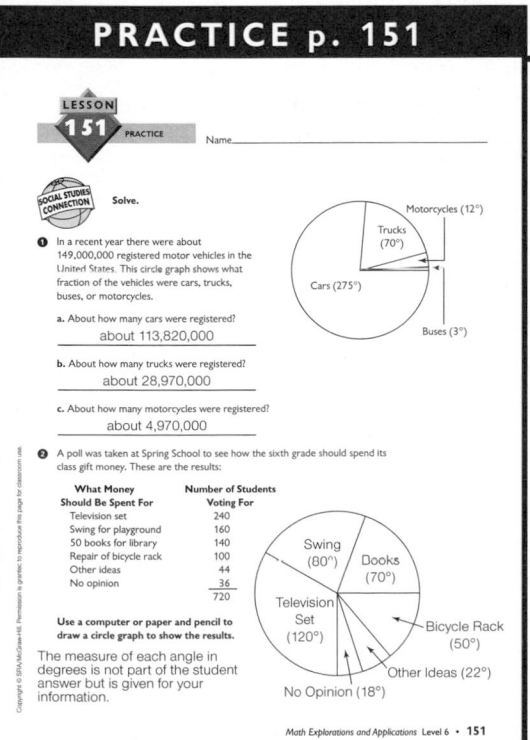

LESSON 151 PRACTICE   Name _____

SOCIAL STUDIES CONNECTION   Solve.

❶ In a recent year there were about 149,000,000 registered motor vehicles in the United States. This circle graph shows what fraction of the vehicles were cars, trucks, buses, or motorcycles.

Motorcycles (12°)
Trucks (70°)
Cars (275°)
Buses (3°)

a. About how many cars were registered?
about 113,820,000

b. About how many trucks were registered?
about 28,970,000

c. About how many motorcycles were registered?
about 4,970,000

❷ A poll was taken at Spring School to see how the sixth grade should spend its class gift money. These are the results:

What Money Should Be Spent For	Number of Students Voting For
Television set	240
Swing for playground	160
50 books for library	140
Repair of bicycle rack	100
Other ideas	44
No opinion	36
	720

Use a computer or paper and pencil to draw a circle graph to show the results.

The measure of each angle in degrees is not part of the student answer but is given for your information.

Swing (80°)
Books (70°)
Television Set (120°)
Bicycle Rack (50°)
Other Ideas (22°)
No Opinion (18°)

Math Explorations and Applications Level 6 • 151

LESSON 151 ENRICHMENT   Name _____

Take a survey of what your friends like to do for fun on weekends. Use **The Cruncher: Go for Fun Survey** project to help you total your survey responses and then graph your results.

Begin by developing appropriate questions for your survey.

❶ What questions might you ask about what your friends like to do when they are at home?
Answers will vary.

❷ What questions might you ask about what your friends like to do when they go out?
_____

Take a survey of your friends and enter the data in The Cruncher.

❸ Make a circle graph of your results.

❹ Make a bar graph of your results.

Math Explorations and Applications Level 6 • 151

---

③ Wrap-Up ⏱ 5 MINUTES

In Closing To summarize the lesson, ask students to explain how circle graphs are similar to and different from bar graphs. Ask them to describe what circle graphs show about data and to suggest what kinds of data circle graphs are most useful for showing.

Informal Assessment Circulate through the room and observe students as they make graphs of the car data. Check to see that they are correctly using the protractor to make the central angles and that they label their graphs appropriately. You may wish to ask students to summarize what their graphs show about the data or to describe interesting facts about the data.

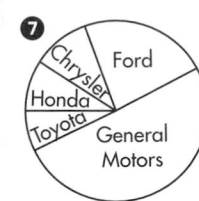

Assessment Criteria

Did the student . . .

✓ demonstrate ability to read and interpret a circle graph?

✓ express understanding of the kinds of information about data a circle graph provides?

✓ demonstrate ability to make a circle graph from a given set of data?

Homework Have students determine how they or one of their pets spends a typical day. Have them list the daily activities and give the time in hours for each, as well as the percent of the whole day that each activity fills. Ask them to make a circle graph to show their data.

Student Edition pages 538–539

LESSON 152

Right Triangles: Squares of Sides

LESSON PLANNER

Objectives

▶ to provide an opportunity to explore the Pythagorean theorem

▶ to provide practice using the Pythagorean theorem to find the length of a triangle's hypotenuse given the lengths of the two shorter sides

Context of the Lesson This is an enrichment lesson relating previous work with angles and sides of polygons to finding areas and square roots.

MANIPULATIVES

calculators*

graph paper

Program Resources

Practice Master 152

Enrichment Master 152

For extra practice:
CD-ROM* Lesson 152

① Warm-Up ⏱ 5 MINUTES

Problem of the Day Present the following problem to the class: The sum of the squares of four consecutive numbers is 734. What are the numbers? (12, 13, 14, and 15)

Problem-Solving Strategies Ask students who have solved the Problem of the Day to share how they solved it and any strategies they used.

Ask students to give the squares of the following numbers: 1, 2, 3, 4, 5, 6, 7, 70, 80, 90, and 900. (1, 4, 9, 16, 25, 36, 49, 4900, 6400, 8100, and 810,000)

② Teach

COOPERATIVE LEARNING **Using the Student Pages** Have students work on the problems on pages 538–539 in pairs or small groups. You may want to have **graph paper** available for students. Explain that the examples provided do not prove that the Pythagorean theorem is true, but they indicate that it might be true. Point out that the proof is too complicated to present now, but the theorem can indeed be proved true for all right triangles.

538 Geometry

Right Triangles: Squares of Sides

Look at △ABC. The length of AC is 1 centimeter, and the length of CB is 1 centimeter.

① What is the area of the red square? **1 cm²**

② What is the area of the green square? **1 cm²**

③ What is the area of the blue square? (Hint: Add the areas of the four triangles that make up the blue square.) **2 cm²**

④ Is it true that the sum of the areas of the squares on the two short sides of right triangle ABC is the same as the area of the square on the long side? **yes**

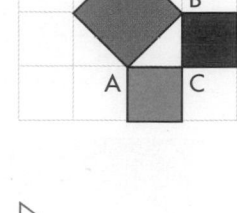

On your paper very carefully draw a right triangle in which the two shorter sides are 3 centimeters long and 4 centimeters long.

⑤ Measure the length of the longest side. **about 5 cm**

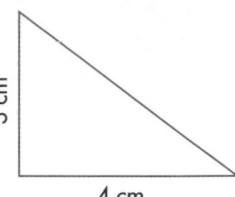

⑥ What is the area of a square with each side 3 cm long? **9 cm²**

⑦ What is the area of a square with each side 4 cm long? **16 cm²**

⑧ What is the area of a square with each side 5 cm long? **25 cm²**

⑨ Is it true in your right triangle that the area of the square on the longest side equals the sum of the areas of the squares on the shorter sides? **yes**

The long side of the right triangle is called the **hypotenuse.** More than 2500 years ago, a Greek mathematician named Pythagoras proved that for any right triangle, the area of the square of the hypotenuse is equal to the sum of the areas of the squares of the other two sides.

538 · Geometry

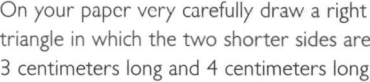

Art Connection Invite students to use graph paper to create a design that consists of tessellating triangles. Ask them to color in a portion of the design that would make a larger triangle. Invite them to illustrate the Pythagorean theorem by measuring the legs and calculating the hypotenuse from the data.

RETEACHING

Reteaching is not needed at this time.

538 Geometry

*available separately

The statement that Pythagoras proved is called the **Pythagorean theorem.** You can use the Pythagorean theorem to find the length of one side of a right triangle if you know the lengths of the other two sides.

Example:

Antonio walked 2 kilometers south and then 3 kilometers east. About how far will he have to go if he walks directly back to his starting point?

$$2 \times 2 = 4$$
$$3 \times 3 = 9$$
$$4 + 9 = 13$$

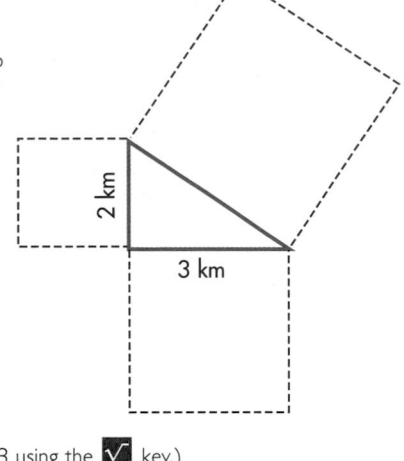

So the area of the big square is 13 square kilometers. Using a calculator, we can find a number that we can multiply by itself to get about 13.

$$3.605 \times 3.605 = 12.996025$$
$$3.606 \times 3.606 = 13.003236$$

(We could also have found the square root of 13 using the $\sqrt{}$ key.)

A side of the big square is a bit more than 3.6 kilometers. So Antonio must walk a bit more than 3.6 kilometers back to the starting point.

10 In each case the lengths of the two shorter sides of a right triangle are given. Find the length of the hypotenuse. Use the Pythagorean theorem. Give answers to the nearest tenth of a centimeter.

a. 6 cm, 8 cm **10 cm** **b.** 5 cm, 12 cm **13 cm** **c.** 9 cm, 12 cm **15 cm**

d. 1 cm, 1 cm **1.4 cm** **e.** 4 cm, 6 cm **7.2 cm** **f.** 2 cm, 3 cm **3.6 cm**

g. 3 cm, 6 cm **6.7 cm** **h.** 1 cm, 2 cm **2.2 cm** **i.** 2 cm, 2 cm **2.8 cm**

11 Use a protractor and a ruler to carefully draw each right triangle described in problem 10. Then measure the length of each hypotenuse. Are these measurements the same as the calculations you made in problem 10? **They should be close.**

12 Crystal is walking around a park by going 40 feet west and 30 feet north. How much shorter would her walk be if she cut through the park diagonally? **20 feet shorter**

13 Is it possible for a hypotenuse to be one of the sides of the right angle in a right triangle? **no**

Unit 6 Lesson 152 • **539**

Have students estimate the square roots first, then check their answers with a **calculator***. Note that if students work carefully, their measurements for problem 11 should be close to the values calculated for problem 10 on page 539.

❸ Wrap-Up ⏱ 5 MINUTES

In Closing To summarize the lesson, ask students to explain how to find the hypotenuse of a right triangle given the lengths of the other two sides.

ALTERNATIVE ASSESSMENT **Performance Assessment** Tell students that a ramp is being built from the edge of a 6-foot tall dock to a point on the ground 8 feet from the base of the dock. Ask them to tell, step by step, how they would find the length of the ramp.

Assessment Criteria

Did the student . . .

✓ express understanding of the relationship between the lengths of the two shorter sides and the hypotenuse of any right triangle?

✓ demonstrate understanding of the procedure for approximating the square root of a number?

Homework Have interested students do research to find out more about the life and work of Pythagoras, including his academy and the society he started that bears his name. Students may also research other cultures, such as the Chinese and Babylonians, who knew and used the Pythagorean theorem many centuries before Pythagoras was born. Invite students to present their findings to the class.

GIFTED & TALENTED **Meeting Individual Needs** Challenge students to explain how to find the length of a side of a right triangle given the length of another side and the hypotenuse. (square each; subtract the square of the other side from the square of the hypotenuse; find the square root of that difference)

Using the Student Pages
Use this Unit Review as a preliminary unit test to indicate areas in which an individual student is having difficulty or in which the entire class may need help. If students do not do well on the Unit Review, you may want to spend a day or so helping them overcome their individual difficulties before they take the Unit Test.

Next to each instruction line is a list of the lessons in the unit covered in that set of problems. Students can refer to the specific lesson for additional instruction if they need help. You can also use this information to make additional assignments based on the previous lesson concepts.

Problems 1–5
If a student misses more than one of these problems involving finding area, check to see what the difficulty is. Redevelop the formulas as shown in the appropriate lessons for those students who have difficulty remembering them. Help those students who have trouble deciding which lengths or distances to measure. Encourage those students who have trouble solving problem 4 to break up the figures into smaller parts that they can handle.

Problems 6–8
If either problem 6 or 7 is missed, have the student draw a picture of the figure, tell what information is needed, and explain how he or she could check to see if a given answer was correct. Give similar extra help to students who miss problem 8, but point out the need for getting successively better approximations.

Problems 9 and 10
Have students who missed either of these problems about finding volume and surface area build a model with cubes and then do the problem. They should explain whether they are being asked to find the total number of cubes or the squares showing and then try to find a more efficient procedure for getting the answer.

Find the area in square centimeters of each of these figures.

Lessons 128–131

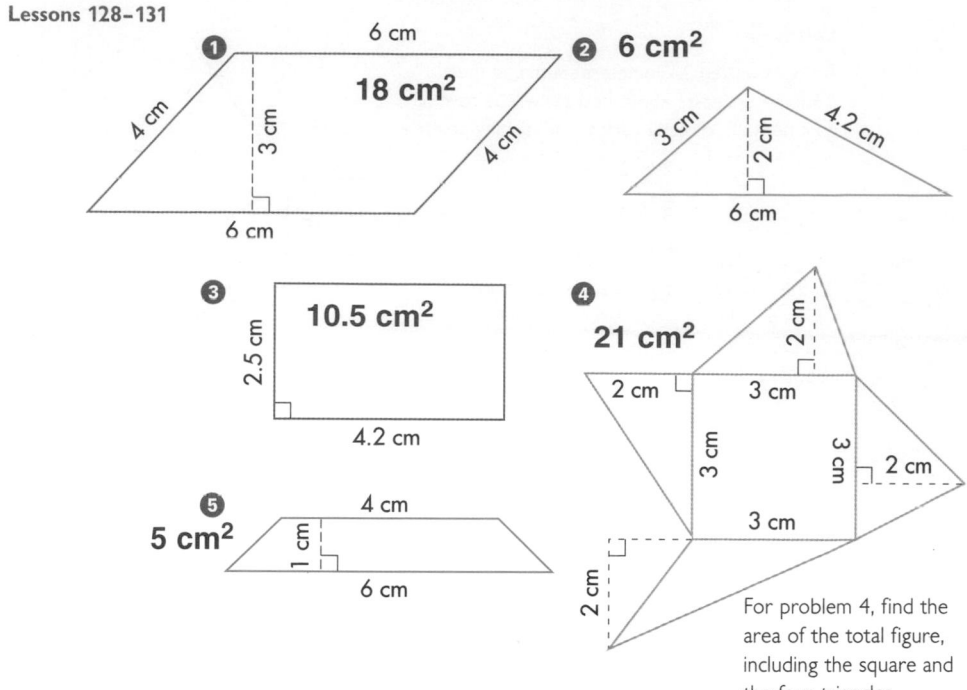

For problem 4, find the area of the total figure, including the square and the four triangles.

Lessons 125, 126, 135, and 136

Solve the following problems.

6 The area of a rectangle is 28 square centimeters, and its base is 7 centimeters long. What is its height? **4 cm**

7 The area of a square is 81 square centimeters. What is the length of a side? **9 cm**

8 The area of a square is 10 square centimeters. To the nearest tenth of a centimeter, how long is a side? **3.2 cm**

9 A rectangular box is 7 centimeters long, 3 centimeters wide, and 4 centimeters tall. What is the volume of the box in cubic centimeters? **84 cm³**

10 What is the total area of the six faces of the box in problem 9? **122 cm²**

540 · Geometry

RETEACHING

Students who have difficulty with this Unit Review should have further opportunity to review and to practice the skills before they proceed. For each set of problems there are specific suggestions for reteaching. These suggestions can be found in the margins.

Lesson 139   Answer the following questions.

Remember: There are 100 centimeters in a meter.
　　　　　　　There are 1000 meters in a kilometer.

⑪ How many grams are in a kilogram? **1000**

⑫ How many centigrams are in a gram? **100**

⑬ How many centimeters are in a kilometer? **100,000**

⑭ How many centiliters are in a kiloliter? **100,000**

⑮ At which of these outdoor temperatures would you be most comfortable?

　　a. 0°C　**b.** 20°C　**c.** 50°C　**d.** 70°C　**e.** 100°C

Lesson 144   Use your protractor to measure each of these angles.

⑯ ∠A **46°** **⑰** ∠B **98°** **⑱** ∠C **36°** **⑲** ∠JEF **61°**

⑳ ∠JHI **61°** **㉑** ∠DEH **61°** **㉒** ∠FEH **119°** **㉓** ∠GHE **119°**

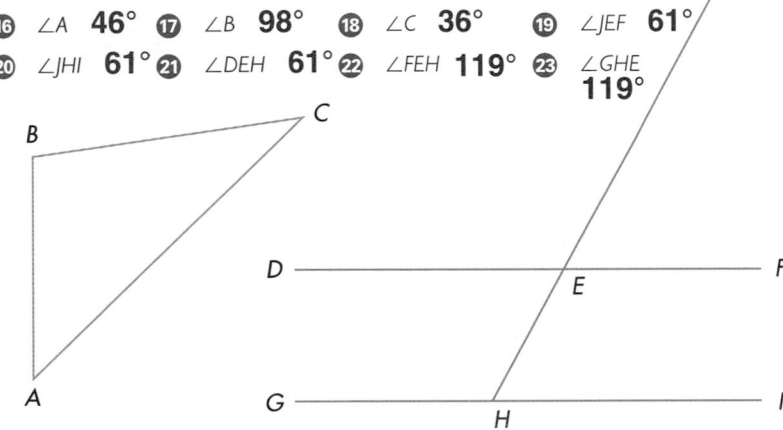

Lessons 143 and 148   Answer the following questions.

㉔ If two lines are perpendicular, what is the measure of the angle they make when they meet? **90°**

㉕ How many planes contain both points A and B? **an infinite number**

B
•

A
•

PRACTICE p. 153

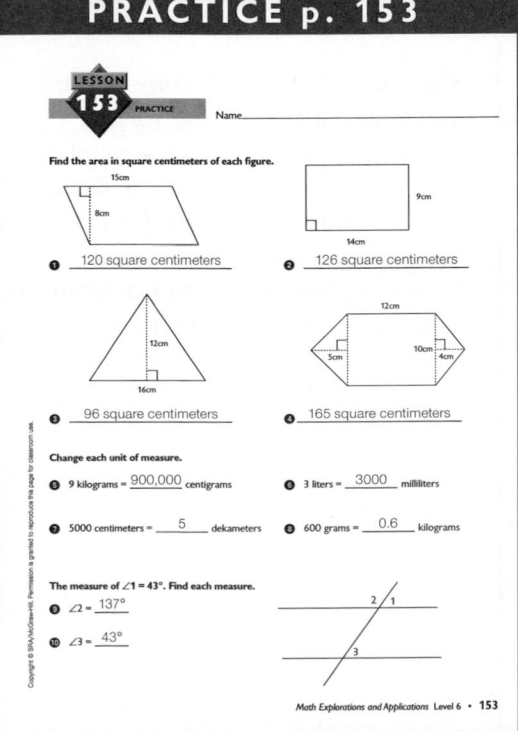

ENRICHMENT p. 153

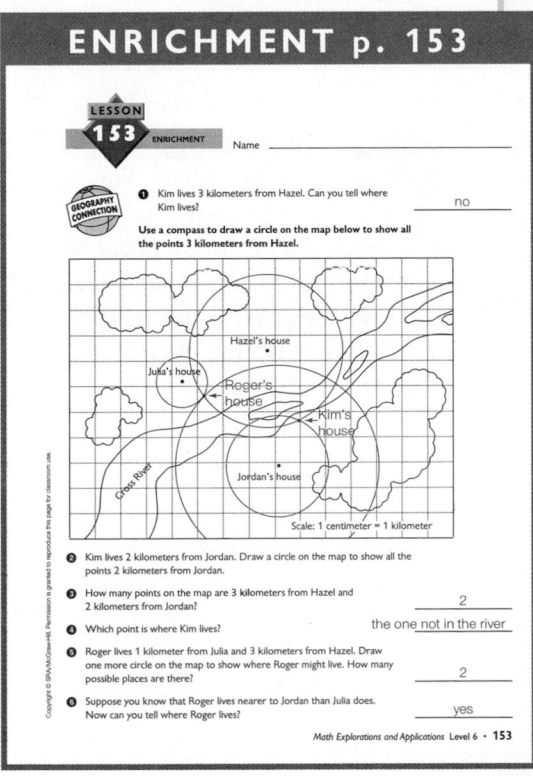

Problems 11–15 Check to see whether students who missed more than one of these problems involving converting among metric units have overlooked the conversion data at the top of the page. Have them redo the problems. Basic facts about the Celsius scale should help students who miss problem 15. Remind them that 0° is the temperature at which water freezes, 100° is the temperature at which water boils, and that about 37° is normal human body temperature, which would be a very hot day.

Problems 16–23 Give reteaching to students who miss more than two of these problems involving measuring angles by more than 2° by referring to the suggestions in Lesson 144.

Problems 24 and 25 Students who miss problem 24 should be asked to identify and then draw perpendicular lines. Next have them measure the right angles formed. Try to go through problem 25 with those students who had an incorrect answer. Use a piece of paper or cardboard as a model of a plane. Rotate the paper so that it swings on the line through A and B as though swinging on a hinge. The students should then be able to see that there is an infinite number of planes through A and B.

 **Portfolio Assessment** If you have not already assigned the Portfolio Assessment task provided on Assessment Blackline Masters page 91, it can be used at this time to evaluate students' ability to solve problems involving area, perimeter, and angle measurement.

 **Performance Assessment** The Performance Assessment Task 2 provided on Assessment Blackline Masters pages 82–83 can be used at this time to evaluate students' proficiency with measurement, angles, and constructions. You may want to administer this assessment with individual students or in small groups.

Unit Project If you have not already assigned the "Melting Ice Cubes" project on pages 550 and 551, you may wish to do so at this time. This project is a good opportunity for students to apply the concept of setting up an experiment and analyzing results using surface area in real-world problem solving.

Unit 6 Practice

Using the Student Pages The purpose of Lesson 154 is to provide additional practice for those students who demonstrated a need for it on the Unit Review. You may wish to assign only the specific exercises in each Unit Practice in which students need further reinforcement. Each instruction line gives the lessons in the unit it covers so that you or students can refer to the specific lesson for additional review and instruction.

 Students who do not require additional practice on specific concepts may enjoy playing any of the games you have played so far, such as the "Three Questions" game on page 473, which involves classifying polygons and using deductions. These students may also help by practicing flashcard drills and playing appropriate games with students who need remedial practice or by actually teaching certain procedures to other students.

Unit 6 Practice

Lessons 128–131   Find the area in square centimeters of each of these figures.

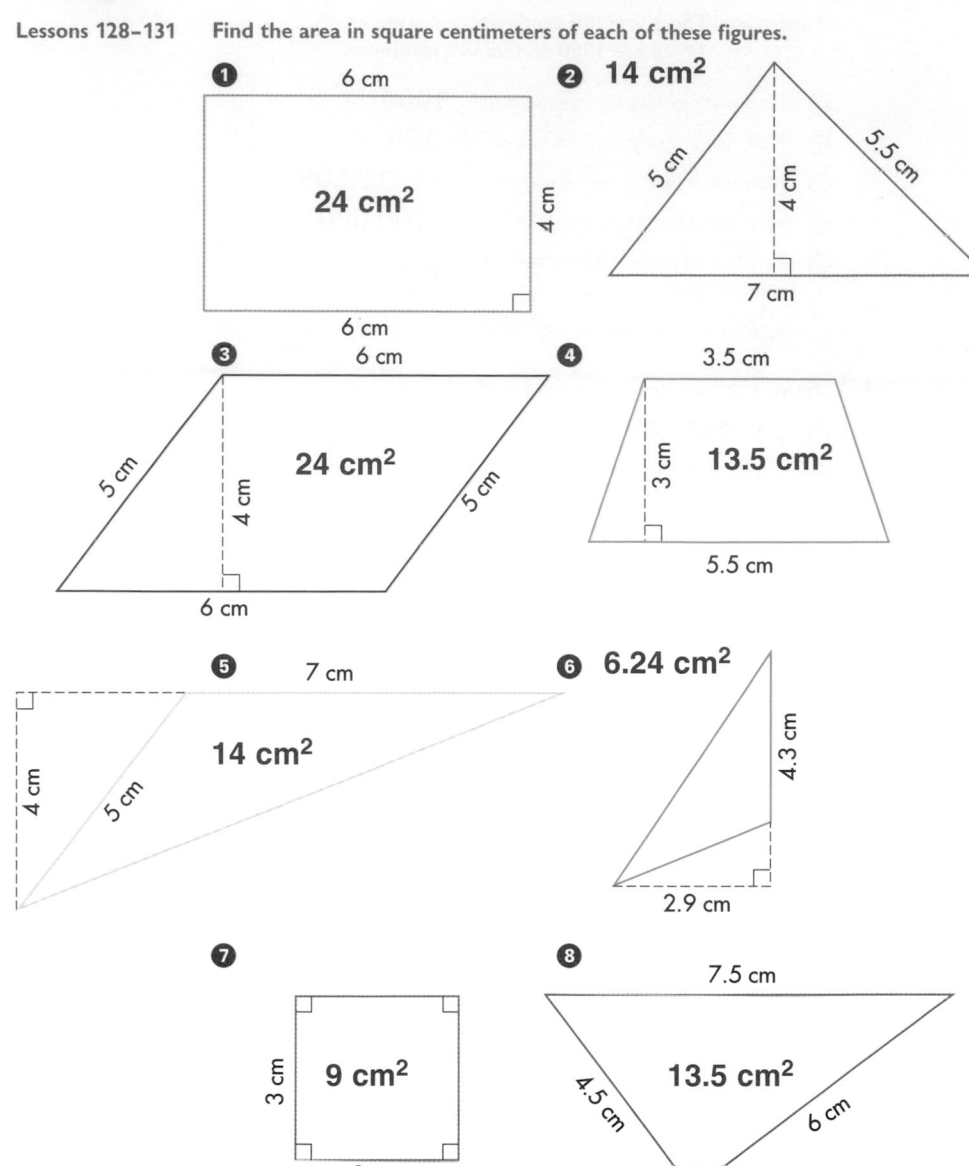

❶ 6 cm · 24 cm² · 6 cm · 4 cm

❷ 14 cm² · 5 cm · 4 cm · 5.5 cm · 7 cm

❸ 6 cm · 5 cm · 24 cm² · 4 cm · 5 cm · 6 cm

❹ 3.5 cm · 3 cm · 13.5 cm² · 5.5 cm

❺ 7 cm · 4 cm · 5 cm · 14 cm²

❻ 6.24 cm² · 4.3 cm · 2.9 cm

❼ 3 cm · 9 cm² · 3 cm

❽ 7.5 cm · 4.5 cm · 13.5 cm² · 6 cm

542 · Geometry

 **Technology Connection** You may want to refer students to the software *Home Grade Level Math Programs* from Josten Home Learning (Mac, IBM, for grade 6) for further practice with math topics commonly taught at the sixth grade level.

RETEACHING

Students who have difficulty with this Unit Practice should have further opportunity to review and to practice the skills before they proceed. Beside each set of problems is a reference to the lesson or lessons from which the problems were taken. You may want to review the individual lessons with students who are having difficulty with them.

Lessons 124, 128, 131, and 152

Answer the following questions.

9 Find the area in square centimeters of each of the three squares and the triangle.

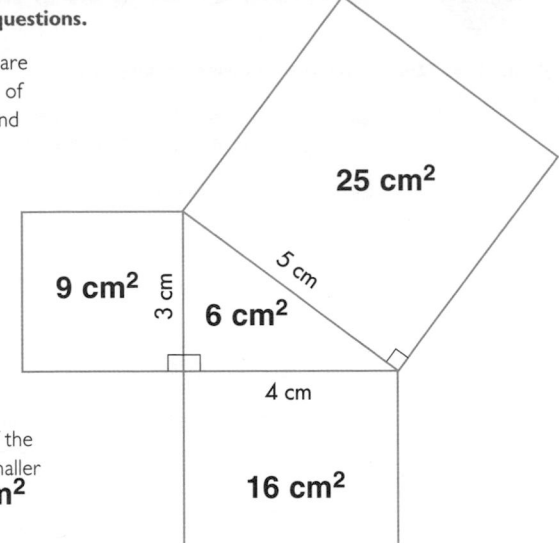

25 cm²

9 cm²

3 cm

6 cm²

5 cm

4 cm

16 cm²

10 What is the sum of the areas of the two smaller squares? **25 cm²**

11 How does the answer to problem 10 compare to the area of the largest square?

They are the same.

12 What is the total area of the figure at the right? **30 cm²**

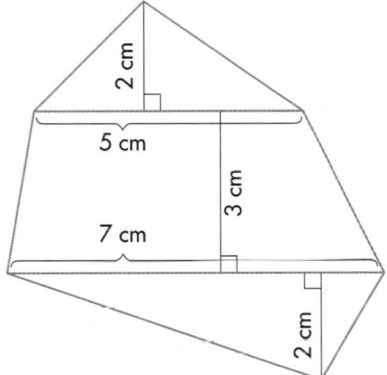

2 cm

5 cm

3 cm

7 cm

2 cm

Unit 6 Practice • **543**

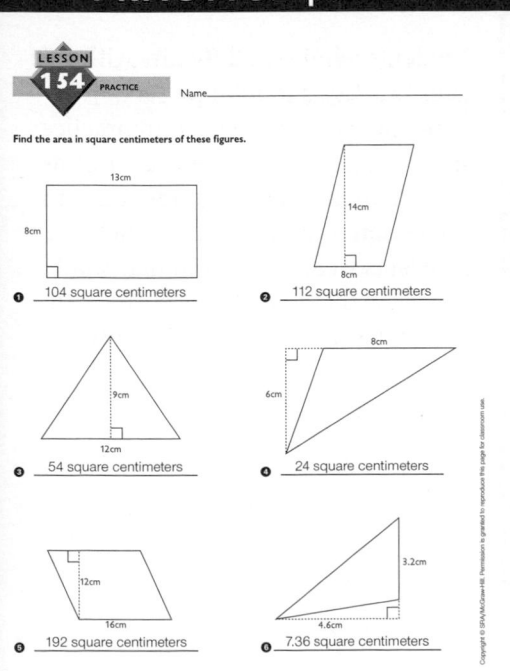
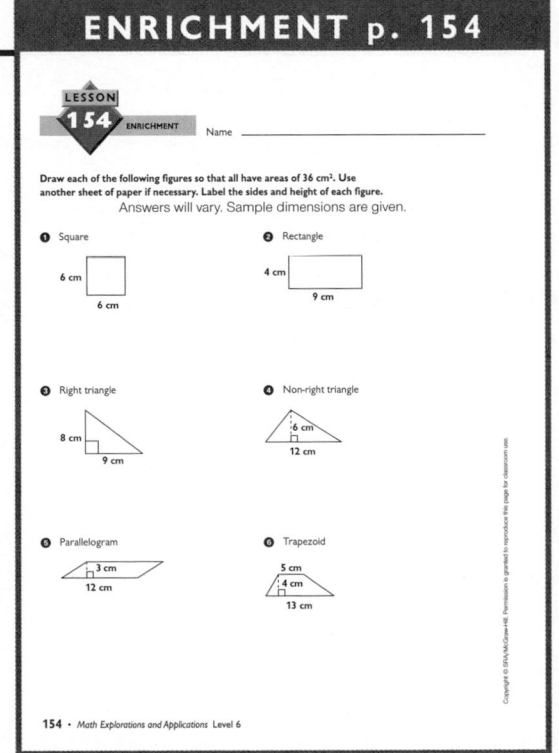

Using the Student Pages The purpose of Lesson 155 is to provide additional practice for those students who demonstrated a need for it on the Unit Review. You may wish to assign only the specific exercises in each Unit Practice in which students need further reinforcement. Each instruction line gives the lessons in the unit it covers so that you or students can refer to the specific lesson for additional review and instruction.

 Students who do not require additional practice on specific concepts may enjoy playing any of the games you have played so far, such as the "Three Questions" game on page 473, which involves classifying polygons and using deductions. These students may also help by practicing flashcard drills and playing appropriate games with students who need remedial practice or by actually teaching certain procedures to other students.

Lessons 125, 126, 135, and 136

Solve the following problems.

1 The area of a rectangle is 56 square centimeters. The length of its base is 8 centimeters. What is its height? **7 cm**

2 The area of a triangle is 56 square centimeters. The length of its base is 8 centimeters. What is its height? **14 cm**

3 The area of a square is 100 square centimeters. What is the length of a side? **10 cm**

4 The area of a square is 169 square centimeters. What is the length of a side? **13 cm**

5 The area of a square is 2 square centimeters. To the nearest tenth of a centimeter, what is the length of a side? **1.4 cm**

6 What is the volume in cubic centimeters of a rectangular box that is 4 centimeters long, 4 centimeters wide, and 4 centimeters tall? **64 cm³**

7 What is the volume in cubic centimeters of a rectangular box that is 3 centimeters long, 2 centimeters wide, and 1 centimeter tall? **6 cm³**

8 What is the volume in cubic centimeters of a rectangular box that is 3.2 centimeters long, 1.5 centimeters wide, and 5 centimeters tall? **24 cm³**

9 What is the total area of the six faces of the box

   a. in problem 6? **96 cm²**

   b. in problem 7? **22 cm²**

   c. in problem 8? **56.6 cm²**

Lesson 139

If necessary, use the table on page 490 to help solve these problems.

10 ■ grams = 1 kilogram
1000

11 ■ meters = 5 kilometers
5000

12 ■ meters = 1 kilometer
1000

13 ■ meters = 4.7 kilometers
4700

14 ■ grams = 5 kilograms
5000

15 ■ milligrams = 8.64 grams
8640

16 ■ grams = 4.7 kilograms
4700

17 ■ millimeters = 8.64 meters
8640

18 ■ liters = 2500 milliliters
2.5

19 ■ centimeters = 3.6 meters
360

Students who have difficulty with this Unit Practice should have further opportunity to review and to practice the skills before they proceed. Beside each set of problems is a reference to the lesson or lessons from which the problems were taken. You may want to review the individual lessons with students who are having difficulty with them.

Lesson 137   **Answer the following questions.**

20 Lola and Omar were ice-skating outside on a frozen pond. They looked at a thermometer. Which of these temperatures might they have seen? (More than one answer may be correct.)

(**a.**) –20°C   (**b.**) –5°C   **c.** 15°C   **d.** 25°C   **e.** 35°C

21 At which of these temperatures would it generally be most comfortable to go swimming?

a. 10°C   **b.** 16°C   (**c.**) 27°C   **d.** 50°C   **e.** 80°C

22 What is the normal boiling point of water?

a. 51°C   (**b.**) 100°C   **c.** 168°C   **d.** 212°C   **e.** 508°C

23 How many feet are in 12 yards? **36**

24 How many pounds are in 192 ounces? **12**

Lesson 148   **Use the figures at the right to answer these questions.**

25 How many lines can be drawn through the points M and N? **1**

•N

26 How many planes could go through the points M and N?

an infinite number

•M

27 Suppose two lines meet at point M. Will they meet at any other points?

no

28 Suppose two planes meet at point M. Will they meet at any other points? **yes**

29 Line AB is perpendicular to plane p. What is the relationship of line AB to a line in plane p that meets AB? What is the relationship of line AB to a line in plane p that does not meet AB?

perpendicular; skew

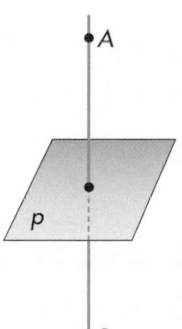

PRACTICE p. 155

LESSON **155** PRACTICE   Name_____

Solve these problems.

❶ The area of a rectangle is 100 square centimeters. The length of the base is 20 centimeters. What is the height? ___5 cm___

❷ The area of a square is 196 square centimeters. What is the length of a side? ___14 cm___

❸ What is the volume in cubic centimeters of a rectangular box that is 4 centimeters long, 5 centimeters wide, and 3 centimeters high? ___60 cubic centimeters___

❹ What is the total area of the six faces of the box in problem 3? ___94 square centimeters___

Change each measurement.

❺ 4000 grams = ___4___ kilograms   ❻ 2 kilometers = ___2000___ meters

❼ 8 liters = ___800___ centiliters   ❽ 50 centimeters = ___500___ millimeters

Choose the correct answer.

❾ What is the normal freezing point of water? ___b___
a. –32°C   b. 0°C   c. 32°C   d. 100°C   e. 212°C

Solve.

❿ How many lines can be drawn between points A, B, and C? ___3 lines___

*Math Explorations and Applications Level 6 • **155***

ENRICHMENT p. 155

LESSON **155** ENRICHMENT   Name_____

Find the area of all surfaces that could be seen if you were able to rotate the object below. Do not include the bottom.

1 cm ⬜ 1 cm
   1 cm

All cubes are 1 cm on a side.

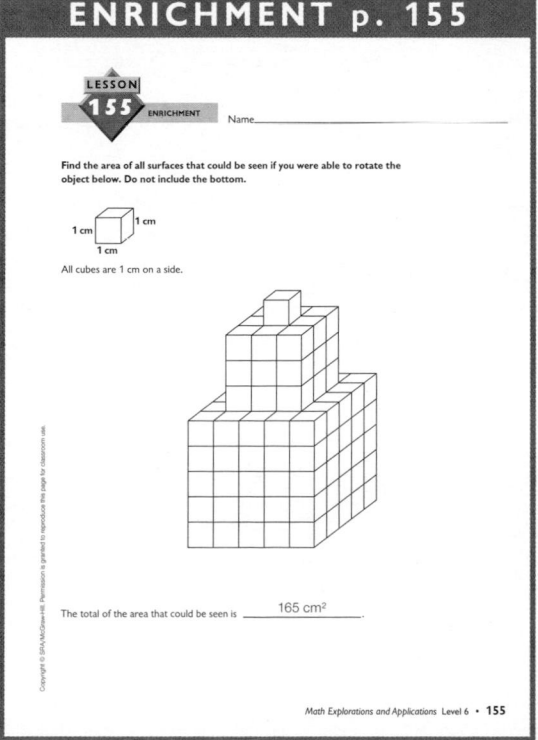

The total of the area that could be seen is ___165 cm²___.

*Math Explorations and Applications Level 6 • **155***

Using the Student Pages The purpose of Lesson 156 is to provide additional practice for those students who demonstrated a need for it on the Unit Review. You may wish to assign only the specific exercises in each Unit Practice in which students need further reinforcement. Each instruction line gives the lessons in the unit it covers so that you or students can refer to the specific lesson for additional review and instruction.

 Students who do not require additional practice on specific concepts may enjoy playing any of the games you have played so far, such as the "Three Questions" game on page 473, which involves classifying polygons and using deductions. These students may also help by practicing flashcard drills and playing appropriate games with students who need remedial practice or by actually teaching certain procedures to other students.

Students can use **The Cruncher*:** *Go for Fun Survey* spreadsheet to help them create a circle graph for problem 19.

 You may want to use the Cumulative Review on page 587 after this lesson.

Lessons 144–147

Find the measure of each angle. If you can do this without actually measuring in some cases, do so.

❶ ∠A **50°**

❷ ∠B **96°**

❸ ∠C **34°**

❹ ∠D **134°**

❺ ∠E **100°**

❻ ∠F **51°**

❼ ∠G **75°**

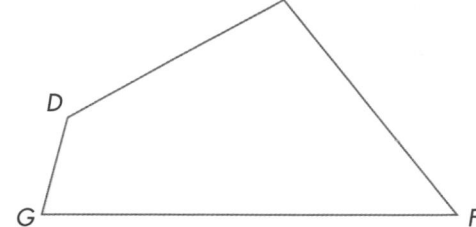

❽ ∠MKH **121°**

❾ ∠GKL **121°**

❿ ∠KLJ **121°**

⓫ ∠MKG **59°**

⓬ ∠HKL **59°**

⓭ ∠JLN **59°**

⓮ ∠KLI **59°**

⓯ ∠GKH **180°**

Line GH is parallel to line IJ.

546 · Geometry

RETEACHING

Students who have difficulty with this Unit Practice should have further opportunity to review and to practice the skills before they proceed. Beside each set of problems is a reference to the lesson or lessons from which the problems were taken. You may want to review the individual lessons with students who are having difficulty with them.

*available separately

Answers to problem 19:

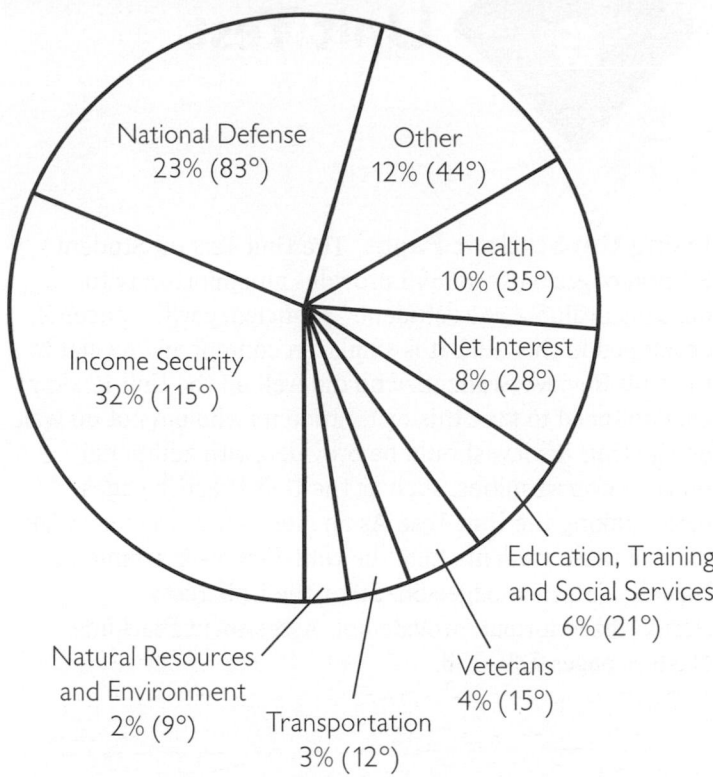

For your information, the size (in degrees) of each sector is shown above. The students should not have this information on their graphs. Some answers may vary by a percent or a degree, depending on the way rounding was done.

Lesson 151

Study this circle graph. Then answer the questions.

⑯ In 1995 what percent of the government's money came from individual income taxes?
39%

⑰ In 1995 the government received about $1519 billion (including money it borrowed). How many dollars came from

a. individual income taxes?
$592.4 billion
b. social insurance taxes and contributions?
$486.1 billion
c. corporation income taxes?
$15.2 billion
d. borrowing? **$167.1 billion**

e. excise taxes? **$60.8 billion**

Where Our Government Gets Its Money Fiscal Year 1995
(Oct. 1, 1994–Sept. 30, 1995)

⑱ This chart shows how our government spent its money in fiscal year 1995. Use a computer or other means to draw and complete the chart. You may also want to use a calculator.

Spending Category	Amount (billions of dollars)	Percent
Income security	556.3	**37**
National defense	272.0	**18**
Other	29.7	**2**
Health	275.3	**18**
Net interest	232.3	**15**
Education, training, and social services	54.2	**4**
Veterans	38.0	**2.5**
Transportation	39.3	**2.5**
Natural resources and environment	22.1	**1**

⑲ Work in groups to make a circle graph to show this information.
See graph in margin.

Use the Cumulative Review on page 587 after this lesson.

Unit 6   Lesson 156 • **547**

PRACTICE p.156

LESSON 156 PRACTICE   Name_____

Find the measure of each angle. If you can do this without actually measuring in some cases, do so.

① ∠A = **38°**
② ∠B = **105°**
③ ∠C = **37°**

④ ∠D = **57°**
⑤ ∠E = **123°**
⑥ ∠F = **95°**
⑦ ∠G = **85°**

Line MN is parallel to line OP.

⑧ ∠QSN = **50°**
⑩ ∠MST = **50°**
⑫ ∠NST = **130°**

⑨ ∠STP = **50°**
⑪ ∠PTR = **130°**
⑬ ∠OTR = **50°**

⑭ Make a circle graph for the table.

Income Category	Amount
Baby-sitting	$50
Walking dog	$10
Washing cars	$15
Mowing lawns	$45

156 • Math Explorations and Applications Level 6

ENRICHMENT p.156

LESSON 156 ENRICHMENT   Name_____

Tell how many triangles could be made, given the information in each exercise. Write not possible, one, or many. If at least one triangle is possible, draw one and label the given measurements.

① One angle measures 38°, and another measures 76°.
many

② One side measures 3 cm, another measures 4 cm, and the angle between them measures 40°.
one

③ Two angles are right angles.
not possible

④ One side measures 5 cm, and another measures 7 cm.
many

⑤ One angle measures 97°, and another measures 108°.
not possible

⑥ Sides measure 3 cm, 4 cm, and 6 cm.
one

⑦ One angle is right and another is acute.
many

⑧ Sides measure 2 cm, 3 cm, and 6 cm.
not possible

156 • Math Explorations and Applications Level 6

Using the Student Pages The Unit Test on Student Edition pages 548 and 549 provides an opportunity to formally evaluate your students' proficiency with concepts developed in this unit. It is similar in content and format to the Unit Review. Students who did well on the Unit Review may not need to take this test. Students who did not do well on the Unit Review should be provided with additional practice opportunities, such as the Unit Practice pages, before taking the Unit Test. As an alternative, you may wish to have these students take the Unit Test on Assessment Blackline Masters pages 56–59 or the Unit Test in standardized format, provided on Assessment Blackline Masters pages 129–133.

UNIT | ASSESSMENT
6

Unit Test

Find the area in square centimeters of each of these figures.

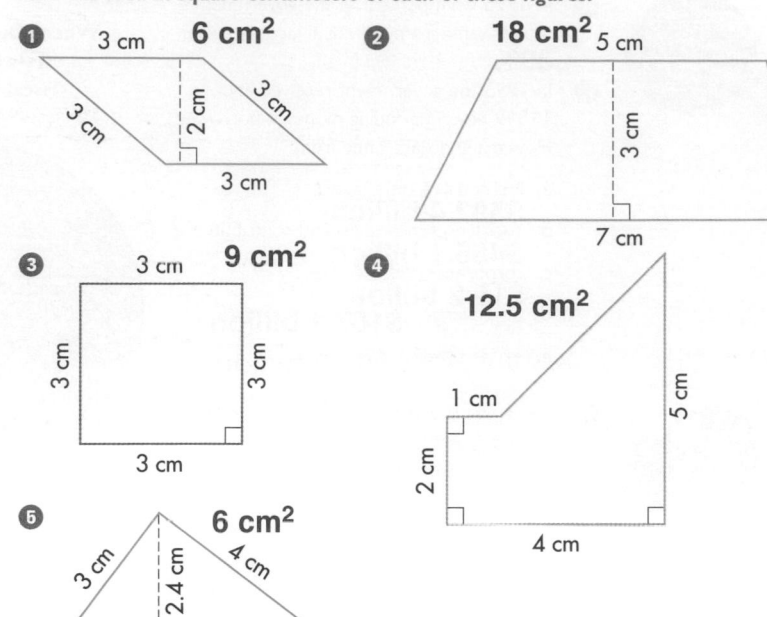

Solve the following problems.

6 The area of a rectangle is 35 square centimeters, and its height is 7 centimeters. What is the length of its base? **5 cm**

7 The area of a square is 49 square centimeters. What is the length of a side? **7 cm**

8 The area of a square is 5 square centimeters. To the nearest tenth of a centimeter, how long is a side? **2.2 cm**

9 Each side of a cube is 3 centimeters long. What is the volume of the cube in cubic centimeters? **27 cm³**

10 What is the total area of the six faces of the cube in problem 9? **54 cm²**

548 • Geometry

Answer the following questions.

Remember: There are 1000 millimeters in a meter. There are 10 meters in a dekameter.

⑪ How many milligrams are in a gram? **1000**

⑫ How many grams are in a dekagram? **10**

⑬ How many milligrams are in a dekagram? **10,000**

⑭ How many milliliters are in a dekaliter? **10,000**

⑮ At which of these room temperatures are most people comfortable?

    a. 0°C   **(b.)** 19°C   **c.** 37°C   **d.** 64°C   **e.** 98°C

Use your protractor to measure each of these angles.

⑯ ∠A **13°**   ⑰ ∠B **14°**   ⑱ ∠C **153°**   ⑲ ∠DEG **54°**

⑳ ∠IJG **54°**   ㉑ ∠HJK **54°**   ㉒ ∠GJK **126°**   ㉓ ∠GEF **126°**

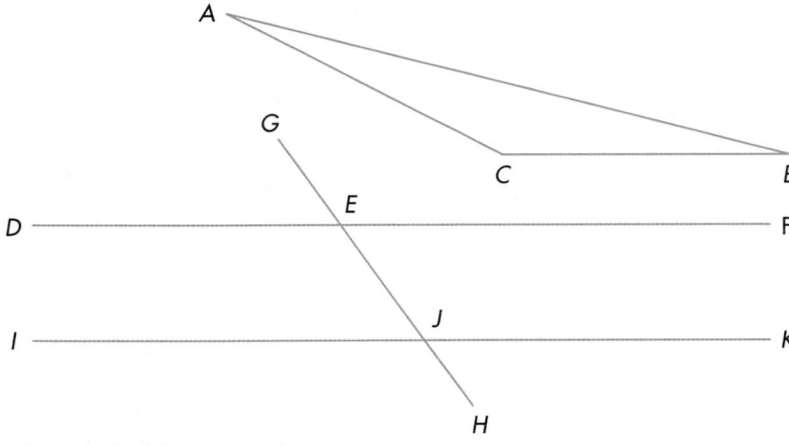

Answer the following questions.

㉔ How many planes contain the points A, B, and C? **only 1**

㉕ How many straight lines contain all three of the points A, B, and C? **none**

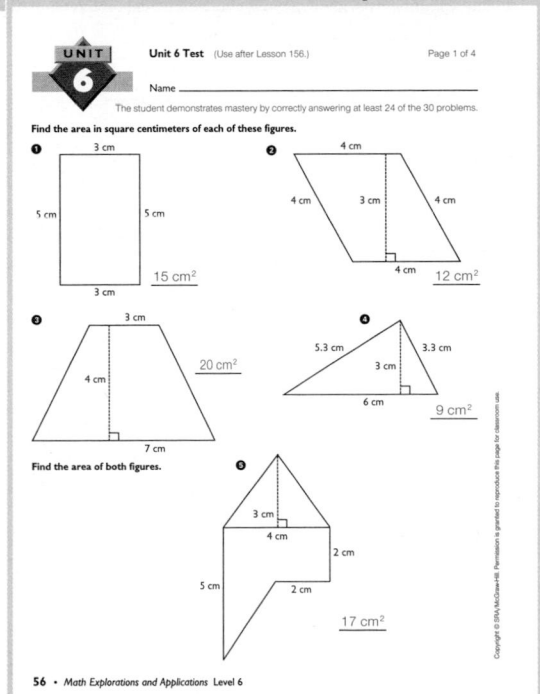

PRESENTING THE PROJECT

Project Objectives

▶ to introduce students to some of the problems normally encountered in setting up an experiment

▶ to explore the relationship between surface area and the time it takes an ice cube to melt

 **MANIPULATIVES**

molds for making ice of various shapes

funnels* (one for each student or group of students)

jars, cups, or glasses for collecting water that drips as the ice melts

large freezer

Although you can do this project having students working alone, having students work in small cooperative groups will allow for much more discussion and analysis. It will also greatly simplify gathering materials and setting up the work area. You might want to use the following four steps in order to complete the activity:

1. Allow several days for students to experiment. Have students make ice in various shapes and attempt to measure how long it takes the ice to melt. Several problems arise, which the groups need to resolve.

   ▶ Have a supply of **molds** available, provide instruction on making clay or cardboard molds, or use different sizes of paper cups. Being able to tell when the ice has melted can be difficult. One solution is to put the ice in funnels with stems of the same diameter. Then declare that the ice has melted when it becomes small enough to fall through the stem. Another solution is to collect the water from the **funnels*** and declare that the ice has melted when a certain volume of water has been collected.

   ▶ How much water you would want to freeze will depend on the molds that are available and the time you have in the school day. In general, small amounts of water will be best for most classrooms (about 2 ounces or 60 milliliters of water being ideal).

2. Bring the groups together to establish rules for the contest. Decide on how much water is to be used, what types of molds will be allowed, and how the winning group will be determined.

Melting Ice Cubes

◆ Does the shape that ice is in affect the time it takes to melt?

To find out, have an ice cube melting contest.

Here are the rules.

A. Each person is allowed to freeze 2 ounces of water.

B. You can freeze it in any shape.

C. Everyone's ice is put into and taken out of the freezer at the same time.

D. The person whose ice lasts the longest is the winner.

Record the results in a table such as the one shown below.

Description of containers	Time taken from freezer	Time ice becomes water	Time to thaw	Comment

*available separately

Here are some things to consider before beginning.

Since water expands when it freezes, don't use closed containers or glass containers to freeze your ice.

Let your ice melt in a place where the water will be collected in a pan.

Think about the possible effects of surface area and volume.

Repeat the contest. Work in small groups to design your shapes. Is there a "best shape" that allows the ice to last the longest?

In your Math Journal write an explanation of why you think a particular shape is the best or why you think the shape doesn't make a difference.

Unit 6 Wrap-Up • **551**

Why teach it at this time?

This project correlates with some of the volume activities in this unit. It specifically correlates with and extends the concepts developed on page 440.

3. Designate an area of the classroom where the students can set up the contest and watch it while doing other class work. Students can use a blank **Cruncher*** spreadsheet to display their data.

4. When the contest is over, use page 440 as a guide to help the class see that the most important factor that determines how fast the ice melts is the ratio of the volume of ice to its surface area; the more surface area, the faster the melting.

What Is a Math Project? If this is the first time you have used math projects in your classroom, you may want to refer to pages 98–99 in this Teacher's Guide for more detailed information about effectively implementing and assessing projects.

Assessing the Project Make a special note of those students who are quick to resolve some of the technical problems associated with running the contest. Students who are good at this sort of problem solving show evidence of higher order thinking.

 **Science, Math & YOU** *Motion Measures,* published by SRA, is one of four units that provide a variety of hands-on projects that integrate real-world math and science. These projects can be used with small groups or with individual students. The four units in *Science, Math & YOU* are *Weather Counts, Life Adds Up, Motion Measures,* and *Circling the Sun.* Use projects from *Motion Measures* with this unit to provide practice with making measurements and analyzing data.

COOPERATIVE LEARNING **Math CrossSections** SRA's *Math CrossSections* is a set of eight units that provide real-world math projects related to famous places in the United States. These open-ended projects focus on problem solving and reinforce reading, research, and study skills. The eight units are:

The White House (Washington, D.C.)
747 DFW (Texas)
California's Giant Sequoias (California)
Pencil Making (Tennessee)
Barging Through the Locks (Michigan)
Atlanta's Olympic Stadium (Georgia)
Madison Square Garden (New York)
The Denver Mint (Colorado)

Use projects from *Atlanta's Olympic Stadium* to provide students with further opportunity to analyze measurements.

Cumulative Review
Use after Lesson 4

Write the numbers in standard form.

1. $4000 + 700 + 60 + 5$ **4765**
2. $8000 + 200 + 70 + 6$ **8276**
3. $3000 + 50 + 1$ **3051**
4. $40,000 + 600 + 70$ **40,670**
5. $5 + 600 + 40,000$ **40,605**
6. $300,000 + 4000 + 70$ **304,070**
7. 3 tenths, 2 hundredths, 5 thousandths **0.325**
8. $0.6 + 0.08 + 0.003$ **0.683**
9. 0 tenths, 4 hundredths, 2 thousandths **0.042**
10. $0.04 + 0.002 + 0.1$ **0.142**
11. $0.005 + 0.4 + 0.02$ **0.425**
12. $0.004 + 0.06$ **0.064**

Copy each pair of numbers but replace ■ with <, >, =.

13. $3.7 ■ 2.9$ **>**
14. $0.4 ■ 0.04$ **>**
15. $0.678 ■ 0.7$ **<**

The point A is the number 0, and the point B is the number 1.

16. What fraction tells us where point R is?
    a. $\frac{1}{2}$ (b.) $\frac{1}{3}$ c. $\frac{2}{3}$
17. What fraction tells us where point S is?
    a. $\frac{1}{4}$ b. $\frac{9}{10}$ (c.) $\frac{3}{4}$

Solve these problems.

18. Of the 32 students in Juan's class, 18 are wearing sneakers today. Are the majority of his classmates wearing sneakers? **yes**
19. A CD player that regularly sells for $80 is on sale for $62.95. Is that more than $\frac{1}{5}$ off the usual price? **yes**

Solve for n.

20. $6 + 7 = n$ **13**
21. $15 - 4 = n$ **9**
22. $n = 9 + 4$ **13**
23. $n = 12 - 8$ **4**
24. $11 - 5 = n$ **6**
25. $n = 16 - 7$ **9**

Cumulative Review
Use after Lesson 8

Write the numbers in standard form.

1. $4 + 700 + 600,000$ **600,704**
2. $0.3 + 0.05 + 0.009$ **0.359**
3. $30 + 8000 + 20,000 + 700,000$ **728,030**
4. $0.004 + 0.5 + 0.08$ **0.584**
5. $4000 + 20 + 7$ **4027**
6. $0.03 + 2 + 0.006$ **2.036**

Copy each pair of numbers but replace ■ with <, >, or =.

7. $0.7 ■ 0.69$ **>**
8. $0.42 ■ 0.042$ **>**
9. $9.0 ■ 0.9$ **>**

Solve for n. Watch the signs.

10. $27 \div 9 = n$ **3**
11. $6 \times 9 = n$ **54**
12. $n = 49 \div 7$ **7**
13. $n = 80 \times 5$ **400**
14. $210 \div 3 = n$ **70**
15. $n = 70 + 80$ **150**

Add. Use shortcuts when you can.

16. $45 + 45$ **90**
17. $73 + 98$ **171**
18. $84 + 15$ **99**
19. $4000 + 26$ **4026**
20. $269 + 331$ **600**
21. $784 + 6$ **790**
22. $72 + 72$ **144**
23. $8000 + 3000$ **11,000**
24. $2003 + 3000$ **5003**
25. $500 + 700$ **1200**
26. $3814 + 4186$ **8000**
27. $4032 + 7153$ **11,185**

Solve these problems.

28. A sports arena has 15,000 seats. About two-thirds of the seats are sold for each event. If tickets cost $15 each, about how much money would the arena collect for 10 events? **$1,500,000**
29. Mara was on vacation with her family for two weeks. There she found 17 new soft drink labels for her collection. If she had 97 labels before the vacation, how many does she have now? **114**
30. Mr. Takamura worked 38 hours last week and 43 hours this week. How many hours has he worked over the past two weeks? **81**

Cumulative Review
Use after Lesson 12

Solve for n.

1. $60 + 7 = n$ **67**
2. $150 \div 3 = n$ **50**
3. $n = 9 \times 4000$ **36,000**

Add. Use shortcuts when you can.

4. $67 + 32 + 48$ **147**
5. $3000 + 2000 + 6000$ **11,000**
6. $250 + 150 + 350$ **750**

Solve these problems. Use shortcuts when you can.

7. $82 - 27$ **55**
8. $100 - 7$ **93**
9. $1000 - 6$ **994**
10. $4027 + 3026$ **7053**
11. $4002 + 2740 + 2000 + 3317$ **12,059**

Use the map to answer these questions.

12. How many miles is it from Miami to Daytona Beach if you go through Vero Beach? **267**
13. How many miles is a round trip between Tampa, Daytona Beach, and Vero Beach? **433**
14. Which round trip is longer:
    (a.) Miami—Gainesville—Miami?
    b. Miami—Vero Beach—Tampa—Ft. Myers—Miami?

Multiply.

15. 30×70 **2100**
16. 800×60 **48,000**
17. 200×700 **140,000**
18. 78×6 **468**
19. 624×5 **3120**
20. 800×7 **5600**
21. 420×8 **3360**
22. 615×90 **55,350**
23. 300×70 **21,000**
24. 700×9 **6300**
25. 3500×400 **1,400,000**

Cumulative Review
Use after Lesson 15

Copy each pair of numbers but replace ■ with <, >, or =.

1. $0.06 ■ 0.059$ **>**
2. $0.72 ■ 0.072$ **>**
3. $9.1 ■ 0.199$ **>**

Solve for n. Watch the signs.

4. $2700 \div 90 = n$ **30**
5. $600 \times 9 = n$ **5400**
6. $n = 420 \div 7$ **60**
7. $5124 + 6387 = n$ **11,511**
8. $416 \times 2 = n$ **832**
9. $6947 - 3258 = n$ **3689**
10. $937 \times 4 = n$ **3748**
11. $250 \div 5 = n$ **50**
12. $500 - 6 = n$ **494**

Choose the correct answer.

13. 17×48 (a.) 816   b. 416   c. 1480
14. $7105 - 2929$ a. 3276   b. 10,034   (c.) 4176
15. 326×311 a. 10,138   (b.) 101,386   c. 11,386
16. $9472 + 6314$ a. 1586   b. 13,986   (c.) 15,786

Divide.

17. $6)\overline{48}$ **8**
18. $3)\overline{15}$ **5**
19. $4)\overline{36}$ **9**
20. $9)\overline{54}$ **6**
21. $7)\overline{567}$ **81**
22. $6)\overline{2436}$ **406**
23. $3)\overline{25,578}$ **8526**
24. $8)\overline{76,144}$ **9518**
25. $321,088 \div 2$ **160,544**
26. $9880 \div 4$ **2470**
27. $33,264 \div 9$ **3696**

Solve these problems.

28. Mr. Wang is buying carpet for his home office. The office is 4 meters wide and 8 meters long. The carpeting he likes is 4 meters wide and costs $109.95 a meter. How much carpeting should he buy, and how much will it cost? **8m; $879.60**
29. Forty students from Rugged High are going on a camping trip. If six students can fit in a van, how many vans will they need to take? **7**
30. Claudia's team cycled 457 kilometers in six days. If they rode about the same distance each day, about how many kilometers did they ride each day? **about 76 km**

Cumulative Review
Use after lesson 19

Solve for n. Watch the signs.

1 2400 ÷ 60 = n **40**
2 2500 × 4 = n **10,000**
3 n = 2025 ÷ 25 **81**

Divide.

4 32)960 **30**
5 42)252 **6**
6 90)90,900 **1010**

7 87)609 **7**
8 28)12,068 **431**
9 250)7500 **30**

10 198)64,350 **325**
11 770)15,400 **20**
12 74)30,710 **415**

Choose the correct answer.

13 57 × 1247 a. 7109 **b. 71,079** c. 717,079
14 83 × 69 **a. 5727** b. 4727 c. 3727
15 2845 − 391 a. 2645 b. 2556 **c. 2454**

Solve these problems.

16 Fred's travel club is planning a hiking trip to Scotland. There are 36 members of the club, who will share the cost equally. If the total cost of the trip is $21,672, how much will each member pay? **$602**

17 Carlos earns $7.25 an hour fixing bicycles. How much will he earn for 12 hours of work? **$87.00**

18 Ms. Chen earns $39,000 a year. She is paid every week. About how much is she paid each week? **$750**

19 Willy's checking account has $1145.89 in it. If he writes four checks, each for $150, how much will he have left in the account? **$545.89**

20 Which job pays the highest salary, one that pays $40,000 a year, one that pays $3500 a month, or one that pays $850 each week? **$850 each week**

Cumulative Review
Use after Lesson 23

Copy and complete the number sequences.

1 3997, 3998, 3999, ■, ■, ■, 4004 **4000, 4001, 4002, 4003**
2 99,996; 99,997; ■; ■; ■; 100,003 **99,998; 99,999; 100,000; 100,001; 100,002**

Round each number to the nearest ten.

3 58 **60**
4 84 **80**
5 22 **20**
6 97 **100**

Round each number to the nearest hundred.

7 237 **200**
8 444 **400**
9 877 **900**
10 550 **500 or 600**

Round each number to the nearest thousand.

11 1045 **1000**
12 1382 **1000**
13 6500 **6000 or 7000**
14 7596 **8000**

Round each number to the nearest whole number.

15 71.3 **71**
16 54.9 **55**
17 87.5 **87 or 88**
18 39.6 **40**

Write the missing items.

Temperature	Change	New Temperature
19 15°C	down 20°	**−5°C** ■
20 −10°C	down 5°	**−15°C** ■

Add or subtract. Watch for negative numbers.

21 100 − 200 **−100**
22 (−100) + 50 **−50**
23 (−150) − 50 **−200**

Solve these problems.

24 Miranda is driving to Jerome, 1977 kilometers away. She wants to spend four days driving and drive about the same distance each day. About how far should she plan to drive each day? **about 494.25 km**

25 Jared has $43.75 in his checking account. Does he have enough money in his account to buy six paperbacks that are on sale for $6.95 each? Can he buy seven paperbacks? **yes; no**

Cumulative Review
Use after Lesson 26

Solve these problems. Watch the signs.

1 745 + 248 **993**
2 1073 × 98 **105,154**
3 8400 − 15 **8385**
4 3)4050 **1350**
5 6741 × 63 **424,683**

6 784 × 126 **98,784**
7 8072 + 725 **8797**
8 8000 × 3000 **24,000,000**
9 70)2240 **32**
10 2500 − 700 **1800**

11 932 + 359 **1291**
12 208 × 34 **7072**
13 13)5226 **402**
14 600 − 207 **393**
15 24,067 − 15,315 **8752**

Round each number to the nearest whole number.

16 7.3 **7**
17 54.5 **54 or 55**
18 82.4 **82**
19 59.6 **60**

Add or subtract. Watch for negative numbers.

20 200 − 200 **0**
21 (−10) + 15 **5**
22 (−15) − 15 **−30**
23 7 − 15 **−8**

Multiply. Watch for negative numbers.

24 −5 × 8 **−40**
25 10 × −6 **−60**
26 −12 × 4 **−48**
27 7 × 7 **49**

Divide. Round decimal quotients to the nearest whole number.

28 2496 ÷ 60 **41.6→42**
29 25,000 ÷ 48 **520.8→521**
30 50,622 ÷ 78 **649**
31 522 ÷ 6 **87**

Solve these problems.

32 Maria had a checking account balance of $183. What would her new balance be after writing a check for $200? **−$17**

33 At Frank's Fruit Market, apples are $0.79 a pound and melons cost $1.29 each. How much will Simone pay for two pounds of apples and three melons? **$5.45**

34 A Landrider holds seven passengers. How many Landriders are needed to transport 30 people? **5**

35 Thirty-six golf balls sell for $54 at Sid's Sports. Do you think Sid will sell you a ball for $1.25? **no**

Cumulative Review
Use after Lesson 30

Round each number to the nearest whole number.

1 14.3 **14**
2 5.4 **5**
3 40.45 **40**
4 9.67 **10**

Choose the correct answer. Watch the signs.

5 34 × 50 a. 170 **b. 1700** c. 17,000
6 3000 − 127 a. 1873 **b. 2873** c. 1730
7 42,000 ÷ 300 **a. 140** b. 1400 c. 14,000

Add or subtract.

8 0.8 − 0.2 **0.6**
9 0.75 + 0.25 **1**
10 0.5 − 0.44 **0.06**
11 7.6 − 1.5 **6.1**

Multiply.

12 10 × 2.7 **27**
13 100 × 0.06 **6**
14 1.726 × 1000 **1726**

Divide.

15 24 ÷ 10 **2.4**
16 2.5 ÷ 1000 **0.0025**
17 314.2 ÷ 100 **3.142**

Complete.

18 2 m = ■ cm **200**
19 0.6 L = ■ mL **600**
20 4000 g = ■ kg **4**

Multiply.

21 7.1 × 4 **28.4**
22 5.5 × 8 **44.0**
23 0.8 × 7 **5.6**
24 0.04 × 6 **0.24**
25 15.3 × 9 **137.7**
26 2.84 × 12 **34.08**
27 32 × 5.8 **185.6**
28 41 × 0.06 **2.46**

Solve these problems.

29 Emma's gerbil weighs 140 grams. What is its weight in kilograms? **0.140 kg**

30 Phillip went to the grocery store and bought a carton of juice for $2.49, a loaf of bread for $2.19, and a box of cereal for $2.99. How much change should he receive if he pays with a $10 bill? **$2.33**

Cumulative Review
Use after Lesson 36

Copy each pair of numbers but replace ■ with <, >, or =.

1. 0.006 ■ 0.058 **<**
2. 1.72 ■ 1.720 **=**
3. 9.1 ■ 1.99 **>**

Multiply or divide.

4. 7.1 × 100 **710**
5. 25.5 ÷ 10 **2.55**
6. 1000 × 0.06 **60**
7. 0.05 ÷ 100 **0.0005**

Complete.

8. 2000 cm = ■ m **20**
9. 600 mL = ■ L **0.6**
10. 4.5 kg = ■ g **4500**

Multiply.

11. 4.1 × 1.8 **7.38**
12. 0.5 × 6 **3.0**
13. 1.01 × 0.09 **0.0909**
14. 305 × 3.3 **1006.5**

For each of the following problems, write two more problems that would have the same answer. **Answers will vary. Examples are given.**

15. $4.1\overline{)88.8}$ → $0.41\overline{)8.88}$, $0.041\overline{)0.888}$
16. $0.65\overline{)41.78}$ → $0.065\overline{)4.178}$, $0.0065\overline{)0.4178}$
17. $1.2\overline{)413}$ → $0.12\overline{)41.3}$, $0.012\overline{)4.13}$
18. $305\overline{)0.56}$ → $30.5\overline{)0.056}$, $3050\overline{)5.6}$

Divide. Round quotients to the nearest hundredth.

19. $0.8\overline{)14}$ **17.5**
20. $0.045\overline{)5}$ **111.11**
21. $0.75\overline{)200}$ **266.666 → 266.67**
22. $400\overline{)6252}$ **15.63**

Add or subtract.

23. 35 − 65 **−30**
24. (−20) + 7 **−13**
25. (−5) − 9 **−14**
26. −4 + 12 **8**

Solve these problems.

27. Jonathan measured the length of a rectangular field to be 200 m and the width to be 50 m. If the true length and width of the field are 0.5 m greater than his measurements, what are the true perimeter and area? **502 m; 10,125.25 m²**
28. Suppose the true length and width are 0.5 less than Jonathan's measurements. What are the true perimeter and the true area? **perimeter = 498 m; area = 9875.25 m²**
29. Ralph had a $20 bill. After shopping, he had $5.75 left. How much did he spend shopping? **$14.25**
30. Alana wants to buy six jars of peanut butter that cost $2.79 each. What will the total cost be? **$16.74**

Cumulative Review
Use after Lesson 41

Solve for n. Watch the signs.

1. 240 ÷ 80 = n **3**
2. 2.5 × 4 = n **10**
3. n = 2.25 ÷ 25 **0.09**

Divide. Round quotients to the nearest hundredth.

4. $33\overline{)9.9}$ **0.3**
5. $2.4\overline{)9600}$ **4000**
6. $60\overline{)606}$ **10.1**
7. $83\overline{)1410}$ **16.987 → 16.99**

Solve. Do as many as you can without paper and pencil.

8. 20 × 20 = ■ **400**
9. ■ = 6 × 7 **42**
10. 4 × 800 = ■ **3200**
11. ■ = 19 × 100 **1900**
12. ■ = 160 + 129 **289**
13. 540 ÷ 6 = ■ **90**

Write in exponential form.

14. 4 × 4 × 4 × 4 **4^4**
15. 12 × 12 × 12 × 12 × 12 × 12 **12^6**
16. 6 × 6 × 6 × 6 × 6 **6^5**
17. 205 × 205 × 205 × 205 **205^4**

Write in standard form.

18. 10×4^3 **640**
19. 6×7^2 **294**
20. 3×10^5 **300,000**
21. 4×10^4 **40,000**
22. 2×10^6 **2,000,000**
23. 10^3 **1000**
24. 9×10^2 **900**
25. 58×10^5 **5,800,000**

Solve these problems.

26. The floor of a rectangular room is 3.5 meters long and 2.6 meters wide. How many 0.1-meter square tiles are needed to cover this rectangular floor? **910**
27. Megan is choosing one photograph and one painting to hang on the wall. She has ten photographs and six paintings from which she can choose. How many different combinations could she choose? **60**
28. Olga works part-time at the florist, where she earns $5.50 an hour. She has forgotten how many hours she worked last week, but her paycheck was $71.50. How many hours did she work? **13**
29. Jason is saving money for a new pair of tennis shoes that costs $64. If he saves $7 a week, how many weeks will it be before he can buy the shoes? **10 weeks**
30. Apples are on sale for 59¢ a pound. How much will 5 pounds cost? **$2.95**

Cumulative Review
Use after Lesson 47

Complete.

1. 200 cm = ■ dm **20**
2. 0.6 kg = ■ g **600**
3. 300 mL = ■ L **0.3**

Add or subtract. Watch the signs.

4. (−5) + 10 **5**
5. (−2) + 2 **0**
6. 10 − 15 **−5**
7. (−2) − 2 **−4**

Write in standard form.

8. 5×10^4 **50,000**
9. 10^8 **100,000,000**
10. $10^5 \times 4$ **400,000**
11. 7×10^3 **7000**

Multiply or divide. Watch the signs.

12. $10^3 \times 10^4$ **10^7 (10,000,000)**
13. $10^8 \div 10^6$ **10^2 (100)**
14. $10^{12} \div 10^5$ **10^7 (10,000,000)**
15. $9^2 \times 10^2$ **8100**
16. $5^3 \times 5^3$ **5^6 (15,625)**
17. $6^3 \div 6^2$ **6^1 (6)**
18. $8^5 \div 8^3$ **8^2 (64)**
19. $2^3 \times 2^5$ **2^8 (256)**

Approximate. Use exponential notation. **Accept all reasonable answers.**

20. 318 × 687 **21×10^4**
21. 8499 × 6499 **54×10^6 or 56×10^6**
22. 220 × 55,012 **12×10^6**

Choose a reasonable approximation for each problem.

23. 3.876 − 2.138 a. 0.7 **(b.) 1.7** c. 0.17
24. 784.1 ÷ 36.5 a. 36 b. 210 **(c.) 21**
25. 14.8 × 26.3 a. 3900 **(b.) 390** c. 450
26. 50.38 ÷ 0.765 **(a.) 65** b. 6.5 c. 650

Solve these problems.

27. Jessica usually earns $6 an hour. On holidays she earns time and a half. How much does she earn per hour on a holiday? **$9**
28. A stack of 100 cardboard sheets is 3.8 cm thick. How thick is each sheet? **0.038 cm (or 0.38 mm)**
29. How many hours will you sleep in your lifetime? Make an estimate. **Accept all reasonable estimates.**
30. On the average the moon is about 238,857 miles from Earth. How many baseball bats would be needed to reach the moon if they could be placed end to end? **If a baseball bat is about a yard long, you would need about 4.2×10^8 baseball bats.**

Cumulative Review
Use after Lesson 51

1. $0.032\overline{)0.688}$, $3.2\overline{)68.8}$, $320\overline{)6880}$;
2. $0.005\overline{)412.2}$, $0.05\overline{)4122}$, $5\overline{)412,200}$;
3. $503\overline{)126.2}$, $5.03\overline{)1.262}$, $0.503\overline{)0.1262}$

For each of the following problems, write three more problems that would have the same answer. **Answers will vary. Examples are given above.**

1. $0.32\overline{)6.88}$
2. $0.0005\overline{)41.22}$
3. $50.3\overline{)12.62}$

Multiply or divide. Write answers in exponential form.

4. $10^3 \times 10^4$ **10^7**
5. $10^8 \div 10^6$ **10^2**
6. $10^7 \div 10^2$ **10^5**
7. $(4 \times 10^6) \times (4 \times 10^5)$ **16×10^{11}**
8. $(12 \times 10^{11}) \div (3 \times 10^7)$ **4×10^4**
9. $(3 \times 10^6) \times (2 \times 10^4)$ **6×10^{10}**

Multiply.

10. 4.4 × 3.8 **16.72**
11. 0.5 × 0.6 **0.30**
12. 1.11 × 0.003 **0.00333**
13. 3.05 × 33 **100.65**

Change each percent to a decimal.

14. 20% **0.2**
15. 6.4% **0.064**
16. 55% **0.55**
17. 0.4% **0.004**
18. 95.5% **0.955**

Change each decimal to a percent.

19. 0.45 **45%**
20. 0.5 **50%**
21. 0.06 **6%**
22. 0.025 **2.5%**
23. 0.668 **66.8%**

Find each amount.

24. 6% of 100 **6**
25. 5% of 6 **0.3**
26. 12.5% of 24 **3**
27. 25% of 60 **15**
28. 50% of 50 **25**
29. 7% of 56 **3.92**
30. 8% of 40 **3.2**
31. 75% of 30 **22.5**

Solve these problems.

32. There is a 25% discount on large cactus plants at the Green Thumb nursery. The regular price is $16. What is the sale price? **$12**
33. Loretta wants to buy a personal stereo that lists for $32. If the sales tax is 5%, how much will she have to pay for it? **$33.60**
34. A $60 atlas is on sale at a 10% discount. The sales tax is 6%. With the discount and the tax, what is the cost of the atlas? **$57.24**
35. Ed has $50 to spend at a local music store, where everything is on sale for 25% off. Can he afford to buy both the new Rolling Pebbles double CD that regularly sells for $32 and the new Blueberries three-CD set that usually sells for $30? **yes**

Cumulative Review
Use after Lesson 55

Change each percent to a decimal.

❶ 20% **0.2** ❷ 6.4% **0.064** ❸ 55% **0.55** ❹ 0.4% **0.004** ❺ 95.5% **0.955**

Change each decimal to a percent.

❻ 0.65 **65%** ❼ 0.04 **4%** ❽ 2.5 **250%** ❾ 0.175 **17.5%** ❿ 0.8 **80%**

Multiply. Watch for negative numbers.

⓫ 4 × −7 **−28** ⓬ 9 × −6 **−54** ⓭ 8 × 5 **40** ⓮ −3 × 4 **−12**

Find each amount.

⓯ 12% of 100 **12** ⓰ 10% of 45 **4.5** ⓱ 4% of 60 **2.4** ⓲ 75% of 20 **15**

⓳ 90% of 50 **45** ⓴ 25% of 70 **17.5** ㉑ 35% of 200 **70** ㉒ 3% of 25 **0.75**

In each case calculate the amount of money you would have.

	Principal	Rate of Interest	Number of Years	Amount
㉓	$100	6%	1	■ $106
㉔	$100	7%	2	■
㉕	$200	8%	5	■
㉖	$200	6%	10	■

㉔ **$ 114.49** ㉕ **$293.87** ㉖ **$358.17**

Solve these problems.

㉗ Mr. Yang put $100 in a bank at 5% interest for ten years. Ms. Van Wyck put $80 in a bank at 7% interest for ten years. Who will have more money in the bank after ten years? **Mr. Yang**

㉘ Ms. Gomez put $500 in the bank at 6% interest. How long must she leave the money in the account in order to double the amount she deposited? **12 years**

㉙ The Generosity Bank pays 5% interest compounded quarterly. If you were to deposit $1000 in that bank, how much money will you have after one-quarter of a year? How much will you have after six months? After one year? **$1012.50; $1025.16; $1050.95**

㉚ Adam bought a baseball glove on sale for $60. That was 25% less than the regular price. What was the regular price of the glove? **$80**

Cumulative Review
Use after Lesson 59

Write in standard form.

❶ 10×5^3 **1250** ❷ 2×7^3 **686** ❸ 5×10^4 **50,000** ❹ $10^2 \times 2^3$ **800**

Multiply.

❺ 4.5 × 20 **90** ❻ 0.5 × 0.006 **0.003** ❼ 1.01 × 0.95 **0.9595** ❽ 105 × 3.03 **318.15**

Solve for n. Watch the signs.

❾ 4800 ÷ 80 = n **60** ❿ 2.5 × 400 = n **1000** ⓫ n = 62.5 ÷ 50 **1.25**

Choose the correct answer. Watch the signs.

⓬ 24 × 500   a. 120   b. 1200   (c.) 12,000

⓭ 4000 − 4   a. 3600   b. 3960   (c.) 3996

⓮ 120,000 ÷ 400   a. 30   (b.) 300   c. 3000

⓯ 27 × 53   a. 761   b. 981   (c.) 1431

⓰ 4973 + 8412   (a.) 13,385   b. 13,985   c. 14,285

Which of these numbers are divisible by 2? by 5? by both 2 and 5?

⓱ 20 **both 2 and 5** ⓲ 64 **2** ⓳ 55 **5** ⓴ 400 **both 2 and 5** ㉑ 95 **5**

Which of these numbers are divisible by 3? by 6? by both 3 and 6?

㉒ 27 **3** ㉓ 66 **both 3 and 6** ㉔ 54 **both 3 and 6** ㉕ 213 **3** ㉖ 954 **both 3 and 6**

Solve these problems.

㉗ A $300 stereo is on sale at a 20% discount. The sales tax is 6%. How much will the stereo cost? **$254.40**

㉘ Carlos deposited $5000 in a bank to open an account. The bank pays 4% interest compounded quarterly. How much will he have in the account in a year? **$5203.02**

㉙ Which costs less, a stereo system regularly priced at $289 on sale at $50 off or on sale at 20% off? **20%**

㉚ A stack of ten identical calculators weighs 1.1 kg. About how much does each calculator weigh? **0.11 kg (or 110 g)**

Cumulative Review
Use after Lesson 64

Divide. Round decimal quotients to the nearest whole number.

❶ 4410 ÷ 70 **63** ❷ 35,000 ÷ 72 **486.1 → 486** ❸ 16,308 ÷ 27 **604**

❹ 592 ÷ 8 **74** ❺ 23,874 ÷ 46 **519** ❻ 1671 ÷ 31 **53.9 → 54**

Write in standard form.

❼ 5×10^4 **50,000** ❽ 10^8 **100,000,000** ❾ $10^5 \times 4$ **400,000** ❿ 7×10^3 **7000** ⓫ $10^4 \times 2$ **20,000**

List the factors for each number.

⓬ 20 **1, 2, 4, 5, 10, 20** ⓭ 64 **1, 2, 4, 8, 16, 32, 64** ⓮ 556 **1, 2, 4, 139, 278, 556** ⓯ 140 **1, 2, 4, 5, 7, 10, 14, 20, 28, 35, 70, 140** ⓰ 1548 **1, 2, 3, 4, 6, 9, 12, 18, 36, 43, 86, 129, 172, 258, 387, 516, 774, 1548**

Show the prime factorization for each number.

⓱ 20 $2^2 \times 5$ ⓲ 64 2^6 ⓳ 556 $2^2 \times 139$ ⓴ 140 $2^2 \times 5 \times 7$ ㉑ 1548 $2^2 \times 3^2 \times 43$

Change each percent to a decimal and each decimal to a percent.

㉒ 40% **0.4** ㉓ 0.064 **6.4%** ㉔ 0.55 **55%** ㉕ 0.8% **0.008** ㉖ 78.6 **7860%**

Find the cost, with tax, of each item.

㉗ an $80 jacket with 5% sales tax **$84**

㉘ a $59.95 fishing rod with 7% sales tax **$64.15**

Find the discount price of each item.

	Regular Price	Discount	Discount Price
㉙	$25	10%	■ **$22.50**
㉚	$1.75	20%	■ **$1.40**
㉛	$150	20%	■ **$120.00**
㉜	$84	25%	■ **$63.00**
㉝	$195	10%	■ **$175.50**
㉞	$62.50	10%	■ **$56.25**
㉟	$75	20%	■ **$60**

Cumulative Review
Use after Lesson 68

Round each number to the nearest whole number.

❶ 24.3 **24** ❷ 5.47 **5** ❸ 400.65 **401** ❹ 99.499 **99**

Copy each pair of numbers but replace ● with <, >, or =.

❺ 0.6 ● 0.58 **>** ❻ 2.62 ● 2.620 **=** ❼ 9.1 ● 9.09 **>**

Complete.

❽ 5000 mL = ■ L **5** ❾ 600 mm = ■ m **0.6** ❿ 6.25 kg = ■ g **6250**

⓫ 2.4 m = ■ cm **240** ⓬ 325 mg = ■ g **0.325** ⓭ 4.7 L = ■ mL **4700**

Solve these problems.

⓮ $\frac{1}{3}$ of 15 **5** ⓯ $\frac{2}{5}$ of 25 **10** ⓰ $\frac{4}{5}$ of 40 **32** ⓱ $\frac{5}{6}$ of 12 **10**

⓲ $\frac{2}{3}$ of $\frac{3}{4}$ **$\frac{6}{12}$ (or $\frac{1}{2}$)** ⓳ $\frac{1}{2}$ of $\frac{5}{6}$ **$\frac{5}{12}$** ⓴ $\frac{1}{4}$ of $\frac{1}{3}$ **$\frac{1}{12}$** ㉑ $\frac{3}{8}$ of $\frac{1}{2}$ **$\frac{3}{16}$**

Complete.

㉒ $\frac{1}{4} = \frac{?}{8}$ **2** ㉓ $\frac{2}{5} = \frac{?}{15}$ **6** ㉔ $\frac{2}{3} = \frac{?}{9}$ **6** ㉕ $\frac{4}{5} = \frac{16}{?}$ **20**

Solve these problems.

㉖ A $250 ping-pong table is on sale at a 10% discount. The sales tax is 8%. How much will the table cost? **$243**

㉗ Hakim deposited $2000 in a bank to open an account. The bank pays 5% interest compounded monthly. How long will it take Hakim to earn over $100 in interest? **1 year (12 months)**

㉘ A motorcycle discounted 20% is on sale for $1600. What is the regular price of the motorcycle? **$2000**

㉙ Mrs. Pulaski earns about $650 a week. What is her annual pay? **about $33,800**

㉚ A school band is selling concert tickets for $3.50. If they sell 150 tickets, how much money will they raise? **$525**

Cumulative Review
Use after Lesson 72

Add or subtract. Watch the signs.

1. $(-4) + 5$ **1**
2. $(-2) + 4$ **2**
3. $7 - 12$ **−5**
4. $20 - 10$ **10**
5. $(-20) - 20$ **−40**
6. $(-15) + 6$ **−9**

Multiply or divide. Watch the signs.

7. $10^3 \times 10^2$ **10^5**
8. $10^8 \div 10^1$ **10^7**
9. $10^{10} \div 10^4$ **10^6**
10. $10^{12} \div 10^7$ **10^5**
11. $10^2 \times 10^1$ **10^3**
12. $10^5 \times 10^3$ **10^8**

Reduce each fraction completely.

13. $\frac{6}{10}$ **$\frac{3}{5}$**
14. $\frac{4}{6}$ **$\frac{2}{3}$**
15. $\frac{5}{100}$ **$\frac{1}{20}$**
16. $\frac{21}{60}$ **$\frac{7}{20}$**
17. $\frac{30}{96}$ **$\frac{5}{16}$**

Find the greatest common factor of each pair of numbers.

18. 10 and 12 **2**
19. 8 and 20 **4**
20. 5 and 15 **5**
21. 48 and 54 **6**

Find the least common multiple of each pair of numbers.

22. 2 and 5 **10**
23. 4 and 10 **20**
24. 8 and 12 **24**
25. 9 and 12 **36**

Copy each pair of numbers but replace ● with <, >, =.

26. $\frac{2}{3}$ ● $\frac{3}{8}$ **>**
27. $\frac{2}{5}$ ● $\frac{5}{6}$ **<**
28. $\frac{5}{12}$ ● $\frac{1}{2}$ **<**

Add or subtract. Watch the signs.

29. $\frac{2}{3} + \frac{3}{4}$ **$1\frac{5}{12}$**
30. $\frac{5}{8} - \frac{1}{3}$ **$\frac{7}{24}$**
31. $\frac{7}{10} - \frac{2}{5}$ **$\frac{3}{10}$**
32. $\frac{1}{2} + \frac{5}{7}$ **$1\frac{3}{14}$**

Solve these problems.

33. Before her trip the odometer on Elena's car read 8507 miles. After the trip it read 9225 miles. How far did she drive on the trip? **718 miles**
34. Alex bought two boxes of cereal at $3.79 each and 4 pounds of grapes at $0.89 a pound. He paid with a $20 bill. How much change should he get? **$8.86**
35. Donna earns $6.50 an hour at her part-time job. How much will she earn if she works 15 hours? **$97.50**

Cumulative Review
Use after Lesson 76

Add or subtract. Watch the signs.

1. $\frac{2}{5} + \frac{1}{4}$ **$\frac{13}{20}$**
2. $\frac{7}{8} - \frac{2}{3}$ **$\frac{5}{24}$**
3. $\frac{9}{10} - \frac{1}{5}$ **$\frac{7}{10}$**
4. $\frac{3}{4} - \frac{1}{3}$ **$\frac{5}{12}$**

Change each percent to a decimal.

5. 30% **0.3**
6. 5.6% **0.056**
7. 55.5% **0.555**
8. 2.91% **0.0291**

Change each decimal to a percent.

9. 0.0007 **0.07%**
10. 0.85 **85%**
11. 4.5 **450%**
12. 0.038 **3.8%**

Find the least common multiple of each set of numbers.

13. 3, 6, and 12 **12**
14. 2, 3, and 8 **24**
15. 2, 4, 6, and 9 **36**

Add.

16. $\frac{1}{4} + \frac{2}{3} + \frac{1}{6}$ **$1\frac{1}{12}$**
17. $\frac{3}{5} + \frac{1}{3} + \frac{2}{15}$ **$1\frac{1}{15}$**
18. $\frac{3}{8} + \frac{1}{4} + \frac{1}{12}$ **$\frac{17}{24}$**

Solve these problems.

19. If you roll a 0–5 number cube, what is the probability of getting a 3? **$\frac{1}{6}$**
20. If you roll a 0–5 cube, what is the probability of getting a number greater than 3? **$\frac{2}{6}$ (or $\frac{1}{3}$)**
21. If you roll a 0–5 cube, what is the probability of getting a 7? **0**
22. You roll a 0–5 cube 60 times. About how many times would you expect to roll a 4? a number other than 4? **10; 50**
23. You roll a 5–10 cube 90 times. About how many times would you expect to roll either a 9 or a 10? **30**
24. Of the 25 students in a kindergarten class, $\frac{3}{5}$ are boys. How many boys are in the class? **15**
25. To override the governor's veto in a certain state, the State Senate must pass a bill with a $\frac{2}{3}$ vote. If there are 49 members of the State Senate, how many must vote for the bill to override the veto? **33**

Cumulative Review
Use after Lesson 81

Copy each pair of numbers but replace ● with <, >, or =.

1. $\frac{2}{3}$ ● $\frac{14}{21}$ **=**
2. $\frac{4}{5}$ ● $\frac{5}{6}$ **<**
3. $\frac{7}{12}$ ● $\frac{1}{2}$ **>**

Watch the signs and reduce your answers.

4. $\frac{2}{3} + \frac{1}{4}$ **$\frac{11}{12}$**
5. $\frac{3}{8} \times \frac{1}{3}$ **$\frac{1}{8}$**
6. $\frac{3}{10} - \frac{1}{5}$ **$\frac{1}{10}$**
7. $\frac{3}{4} \times \frac{1}{5}$ **$\frac{3}{20}$**
8. $0.5 + 0.45$ **0.95**
9. $0.73 - 0.11$ **0.62**
10. $0.75 - 0.5$ **0.25**
11. 0.5×0.47 **0.235**

Change each improper fraction to a mixed or whole number.

12. $\frac{3}{2}$ **$1\frac{1}{2}$**
13. $\frac{5}{4}$ **$1\frac{1}{4}$**
14. $\frac{18}{5}$ **$3\frac{3}{5}$**
15. $\frac{10}{7}$ **$1\frac{3}{7}$**
16. $\frac{25}{10}$ **$2\frac{1}{2}$**

Find the decimal equivalent or an approximation to the nearest hundredth.

17. $1\frac{1}{4}$ **1.25**
18. $\frac{5}{6}$ **0.83**
19. $\frac{8}{5}$ **1.6**
20. $\frac{7}{10}$ **0.7**
21. $5\frac{1}{3}$ **5.33**

Add or subtract.

22. $2\frac{2}{5} + 1\frac{1}{5}$ **$3\frac{3}{5}$**
23. $5\frac{7}{8} - 2\frac{2}{3}$ **$3\frac{5}{24}$**
24. $9\frac{7}{10} - 7\frac{2}{5}$ **$2\frac{3}{10}$**
25. $4\frac{3}{4} + 2\frac{1}{3}$ **$7\frac{1}{12}$**

Solve these problems.

26. You roll a 0–5 number cube 120 times. About how many times would you expect to roll an even number? **60**
27. A school van holds eight band members and their instruments. How many vans are needed to transport the 44 members of the band to their concert in Little Falls? **6**
28. You open a savings account with a $2000 deposit. How much money will you have in your account after one year if the bank pays 4% interest compounded semi-annually? **$2080.80**
29. If it takes $1\frac{1}{2}$ hours to clean your room and $2\frac{1}{4}$ hours to mess it up properly again, how long does it take to clean and then mess up your room again? **$3\frac{3}{4}$ hours**
30. A recipe calls for $1\frac{1}{4}$ cups of olive oil. You need to triple the recipe but you only have $\frac{3}{4}$ cups of olive oil at home. How much more olive oil do you need to buy? **$3\frac{3}{4}$ C**

Cumulative Review
Use after Lesson 86

Copy each pair of numbers but replace ● with <, >, or =.

1. $\frac{2}{5}$ ● $\frac{4}{10}$ **=**
2. $\frac{4}{7}$ ● $\frac{5}{6}$ **<**
3. $\frac{7}{8}$ ● $\frac{11}{12}$ **<**
4. 0.02 ● 0.14 **<**
5. 0.4 ● 0.04 **>**
6. 7.2 ● 7.20 **=**

Find the least common multiple of each set of numbers.

7. 2 and 7 **14**
8. 8 and 12 **24**
9. 3, 4, and 5 **60**
10. 4, 6, and 10 **60**

Solve for n.

11. $\frac{1}{7} \times 14 = n$ **2**
12. $\frac{2}{3} \times 24 = n$ **16**
13. $n = \frac{3}{4} \times 16$ **12**

Complete.

14. 500 cm = ■ m **5**
15. 0.65 kg = ■ g **650**
16. 3000 mL = ■ L **3**

Divide. Reduce when possible.

17. $12 \div \frac{1}{4}$ **48**
18. $\frac{3}{8} \div \frac{1}{2}$ **$\frac{3}{4}$**
19. $\frac{3}{5} \div \frac{1}{5}$ **3**
20. $\frac{3}{4} \div \frac{1}{4}$ **3**

The Scale and Fin Highway runs from Tuna to Pompano.

Tuna —4 km— Mackerel —7.5 km— Salmon —13 km— Sea Bass —7 km— Flounder —16 km— Pompano

How many kilometers is it from

21. Tuna to Salmon? **11.5 km**
22. Mackerel to Flounder? **27.5 km**
23. Sea Bass to Pompano and back? **46 km**
24. Flounder to Tuna, then back to Sea Bass? **56 km**

Solve this problem.

25. At Best Deal Rent-a-Car, you can rent a small car for $25.95 a day with 500 free miles and $0.10 a mile for any miles over 500. What will it cost to rent for three days and drive for 750 miles? **$102.85**

Cumulative Review

Use after Lesson 90

Find the greatest common factor of each set of numbers.

1 12 and 16 **4** **2** 8 and 11 **1**

3 2, 4, and 10 **2** **4** 4, 16, and 20 **4**

Write in standard form.

5 10×3^2 **90** **6** $6^2 \times 7^2$ **1764** **7** 5×10^5 **500,000**

Solve for *n*.

8 $12 \div \frac{1}{2} = n$ **24** **9** $\frac{2}{5} \times 20 = n$ **8** **10** $n = \frac{3}{4} \div \frac{1}{6}$ $4\frac{1}{2}$ (or $\frac{9}{2}$)

Change each improper fraction to a mixed or whole number.

11 $\frac{6}{2}$ **3** **12** $\frac{5}{3}$ $1\frac{2}{3}$ **13** $\frac{12}{5}$ $2\frac{2}{5}$ **14** $\frac{16}{7}$ $2\frac{2}{7}$ **15** $\frac{25}{15}$ $1\frac{2}{3}$

For each set of numbers, find the mean, median, and mode.

16 2, 3, 5, 8, 10, 2 **5, 4, 2**

17 4, 4, 7, 10, 10, 10, 11 **8, 10, 10**

18 1, 1, 5, 2, 15, 18, 7 **7, 5, 1**

19 5.5, 6.5, 8, 8, 9.5, 10.5 **8, 8, 8**

20 15, 12.5, 8, 12.5, 12.5, 5.5, 3, 0 **8, 8, 12.5**

Solve these problems.

21 Arturo starting riding his bike at 9:45 A.M. and finished at 12:20 P.M. For how long did he ride? **2 hrs 35 min**

22 Cassie bought 50 comic books for $0.25 each and sold them all for $0.60 each. How much profit did she make? **$17.50**

23 Which is the better buy, a 10-kilogram bag of Doggie Delights that sells for $14.95, or a 7-kilogram bag of the same product that sells for $9.79? **7-kilogram bag for $9.79**

24 Mackenzie can do 20 sit-ups in 30 seconds. If she keeps up that rate, how many sit-ups would she do in three minutes? **120**

25 Kyle took six tests and got these scores: 90, 70, 69, 60, 95, and 75. Then he scored 90 on the next three tests. What was his mean score for the tests? What was his median score? What was the mode of his scores? Which measure of average best represents his test performance? **81; 90; 90; The median or mode best show how well Kyle is doing now. The mean best shows how Kyle has done overall.**

Cumulative Review

Use after Lesson 94

Answers will vary. Examples are given.

Write three fractions equal to the given fraction.

1 $\frac{2}{3}$ $\frac{4}{6}, \frac{8}{12}, \frac{20}{30}$ **2** $\frac{8}{5}$ $\frac{16}{10}, \frac{80}{50}, \frac{32}{20}$ **3** $\frac{4}{7}$ $\frac{8}{14}, \frac{12}{21}, \frac{40}{70}$ **4** $\frac{5}{4}$ $\frac{4}{3}, \frac{3}{12}, \frac{12}{...}$ ... $\frac{5}{4}$ $\frac{4}{3}$ $\frac{3}{12}$

For each set of numbers, find the mean, median, and mode.

5 12, 3, 5, 14, 10, 9, 10 **9; 10; 10** **6** 4, 4, 9, 12, 10, 12, 12 **9; 10; 12**

7 1, 1, 5, 2, 2, 5, 8, 1, 7 **3.6; 2; 1** **8** 2, 7, 4, 5, 8, 1, 8 **5; 5; 8**

Solve each proportion.

9 $\frac{2}{5} = \frac{n}{10}$ **4** **10** $\frac{3}{8} = \frac{n}{24}$ **9** **11** $\frac{4}{9} = \frac{24}{n}$ **54** **12** $\frac{1}{8} = \frac{n}{32}$ **4**

Each pair of figures is similar. Give the missing side lengths.

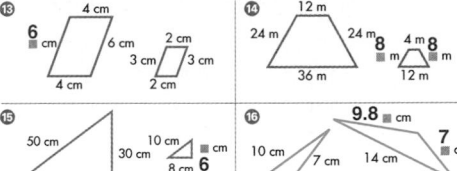

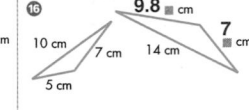

Multiply.

17 $\frac{1}{3} \times 27$ **9** **18** $\frac{1}{8}$ of $\frac{7}{8}$ $\frac{7}{64}$ **19** $\frac{1}{4} \times \frac{5}{8}$ $\frac{5}{32}$ **20** $16 \times \frac{3}{8}$ **6**

Add or subtract.

21 $\frac{4}{7} - \frac{2}{7}$ $\frac{2}{7}$ **22** $\frac{5}{8} + \frac{3}{4}$ $1\frac{3}{8}$ **23** $2\frac{3}{4} + \frac{1}{2}$ $3\frac{1}{4}$ **24** $4\frac{2}{3} - 1\frac{1}{6}$ $3\frac{1}{2}$

Divide.

25 $\frac{2}{3} \div \frac{1}{6}$ **4** **26** $8 \div \frac{1}{3}$ **24** **27** $2\frac{4}{9} \div \frac{1}{6}$ $14\frac{2}{3}$ **28** $\frac{1}{4} \div \frac{1}{2}$ $\frac{1}{3}$

Solve these problems.

29 Which costs more, a $60 tennis racquet marked $\frac{1}{3}$ off" or marked $\frac{1}{3}$ of the regular price"? $\frac{1}{3}$ **off**

30 On a map with a scale of 1 inch = 22 miles, how far apart are two cities that are 6 inches apart on the map? **132 miles**

Cumulative Review

Use after Lesson 99

Find the greatest common factor of each set of numbers.

1 12 and 18 **6** **2** 9 and 10 **1**

3 2, 5, and 10 **1** **4** 4, 12, and 16 **4**

Solve for *n*.

5 $16 \div \frac{1}{2} = n$ **32** **6** $\frac{4}{5} \times 15 = n$ **12** **7** $n = \frac{3}{8} \div \frac{1}{4}$ $1\frac{1}{2}$

Solve each proportion.

8 $\frac{2}{7} = \frac{n}{21}$ **6** **9** $\frac{3}{4} = \frac{n}{24}$ **18** **10** $\frac{3}{8} = \frac{n}{20}$ **7.5** **11** $\frac{1}{6} = \frac{n}{36}$ **6**

12 The table below shows sales of widgets by the Wee Widget Division of International Gadget. Use the data to make two bar graphs—one to show a rapid increase in sales from year to year, and one to show a more modest growth in sales. Then write an explanation of your strategy for showing the sales in two different lights.

12 Check students' graphs carefully.

Year	Widget Sales	Year	Widget Sales
1993	125,000	1996	155,000
1994	130,000	1997	160,000
1995	140,000	1998	175,000

On a sheet of graph paper draw coordinate axes so that each is at least six units long. Then plot and label each of these points:

Check students' graphs.

13 (3, 4) **14** (4, 3) **15** (5, 0) **16** (0, 3)

[graph showing points (3, 4), (0, 3), (4, 3), (5, 0)]

Solve these problems.

17 Which costs more, an $80 CD player marked $\frac{1}{4}$ off" or the same player on sale for 20% off? How much more? **the one marked 20% off; $4**

18 At the same time a flag pole that is 28 feet tall casts a 16-foot shadow, a road sign nearby casts a 4-foot shadow. How tall is the sign? **7 ft**

19 Angela started hiking at 11:40 A.M. and finished at 1:25 P.M. She hiked at a rate of 3.5 miles an hour. For how long did she hike? **1 hr 45 min**

20 Rashid bought a bicycle for $120 and sold it for 15% less than he paid. For how much did he sell it? **$102**

Cumulative Review

Use after Lesson 103

For each of the following figures, tell how many lines of symmetry there are.

1 **3** **2** **0** **3** **1** **4** **8**

Copy each pair of numbers, but replace ● with <, >, or =.

5 $\frac{2}{5}$ ● $\frac{4}{10}$ **=** **6** $\frac{4}{7}$ ● $\frac{5}{6}$ **<** **7** $\frac{7}{8}$ ● $\frac{11}{12}$ **<**

8 0.02 ● 0.14 **<** **9** 0.4 ● 0.04 **>** **10** 7.2 ● 7.20 **=**

Copy each ordered pair. Replace x or y with the correct number so that the ordered pair satisfies the rule $x \boxed{\times 4} y$.

11 (2, y) **8** **12** (4.5, y) **18** **13** (x, 12) **3** **14** (x, 2.4) **0.6**

Alan Isleshoot is a professional basketball player. The table shows some of his shooting statistics.

Game	1	2	3	4	5
Shot Attempts	19	13	22	16	11
Shots Made	12	8	14	10	7

Make a graph using this information. Then use the graph to estimate how many shots Alan might expect to make if the number of shots he attempts is **Check students' graphs carefully.**

15 25? **16** **16** 8? **5** **17** 32? **20** **18** 35? **22**

19 Make a line graph of the temperatures shown in the table below. **Check students' graphs carefully.**

Day	1	2	3	4	5	6	7	8	9
Temperature (°C)	4	3	5	−1	0	−2	−3	1	3

Solve this problem.

20 Which is the better buy, a 12-ounce bottle of shampoo that sells for $8.95 or a 32-ounce bottle of the same shampoo that sells for $26.95? **12-ounce bottle for $8.95**

Cumulative Review

Use after Lesson 108

Add or subtract.

1 $\frac{4}{11} - \frac{2}{11}$ $\frac{2}{11}$　**2** $1\frac{5}{8} + 2\frac{3}{4}$ $4\frac{3}{8}$　**3** $5 - \frac{3}{8}$ $4\frac{5}{8}$　**4** $3\frac{2}{5} - 1\frac{5}{6}$ $1\frac{17}{30}$

For each of the following problems, write two more problems that would have the same answer. **Answers will vary. Examples are given.**

5 $0.12\overline{)4.8}$　**6** $0.003\overline{)47.25}$　**7** $10^1 \times 10^4$　**8** $10^7 \div 10^5$
$1.2\overline{)48},\ 0.012\overline{)0.48}$　$0.03\overline{)472.5},\ 0.3\overline{)4725}$　$10^2 \times 10^3,\ 10^7 \div 10^2$
List the factors of each number.　$10^1 \times 10^1,\ 10^9 \div 10^7$

12 1, 2, 4, 5, 8, 10, 20, 29, 40, 58, 116, 145, 232, 290, 580, 1160

13 1, 2, 4, 8, 16, 131, 262, 524, 1048, 2096

　　　　　　　1, 2, 4, 8,　　1, 2, 3, 4, 6, 12, 43,
9 201　**10** 64　**11** 516　**12** 1160　**13** 2096
1, 3, 67, 201　16, 32, 64　86, 129, 172, 258, 516

Copy and complete the tables so that each ordered pair satisfies the given rule.

$$x \longrightarrow \boxed{\times 3} \longrightarrow y$$

14

x	0	3	−2	−2.5	−4
y	▪	▪	▪	▪	▪

　　　0　9　−6　−7.5　−12

15 Graph each set of ordered pairs in the above table.
Check students' graphs carefully.

Do each chain calculation from left to right, unless you find a faster way to get the answer.

16 $4 + 2 \times 6 - 12 - 4 \div 5$ **4**

17 $10 + 9 + 3 + 7 + 1 + 10 + 10 + 10$ **60**

18 $1 \times 2 \times 3 \times 4 \times 5 \times 6 \times 0$ **0**

Solve these problems.

19 You roll a 5–10 number cube 90 times. About how many times would you expect to roll a number greater than 5? **75**

20 Janine wants to buy a coat that regularly sells for $80 but is now on sale for 20% off. If the sales tax is 6%, what will the coat cost her? **$67.84**

Cumulative Review

Use after Lesson 113

Solve. Watch the signs.

1 $700 - 600$ **100**　**2** 700×600 **420,000**　**3** $6 \times 10^2 \times 70$ **42,000**

Choose the correct answer without calculating.

4 1.2×1.2　a. 0.144　**b.** 1.44　c. 14.4

5 24×2.5　a. 6　**b.** 60　c. 600

6 0.15×0.15　**a.** 0.0225　b. 0.225　c. 2.25

7 3.2×0.8　a. 0.256　**b.** 2.56　c. 25.6

Copy each pair of numbers, but replace ● with <, >, or =.

8 2.5 ● 2.25 **>**　**9** 0.047 ● 0.074 **<**　**10** 0.875 ● 0.9 **<**

For each sequence write the missing terms. Tell what your pattern is.

Answers may vary. Sample answers are given.

11 1, 5, 9, 13, __17__, __21__, __25__ **+4**

12 2, 3, 5, 9, 17, __33__, __65__, __129__ $+2^0, +2^1, +2^2, +2^3, \dots$

13 1, 3, 7, 15, __31__, __63__, __127__ $+2^1, +2^2, +2^3, \dots$

14 40, 37, __34__, 31, __28__, __25__, 22 **−3**

Write each of these rules in the long form, using arrows.

15 $2x - 3 = y$　**16** $y = 4x$　**17** $\frac{1}{2}x + 3 = y$

18 Use a computer or other means to complete the table and graph the function. **Check students' graphs carefully.**

$y = 2x - 5$

x	1	4	▪	▪	▪	▪
y	▪	▪	7	−9	1	9	−7

　−3　3　6　−2　3　7　−1

15 $x \longrightarrow \boxed{\times 2} \longrightarrow n \longrightarrow \boxed{-3} \longrightarrow y$

16 $x \longrightarrow \boxed{\times 4} \longrightarrow y$

17 $x \longrightarrow \boxed{\times \frac{1}{2}} \longrightarrow n \longrightarrow \boxed{+3} \longrightarrow y$

Solve these problems.

19 You roll a 5–10 number cube. What is the probability of getting a 5 or a 6? $\frac{2}{6}$ (or $\frac{1}{3}$)

20 A taxi cab company charges $2 for the first mile of a trip and $0.35 for each additional one fourth of a mile. What is the cost of a 2.5 mile trip? **$4.10**

Cumulative Review

Use after Lesson 118

Change each improper fraction to a mixed or whole number.

1 $\frac{5}{2}$ $2\frac{1}{2}$　**2** $\frac{7}{4}$ $1\frac{3}{4}$　**3** $\frac{18}{7}$ $2\frac{4}{7}$　**4** $\frac{10}{3}$ $3\frac{1}{3}$　**5** $\frac{25}{25}$ **1**

Find the decimal equivalent or a decimal approximation to the nearest thousandth.

6 $1\frac{1}{5}$ **1.2**　**7** $\frac{5}{8}$ **0.625**　**8** $\frac{8}{7}$ **1.143**　**9** $\frac{9}{10}$ **0.9**　**10** $6\frac{2}{3}$ **6.667**

Answers will vary.
Write three fractions equal to the given fraction. **Examples are given.**

11 $\frac{2}{5}$　**12** $\frac{9}{4}$　**13** $\frac{5}{7}$　**14** $\frac{15}{1}$　**15** $\frac{8}{3}$
$\frac{4}{10}, \frac{6}{15}, \frac{12}{30}$　$\frac{18}{8}, \frac{27}{12}, \frac{45}{20}$　$\frac{50}{70}, \frac{15}{21}, \frac{10}{14}$　$\frac{30}{1}, \frac{30}{4}, \frac{30}{10}$　$\frac{2}{3}, \frac{4}{6}, \frac{16}{24}$

Graph the function for each function rule.
Check students' graphs carefully.

16 $2x + 4 = y$　**17** $y = 3x - 2$　**18** $\frac{1}{2}x + 5 = y$

Solve for n.

19 $8 \times 8 = n$ **64**　**20** $60 \times 60 = n$ **3600**　**21** $39 \times 41 = n$ **1599**

22 $75 \times 7 = n$ **525**　**23** $81 \times 5 = n$ **405**　**24** $810 \times 5 = n$ **4050**

25 Use a computer or other means to complete the table and graph the function.

$y = 2x^2 + 3x + 2$

x	0	1	2	3	0.5	1.5	2.5
y	▪	▪	▪	▪	▪	▪	▪

Check students' graphs carefully.

　2　7　16　29　4　11　22

26 Draw three rectangles that meet the conditions of the function $y = 3x + 1$, where x is the length of the shorter side and y is the length of the longer side.

26 Answers will vary. Check sides of students' drawings to make sure they meet the terms of the equation.

For each pair of figures, tell whether a rotation, a reflection, or a translation could be used to move one figure on top of the other.

27 reflection　**28** translation

29 rotation　**30** reflection

Cumulative Review

Use after Lesson 123

Write in standard form.

1 10×3^3 **270**　**2** $8^2 \times 5^2$ **1600**　**3** 25×10^3 **25,000**

Add or subtract. Watch the signs.

4 $\frac{2}{5} + \frac{3}{4}$ $1\frac{3}{20}$　**5** $\frac{5}{8} - \frac{1}{24}$ $\frac{11}{24}$　**6** $\frac{7}{10} - \frac{3}{5}$ $\frac{1}{10}$　**7** $\frac{3}{8} + \frac{5}{12}$ $\frac{19}{24}$

For each graph determine a function rule.

8

$y = x + 2$

9

$y = 3x$

Solve for n. Use shortcuts when you can.

10 $14 - 2.5 = n$ **11.5**　**11** $n \times 30 = 900$ **30**　**12** $120 + n = 150$ **30**

13 $\frac{17}{43} \times 0 = n$ **0**　**14** $1000 \div 50 = n$ **20**　**15** $729 \div n = 1$ **729**

Use 3.14 for π to find the approximate circumference of a circle with a diameter of

16 10 meters. **31.4 m**　**17** 20 meters. **62.8 m**　**18** 8 centimeters. **25.12 m**

Multiply or divide. Watch the signs.

19 $2.25 \div 100$ **0.0225**　**20** 0.078×1000 **78**

21 $294 \div 1000$ **0.294**　**22** 9.001×10 **90.01**

23 $34.3 \div 1000$ **0.0343**　**24** 8.63×100 **863**

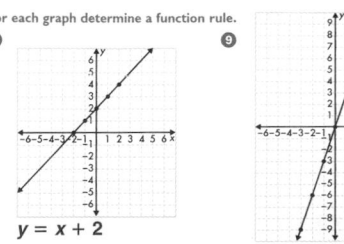

What are the coordinates of

25 point A? **(2, −3)**　**26** point B? **(−1, 4)**

27 point C? **(−3, 0)**　**28** point D? **(0, 5)**

29 point E? **(3, 3)**　**30** point F? **(−2, −1)**

Cumulative Review
Use after Lesson 126

Solve for *n*. Use shortcuts when you can.

1. $30 - 12.9 = n$ **17.1**
2. $n \times 40 = 1600$ **40**
3. $50 \times 50 = n$ **2500**
4. $100 \div 0.20 = n$ **500**

Graph the function for each function rule. **Check students' graphs carefully.**

5. $x + 3 = y$
6. $y = 2x - 4$
7. $2x + 5 = y$

Copy each pair of numbers but replace ● with <, >, or =.

8. $\frac{1}{2}$ ● $\frac{12}{24}$ **=**
9. $\frac{7}{8}$ ● $\frac{20}{24}$ **>**
10. $1\frac{5}{6}$ ● $\frac{13}{6}$ **<**

Find the area of the rectangles with these bases and heights.

11. base = 10 cm, height = 30 cm **300 cm²**
12. base = 48 cm, height = 60 cm **2880 cm²**
13. base = 1.5 m, height = 0.5 m **0.75 m²**
14. base = 0.14 m, height = 0.4 m **0.056 m²**

Find the volume of boxes with the following dimensions.

15. length = 5 cm, width = 6 cm, height = 8 cm **240 cm³**
16. length = 4 m, width = 6 m, height = 3 m **72 m³**
17. length = 10 cm, width = 12 cm, height = 8 cm **960 cm³**
18. length = 2 dm, width = 2 dm, height = 3 dm **12 dm³**

Solve these problems.

19. What is the total area of the top and four sides of a building that is 22 meters long, 18 meters wide, and 11 meters tall? **1276 m²**
20. What is the total price, including tax, of a mountain bike that regularly sells for $240, but is now on sale for 25% off? The sales tax is 6.5%. **$191.70**

580 · Cumulative Review

Cumulative Review
Use after Lesson 129

Answers may vary. Examples are given.

For each sequence write the missing terms. Tell what your pattern is.

1. 1, 4, 8, 13, **19**, **26**, **34** +3, +4, +5, ...
2. 2, 3, 5, 6, 8, **9**, **11**, **12** +1, +2, +1, +2, ...
3. 1, 3, 7, 13, **21**, **31**, **43** +2, +4, +6, +8, ...
4. 50, 45, **40**, **35**, **30**, 25, 20 **−5**

Choose the correct answer without calculating.

5. 1.1×1.1 a. 0.121 **(b.)** 1.21 c. 12.1
6. 20×0.35 **(a.)** 7 b. 70 c. 700
7. 0.25×0.25 **(a.)** 0.0625 b. 0.625 c. 6.25

Calculate the perimeter and the area of a rectangle having the given measurements.

8. length = 25 cm, width = 30 cm, perimeter = ■, area = ■
110 cm 750 cm²
9. length = 40 cm, width = 500 cm, perimeter = ■, area = ■
1080 cm 20,000 cm²
10. length = 80 cm, width = 120 cm, perimeter = ■, area = ■
400 cm 9600 cm²

For each of these right triangles name the right angle, base, and height. **See below.***

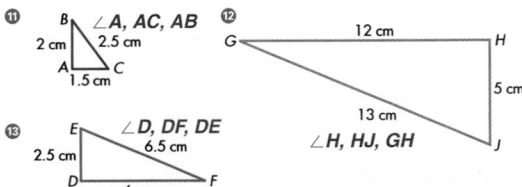

11. **∠A, AC, AB**
12. **∠H, HJ, GH**
13. **∠D, DF, DE**

Find the area of right triangles with these bases and heights.

14. base = 10 cm, height = 15 cm **75 cm²**
15. base = 22 cm, height = 30 cm **330 cm²**

*The base and the height are interchangeable.

Cumulative Review · 581

Cumulative Review
Use after Lesson 134

Divide. Round decimal quotients to the nearest tenth when necessary.

1. $305 \div 7$ **43.6**
2. $952 \div 21$ **45.3**
3. $320 \div 20$ **16**
4. $1658 \div 96$ **17.3**
5. $2652 \div 13$ **204**
6. $814 \div 6$ **135.7**
7. $450 \div 90$ **5**
8. $3072 \div 64$ **48**

Multiply. Use shortcuts when you can.

9. 30×30 **900**
10. 81×79 **6399**
11. 500×50 **25,000**
12. 60×60 **3600**
13. 93×10 **930**
14. 250×40 **10,000**
15. 302×7 **2114**
16. 41×300 **12,300**

Graph the function for each function rule. **Check students' graphs carefully.**

17. $x + 6 = y$
18. $y = 2x - 2$
19. $3x + 4 = y$

Find the area of each trapezoid.

20. 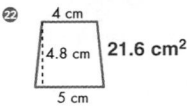 **128 cm²**
21. **28.5 cm²**
22. 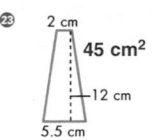 **21.6 cm²**
23. **45 cm²**

For problems 24 and 25, *B* is the length of the longer base of a trapezoid, and *b* is the length of the shorter base. The length of the segment halfway between the bases and parallel to them is *m*. Find *m*.

24. $B = 10$ cm, $b = 6$ cm, $m = ?$ **8 cm**
25. $B = 25$ cm, $b = 12$ cm, $m = ?$ **18.5 cm**
26. Draw a right scalene triangle. **Drawings may vary. A scalene triangle has three sides of different lengths.**
27. Is every rhombus a square? **no**
28. Is every square a rhombus? **yes**
29. Is every quadrilateral a parallelogram? **no**
30. Is every trapezoid a quadrilateral? **yes**

582 · Cumulative Review

Cumulative Review
Use after Lesson 139

Use 3.14 for π to find the approximate circumference of a circle with a diameter of

1. 12 meters. **37.68 m**
2. 15 meters. **47.1 m**
3. 6 centimeters. **18.84 cm**

Multiply or divide. Watch the signs.

4. $2.25 \div 100$ **0.0225**
5. 0.078×1000 **78**
6. 9.001×10 **90.01**
7. $34.3 \div 1000$ **0.0343**
8. 5.1×1000 **0.0051**
9. $200.5 \div 100$ **2.005**
10. 0.003×100 **0.3**
11. $25 \times 100,000$ **2,500,000**
12. $10,000 \times 0.002$ **20**
13. $10 \div 20$ **0.5**
14. $25 \div 100,000$ **0.00025**
15. $2.5 \times 10,000$ **25,000**

16. Use a computer or other means to draw and complete this chart. Round each length to the nearest hundredth of a centimeter.

Area of square (cm²)	10	20	40	2	4	6	12
Length of side (cm)	■	■	■	■	■	■	■
	3.16	4.47	6.32	1.41	2	2.45	3.46

Convert these measurements.

17. 3.82 meters to centimeters **382 cm**
18. 472.5 meters to kilometers **0.4725 km**
19. 0.24 kilograms to grams **240 g**
20. 0.034 kilometers to meters **34 m**

Solve these problems.

21. Draw a right isosceles triangle with an area of 32 cm². Use a centimeter ruler or centimeter grid paper. **The triangle should be as follows:**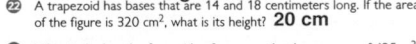
22. A trapezoid has bases that are 14 and 18 centimeters long. If the area of the figure is 320 cm², what is its height? **20 cm**
23. What is the length of one side of a square that has an area of 625 m²? **25 m**
24. Rachel walks about 4 kilometers in an hour. It usually takes about 28 minutes to walk from her house to her piano teacher's house. About how far is it from Rachel's house to her teacher's house? **a little less than 2 km**
25. Jack measured a stack of 50 identical magazines. It was 38.8 centimeters high. How thick was each magazine? **about 0.776 cm**

Cumulative Review · 583

Cumulative Review
Use after Lesson 144

What are the coordinates of

1 point A? **2** point B?
(−3, 2) **(1, 5)**

3 point C? **4** point D?
(−6, −2) **(4, 3)**

5 point E?
(0, 2)

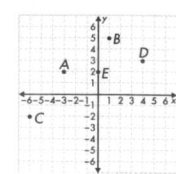

Find the area of the right triangles with these bases and heights.

6 base = 12 cm, height = 14 cm **7** base = 20 cm, height = 25 cm
84 cm² **250 cm²**

For each sequence write the missing terms. Tell what your pattern is.

Answers will vary. Examples are given.

8 1, 5, 10, 16, __23__ , __31__ , __40__ +4, +5, +6, +7, . . .

9 2, 4, 8, 14, 22, __32__ , __44__ , __58__ +2, +4, +6, +8, . . .

10 1, 2, 5, 14, 41, __122__ , __365__ , __1094__ +3⁰, +3¹, +3², +3³, . . .

Add or subtract. Completely reduce your answer.

11 $\frac{1}{2} + \frac{1}{3}$ $\frac{5}{6}$ **12** $\frac{2}{5} + \frac{3}{4}$ $1\frac{3}{20}$ **13** $\frac{5}{6} - \frac{1}{2}$ $\frac{1}{3}$ **14** $\frac{7}{8} - \frac{1}{4}$ $\frac{5}{8}$ **15** $\frac{4}{5} - \frac{1}{10}$ $\frac{7}{10}$

16 $\frac{2}{3} + \frac{1}{2}$ $1\frac{1}{6}$ **17** $\frac{5}{8} + \frac{1}{12}$ $\frac{17}{24}$ **18** $\frac{9}{10} - \frac{3}{5}$ $\frac{3}{10}$ **19** $\frac{4}{5} - \frac{3}{4}$ $\frac{1}{20}$ **20** $\frac{1}{6} + \frac{3}{8}$ $\frac{13}{24}$

Tell whether each angle is obtuse, right, or acute.

21 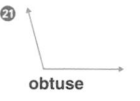 **22** 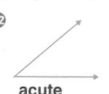 **23**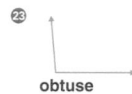

obtuse   acute   obtuse

 Solve these problems.

24 A bag of cherries weighs 2.5 pounds. How many ounces is that? **40**

25 A rectangular room is $17\frac{3}{4}$ feet long and $10\frac{1}{2}$ feet wide. What is the area of the floor of the room? **$186\frac{3}{8}$ ft**

Cumulative Review
Use after Lesson 148

Answers may vary. Examples are given.

For each sequence write the missing terms. Tell what your pattern is.

1 1, 8, 15, 22, __29__ , __36__ , __43__ +7

2 2, 5, 11, 23, 47, __95__ , __191__ , __383__ ×2 +1

3 1, 4, 16, 64, __256__ , __1024__ , __4096__ ×4

Add or subtract. Completely reduce your answer.

4 $\frac{1}{5} + \frac{1}{3}$ $\frac{8}{15}$ **5** $\frac{2}{3} + \frac{3}{8}$ $1\frac{1}{24}$ **6** $\frac{5}{6} - \frac{1}{4}$ $\frac{7}{12}$ **7** $\frac{7}{9} - \frac{2}{5}$ $\frac{17}{45}$ **8** $\frac{4}{5} - \frac{7}{10}$ $\frac{1}{10}$

Tell whether each triangle is obtuse, right, or acute.

9  **10**  right **11**
obtuse   acute

In the figure below, lines AC, DF, and JK are parallel to each other. The measure of ∠1 is 50 degrees.

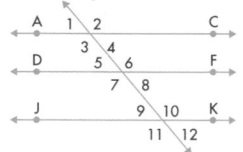

Determine the measure of each of the following angles.

17 ∠2 **18** ∠4 **19** ∠3 **20** ∠9 **21** ∠6
130° 50° 130° 50° 130°

Determine the measure of the third angle.

22 38° **23** 55°

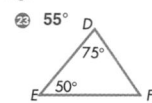

Answers may vary. Examples are given.

Give examples of each of these.

24 A line and a plane that meet at one point

25 A line and a plane that are parallel **a line on the floor and the ceiling**

26 the line between two side walls and the ceiling

Cumulative Review
Use after Lesson 151

Multiply or divide. Watch the signs.

1 1.25 ÷ 1000 **2** 0.078 × 10 **3** 5.001 × 100
0.00125 **0.78** **500.1**

4 44.4 ÷ 1000 **5** 5.5 ÷ 1000 **6** 500.5 ÷ 10,000
0.0444 **0.0055** **0.05005**

7 0.005 × 100 **8** 5 × 100,000 **9** 999 ÷ 1000
0.5 **500,000** **0.999**

Convert these measurements.

10 3.12 decimeters to centimeters **11** 76.5 meters to kilometers
31.2 cm **0.0765 km**

12 0.744 kilograms to grams **13** 0.0834 kilometers to meters
744 g **83.4 m**

14 5 feet to inches **15** 80 ounces to pounds
60 in. **5 lb**

16 4 quarts to cups **17** 14 minutes to seconds
16 cups **840 seconds**

Graph the function for each function rule. **Check students' graphs carefully.**

18 $x - 3 = y$ **19** $y = \frac{1}{2}x + 3$ **20** $3x - 2 = y$

Find the area of the triangles with these bases and heights.

21 base = 12 m, height = 8.5 m **22** base = 2.2 cm, height = 3 cm
51 m² **3.3 cm²**

23 Dave and Belinda recorded the number and kinds of vehicles that passed through an intersection of their town. The table shows their results. Use a computer or other means to make a circle graph to show the information in the chart.

Type of vehicle	Number seen
Sedan	55
Coupe	24
Station wagon	8
Van	18
Sports utility	27
Sports car	12
Truck	6

24 Examples: two books, a large paper clip and a small paper clip, a large pizza and a small pizza

Solve.

24 List five pairs of similar objects from everyday life.

25 Draw any triangle. Use a compass and a straightedge to construct a triangle congruent to it. **Drawings will vary.**

Cumulative Review
Use after Lesson 156

Tell whether each triangle is obtuse, right, or acute.

1 right **2** obtuse **3** acute

Find the decimal equivalent or an approximation to the nearest hundredth.

4 $2\frac{1}{9}$ **5** $\frac{7}{10}$ **6** $\frac{9}{5}$ **7** $\frac{19}{25}$ **8** $7\frac{5}{7}$
2.11 **0.7** **1.8** **0.76** **7.71**

Choose the correct answer without using paper or a calculator.

9 11 × 1.1 **a.** 1.21 **b.** 12.1 **c.** 121

10 30 × 0.25 **a.** 7.5 **b.** 75 **c.** 750

11 0.5 × 0.05 **a.** 0.025 **b.** 0.25 **c.** 2.5

In each case the lengths of the two shorter sides of a right triangle are given. Find the length of the hypotenuse. Give answers to the nearest tenth of a centimeter.

12 4 cm, 6 cm **13** 2 cm, 5 cm **14** 7 cm, 10 cm
7.2 cm **5.4 cm** **12.2 cm**

Find the area in square centimeters of each of these figures.

15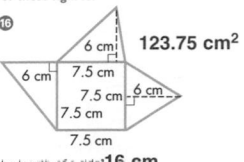
24 cm²

16 **123.75 cm²**

Solve these problems.

17 The area of a square is 256 cm². What is the length of a side? **16 cm**

18 What is the volume in cubic centimeters of a rectangular box that is 5.6 centimeters long, 2.2 centimeters wide, and 4.0 centimeters tall? **49.28 cm³**

19 The formula for converting between degrees Celsius (C) and degrees Fahrenheit (F) is F = $\frac{9}{5}$C + 32. Water boils at 100°C. What is the boiling point of water in degrees Fahrenheit? **212°F**

20 How many milliliters are in a centiliter? **10**

Metric System

Length		Weight (mass)		Liquid Volume (capacity)	
millimeter (mm)	0.001 m	milligram (mg)	0.001 g	milliliter (mL)	0.001 L
centimeter (cm)	0.01 m	centigram (cg)	0.01 g	centiliter (cL)	0.01 L
decimeter (dm)	0.1 m	decigram (dg)	0.1 g	deciliter (dL)	0.1 L
meter (m)	1 m	gram (g)	1 g	liter (L)	1 L
dekameter (dam)	10 m	dekagram (dag)	10 g	dekaliter (daL)	10 L
hectometer (hm)	100 m	hectogram (hg)	100 g	hectoliter (hL)	100 L
kilometer (km)	1000 m	kilogram (kg)	1000 g	kiloliter (kL)	1000 L

◆ Units of area are derived from units of length.

square centimeter (cm²)   1 cm² = 0.0001 m²
square meter (m²)   1 m² = 10,000 cm²
square kilometer (km²)   1 km² = 1,000,000 m²

◆ Units of volume can also be derived from units of length.

cubic centimeter (cm³)   **cubic meter** (m³)   1 m³ = 1,000,000 cm³

◆ Descriptions of some common units:

kilometer   *You can walk a kilometer in about 12 minutes.*
meter   *Most classroom doors are about 1 meter wide.*
centimeter   *This line segment is 1 centimeter long.* ———
millimeter   *This line segment is 1 millimeter long.* -
liter   *Four average-sized glasses hold about 1 liter of liquid all together.*
milliliter   *This cube holds about 1 milliliter of liquid.*

kilogram   *A pair of size-10 men's shoes weighs about 1 kilogram.*
gram   *A nickel weighs about 5 grams.*

Customary System

◆ **Length**

inch (in.)   1 in. = $\frac{1}{12}$ ft
  $\frac{1}{36}$ yd

foot (ft)   1 ft = 12 in.
  $\frac{1}{3}$ yd

yard (yd)   1 yd = 36 in.
  3 ft

mile (mi)   1 mi = 5280 ft
  1760 yd

◆ **Area**

square inch (sq in. or in.²)
square foot (sq ft or ft²)   1 ft² = 144 in.²
square yard (sq yd or yd²)   1 yd² = 9 ft²
acre (A)   1 A = 4840 yd²
square mile (sq mi or mi²)   1 mi² = 640 A

◆ **Weight**

ounce (oz)   1 oz = $\frac{1}{16}$ lb
pound (lb)   1 lb = 16 oz
ton (T)   1 T = 2000 lb

◆ **Volume**

cubic inch (cu in. or in.³)
cubic foot (cu ft or ft³)   1 ft³ = 1728 in.³
cubic yard (cu yd or yd³)   1 yd³ = 27 ft³

◆ **Liquid Volume (capacity)**

fluid ounce (fl oz)   1 fl oz = $\frac{1}{8}$ cup

cup (c)   1 c = 8 fl oz
  $\frac{1}{2}$ pt

pint (pt)   1 pt = 16 fl oz
  2 c
  $\frac{1}{2}$ qt

quart (qt)   1 qt = 32 fl oz
  4 c
  $\frac{1}{4}$ gal

gallon (gal)   1 gal = 128 fl oz
  16 c
  8 pt
  4 qt

Formulas

Circle

area = πr^2
diameter = $2r$
circumference = πd

Parallelogram

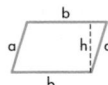

area = bh
perimeter = $2a + 2b$

Square

area = s^2
perimeter = $4s$

Rectangle

area = $l \times w$
perimeter = $2l + 2w$

Triangle

area = $\frac{1}{2}bh$
perimeter = $a + b + c$

Trapezoid

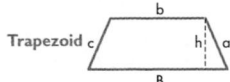

area = $\frac{h(B + b)}{2}$
perimeter = $a + b + c + B$

Volume $V = lwh$

Interest $I = prt$ (principal × rate × time)

Probability $\dfrac{\text{number of favorable outcomes}}{\text{number of possible outcomes}}$

Temperature Conversions   Fahrenheit to Celsius   C° = (F° − 32) × $\frac{5}{9}$
Celsius to Fahrenheit   F° = $\frac{9}{5}$C° + 32

Finding Total Degrees of Angles of Regular Polygons   180 × (n − 2), where n = number of sides

Pythagorean Theorem $a^2 + b^2 = c^2$, where c is the hypotenuse of a right triangle and a and b are the other sides

Formula for a Straight Line $y = Ax + B$, where A is the number of steps to the right for each step up, and B is the y-coordinate for x = 0

acute angle   base

A

acute angle An angle that measures less than 90°. These are acute angles:

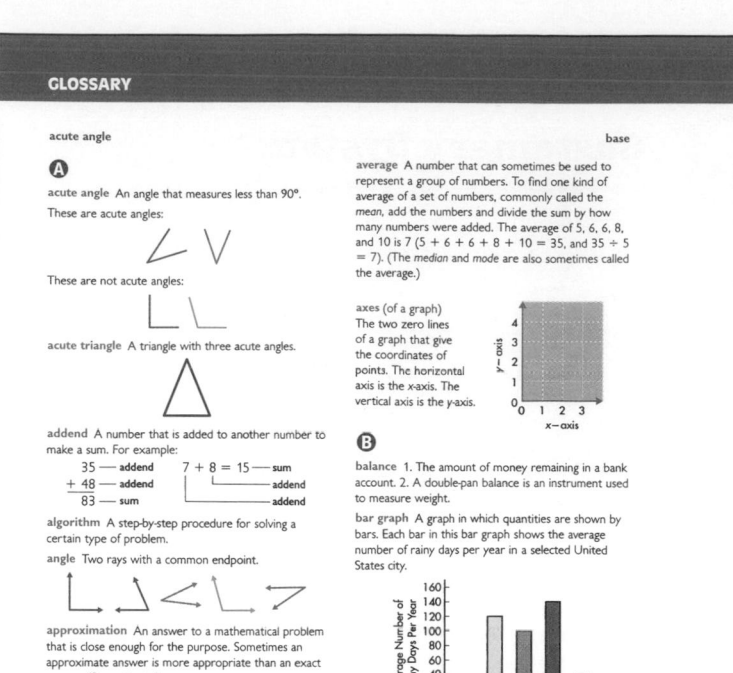

These are not acute angles:

acute triangle A triangle with three acute angles.

addend A number that is added to another number to make a sum. For example:

$$\begin{array}{rl} 35 & \text{— addend} \\ + 48 & \text{— addend} \\ \hline 83 & \text{— sum} \end{array}$$

7 + 8 = 15 — sum
— addend
— addend

algorithm A step-by-step procedure for solving a certain type of problem.

angle Two rays with a common endpoint.

approximation An answer to a mathematical problem that is close enough for the purpose. Sometimes an approximate answer is more appropriate than an exact answer. (See *estimate*.)

arc A part of a circle.

area The number of square units enclosed by a figure. The area of this rectangle is 6 square centimeters.

arrow operation A notation for showing an action of a function machine. In 7 —(× 8)→ 56 , 7 goes in and is multiplied by 8 to give 56. The function rule in this case is ×8. In the operation

6 ←(− 5)— 11 , 11 goes in and 5 is subtracted from it to give 6. The function rule in this case is −5.

average A number that can sometimes be used to represent a group of numbers. To find one kind of average of a set of numbers, commonly called the *mean*, add the numbers and divide the sum by how many numbers were added. The average of 5, 6, 6, 8, and 10 is 7 (5 + 6 + 6 + 8 + 10 = 35, and 35 ÷ 5 = 7). (The *median* and *mode* are also sometimes called the average.)

axes (of a graph) The two zero lines of a graph that give the coordinates of points. The horizontal axis is the *x-axis*. The vertical axis is the *y-axis*.

B

balance 1. The amount of money remaining in a bank account. 2. A double-pan balance is an instrument used to measure weight.

bar graph A graph in which quantities are shown by bars. Each bar in this bar graph shows the average number of rainy days per year in a selected United States city.

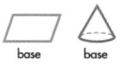

base 1. A side of a polygon or a surface of a space figure.

base   base

2. The number to be raised to a power. In the expression 3ⁿ, 3 is the base.

592 • Glossary

---

bound   cube

bound A number that an answer must be greater than or less than. For example, 36 × 21 must be less than 40 × 30, or 1200. So 1200 is an upper bound. The answer to 36 × 21 must be greater than 30 × 20, or 600. So 600 is a lower bound.

C

Celsius (C) A temperature scale named after a Swedish astronomer, in which 0° is the temperature at which water freezes and 100° is the temperature at which water boils under standard conditions.

circle A figure (in a plane) in which all points are the same distance from a point called the center. In this figure, for example, points A, B, and C are the same distance from point O, the center of the circle.

circumference The distance around a circle.

clipped range In a set of numbers, the range calculated without the greatest and least values.

common denominator A common multiple of two or more denominators. For example, 56 is a common denominator of $\frac{1}{7}$ and $\frac{3}{8}$.

composite function A function with two or more operations. For example:

x —(× 3)→ n —(+ 5)→ y

composite number A whole number having factors other than 1 and itself.

compound interest Interest that is paid on the previous interest as well as on the principal.

concave Shape of a figure in which there exists a line segment between two points of the figure that goes outside the figure.

cone A figure made by connecting every point of a circle to a point not in the plane of the circle.

congruent Figures that are the same size and same shape; that is, they fit perfectly when placed on top of each other.

These triangles are congruent:

These are not:

convex Shape of a figure in which every line segment between two points of the figure remains entirely inside the figure. (See *concave*.)

coordinates Numbers that give the position of a point on a graph. In the figure shown, for example, the coordinates of point A are (2,3). The *x*-coordinate is 2. The *y*-coordinate is 3.

cube A solid figure with six congruent square faces. For example:

Glossary • 593

---

cylinder   Fahrenheit

cylinder A figure with two parallel bases that are usually congruent circles.

D

decimal point A dot used to separate the ones digit from the tenths digit.

degree 1. A unit for measuring temperature. 2. A unit for measuring angles.

denominator The part of a fraction written below the line. The part written above the line is called the numerator. The denominator tells how many equal parts something is divided into; the numerator tells how many of those parts are being referred to. In the fraction $\frac{3}{4}$ the denominator (4) indicates that something is divided into four equal parts. The numerator (3) says to consider three of those parts.

deposit To add money to a bank account. (Also, the amount of money added.)

diagonal A segment that joins two nonadjacent vertices of a polygon.

diameter A line segment, going through the center of a circle, that starts at one point on the circle and ends at the opposite point on the circle. (Also, the length of that line segment.) AB is a diameter of this circle.

difference The amount by which one number is greater or less than another number. For example:

$$\begin{array}{rl} 43 & \text{— minuend} \\ - 16 & \text{— subtrahend} \\ \hline 27 & \text{— difference} \end{array}$$

10 − 7 = 3 — difference
— subtrahend
— minuend

digit Any of the numbers 0, 1, 2, 3, 4, 5, 6, 7, 8, and 9. The two digits in 15 are 1 and 5.

dividend A number that is divided by the divisor. (See *divisor*.) For example:

6 ÷ 3 = 2
— quotient
— divisor
— dividend

$$\begin{array}{r} 43 \text{ — quotient} \\ 8\overline{)347} \text{ — dividend} \\ \underline{32} \\ 27 \\ \underline{24} \\ 3 \end{array}$$

divisor A number that the dividend is divided by. (See *dividend*.)

E

equation A mathematical statement with an equal sign stating that two quantities are equal. For example, 4 + 2 = 6 and 6 + n = 10 are equations.

equilateral triangle A triangle with all three sides the same length. For example:

equivalent fractions Fractions that have the same value. The fractions $\frac{2}{6}$, $\frac{4}{12}$, and $\frac{1}{3}$ are equivalent fractions.

estimate A judgment about the size or quantity of something. (Also, to make such a judgment.) (See *approximation*.)

even number Any multiple of 2. The numbers 0, 2, 4, 6, 8, and so on are even numbers.

exponent A number written slightly above and to the right of the base. It tells how many times the base is to be used as a factor. In the expression 3⁴, 4 is the exponent.

F

factor 1. A whole number that divides evenly into a given second whole number. 2. One of the numbers multiplied to give a product.

Fahrenheit (F) A temperature scale named for a German physicist, in which 32° is the temperature at which water freezes and 212° is the temperature at which water boils under standard conditions.

594 • Glossary

---

fraction   line

fraction Examples of fractions are $\frac{1}{2}$, $\frac{3}{4}$, and $\frac{7}{8}$. The fraction $\frac{3}{4}$ means that something is divided into four equal parts and that we are considering three of those parts. (See *denominator* and *numerator*.)

function machine A device (sometimes imaginary) that does the same thing to every number that is put into it. (See *arrow notation*.)

function rule See *arrow notation*.

G

greatest common factor The greatest number that divides two or more numbers with no remainders.

H

hexagon A polygon with six sides.

hundredth If a whole is divided into 100 equal parts, each part is one hundredth of the whole.

hypotenuse The longest side of a right triangle.

identity function A function that always gives back the same number that is put in.

improper fraction A fraction in which the numerator is greater than or equal to the denominator.

inequality A statement that tells which of two numbers is greater. For example, 4 > 3 is read "4 is greater than 3." The expression 3 + 6 < 10 is read "3 plus 6 is less than 10."

interest The payment made by a bank to those who have deposited money there.

intersecting lines Lines that meet. In this figure, lines AB and CD intersect at point E:

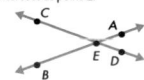

inverse operation An operation that undoes the results of another operation. Multiplication and division are inverse operations; addition and subtraction are inverse operations.

—(× 3)→ is the inverse of —(÷ 3)→

—(− 6)→ is the inverse of —(+ 6)→

isosceles trapezoid A trapezoid with two equal sides. This is an isosceles trapezoid:

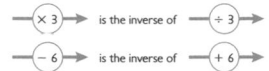

isosceles triangle A triangle with two equal sides. These are isosceles triangles:

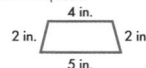

L

least common multiple (LCM) The least number (except 0) that is a multiple of two or more numbers.

line A set of points continuing without end in both directions.

Glossary • 595

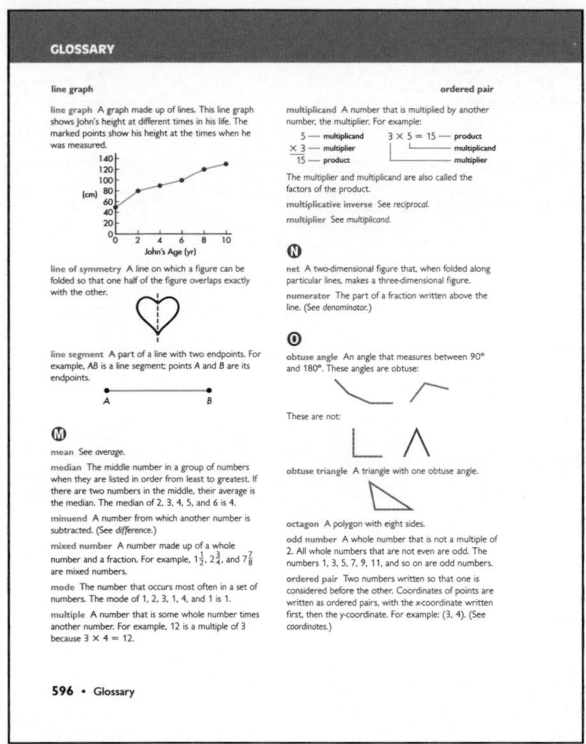

line graph   **ordered pair**

line graph A graph made up of lines. This line graph shows John's height at different times in his life. The marked points show his height at the times when he was measured.

line of symmetry A line on which a figure can be folded so that one half of the figure overlaps exactly with the other.

line segment A part of a line with two endpoints. For example, AB is a line segment; points A and B are its endpoints.

M

mean See *average.*

median The middle number in a group of numbers when they are listed in order from least to greatest. If there are two numbers in the middle, their average is the median. The median of 2, 3, 4, 5, and 6 is 4.

minuend A number from which another number is subtracted. (See *difference.*)

mixed number A number made up of a whole number and a fraction. For example, $1\frac{1}{2}$, $2\frac{3}{4}$, and $7\frac{7}{8}$ are mixed numbers.

mode The number that occurs most often in a set of numbers. The mode of 1, 2, 3, 1, 4, and 1 is 1.

multiple A number that is some whole number times another number. For example, 12 is a multiple of 3 because $3 \times 4 = 12$.

multiplicand A number that is multiplied by another number, the multiplier. For example:

$$5 \quad \text{multiplicand}$$
$$\times\ 3 \quad \text{multiplier}$$
$$\overline{15} \quad \text{product}$$

$$3 \times 5 = 15 \quad \text{product}$$

The multiplier and multiplicand are also called the factors of the product.

multiplicative inverse See *reciprocal.*

multiplier See *multiplicand.*

N

net A two-dimensional figure that, when folded along particular lines, makes a three-dimensional figure.

numerator The part of a fraction written above the line. (See *denominator.*)

O

obtuse angle An angle that measures between 90° and 180°. These angles are obtuse:

These are not:

obtuse triangle A triangle with one obtuse angle.

octagon A polygon with eight sides.

odd number A whole number that is not a multiple of 2. All whole numbers that are not even are odd. The numbers 1, 3, 5, 7, 9, 11, and so on are odd numbers.

ordered pair Two numbers written so that one is considered before the other. Coordinates of points are written as ordered pairs, with the x-coordinate written first, then the y-coordinate. For example: (3, 4). (See *coordinates.*)

596 • Glossary

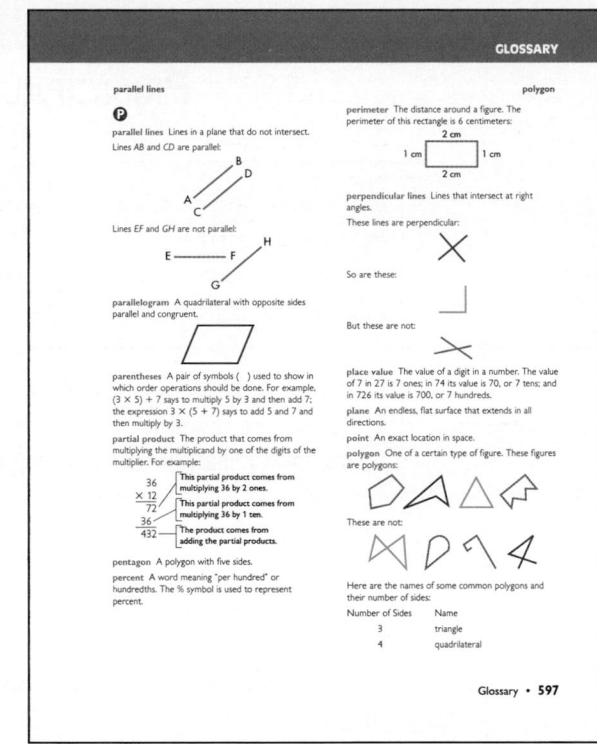

parallel lines   **polygon**

P

parallel lines Lines in a plane that do not intersect. Lines AB and CD are parallel.

Lines EF and GH are not parallel:

parallelogram A quadrilateral with opposite sides parallel and congruent.

parentheses A pair of symbols ( ) used to show in which order operations should be done. For example, $(3 \times 5) + 7$ says to multiply 5 by 3 and then add 7; the expression $3 \times (5 + 7)$ says to add 5 and 7 and then multiply by 3.

partial product The product that comes from multiplying the multiplicand by one of the digits of the multiplier. For example:

$$36$$
$$\times\ 12$$
$$\overline{72}$$ ← This partial product comes from multiplying 36 by 2 ones.
$$36$$ ← This partial product comes from multiplying 36 by 1 ten.
$$\overline{432}$$ ← The product comes from adding the partial products.

pentagon A polygon with five sides.

percent A word meaning "per hundred" or "hundredths." The % symbol is used to represent percent.

perimeter The distance around a figure. The perimeter of this rectangle is 6 centimeters:

perpendicular lines Lines that intersect at right angles.

These lines are perpendicular:

So are these:

But these are not:

place value The value of a digit in a number. The value of 7 in 27 is 7 ones; in 74 its value is 70, or 7 tens; and in 726 its value is 700, or 7 hundreds.

plane An endless, flat surface that extends in all directions.

point An exact location in space.

polygon One of a certain type of figure. These figures are polygons:

These are not:

Here are the names of some common polygons and their number of sides:

Number of Sides	Name
3	triangle
4	quadrilateral

Glossary • 597

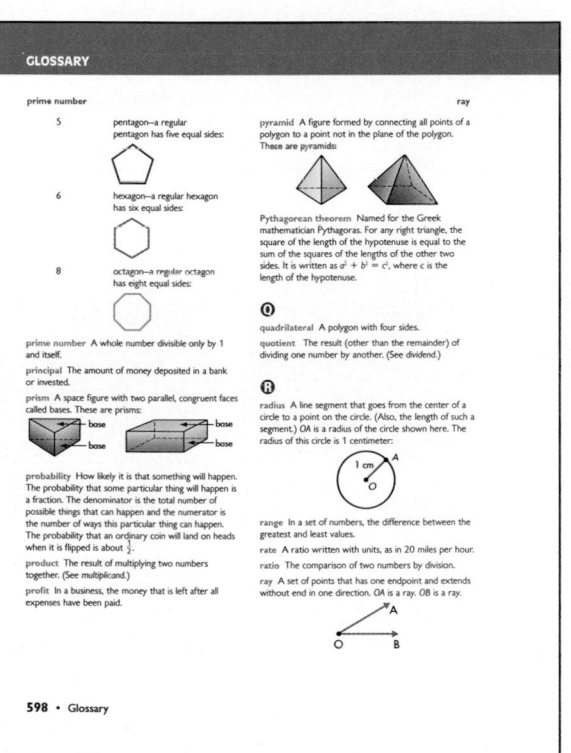

prime number   **ray**

5	pentagon—a regular pentagon has five equal sides:
6	hexagon—a regular hexagon has six equal sides:
8	octagon—a regular octagon has eight equal sides:

prime number A whole number divisible only by 1 and itself.

principal The amount of money deposited in a bank or invested.

prism A space figure with two parallel, congruent faces called bases. These are prisms:

probability How likely it is that something will happen. The probability that some particular thing will happen is a fraction. The denominator is the total number of possible things that can happen and the numerator is the number of ways this particular thing can happen. The probability that an ordinary coin will land on heads when it is flipped is about $\frac{1}{2}$.

product The result of multiplying two numbers together. (See *multiplicand.*)

profit In a business, the money that is left after all expenses have been paid.

pyramid A figure formed by connecting all points of a polygon to a point not in the plane of the polygon. These are pyramids:

Pythagorean theorem Named for the Greek mathematician Pythagoras. For any right triangle, the square of the length of the hypotenuse is equal to the sum of the squares of the lengths of the other two sides. It is written as $a^2 + b^2 = c^2$, where c is the length of the hypotenuse.

Q

quadrilateral A polygon with four sides.

quotient The result (other than the remainder) of dividing one number by another. (See *dividend.*)

R

radius A line segment that goes from the center of a circle to a point on the circle. (Also, the length of such a segment.) OA is a radius of the circle shown here. The radius of this circle is 1 centimeter:

range In a set of numbers, the difference between the greatest and least values.

rate A ratio written with units, as in 20 miles per hour.

ratio The comparison of two numbers by division.

ray A set of points that has one endpoint and extends without end in one direction. OA and OB is a ray.

598 • Glossary

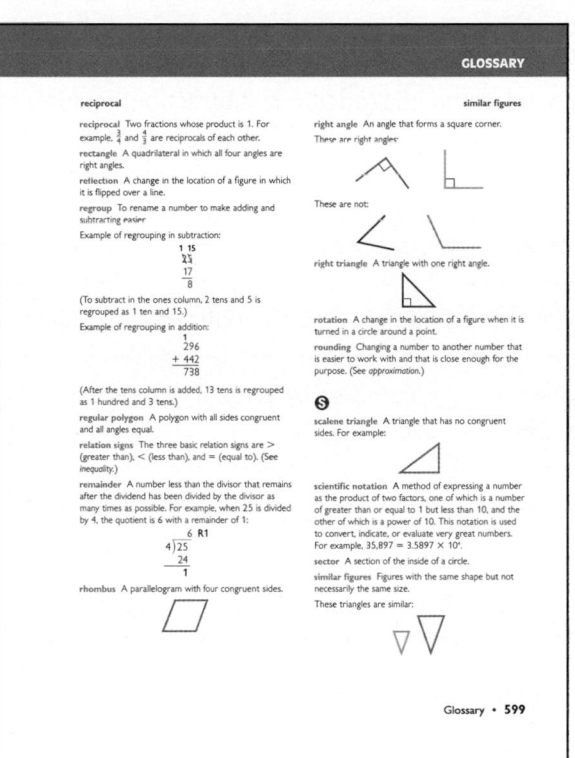

reciprocal   **similar figures**

reciprocal Two fractions whose product is 1. For example, $\frac{3}{4}$ and $\frac{4}{3}$ are reciprocals of each other.

rectangle A quadrilateral in which all four angles are right angles.

reflection A change in the location of a figure in which it is flipped over a line.

regroup To rename a number to make adding and subtracting easier.

Example of regrouping in subtraction:

$$\begin{array}{r} 1\ 15 \\ 2\cancel{5} \\ -\ 17 \\ \hline 8 \end{array}$$

(To subtract in the ones column, 2 tens and 5 is regrouped as 1 ten and 15.)

Example of regrouping in addition:

$$\begin{array}{r} 1 \\ 296 \\ +\ 442 \\ \hline 738 \end{array}$$

(After the tens column is added, 13 tens is regrouped as 1 hundred and 3 tens.)

regular polygon A polygon with all sides congruent and all angles equal.

relation signs The three basic relation signs are > (greater than), < (less than), and = (equal to). (See *inequality.*)

remainder A number less than the divisor that remains after the dividend has been divided by the divisor as many times as possible. For example, when 25 is divided by 4, the quotient is 6 with a remainder of 1:

$$\begin{array}{r} 6\ \text{R1} \\ 4\overline{)25} \\ 24 \\ \hline 1 \end{array}$$

rhombus A parallelogram with four congruent sides.

right angle An angle that forms a square corner. These are right angles:

These are not:

right triangle A triangle with one right angle.

rotation A change in the location of a figure when it is turned in a circle around a point.

rounding Changing a number to another number that is easier to work with and that is close enough for the purpose. (See *approximation.*)

S

scalene triangle A triangle that has no congruent sides. For example:

scientific notation A method of expressing a number as the product of two factors, one of which is a number of greater than or equal to 1 but less than 10, and the other of which is a power of 10. This notation is used to convert, indicate, or evaluate very great numbers. For example, $35,897 = 3.5897 \times 10^4$.

sector A section of the inside of a circle.

similar figures Figures with the same shape but not necessarily the same size.

These triangles are similar:

Glossary • 599

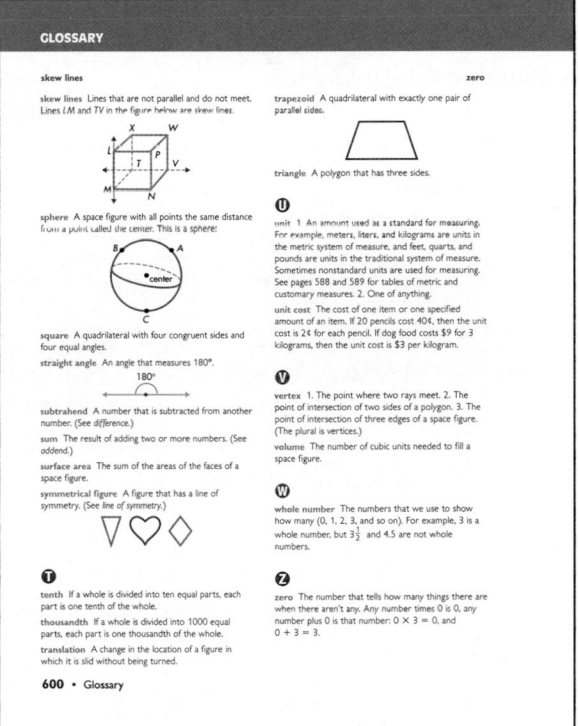

skew lines   **zero**

skew lines Lines that are not parallel and do not meet. Lines LM and TV in the figure below are skew lines.

sphere A space figure with all points the same distance from a point called the center. This is a sphere:

square A quadrilateral with four congruent sides and four equal angles.

straight angle An angle that measures 180°.

subtrahend A number that is subtracted from another number. (See *difference.*)

sum The result of adding two or more numbers. (See *addend.*)

surface area The sum of the areas of the faces of a space figure.

symmetrical figure A figure that has a line of symmetry. (See *line of symmetry.*)

T

tenth If a whole is divided into ten equal parts, each part is one tenth of the whole.

thousandth If a whole is divided into 1000 equal parts, each part is one thousandth of the whole.

translation A change in the location of a figure in which it is slid without being turned.

trapezoid A quadrilateral with exactly one pair of parallel sides.

triangle A polygon that has three sides.

U

unit 1. An amount used as a standard for measuring. For example, meters, liters, and kilograms are units in the metric system of measure, and feet, quarts, and pounds are units in the traditional system of measure. Sometimes nonstandard units are used for measuring. See pages 588 and 589 for tables of metric and customary measures. 2. One of anything.

unit cost The cost of one item or one specified amount of an item. If 20 pencils cost 40¢, then the unit cost is 2¢ for each pencil. If dog food costs $9 for 3 kilograms, then the unit cost is $3 per kilogram.

V

vertex 1. The point where two rays meet. 2. The point of intersection of two sides of a polygon. 3. The point of intersection of three edges of a space figure. (The plural is vertices.)

volume The number of cubic units needed to fill a space figure.

W

whole number The numbers that we use to show how many (0, 1, 2, 3, and so on). For example, 3 is a whole number, but $3\frac{1}{2}$ and 4.5 are not whole numbers.

Z

zero The number that tells how many things there are when there aren't any. Any number times 0 is 0, and any number plus 0 is that number: $0 \times 3 = 0$, and $0 + 3 = 3$.

600 • Glossary

Glossary

GAME DIRECTORY

Game	Principal Skills	Begin Using* Student's Edition	Teacher's Guide
Roll and Regroup a Number	Understanding place value; regrouping (writing numbers in standard form)	page 9	Lesson 2
Roll-Sub-Add	Adding and subtracting mentally	page 14	Lesson 4
Busy Bee	Using probabilistic concepts; using addition facts		Lesson 4
Multifact	Using multiplication facts; adding and subtracting mentally	page 16	Lesson 5
Marathon 1	Solving missing-factor problems related to multiplication facts		Lesson 5
Marathon 2	Solving missing-factor problems related to multiplication facts		Lesson 5
Cubo	Using mental arithmetic (addition, subtraction, multiplication, division)	page 18	Lesson 6
Cube-O-Mat	Using mental arithmetic (addition, subtraction, multiplication, division)		Lesson 7
Harder Cube-O-Mat	Using mental arithmetic (addition, subtraction, multiplication, division)		Lesson 7
Transaction	Adding and subtracting whole numbers; maintaining a record of money transactions		Lesson 9
Don't Go Over 1000	Using multidigit addition and mathematical reasoning	page 35	Lesson 10
Roll a Problem (Multiplication)	Multiplying two-digit numbers by two-digit numbers; using intuitive notions of probability	page 46	Lesson 13
Roll a Problem (Division)	Dividing three-digit numbers by two-digit numbers; using intuitive notions of probability	page 63	Lesson 16
Roll and Divide	Dividing mentally; using mathematical reasoning	page 67	Lesson 17
Key Keys	Mental arithmetic; using a calculator	page 73	Lesson 19
Approximation	Approximating answers to multidigit computations; rounding numbers	page 75	Lesson 20
Roller Coaster 1	Approximating products of multidigit numbers		Lesson 20
Roller Coaster 2	Approximating sums, differences, products, and quotients		Lesson 20
Numbo Jumbo	Using direct and indirect reasoning	page 95	Lesson 26
Harder Roll a Decimal	Using place value; subtracting decimals	page 105	Lesson 27

GAME DIRECTORY

GAME	PRINCIPAL SKILLS	BEGIN USING* Student's Edition	BEGIN USING* Teacher's Guide
Harder Transaction	Adding and subtracting decimals; maintaining a record of money transactions		Lesson 27
Make 25	Multiplying decimals; approximating products of two decimals	page 127	Lesson 34
Tips	Finding percents (10%, 15%, 20%); probabilistic thinking	page 179	Lesson 48
5% Tax	Finding percents mentally; adding decimals (money) mentally		Lesson 48
Harder 5% Tax	Finding percents mentally; adding decimals (money) mentally		Lesson 48
$50 Price	Approximating and calculating percent discounts, using mental arithmetic	page 185	Lesson 50
Discount	Finding percents mentally; subtracting decimals (money) mentally		Lesson 50
Harder Discount	Finding percents mentally; subtracting decimals (money) mentally		Lesson 50
Tiling	Using divisibility		Lesson 59
Find the Treasure	Using flow charts; using probabilistic concepts		Lesson 60
Harder Find the Treasure	Using flow charts; using probabilistic concepts		Lesson 60
Fractions of 60	Finding fractions of whole numbers; using division, multiplication, and addition	page 241	Lesson 65
Up to 1	Finding decimal equivalents; comparing fractions and decimals	page 245	Lesson 67
Equivalence 2	Recognizing fraction and decimal equivalents; solving missing-numerator and missing-denominator problems		Lesson 67
Equivalence 1	Recognizing equivalent fractions; solving missing-numerator and missing-denominator problems		Lesson 68
Greatest Common Factor	Finding the greatest common factor of two numbers; forming pairs of numbers that have great common factors	page 253	Lesson 69
Cosmic Cafe	Finding the least common multiple of two numbers		Lesson 71
Circo 11	Recognizing when a set of fractions adds up to greater than $\frac{1}{2}$	page 265	Lesson 73
Harder Cosmic Cafe	Finding the least common multiple of three numbers		Lesson 74
Roll a 15	Using intuitive notions of probability	page 272	Lesson 75

GAME DIRECTORY

Game	Principal Skills	Begin Using* Student's Edition	Teacher's Edition
Routes	Working with a network diagram; using intuitive notions of probability		Lesson 75
Harder Routes	Working with a network diagram; using intuitive notions of probability		Lesson 75
Anything But 10	Applying intuitive notions of probability; practicing addition	page 274	Lesson 76
Fringo Factory	Converting improper fractions to mixed numbers		Lesson 78
Harder Fringo Factory	Converting improper fractions to mixed numbers		Lesson 78
Up to 2	Finding decimal equivalents; comparing fractions and decimals	page 282	Lesson 79
Make 1	Approximating sums and differences of fractions; adding and subtracting fractions	page 289	Lesson 80
Make 2	Finding decimal equivalents; adding and comparing fractions and decimals	page 296	Lesson 82
Pentathlon	Using statistics and averaging		Lesson 88
Inverso	Approximating the multiplicative inverse (in decimal form) of multidigit numbers; using a calculator	page 335	Lesson 94
Hockey	Moving a point on a four-quadrant grid		Lesson 98
Get the Point	Plotting points on a four-quadrant grid; estimating the position of a point based on information about the regions formed by two lines through that point.	page 374	Lesson 105
Find the Function Rule	Determining simple function rules using ordered pairs	page 387	Lesson 109
Three Questions	Naming and classifying triangles and quadrilaterals; using deduction	page 473	Lesson 134

*These games and their variations should be used many times throughout the year. Feel free to use them again any time after they are introduced.
**Games in red are from the Game Mat set.

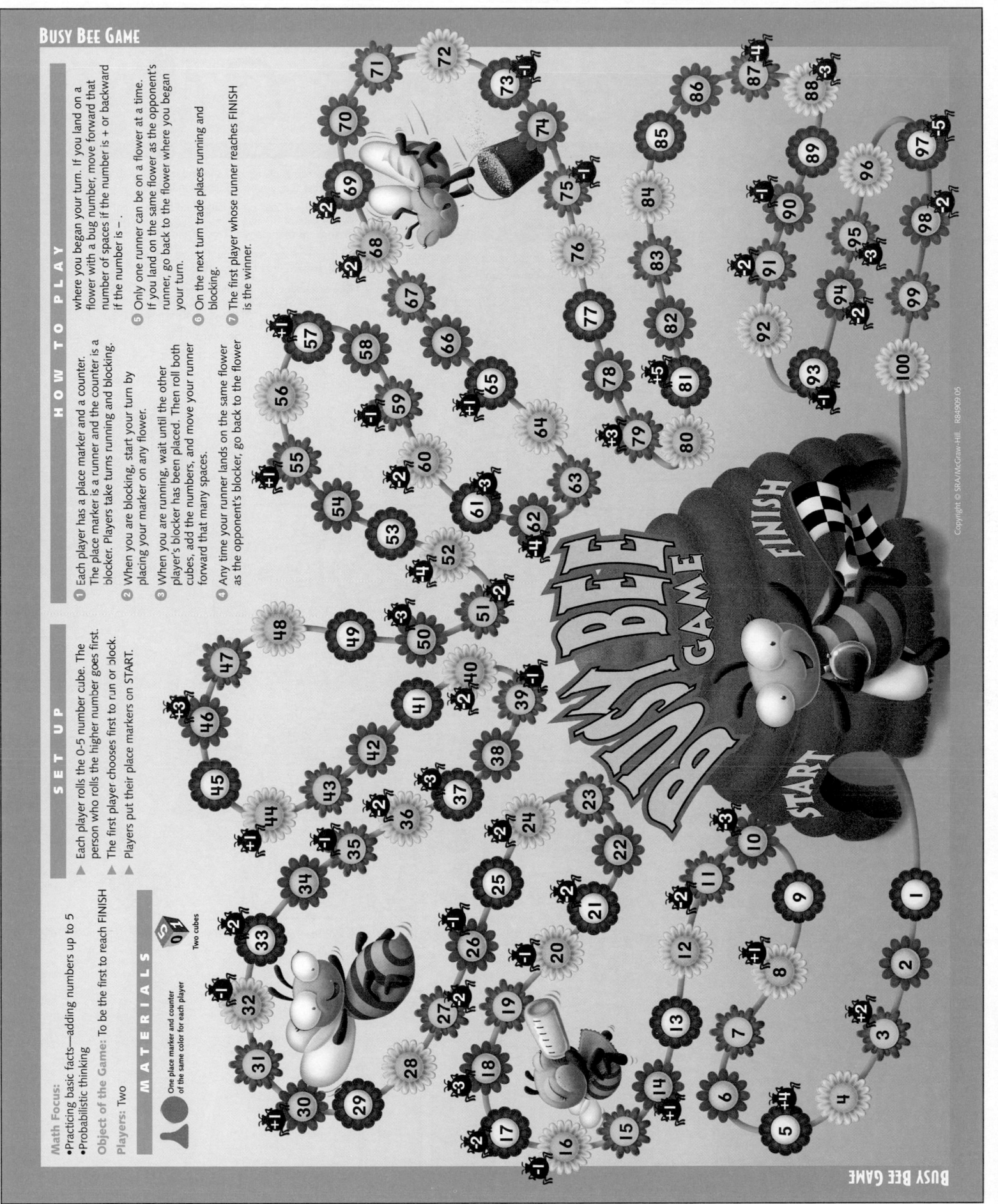

BUSY BEE GAME

Math Focus:
• Practicing basic facts—adding numbers up to 5
• Probabilistic thinking

Object of the Game: To be the first to reach FINISH

Players: Two

MATERIALS
One place marker and counter of the same color for each player

Two cubes

SET UP
▲ Each player rolls the 0–5 number cube. The person who rolls the higher number goes first.
▲ The first player chooses first to run or block.
▲ Players put their place markers on START.

HOW TO PLAY
1. Each player has a place marker and a counter. The place marker is a runner and the counter is a blocker. Players take turns running and blocking.
2. When you are blocking, start your turn by placing your marker on any flower.
3. When you are running, wait until the other player's blocker has been placed. Then roll both cubes, add the numbers, and move your runner forward that many spaces.
4. Any time your runner lands on the same flower as the opponent's blocker, go back to the flower where you began your turn. If you land on a flower with a bug number, move forward that number of spaces if the number is + or backward if the number is −.
5. Only one runner can be on a flower at a time. If you land on the same flower as the opponent's runner, go back to the flower where you began your turn.
6. On the next turn trade places running and blocking.
7. The first player whose runner reaches FINISH is the winner.

603

COSMIC CAFE GAME

Math Focus: Finding the least common multiple of two numbers

Object of the Game: To be the last player on the board

Players: Two, three, or four

MATERIALS

Place markers

Cube

SET UP

▶ Put your place marker on the space marked START.

▶ Everyone rolls the 0-5 number cube. The person who rolls the highest number goes first.

HOW TO PLAY

❶ Take turns rolling the cube and moving your place marker the number of spaces indicated.

❷ When you land on a space, find the least common multiple of the two numbers there. Then move forward that many spaces to end your turn.

❸ If you roll a 0, you cannot move and must remain on that space until the next turn.

❹ Keep taking turns until all players except one have reached STOP. (If you roll exactly or more than enough to reach STOP, you must move there.)

❺ The last player on the board is the winner.

COSMIC CAFE GAME
HARDER

Math Focus: Finding the least common multiple of three numbers

Object of the Game: To be the last player on the board

Players: Two, three, or four

MATERIALS

Place markers

Cube

SET UP

▶ Put your place marker on the space marked START.

▶ Everyone rolls the 0–5 number cube. The person who rolls the highest number goes first.

HOW TO PLAY

❶ Take turns rolling the cube and moving your place marker the number of spaces indicated.

❷ When you land on a space, find the least common multiple of the three numbers there. Then move forward that many spaces to end your turn.

❸ If you roll a 0, you cannot move and must remain on that space until the next turn.

❹ Keep taking turns until all players except one have reached STOP. (If you roll exactly or more than enough to reach STOP, you must move there.)

❺ The last player on the board is the winner.

Math Focus: Using mental arithmetic (all operations)

Object of the Game: To have three counters in a row

Players: Two

MATERIALS

Two cubes   Two cubes

Five counters of the same color for each player, or five pennies and five nickels

SET UP

- Each player rolls the 0-5 number cube. The person who rolls the higher number goes first. The first player chooses pennies or nickels as counters. The second player uses what is left.
- Agree on the game card you will use for this game. Both players use the same card.

HOW TO PLAY

1. Take turns rolling all four cubes. Try to make one of the numbers on the card by using any combination of the four operations (+, −, ×, or ÷) on the numbers rolled. Use the number on each cube only once.
2. If you roll the same number on two cubes, you must use both.
3. If you can make one of the numbers on the card, place one of your counters on it. If you cannot make one of the numbers on the card, you must wait until the next turn to try again.
4. The first player to have three counters in a row (horizontally, vertically, or diagonally) is the winner.

HARDER CUBE-O-MAT

Math Focus: Using mental arithmetic (all operations)

Object of the Game: To have four counters in a row

Players: Two

MATERIALS

Two cubes

Two cubes

13 counters of the same color for each player, or 13 pennies and 13 nickels

SET UP

▲ Each player rolls a 0-5 number cube. The person who rolls the higher number goes first.

▲ The first player chooses pennies or nickels as counters. The second player uses what is left.

▲ Agree on the game card you will use for this game. Both players use the same card.

HOW TO PLAY

1 Take turns rolling all four cubes. Try to make one of the numbers on the card by using any combination of the four operations (+, −, ×, or ÷) on the numbers rolled. Use the number on each cube only once.

2 If you roll the same number on two cubes, you must use both.

3 If you can make one of the numbers on the card, place one of your counters on it. If you cannot make one of the numbers on the card, you must wait until the next turn to try again.

4 The first player to have four counters in a row (horizontally, vertically, or diagonally) is the winner.

5	27	10	14	6
13	16	20	17	28
9	23	15	21	11
26	19	22	18	24
8	25	12	29	7

11	32	16	29	12
28	19	25	20	33
15	24	23	26	17
35	22	27	21	30
14	31	18	34	13

607

DISCOUNT GAME

Reg. $380.00
20% off
$304.00

Reg. $35.00
10% off
$31.50

Reg. $150.00
20% off
$120.00

Reg. $25.00
10% off
$22.50

$56.00

Reg. $300.00
20% off
$240.00

$45.00

Reg. $90.00
20% off
$72.00

Reg. $70.00
20% off

Reg. $60.00
25% off

DISCOUNT GAME

GO DISCOUNT STORE

PENALTY

Reg. $250.00
25% off
$187.50

Math Focus:
• Calculating percents mentally
• Mental arithmetic (subtraction)

Object of the Game: To have the most counters at the end of the game

Players: Two, three, or four

$192.00

Reg. $240.00
20% off

MATERIALS

Place markers

Cube

16 counters or pennies

SET UP

▶ Cover every circle on the mat with a counter.
▶ Put your place marker on the space marked GO.

▶ Everyone rolls the 0-5 number cube. The person who rolls the highest number goes first.

Reg. $15.00
10% off
$13.50

$36.00

Reg. $40.00
10% off

HOW TO PLAY

❶ Take turns rolling the cube and moving your place marker the number of spaces indicated.

❷ If you land on a space with a counter, determine the discounted price of the item shown by using mental arithmetic. Do not use pencil and paper or a calculator.

❸ To check your answer, look under the counter. If you are correct, keep the counter; if you are incorrect, replace the counter.

❹ If you roll a 0, you must wait until your next turn to roll again. You cannot try for a counter if you roll a 0.

❺ If you land on the space marked PENALTY, you must, if possible, place one of your counters on an empty circle.

❻ The player with the most counters at the end of the game wins.

$47.50

Reg. $10.00
15% off

Reg. $30.00
5% off

Reg. $20.00
30% off

Reg. $50.00
5% off
$8.50

$28.50

$14.00

DISCOUNT GAME

Reg. $210.00
30% off
$147.00

Reg. $75.00
20% off
$60.00

Reg. $18.00
5% off
$17.10

Reg. $35.00
10% off
$31.50

$7.70

Reg. $11.00
30% off

Reg. $55.00
20% off
$44.00

$60.00

Reg. $80.00
25% off

Reg. $12.50
10% off
$11.25

HARDER

DISCOUNT GAME

PENALTY

Math Focus:
• Calculating percents mentally
• Mental arithmetic (subtraction)

Object of the Game: To have the most counters at the end of the game

Players: Two, three, or four

MATERIALS

Place markers

Cube

16 counters or pennies

Reg. $190.00
20% off
$152.00

$61.75

Reg. $65.00
5% off

SET UP

► Cover every circle on the mat with a counter.
► Put your place marker on the space marked GO.

► Everyone rolls the 0-5 number cube. The person who rolls the highest number goes first.

HOW TO PLAY

❶ Take turns rolling the cube and moving your place marker the number of spaces indicated.

❷ If you land on a space with a counter, determine the discounted price of the item shown by using mental arithmetic. Do not use pencil and paper or a calculator.

❸ To check your answer, look under the counter. If you are correct, keep the counter; if you are incorrect, replace the counter.

❹ If you roll a 0, you must wait until your next turn to roll again. You cannot try for a counter if you roll a 0.

❺ If you land on the space marked PENALTY, you must, if possible, place one of your counters on an empty circle.

❻ The player with the most counters at the end of the game wins.

$199.75

Reg. $235.00
15% off

Reg. $9.50
10% off
$8.55

$30.00

Reg. $40.00
25% off

Reg. $14.00
20% off
$11.20

Reg. $12.00
25% off
$9.00

Reg. $23.00
20% off
$18.40

DISCOUNT STORE
GO

HARDER DISCOUNT GAME

EQUIVALENCE 1

Math Focus:
- Solving missing numerator and missing denominator problems
- Recognizing equivalent fractions

Object of the Game: To have the most counters at the end of the game

Players: Two or three

MATERIALS

Place markers

Cube

50 counters or pennies per player

SET UP

► Cover one circle in each box with a counter.

► Place the extra counters on the space marked BANK.

► Put your place marker on the space marked START.

► Everyone rolls the 0-5 number cube. The person who rolls the highest number goes first.

HOW TO PLAY

1. Take turns rolling the cube and moving your place marker the number of spaces indicated.

2. To win the counter in the space where you land, say the number that is under the counter.

3. Check your answer by looking under the counter. If you are correct, keep the counter; if you are incorrect, replace the counter.

4. If you give an incorrect answer and roll a 0 on the next turn, you may try again to win the counter by saying the correct number.

5. You can win a counter only if one is available on the space where you land.

6. Collect two counters from the BANK each time you pass or land on the space marked START.

7. After all the counters in the boxes have been won, the player with the most counters is the winner.

BANK

Start

$$\frac{1}{2} = 0.5$$

$$\frac{1}{4} = 0.25$$

$$\frac{1}{3} = 0.333$$

$$\frac{1}{5} = 0.2$$

$$\frac{5}{8} = 0.625$$

$$\frac{6}{8} = 0.75$$

$$\frac{4}{5} = 0.8$$

$$\frac{3}{4} = 0.75$$

$$\frac{2}{4} = 0.5$$

$$\frac{1}{8} = 0.125$$

$$\frac{4}{8} = 0.5$$

$$\frac{2}{3} = 0.667$$

$$\frac{3}{3} = 1.0$$

$$\frac{3}{6} = 0.5$$

$$\frac{3}{8} = 0.375$$

$$\frac{2}{5} = 0.4$$

$$\frac{2}{6} = 0.333$$

$$\frac{3}{5} = 0.6$$

$$\frac{5}{5} = 1.0$$

$$\frac{2}{8} = 0.25$$

$$\frac{4}{6} = 0.667$$

EQUIVALENCE 2

Math Focus: Finding fraction-decimal equivalents

Object of the Game: To have the most counters at the end of the game

Players: Two or three

MATERIALS

Place markers — Cube — 50 counters or pennies per player

SET UP

▶ Cover one circle in each box with a counter.

▶ Place the extra counters in the space marked BANK.

▶ Put your place marker on the space marked START.

▶ Everyone rolls the 0-5 number cube. The person who rolls the highest number goes first.

HOW TO PLAY

❶ Take turns rolling the cube and moving your place markers the number of spaces indicated.

❷ To win the counter in the space where you land, say the number that is under the counter.

❸ Check your answer by looking under the counter. If you are correct, keep the counter; if you are incorrect, replace the counter.

❹ If you give an incorrect answer and roll a 0 on the next turn, you may try again to win the counter by saying the correct number.

❺ You can win a counter only if one is available on the space where you land.

❻ Collect two counters from the BANK each time you pass or land on the space marked START.

❼ After all the counters in the boxes have been won, the player with the most counters is the winner.

BANK

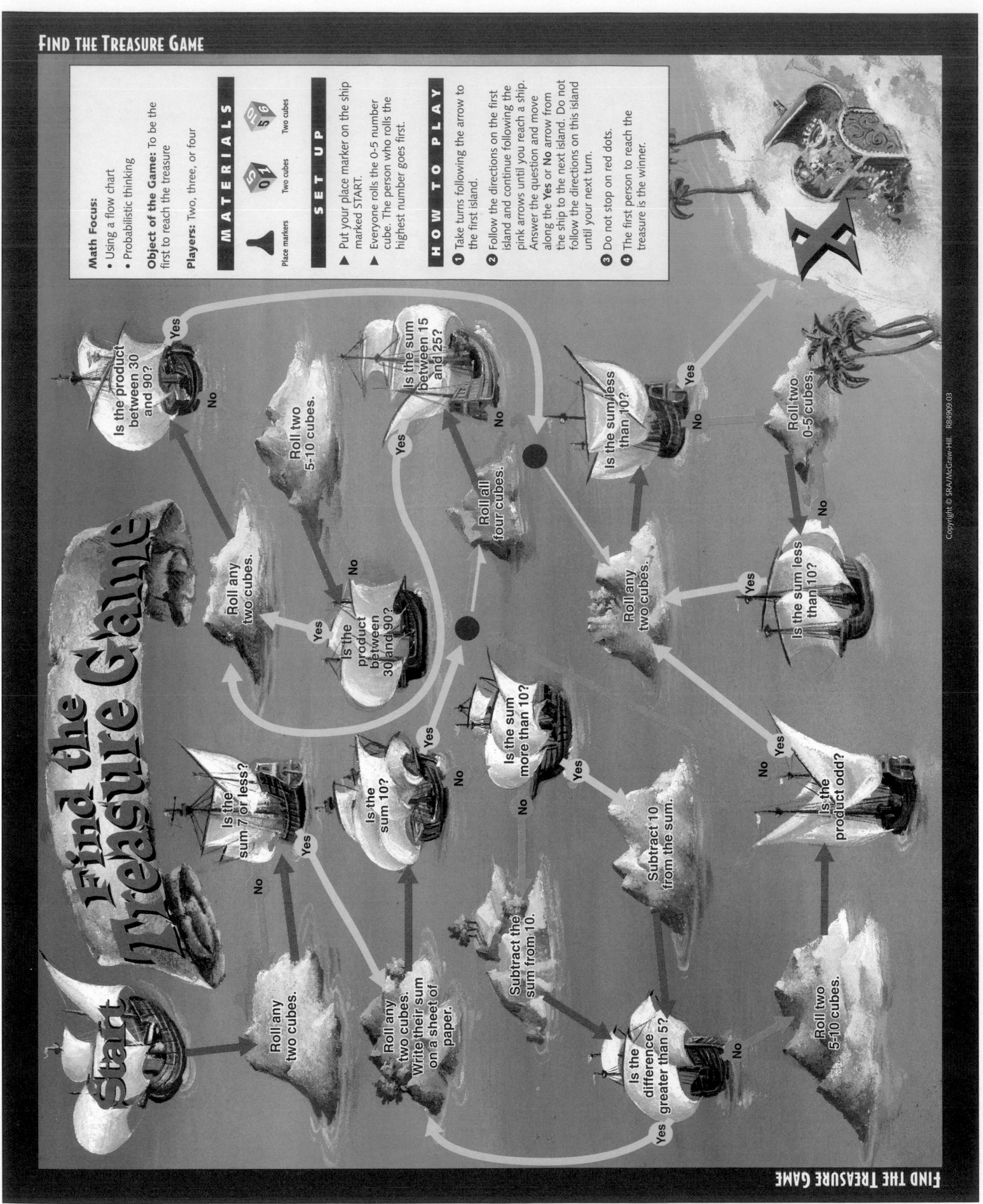

Find the Treasure Game

Math Focus:
- Using a flow chart
- Probabilistic thinking

Object of the Game: To be the first to reach the treasure

Players: Two, three, or four

MATERIALS

Place markers   Two cubes   Two cubes

SET UP

▲ Put your place marker on the ship marked START.

▲ Everyone rolls the 0–5 number cube. The person who rolls the highest number goes first.

HOW TO PLAY

1. Take turns following the arrow to the first island.
2. Follow the directions on the first island and continue following the pink arrows until you reach a ship. Answer the question and move along the **Yes** or **No** arrow from the ship to the next island. Do not follow the directions on this island until your next turn.
3. Do not stop on red dots.
4. The first person to reach the treasure is the winner.

Start

Roll any two cubes.

Roll any two cubes. Write their sum on a sheet of paper.

Is the sum 7 or less?

Is the sum 10?

Is the sum more than 10?

Subtract the sum from 10.

Is the difference greater than 5?

Subtract 10 from the sum.

Is the product odd?

Roll two 5–10 cubes.

Roll two 5–10 cubes.

Roll any two cubes.

Is the product between 30 and 90?

Is the product between 30 and 90?

Roll all four cubes.

Is the sum between 15 and 25?

Is the sum less than 10?

Is the sum less than 10?

Roll two 0–5 cubes.

Yes   No

Copyright © SRA/McGraw-Hill.   R8490903

612

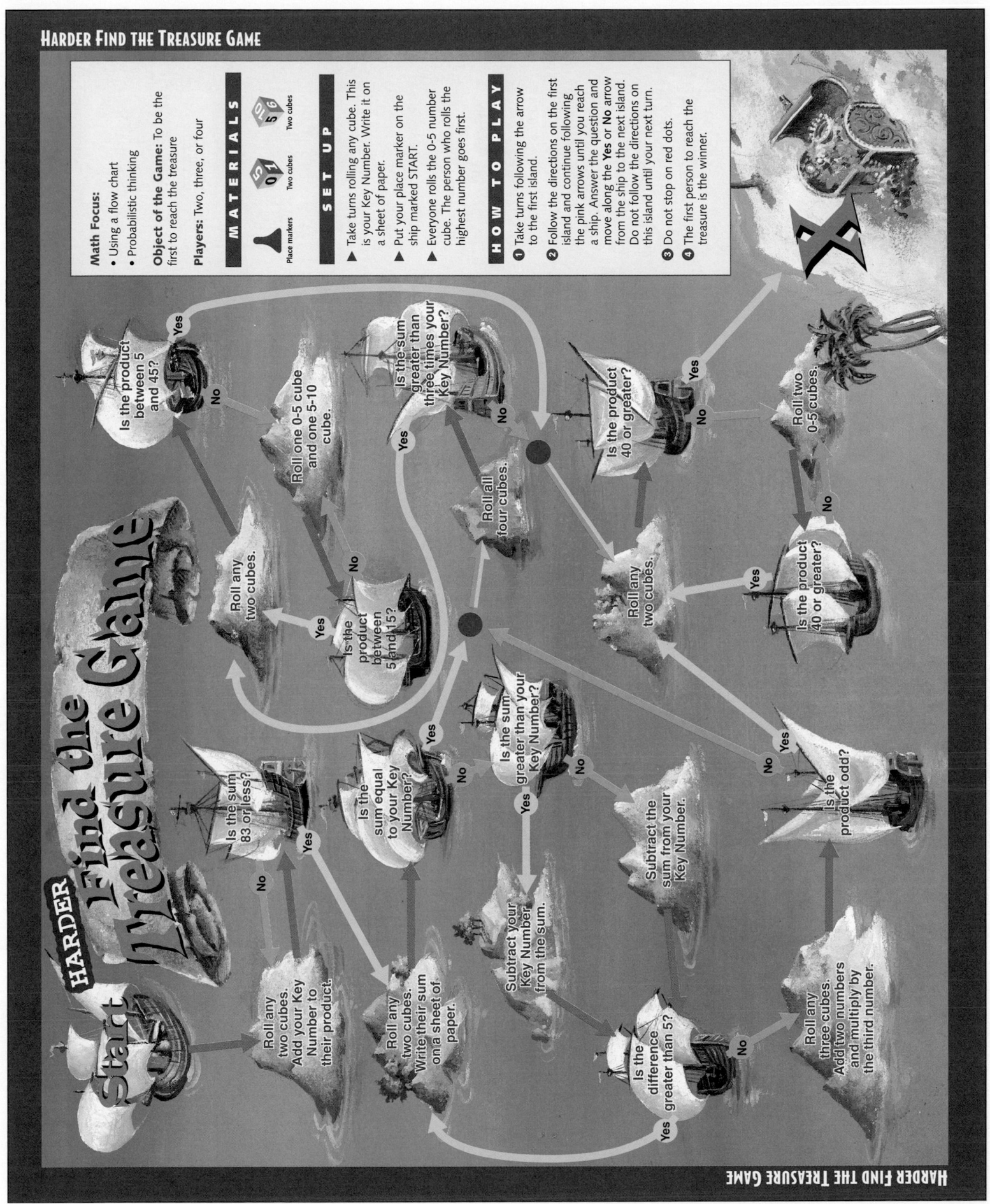

HARDER Find the Treasure Game

Math Focus:
- Using a flow chart
- Probabilistic thinking

Object of the Game: To be the first to reach the treasure

Players: Two, three, or four

MATERIALS

Place markers

0 1 Two cubes

5 6 10 Two cubes

SET UP

▲ Take turns rolling any cube. This is your Key Number. Write it on a sheet of paper.

▲ Put your place marker on the ship marked START.

▲ Everyone rolls the 0-5 number cube. The person who rolls the highest number goes first.

HOW TO PLAY

1. Take turns following the arrow to the first island.

2. Follow the directions on the first island and continue following the pink arrows until you reach a ship. Answer the question and move along the **Yes** or **No** arrow from the ship to the next island. Do not follow the directions on this island until your next turn.

3. Do not stop on red dots.

4. The first person to reach the treasure is the winner.

Start

Roll any two cubes. Add your Key Number to their product.

Roll any two cubes. Write their sum on a sheet of paper.

Is the sum 83 or less?

Is the sum equal to your Key Number?

Subtract your Key Number from the sum.

Is the difference greater than 5?

Roll any three cubes. Add two numbers and multiply by the third number.

Is the sum greater than your Key Number?

Subtract the sum from your Key Number.

Is the product odd?

Is the sum greater than three times your Key Number?

Roll one 0-5 cube and one 5-10 cube.

Is the product between 5 and 45?

Roll any two cubes.

Is the product between 5 and 15?

Roll all four cubes.

Is the product 40 or greater?

Roll any two cubes.

Is the product 40 or greater?

Roll two 0-5 cubes.

613

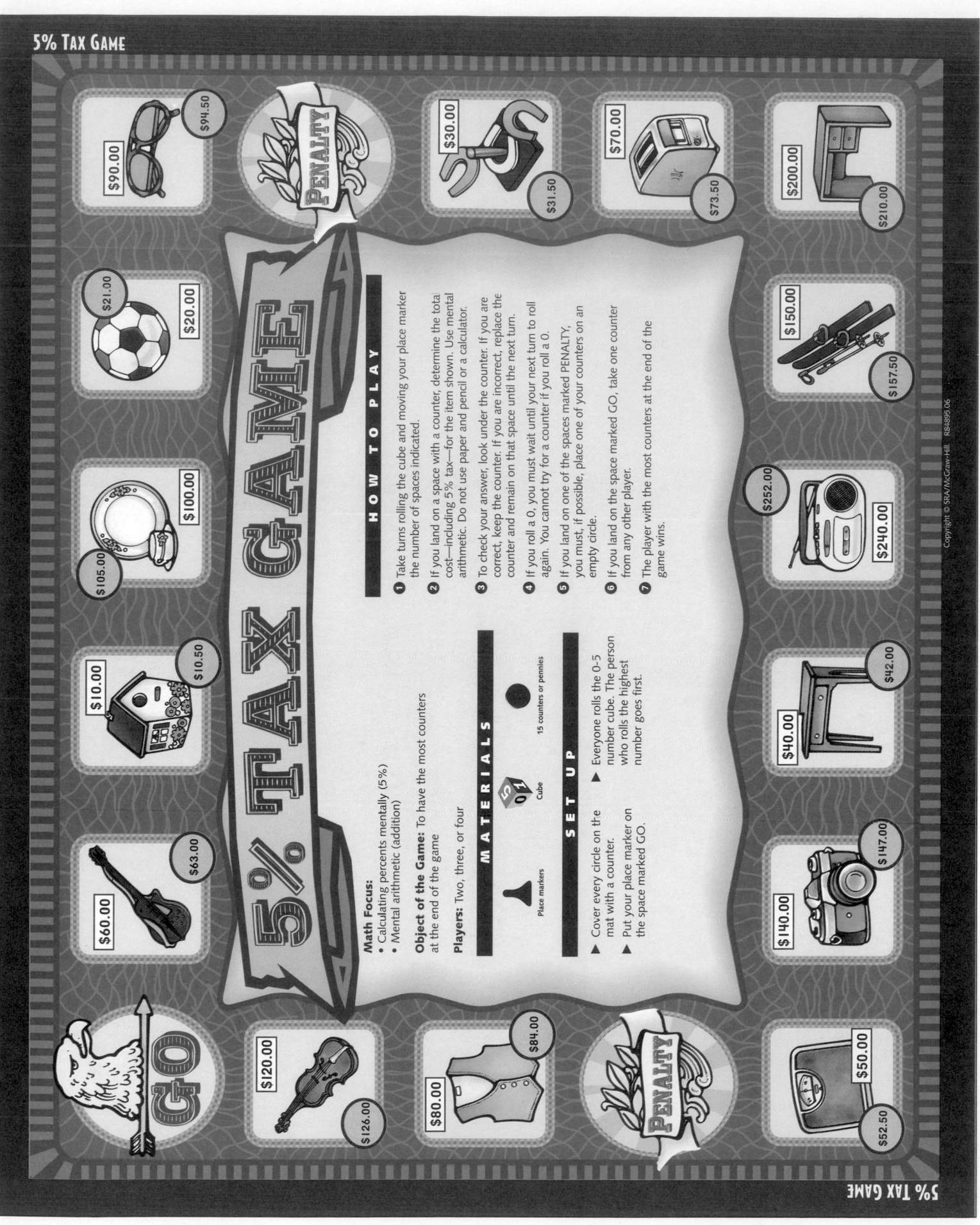

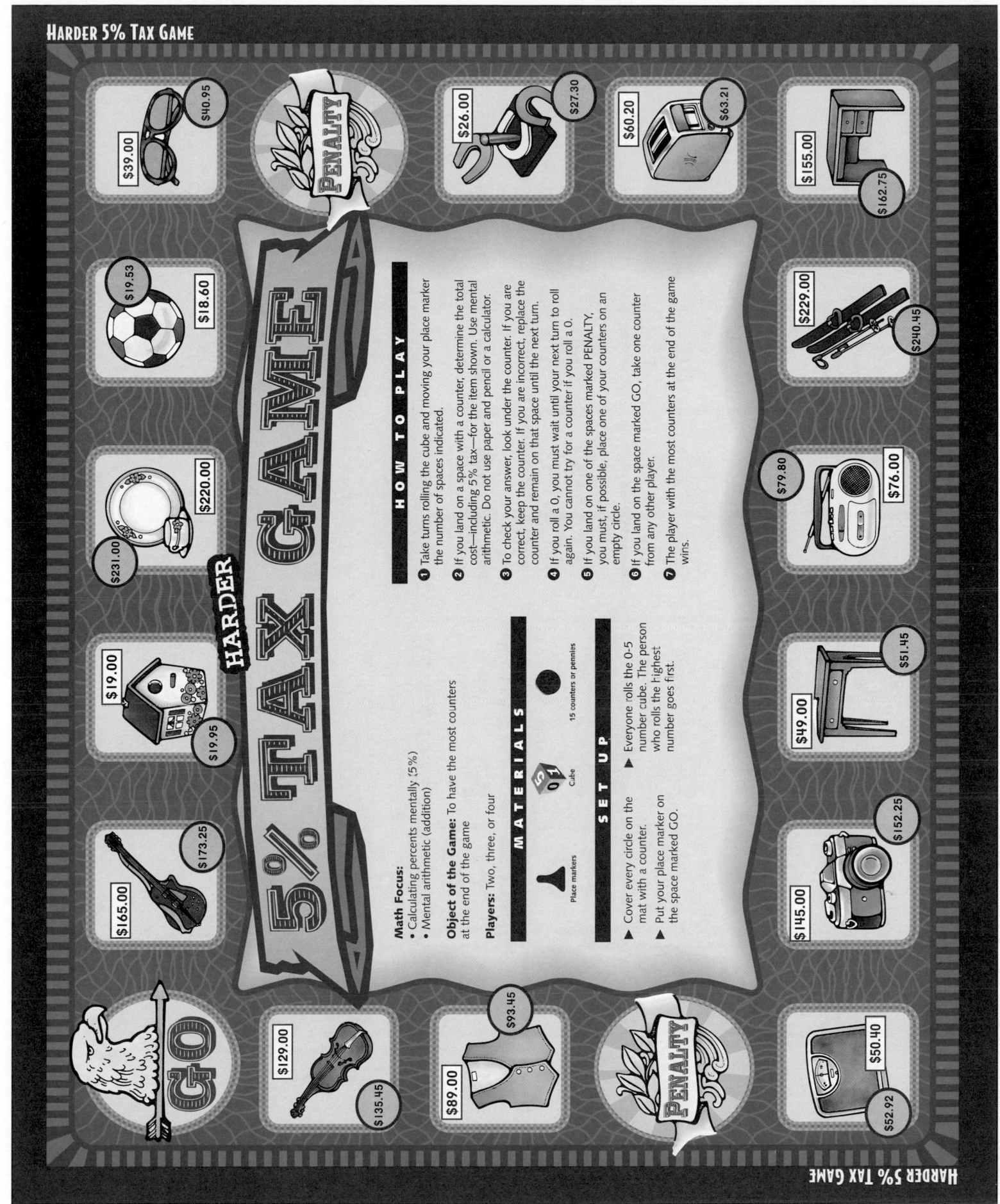

HARDER

5% TAX GAME

Math Focus:
- Calculating percents mentally (5%)
- Mental arithmetic (addition)

Object of the Game: To have the most counters at the end of the game

Players: Two, three, or four

MATERIALS

Place markers

Cube

15 counters or pennies

SET UP

▶ Cover every circle on the mat with a counter.

▶ Put your place marker on the space marked GO.

▶ Everyone rolls the 0-5 number cube. The person who rolls the highest number goes first.

HOW TO PLAY

1. Take turns rolling the cube and moving your place marker the number of spaces indicated.

2. If you land on a space with a counter, determine the total cost—including 5% tax—for the item shown. Use mental arithmetic. Do not use paper and pencil or a calculator.

3. To check your answer, look under the counter. If you are correct, keep the counter. If you are incorrect, replace the counter and remain on that space until the next turn.

4. If you roll a 0, you must wait until your next turn to roll again. You cannot try for a counter if you roll a 0.

5. If you land on one of the spaces marked PENALTY, you must, if possible, place one of your counters on an empty circle.

6. If you land on the space marked GO, take one counter from any other player.

7. The player with the most counters at the end of the game wins.

$40.95 — $39.00

PENALTY

$26.00 — $27.30

$60.20 — $63.21

$155.00 — $162.75

$19.53 — $18.60

$229.00 — $240.45

$220.00 — $231.00

$79.80 — $76.00

$19.00 — $19.95

$51.45 — $49.00

$173.25 — $165.00

$152.25 — $145.00

GO

$129.00 — $135.45

$93.45 — $89.00

PENALTY

$50.40 — $52.92

615

Math Focus: Converting improper fractions to mixed numbers

Object of the Game: To have four counters in a row

Players: Two

Two cubes

Two cubes

20 counters of the same color for each player, or 20 pennies and 20 nickels

GAME
HOME OF MIXED NUMBERS

▶ Each player rolls a 0-5 number cube. The person who rolls the higher number goes first.

▶ The first player chooses pennies or nickels as counters. The second player uses what is left.

❶ Take turns rolling any two number cubes. Use the numbers to create an improper fraction. For example, if you roll a 3 and a 7, the improper fraction is 7/3.

❷ After making an improper fraction, find a mixed number equivalent of that fraction, and cover it with one of your counters. Only one counter can be in each square.

❸ If you roll a 0 on one of your cubes, roll that cube again.

❹ The first player to have four counters in a row (in any direction) wins.

$1\frac{3}{4}$	$1\frac{1}{2}$	$1\frac{1}{7}$	$2\frac{1}{4}$	$1\frac{1}{2}$
$1\frac{1}{6}$	$2\frac{1}{3}$	2	$2\frac{1}{2}$	$1\frac{1}{4}$
9	4	$1\frac{4}{5}$	$1\frac{2}{7}$	$1\frac{2}{3}$
$4\frac{1}{2}$	$1\frac{3}{7}$	7	$1\frac{1}{3}$	$1\frac{1}{2}$
6	1	$3\frac{1}{3}$	$1\frac{3}{5}$	2
$1\frac{1}{8}$	$1\frac{2}{5}$	$1\frac{2}{3}$	10	$1\frac{3}{4}$
3	$2\frac{2}{3}$	$1\frac{1}{9}$	$3\frac{1}{2}$	$1\frac{1}{3}$
$1\frac{1}{5}$	8	5	$1\frac{1}{4}$	3

IMPROPER FRACTIONS

FRINGO FACTORY

FRINGO FACTORY GAME

Math Focus: Recognizing the equivalents of proper and improper fractions

Object of the Game: To have four counters in a row

Players: Two

MATERIALS

Two cubes   Two cubes

20 counters of the same color for each player, or 20 pennies and 20 nickels

SET UP

► Each player rolls a 0-5 number cube. The person who rolls the higher number goes first.

► The first player chooses pennies or nickels as counters. The second player uses what is left.

HOW TO PLAY

❶ Take turns rolling any two number cubes. Use the numbers to create a proper or improper fraction. For example, if you roll a 3 and a 7, you could make 3/7 or 7/3.

❷ After making a fraction, find the equivalent of that fraction and cover it with one of your counters. Only one counter can be in each square.

❸ If you roll a 0 on one of your cubes, roll that cube again.

❹ The first player to have four counters in a row (in any direction) wins.

HARDER

FRINGO FACTORY

GAME

HOME OF MIXED NUMBERS

$1\frac{3}{7}$	$2\frac{1}{4}$	2	$1\frac{3}{4}$	$1\frac{1}{2}$	$1\frac{1}{4}$
$\frac{3}{4}$	$\frac{5}{8}$	$\frac{1}{2}$	$\frac{3}{8}$	$\frac{1}{4}$	$\frac{1}{8}$
1	$1\frac{1}{5}$	$1\frac{2}{5}$	$1\frac{3}{5}$	$1\frac{4}{5}$	2
$\frac{6}{7}$	$\frac{5}{7}$	$\frac{4}{7}$	$\frac{3}{7}$	$\frac{2}{7}$	$\frac{1}{7}$
2	$1\frac{5}{6}$	$1\frac{2}{3}$	$1\frac{1}{2}$	$1\frac{1}{3}$	$1\frac{1}{6}$
$\frac{8}{9}$	$\frac{7}{9}$	$\frac{5}{9}$	$\frac{4}{9}$	$\frac{2}{9}$	$\frac{1}{9}$
3	$2\frac{1}{2}$	2	$1\frac{1}{2}$	1	$\frac{1}{9}$
$3\frac{1}{2}$	4	$4\frac{1}{2}$	5	6	7
$3\frac{1}{3}$	3	$2\frac{2}{3}$	$2\frac{2}{3}$	2	$1\frac{2}{3}$
9	$1\frac{1}{9}$	$1\frac{1}{8}$	$1\frac{1}{7}$	6	10

IMPROPER FRACTIONS

FRINGO FACTORY

$\frac{7}{4}$ $\frac{5}{7}$ $\frac{10}{3}$

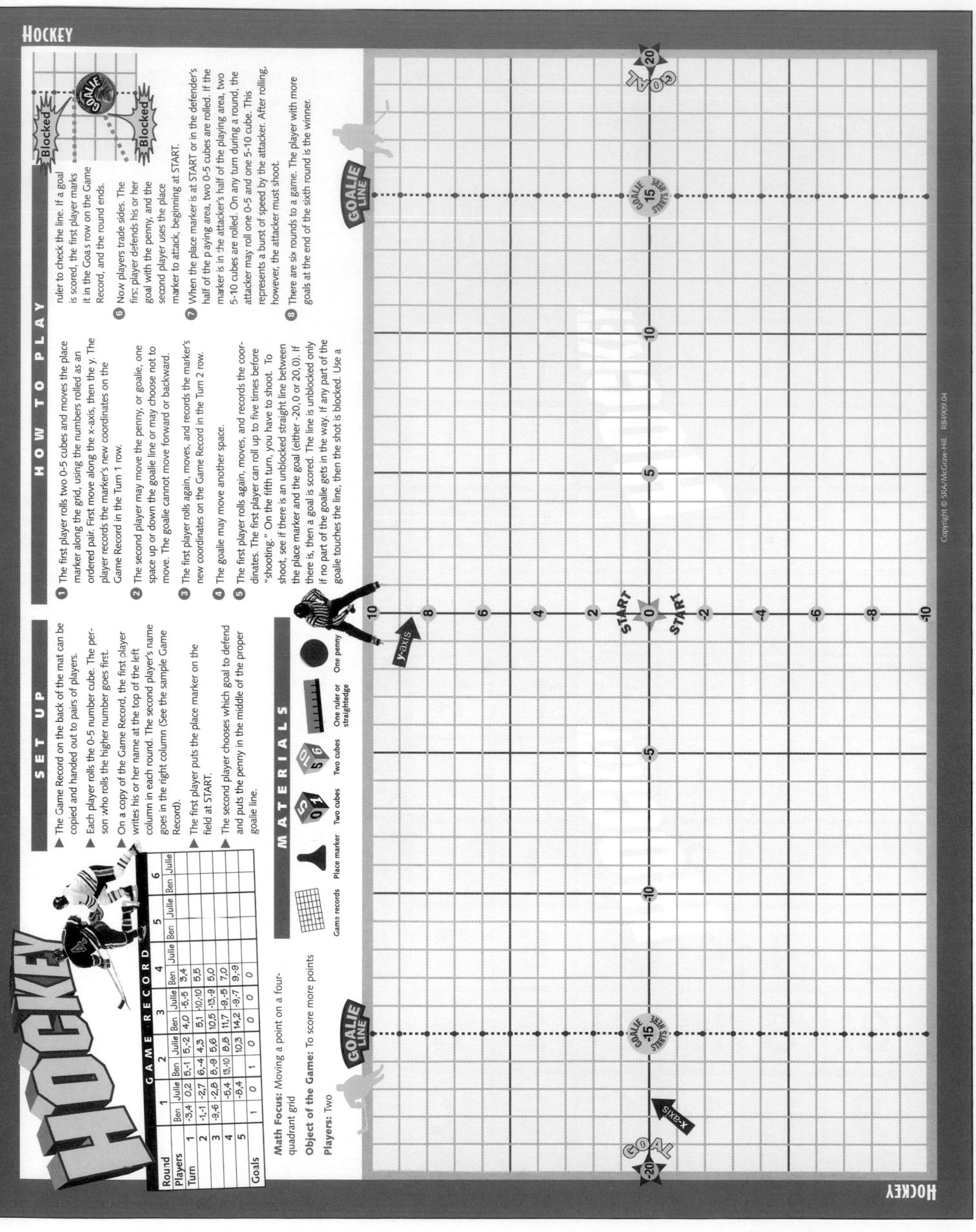

HOCKEY

Math Focus: Moving a point on a four-quadrant grid

Object of the Game: To score more points

Players: Two

GAME RECORD

Round	1		2		3		4		5		6	
Players	Ben	Julie	Ben	Julie	Ben	Julie	Ben	Julie	Ben	Julie	Ben	Julie
Turn 1	-3,4	0,2	5,-1	5,-2	4,0	-5,-5	5,4					
Turn 2	-1,-1	-2,7	6,4	4,3	5,1	10,-10	5,5					
Turn 3	-9,-6	-2,8	8,-9	5,6	10,5	-13,-9	5,0					
Turn 4		-5,-4	13,10	8,8	11,7	-9,-5	7,0					
Turn 5		-8,4	10,3	14,2	-9,-7	9,9						
Goals	1	0	1	0	0	0						

SET UP

▶ The Game Record on the back of the mat can be copied and handed out to pairs of players.

▶ Each player rolls the 0–5 number cube. The person who rolls the higher number goes first.

▶ On a copy of the Game Record, the first player writes his or her name at the top of the left column in each round. The second player's name goes in the right column (See the sample Game Record).

▶ The first player puts the place marker on the field at START.

▶ The second player chooses which goal to defend and puts the penny in the middle of the proper goalie line.

MATERIALS

Game records

Place marker

One penny

Two cubes — Two 0–5 cubes

Two cubes — Two 5–10 cubes

One ruler or straightedge

HOW TO PLAY

1. The first player rolls two 0–5 cubes and moves the place marker along the grid, using the numbers rolled as an ordered pair. First move along the x-axis, then the y. The player records the marker's new coordinates on the Game Record in the Turn 1 row.

2. The second player may move the penny, or goalie, one space up or down the goalie line or may choose not to move. The goalie cannot move forward or backward.

3. The first player rolls again, moves, and records the marker's new coordinates on the Game Record in the Turn 2 row.

4. The goalie may move another space.

5. The first player rolls again, moves, and records the coordinates. The first player can roll up to five times before "shooting." On the fifth turn, you have to shoot. To shoot, see if there is an unblocked straight line between the place marker and the goal (either -20,0 or 20,0). If there is, then a goal is scored. The line is unblocked only if no part of the goalie gets in the way. If any part of the goalie touches the line, then the shot is blocked. Use a

6. ruler to check the line. If a goal is scored, the first player marks it in the Goals row on the Game Record, and the round ends.

7. Now players trade sides. The first player defends his or her goal with the penny, and the second player uses the place marker to attack, beginning at START.

8. When the place marker is at START or in the defender's half of the playing area, two 0–5 cubes are rolled. If the marker is in the attacker's half of the playing area, two 5–10 cubes are rolled. On any turn during a round, the attacker may roll one 0–5 and one 5–10 cube. This represents a burst of speed by the attacker. After rolling, however, the attacker must shoot.

9. There are six rounds to a game. The player with more goals at the end of the sixth round is the winner.

Blocked — GOALIE — Blocked

y-axis

x-axis

10   8   6   4   2   START 0 START -2   -4   -6   -8   -10

GOAL -20   GOALIE LINE -15   -10   -5   5   10   GOALIE LINE 15   GOAL 20

Copyright © SRA/McGraw-Hill. R84909-04

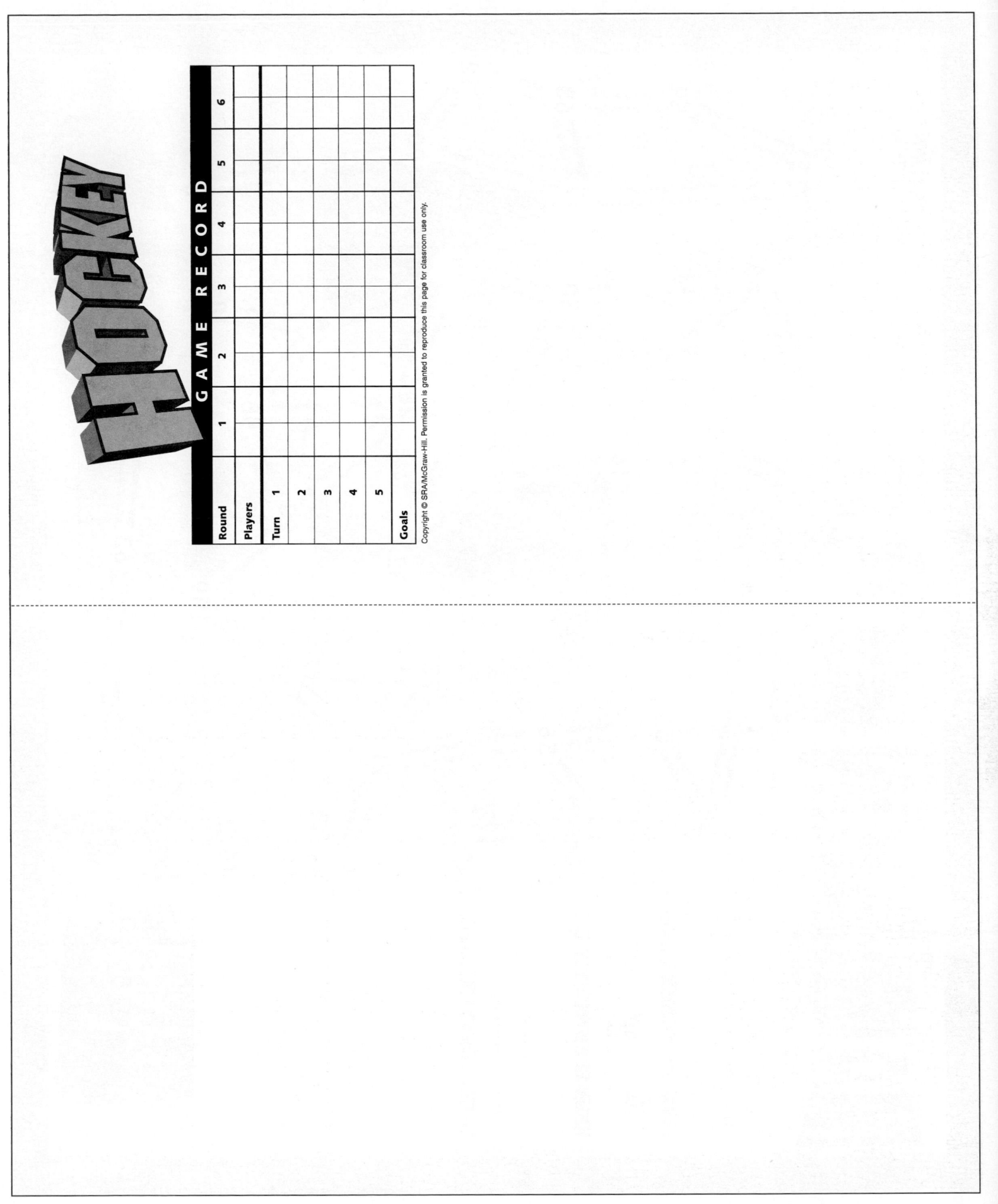

HOCKEY

GAME RECORD

Round		1	2	3	4	5	6
Players							
Turn	1						
	2						
	3						
	4						
	5						
Goals							

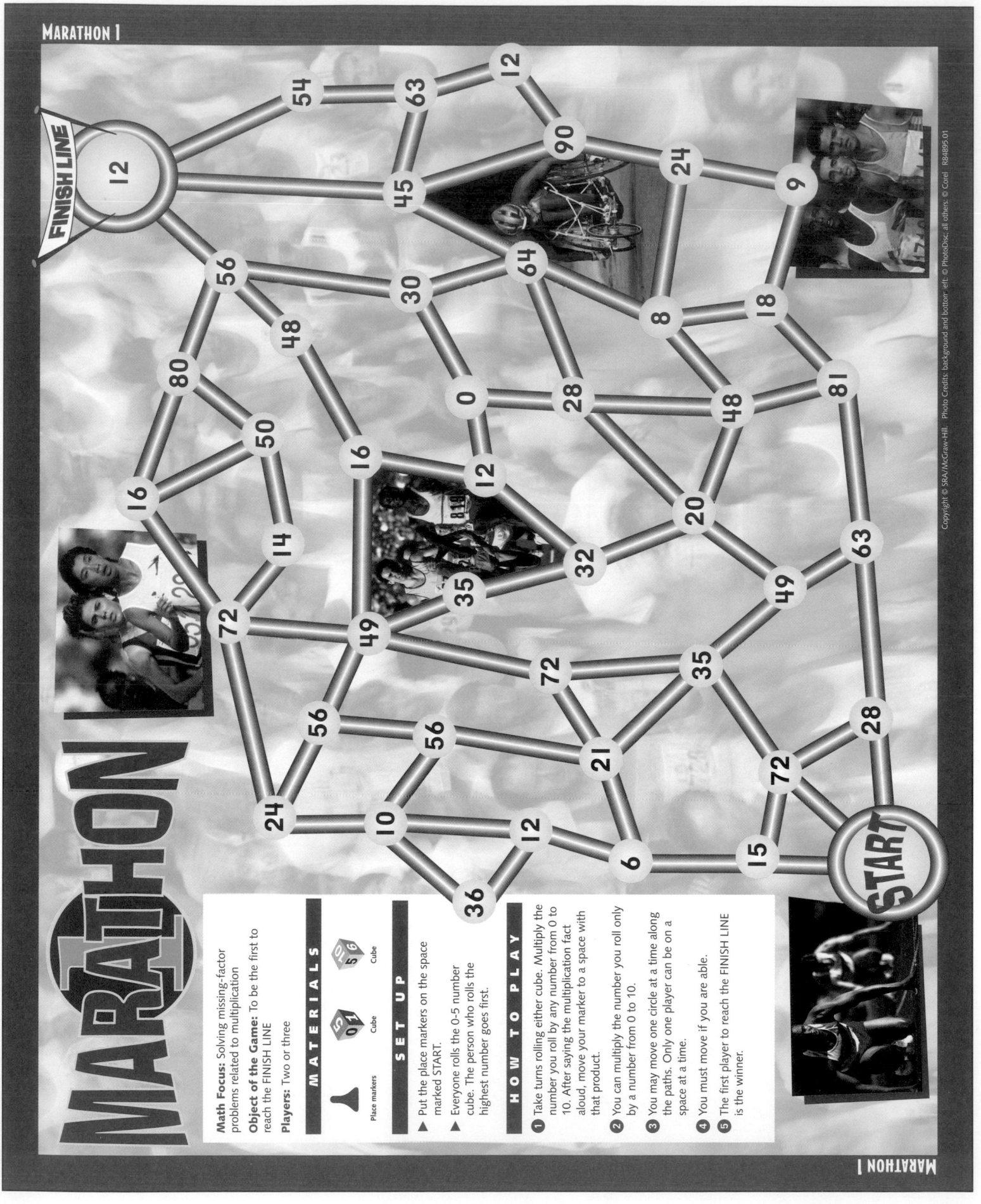

MARATHON

Math Focus: Solving missing-factor problems related to multiplication

Object of the Game: To be the first to reach the FINISH LINE

Players: Two or three

MATERIALS

Place markers   Cube   Cube

SET UP

▶ Put the place markers on the space marked START.

▶ Everyone rolls the 0–5 number cube. The person who rolls the highest number goes first.

HOW TO PLAY

1. Take turns rolling either cube. Multiply the number you roll by any number from 0 to 10. After saying the multiplication fact aloud, move your marker to a space with that product.

2. You can multiply the number you roll only by a number from 0 to 10.

3. You may move one circle at a time along the paths. Only one player can be on a space at a time.

4. You must move if you are able.

5. The first player to reach the FINISH LINE is the winner.

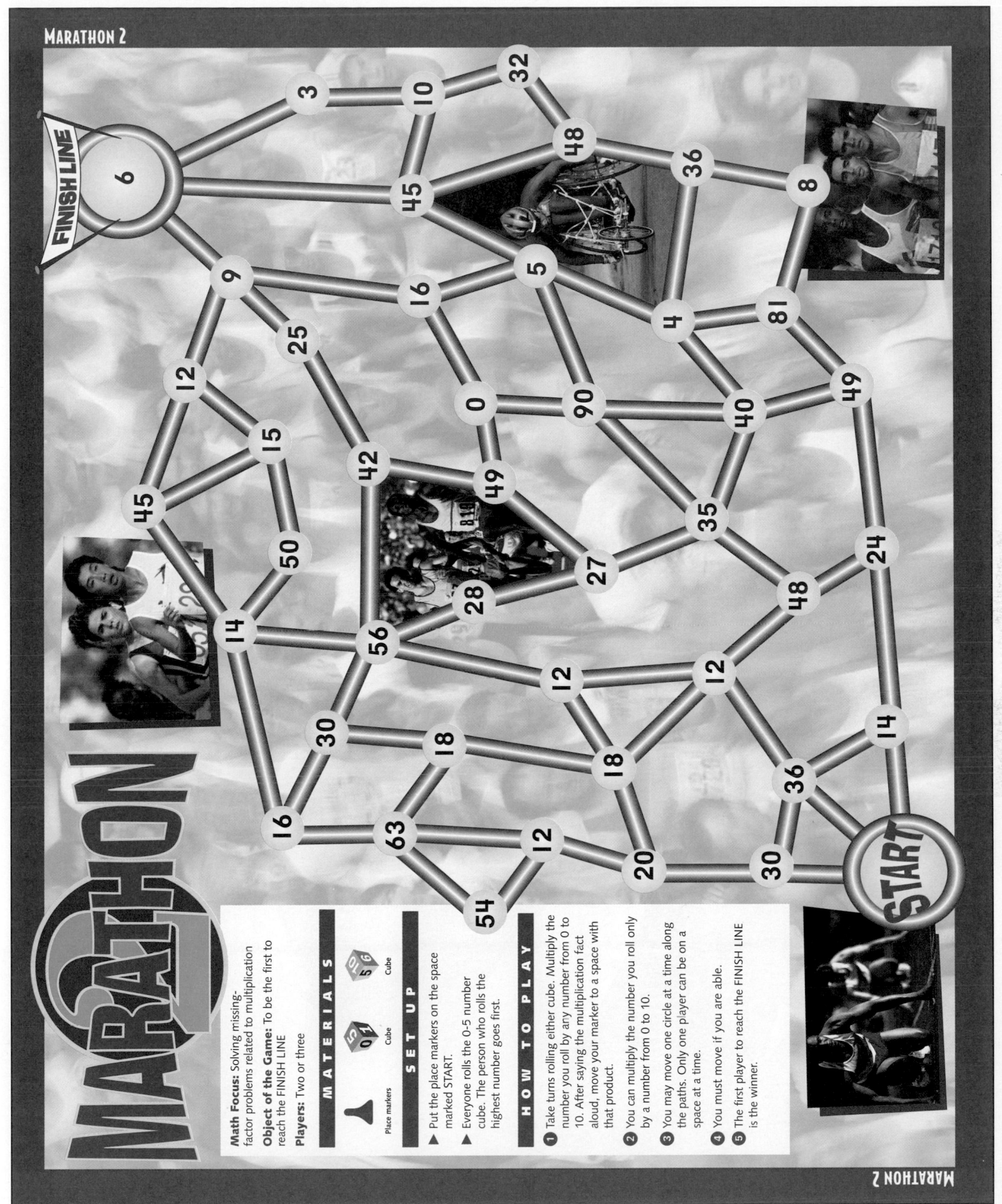

MARATHON 2

Math Focus: Solving missing-factor problems related to multiplication

Object of the Game: To be the first to reach the FINISH LINE

Players: Two or three

MATERIALS

Place markers   Cube   Cube

SET UP

▲ Put the place markers on the space marked START.

▲ Everyone rolls the 0–5 number cube. The person who rolls the highest number goes first.

HOW TO PLAY

1. Take turns rolling either cube. Multiply the number you roll by any number from 0 to 10. After saying the multiplication fact aloud, move your marker to a space with that product.

2. You can multiply the number you roll only by a number from 0 to 10.

3. You may move one circle at a time along the paths. Only one player can be on a space at a time.

4. You must move if you are able.

5. The first player to reach the FINISH LINE is the winner.

622

How to Play Pentathlon

Math Focus:
- Analyzing data
- Calculating the average of two numbers

Object of the Game: To be the overall winner of five track and field events

Players: Two, three, or four

MATERIALS

Stat sheets   Game cards   Calculator

SET UP

► Make copies of the cards and cut them out, keeping the cards for each event together.

► Before cutting, the copies can be enlarged for easier handling.

HOW TO PLAY

1. Place each set of game cards face down on the appropriate event. Play begins at the 400-meter dash. Players take turns drawing cards and writing the results on their stat sheets.

2. Players then compare results to determine their standing (first, second, third, or fourth) and write this down on their stat sheets. For races, the fastest time wins; for the jumps and the shot put, the longest distance wins.

3. Place all the cards on the bottom of the deck, and move on to the next event. Play continues around the board *twice*.

4. After the second turn at each event, all players average their scores to determine the final winner of each event and to record their final standings.

5. After players have averaged all five events and recorded their final standings, they calculate their overall score. Every first-place finish in the final standings is worth ten points, every second place is worth five, every third place is worth three, and every fourth-place finish earns one point.

6. The player with the most points wins the pentathlon.

Game Cards

400 Meter	Long Jump	Shot Put	100 Meter	High Jump
42.0 sec	6.35 m	17.32 m	10.20 sec	2.16 m
41.9 sec	6.37 m	18.14 m	10.05 sec	2.18 m
41.8 sec	6.76 m	19.61 m	9.95 sec	2.24 m
38.6 sec	6.82 m	21.03 m	10.14 sec	2.23 m
43.0 sec	6.78 m	21.16 m	10.06 sec	2.25 m
41.5 sec	6.72 m	22.41 m	10.25 sec	2.36 m
42.1 sec	6.40 m	17.61 m	9.14 sec	2.17 m
41.7 sec	6.50 m	18.16 m	10.01 sec	2.19 m
42.5 sec	6.60 m	19.01 m	11.05 sec	2.20 m
42.2 sec	6.70 m	21.42 m	9.80 sec	2.26 m
41.6 sec	6.43 m	22.00 m	9.89 sec	2.29 m
42.3 sec	6.67 m	22.50 m	10.11 sec	2.35 m
42.4 sec	6.51 m	17.03 m	10.31 sec	2.40 m
41.4 sec	6.71 m	20.43 m	9.99 sec	2.15 m
42.7 sec	6.36 m	20.00 m	10.20 sec	2.50 m
41.0 sec	6.66 m	19.00 m	9.97 sec	2.45 m

Stat Sheet

Event	Results	Standing	Average	Final Standing	Score
400 Meter					
400 Meter					
Long Jump					
Long Jump					
Shot Put					
Shot Put					
100 Meter					
100 Meter					
High Jump					
High Jump					
				Overall Score	

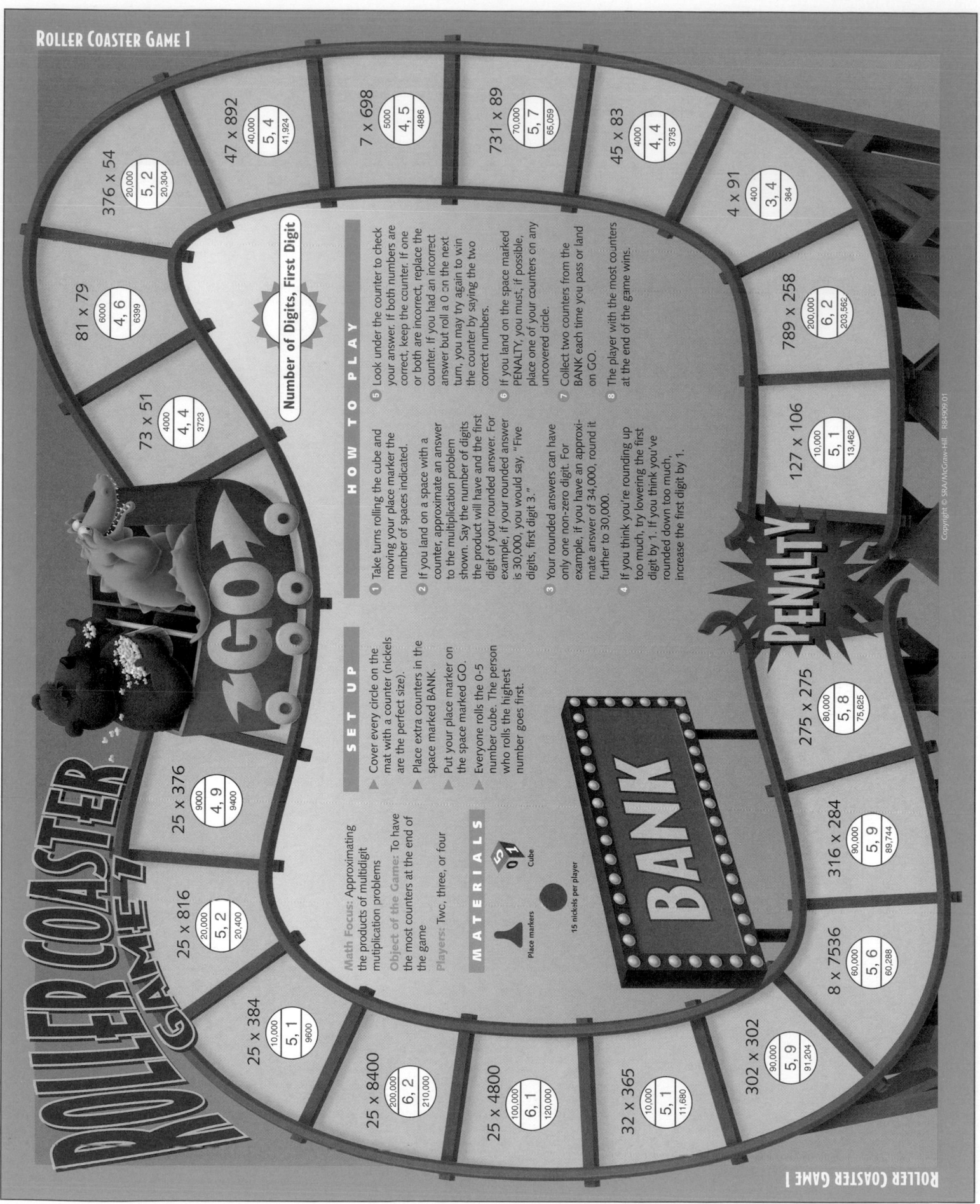

ROLLER COASTER GAME 1

Math Focus: Approximating the products of multidigit multiplication problems

Object of the Game: To have the most counters at the end of the game

Players: Two, three, or four

MATERIALS

Place markers

Cube

15 nickels per player

SET UP

▲ Cover every circle on the mat with a counter (nickels are the perfect size).

▲ Place extra counters in the space marked BANK.

▲ Put your place marker on the space marked GO.

▲ Everyone rolls the 0–5 number cube. The person who rolls the highest number goes first.

Number of Digits, First Digit

HOW TO PLAY

1 Take turns rolling the cube and moving your place marker the number of spaces indicated.

2 If you land on a space with a counter, approximate an answer to the multiplication problem shown. Say the number of digits the product will have and the first digit of your rounded answer. For example, if your rounded answer is 30,000, you would say, "Five digits, first digit 3."

3 Your rounded answers can have only one non-zero digit. For example, if you have an approximate answer of 34,000, round it further to 30,000.

4 If you think you're rounding up too much, try lowering the first digit by 1. If you think you've rounded down too much, increase the first digit by 1.

5 Look under the counter to check your answer. If both numbers are correct, keep the counter. If one or both are incorrect, replace the counter. If you had an incorrect answer but roll a 0 on the next turn, you may try again to win the counter by saying the two correct numbers.

6 If you land on the space marked PENALTY, you must, if possible, place one of your counters on any uncovered circle.

7 Collect two counters from the BANK each time you pass or land on GO.

8 The player with the most counters at the end of the game wins.

Board spaces

25 × 376 — 9000 — 4, 9 — 9400

25 × 816 — 20,000 — 5, 2 — 20,400

25 × 384 — 10,000 — 5, 1 — 9600

25 × 8400 — 200,000 — 6, 2 — 210,000

25 × 4800 — 100,000 — 6, 1 — 120,000

32 × 365 — 10,000 — 5, 1 — 11,680

302 × 302 — 90,000 — 5, 9 — 91,204

8 × 7536 — 60,000 — 5, 6 — 60,288

316 × 284 — 90,000 — 5, 9 — 89,744

275 × 275 — 80,000 — 5, 8 — 75,625

81 × 79 — 6000 — 4, 6 — 6399

73 × 51 — 4000 — 4, 4 — 3723

376 × 54 — 20,000 — 5, 2 — 20,304

47 × 892 — 40,000 — 5, 4 — 41,924

7 × 698 — 5000 — 4, 5 — 4886

731 × 89 — 70,000 — 5, 7 — 65,059

45 × 83 — 4000 — 4, 4 — 3735

4 × 91 — 400 — 3, 4 — 364

789 × 258 — 200,000 — 6, 2 — 203,562

127 × 106 — 10,000 — 5, 1 — 13,462

BANK

PENALTY

GO

624

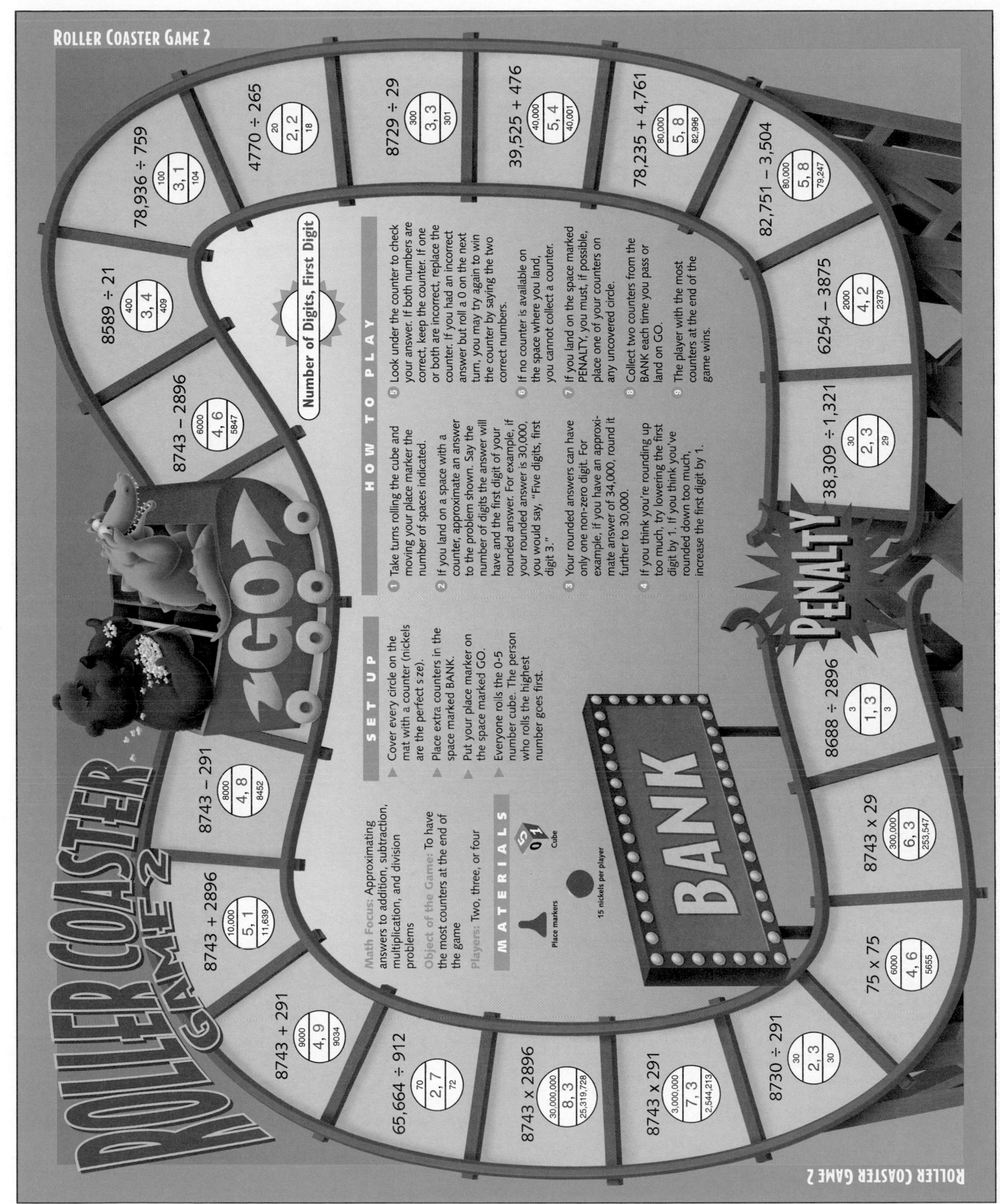

ROLLER COASTER GAME 2

Number of Digits, First Digit

SET UP

▲ Cover every circle on the mat with a counter (nickels are the perfect size).

▲ Place extra counters in the space marked BANK.

▲ Put your place marker on the space marked GO.

▲ Everyone rolls the 0–5 number cube. The person who rolls the highest number goes first.

HOW TO PLAY

1. Take turns rolling the cube and moving your place marker the number of spaces indicated.

2. If you land on a space with a counter, approximate an answer to the problem shown. Say the number of digits the answer will have and the first digit of your rounded answer. For example, if your rounded answer is 30,000, you would say, "Five digits, first digit 3."

3. Your rounded answers can have only one non-zero digit. For example, if you have an approximate answer of 34,000, round it further to 30,000.

4. If you think you're rounding up too much, try lowering the first digit by 1. If you think you've rounded down too much, increase the first digit by 1.

5. Look under the counter to check your answer. If both numbers are correct, keep the counter. If one or both are incorrect, replace the counter. If you had an incorrect answer but roll a 0 on the next turn, you may try again to win the counter by saying the two correct numbers.

6. If no counter is available on the space where you land, you cannot collect a counter.

7. If you land on the space marked PENALTY, you must, if possible, place one of your counters on any uncovered circle.

8. Collect two counters from the BANK each time you pass or land on GO.

9. The player with the most counters at the end of the game wins.

Math Focus: Approximating answers to addition, subtraction, multiplication, and division problems

Object of the Game: To have the most counters at the end of the game

Players: Two, three, or four

MATERIALS

Place markers

Cube

15 nickels per player

Board spaces (with problem, and circle showing answer digits/first digit and full answer):

- 8743 + 2896 — 10,000 / 5, 1 / 11,639
- 8743 + 291 — 9000 / 4, 9 / 9034
- 65,664 ÷ 912 — 70 / 2, 7 / 72
- 8743 x 2896 — 30,000,000 / 8, 3 / 25,319,728
- 8743 x 291 — 3,000,000 / 7, 3 / 2,544,213
- 8730 ÷ 291 — 30 / 2, 3 / 30
- 75 x 75 — 6000 / 4, 6 / 5655
- 8743 x 29 — 300,000 / 6, 3 / 253,547
- 8688 ÷ 2896 — 3 / 1, 3 / 3
- 38,309 ÷ 1,321 — 30 / 2, 3 / 29
- 6254 – 3875 — 2000 / 4, 2 / 2379
- 82,751 – 3,504 — 80,000 / 5, 8 / 79,247
- 78,235 + 4,761 — 80,000 / 5, 8 / 82,996
- 39,525 + 476 — 40,000 / 5, 4 / 40,001
- 8729 ÷ 29 — 300 / 3, 3 / 301
- 4770 ÷ 265 — 20 / 2, 2 / 18
- 78,936 ÷ 759 — 100 / 3, 1 / 104
- 8589 ÷ 21 — 400 / 3, 4 / 409
- 8743 – 2896 — 6000 / 4, 6 / 5847
- 8743 – 291 — 8000 / 4, 8 / 8452

BANK

PENALTY

GO

ROUTES

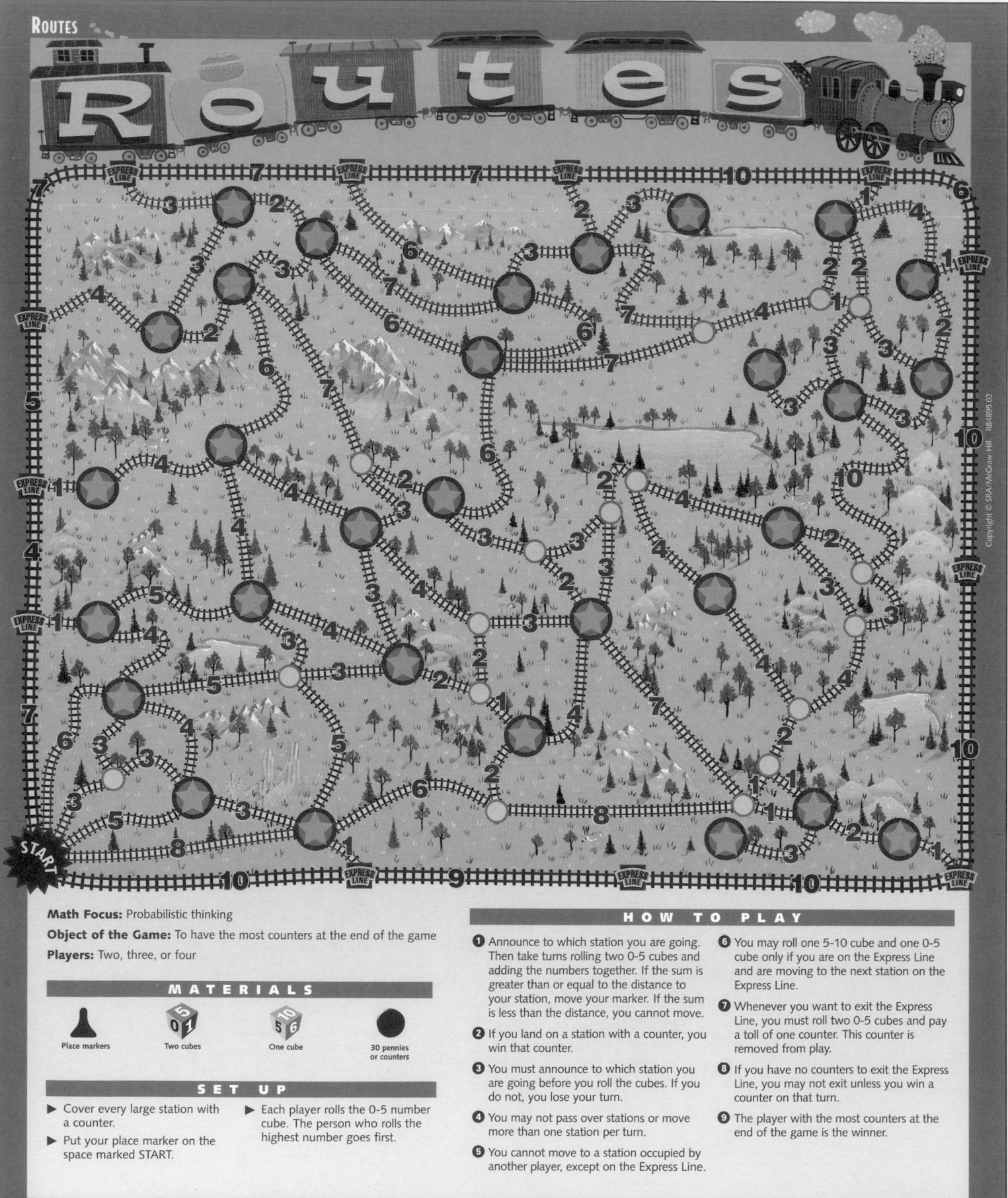

Math Focus: Probabilistic thinking

Object of the Game: To have the most counters at the end of the game

Players: Two, three, or four

MATERIALS

Place markers   Two cubes   One cube   30 pennies or counters

SET UP

► Cover every large station with a counter.

► Put your place marker on the space marked START.

► Each player rolls the 0-5 number cube. The person who rolls the highest number goes first.

HOW TO PLAY

❶ Announce to which station you are going. Then take turns rolling two 0-5 cubes and adding the numbers together. If the sum is greater than or equal to the distance to your station, move your marker. If the sum is less than the distance, you cannot move.

❷ If you land on a station with a counter, you win that counter.

❸ You must announce to which station you are going before you roll the cubes. If you do not, you lose your turn.

❹ You may not pass over stations or move more than one station per turn.

❺ You cannot move to a station occupied by another player, except on the Express Line.

❻ You may roll one 5-10 cube and one 0-5 cube only if you are on the Express Line and are moving to the next station on the Express Line.

❼ Whenever you want to exit the Express Line, you must roll two 0-5 cubes and pay a toll of one counter. This counter is removed from play.

❽ If you have no counters to exit the Express Line, you may not exit unless you win a counter on that turn.

❾ The player with the most counters at the end of the game is the winner.

ROUTES

626

HARDER ROUTES

Math Focus: Probabilistic thinking

Object of the Game: To be the first to reach FINISH

Players: Two, three, or four

MATERIALS

Place markers

Cube

SET UP

▶ Put your place marker on the space marked START.

▶ Everyone rolls the 0-5 number cube. The person who rolls the highest number goes first.

HOW TO PLAY

❶ Take turns announcing to which intersection you are going. Then roll the 0-5 cube. If the number you roll is greater than or equal to the distance to your intersection, move your marker. If the number is less than the distance, you cannot move.

❷ You must announce to which intersection you are going before you roll the cube. If you do not, you lose your turn.

❸ You cannot move to an intersection occupied by another player.

❹ You may not pass over intersections or move more than one intersection per turn.

❺ The first player to land on FINISH is the winner.

TRAN$ACTION

SUNDAY	MONDAY	TUESDAY	WEDNESDAY	THURSDAY	FRIDAY	SATURDAY
START $1000 $1000 — Your balance is $1000	**1** Speeding Ticket — Pay $___	**2** Doctor Bill — Pay $___	**3** Electric Bill — Pay $__	**4** Pay Day — Earn $__	**5** Health Food Store — Pay $__	
6 Visit Museum — FREE	**7** Concert Tickets — Pay $__	**8** Win a Contest — Earn $___	**9** Supermarket — Pay $__	**10** Telephone Bill — Pay $__	**11** Go Back 7 Spaces	**12** New Shirt — Pay $__
13 Visit Zoo — FREE	**14** Dry cleaning — Pay $__	**15** Pay Day — Earn $___	**16** Income Tax — Pay $___	**17** Holiday — No Bills Today	**18** Buy a Plant — Pay $__	**19** Water Bill — Pay $__
20 Go for a Bicycle Ride — FREE	**21** Visit Amusement Park — Pay $__	**22** Life Insurance — Pay $__	**23** Go Back 7 Spaces	**24** Supermarket — Pay $__	**25** Go Ahead 2 Spaces	**26** Television Repair — Pay $__
27 Go Roller Skating — FREE	**28** Eat in Restaurant — Pay $__	**29** Buy a Book — Pay $__	**30** Buy Gift — Pay $___	**31** Go Back 7 Spaces	FINISH — Wait until all players finish	

Math Focus:
- Adding and subtracting amounts of money (dollars)
- Maintaining a record of money transactions

Object of the Game: To have the greatest balance at the end of the game

Players: Two or three

MATERIALS

 Place markers

  Two cubes

  Two cubes

 One score sheet per player

SET UP

▶ The blank balance sheet for "Harder Transaction" can be photocopied for students to use.

▶ Put your place markers on the space marked START.

▶ On your score sheet write "Start" under DATE and "$1000" under BALANCE.

▶ Everyone rolls one 0-5 number cube. The person who rolls the highest number goes first.

DATE	EARN	PAY	BALANCE
Start			$1000
3		−$24	$ 976
8	+$861		$1837
11			
4	+76		$1913
6		−$45	$1868

HOW TO PLAY

1 Take turns rolling one 0-5 cube and moving your place marker the correct number of spaces.

2 When you land on a space that says "Earn" or "Pay," roll one cube for each blank line in the amount. Arrange the digits in the best order. Try to earn the most and pay the least. For example, if you roll a 7, 0, and 2 and have to pay, make the amount $207. If you are earning, make the amount $720.

3 Zero cannot be used as the first digit of an amount. Also, 10 cannot be used. If you roll a 10, roll that cube again.

4 On every turn write down what you earn or pay under the correct column, then add what you earned or subtract what you paid in the BALANCE column. Also, write down the date of each transaction.

5 Keep playing until everyone reaches FINISH or runs out of money.

6 The player with the greatest correct balance wins. Players must check the winner's addition and subtraction. Add to find each total in the winner's PAY column and EARN column. Then add the EARN total to $1000 and subtract the PAY total. This balance should match the winner's final balance. If there is a mistake in the balance, the player with the greatest correct balance wins instead.

Reminder: If you land on a space that says "Pay $_ _," roll two 0-5 cubes and choose the lesser amount to pay. If you land on a space that says "Earn $_ _," roll two 5-10 cubes and choose the greater combination of digits.

HARDER TRAN$ACTION

SUNDAY	MONDAY	TUESDAY	WEDNESDAY	THURSDAY	FRIDAY	SATURDAY

$1000 START $1000
Your balance is $1000

1 Speeding Ticket — Pay $__.__

2 Doctor Bill — Pay $__.__

3 Electric Bill — Pay $__.__

4 Pay Day — Earn $__.__

5 Supermarket — Pay $__.__

6 Visit Museum — FREE

7 Snack — Pay $__.__

8 Win a contest — Earn $__.__

9 Supermarket — Pay $__.__

10 Telephone Bill — Pay $__.__

11 Go Back 7 Spaces

12 New Shirt — Pay $__.__

13 Visit Amusement Park — Pay $__.__

14 Concert Tickets — Pay $__.__

15 Pay Day — Earn $__.__

16 Income Tax — Pay $__.__

17 Holiday — No Bills Today

18 Buy Compact Discs — Pay $__.__

19 Water Bill — Pay $__.__

20 Go for a Bicycle Ride — FREE

21 Visit Zoo — Pay $__.__

22 Life Insurance — Pay $__.__

23 Go Back 7 Spaces

24 Health Food Store — Pay $__.__

25 Go Ahead 2 Spaces

26 Television Repair — Pay $__.__

27 Play Tennis — FREE

28 Eat in Restaurant — Pay $__.__

29 New Jeans — Pay $__.__

30 Buy Gift — Pay $__.__

31 Go Back 7 Spaces

FINISH — Wait until all players finish

Math Focus:
- Adding and subtracting amounts of money (dollars and cents)
- Maintaining a record of money transactions

Object of the Game: To have the greatest balance at the end of the game

Players: Two or three

MATERIALS

Place markers

Two cubes

Two cubes

One score sheet per player

SET UP

- The blank balance sheet below can be photocopied for students to use.
- Put your place markers on the space marked START.
- On your score sheet write "Start" under DATE and "$1000" under BALANCE.
- Everyone rolls one 0-5 number cube. The person who rolls the highest number goes first.

DATE	EARN	PAY	BALANCE

HOW TO PLAY

1. Take turns rolling one 0-5 cube and moving your place marker the correct number of spaces.

2. When you land on a space that says "Earn" or "Pay," roll one cube for each blank line in the amount. Arrange the digits in the best order. Try to earn the most and pay the least. For example, if you roll a 7, 1, and 2 and have to pay, make the amount $1.27. If you are earning, make the amount $7.21.

3. Zero cannot be used as the first digit of an amount. Also, 10 cannot be used. If you roll a 10, roll that cube again.

4. On every turn write down what you earn or pay under the correct column, then add what you earned or subtract what you paid in the BALANCE column. Also write down the date of each transaction.

5. Keep playing until everyone reaches FINISH or runs out of money.

6. The player with the greatest correct balance wins. Players must check the winner's addition and subtraction. Add to find each total in the winner's PAY column and the EARN column. Then add the EARN total to $1000 and subtract the PAY total. This balance should match the winner's final balance. If there is a mistake in the balance, the player with the greatest correct balance wins instead.

Reminder: If you land on a space that says "Pay $_ _," roll two 0-5 cubes and choose the lesser amount to pay. If you land on a space that says "Earn $_ _._ _," roll four 5-10 cubes and choose the greatest combination of digits.

629

INDEX

A

Act It Out, 208–209, 298–301, 350–353
  Is Business Booming?, 350–353
  A Material Problem with Fractions,
    298–301
  Tricky Nines, 208–209
Acute angles, 503–506, 509
Addition
  basic facts, 14–15, 18–19, 371, 378–379,
    399
  decimals, 102–107, 133–134, 164–166,
    169–170, 228–233, 278–279, 286–287,
    290
  estimating sums, 36, 64, 68–69, 106–107,
    134, 204–205, 242, 267, 270–271, 278,
    280–281, 286–287, 290, 298, 314–315
  fractions, like denominators, 242, 262, 264,
    266, 270, 298, 330–331, 333, 407, 410,
    498
  fractions, unlike denominators, 253,
    262–265, 266–267, 269–270, 278, 280,
    293, 298, 330–331, 336, 407, 410, 498
  missing addends, 139, 346, 381, 399, 502,
    518
  mixed numbers, 286–289, 290, 298,
    330–331, 333, 335–336, 407, 409
  money, 64, 68–69, 104, 106–107, 134, 179,
    314–315,
  multidigit, 16, 24–27, 30–35, 90–92,
    116–117, 124–125, 128, 217, 308–309,
    310–311
  negative numbers, 82–84, 89, 91, 93, 96,
    156, 346, 371, 378–379, 397, 399
  three or more addends, 8, 26–27, 30, 125,
    128, 382, 401, 522
Advertising, 338–339
Algebra
  coordinate graphing, 353–355, 363,
    365–367, 369, 372–375, 377, 402–405,
    426–428
  formulas, 390–393, 415, 421–422, 438,
    444–445, 453, 457, 460, 465, 476, 519,
    590–591
  functions, 302–303, 354–355, 362–363,
    370–371, 378–381, 386–387, 396–400,
    402–405, 410–413, 416–419, 426–427,
    429–433
  graphing functions, 354–355, 362–363,
    370–373, 378–381, 396–397, 399,
    402–405, 410–413, 415–419, 426–427,
    429–433

integers (negative numbers), 82–85, 87–89,
    91, 93, 96, 156, 346, 369, 370–373, 375,
    378–381, 390, 397, 399, 426–429,
    432–433
inverse operations, 196–197, 304, 380
missing term problems, 50, 139, 204–205,
    239, 279, 302–303, 346, 380–381, 390,
    399, 419, 476–477, 502–503, 518, 540,
    544
variables, 50, 204–205, 239, 324, 326, 328,
    346, 355, 362–363, 370–371, 378–381,
    386–387, 390–393, 395–405, 410–419,
    421–422, 426–427, 429–433, 438,
    444–445, 453, 457, 460, 464–465, 472,
    476, 519, 590–591
writing equations and expressions from
    situations, 390–393, 404–405, 410–411
writing equations from graphs or tables,
    400–401, 416–418, 421, 427, 429, 431,
    433
Algebra Readiness, 142, 204–205, 239,
    302–303, 352, 354, 362, 370, 378–381,
    386–387, 390–393, 398–400, 402–407,
    410–419, 421–422, 438, 444–446, 448,
    453, 457, 460, 465, 476, 573–575,
    577–580, 582
All About Sam, 286
All in a Day, 402
All the Money in the World, 66
Amazing Biofacts, 134
Amazing Buildings, 470
Analyzing Answers, 31, 53, 113, 115, 257, 263,
    277, 301, 355, 373, 399
*And Then There Was One: The Mysteries of
    Extinction*, 408
Angles
  acute angles, 503–506, 509
  copying, 530–531
  corresponding, 510–513, 516–517
  measuring, 506–509, 518–520, 541, 546,
    549
  obtuse angles, 503–506, 509
  of polygons, 519–520, 591
  right angles, 452–453, 503–505, 509
  straight, 514–517
  supplementary, 514–517
  vertical, 510–513, 516–517
Anno's Magic Seeds, 378
Anno's Mysterious Multiplying Jar, 17, 603
Anything but 10 Game, 274–275
Approximation, *See* Estimation
Approximation, 75
Approximation Game, 75, 601

Area
  complicated figures, 450, 462–463, 485
  estimating, 21, 414, 441, 444, 452
  on a grid, 466–467, 487
  parallelograms, 457–458, 460, 472, 476,
    485, 540, 542–543, 548, 590
  rectangles, 116–117, 410–411, 438–440,
    447–448, 484, 499, 540, 542–543, 548,
    590
  right triangles, 452–455, 485, 542–543
  square units, 439, 588, 589
  of surfaces, 440–443, 446, 550–551
  trapezoids, 464–465, 476, 486, 540,
    542–543, 548, 590
  triangles, 460–463, 476, 540, 542–543,
    548, 590
Area, 466
"Arithmetic", 22
Art Connection, 303, 305, 308, 326, 374, 456,
    515, 523, 538
Assessment, 48–49, 90–91, 96–97, 136–137,
    164–165, 170–171, 200–201, 228–229,
    232–233, 292–293, 330–331, 336–337,
    394–397, 426–427, 432–433, 484–487,
    540–541, 548–549, 552–587
  Analyzing Answers, 31, 53, 113, 115, 257,
    263, 277, 301, 355, 373, 399
  Informal Assessment, 11, 19, 39, 47, 73, 83,
    89, 109, 115, 123, 135, 161, 163, 181,
    207, 209, 227, 249, 257, 263, 277, 281,
    285, 297, 301, 313, 329, 345, 347, 361,
    367, 377, 381, 389, 415, 423, 443, 463,
    467, 475, 483, 509, 513, 525, 537
  Mastery Checkpoints, 7, 11, 13, 31, 43, 57,
    71, 77, 105, 119, 133, 157, 189, 203, 265,
    289, 307, 317, 353, 355, 401, 517
  Performance Assessment, 49, 63, 81, 87, 91,
    113, 127, 137, 153, 165, 185, 195, 199,
    201, 213, 221, 225, 229, 243, 247, 253,
    261, 269, 279, 291, 293, 303, 307, 317,
    321, 323, 327, 331, 349, 369, 379, 387,
    393, 397, 399, 413, 419, 427, 439, 447,
    451, 455, 459, 465, 471, 487, 489, 493,
    501, 505, 521, 527, 533, 539, 541
  Portfolio Assessment, 15, 27, 35, 49, 67, 91,
    121, 137, 145, 147, 151, 165, 179, 189,
    201, 217, 229, 273, 293, 309, 331, 363,
    373, 397, 405, 411, 425, 427, 477, 481,
    487, 495, 497, 541
  Self Assessment, 15, 17, 19, 23, 57, 141,
    289, 385, 401, 409
At Risk, 38, 76, 296, 536

Averages
    mean, 314-324, 331, 334, 337, 365, 371, 407
    median, 318-323, 331, 334, 337
    mode, 318-324, 331, 334, 337
Axes (graphs), 353

B

Babylon numeration system, 99
Bar graphs, 342-343, 349
Base (exponents), 143
Base (of figures), 438
Basic facts, 15, 17, 19
Bingo Brown and the Language of Love, 315
A Birthday Present Project, 234-235
Brain Teasers and Mind-Benders, 496
The Bunyans, 248
Busy Bee Game Mat, 600, 603
Buy Now, Pay Later, 131

C

Calculators
    decimals, 123, 144, 192-193, 197, 276,
        278-279, 315, 335, 422, 478-481, 547
    exponents, 145, 162-163, 192
    fractions, 72, 258, 276, 278-279, 306
    integers, 84-85, 89
    order of operations, 406
    percents, 182-185, 193-195, 198-199, 203,
        231, 235, 276, 547
    square roots, 478-481
    whole numbers, 33, 72-75, 152-153,
        159-161, 315, 388, 446-447, 449-451,
        536
Calculator Riddles, 206
Capacity
    customary units, 494-495, 589
    estimating, 5, 110, 114, 122, 383, 483,
        496-497
    metric units, 112-113, 490-493, 588
Cardinal directions, 502-503
Celsius, 82, 91, 94, 368-369, 390-393, 424,
    483, 591
Center (circle), 528-529
Centigram, 490-491, 588
Centiliter, 491, 588
Centimeter, 4-5, 112-113, 490-492, 588
Chain calculations, 401
Charlie and the Great Glass Elevator, 362
Charts, *See* Statistics
Children's Atlas of the United States, 26

The Children's Space Atlas, 260
Circle graphs, 342-345, 534-537
Circles, 420-422, 528-529
    center, 528-529
    circumference, 420-423, 427, 430, 433,
        459, 590
    compass, 528-533
    diameter, 420-422, 528, 590
    pi (π), 422
    radius, 421, 528
Circo 11 Game, 265, 288, 602
Circumference, 420-423, 427, 430, 433, 459,
    590
Classifying figures, 468-475, 509
Classroom Grade Level Math Programs, 142,
    507
Clever Counting Project, 98-99
Common denominator, 258-260, 262-264,
    286-287, 324
Common factors, 251-254, 498
Comparing decimals, 11, 105, 245, 282
Comparing fractions, 245, 258-261, 267,
    282-283
Compass (cardinal directions), 502-503
Compass (circle), 528-533
Competition Thinking Story, 188-189,
    206-207, 220-221, 224-225
Complicated figures-area, 462-463
Composite functions, 378-381, 386, 398-399,
    402-405, 416-418
    graphing, 378-379
Composite numbers, 222-223
Compound interest, 190-195, 200-201,
    229-231, 233-235
Computers
    charts/tables, 112, 134-135, 149, 153, 160,
        230, 275, 309, 312, 325, 327, 345, 365,
        371, 379, 381, 383, 410-411, 412-413,
        414, 497, 521, 535, 547
    The Cruncher, 33, 65-66, 69, 83, 109, 112,
        118, 126, 133, 135, 151, 160, 177-178,
        181, 191-192, 194, 209, 230, 245, 249,
        267, 275, 283, 291, 295-296, 306, 309,
        312, 315, 321, 323, 331, 345, 352, 365,
        369, 371-372, 379, 383, 405, 421-422,
        425, 445, 451, 477, 519, 535-536, 547
    functions, 371, 379, 410-411, 412-413, 414
    graphs, 344, 352, 365, 369, 371-372, 379,
        383, 413, 425, 535-536, 546
    spreadsheets, 33, 65-66, 69, 83, 118, 126,
        177-178, 181, 191, 194, 245, 267, 283,
        291, 295-296, 306, 315, 421-422, 445,
        519, 537

Congruency, 356-357, 360-361, 526-527,
    532-533
Cookies, 51
Cooperative Learning, 4-5, 9, 14, 16, 18, 35,
    44, 46, 54, 63, 67, 73-75, 86, 95, 98-99,
    105-106, 120-121, 124, 127, 139,
    158-159, 161, 163, 172-173, 179,
    184-185, 222, 234-235, 241, 245, 253,
    265, 272-277, 282-283, 289, 294,
    296-297, 299, 311, 315, 318, 326, 328,
    335, 338-339, 343-344,372, 374-375,
    382, 387, 389, 421, 424, 446, 449, 467,
    473, 483, 496, 522, 526, 538, 550-551
Coordinates, 352-355, 374-375, 402-403
*Core Concepts in Math: Mastering Decimals
    and Percents,* 182
*Core Concepts in Math: Mastering
    Equations, Roots, and Exponents,* 149
Core Concepts in Math: Mastering Fractions,
    267
*Core Concepts in Math: Mastering Informal
    Geometry,* 441
*Core Concepts in Math: Problem Solving
    Series,* 41
*Core Concepts in Math: Problem Solving
    with Tables, Graphs, and Statistics,* 366
Corresponding angles, 510-513, 516-517
Cosmic Cafe Game Mat, 259-260, 602, 604
Cosmic Golf, 503
Counting on Frank, 40
Create Your Own Rainbirds, 460
Cross Curriculum Connections
    Art Connection, 303, 305, 308, 326, 374,
        456, 515, 523, 538
    Geography Connection, 21, 29, 32, 82, 85,
        308-309, 326-327, 424-425, 502-503,
        506, 554, 571
    Language Arts Connection, 88, 328, 504
    Literature Connection, 5, 9, 17, 18, 22, 26,
        29, 34, 38, 40, 46, 51, 55, 60, 66, 69, 72,
        75, 80, 83, 84, 102, 108, 111, 114, 117,
        122, 126, 128, 131, 134, 140, 144, 150,
        152, 155, 160, 178, 180, 184, 187, 190,
        193, 198, 206, 210, 218, 238, 245, 248,
        251, 256, 260, 262, 271, 275, 278, 280,
        282, 286, 290, 296, 300, 302, 312, 315,
        350, 362, 365, 371, 375, 378, 384, 386,
        398, 402, 408, 414, 421, 440, 445, 452,
        460, 466, 470, 474, 476, 480, 482, 488,
        492, 496, 498, 502, 508, 512, 518, 524,
        529, 535
    Math Connection, 494

Music Connection, 14, 16
Physical Education Connection, 197, 270, 290, 320, 346
Real-World Connection, 85, 124, 181, 194, 205, 291, 309, 317, 346, 383, 390, 392, 407, 454, 462, 494, 514
Science Connection, 148–149, 153, 197, 320, 342–343, 368–369, 376, 383, 386, 424
Social Studies Connection, 9, 61, 78, 98, 110, 145, 158–160, 183, 240, 306–307, 322, 325, 344, 368, 428, 439, 490, 534–535, 547
Technology Connection, 5, 20, 24, 33, 37, 41, 50, 61, 65, 68, 74, 79, 85, 103, 107, 125, 139, 142, 149, 182, 186, 211, 219, 223, 239, 250, 255, 259, 267, 271, 276, 283, 295, 319, 351, 366, 359, 372, 391, 403, 417, 422, 441, 444, 450, 453, 457, 461, 473, 479, 491, 499, 503, 507, 519, 530, 536, 547
Cruncher, 33, 65–66, 69, 83, 109, 112, 118, 126, 133, 135, 151, 160, 177–178, 181, 191–192, 194, 209, 230, 245, 249, 267, 275, 283, 291, 295–296, 306, 309, 312, 315, 321, 323, 331, 345, 352, 365, 369, 371–372, 379, 383, 405, 421–422, 425, 445, 451, 477, 519, 535–536, 547
Cube-O-Mat Game Mat, 21–22, 601, 606
Cubes, 441, 447
Cubic units (volume), 444–445
Cubo Game, 18, 416, 420, 601
Cultural Diversity, 116, 220, 304, 442, 469
Cumulative Review, 552–587
Cup, 494–495, 589
Current U.S. Weather, 351
Customary measurement system, *See* Measurement

D

Days, 494–495
Dear Mr. Henshaw, 55
Decagons, 521
Decimal equivalents–fractions, 244–248, 250, 258, 278, 281–283, 292–293, 296, 306, 330–331, 333, 335, 336–337, 526
Decimals
    adding, 102–107, 133, 134, 164–166, 169–170, 228–233, 278–279, 286–287, 290
    comparing/ordering, 11, 12, 105, 245, 282

dividing by a decimal, 128–133, 137, 164, 167, 169–171, 389
dividing by a power of ten, 111–113, 126–127, 136–137, 164–166, 169–171, 176, 180, 423, 488–489
dividing by a whole number, 130–133, 279
multiplying by a decimal, 115–119, 126–127, 136–137, 164, 166, 170–171, 178, 389, 439, 455
multiplying by a power of ten, 110, 112–113, 126–127, 136–137, 164–166, 170–171, 176, 180, 423, 482, 488–489
multiplying by a whole number, 114–115, 136–137, 164, 166, 170–171, 178, 314, 362, 389, 439, 482
place value, 10–11, 105, 179
relating to fractions, 244–248, 250, 258, 278, 280–283, 290, 292–293, 296, 306, 330–331, 333, 335, 336–337, 526
relating to percents, 176–179, 200–201, 228–233, 526
rounding, 78–81, 131–133, 180–181, 478–481
subtracting, 102–107, 133, 164–166, 169–170, 228–233, 278–279, 290, 298
Decigram, 491, 588
Deciliter, 491, 588
Decimeter, 112–113, 491–492, 588
Deficit, 158–160
Dekagram, 491, 588
Dekaliter, 491, 588
Dekameter, 112, 491, 588
Denominators, common, 258–260, 262–264, 286–287, 324
Diagonals, 521
Diagram, 44
Diameter, 420–422, 528, 590
Diet for a Small Terrier Thinking Story, 376–377, 384–385, 408–409
Directions-cardinal, 502–503
Discount Game Mat, 183–184, 602, 608
Discounts-percent, 180–190, 192, 197–203, 228–229, 231–233
Divide and Roll Game, 65
Divisibility, 208–218
Division
    basic facts, 16–19, 50, 217
    by multiples and powers of ten, 74, 111–113, 126–127, 136–137, 164–166, 169–171, 176, 180, 423, 488–489
    decimals, 111–113, 126–133, 136–137, 164–167, 169–171, 176, 180, 279, 389, 423, 488–489

estimating quotients, 76, 93, 129, 163, 389
exponents, 152–153, 155–157, 163
fractions, 298–301, 304–307, 330–331, 333, 336
missing terms, 205, 279, 380–381, 419
money, 128
multidigit divisors, 58–63, 93, 96–97, 217, 279, 322, 455
one-digit divisors, 54–57, 90–91, 96–97, 210, 255, 322, 380, 455
remainders, 50–56, 58, 208, 211, 214, 219, 258–259
Divisors, 218–219
Dominoes: Basic Rules and Variations, 80, 262
Don't Go Over 1000 Game, 34–35, 90, 601
Do You Wanna Bet?, 275

E

Eagle Eye Mystery, 422
Earthworks Group, 187
Ed Emberly's Picture Pie, 282
The Efficiency Experts Thinking Story, 108–109, 140–141, 150–151
Eisenhower National Clearinghouse, 5
Energy Savers Thinking Story, 246–247, 256–257, 268–269, 284–285
Equilateral triangles, 468–469
Equivalence 1 Game Mat, 248–249, 602, 610
Equivalence 2 Game Mat, 245–246, 602, 611
Equivalent fractions, 248–249
ESL, 23, 45, 52, 88, 132, 202, 221, 259, 388, 475, 513
Estimating
    area, 21, 414, 441, 444, 452
    capacity, 5, 110, 114, 122, 383, 483, 496–497
    differences, 36, 103, 106–107, 290, 298
    length, 5, 7, 77, 110, 114, 121, 122, 161, 254, 386, 420, 449, 464, 483, 494
    products, 47, 76–79, 84–85, 93, 115, 136, 162–163, 178, 314, 389, 455
    quotients, 76–77, 93, 129, 163, 389
    sums, 36, 64, 68–69, 106–107, 134, 204–205, 242, 267, 270–271, 278, 280–281, 286–287, 290, 298, 314 315
    weight, 5, 110, 114, 122, 135, 254, 294, 442–443, 483, 501
    volume, 452, 496–497
Exponential form, 143–145, 148–149, 151–154, 164–165, 167, 169–170

Exponents
  approximation, 154–157
  base, 143
  division, 152–153, 155–157, 163
  evaluating expressions, 143–145, 490
  exponential form, 143–145, 148–149,
    151–154, 164–165, 167, 169–170
  multiplication, 152–157, 162–163, 167

F

Factors, 218–225
  greatest common, 252–253
Fahrenheit, 390–393, 591
Fair Advertising Project, 338–339
$50 Price Game, 184–185, 602
*50 Simple Things You Can Do to Save the
  Earth*, 187
Find the Function Rule Game, 386–387, 603
Find the Treasure Game Mat, 220, 602, 612
Figures
  classifying, 468–475, 509
  congruent, 356, 526–527, 532–533
  similar, 328–329, 526–527
Five in a Row, 219
5% Tax Game Mat, 177–178, 602, 614
Fluid ounce, 494–495, 589
Foot, 120–121, 494–495, 589
Formulas, 390–393, 590–591
  angles of a polygon, 519, 591
  area of parallelograms, 457, 460, 476, 590
  area of rectangles, 438, 590
  area of right triangles, 453
  area of trapezoids, 465, 476, 590
  area of triangles, 460, 476, 590
  circumference, 421–422, 590
  perimeter, 415, 476, 590
  volume, 444–445, 591
Fractions
  adding (like denominators), 242, 262, 264,
    266, 270, 298, 330–331, 333, 407, 410,
    498
  adding (unlike denominators), 253,
    262–265, 266–267, 269–270, 278, 280,
    293, 298, 289, 296, 330–331, 336, 407,
    410, 498
  adding mixed numbers, 286–289, 290, 298,
    330–331, 333, 335–336, 407, 409
  common denominator, 258–260, 262–264,
    286–287, 324
  comparing/ordering, 245, 258–261, 267,
    282–283, 285, 382

  decimal equivalents, 244–248, 250, 258,
    278, 281–283, 292–293, 296, 306,
    330–331, 333, 335, 336–337, 526
  dividing by a whole number, 305–306
  dividing by a fraction or mixed number,
    298–301, 304–307, 330–331, 333, 336
  equivalent, 248–249, 258, 262, 264–265,
    328
  mixed numbers and improper fractions,
    280–283, 288
  multiplying by a fraction or mixed number,
    242, 254, 257, 292–293, 306–307,
    330–333, 336–337
  multiplying by a whole number, 239,
    302–303, 332, 335–337
  of a number, 238–241, 243–244, 292–293,
    332, 335–337, 455
  of a whole, 12–13, 238, 374, 503
  reciprocals, 304–306, 335
  reduced form, 249–253, 498
  subtracting (like denominators), 262–263,
    330, 336
  subtracting (unlike denominators),
    262–265, 278, 293, 330–331, 336, 498
  subtracting mixed numbers, 287–289,
    330–331, 333, 336
Fractions of 60 Game, 239–241, 602
Fringo Factory Game Mat, 281, 603, 616
Functions
  composite, 378–381, 386–387, 398–399,
    402–405
  graphing, 354–355, 362–363, 370–373,
    378–381, 396–397, 399, 402–405,
    410–413, 415–419, 426–427, 429–433
  inverse, 302–303, 380–381
  nonlinear, 410–413
  rules, 302–303, 354–355, 362–363,
    370–371, 378–381, 386–387, 395–405,
    410–413, 416–419, 427, 429, 431, 433
  standard notation, 398–401
  tables, 370–371, 378–381, 386–387,
    396–401, 410–415, 426–427, 429,
    431–433

G

Galileo Lesson Plans, 461
Gallon, 494–495, 589
Game Mats
  Busy Bee, 15, 601, 630
  Cosmic Cafe, 259–260, 602, 604
  Cube-O-Mat, 21–22, 601, 606

  Discount, 183–184, 602, 608
  Equivalence 1, 248–249, 602, 610
  Equivalence 2, 245–246, 602, 611
  Find the Treasure, 220, 602, 612
  5% Tax, 177–178, 602, 614
  Fringo Factory, 281, 603, 616
  Harder Cosmic Cafe, 267–268, 602, 605
  Harder Cube-O-Mat, 21–22, 601, 607
  Harder Discount, 602, 609
  Harder Find the Treasure, 220, 602, 613
  Harder 5% Tax, 178, 602, 615
  Harder Fringo Factory, 281, 603, 617
  Harder Routes, 272, 603, 627
  Harder Transaction, 104, 602, 629
  Hockey, 352, 603, 618–619
  Marathon 1, 17, 601, 620
  Marathon 2, 17, 601, 621
  Pentathlon, 315–316, 603, 622–623
  Roller Coaster 1, 75–76, 601, 624
  Roller Coaster 2, 76, 601, 625
  Routes, 272, 603, 626
  Transaction, 30, 601, 628
Games
  Anything but 10, 274–275, 603
  Approximation, 75, 601
  Circo 11, 265, 288, 602
  Cubo, 18, 416, 420, 601
  Don't Go Over 1000, 35, 90, 601
  $50 Price Game, 184–185, 602
  Find the Function Rule, 386–387, 603
  Fractions of 60, 239–241, 602
  Get the Point, 374–375, 603
  Greatest Common Factor, 251–253, 602
  Harder Roll a Decimal, 104–105, 601
  Inverso, 335, 603
  Key Keys, 73, 601
  Make 1, 287–289, 603
  Make 2, 295–296, 603
  Make 25, 125–127, 602
  Multifact, 16, 601
  Numbo Jumbo, 92, 95, 601
  Roll a 15, 272–273, 602
  Roll a Problem, 46, 90, 380, 402, 601
  Roll a Problem (Division), 60, 62–63, 90,
    601
  Roll and Divide, 67, 601
  Roll and Regroup a Number, 9, 601
  Roll-Sub-Add, 14, 601
  Three Questions, 473, 603
  Tiling, 215–216, 602
  Tips, 177–179, 602
  Up to 1, 245, 602
  Up to 2, 282–283, 603

Geography Connection, 21, 29, 32, 82, 85, 308–309, 326–327, 424–425, 502–503, 506, 554, 571

Geometry
angles, *See* Angles
area, *See* Area
circle, 420–422, 528–529
circumference, 420–423, 427, 430, 433, 459, 590
classifying figures, 468–475, 509
congruence, 356–361, 526–527, 532–533
cube, 441, 447
decagon, 521
diameter, 420–422, 528, 590
heptagon, 519, 521
hexagon, 519, 521
line, 456, 522–525
line segment, 522
net, 441
nonagon, 521
octagon, 519, 521
parallel, 456, 510
parallelogram, 456–459, 470–473
pentagon, 519, 521
perimeter, 391, 404, 414–415, 448–451, 459, 476, 590
perpendicular, 457
plane, 523–524
point, 522–525
Pythagorean Theorem, 538–539
quadrilateral, 456–459, 470–475, 521
radius, 421, 528
ray, 503, 525
rectangle, 470–473
rectangular prism, 445
reflection, 357–358, 360–361
rhombus, 470–473
rotation, 356–358, 360–361, 502–503
similarity, 328–329, 526–527
spatial visualization, 6–7, 139, 441
square, 470–473, 478–481
symmetry, 357–361
translation, 356–358, 360–361
trapezoid, 459, 464–465, 470–473
triangle, 460–463, 468–469, 472–475, 509, 521
vertex, 406
volume, 444–451, 496–497
Geometry (book), 457
Geometry (Internet site), 499
Geometry Inventory, 530
Get the Point Game, 374–375, 603
Gifted & Talented, 35, 39, 85, 103, 147, 160,

179, 192, 212, 215, 225, 240, 242, 269, 307, 316, 323, 359, 390, 445, 458, 465, 501, 521, 531, 539
Gold and Silver, 126
A Grain of Rice, 365
Gram, 112–113, 490–492, 588
Graphing, 342–349, 352–355, 374–375, 397, 399
bar, 342–345, 349
circle, 342–345, 534–537
composite functions, 378–379, 402–403
coordinate, 352–355, 374–375, 402–403
functions, 354–355, 362–363, 370–373, 378–381, 396–397, 399, 402–405, 410–413, 415–419, 426–427, 429–433
inverse functions, 380–381
line, 344, 346, 348–349, 354–355, 364–369, 377, 410
linear functions, 354–355, 362–363, 370–373, 378–381, 396–397, 399, 402–405, 415–419, 426–427, 429–433
negative numbers, 368–375
nonlinear functions, 410–413
perimeter function, 414–415
picture, 347, 349
temperature, 424–425
Graph Power, 372, 536
Greatest Common Factor Game, 251–253, 602
The Greedy Triangle, 518
Grids
area, 466–467
coordinates, 353–355, 374–375, 402–405
Gulliver's Travels, 302

H

Hands on Math 3, 403
Harder Cosmic Cafe Game Mat, 267–268, 602, 615
Harder Cube-O-Mat Game Mat, 21–22, 601, 607
Harder Find the Treasure Game Mat, 220, 602, 613
Harder 5% Tax Game Mat, 178, 602, 615
Harder Fringo Factory Game Mat, 281, 603, 617
Harder Roll a Decimal Game, 104–105, 601
Harder Routes Game Mat, 272, 603, 627
Harder Transaction Game Mat, 104, 602, 629
Hectogram, 491, 588
Hectoliter, 588

Hectometer, 112–113
Heptagon, 519, 521
Hexagon, 519, 521
The Hoboken Chicken Emergency, 312
Hockey Game Mat, 352, 603, 618–619
Hour, 494–495
How Much, How Many?, 122
How Much Is a Million?, 155
How to Count Sheep Without Falling Asleep, 34
How to Get Fabulously Rich, 535
Hundred-millions, 8
Hundred-thousands, 8
Hundreds, 8–9
Hundredths, 10–11
Hypotenuse, 538–539

I

If You Made a Million, 193
Improper fractions, 280–283
In the Neighborhood, 276
Inch, 120–121, 494–495, 589
Inflation: When Prices Go Up, Up, Up, 198
Informal Assessment, 11, 19, 39, 47, 73, 83, 89, 109, 115, 123, 135, 161, 163, 181, 207, 209, 227, 249, 257, 263, 277, 281, 285, 297, 301, 313, 329, 345, 347, 361, 367, 377, 381, 389, 415, 423, 443, 463, 467, 475, 483, 509, 513, 525, 537
Integers, 82–85, 87–89, 91, 93, 96, 156, 346, 369, 370–373, 375, 378–381, 390, 397, 399, 426–429, 432–433
Integrated Problem Solving, 22–23, 38–39, 70–71, 86–87, 108–109, 140–141, 150–151, 188–189, 206–207, 220–221, 224–225, 246–247, 256–257, 268–269, 284–285, 376–377, 384–385, 408–409, 442–443, 474–475, 500–501
Interest, 190–195, 200–201, 229–231, 233 235
Internet
Current U.S. Weather, 351
Eisenhower National Clearinghouse, 5, 333
Galileo Lesson Plans, 461
Geometry, 499
Interpreting data, 388
Intuitive geometry, 374–375
Inverse functions, 302–303, 380–381
graphing, 380–381
Inverso Game, 335, 603

Is a Blue Whale the Biggest Thing There Is?, 398
Is Business Booming? Act It Out, 350–353
Isosceles triangles, 468–469

J

Jason and the Money Tree, 111

K

Key Keys Game, 73, 601
Kid Power, 178
The *Kids' Complete Guide to Money*, 117
Kid's Money Book, 184
Kilogram, 491–492, 588
Kiloliter, 490, 588
Kilometer, 112, 491–492, 588

L

Language Arts Connection, 88, 328, 504
Laser disc, 41, 50, 65, 79, 85, 103, 149, 182,
    239, 250, 267, 283, 366, 479
    *Core Concepts in Math: Mastering
        Decimals and Percents*, 182
    *Core Concepts in Math: Mastering
        Equations, Roots, and Exponents*, 149
    *Core Concepts in Math: Mastering
        Fractions*, 267
    *Core Concepts in Math: Mastering
        Informal Geometry*, 441
    *Core Concepts in Math: Problem Solving
        Series*, 41
    *Core Concepts in Math: Problem Solving
        with Tables, Graphs, and Statistics*, 366
    *Modumath: Arithmetic, Adding and
        Subtracting Decimal Fractions*, 103
    *Modumath: Arithmetic, Changing
        Fractions to Decimals*, 283
    *Modumath: Arithmetic, Dividing Whole
        Numbers*, Part 1, 50
    *Modumath: Arithmetic, Multiplying
        Fractions*, 65, 239
    *Modumath: Arithmetic, Renaming
        Fractions*, 250
    *Modumath: Arithmetic, Rounding
        Numbers*, 79
    Modumath: Arithmetic, Signed Numbers,
        85
    Modumath: Arithmetic, Square Roots, 479

Learning Styles, 6, 10, 25, 56, 141, 177, 180,
    196, 267, 273, 358, 444, 477, 509, 520
Least common multiples, 261, 266–267
Length
    customary, 494–495, 589
    determining from given areas, 476–477
    estimating, 5, 7, 77, 110, 114, 121, 122, 161,
        254, 386, 420, 449, 464, 483, 494
    metric, 112–113, 490–493, 588
Let's Investigate Area and Volume, 445
Let's Investigate Calculators, 84
Let's Investigate Circles, 529
Let's Investigate Quadrilaterals, 512
The Librarian Who Measured the Earth, 421
Library Research Project, 434–435
Linear functions-graphing, 354–355,
    362–363, 370–373, 378–381, 396–397,
    399, 402–405, 415–419, 426–427,
    429–433
Line graphs, 344, 346, 348–349, 354–355,
    364–369, 377, 410
Lines, 522–523
    parallel, 456, 510
    perpendicular, 457
    skew, 522
    of symmetry, 357–361
Line segments, 522
Liter, 112–113, 490–491, 588
Literature Connection, 5, 9, 17, 18, 22, 26, 29,
    34, 38, 40, 46, 51, 55, 60, 66, 69, 72, 75,
    80, 83, 84, 102, 108, 111, 114, 117, 122,
    126, 128, 131, 134, 140, 144, 150, 152,
    155, 160, 178, 180, 184, 187, 190, 193,
    198, 206, 210, 218, 238, 245, 248, 251,
    256, 260, 262, 271, 275, 278, 280, 282,
    286, 290, 296, 300, 302, 312, 315, 350,
    362, 365, 371, 375, 378, 384, 386, 398,
    402, 408, 414, 421, 440, 445, 452, 460,
    466, 470, 474, 476, 480, 482, 488, 492,
    496, 498, 502, 508, 512, 518, 524, 529,
    535 *See also individual book titles.*
The Liter Is, 492
Lunch Money, 108

M

Magnification, 152
Make 1 Game, 287–289, 603
Make 25 Game, 125–127, 602
Make 2 Game, 295–296, 603
Maps, 21, 32, 34, 146, 308–309, 326, 554
The Map with a Gap, 190

Marathon 1 Game Mat, 17, 601, 620
Marathon 2 Game Mat, 17, 601, 621
Mass/weight
    customary units, 494–495, 589
    estimating, 5, 110, 114, 122, 135, 254, 294,
        442–443, 483, 501
    metric units, 112–113, 490–493, 588
Mastering Math, 68
Mastering Math II, 491
Mastery Checkpoints, 7, 11, 13, 31, 43, 53, 57,
    71, 77, 105, 119, 133, 157, 189, 203, 265,
    289, 307, 317, 353, 355, 401, 517
A Material Problem with Fractions Act It
    Out, 298–301
Math Ace, 259
Math-a-Magic Number Tricks for Magicians,
    296
Math and Society, 160
Math Connection, 494
Math Curse, 238
Mathematics, 502
*Mathematics Curriculum and Teaching
    Program*, 271, 473
Math for Every Kid, 508
Math for Smarty Pants, 251
Math Fun: Test Your Luck, 271
Math Fun with Money Puzzlers, 69
Math Fun with Trick Lines and Shapes, 524
Math Journal, 5–6, 9, 22, 35, 38, 46, 70, 74,
    89, 99, 108, 127, 140, 150, 161, 188, 192,
    203, 206, 210–211, 213, 220, 224, 241,
    246, 256, 261, 268, 283–284, 289, 296,
    329, 345, 349, 376, 384, 408–409, 447,
    455, 467, 474, 480–481, 495, 497, 500,
    509, 524–525, 527, 537, 551
Mathematical Reasoning, 9, 14, 35, 46, 63, 73,
    75, 95, 105, 127, 179, 245, 265, 272,
    274, 282–283, 296, 374–375, 387, 473
Math Manipulatives, 111, 264, 445, 529–530,
    532, 535
The Math Map Trip, 453
Math Mini-Mysteries, 29
*Math Mystery Theatre, The Curse of King
    Tut Tut Cubit*, 450
*Math Mystery Theatre, Decimal
    Disagreement: The War of the Rose*,
    125
*Math Mystery Theatre: Decimal Disaster, or
    the Case of the Maltese Fraction*, 139
*Math Mystery Theatre: Great Numbers Bank
    Robbery*, 223
*Math Mystery Theatre: Mathman and
    Chickadee vs. the Questioner*, 65

Math Mystery Theatre: Mission Division: World's Secret Formula, 61
Math Mystery Theatre: The Ten Percenters, 107
MathSmart Junior, 83
Math Wiz, 384
Math Workshop, 519
Matilda, 114
Maya numeration system, 99
The Meal a Mile Long, 210
Mean, 314–323
Measurement
   angles, 506–509, 518–520, 541, 546, 549
   converting units, 490–495, 588–589
   cubic units, 444–445
   customary units, 120–121, 494–495, 589
   metric units, 112–113, 122–123, 490–493, 588
   precision, 120–123
   square units, 438–439
   temperature, 368–369, 390, 424–425, 483, 591
   time, 155, 494–495
Measuring Up, 482
Median, 318–323
Meeting Individual Needs
   At Risk, 38, 76, 296, 536
   ESL, 23, 45, 52, 88, 132, 202, 221, 259, 388, 475, 513
   Gifted & Talented, 35, 39, 85, 103, 147, 160, 179, 192, 212, 215, 225, 240, 242, 269, 307, 316, 323, 359, 390, 445, 458, 465, 501, 521, 531, 539
   Learning Styles, 6, 10, 25, 56, 141, 177, 180, 196, 267, 273, 358, 444, 477, 509, 520
   Special Needs, 19, 26, 37, 41, 55, 63, 104, 119, 133, 143, 147, 153, 188, 214, 223, 247, 252, 260, 285, 287, 306, 313, 321, 353, 378, 380, 404, 412, 418, 422, 441, 455, 459, 462, 466, 481, 492, 505, 516
Megagram, 588
Megaliter, 491, 588
Megameter, 491, 588
Melisande, 386
Melting Ice Cubes Project, 550–551
Mental Math, *See every lesson* Warm-Up
Mental Math Games, 74
Meter, 112–113, 490–492, 588
Metric units, *See* Measurement
Micro Aliens: Dazzling Journeys with an Electron Microscope, 488
Microgram, 588
Microliter, 491, 588

Micrometer, 491, 588
Mid-Unit Review, 48–49, 136–137, 200–201, 292–293, 394–397, 484–487
Mighty Mac Cosmic Geometry, 444
Mighty Math Calculating Crew, 33
Mighty Math Geometry, 359
Mile, 33, 494–495, 589
Milligram, 112–113, 491–492, 588
Milliliter, 490–492, 588
Millimeter, 112–113, 490–492, 588
Millions, 8
Minute, 494–495
Mixed numbers, 12–13, 280–283, 286–291
   addition, 286–289, 290, 298, 330–331, 333, 335–336, 407, 409
   division, 305–306
   multiplication, 305–306
   subtraction, 287–289, 330–331, 333, 336
Mixed practice
   addition and subtraction, 15, 30
   addition, subtraction, and multiplication, 43, 47
   all operations, 19–20, 74, 90, 138, 204–205, 217, 255, 382, 388, 401, 423, 438, 455
   decimals, 126, 133–134, 278, 389
   fractions, 278, 407, 498
   multiplication and division, 17, 61, 93
Mode, 318–323
Modumath: Arithmetic, Adding and Subtracting Decimal Fractions, 103
Modumath: Arithmetic, Changing Fractions to Decimals, 283
Modumath: Arithmetic, Dividing Whole Numbers, Part 1, 50
Modumath: Arithmetic, Multiplying Fractions, 239
Modumath: Arithmetic, Renaming Fractions, 250
Modumath: Arithmetic, Rounding Numbers, 79
Modumath: Arithmetic, Signed Numbers, 85
Modumath: Arithmetic, Square Roots, 479
Money, computing with, 38–39, 45, 55, 58, 64–65, 68–69, 86–87, 91, 94, 104–107, 119, 124–125, 128, 132–133, 134–135, 157, 165, 168–169, 176–203, 206–207, 228–235, 284–285, 294–295, 304, 313–315, 350, 392–393, 405 *See also* Addition, Division, Multiplication, *and* Subtraction
Mr. Muddle's Extra-Large Problems Thinking Story, 22–23, 38–39, 70–71, 86–87

Multifact Game, 16, 601
Multiples, 218–219
   least common, 261, 266–267
   of nine, 208–209
Multiplication
   basic facts, 16–19, 217, 371, 398–399
   by multiples and powers of ten, 36–39, 41, 44, 72, 74, 110, 112–113, 126–127, 136–137, 164–166, 170–171, 176, 180, 351, 354, 423, 482, 488–490
   checking products, 226–227
   decimals, 115–119, 126–127, 130–133, 136–137, 164, 166, 170–171, 178, 279, 389, 439, 455
   estimating products, 47, 76–79, 84–85, 93, 115, 136, 162–163, 178, 314, 389, 455
   exponents, 152–157, 162–163, 167
   fractions, 239, 242, 254, 257, 292–293, 302–303, 306–307, 330–333, 335–337
   missing factor problems, 204–205, 302–303, 380–381, 399, 476–477
   money, 68, 91, 94, 119, 392–393
   multidigit multipliers, 42–43, 60–61, 74, 92, 146, 217,
   negative numbers, 88–89, 91, 93, 96, 370–371
   one-digit multipliers, 40–43, 92, 209, 488
Multiplicative inverse, 304–305
Music Connection, 14, 16

N

Negative numbers, 82–85, 87–89, 91, 93, 96, 156, 346, 369, 370–373, 375, 378–381, 390, 397, 399, 426–429, 432–433
   addition, 82–84, 89, 91, 93, 96, 156, 346, 371, 378–379, 397, 399
   graphing, 368–375, 378–381, 402–405, 426–428, 432–433
   multiplication, 88–89, 91, 93, 96, 370–371
   subtraction, 84–85, 91, 93
Nets, 441
Nonagons, 521
Nonlinear functions—graphing, 410–413
Number
   exponential form, 143–145, 148–149, 151–154, 164–165, 167, 169–170
   exponents, 143–157, 162–165, 167, 169–170, 412–413, 490
   negative numbers, 82–85, 87–89, 91, 93, 96, 156, 346, 369, 370–373, 375, 378–381, 390, 397, 399, 426–429, 432–433

number line, 12, 79–80, 82
   scientific notation, 162–163
Number line, 12, 79–80, 82
NumberMaze, 255
Number Munchers, 37
Number patterns, 265, 357, 400–401
Number sense
   comparing/ordering, 9–11, 12–13, 105,
      245, 258–259, 261, 267, 282–283, 285
   estimating/approximating, 47, 64, 68–69,
      76–77, 79, 81, 84–85, 90, 93, 96,
      102–103, 106–107, 115, 129, 130, 134,
      136, 138, 154–155, 161–163, 178,
      204–205, 222–223, 242, 267, 270–271,
      274–275, 278, 280–283, 286–287, 290,
      298, 314–315, 335, 368–369, 375, 389,
      410–412, 424, 455–457, 460–461
   place value, 8–11, 35, 46, 63, 75, 105, 179
   rounding, 78–81, 93, 131, 478–479
Number theory
   common factors, 251–254, 498
   common multiples, 258–261, 266–269
   composite numbers, 222–223
   divisibility, 208–218
   factors, 218–225
   prime factorization, 222–225, 229, 231,
      233, 261, 266
   prime numbers, 222–223
   square roots, 478–481, 539
Numbo Jumbo, 95, 601
Numeration systems, 98–99

O

Obtuse angles, 503–506, 509
Octagons, 521
Ones, 8, 11
On Target Multiply and Divide, 211
On the Move Thinking Story, 442–443,
   474–475, 500–501
Operation Neptune, 186
Operational facts, 15, 17, 19
Operations—order of, 406–407
Ordering
   decimals, 12, 245, 282–283
   fractions, 245, 259, 282–283
Ordered pairs, 353–355, 362–363, 370–371,
   386
Organizing and Interpreting Points on a
   Graph, 350
Origami in the Classroom, 414
Ounce, 494–495, 589
Our Solar System, 278

P

Pablo Picasso, 474
Parallel lines, 456, 510
Parallelograms, 456–459, 470–473
   area, 457–458, 460, 472, 476, 485, 540,
      542–543, 548, 590
Partial product, 42
Patterns, computational, 20, 23, 25–26, 29,
   36–37, 41, 44, 60–61, 64, 72, 74,
   110–111, 118, 126, 164, 166, 204–205,
   319, 332, 351, 354, 362, 382, 407, 419,
   423, 438, 455, 480–481
Patterns, number, 265, 357, 400–401
Pentagons, 519, 521
Pentathlon Game Mat, 315–316, 603,
   622–623
Per capita, 158–159
Percents
   on a calculator, 182–184
   changing to decimals, 176–178, 228, 230,
      232
   discount, 180–190, 192, 197–203,
      228–229, 231–233, 375
   interest, 190–195, 200–201, 229–231,
      233–235
   of a number, 176–177, 182–183, 187, 196,
      200, 202, 205, 228, 230, 232, 276–277,
      345, 383, 405, 535, 547
   reversing, 196–199
   tax, 177, 179, 182–189, 196–203, 228–229,
      231–233, 368–369, 375
Performance Assessment, 49, 63, 81, 87, 91,
   113, 127, 137, 153, 165, 185, 195, 199,
   201, 213, 221, 225, 229, 243, 247, 253,
   261, 269, 279, 291, 293, 303, 307, 317,
   321, 323, 327, 331, 349, 369, 379, 387,
   393, 397, 399, 413, 419, 427, 439, 447,
   451, 455, 459, 465, 471, 487, 489, 493,
   501, 505, 521, 527, 533, 539, 541
Perimeter, 391, 404, 414–415, 448–451, 459,
   476, 590
Perimeter functions—graphing, 414–415
Perpendicular lines, 457
The Phantom Tollbooth, 245
Physical Education Connection, 197, 270,
   290, 320, 346
Pi (π), 422, 459
Picture graph, 347, 349
Pint, 494–495, 589
Place value, 8–11, 35, 46, 63, 75, 105, 179
   decimals, 10–11, 105, 179
   hundred-millions, 8

hundred-thousands, 8
hundreds, 8–9
hundredths, 10–11
millions, 8
ones, 8–11
ten-millions, 8
ten-thousands, 8
tens, 8–10
tenths, 10–11
thousands, 8
thousandths, 10–11
Planes, 523–524
Planning a Trip Project, 172–173
Play with Your Triangle, 218
Points (graphs), 353–355
Points (lines), 522
Polygons—angles in, 518–521
Portfolio Assessment, 15, 27, 35, 49, 67, 91,
   121, 137, 145, 147, 151, 165, 179, 189,
   201, 217, 229, 273, 293, 309, 331, 363,
   373, 397, 405, 411, 425, 427, 477, 481,
   487, 495, 497, 541
Possibilities, 146–147
Pound, 494–495, 589
Powers of ten, 36–37, 110–113, 488–489
Precision of measurement, 120–123
Presidential Puzzles, 375
Prevocational Math Series, 295
Prime factorization, 222–225, 229, 231, 233,
   261, 266
Prime numbers, 222–223
Principal, 190–191
Probability, 270–277
   analyzing, 274–277
Problem of the Day, *See every lesson* Warm-
   Up
Problem Solving
   applications, 5–7, 13, 20–21, 25, 27, 29–34,
      37, 39, 41, 43–45, 49, 51–53, 55, 57, 59,
      61–62, 65–66, 68–69, 75–77, 80–81, 85,
      89, 91, 94, 96–97, 103–104, 106–107,
      113, 119–120, 124–125, 132–133, 135,
      137, 139, 147, 155–158, 160–161, 165,
      168–169, 171, 178, 181, 183–184,
      186–187, 193–195, 198–199, 201–203,
      214–216, 228–230, 232–233, 239–240,
      243, 255, 264, 267, 270–273, 275–277,
      279, 286, 290–291, 293–295, 297,
      307–309, 312–313, 316–318, 320–323,
      325–328, 329, 331, 334, 337, 342–348,
      358, 360, 363–367, 369, 372–373, 379,
      383, 386, 388, 390–393, 400, 403–405,
      414–415, 418–419, 422–425, 427, 432,

441, 447, 453–454, 461–462, 464, 466, 469–472, 476–477, 479, 481–483, 489–491, 493, 495–497, 511–512, 515, 519–520, 535, 539–540, 548, 552–553, 555–565, 567–577, 580, 583–584, 587

  logical reasoning, 40, 91, 95, 207, 242, 274, 362, 473

  multiple solutions, 24, 33, 157, 158, 277, 446

  multi-step problems, 27, 43, 58, 84, 196, 264, 304, 350

  no solutions, 29–30, 53, 199, 229, 324, 470, 477

  Thinking Stories (integrated problem solving), 22–23, 38–39, 70–71, 86–87, 108–109, 140–141, 150–151, 188–189, 206–207, 220–221, 224–225, 246–247, 256–257, 268–269, 284–285, 376–377, 384–385, 408–409, 442–443, 474–475, 500–501

Problem-solving strategies
  check for reasonableness, 45, 77, 133, 257
  choose the operation, 34, 68–69, 106, 290–291
  conduct an experiment, 135, 155
  interpret data, 347, 367, 410
  interpret quotient/remainder, 51–53
  too much information, 44, 414
  use estimation, 41, 66, 389
  use guess and check, 20, 116, 154, 226, 378
  use manipulatives, 448, 506
  use/draw a picture or diagram, 66, 110, 120, 146–147, 214, 438
  use/find a pattern, 142, 145, 388, 400, 456, 522
  use/make a table, 235, 294–295, 373, 521

Products–checking, 226–227

Project, 98–99, 172–173, 234–235, 338–339, 434–435, 550–551
  A Birthday Present, 234–235
  Clever Counting, 98–99
  Fair Advertising, 338–339
  Library Research, 434–435
  Melting Ice Cubes, 550–551
  Planning a Trip, 172–173

Proportions, 324–329

Protractor, 506–508

Pumpkins, 46

Pythagorean Theorem, 538–539

Q

Quadrilateral, 456–459, 470–475, 521

Quart, 494–495, 589

R

Radius, 421, 528

Rajah's Rice, 144

Rand McNally's Children's Atlas of the United States, 26

Rates, 314–317

Ratios, 310–314

Rays, 525

Real-World Connection, 85, 124, 181, 194, 205, 291, 309, 317, 346, 383, 390, 392, 407, 454, 462, 494, 514

Recipes, 290–291

Reciprocal, 304–305
  approximating, 335

Rectangles, 470–473
  area, 438–439, 590

Rectangular prism, 444–447

Reducing fractions, 250–252, 254

Reflection, 356–361

Regrouping, 9

Regular polygons, 520

Rhombus, 470–471

Right angles, 452–453, 503–505, 509

Right triangles, 452–454, 468–469, 538–539
  area, 452–454

Roll a 15 Game, 272–273, 602

Roll a Problem Game, 46, 90, 380, 402, 601

Roll a Problem Game (Division), 60, 62–63, 90, 601

Roll and Divide Game, 66–67, 601

Roll and Regroup a Number Game, 9, 601

Roller Coaster 1 Game Mat, 75–76, 601, 624

Roller Coaster 2 Game Mat, 76, 601, 625

Roll-Sub-Add Game, 14–15, 601

Roman numerals, 98

Rotation, 356–358, 360–361, 502–503

Rounding, 78–81, 93, 131, 478–479
  to hundred thousands, 79
  to hundreds, 78–79
  to hundredths, 131
  to millions, 79
  to tens, 78
  to thousands, 78–79
  to whole numbers, 78–79, 93

Routes Game Mat, 272, 603, 626

S

Sales tax, 177, 179, 182–189, 196–203, 228–229, 231–233, 368–369, 375

Sarah, Plain and Tall, 38

Savings accounts, 234–235

Scalene triangles, 468–469

Science Connection, 148–149, 153, 197, 320, 342–343, 368–369, 376, 383, 386, 424

The Science Chef, 290

Scientific notation, 162–163

Sea Squares, 480

Sector, 535

Self Assessment, 15, 17, 19, 23, 57, 141, 289, 385, 401, 409

Sequence, 400

Shapes
  angles in, 518–521
  decagons, 521
  heptagons, 519, 521
  hexagons, 519, 521
  nonagons, 521
  octagons, 519, 521
  parallelograms, 456–459, 470–473
  pentagons, 519, 521
  properties, 473
  quadrilaterals, 456–459, 470–475, 521
  rectangles, 470–473
  regular polygons, 520
  rhombus, 470–473
  trapezoids, 459, 464–465, 470–473
  triangles, 460–463, 468–469, 472–475, 509, 521

Sideways Arithmetic from Wayside School, 256

Similar figures, 328–329, 526–527

Skew lines, 522

Skyscraper, 5

Smart Spending, 102

The Sneaky Square and 113 Other Math Activities for Kids, 18

Social Studies Connection, 9, 61, 78, 98, 110, 145, 158–160, 183, 240, 306–307, 322, 325, 344, 368, 428, 439, 490, 534–535, 547

Software, 20, 24, 33, 37, 50, 65, 68, 72, 74, 79, 85, 103, 142, 149, 182, 186, 211, 219, 239, 250, 255, 259, 267, 271, 276, 283, 295, 319, 359, 372, 391, 403, 422, 441, 444, 453, 457, 473, 479, 491, 503, 507, 519, 530, 536, 542

Classroom Grade Level Math Programs, 142, 507
Core Concepts in Math: Mastering Decimals and Percents, 182
Core Concepts in Math: Mastering Equations, Roots, and Exponents, 149
Core Concepts in Math: Mastering Fractions, 267
Core Concepts in Math: Mastering Informal Geometry, 441
Cosmic Golf, 503
Eagle Eye Mystery, 422
Five in a Row, 219
Geometry, 457, 499
Geometry Inventory, 530
Graph Power, 372, 536
Hands on Math 3, 403
Home Grade Level Math Programs, 542
In The Neighborhood, 276
Mastering Math, 68
Mastering Math II, 491
Math Ace, 259
Mathematics Curriculum and Teaching Program, 271, 473
The Math Map Trip, 453
Math Workshop, 519
Mental Math Games, 74
Mighty Mac Cosmic Geometry, 444
Mighty Math Calculating Crew, 33
Mighty Math Geometry, 359
Modumath: Arithmetic, Adding and Subtracting Decimal Fractions, 103
Modumath: Arithmetic, Changing Fractions to Decimals, 283
Modumath: Arithmetic, Dividing Whole Numbers, Part 1, 50
Modumath: Arithmetic, Multiplying Fractions, 239
Modumath: Arithmetic, Renaming Fractions, 250
Modumath: Arithmetic, Rounding Numbers, 79
Modumath: Arithmetic, Signed Numbers, 85
Modumath: Arithmetic, Square Roots, 479
NumberMaze, 255
Number Munchers, 37
On Target Multiply and Divide, 211
Operation Neptune, 186
Prevocational Math Series, 295
Spotlight: Fractions and Decimals, 319
The Table Top, Senior Edition, 391
Turbo Math Facts, 20
Word Problem Square Off: Level A, 24

Special Needs, 19, 26, 37, 41, 55, 63, 104, 119, 133, 143, 147, 153, 188, 214, 223, 247, 252, 260, 285, 287, 306, 313, 321, 353, 378, 380, 404, 412, 418, 422, 441, 455, 459, 462, 466, 481, 492, 505, 516
Spotlight: Fractions and Decimals, 319
Spreadsheets, 65, 69, 112, 118, 160, 177–178, 181, 184, 194, 245, 267, 275–276, 283, 291, 295–296, 306, 309, 312, 315, 325–326, 365, 369, 371, 379, 383, 421–422, 425, 445, 519, 535–536
Square roots, 478–481, 539
  symbol, 479
Square units (area), 439
Squares, 470–471, 590
Standard form, 8, 11
Standard notation-functions, 398–399
Statistics
  averages, 314–324, 331, 334, 337, 365, 371, 407
  bar graphs, 342–345, 349
  charts/tables, 85, 112, 134, 149, 153, 159, 209, 213, 235, 276, 307, 309, 312–313, 325, 327, 342–343, 345, 351, 364, 372, 383, 388–389, 390–395, 414–415, 421, 424, 435, 479–481, 497–498, 521, 535–537, 547
  circle graphs, 342–345, 534–537
  collecting data, 22–23, 276–277, 344–345
  line graphs, 344, 346, 348–349, 354–355, 364–369
  picture graphs, 347, 349
  tallying, 276
Straight angles, 514–517
Straight lines, 524
The Story of the New York Stock Exchange, 280
Subtraction
  basic facts, 14–15, 18–19, 217, 371, 380–381
  decimals, 102–107, 133, 164–166, 169–170, 228–233, 278–279, 290, 298
  estimating differences, 36, 103, 106–107, 290, 298
  fractions (like denominators), 262–263, 330, 336
  fractions (unlike denominators), 262–265, 278, 293, 330–331, 336, 498
  missing term problems, 205, 380–381, 399
  mixed numbers, 287–289, 330–331, 333, 336
  money, 68–69, 104, 107, 168

multidigit numbers, 28–31, 92, 142–143, 149, 217, 310–311, 351, 354–355, 518
negative numbers, 82–84, 89, 91, 93, 96, 156, 346, 390
Supergrandpa, 128
Supplementary angles, 514–517
Surface area, 440–443, 446, 550–551
Surplus, 158–160
Symmetry, 356–361

T

Tables, *See* Statistics
The Table Top, Senior Edition, 391
Take Me to Your Liter: Math and Science Jokes, 140
Tax rate, 186–187
Technology Connection, 5, 20, 24, 33, 37, 41, 50, 61, 65, 68, 74, 79, 85, 103, 107, 125, 139, 142, 149, 182, 186, 211, 219, 223, 239, 250, 255, 259, 267, 271, 276, 283, 295, 319, 351, 359, 366, 372, 391, 403, 422, 441, 444, 450, 453, 457, 461, 473, 479, 491, 499, 503, 507, 519, 530, 536, 542
  Laser disc, 41, 50, 65, 79, 85, 103, 182, 239, 250, 267, 283, 366, 479
  Software, 20, 24, 33, 37, 50, 65, 68, 72, 74, 79, 85, 103, 142, 149, 182, 186, 211, 219, 239, 250, 255, 259, 267, 271, 276, 283, 295, 319, 359, 372, 391, 403, 417, 422, 441, 444, 453, 457, 473, 479, 491, 503, 507, 519, 530, 536, 542
  Video, 50, 61, 65, 79, 85, 103, 107, 125, 223, 239, 250, 271, 283, 450, 473, 479
Temperature
  average monthly, 424–425
  Celsius, 82, 91, 94, 368–369, 390–393, 424, 483, 591
  Fahrenheit, 390–393, 591
  graphing, 424–425
Ten-millions, 8
Ten-thousands, 8
Tens, 8–10
Tenths, 10–11
Thinking Story, 22–23, 38–39, 70–71, 86–87, 108–109, 140–141, 150–151, 188–189, 206–207, 220–221, 224–225, 246–247, 256–257, 268, 269, 284–285, 376–377, 384–385, 408–409, 442–443, 474–475, 500–501
  Competition, 188–189, 206–207, 220–221, 224–225

Diet for a Small Terrier, 376–377, 384–385, 408–409

The Efficiency Experts, 108–109, 140–141, 150–151

Energy Savers, 246–247, 256–257, 268–269, 284–285

Mr. Muddle's Extra-Large Problems, 22–23, 38–39, 70–71, 86–87

On the Move, 442–443, 474–475, 500–501

Thousands, 8

Thousandths, 10–11

Three-dimensional figures
    classifying, 472
    cubes, 441, 447
    nets, 441
    visualizing, 6–7, 139, 441

Three Questions Game, 473, 603

Tiling Game, 215–216, 602

Timetable, 312–313

Tips Game, 177–179, 602

Toothpaste Millionaire, 72

Top Dog, 29

Transaction Game Mat, 30, 601, 628

Translation, 356–361

Trapezoids, 459, 464–465, 470–473
    area, 464–465, 476, 590

Tree diagram, 146

Triangles, 460–463, 468–469, 472–475, 509, 521
    acute triangles, 509
    area, 460–463, 476, 590
    copying, 532–533
    equilateral triangles, 468–469
    hypotenuse, 538–539
    isosceles triangles, 468–469
    obtuse triangles, 509
    Pythagorean theorem, 539
    right triangles, 452–454, 468–469, 509, 538–539
    scalene triangles, 468–469

Triangles and Pyramids, 452

Tricky Nines Act It Out, 208–209

Turbo Math Facts, 20

263 Brain Busters: Just How Smart Are You, Anyway?, 180

U

Unit Practice, 92–95, 166–169, 230–231, 332–335, 428–431, 542–547

Unit Review, 90–91, 164–165, 228–229, 330–331, 426–427, 540–541

Unit Test, 96–97, 170–171, 232–233, 336–337, 432–433, 548–549

Unit Wrap-Up, 98–99, 172–173, 234–235, 338–339, 434–435, 550–551

Up to 1 Game, 245, 602

Up to 2 Game, 282–283, 603

V

Variables, 50, 204–205, 239, 324, 326, 328, 346, 355, 362–363, 370–371, 378–381, 386–387, 390–393, 395–405, 410–419, 421–422, 426–427, 429–433, 438, 444–445, 453, 457, 460, 464–465, 472, 476, 519, 590–591

Venn Diagram, 210–211

Vertex, 506

Vertical angles, 510–513

Video, 50, 61, 65, 79, 85, 103, 107, 125, 139, 223, 239, 250, 271, 283, 450, 473, 479
    Mathematics Curriculum and Teaching Program, 271, 473
    Math Mystery Theatre: The Curse of King Tut Tut Cubit, 450
    Math Mystery Theatre: Decimal Disagreement: The War of the Rose, 125
    Math Mystery Theatre: Decimal Disaster, or the Case of the Maltese Fraction, 139
    Math Mystery Theatre: Great Numbers Bank Robbery, 223
    Math Mystery Theatre: Mathman and Chickadee vs. The Questioner, 65
    Math Mystery Theatre: Mission Division: World's Secret Formula, 61
    Math Mystery Theatre: The Ten Percenters, 107
    Modumath: Arithmetic, Adding and Subtracting Decimal Fractions, 103
    Modumath: Arithmetic, Changing Fractions to Decimals, 283
    Modumath: Arithmetic, Dividing Whole Numbers, Part 1, 50
    Modumath: Arithmetic, Multiplying Fractions, 239
    Modumath: Arithmetic, Renaming Fractions, 250
    Modumath: Arithmetic, Rounding Numbers, 79
    Modumath: Arithmetic, Signed Numbers, 85
    Modumath: Arithmetic, Square Roots, 479

Volume, 112–113, 444–451, 490–497
    cubic units, 444–451, 588
    customary, 589
    estimating, 452, 496–497
    metric, 112–113, 588

W

Weight/mass
    customary, 494–495, 589
    estimating, 5, 110, 114, 122, 135, 254, 294, 442–443, 483, 501
    metric, 112–113, 490–493, 588

The Westing Game, 150

What Do You Mean by Average?, 60

What's Cooking, Jenny Archer?, 371

Whole numbers and fractions, 238–241

Willoughby, Stephen, T19, T21, T22, 5, 25, 87, 145, 219, 358, 392, 480, 531

Woodsong, 300

Woodworking for Kids, 440

Word Problem Square Off: Level A, 24

Y

Yard, 494–495, 589

You Can't Count a Billion Dollars, 9

Yuki numeration system, 99

SCOPE & SEQUENCE

	K		Level 1				Level 2				Level 3				Level 4						Level 5						Level 6						Glencoe*		
Units	1	2	1	2	3	4	1	2	3	4	1	2	3	4	1	2	3	4	5	6	1	2	3	4	5	6	1	2	3	4	5	6	6	7	8
Addition (whole numbers)																																			
Meaning of addition	•	•	•																																
Basic facts		✓	✓	•	✓	•	✓	•	•	•	✓	•	•	•	✓	•	✓	•	•	•	•	•					•	•	•	•	•	•			
Missing addend problems	•	•		•	✓		•	•	•	•	•	•	•	•	•	•	•	•			•	•					•	•	•	•	•	•			
Three or more addends			•	•		•	•	•	•	✓	•	•	•	•	•	•	•	•			•	•					•	•	•	•		•		•	•
Two-digit numbers			•	✓	✓	•	✓	✓	•	•	•	•	•	•	✓	•	•	•	•		•	•					•	•	•	•	•	•		•	•
Three-digit numbers							✓	✓	•	•	•	✓	•	•	•	•	•	•	•		✓	•	•	•			✓	•	•	•	•	•		•	•
Greater numbers								•	✓	•	•	•	•	•	•	•	•	•	•		✓	•	•				✓	•	•	•	•	•		•	•
Adding money	•	✓	•	✓	✓	•	•	•	•	•	•	•	•	•	•	•	•	•			•	•					•	•	•	•	•	•		•	•
Estimating sums			•	•	•		•	•	✓		✓		•	•	✓	•	•	•	•		✓	•					•	•	•		•			•	•
Algebra																																			
Properties of whole numbers			•	•		•	•	•		•		•		•		•		•	•		•	•					•							•	•
Integers (negative numbers)	•		•		•		•		•	•		•	•		•		•		•		•	•					•		•		•			•	•
Operations with integers										•					•	•		•			•						•	•		•				•	•
Missing term problems	•	•	•	✓	•	•	•	•	•	•	•	•	•	•	•	•	•	•	•		•	•	•				•	•	•	•	•	•		•	•
Make and solve number sentences and equations			•	•	•	•	•	•	•	•	•	•	•	•	•	•	•	•			•	•					•	•	•	•	•	•		•	•
Variables										•	•	•	•	•	•	•	•	•	•	•	•	•	•	•			•	•	•	•	•	•		•	•
Parentheses and order of operations										•	•	•	•		•	•		•			•	•		•				•			•	•		•	•
Inverse operations							•	•		•	✓		•	•	•		•	•	•		•						•	•	•					•	•
Function machines/tables	•	•		•	•	•	•	•		•			•	•	•	•	•	•		✓								•	•	✓		•		•	•
Function rules	•	•		•	•	•				•			•		✓		•	•	•	✓	•	•						•	•	✓		•		•	•
Inverse functions							•	•		•	•		•					✓		•		✓						•	•					•	•
Composite functions										•	•		•					✓		•		✓						•						•	•
Coordinate graphing																																			
One quadrant										•	•		•		•	•	•				✓							•		✓		•		•	•
Four quadrants																					✓							•		•		•		•	•
Graphing linear functions															•	✓	•	•	•		✓							•		✓		•		•	•
Graphing nonlinear functions																														•		•			•
Using formulas										•	•		•					•	•	•	•	•						•				•		•	•
Square numbers										•			•		•	•	•			•				•		•				•		•		•	•
Square roots																											•	•		•		•		•	•
Decimals and money																																			
Place value											•		•	•	•	•	•		•		✓	•					•	•	•	•			•	•	•
Comparing and ordering											•	•	✓	•	•	•		•		✓	•	•	✓	•			•	•	•	•			•	•	•
Rounding												•	•			•	•	•	•	•	•	•					•	•	•				•	•	•
Relating decimals and fractions											•	•		•					✓			✓	•	•	•	•			•				•	•	•
Relating decimals and percents																			•					✓	•				•				•	•	•
Adding											✓	•	•	•	•	•	•	•	✓	✓	•	•	•	•		✓	•	•					•	•	•
Estimating sums													•	•	•	•	•	•	✓	•		•	•	•		•	•						•	•	•
Subtracting											✓	•	•	•	•	•	•	•	✓	✓	•	•	•	•		✓	•	•					•	•	•
Estimating differences													•	•		•	•	•	✓		•		•	•		•	•						•	•	•
Multiplying by powers of 10																			✓	✓	•	•	•	•		•	•						•	•	•
Multiplying by a whole number													•		•			•	•	•	✓	•	•	•		✓	•						•	•	•
Multiplying by a decimal															•					•			✓	•		✓	•						•	•	•
Estimating products																•		•	•	✓	•	•	•	•		•	•						•	•	•
Dividing by powers of 10																			✓	✓	•	•	•	•		•	•						•	•	•
Dividing by a whole number																			•	•	•	✓	•	✓	•	•	•						•	•	•
Dividing by a decimal																				•				✓	•								•	•	•
Estimating quotients																			•			•			•	•		•						•	•	•
Identifying and counting currency	•	✓	•	•	✓	✓	•			•	•	•	✓		•	•		•	•		•												•	•	•
Exchanging money	•	•		•	✓	✓	•	•	•	✓	•	•	•	•	•	•	•				•						•	•	•				•	•	•
Making change			•	•	•	✓	•	•	•	•	•	•	•	•	•	•	•		✓	•	•						•						•	•	•
Computing with money			•	✓	✓	✓	•	•	•	•	•	•	•	•	•	•	•	•	✓		•	•	•	•		•	•	•	•	•	•	•	•	•	•
Division (whole numbers)																																			
Meaning of division	•	•		•	•		•	•		•	•																								
Basic facts							•		•	✓	•	•	•	✓	✓	•	•	•	•		•	•					•	•	•	•		•			
Remainders							•	•		•	✓	•	•	✓	✓	•	•	✓	•		•	✓					•	•	•		•				
Missing term problems							•	•		•	•	•	•	•	•	•	•	•			•	•					•	•							
One-digit divisors							•	•		•	•	•	•	•	•	✓	•	✓	•		•	•					✓	•	•	•		•		•	•
Two-digit divisors												•	•			✓	•	✓	•		•	•					•	•	•					•	•
Greater divisors																•		•	•		•	•	•				•	•	•					•	•
Dividing by multiples of 10											•	•		•		•	•	•	•		•	•					•	•	•	•		•		•	•
Dividing money																•	•	•	•		•	✓					•							•	•
Estimating quotients																•	•	•	•		•	•	•	✓	•		•	✓	•						•
Fractions																																			
Fractions of a whole	•	✓		•	•		✓	•		•	✓	•	•		•			•	•		✓						•		•	•			•	•	
Fractions of a set					•			•		•	✓	•	•					•			✓		✓				•			•					
Fractions of a number				•	•	•		•		•	•	•	•	•				•			✓	•		•			•			•					
Comparing/ordering				•			•			•	•		•					•			•						•			•					
Equivalent fractions				•			•			•	•		•					•			•						•			•					
Reduced form																		•			•						•			•					
Mixed numbers and improper fractions									•	•	•							•			•		✓				•			•					
Adding—like denominators											•							✓			•	✓	•				•	•	•	•		•			

Scope & Sequence

	K		Level 1				Level 2				Level 3				Level 4						Level 5						Level 6						Glencoe*		
Units	1	2	1	2	3	4	1	2	3	4	1	2	3	4	1	2	3	4	5	6	1	2	3	4	5	6	1	2	3	4	5	6	6	7	8

Fractions (continued)

	K		L1				L2				L3				L4						L5						L6						G		
Adding—unlike denominators																•			✓			✓	•	•				✓		•	•		•	•	•
Adding mixed numbers																			✓			✓	•	•				✓		•	•		•	•	•
Subtracting—like denominators																			✓			✓	•	•					•	•	•		•	•	•
Subtracting—unlike denominators																			✓			✓	•	•					•	•	•		•	•	•
Subtracting mixed numbers																			✓			✓	•	•					•	•	•		•	•	•
Multiplying by a whole number																							•	•				✓	•	•	•		•	•	•
Multiplying by a fraction or mixed number																•								✓				✓	•	•	•		•	•	•
Reciprocals																												✓					•	•	•
Dividing a fraction by a whole number																												✓					•	•	•
Dividing by a fraction or mixed number																												✓	•				•	•	•

Geometry

	K		L1				L2				L3				L4						L5						L6						G		
Identifying/drawing figures	•	•	•	•	•	•	•	•	•	•	•	•	•	•	•	•	•	•	•	•	•	•	•	•			•						•	•	•
Classifying figures	•	•	•	•	•	•				•			•		•		•	•	•		•												•	•	•
Classifying triangles													•				•				•												•	•	•
Classifying quadrilaterals					•				•				•				•	•		•		•											•	•	•
Solid figures			•		•		•		•				•				•				•		•		•			•	•				•	•	•
Spatial visualization															•	•			•		•		•		•			•	•				•	•	•
Congruence	•	•			•	•		✓					•				•				•												•	•	•
Similarity													•				•					•	•					•					•	•	•
Symmetry	•	•		•	•	•		•					•				•				•							•	•				•	•	•
Translation/reflection/rotation												•				•	•				•							•	•				•	•	•
Measuring and classifying angles													•			•	•				•		•	•								✓	•	•	•
Parallel and perpendicular lines													•				•	•															•	•	•
Relationships with parallel lines																																✓	•	•	•
Perimeter		•			•		•		•				•		•	•	•		•			•		•									•	•	•
Radius and diameter											•	•				•	•				•												•	•	•
Circumference													•	•			•				•												•	•	•
Areas of triangles																					•												•	•	•
Areas of quadrilaterals											•			•	•	•	•	•	•	•	•	•	•	•	•								•	•	•
Surface area																																	•	•	•
Volume													•			•	•		•														•	•	•
Pythagorean Theorem																																	•	•	•

Manipulatives

	K		L1				L2				L3				L4						L5						L6						G		
Used in concept development	•	•	•	•	•	•	•	•	•	•	•	•	•	•	•	•	•	•	•	•	•	•	•	•	•	•	•	•	•	•	•	•	•	•	•
Used in reteaching and individualized instruction	•	•	•	•	•	•	•	•	•	•	•	•	•	•	•	•	•	•	•	•	•	•	•	•	•	•	•	•	•	•	•	•	•	•	•

Measurement

	K		L1				L2				L3				L4						L5						L6						G		
Length																																			
Estimate	✓		•	•	•	•	•				•	•	✓	•	•	•	•	•	•	✓	•	•	•	•	✓	•	•		•		•		•	•	•
Compare	✓		•	•	•	•	•				•	•	✓	•	•	•	•	•	•	•	•	•	•	•			•		•				•	•	•
Use nonstandard units	✓		•	•	•	•	•				•	•	•			•	•		•	•			•	•									•		
Use customary units			•	•	•	•	✓	•	•	•	•	•	•	✓	•	•	•	•	•	•	•	•	•	•	•	•	•	•	•	•	•		•	•	•
Use metric units			•	•	•	•	✓	•	•	•	•	•	•	✓	•	•	•	•	•	✓	•	•	•	•	✓	•	•	•	•	•	•		•	•	•
Mass/Weight																																			
Estimate	✓	•	•			•	•			•	•				•	•	•	•	•		•	•		•			•						•	•	•
Compare	✓	•	•			•	•		•		•		✓	•	•	•		•	•		•	•		•			•						•	•	•
Use nonstandard units	✓	•				•	•				•																						•		
Use customary units			•	•		•		•		•			✓	•	•	•		•	•								•	•	•	•	•		•	•	•
Use metric units			•	•	•	•	•		•		•		✓	•	•	•		•	•								•	•	•	•	•		•	•	•
Capacity																																			
Estimate	•	•		•	•		•			•			•			•					•	•			•		•	•	•		•		•	•	•
Compare				•	•		•			•			•	•		•					•	•			•			•			•		•	•	•
Use nonstandard units				•	•	•							•																				•	•	•
Use customary units				•		•		•		•			•	•	•	•	•	•									•	•	•	•	•		•	•	•
Use metric units				•				•		•			•	•	•	•	•	•									•	•	•	•	•		•	•	•
Temperature																																			
Estimate	•			•	•																												•	•	•
Use degrees Fahrenheit							•			•		•	•		•		•		•		•	•								•	•	•	•	•	•
Use degrees Celsius																					•	•											•	•	•
Converting within customary system							•	•	•		•		•		•	•	•	•	•	•	•	•						•					•	•	•
Converting within metric system							•	•	•		•		•		•	•	•	•	•	•	•	•						•					•	•	•
Telling time																																			
To the hour		✓					•			•	•	✓	•	•		•	•		•																
To the half hour		•					•			•	•	✓	•	•		•	•																		
To the quarter hour		•					•			•	•	✓	•	•		•	•																		
To the minute										✓	•	✓				•	•		•																
Adding and subtracting time			•	•	•	•		•							•	•					•	•			•			•						•	
A.M. and P.M.															•	•					•	•		•			•				•				
Estimating time	•	•	•	•	•	•		•																											
Calculating elapsed time				•	•	•	•	•	•	•	•				•	•	•	•	•	•	•	•	•	•									•	•	•
Reading a calendar	•	•																																	
Reading a map		•		•			•	•	•	•				•	•	•	•				•	•					•	•					•	•	•

✓ indicates Mastery Checkpoints • *Mathematics: Applications and Connections* Courses 1–3, Levels 6–8 © 1999 **Scope & Sequence**

Scope & Sequence

Mental Arithmetic

Skill	K1	K2	L1-1	L1-2	L1-3	L1-4	L2-1	L2-2	L2-3	L2-4	L3-1	L3-2	L3-3	L3-4	L4-1	L4-2	L4-3	L4-4	L4-5	L4-6	L5-1	L5-2	L5-3	L5-4	L5-5	L5-6	L6-1	L6-2	L6-3	L6-4	L6-5	L6-6	G6	G7	G8
Basic fact strategies–addition and subtraction																																			
Use patterns		•	•	•	•	✓	•																										•	•	•
Count on	•	•	✓	✓	✓	✓	•																												
Count up or back		•	✓	✓	✓	✓	•																												
Use doubles				✓	•	✓	•				•	•																							
Use doubles plus 1				✓	•	✓	•					•																							
Make 10	•		•	•	•	•		•																											
Use properties				•	•																														
Use related facts				•	•							•																							
Basic fact strategies–multiplication and division																																			
Use patterns											•		•	•		•																	•	•	•
Use skip-counting						•		•		•			•		•	•																			
Use properties													•			•																			
Use related facts												✓			•	•			•		•														
Chain calculations			•	•	•	•	•	•	•	•	•	•	•	•	•	•	•	•	•	•	•		•	•	•	•	•	•		•	•		•	•	•
Multidigit addition and subtraction								•	•	•	•	•	•	•	•	•	•	•	•	•	•	•	•	•	•	•	•	•	•	•	•	•	•	•	•
Multidigit multiplication and division												•			•	•	•	•	•	•	•	•	•	•	•	•	•	•	•	•	•	•	•	•	•
Multiples and powers of 10					•	✓					•		•	•	•	•	•	•	•	•	•	•	•	•	•	•	•	•	•	•	•	•	•	•	•
Using computational patterns			•	•	•	✓	•	•	•	•	•	•	•	•	•	•	•	•	•	•	•	•	•	•	•	•	•	•	•	•	•	•	•	•	•
Approximation			•	•	•	•	✓	•	•	•	✓	•	•	•	•	•	•	•	•	•	•	•	•	•	•	•	•	•	•	•	•	•	•	•	•
Find a fraction of a number				•	•	•		•					•			•					•						•		•				•	•	•
Find a percent of a number																										•		•	•	•			•	•	•
Use divisibility rules																					•							•	•				•	•	•
Find equivalent fractions, decimals, and percents										•	•						•					•		•			•		•	•			•	•	•

Multiplication (whole numbers)

Skill	K1	K2	L1-1	L1-2	L1-3	L1-4	L2-1	L2-2	L2-3	L2-4	L3-1	L3-2	L3-3	L3-4	L4-1	L4-2	L4-3	L4-4	L4-5	L4-6	L5-1	L5-2	L5-3	L5-4	L5-5	L5-6	L6-1	L6-2	L6-3	L6-4	L6-5	L6-6	G6	G7	G8
Meaning of multiplication		•		•	•	•					•		•			•		•			•														
Basic facts						•				✓		✓	•	•	•	•	✓	•	•	•	•	•	•	•	•	•	•	•	•	•	•	•			
Missing factor problems										•			•	•		•	•	•	•	•	•	•	•	•	•	•	•	•	•	•					
One-digit multipliers										•				✓	•	•	•	•	•	✓	•	•	•	•	✓	•	•	•	•	•	•	•	•	•	•
Two-digit multipliers													•	•	•	•	•	•	•	✓	•	•	•	✓	•	•	•	•	•	•	•	•	•	•	•
Greater multipliers													•	•	•	✓	•	•	✓	•	•	•	✓	•	•	•	•	•	•	•	•	•	•	•	•
Multiplying by multiples of 10										✓	•	•	•	•	•	•	✓	•	•	✓	•	•	✓	•	•	•	•	•	•	•	•	•	•	•	•
Multiplying money										•		•			•	•	•	•	✓	•	•	•	•	•	•			•					•	•	•
Estimating products										•		•		•	•	•	•	•	✓	•	•	•	✓	•	•								•	•	•

Number and numeration

Skill	K1	K2	L1-1	L1-2	L1-3	L1-4	L2-1	L2-2	L2-3	L2-4	L3-1	L3-2	L3-3	L3-4	L4-1	L4-2	L4-3	L4-4	L4-5	L4-6	L5-1	L5-2	L5-3	L5-4	L5-5	L5-6	L6-1	L6-2	L6-3	L6-4	L6-5	L6-6	G6	G7	G8
Reading and writing numbers	✓	•	✓	✓	•	✓	✓		•	✓		•	✓			•	✓				•		✓				✓								
Number lines		•	•	✓	•	•	•	•			•		•		•		•		•		•			•	•		•	•					•	•	•
Counting	✓	•	•	✓	•	•	✓	✓		•	•	✓			•	✓	•				✓														
Skip counting		•	•	•	•	•		•			•	✓	•		•	•																			
Ordinal numbers	•	•	•	•																															
Place value		•		•	•	•	•	•	•		•		•	•	•	•	•		•	✓		•		•	✓	•	•		•			•	•	•	
Roman numerals									•				•			•	•		•																
Comparing and ordering numbers	✓	•		•	•	✓	•	•		•	•	•	•	•		•	•		•	✓		•		✓	•		•	•					•	•	•
Rounding									•		•	•	•	•		•	•	•	•		•	•	•	•					•				•	•	•
Estimation/Approximation		•	•	•	•			•			•		•	•	•	✓	•				✓						•						•	•	•
Integers (negative numbers)			•		•		•		•		•		•		•	•					•			•				•		•			•	•	•
Even/odd numbers			•	•		•		✓	•	•			•		•	•	•	•																	
Prime and composite numbers															•		•					•					•						•	•	•
Factors and prime factorization															•	•	•	•				•					•	•	•				•	•	•
Common factors															•							•						•	•		•		•	•	•
Common multiples															•						•	•						•					•	•	•
Checking divisibility																					•							•	•				•	•	•
Exponents												•					•		•	•				•			•						•	•	•
Exponential notation and scientific notation																•		•										•					•	•	•
Square roots																																	•	•	•

Patterns, Relations, and Functions

Skill	K1	K2	L1-1	L1-2	L1-3	L1-4	L2-1	L2-2	L2-3	L2-4	L3-1	L3-2	L3-3	L3-4	L4-1	L4-2	L4-3	L4-4	L4-5	L4-6	L5-1	L5-2	L5-3	L5-4	L5-5	L5-6	L6-1	L6-2	L6-3	L6-4	L6-5	L6-6	G6	G7	G8
Classifying objects	✓	•	•	•																															
Number patterns	•	•	✓	•	•	•	•	•	•	•	•	•	•	•	•	•	•	•	•	•	•		•	•			•	•					•	•	•
Picture patterns	✓		•	•	•	•																													
Geometric patterns	✓	•	•	•	•			•	✓			•	•	•																			•	•	•
Ordered pairs															•	•	•	•			✓		•	•							•		•	•	•
Graphing ordered pairs															•	•		•	•		✓		•	•								✓	•	•	•
Inequalities	✓	•		•	•	✓	•	•	✓	•	✓	•		•	•	•			•		✓	•		•		•	•		•				•	•	•
Function machines/tables	•	•		•	•	•	•	•	•	•	•	•	•	•	•	•	•	•	•	•	•	✓					•	✓					•	•	•
Function rules	•	•		•	•	•	•	•	•	•	•	•	•	•	•	•	•	•	•	•	✓	•					•	✓					•	•	•
Graphing functions															•			•			✓	•						✓					•	•	•

Probability

Skill	K1	K2	L1-1	L1-2	L1-3	L1-4	L2-1	L2-2	L2-3	L2-4	L3-1	L3-2	L3-3	L3-4	L4-1	L4-2	L4-3	L4-4	L4-5	L4-6	L5-1	L5-2	L5-3	L5-4	L5-5	L5-6	L6-1	L6-2	L6-3	L6-4	L6-5	L6-6	G6	G7	G8
Determining possible outcomes		•				•					•					•	•				•			•		•		•		•			•	•	•
Predicting outcomes		•	•	•			•				•				•	•	•				•			•		•		•		•			•	•	•
Conducting experiments		•	•				•								•						•			•		•		•		•			•	•	•
Experimental probability																					•			•		•		•		•			•	•	•
Theoretical probability																					•			•		•		•		•			•	•	•
Using probability to plan strategies			•	•	•	•		•			•	•	•	•	•	•	•	•	•	•	•	•	•	•	•	•	•	•	•	•	•	•	•	•	•

Problem Solving

Work with various problem types
- Multi-step problems
- Multiple solutions
- No solutions

Use logical reasoning, including:
- Interpreting data
- Checking reasonableness
- Solving problems with too much information
- Interpreting the quotient and remainder
- Choosing the appropriate operation
- Using estimation
- Using guess and check

Choose an appropriate strategy, including:
- Solving a simpler problem
- Eliminating possibilities
- Acting it out
- Using/finding a pattern
- Using/making a table
- Using/drawing a picture or diagram
- Using manipulatives
- Conducting an experiment

Ratio and Proportion

	K1	K2	L1-1	L1-2	L1-3	L1-4	L2-1	L2-2	L2-3	L2-4	L3-1	L3-2	L3-3	L3-4	L4-1	L4-2	L4-3	L4-4	L4-5	L4-6	L5-1	L5-2	L5-3	L5-4	L5-5	L5-6	L6-1	L6-2	L6-3	L6-4	L6-5	L6-6	G6	G7	G8
Meaning/use of ratio and proportion															●						●	✓	●	●			●	●					●	●	●
Rates																●	●	●	●	●		●	✓			●	●	✓	●	●		●	●	●
Similar figures															●						●							●		●	●		●	●	●
Map scales											●	●									●	●		●		●							●	●	●
Meaning of percent																					●			●									●	●	●
Percent of a number																		●				✓			✓	●		●	●	●		●	●	●
Percent discounts																						✓			✓	●						●	●	●
Sales tax											●					●	●					✓			✓	●		●				●	●	●
Simple/compound interest															●						●			●	●							●	●	●

Statistics and graphing

	K1	K2	L1-1	L1-2	L1-3	L1-4	L2-1	L2-2	L2-3	L2-4	L3-1	L3-2	L3-3	L3-4	L4-1	L4-2	L4-3	L4-4	L4-5	L4-6	L5-1	L5-2	L5-3	L5-4	L5-5	L5-6	L6-1	L6-2	L6-3	L6-4	L6-5	L6-6	G6	G7	G8
Surveying	●	●	●			●			●			●			●		●			●		●			●	●			●		●		●	●	●
Tallying	●		●			●		●			●			●	●	●			●			●			●			●		●		●	●	●
Making tables with data	●	●	●	●	●	●	●	●		●	●	●	●	●	●	●	●	●	●		●	✓	●	●			●	●		●		●	●	●
Real and picture graphs	●	●	●			●			●			●			●	●											●			●		●	●	●
Bar graphs	●	●	●			●		●	●			●			●		●			●	●						●			●		●	●	●
Line graphs											●	●			●	●	●	●	●	●	●			●			●			●		●	●	●
Circle graphs															●						●					●		●		●		●	●	●
Finding the mean															●	●					●	✓	●	●			✓	●		●		●	●	●
Finding the median															●	●					●	●					●			●		●	●	●
Finding the mode															●						●	●					●			●		●	●	●

Subtraction (whole numbers)

	K1	K2	L1-1	L1-2	L1-3	L1-4	L2-1	L2-2	L2-3	L2-4	L3-1	L3-2	L3-3	L3-4	L4-1	L4-2	L4-3	L4-4	L4-5	L4-6	L5-1	L5-2	L5-3	L5-4	L5-5	L5-6	L6-1	L6-2	L6-3	L6-4	L6-5	L6-6	G6	G7	G8
Meaning of subtraction	●	●					●																												
Basic facts		●	✓	✓	●	●	✓	●	●	●	✓	●	●	●	✓	●	●	●	●																
Missing term problems			●	●	●	●		●	●		●	●			●	●																			
Two-digit numbers			✓	✓	✓	●	✓	●	●	●	✓	●	●	●	●	●	●	●	●																
Three-digit numbers							✓	✓	●	●	●	●	●	●	✓	●	●	●	●		✓	●	●												
Greater numbers							●	✓	●	●	●	●	●	●	✓	●	●	●	●		✓	●	●												
Subtracting money			●	✓		●	●	●	●		●	●	●	●	●	●	●	●	●	✓	●					✓	●						●	●	●
Estimating differences					●	●			●		●	✓		●	●	●	●	●	✓	●					✓	●	●						●	●	●

Technology

Calculators

	K1	K2	L1-1	L1-2	L1-3	L1-4	L2-1	L2-2	L2-3	L2-4	L3-1	L3-2	L3-3	L3-4	L4-1	L4-2	L4-3	L4-4	L4-5	L4-6	L5-1	L5-2	L5-3	L5-4	L5-5	L5-6	L6-1	L6-2	L6-3	L6-4	L6-5	L6-6	G6	G7	G8
Counting	●	●		●			●			●																									
Skip counting	●			●			●		●											✓															
Computation with whole numbers	●	●	●			●		●			●	●	●	●	●	●	●	●	●	✓	●	●					●	●		●		●	●	●	●
Computation with decimals								●			●				●	●	●	●			●	●		●			●		●				●	●	●
Computation with fractions															●						●	●					●						●	●	●
Computation with integers (negative numbers)											●				●	●					●						●						●	●	●
Using function rules			●				●				●	●			●	●		●	●								●			●		●	●	●	●
Order of operations											●	●				●											●			●		●	●	●	●
Function keys													●	●	●	●		●	●							●		●		●		●	●	●	●

Computers

	K1	K2	L1-1	L1-2	L1-3	L1-4	L2-1	L2-2	L2-3	L2-4	L3-1	L3-2	L3-3	L3-4	L4-1	L4-2	L4-3	L4-4	L4-5	L4-6	L5-1	L5-2	L5-3	L5-4	L5-5	L5-6	L6-1	L6-2	L6-3	L6-4	L6-5	L6-6	G6	G7	G8
Spreadsheets													●		●	●	●	●	●	●	●	●	●	●	●	●	●	●	●	●	●	●	●	●	●
Functions											●	●			●	●	●	●			●	●					●						●	●	●
Graphs											●	●				●					●	●					●						●	●	●
Charts and tables											●	●	●	●	●	●	●	●	●		●	●		●			●	●		●		●	●	●	●